NEW *Speaking Out: Videos in Abnormal Psychology Volume II* on MyPsychLab!

BIPOLAR DISORDER

Interview with
FELICIANO

Day in the Life:
FELICIANO

POST TRAUMATIC STRESS DISORDER

Interview with
BONNIE

Day in the Life:
BONNIE

IMPULSE CONTROL DISORDER

Interview with
ED

Day in the Life:
ED

ANOREXIA NERVOSA DISORDER

Interview with
NATASHA

Day in the Life:
NATASHA

DEMENTIA DISORDER

Interview with
ALVIN

Day in the Life:
ALVIN

ASPERGER'S SYNDROME DISORDER

Interview with
DAVID

Day in the Life:
DAVID

Also on MyPsychLab:
Speaking Out: Videos in Abnormal Psychology Volume I

MAJOR DEPRESSION

EVERETT
"You feel absolute worthlessness. You feel there is no hope for the future."

BULIMIA

JESSICA
"I started out with a diet for me."

SCHIZOPHRENIA

LARRY
"My voices had gotten the most of me . . ."

SCHIZOAFFECTIVE DISORDER

JOSH
"When I was first in the hospital, I thought I was in the middle of a massacre . . ."

ADHD

JIMMY
"I think without it (medicine) I would be dreaming the whole entire day."

AUTISM

XAVIER
"He is now talking, which was a blessing."

PLUS videos covering Obsessive-Compulsive Disorder, Hyphochondriasis, Post Traumatic Stress Disorder, Social Phobia, HIV, Bipolar Mood Disorder with Psychotic Features, Borderline Personality Disorder, Alcoholism, and Gender Identity Disorder.

ABNORMAL PSYCHOLOGY

SIXTH EDITION

Thomas F. Oltmanns
WASHINGTON UNIVERSITY IN ST. LOUIS

Robert E. Emery
UNIVERSITY OF VIRGINIA

PRENTICE HALL

Boston   Columbus   Indianapolis   New York   San Francisco   Upper Saddle River
Amsterdam   Cape Town   Dubai   London   Madrid   Milan   Munich   Paris   Montreal   Toronto
Delhi   Mexico City   Sao Paulo   Sydney   Hong Kong   Seoul   Singapore   Taipei   Tokyo

Editorial Director: Leah Jewell
Executive Editor: Jeff Marshall
Associate Editor: LeeAnn Doherty
Director of Marketing: Brandy Dawson
Marketing Manager: Nicole Kunzmann
Managing Editor: Maureen Richardson
Project Manager: Marianne Peters-Riordan
Copy Editor: Martha Williams
Proofreader: Marne Evans
Senior Operations Supervisor: Sherry Lewis
Senior Art Director: Nancy Wells
Art Director, cover and interior: Suzanne Duda

Designer, cover and interior: Carmen DiBartolomeo, Red Kite Project
Manager, Visual Research: Beth Brenzel
Photo Researcher: Rachel Lucas
Manager, Rights and Permissions: Zina Arabia
Image Permission Coordinator: Fran Toepfer
Manager, Cover Visual Research & Permissions: Karen Sanatar
Full-Service Project Management and Composition: Preparé, Inc.
Printer/Binder: Courier Companies, Inc.
Cover Printer: Phoenix Color Corp.

This book was set in 11/12.5 Garamond.

Credits and acknowledgments borrowed from other sources and reproduced, with permission, in this textbook appear on appropriate page within text (or on page 643–644).

Library of Congress Cataloging-in-Publication Data
Oltmanns, Thomas F.
  Abnormal psychology / Thomas F. Oltmanns, Robert E. Emery—6th ed.
    p. cm.
Includes bibliographical references and index.
ISBN 978-0-205-68953-8 (alk. paper)
1. Psychology, Pathological. 2. Mental illness. I. Emery, Robert E. II. Title
RC454.O44 2010
616.89—dc22   2009003989

To Gail, Josh, Sara, Billy, Presley, and Riley—T.F.O.
To Margaret J. Emery, 1923-2006—R.E.E.

Prentice Hall
is an imprint of

www.pearsonhighered.com

Student Edition: ISBN 10: 0-205-68953-1
                  ISBN 13: 978-0-205-68953-8
Exam Copy: ISBN 13: 978-0-205-68954-5
                  ISBN 10: 0-205-68954-X

Brief Contents

Contents

3 TREATMENT OF PSYCHOLOGICAL DISORDERS 60

4 CLASSIFICATION AND ASSESSMENT OF ABNORMAL BEHAVIOR 88

5 MOOD DISORDERS AND SUICIDE 120

6 ANXIETY DISORDERS 162

7   ACUTE AND POSTTRAUMATIC STRESS DISORDERS, DISSOCIATIVE DISORDERS, AND SOMATOFORM DISORDERS   196

8   STRESS AND PHYSICAL HEALTH   230

9 PERSONALITY DISORDERS 256

10 EATING DISORDERS 294

11 SUBSTANCE USE DISORDERS   320

12 SEXUAL AND GENDER IDENTITY DISORDERS   358

13 SCHIZOPHRENIC DISORDERS 394

14 DEMENTIA, DELIRIUM, AND AMNESTIC DISORDERS 432

15 MENTAL RETARDATION AND PERVASIVE DEVELOPMENTAL DISORDERS 462

16 PSYCHOLOGICAL DISORDERS OF CHILDHOOD 496

17 ADJUSTMENT DISORDERS AND LIFE-CYCLE TRANSITIONS 530

18 MENTAL HEALTH AND THE LAW 558

DSM-IV-TR TABLES

Preface

Emotional suffering touches all of our lives at some point in time. Psychological problems affect many of us directly and all of us indirectly—through our loved ones, friends, and the strangers whose troubled behavior we cannot ignore. Abnormal psychology is not about "them." Abnormal psychology is about all of us.

Abnormal psychology today is also about scientific inquiry. We once again bring both the science and the personal aspects of abnormal psychology to life in this sixth edition of our text. We answer pressing intellectual and human questions as accurately, sensitively, and completely as possible, given the pace of new discoveries. Throughout this book, we offer an engaging yet rigorous treatment of abnormal psychology, the latest research and theory, and the urgent needs of the people behind the disorders.

WHAT'S NEW IN THE SIXTH EDITION?

In this sixth edition of our text, we have expanded our focus on critical thinking in several ways. Most obviously, we added a new feature called **The Big Picture: Critical Thinking Review**. **The Big Picture** poses a series of integrative "big picture" questions that challenge students to think critically about major substantive and conceptual themes in each chapter. Margin questions call students' attention to the "big picture" while reading the chapter. At the end of the chapter, **The Big Picture: Critical Thinking Review** highlights the most important challenges and provides handy page references for review purposes. We also revised and expanded our **Critical Thinking Matters** boxes. This feature, found in every chapter, delves into some timely, often controversial issues (e.g., the purported link between vaccines and autism). We encourage students to think critically—to be *inquiring skeptics*—in evaluating scientific information and pseudoscientific information, especially on the Internet and in the media. We have also expanded the series of

video interviews (that we helped to develop and edit) called *Speaking Out.* Most importantly, the sixth edition continues to offer an engaging presentation of psychological science including hundreds of updates using the latest research. We carefully edited material that had become dated. The result is a book approximately 40 pages shorter than the fifth edition, making the material more accessible to students.

Critical Thinking Matters

Our **Critical Thinking Matters** feature addresses a concern that instructors raise repeatedly, and we wholeheartedly share: Students need to think critically about science and pseudoscience, especially in the Internet Age. Psychological disorders are frightening and burdensome to individuals, families, and society. Yet, any intellectually honest professional would admit that we simply do not have all the answers to many of the pressing questions posed to mental health experts. True, science is constantly moving forward as we uncover valuable new information about the causes and treatment of mental disorders. Some scientific leads prove to be misleading, however, and pseudoscientific misinformation (and outright charlatanism) abounds, especially on the Internet and in the popular media. In this new edition, we have added more critical thinking questions to each chapter. As noted, we have also added a **The Big Picture: Critical Thinking Review** at the end of each chapter. In this new highlight, we review the most important critical thinking questions, provide brief answers, and direct the student to those pages where the question is addressed in greater detail.

Critical thinking *matters* because psychological problems matter deeply to those who suffer and to their loved ones. Good research tells us—and them—which treatments work, and which ones don't, as well as what might cause mental illness, and what doesn't. Critical thinking *matters* because students in abnormal psychology surely will not remember all the details they learn in this course. In fact, they shouldn't focus exclusively on factual details, because the details will change with new scientific developments. If students can learn to think critically about abnormal psychology, the lesson will last a lifetime and be used repeatedly, not only in understanding psychological problems, but also in every area of life.

Our **Critical Thinking Matters** features help students to *think* about science, about pseudoscience, and about themselves. For example, in Chapter 2 we address the belief, currently promoted widely on the Internet and in the popular media, that mercury in widely used measles/mumps/rubella (MMR) vaccinations in the 1990s caused an epidemic of autism (and perhaps a host of other psychological problems for children). **Critical Thinking** Matters outlines the concerns of the frightened public, but goes on to point out (1) the failure to find support for this fear in numerous, large-scale scientific studies; (2) the scientific stance that the burden of proof lies with the proponents of any hypothesis, including speculations about MMR; (3) the widely ignored fact that 10 of the original 13 authors who raised the theoretical possibility *publicly withdrew their speculation about autism and MMR*; and (4) the fact the findings of legal actions, sadly, do not necessarily reach conclusions consistent with scientific knowledge. As we discuss in the text in Chapter 16, moreover, the apparent epidemic of autism very likely resulted from increased awareness of the disorder and loosened criteria for diagnosing autism.

Getting Help

We want students to think critically about disorders *and* to be sensitive to the struggles of individuals with psychological problems. As scientist-practitioners, we see these dual goals not only as compatible, but also as essential. One way that we underscore the personal nature of emotional problems is in our **Getting Help** features found in every chapter. In **Getting Help,** we directly address the personal side of psychological disorders and try to answer the sorts of questions that students often ask us privately after lecture or during office hours. The **Getting Help** sections give responsible, empirically sound, and concrete guidance on such personal topics as

- What treatments should I seek out for a particular disorder? (See Chapters 2, 6, 10, and 12)

- What can I do to help someone I know who has a psychological problem? (See Chapters 5, 9, 10, and 16)
- How can I find a good therapist? (See Chapters 3, 5, and 12)
- Where can I get reliable information from books, the Internet, or professionals in my community? (See Chapters 1, 5, 7, and 11)
- What self-help strategies can I try or suggest to friends? (See Chapters 6, 11, and 12)

Students can also find research-based information on the effectiveness and efficacy of various treatments in Chapter 3, "Treatment of Psychological Disorders," and in the Treatment headings near the end of every disorder chapter. We cover treatment generally at the beginning of the text but in detail in the context of each disorder, because different treatments are more or less effective for different psychological problems.

New *Speaking Out* Video Interviews

One of the best ways to understand the needs of the people behind the disorders is to hear their stories in their own words. We worked in consultation with Prentice Hall and NKP Productions to produce a video series called *Speaking Out: Interviews with People Who Struggle with Psychological Disorders.* The first 16 cases in the *Speaking Out* series were introduced with the previous edition of our book. Now we have added 6 new cases, addressing the following problem areas: bipolar mood disorder, posttraumatic stress disorder, compulsive gambling, anorexia nervosa, Alzheimer's disease, and Asperger's disorder. These interviews give students a window into the lives of people who are not so different from anyone else, but who happen to struggle with various kinds of mental disorder. The new video cases also include a new, second segment called "A Day in the Life," interviews with friends and family members who discuss their relationships, feelings, and perspectives. We introduce students to each of these people in the appropriate chapters of our book, using their photos and a brief description of relevant issues that should be considered when viewing the **Video Cases.** The full versions of the interviews are available to instructors either on DVD or VHS, along with an Instructor's Video Guide.

We are especially proud of the ***Speaking Out*** videos and view them as a part of our text, not as a supplement, because we were intimately involved with their production. As with the original series, we screened the new video cases, helped to construct and guide the actual interviews, and gave detailed feedback on how to edit the films to make the disorders real for students and fit closely with the organization and themes in our sixth edition.

New Research

The unsolved mysteries of abnormal psychology challenge all of our intellectual and personal resources. In our sixth edition, we include the latest "clues" psychological scientists have unearthed in doing the detective work of research, including references to hundreds of new studies. But the measure of a leading-edge textbook is not merely the number of new references; it is the number of new studies the authors have reviewed and evaluated before deciding which ones to include and which ones to discard. For every new reference in this edition of our text, we have read many additional papers before selecting the one gem to include. Some of the updated research and perspectives in this edition includes

- New information on the prevalence of mental disorders, using recently published data from the replication of the National Comorbidity Survey (NCS-R) (*Chapter 1*)
- Enhanced coverage of genetic perspectives including gene–environment interactions and correlations (*Chapter 2*)
- New evidence on what makes placebos "work," on treatments that harm, "3rd wave" CBT (*Chapter 3*)
- Revised discussion of the strengths and weaknesses of DSM-IV-TR, and updated information regarding the production of DSM-V, which is now well underway and due to be published in 2012 (*Chapter 4*)
- New coverage of nonsuicidal self-injury, one of the fastest-growing and most alarming topics in the field of psychopathology (*Chapter 5*)
- Updated evidence regarding the prevalence of anxiety disorders across the life span (*Chapter 6*)
- Further consideration of *resilience* in response to trauma, questions about secondary trauma, and a new discussion of *hwa-byung,* a disorder unique to Korean culture (*Chapter 7*)

- New research on cultural differences in social support, religion and coping, and the daily experience of pain (*Chapter 8*)
- Updated coverage of impulse control disorders, with a new video case concerning compulsive gambling (*Chapter 9*)
- Latest evidence on redefining, treating (the Maudsley method), and preventing eating disorders; up-to-date consideration of women's portrayal in the media, including death of model Ana Carolina Reston (*Chapter 10*)
- Simplified coverage of the prevalence of substance use disorders, including evidence regarding gender differences from the recent NESARC study (*Chapter 11*)
- New recommendations in the Getting Help section for readers who are concerned about gender identity issues (*Chapter 12*)
- Recent recognition of the limitations of so-called atypical antipsychotic drugs in the treatment of schizophrenia (*Chapter 13*)
- Revised discussion of memory changes associated with normal aging, incorporating new evidence from this rapidly expanding area of research (*Chapter 14*)
- More on the "epidemic of autism," Asperger's disorder, mirror neurons, and genetic screening (*Chapter 15*)
- Updated discussion of adolescent depression, antidepressants, suicide risk; new long-term results on treating adolescent depression and ADHD (including preschoolers); new data on stimulants and growth (*Chapter 16*)
- New discussions of "relational diagnoses," complicated grief, and psychological pain (*Chapter 17*)
- New material on the legal effects of the Virginia Tech shootings, updates on Tarasoff duties, and data on malpractice suits (*Chapter 18*)

THE GOLD STANDARD REMAINS UNCHANGED

We view integration as the gold standard of any forward-looking abnormal psychology text, and the gold standard remains unchanged in the sixth edition of our textbook. We see the most exciting and promising future for abnormal psychology in the integration of theoretical approaches, professional specialties, and science and practice, not in the old, fractured competition among "paradigms," a split between psychology and psychiatry, or the division between scientists and practitioners.

Integrated Understanding of Causes and Treatment

For much of the last century, abnormal psychology was dominated by theoretical paradigms, a circumstance that reminds us of the parable of the seven blind men and the elephant. One blind man grasps a tusk and concludes that an elephant is very much like a spear. Another feels a leg and decides an elephant is like a tree, and so on. Our goal from the first edition of **Abnormal Psychology** has been to show the reader the whole elephant. We do this through our unique *integrative systems approach,* in which we focus on what we know today rather than what we used to think. In every chapter, we consider the latest evidence on the *multiple* risk factors that contribute to psychological disorders, as well as the most effective psychological and biomedical treatments. Even if science cannot yet paint a picture of the whole elephant, we clearly tell the student what we know, what we don't know, and how psychologists think the pieces might fit together.

Pedagogy: Integrated Content and Method

We also continue to bring cohesion to abnormal psychology—and to the student—with pedagogy. Each disorder chapter unfolds in the same way, providing a coherent framework with a *consistent chapter outline.* We open with an Overview followed by one or two extended Case Studies. We then discuss Symptoms, Diagnosis, Frequency, Causes, and finally, Treatment (the same sections as in previous editions but with new, straightforward headings). Each chapter covers the key details of **DSM-IV-TR** throughout.

Abnormal psychology is not only about the latest research, but also about the methods psychologists use (and invent) in order to do scientific detective work. Unlike any other text in this field, we cover the scientific method by offering brief **Research Methods** features in every single chapter. Teaching methods in the context of content helps students appreciate the importance of scientific procedures and assumptions, makes learning research methods more manageable, and gives the text flexibility. By the end of the text, our unique approach allows us to cover research methods in *more* detail than we could reasonably cover in a single, detached chapter.

Many of our students have told us that the typical research methods chapter seems dry, difficult, and—to our great disappointment—irrelevant. These problems never arise with our integrated, contextualized approach to research methods.

Abnormal psychology also is, of course, about real people with real problems. We bring the human, clinical side of abnormal psychology alive with detailed **Case Studies.** The **Case Studies** take the reader along the human journey of pain, triumph, frustration, and fresh starts that is abnormal psychology. The cases help students to think more deeply about psychological disorders, much as our own clinical experience enriches our understanding. (We both have been active clinicians as well as active researchers throughout our careers.) In extended cases near the beginning of each chapter, in briefer cases later, and in first-person accounts throughout, the student sees how ordinary lives are disrupted by psychological problems—and how effective treatment can rebuild shattered lives. The case studies also make the details and complexity of the science concrete, relevant, and essential to the "real world."

Sometimes a study or problem suggests a departure from current thinking or raises side issues that deserve to be examined in detail. We cover these emerging ideas in features identified by the topic at hand. One example of an emerging issue we discuss in this way is whether the female response to stress might be to "tend and befriend" rather than fight or flight (Chapter 8). Other topics include the common elements of suicide (Chapter 5) and a system for classifying different types of rapists (Chapter 12).

SUPPLEMENTS

Supplements for Instructors

Instructor's Resource Manual: 0-205-69131-5 Instructor's Resource Manual contains notes and suggestions on how to integrate the new *Speaking Out* video segments into your course.

Test Item File: 0-205-69129-3 This comprehensive test bank has been updated to include new questions on revised text material. It contains over 1,800 multiple-choice, true/false, short answer, and essay questions. The Test Item File also includes the Total Assessment Guide

(T.A.G.), which organizes test questions by section and according to definitional, factual, conceptual, or applied questions.

***Speaking Out: Interviews with People who Struggle with Psychological Disorders:* Volume I: 0-13-193332-9;** *NEW* **Volume II: 0-13-600303-6** These two sets of video segments allow students to see first-hand accounts of patients with various disorders. Filmed under the editorial direction of Tom Oltmanns and Robert Emery, the interviews were conducted by licensed clinicians and range in length from 10 to 25 minutes. These video segments are available on DVD, and an Instructor's Resource Manual provides background notes and suggested discussion questions. Interviews include

Volume I

Everett—Major Depression
Sarah—Depression/Deliberate Self Harm
Ann—Bipolar Mood Disorder with Psychotic
    Features
Steve—Social Phobia
Dave—Obsessive/Compulsive Disorder
Sara—PTSD
Henry—Hypochondriasis
Julia—HIV
Liz—Borderline Personality Disorder
Jessica—Bulimia Nervosa
Chris—Alcoholism
Larry—Schizophrenia
Josh—Schizoaffective Disorder
Xavier—Autism
Jimmy—Attention-Deficit/Hyperactivity
    Disorder (ADHD)
Denise—Gender Identity Disorder

NEW Volume II

Feliziano—Bipolar Disorder
Bonnie—Posttraumatic Stress Disorder
Ed—Compulsive Gambling
Natasha—Anorexia Nervosa
Alvin—Dementia Disorder
David—Asperger's Disorder

Patients as Educators: Video Cases in Abnormal Psychology Created by James H. Scully, Jr., M.D., and Alan M. Dahms, Ph.D., Colorado State University, this VHS tape includes a series of 10 patient interviews illustrating a range of disorders. Each interview is preceded by a brief history of the patient and a synopsis of some major symptoms of the disorder and ends with a summary and brief analysis.

ABCNEWS **ABC News Videos for Abnormal Psychology, Series III** Qualified adopters can obtain this series consisting of segments from the *ABC Nightly News with Peter Jennings, Nightline, 20/20, Prime Time Live,* and *The Health Show.* The programs cover issues such as drugs and alcoholism, psychotherapy, autism, crime motivation, depression, and others. Contact your Pearson representative for more details.

MyTest Testing Software: 0-205-68955-8 This test-generating software provides instructors "best in class" features in an easy to use program. Create tests and easily select questions with drag-and-drop or point-and-click functionality. Add or modify test questions using the built-in Question Editor and print tests in a variety of formats. The program comes with full technical support.

Pearson Education Online Catalog Page— Instructors' Resource Center (www.pearsonhighered.com) This site is password-protected for instructors' use only and allows you online access to all Pearson psychology supplements at any time. You'll find a multitude of resources—both text-specific and nontext-specific—for teaching abnormal psychology. From this site, you can download any of this text's key supplements, including the Instructor's Resource Manual, Test Item File, and PowerPoint presentations. Contact your local sales representative for the User ID and Password to access this site.

PowerPoint Presentation: 0-205-690002-5 These presentations highlight key points and include important tables, figures, and graphics from the text.

MyPsychLab This robust course management platform enables instructors to assign tests, quizzes, and projects online and view the results of those assignments as a class aggregate, or as focused on a student-by-student, text section-by-text section basis. Based upon these assignment results, instructors are presented with a detailed teaching plan to bolster student comprehension of any topic areas not well understood, and to supplement all other chapter sections. A series of self-diagnostic tests serve as the foundation of this exciting new platform, which also includes and integrates assignments, remediation content, and study activities that feed results into the platform's gradebook. The diversified collection of study content and activities encompasses

Live!Psych animations, patient interview videos, the American Psychological Association (APA) reader *Current Directions in Abnormal Psychology*, author-recommended Web sites, and more. All supplementary resources are also housed on the MyPsychLab platform.

Student Supplements

 Research Navigator™ *Research Navigator™* is an online resource that features three exclusive databases full of source material, including

EBSCO's **ContentSelect™** Academic Journal Database, organized by subject. Each subject contains 50 to 100 of the leading academic journals by keyword, topic, or multiple topics. Articles include abstract and citation information and can be cut, pasted, e-mailed, or saved for later use.
The New York Times Search-by-Subject One Year Archive, organized by subject and searchable by keyword or multiple keywords. Instructors and students can view the full text of the article.
Best of the Web Link Library, organized by subject, offers editorially selected "best of the Web" sites. Link Libraries are continually scanned and kept up-to-date, providing the most relevant and accurate links for research assignments.

To see how this resource works, take a tour at *www.researchnavigator.com,* or ask your local Pearson representative for more details.

Study Guide: 0-205-69130-7 The Study Guide includes numerous review and study questions and other learning aids to help reinforce students' understanding of the concepts covered in the text.

 Current Directions in Abnormal Psychology, 2nd edition: 0-205-59741-6 Prentice Hall is pleased to continue to support the **American Psychological Society (APS)** reader series **Current Directions in Psychological Science.** You can package the *Current Directions in Abnormal Psychology* reader with this text. (ISBN 0-205-59741-6)

This reader contains selected articles from APS's journal *Current Directions in Psychological Science. Current Directions* was created as a means by which scientists could quickly and easily learn about new and significant research developments outside their major field of study. The journal's concise reviews span all of scientific psychology, and because of the journal's accessibility to audiences outside specialty areas, it is a natural fit for use in college courses. These readers offer a rich resource that connects students and scholars directly to leading scientists working in psychology today.

The American Psychological Society is the only association dedicated solely to advancing psychology as a science-based discipline. APS members include the field's most respected researchers and educators representing the full range of topics within psychological science. The society is widely recognized as a leading voice for the science of psychology in Washington and is focused on increasing public understanding and use of the knowledge generated by psychological research.

Abnormal Psychology Casebook: A New Perspective: 0-13-093787-8 This text, by Andrew R. Getzfeld, uses clear, accessible language and explanations and features real cases based on a variety of psychopathologies—all involving patients/clients from a wide variety of cultural, ethnic, racial, religious, social, and socioeconomic backgrounds—and all based on the author's own experiences as a practicing social worker and psychologist.

CourseSmart eTextbook: 0-205-68956-6 This offers students an online subscription to ***Abnormal Psychology, Sixth Edition*** at a 50 percent savings. With the CourseSmart textbook, students can search the text, make notes online, print out reading assignments that incorporate lecture notes, and bookmark important passages. Ask your Pearson representative for details, or visit www.coursesmart.com.

ACKNOWLEDGMENTS

Writing and revising this textbook is a never-ending task that fortunately is also a labor of love. This sixth edition is the culmination of years of effort and is the product of many people's hard work. The first people we wish to thank for their important contributions to making this the text of the future, not of the past, are the following expert reviewers who have unselfishly offered us a great many helpful suggestions, both in this and in previous editions: John Dale Alden, III, Lipscomb University; John Allen, University of Arizona; Hal Arkowitz, University of Arizona; Jo Ann Armstrong, Patrick Henry Community College; Gordon Atlas, Alfred University; Deanna Barch, Washington University; Catherine Barnard, Kalamazoo Community College; Thomas G. Bowers, Pennsylvania State University, Harrisburg; Stephanie Boyd, University of South Carolina; Gail Bruce-Sanford, University of Montana; Ann Calhoun-Seals, Belmont Abbey College; Caryn L. Carlson, University of Texas at Austin; Richard Cavasina, California University of Pennsylvania; Laurie Chassin, Arizona State University; Lee H. Coleman, Miami University of Ohio; Bradley T. Conner, Temple University; Dean Cruess, University of Pennsylvania; Danielle Dick, Washington University; Juris G. Draguns, Pennsylvania State University; William Edmonston, Jr., Colgate University; Ronald Evans, Washburn University; John Foust, Parkland College; Alan Glaros, University of Missouri, Kansas City; Ian H. Gotlib, Stanford University; Irving Gottesman, University of Virginia; Mort Harmatz, University of Massachusetts; Marjorie L. Hatch, Southern Methodist University; Jennifer A. Haythornwaite, Johns Hopkins University; Holly Hazlett-Stevens, University of Nevada, Reno; Brant P. Hasler, University of Arizona; Debra L. Hollister, Valencia Community College; Jennifer Jenkins, University of Toronto; Stuart Keeley, Bowling Green State University; Carolin Keutzer, University of Oregon; Mark H. Licht, Florida State University; Roger Loeb, University of Michigan, Dearborn; Carol Manning, University of Virginia; Richard D. McAnulty, University of North Carolina—Charlotte; Richard McFall, Indiana University; John Monahan, University of Virginia School of Law; Tracy L. Morris, West Virginia University; Dan Muhwezi, Butler Community College; Christopher Murray, University of Maryland; William O'Donohue, University of Nevada—Reno; Joseph J. Palladino, University of Southern Indiana; Demetrios Papageorgis, University of British Columbia; Ronald D. Pearse, Fairmont State College; Seth Pollak, University of Wisconsin; Melvyn G. Preisz, Oklahoma City University; Paul Rasmussen, Furman University; Rena Repetti, University of California, Los Angeles; Karen Clay Rhines, Northampton Community College; Jennifer Langhinrichsen-Rohling, University of South Alabama; Patricia H. Rosenberger, Colorado State University; Catherine Guthrie-Scanes, Mississippi State University; Josh Searle-White, Allegheny College; Forrest Scogin, University of Alabama; Danny Shaw, University of Pittsburgh; Heather Shaw, American Institutes of Research; Janet Simons, Central Iowa Psychological Services; Patricia J. Slocum, College of DuPage; Darrell Smith, Tennessee State University; Randi Smith, Metropolitan State College of Denver; Cheryl Spinweber, University of California, San Diego; Bonnie Spring, The Chicago Medical School; Laura Stephenson, Washburn University; Eric Stice, University of Texas; Alexandra Stillman, Utah State University; Joanne Stohs, California State, Fullerton; Martha Storandt, Washington University; Milton E. Strauss, Case Western Reserve University; Amie Grills-Taquechel, University of Houston; J. Kevin Thompson, University of South Florida; Julie Thompson, Duke University; Robert H. Tipton, Virginia Commonwealth University; Douglas Whitman, Wayne State University; Michael Wierzbicki, Marquette University; Robert D. Zettle, Wichita State University; Ken Winters, University of Minnesota; and Eleanor Webber, Johnson State College.

We have been fortunate to work in stimulating academic environments that have fostered our interests in studying abnormal psychology and in teaching undergraduate students. We are particularly grateful to our colleagues at the University of Virginia: Eric Turkheimer, Irving Gottesman (now at the University of Minnesota), Mavis Hetherington, John Monahan, Joseph Allen, Dan Wegner (now at Harvard), David Hill, Jim Coan, Bethany Teachman, Amori Mikami, Cedric Williams, and Peter Brunjes for extended and ongoing discussions of the issues that are considered in this book. More recently, Deanna Barch, Bob Krueger, Danielle Dick, Martha Storandt, and Randy Larsen (all in the Department of Psychology at Washington University) have added an important new perspective to our views regarding many important topics in this field. Close friends and colleagues at Indiana University have also served in this role, especially Dick McFall, Rick Viken, and Alexander Buchwald. Many undergraduate and graduate students who have taken our courses also have helped to shape the viewpoints that are expressed here. They are too numerous to identify individually, but we are grateful for the intellectual challenges and excitement that they have provided over the past several years.

Many other people have contributed to the text in important ways. Once again, Kimberly Carpenter Emery did extensive legal research for Chapter 18. Danielle Dick contributed substantial expertise regarding new developments in behavior genetics and gene identification methods. Martha Storandt and Carol Manning provided extensive consultation on issues related to dementia and other cognitive disorders. Jennifer Hill, Erin Horn, and Nick Eaton provided important help with library research and manuscript preparation.

We also would like to express our deep appreciation to the Prentice Hall team who share our pride and excitement about this text, and who have worked long and hard to make it the very best text. Major contributors include Jeff Marshall, Executive Editor; LeeAnn Doherty, Associate Editor; Nicole Kunzmann, Marketing Manager; Maureen Richardson, Managing Editor; Marianne Peters-Riordan, Production Liaison; Leah Jewell, Editorial Director, Social Sciences; Rochelle Diogenes, Editor-in-Chief, Development; Paul DeLuca, Media Editor; Julie Tesser, Photo Researcher; Nancy Wells, Art Director; and Leslie Osher, Creative Design Director.

Finally, we want to express our gratitude to our families for their patience and support throughout our obsession with this text: Gail and Josh Oltmanns, and Sara, Billy, Presley, and Riley Baber; and Kimberly, Maggie, Julia, Bobby, Lucy, and John-John Emery. You remain our loving sources of motivation and inspiration.

—*Tom Oltmanns*
—*Bob Emery*

About the Authors

THOMAS F. OLTMANNS is the Edgar James Swift Professor of Psychology in Arts and Sciences and Professor of Psychiatry at Washington University in St. Louis, where he is also Director of Clinical Training in Psychology. He received his B.A. from the University of Wisconsin and his Ph.D. from the State University of New York at Stony Brook. He was previously a faculty member in the psychology departments at Indiana University (1976 to 1986) and at the University of Virginia (1986 to 2003). He is currently a member of the Board of Directors of the Association for Psychological Science, served as President of the Society for a Science of Clinical Psychology in 1993, and is President-elect of the Society for Research in Psychopathology. Undergraduate students at UVa recognized his teaching by selecting him to receive the "Outstanding Professor Award" in 1997 and 2002. His early research was concerned with the role of cognitive and emotional factors in schizophrenia. His lab is currently conducting a large, prospective study of the trajectory of personality disorders in middle-aged and older adults. His other books include *Schizophrenia* (1980), written with John Neale; *Delusional Beliefs* (1988), edited with Brendan Maher; and *Case Studies in Abnormal Psychology* (8th edition, 2009), written with Michele Martin.

ROBERT E. EMERY is Professor of Psychology and Director of the Center for Children, Families, and the Law at the University of Virginia, where he also served as Director of Clinical Training for nine years. He received a B.A. from Brown University in 1974 and a Ph.D. from SUNY at Stony Brook in 1982. His research focuses on family conflict, children's mental health, and associated legal issues, particularly divorce mediation and child custody disputes. More recently, he has become involved in genetically informed research of selection into and the consequences of major changes in the family environment. Emery has authored over 120 scientific articles and book chapters. His awards include a "Citation Classic" from the Institute for Scientific Information, an Outstanding Research Publication Award from the American Associate for Marriage and Family Therapy, the Distinguished Researcher Award from the Association of Family and Conciliation Courts, and several awards and award nominations for his three books on divorce: *Marriage, Divorce and Children's Adjustment* (2nd edition., 1998, Sage Publications); *Renegotiating Family Relationships: Divorce, Child Custody, and Mediation* (2nd edition., in press, Guilford Press); and *The Truth about Children and Divorce: Dealing with the Emotions So You and Your Children Can Thrive* (2006, Plume). In addition to teaching, research, and administration, he maintains a limited practice as a clinical psychologist and mediator.

ABNORMAL PSYCHOLOGY

EXAMPLES AND DEFINITIONS OF ABNORMAL BEHAVIOR

Mental disorders touch every realm of human experience; they are part of the human experience. They can disrupt the way we think, the way we feel, and the way we behave. They also affect relationships with other people. These problems often have a devastating impact on people's lives. In countries like the United States, mental disorders are the second leading cause of disease-related disability and mortality, ranking slightly behind cardiovascular conditions and slightly ahead of cancer (Lopez et al., 2006). The purpose of this book is to help you become familiar with the nature of these disorders and the various ways in which psychologists and other mental health professionals are advancing knowledge of their causes and treatment.

Many of us grow up thinking that mental disorders happen to a few unfortunate people. We don't expect them to happen to us or to those we love. In fact, mental disorders are very common. At least two out of every four people will experience a serious form of abnormal behavior, such as depression, alcoholism, or schizophrenia, at some point during his or her lifetime. When you add up the numbers of people who experience these problems firsthand as well as through relatives and close friends, you realize that, like other health problems, mental disorders affect all of us. That is why, throughout this book, we will try to help you understand not only the kind of disturbed behaviors and thinking that characterize particular disorders, but also the people to whom they occur and the circumstances that can foster them.

Most importantly, this book is about all of us, not "them"—anonymous people with whom we empathize but do not identify. Just as each of us will be affected by medical problems at some point during our lives, it is also likely that we, or someone we love, will have to cope with that aspect of the human experience known as a disorder of the mind.

OVERVIEW

The symptoms and signs of mental disorders, including such phenomena as depressed mood, panic attacks, and bizarre beliefs, are known as **psychopathology.** Literally translated, this term means *pathology of the mind*. **Abnormal psychology** is the application of psychological science to the study of mental disorders.

In the first four chapters of this book, we will look at the field of abnormal psychology in general. We will look at the ways in which abnormal behaviors are broken down into categories of mental disorders that can be more clearly defined for diagnostic purposes, and how those behaviors are assessed. We will also discuss current ideas about the causes of these disorders and ways in which they can be treated.

This chapter will help you begin to understand the qualities that define behaviors and experiences as being abnormal. At what point does the diet that a girl follows in order to perform at her peak as a ballerina or gymnast become an eating disorder? When does grief following the end of a relationship become major depression? The line dividing normal from abnormal is not always clear. You will find that the issue is often one of degree rather than exact form or content of behavior.

The case studies in this chapter describe the experiences of two people whose behavior would be considered abnormal by mental health professionals. Our first case will introduce you to a person who suffered from one of the most obvious and disabling forms of mental disorder, known as schizophrenia. Kevin's life had been relatively unremarkable for many years. He had done well in school, was married, and held a good job. Unfortunately, over a period of several months, the fabric of his normal life began to fall apart. The transition wasn't obvious to either Kevin or his family, but it eventually became clear that he was having serious problems.

CASE **STUDY** A Husband's Paranoid Schizophrenia

Kevin and Joyce Warner (not their real names*) had been married for 8 years when they sought help from a psychologist for their marital problems. Joyce was 34 years old, worked full time as a pediatric nurse, and was six months pregnant with her first child. Kevin, who was 35 years old, was finishing his third year working as a librarian at a local university. Joyce was extremely worried about what would happen if Kevin lost his job, especially in light of the baby's imminent arrival.

Although the Warners had come for couples therapy, the psychologist soon became concerned about certain eccentric aspects of Kevin's behavior. In the first session, Joyce

*Throughout this text we use fictitious names to protect the identities of the people involved.

described one recent event that had precipitated a major argument. One day, after eating lunch at work, Kevin had experienced sharp pains in his chest and had difficulty breathing. Fearful, he rushed to the emergency room at the hospital where Joyce worked. The physician who saw Kevin found nothing wrong with him, even after extensive testing. She gave Kevin a few tranquilizers and sent him home to rest. When Joyce arrived home that evening, Kevin told her that he suspected that he had been poisoned at work by his supervisor. He still held this belief.

Kevin's belief about the alleged poisoning raised serious concern in the psychologist's mind about Kevin's mental health. He decided to interview Joyce alone so that he could ask more extensive questions about Kevin's behavior. Joyce realized that the poisoning idea was "crazy." She was not willing, however, to see it as evidence that Kevin had a mental disorder. Joyce had known Kevin for 15 years. As far as she knew, he had never held any strange beliefs before this time. Joyce said that Kevin had always been "a thoughtful and unusually sensitive guy." She did not attach a great deal of significance to Kevin's unusual belief. She was more preoccupied with the couple's present financial concerns and insisted that it was time for Kevin to "face reality."

Kevin's condition deteriorated noticeably over the next few weeks. He became extremely withdrawn, frequently sitting alone in a darkened room after dinner. On several occasions, he told her that he felt as if he had "lost pieces of his thinking." It wasn't that his memory was failing, but rather he felt as though parts of his brain were shut off.

Kevin's problems at work also grew worse. His supervisor informed Kevin that his contract would definitely not be renewed. Joyce exploded when Kevin indifferently told her the bad news. His apparent lack of concern was especially annoying. She called Kevin's supervisor, who confirmed the news. He told her that Kevin was physically present at the library, but he was only completing a few hours of work each day. Kevin sometimes spent long periods of time just sitting at his desk and staring off into space and was sometimes heard mumbling softly to himself.

Kevin's speech was quite odd during the next therapy session. He would sometimes start to speak, drift off into silence, then reestablish eye contact with a bewildered smile and a shrug of his shoulders. He had apparently lost his train of thought completely. His answers to questions were often off the point, and when he did string together several sentences, their meaning was sometimes obscure. For example, at one point during the session, the psychologist asked Kevin if he planned to appeal his supervisor's decision. Kevin said,

I'm feeling pressured, like I'm lost and can't quite get here. But I need more time to explore the deeper side. Like in art. What you see on the surface is much richer when you look closely. I'm like that. An intuitive person. I can't relate in a linear way, and when people expect that from me, I get confused.

Kevin's strange belief about poisoning continued to expand. The Warners received a letter from Kevin's mother, who lived in another city 200 miles away. She had become ill after going out for dinner one night and mentioned that she must have eaten something that made her sick. After reading the letter, Kevin became convinced that his supervisor had tried to poison his mother, too.

When questioned about this new incident, Kevin launched into a long, rambling story. He said that his supervisor was a Vietnam veteran, but he had refused to talk with Kevin about his years in the service. Kevin suspected that this was because the supervisor had been a member of army intelligence. Perhaps he still was a member of some secret organization. Kevin suggested that an agent from this organization had been sent by his supervisor to poison his mother. Kevin thought that he and Joyce were in danger. Kevin also had some concerns about Asians, but he would not specify these worries in more detail.

Kevin's bizarre beliefs and his disorganized behavior convinced the psychologist that he needed to be hospitalized. Joyce reluctantly agreed that

this was the most appropriate course of action. She had run out of alternatives. Arrangements were made to have Kevin admitted to a private psychiatric facility, where the psychiatrist prescribed haloperidol (Haldol), a type of antipsychotic medication. Kevin seemed to respond positively to the drug, because he soon stopped talking about plots and poisoning—but he remained withdrawn and uncommunicative. After three weeks of treatment, Kevin's psychiatrist thought that he had improved significantly. Kevin was discharged from the hospital in time for the birth of their baby girl. Unfortunately, when the couple returned to consult with the psychologist, Kevin's adjustment was still a major concern. He did not talk with Joyce about the poisonings, but she noticed that he remained withdrawn and showed few emotions, even toward the baby.

When the psychologist questioned Kevin in detail, he admitted reluctantly that he still believed that he had been poisoned. Slowly, he revealed more of the plot. Immediately after admission to the hospital, Kevin had decided that his psychiatrist, who happened to be from Korea, could not be trusted. Kevin was sure that he, too, was working for army intelligence or perhaps for a counterintelligence operation. Kevin believed that he was being interrogated by this clever psychiatrist, so he had "played dumb." He did not discuss the suspected poisonings or the secret organization that had planned them. Whenever he could get away with it, Kevin simply pretended to take his medication. He thought that it was either poison or truth serum.

Kevin was admitted to a different psychiatric hospital soon after it became apparent that his paranoid beliefs had expanded. This time, he was given intramuscular injections of antipsychotic medication in order to be sure that the medicine was actually taken. Kevin improved considerably after several weeks in the hospital. He acknowledged that he had experienced paranoid thoughts. Although he still felt suspicious from time to time, wondering whether the plot had actually been real, he recognized that it could not really have happened, and he spent less and less time thinking about it.

RECOGNIZING THE PRESENCE OF A DISORDER

Some mental disorders are so severe that the people who suffer from them are not aware of the implausibility of their beliefs. Schizophrenia is a form of **psychosis,** a general term that refers to several types of severe mental disorder in which the person is considered to be out of contact with reality. Kevin exhibited several psychotic symptoms. For example, Kevin's firm belief that he was being poisoned by his supervisor had no basis in reality. Other disorders, however, are more subtle variations on normal experience. We will shortly consider some of the guidelines that are applied in determining abnormality.

Mental disorders are typically defined by a set of characteristic features; one symptom by itself is seldom sufficient to make a diagnosis. A group of symptoms that appear together and are assumed to represent a specific type of disorder is referred to as a **syndrome.** Kevin's unrealistic and paranoid belief that he was being poisoned, his peculiar and occasionally difficult-to-understand patterns of speech, and his oddly unemotional responses are all symptoms of schizophrenia (see Chapter 13). Each symptom is taken to be a fallible, or imperfect, indicator of the presence of the disorder. The significance of any specific feature depends on whether the person also exhibits additional behaviors that are characteristic of a particular disorder.

The duration of a person's symptoms is also important. Mental disorders are defined in terms of *persistent* maladaptive behaviors. Many unusual behaviors and inexplicable experiences are short lived; if we ignore them, they go away. Unfortunately, some forms of problematic behavior are not transient, and they eventually interfere with the person's social and occupational functioning. In Kevin's case, he had become completely preoccupied with his suspicions about poison. Joyce tried for several weeks to ignore certain aspects of Kevin's behavior, especially his delusional beliefs. She didn't want to think about the possibility that his behavior was abnormal and instead chose to explain his problems in terms of lack of maturity or lack of motivation. But as the problems accumulated, she finally decided to seek professional help. The magnitude of Kevin's problem was measured, in large part, by its persistence.

Impairment in the ability to perform social and occupational roles is another consideration in identifying the presence of a mental disorder. Delusional beliefs and disorganized speech typically lead to a profound disruption of relationships with other people. Like Kevin, people who experience these symptoms will obviously find the world to be a strange, puzzling, and perhaps alarming place. And they often elicit the same reactions in other people. Kevin's odd behavior and his inability to concentrate on his work had eventually cost him his job. His problems also had a negative impact on his relationship with his wife and his ability to help care for their daughter.

Kevin's situation raises several additional questions about abnormal behavior. One of the most difficult issues in the field centers on the processes by which mental disorders are identified. Once Kevin's problems came to the attention of a mental health professional, could he

◀ People with schizophrenia sometimes exhibit disorganized behavior, like this hospitalized woman.

have been tested in some way to confirm the presence or absence of a mental disorder?

Psychologists and other mental health professionals do not at present have laboratory tests that can be used to confirm definitively the presence of psychopathology because the processes that are responsible for mental disorders have not yet been discovered. Unlike specialists in other areas of medicine where many specific disease mechanisms have been discovered by advances in the biological sciences, psychologists and psychiatrists cannot test for the presence of a viral infection or a brain lesion or a genetic defect to confirm a diagnosis of mental disorder. Clinical psychologists must still depend on their observations of the person's behavior and descriptions of personal experience.

Is it possible to move beyond our current dependence on descriptive definitions of psychopathology? Will we someday have valid tests that can be used to establish independently the presence of a mental disorder? If we do, what

What kinds of clues suggest that a person may have a mental disorder?

form might these tests take? The answers to these questions are being sought in many kinds of research studies that will be discussed throughout this book.

Before we leave this section, we must also mention some other terms. You may be familiar with a variety of words that are commonly used in describing abnormal behavior. One term is *insanity,* which years ago referred to mental dysfunction but today is a legal term that refers to judgments about whether a person should be held responsible for criminal behavior if he or she is also mentally disturbed (see Chapter 18). If Kevin had murdered his psychiatrist, for example, based on the delusional belief that the psychiatrist was trying to harm him, a court of law might consider whether Kevin should be held to be *not guilty by reason of insanity.*

What is the difference between normal and abnormal behavior?

Another old-fashioned term that you may have heard is *nervous breakdown.* If we said that Kevin had "suffered a nervous breakdown," we would be indicating, in very general terms, that he had developed some sort of incapacitating but otherwise unspecified type of mental disorder. This expression does not convey any specific information about the nature of the person's problems. Some people might also say that Kevin was acting *crazy.* This is an informal, pejorative term that does not convey specific information and carries with it many unfortunate, unfounded, and negative implications. Mental health professionals refer to psychopathological conditions as mental disorders or abnormal behaviors. We will define these terms in the pages that follow.

▼ Andy Warhol was one of the most influential painters of the 20th century. His colleague, Jean-Michel Basquiat, was also an extremely promising artist. His dependence on heroin and his ultimately fatal overdose is one extreme example of the destructive and tragic effects of mental disorder.

DEFINING ABNORMAL BEHAVIOR

Why do we consider Kevin's behavior to be abnormal? By what criteria do we decide whether a particular set of behaviors or emotional reactions should be viewed as a mental disorder? These are important questions because they determine, in many ways, how other people will respond to the person, as well as who will be responsible for providing help (if help is required). Many attempts have been made to define abnormal behavior, but none is entirely satisfactory. No one has been able to provide a consistent definition that easily accounts for all situations in which the concept is invoked (Frances, First, & Pincus, 1995; Zachar & Kendler, 2007).

One approach to the definition of abnormal behavior places principal emphasis on the individual's experience of personal distress. We might say that abnormal behavior is defined in terms of subjective discomfort that leads the person to seek help from a mental health professional. This definition is fraught with problems, however. Kevin's case illustrates one of the major reasons that this approach does not work. Before his second hospitalization, Kevin was unable or unwilling to appreciate the extent of his problem or the impact his behavior had on other people. A psychologist would say that he did not have *insight* regarding his disorder. The discomfort was primarily experienced by Joyce, and she had attempted for many weeks to deny the nature of the problem. It would be useless to adopt a definition that considered Kevin's behavior to be abnormal only after he had been successfully treated.

Another approach is to define abnormal behavior in terms of statistical norms—how common or rare it is in the general population. By this definition, people with unusually high levels of anxiety or depression would be considered abnormal because their experience deviates from the expected norm. Kevin's paranoid beliefs would be defined as pathological because they are idiosyncratic. Mental disorders are, in fact, defined in terms of experiences that most people do not have.

This approach, however, does not specify *how* unusual the behavior must be before it is considered abnormal. Some conditions that are typically considered to be forms of psychopathology are extremely rare. For example, gender identity disorder, the belief that one is a member of the opposite sex trapped in the wrong body, affects less than 1 person out of every 30,000. In contrast, other mental disorders are much more common. In the United States, mood disorders affect 1 out of every 5 people at some point during their lives; alcoholism and other substance use disorders affect approximately 1 out of every 6 people (Kessler et al., 2005).

Another weakness of the statistical approach is that it does not distinguish between deviations that are harmful and those that are not. Many rare behaviors are not pathological. Some "abnormal" qualities have relatively little impact on a person's adjustment. Examples are being extremely pragmatic or unusually talkative. Other abnormal characteristics, such as exceptional intellectual, artistic, or athletic ability, may actually confer an advantage on the individual. For these reasons, the simple fact that a behavior is statistically rare cannot be used to define psychopathology.

Harmful Dysfunction

One useful approach to the definition of mental disorder has been proposed by Jerome Wakefield of Rutgers University (Wakefield, 1999). According to Wakefield, a condition should be considered a mental disorder if, and only if, it meets two criteria:

1. The condition results from the inability of some internal mechanism (mental or physical) to perform its natural function. In other words, something inside the person is not working properly. Examples of such mechanisms include those that regulate levels of emotion and those that distinguish between real auditory sensations and those that are imagined.

2. The condition causes some harm to the person as judged by the standards of the person's culture. These negative consequences are measured in terms of the person's own subjective distress or difficulty performing expected social or occupational roles.

A mental disorder, therefore, is defined in terms of **harmful dysfunction.** This definition incorporates one element that is based as much as possible on an objective evaluation of performance. The natural function of cognitive and perceptual processes is to allow the person to perceive the world in ways that are shared with other people and to engage in rational thought and problem solving. The dysfunctions in mental disorders are assumed to be the product of disruptions of thought, feeling, communication, perception, and motivation.

In Kevin's case, the most apparent dysfunctions involved failures of mechanisms that are responsible for perception, thinking, and communication. Disruption of these systems was presumably responsible for his delusional beliefs and his disorganized speech. The natural function of cognitive and perceptual processes is to allow the person to perceive the world in ways that are shared with other people and to engage in rational thought and problem solving. The natural function of language abilities is to allow the person to communicate clearly with other people. Therefore, Kevin's abnormal behavior can be viewed as a pervasive dysfunction cutting across several mental mechanisms.

The harmful dysfunction view of mental disorder recognizes that every type of dysfunction does not lead to a disorder. Only dysfunctions that result in significant harm to the person are considered to be disorders. This is the second element of the definition. There are, for example, many types of physical dysfunction, such as albinism, reversal of heart position, and fused toes, that clearly represent a significant departure from the way that some biological process ordinarily functions. These conditions are not considered to be disorders, however, because they are not necessarily harmful to the person.

Kevin's dysfunctions were, in fact, harmful to his adjustment. They affected both his family relationships—his marriage to Joyce and his ability to function as a parent—and his performance at work. His social and occupational performances were clearly impaired. There are, of course, other types of harm that are also associated with mental disorders. These include subjective distress, such as high levels of anxiety or depression, as well as more tangible outcomes, such as suicide.

The definition of abnormal behavior presented in the official *Diagnostic and Statistical Manual of Mental Disorders,* published by the American Psychiatric Association and currently in

PEARSON mypsychlab VIDEO CASE

BIPOLAR DISORDER

FELIZIANO

"Depression is the worst part. My shoulders feel weighted down, and your blood feels warmer than it is. You sink deeper and deeper."

As you watch the interview and the day-in-the-life segments, ask yourself what impact Feliziano's depression and hypomania seem to have on his ability to function. Are these mood states harmful?

TABLE 1–1 Summary of the DSM-IV-TR Definition of Mental Disorders

DEFINING CHARACTERISTICS

A behavioral or psychological syndrome (groups of associated features) that is associated with

1. Present distress (painful symptoms), or
2. Disability (impairment in one or more important areas of functioning), or with
3. A significantly increased risk of suffering death, pain, disability, or an important loss of freedom

CONDITIONS EXCLUDED FROM CONSIDERATION

This syndrome or pattern must not be merely

1. An expectable and culturally sanctioned response to a particular event (such as the death of a loved one)
2. Deviant behavior (such as the actions of political, religious, or sexual minorities)
3. Conflicts that are between the individual and society (such as voluntary efforts to express individuality)

---

its fourth revised edition—DSM-IV-TR (APA, 2000)—incorporates many of the factors that we have already discussed. This classification system is discussed in Chapter 4. This definition is summarized in Table 1–1, along with a number of conditions that are specifically excluded from the DSM-IV-TR definition of mental disorders.

The DSM-IV-TR definition places primary emphasis on the consequences of certain behavioral syndromes. Accordingly, mental disorders are defined by clusters of persistent, maladaptive behaviors that are associated with personal distress, such as anxiety or depression, or with impairment in social functioning, such as job performance or personal relationships. The official definition, therefore, recognizes the concept of dysfunction, and it spells out ways in which the harmful consequences of the disorder might be identified.

The DSM-IV-TR definition excludes voluntary behaviors, as well as beliefs and actions that are shared by religious, political, or sexual minority groups (e.g., gays and lesbians). In the 1960s, for example, members of the Yippie Party intentionally engaged in disruptive behaviors, such as throwing money off the balcony at a stock exchange. Their purpose was to challenge traditional values. These were, in some ways, maladaptive behaviors that could have resulted in social impairment if those involved had been legally prosecuted. But they were not dysfunctions. They were intentional political gestures. It makes sense to try to distinguish between voluntary behaviors and mental disorders, but the boundaries between these different forms of behavior are difficult to draw. Educated discussions of these issues depend on the consideration of a number of important questions (see Critical Thinking Matters on page 9).

In actual practice, abnormal behavior is defined in terms of an official diagnostic system. Mental health, like medicine, is an applied rather than a theoretical field. It draws on knowledge from research in the psychological and biological sciences in an effort to help people whose behavior is disordered. Mental disorders are, in some respects, those problems with which mental health professionals attempt to deal. As their activities and explanatory concepts expand, so does the list of abnormal behaviors. The practical boundaries of abnormal behavior are defined by the list of disorders that are included in the official *Diagnostic and Statistical Manual of Mental Disorders*. The categories in that manual are listed inside the back cover of this book. The DSM-IV-TR thus provides another simplistic, though practical, answer to our question as to why Kevin's behavior would be considered abnormal:

▼ Some entertainers participate in bizarre or outrageous skits, as in the hit movie *Jackass*. The behaviors are shocking, but they are voluntary. Unless accompanied by other symptoms, they would not be considered evidence of a mental disorder.

CRITICAL THINKING MATTERS

Is Sexual Addiction a Meaningful Concept?

Stories about mental disorders appear frequently in the popular media. One topic that attracted a frenzy of media attention in 1998 was a concept that has been called "sexual addiction." Shortly after the public learned that President Clinton had had an illicit sexual affair with a young White House intern, newspapers, magazines, and television programs sought interviews with professional psychologists who offered their opinions regarding the president's behavior. Why would he risk his marriage, family, and career—some said the security of the nation—for a casual sexual relationship with someone on his staff?

Many experts responded by invoking the concept of mental disorder, specifically "sexual addiction" (some called it "sexual compulsion," and one even called it the "Clinton syndrome"). The symptoms of this disorder presumably include low self-esteem, insecurity, need for reassurance, and sensation seeking, to name only a few. One expert claimed that fully 20 percent of highly successful men suffer from sexual addiction.

Most of the stories failed to mention that sexual addiction does not appear in the official diagnostic manual. That, by itself, is not an insurmountable problem. Disorders have come and gone over the years, and it's possible that this one might turn out to be useful. Perhaps it will be included in the next edition. We shouldn't reject a new concept simply because it hasn't become part of the official classification system (or accept one on faith, simply because it has). The most important thing is that we *think critically* about the issues that are raised by invoking a concept like sexual addiction.

> ### How is disordered behavior different from immoral behavior or illegal behavior?

At the broadest possible level, we must ask ourselves "What *is* a mental disorder?" How is *disordered* behavior different from immoral behavior or illegal behavior? What is gained by adopting one perspective over another? Another important question is whether sexual addiction is more useful than other similar concepts.

For example, narcissistic personality disorder includes many of the same features (such as lack of empathy, feelings of entitlement, and a history of exploiting others). What evidence supports the value of one concept over another? Has the proposed disorder been defined in a specific way that can be used consistently by mental health professionals? On what basis do the experts claim to know how many people are affected by this condition?

Students who ask these kinds of questions are engaged in critical thinking, a process in which judgments and decisions are based on a careful analysis of the best available evidence. In order to consider these issues, you need to put aside your own subjective feelings and impressions, such as whether you find a particular kind of behavior disgusting, confusing, or frightening. It may also be necessary to disregard opinions expressed by authorities whom you respect (politicians, journalists, and talk-show hosts). Be skeptical. Ask questions. Consider the evidence from different points of view, and remember that some kinds of evidence are better than others.

He would be considered to be exhibiting abnormal behavior because his experiences fit the description of schizophrenia, which is one of the officially recognized forms of mental disorder.

Mental Health Versus Absence of Disorder

The process of defining abnormal behavior raises interesting questions about the way we think about the quality of our lives when mental disorders are *not* present. What is mental health? Is optimal mental health more than the absence of mental disorder? The answer is clearly "yes." If you want to know whether one of your friends is physically fit, you would need to determine more than whether or not she is sick. In the realm of psychological functioning, people who function at the highest levels can be described as *flourishing* (Fredrickson & Losada, 2005; Keyes, 2007). They are typically people who experience many positive emotions, are interested in life, and tend to be calm and peaceful.

Flourishing people also hold positive attitudes about themselves and other people. They find meaning and direction in their lives and develop trusting relationships with other people. Complete mental health implies the presence of these adaptive characteristics. Therefore, comprehensive approaches to mental health in the community must be concerned both with efforts to diminish the frequency and impact of mental disorders and with activities designed to promote flourishing.

Culture and Diagnostic Practice

The process by which the *Diagnostic and Statistical Manual* is constructed and revised is necessarily influenced by cultural considerations. **Culture** is defined in terms of the values, beliefs, and practices that are shared by a specific community or group of people. These values and beliefs have a profound influence on opinions regarding the difference between normal and abnormal behavior (Lopez & Guarnaccia, 2000).

The impact of particular behaviors and experiences on a person's adjustment depends on the culture in which the person lives. To use Jerome Wakefield's (1992) terms, "only dysfunctions that are socially disvalued are disorders" (p. 384). Consider, for example, the DSM-IV-TR concept of female orgasmic disorder, which is defined in terms of the absence of orgasm accompanied by subjective distress or interpersonal difficulties that result from this disturbance (see Chapter 12). A woman who grew up in a society that discouraged female sexuality might not be distressed or impaired by the absence of orgasmic responses. According to DSM-IV-TR, she would not be considered to have a sexual problem. Therefore, this definition of abnormal behavior is not culturally universal and might lead us to consider a particular pattern of behavior to be abnormal in one society and not in another.

There have been many instances in which groups representing particular social values have brought pressure to bear on decisions shaping the diagnostic manual. The influence of cultural changes on psychiatric classification is perhaps nowhere better illustrated than in the case of homosexuality. In the first and second editions of the DSM, homosexuality was, by definition, a form of mental disorder, in spite of arguments expressed by scientists, who argued that homosexual behavior was not abnormal (see Chapter 12). Toward the end of the 1960s, as the gay and lesbian rights movement became more forceful and outspoken, its leaders challenged the assumption that homosexuality was pathological. They opposed the inclusion of homosexuality in the official diagnostic manual. After extended and sometimes heated discussions, the board of trustees of the American Psychiatric Association agreed to remove homosexuality as a form of mental illness. They were impressed by numerous indications, in personal appeals as well as the research literature, that homosexuality, per se, was not invariably associated with impaired functioning. They decided that, in order to be considered a form of mental disorder, a condition ought to be associated with subjective distress or seriously impaired social or occupational functioning. The stage was set for these events by gradual shifts in society's attitudes toward sexual behavior (Bullough, 1976; Minton, 2002). As more and more people came to believe that reproduction was not the main purpose of sexual behavior, tolerance for greater variety in human sexuality grew. The revision of the DSM's system for describing sexual disorders was, therefore, the product of several forces, cultural as well as political. These deliberations are a reflection of the practical nature of the manual and of the health-related professions. Value judgments are an inherent part of any attempt to define "disorder" (Sedgwick, 1981).

Many people think about culture primarily in terms of exotic patterns of behavior in distant lands. The decisions regarding homosexuality and premenstrual dysphoric disorder remind us that the values of our own culture play an intimate role in our definition of abnormal behavior. These issues also highlight the importance of cultural change. Culture is a dynamic process; it changes continuously as a result of the actions of individuals. To the extent that our definition of abnormal behavior is determined by cultural values and beliefs, we should expect that it will continue to evolve over time.

WHO EXPERIENCES ABNORMAL BEHAVIOR?

Having introduced many of the issues that are involved in the definition of abnormal behavior, we now turn to another clinical example. The woman in our second case study, Mary Childress, suffered from a serious eating disorder known as *bulimia nervosa*. Her problems raise additional questions about the definition of abnormal behavior.

▶ How thin is too thin? This young dancer suffers from an eating disorder. Some experts maintain that the differences between abnormal and normal behavior are essentially differences in degree, that is, quantitative differences.

CASE **STUDY** A College Student's Eating Disorder

Mary Childress was, in most respects, a typical 18-year-old sophomore at a large state university. She was popular with other students and a good student, in spite of the fact that she spent little time studying. Everything about Mary's life was relatively normal—except for her bingeing and purging.

Mary's eating patterns were wildly erratic. She preferred to skip breakfast entirely and often missed lunch as well. By the middle of the afternoon, she could no longer ignore the hunger pangs. At that point, on two or three days out of the week, Mary would drive her car to the drive-in window of a fast-food restaurant. Her typical order included three or four double cheeseburgers, several orders of french fries, and a large milkshake (or maybe two). Then she binged, devouring all the food as she drove around town by herself. Later she would go to a private bathroom, where she wouldn't be seen by anyone, and purge the food from her stomach by vomiting. Afterward, she returned to her room, feeling angry, frustrated, and ashamed.

Mary was tall and weighed 110 pounds. She believed that her body was unattractive, especially her thighs and hips. She was extremely critical of herself and had worried about her weight for many years. Her weight fluctuated quite a bit, from a low of 97 pounds when she was a senior in high school to a high of 125 during her first year at the university. Her mother was a "full-figured" woman. Mary swore to herself at an early age that she would never let herself gain as much weight as her mother had.

Purging had originally seemed like an ideal solution to the problem of weight control. You could eat whatever you wanted and quickly get rid of it so you wouldn't get fat. Unfortunately, the vomiting became a vicious trap. Disgusted by her own behavior, Mary often promised herself that she would never binge and purge again, but she couldn't stop the cycle.

> *Disgusted by her own behavior, Mary often promised herself that she would never binge and purge again, but she couldn't stop the cycle.*

For the past year Mary had been vomiting at least once almost every day and occasionally as many as three or four times a day. The impulse to purge was very strong. Mary felt bloated after having only a bowl of cereal and a glass of orange juice. If she ate a sandwich and drank a diet soda, she began to ruminate about what she had eaten, thinking, "I've got to get rid of that!" Usually, before long, she found a bathroom and threw up. Her excessive binges were less frequent than the vomiting. Four or five times a week she experienced an overwhelming urge to eat forbidden foods, especially fast food. Her initial reaction was usually a short-lived attempt to resist the impulse. Then she would space out or "go into a zone," becoming only vaguely aware of what she was doing and feeling. In the midst of a serious binge, Mary felt completely helpless and unable to control herself.

There weren't any obvious physical signs that would alert someone to Mary's eating problems, but the vomiting had begun to wreak havoc with her body, especially her digestive system. She had suffered severe throat infections and frequent, intense stomach pains. Her dentist had noticed problems beginning to develop with her teeth and gums, undoubtedly a consequence of constant exposure to strong stomach acids.

Mary's eating problem started to develop when she was 15. She had been seriously involved in gymnastics for several years but eventually developed a knee condition that forced her to give up the sport. She gained a few pounds in the next month or two and decided to lose weight by dieting. Buoyed by unrealistic expectations about the immediate, positive benefits of a diet that she had seen advertised on television, Mary initially adhered rigidly to its recommended regimen. Six months later, after three of these fad diets had failed, she started throwing up as a way to control her intake of food.

Mary's problems persisted after she graduated from high school and began her college education. She felt guilty and ashamed about her eating problems. She was much too embarrassed to let anyone know what she was doing and would never eat more than a few mouthfuls of food in a public place like the dorm cafeteria. Her roommate, Julie, was from a small town on the other side of the state. They got along reasonably well, but Mary managed to conceal her bingeing and purging, thanks in large part to the fact that she was able to bring her own car to campus. The car allowed her to drive away from campus several times a week so that she could binge.

As you are reading the case, ask yourself about the impact of Mary's eating disorder on her subjective experience and social adjustment. In what ways are these consequences similar to those seen in Kevin Warner's case? How are they different? This case also introduces another important concept associated with the way that we think about abnormal behavior: How can we identify the boundary between normal and abnormal behavior? Is there an obvious distinction between eating patterns that are considered to be part of a mental disorder and those that are not? Or is there a gradual progression from one end of a continuum to the other, with each step fading gradually into the next?

Mary's case illustrates many of the characteristic features of bulimia nervosa. As in Kevin's case, her behavior could be considered abnormal not only because it fit the criteria for one of the categories in DSM-IV-TR but also because she suffered from a dysfunction (in this case, of the mechanisms that regulate appetite) that was obviously harmful. The impact of the disorder was greatest in terms of her physical health: Eating disorders can be fatal if they are not properly treated because they affect so many vital organs of the body, including the heart and kidneys. Mary's social functioning and her academic performance were not yet seriously impaired. There are many different ways in which to measure the harmful effects of abnormal behavior.

Mary's case also illustrates the subjective pain that is associated with many types of abnormal behavior. In contrast to Kevin, Mary was acutely aware of her disorder. She was frustrated and unhappy. In an attempt to relieve this emotional distress, she entered psychological treatment. Unfortunately, painful emotions associated with mental disorders can also interfere with, or delay, the decision to look for professional help. Guilt, shame, and embarrassment often accompany psychological problems and sometimes make it difficult to confide in another person, even though the average therapist has seen such problems many times over.

Frequency in and Impact on Community Populations

Many important decisions about mental disorders are based on data regarding the frequency with which these disorders occur. At least 3 percent of college women would meet diagnostic criteria for bulimia nervosa (see Chapter 10). These data are a source of considerable concern, especially among those who are responsible for health services on college campuses.

Epidemiology is the scientific study of the frequency and distribution of disorders within a population (Gordis, 2004). Epidemiologists are concerned with questions such as whether the frequency of a disorder has increased or decreased during a particular period, whether it is more common in one geographic area than in another, and whether certain types of people—based on such factors as gender, race, and socioeconomic status—are at greater risk than other types for the development of the disorder. Health administrators often use such information to make decisions about the allocation of resources for professional training programs, treatment facilities, and research projects.

Two terms are particularly important in epidemiological research. **Incidence** refers to the number of new cases of a disorder that appear in a population during a specific period of time. **Prevalence** refers to the total number of active cases, both old and new, that are present in a population during a specific period of time (Susser et al., 2006). The *lifetime prevalence* of a disorder is the total proportion of people in a given population who have been affected by the disorder at some point during their lives. Some studies also report 12-month prevalence rates, indicating the proportion of the population that met criteria for the disorder during the year prior to the assessment. Lifetime prevalence rates are higher than 12-month prevalence rates because some people who had problems in the past and then recovered will be counted with regard to lifetime disorders but not be counted for the most recent year.

Lifetime Prevalence and Gender Differences How prevalent are the various forms of abnormal behavior? The best and most recent data regarding this question come from a large-scale study known as the *National Comorbidity Survey Replication* (NCS-R) conducted between 2001 and 2003 (Kessler et al., 2005; Kessler, Merikangas, & Wang, 2007). Members of this research team interviewed a nationally representative sample of approximately 9,000 people living in the continental United States. Questions were asked pertaining to several (but not all) of the major disorders listed in the DSM-IV. The NCS-R found that 46 percent of the people they interviewed received at least one *lifetime* diagnosis, with first onset of symptoms usually occurring during childhood or adolescence. This proportion of the population is much higher than many people expect, and it underscores the point that we made at the beginning of this chapter: All of us can expect to encounter the challenges of a mental disorder—either for ourselves or for someone we love—at some point during our lives.

Figure 1–1 lists some results from this study using lifetime prevalence rates—the number of people who had experienced each disorder at some

Frequency of Mental Disorders in the Community

(Bar chart showing Lifetime Prevalence (percent) on the x-axis from 0 to 18 for the following disorders: Major depression, Alcohol abuse, Drug abuse, Posttraumatic stress disorder, Panic disorder, Bipolar mood disorder, Obsessive–compulsive disorder, Schizophrenia, Bulimia nervosa, Anorexia nervosa)

FIGURE 1–1: Lifetime prevalence rates for various mental disorders (NCS-R data).

Source: From "Lifetime Prevalence and Age-of-Onset Distributions of DSM-IV Disorders in the National Comorbidity Survey Replication" by R. C. Kessler, et al., *Archives of General Psychiatry, 62,* (2005), 593-603. Copyright © 2005 by American Medical Association. Reprinted with permission of the publisher.

point during their lives. The most prevalent specific type of disorder was major depression (17 percent). Substance use disorders and various kinds of anxiety disorders were also relatively common. Substantially lower lifetime prevalence rates were found for schizophrenia and eating disorders (bulimia and anorexia), which affect approximately 1 percent of the population. These lifetime prevalence rates are consistent with data reported by earlier epidemiological studies of mental disorders.

Although many mental disorders are quite common, they are not always seriously debilitating, and some people who qualify for a diagnosis do not need immediate treatment. The NCS-R investigators assigned each case a score with regard to severity, based on the severity of symptoms as well as the level of occupational and social impairment that the person experienced. Averaged across all of the disorders diagnosed in the past 12 months, 40 percent of cases were rated as "mild," 37 percent as "moderate," and only 22 percent as "severe." Mood disorders were the most likely to be rated as severe (45 percent) while anxiety disorders were less likely to be rated as severe (23 percent).

Epidemiological studies such as the NCS-R have consistently found gender differences for many types of mental disorder: Major depression, anxiety disorders, and eating disorders are more common among women; alcoholism and antisocial personality are more common among men. Some other conditions, like bipolar mood disorder, appear with equal frequency in both women and men. Patterns of this sort raise interesting questions about possible causal mechanisms. What conditions would make women more vulnerable to one kind of disorder and men more vulnerable to another? There are many possibilities, including factors such as hormones, patterns of learning, and social pressures. We will discuss gender differences in more detail in subsequent chapters of this book.

Comorbidity and Disease Burden Most severe disorders are concentrated in a relatively small segment of the population. Often these are people who simultaneously qualify for more than one diagnosis, such as major depression and alcoholism. The presence of more than one condition within the same period of time is known as **comorbidity** (or co-occurrence). Twenty-three percent of the people in the NCS-R sample had three or more 12-month disorders, and 50 percent of those cases were rated as being "severe." While mental disorders occur relatively frequently,

the most serious problems are concentrated in a smaller group of people who have more than one disorder. These findings have shifted the emphasis of epidemiological studies from counting the absolute number of people who have any kind of mental disorder to measuring the functional impairment associated with these problems.

Mental disorders are highly prevalent, but how do we measure the extent of their impact on people's lives? And how does that impact compare to the effects of other diseases? These are important questions when policymakers must establish priorities for various types of training, research, and health services.

Epidemiologists measure disease burden by combining two factors: mortality and disability. The common measure is based on time: lost years of healthy life, which might be caused by premature death (compared to the person's standard life expectancy) or living with a disability (weighted for severity). For purposes of comparison among different forms of disease and injury, the disability produced by major depression is considered to be equivalent to that associated with blindness or paraplegia. A psychotic disorder such as schizophrenia leads to disability that is comparable to that associated with quadriplegia.

How does the impact of mental disorders compare to that of other health problems?

The World Health Organization (WHO) sponsored an ambitious study called the Global Burden of Disease Study, which used these measures to evaluate and compare the impact of more than 100 forms of disease and injury throughout the world (Lopez et al., 2006). Although mental disorders are responsible for only 1 percent of all deaths, they produce 47 percent of all disability in economically developed countries, like the United States, and 28 percent of all disability worldwide. The combined index (mortality plus disability) reveals that, as a combined category, mental disorders are the second leading source of disease burden in developed countries (see Figure 1–2 on page 14). Investigators in the WHO study predict that, relative to other types of health problems, the burden of mental disorders will increase by the year 2020. These surprising results indicate strongly that mental disorders are one of the world's greatest health challenges.

Cross-Cultural Comparisons

As the evidence regarding the global burden of disease clearly documents, mental disorders affect people all over the world. That does not

Comparison of the Impact of Mental Disorders and Other Medical Conditions on People's Lives

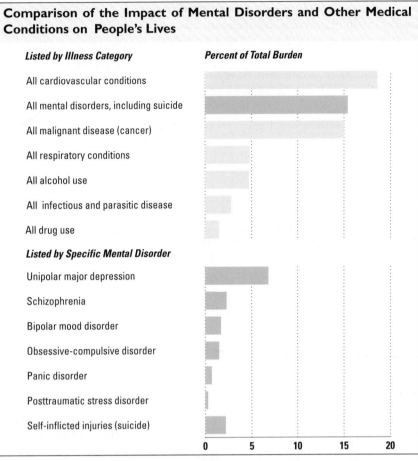

Listed by Illness Category   *Percent of Total Burden*

All cardiovascular conditions

All mental disorders, including suicide

All malignant disease (cancer)

All respiratory conditions

All alcohol use

All infectious and parasitic disease

All drug use

Listed by Specific Mental Disorder

Unipolar major depression

Schizophrenia

Bipolar mood disorder

Obsessive-compulsive disorder

Panic disorder

Posttraumatic stress disorder

Self-inflicted injuries (suicide)

0   5   10   15   20

FIGURE 1–2: Disease burden in economically developed countries measured in disability-adjusted life years (DALYs).

Source: C. L. Murray, and A. D. Lopez, Eds., 1996, *The Global Burden of Disease: A Comprehensive Assessment of Mortality and Disability from Diseases, Injuries, and Risk Factors in 1990 and Projected to 2020,* Cambridge, MA: Harvard University Press.

mean, however, that the symptoms of psychopathology and the expression of emotional distress take the same form in all cultures. Epidemiological studies comparing the frequency of mental disorders in different cultures suggest that some disorders, like schizophrenia, show important consistencies in cross-cultural comparisons. They are found in virtually every culture that social scientists have studied.

Other disorders, like bulimia, are more specifically associated with cultural factors, as revealed by comparisons of prevalence in different parts of the world and changes in prevalence over generations. Almost 90 percent of bulimic patients are women. Within the United States, the incidence of bulimia is much higher among university women than among working women, and it is more common among younger women than among older women. The prevalence of bulimia is much higher in Western nations than in other parts of the world. Furthermore, the number of cases increased dramatically during the latter part of the twentieth century (Keel & Klump, 2003). These patterns suggest that holding particular sets of values related to eating and to women's appearance is an important ingredient in establishing risk for development of an eating disorder.

The strength and nature of the relationship between culture and psychopathology vary from one disorder to the next. Several general conclusions can be drawn from cross-cultural studies of

▶ Mental disorders are found in relatively similar numbers throughout the world, but approaches to treatment vary from one culture to the next. In China, acupuncture is used frequently to treat people who are depressed. Medication and psychotherapy are the most frequently used forms of treatment for depression in the United States and Europe.

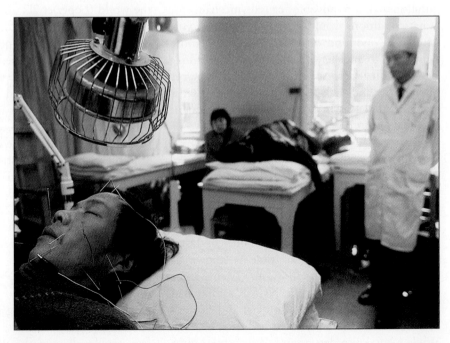

psychopathology (Draguns & Tanaka-Matsumi, 2003), including the following points:

- All mental disorders are shaped, to some extent, by cultural factors.
- No mental disorders are entirely due to cultural or social factors.
- Psychotic disorders are less influenced by culture than are nonpsychotic disorders.
- The symptoms of certain disorders are more likely to vary across cultures than are the disorders themselves.

We will return to these points as we discuss specific disorders, such as depression, phobias, and alcoholism, throughout this book.

THE MENTAL HEALTH PROFESSIONS

People receive treatment for psychological problems in many different settings and from various kinds of service providers. Specialized mental health professionals, such as psychiatrists, psychologists, and social workers, treat fewer than half (40 percent) of those people who seek help for mental disorders (Manderscheid et al., 1999). Roughly one-third (34 percent) are treated by primary care physicians, who are most likely to prescribe some form of medication. The remaining 26 percent of mental health services are delivered by social agencies and self-help groups, such as Alcoholics Anonymous.

Many forms of specialized training prepare people to provide professional assistance to those who suffer from mental disorders. Table 1–2 presents estimated numbers of different types of mental health professionals currently practicing in the United States. The overall number of professionals who provide mental health services expanded dramatically during the 1990s, with most of this growth occurring among nonphysicians (Scheffler, Ivey, & Garrett, 1998). Most of these professions require extensive clinical experience in addition to formal academic instruction. In order to provide direct services to clients, psychiatrists, psychologists, social workers, counselors, nurses, and marriage and family therapists must be licensed in their own specialties by state boards of examiners.

Psychiatry is the branch of medicine that is concerned with the study and treatment of

TABLE 1–2 Estimated Number of Clinically Trained Professionals Providing Mental Health Services in the United States

PROFESSION	NUMBER
Psychiatrists	40,900
Clinical psychologists	77,500
Social workers	194,600
Marriage and family therapists	47,100
Psychiatric nurses	16,600
Counselors	111,900
Psychosocial rehabilitation providers	100,000

Source: F. F. Duffy et al., "Mental Health Practitioners and Trainees," in R. W. Manderscheid and M. J. Henderson, Eds., *Mental Health, United States, 2002.* Rockville, MD; U.S. Department of Health and Human Services, Chapter 21, Table 1 (go to www.mentalhealth.org/publications/allpubs/SMA04-3938).

mental disorders. Psychiatrists complete the normal sequence of coursework and internship training in a medical school (usually four years) before going on to receive specialized residency training (another four years) that is focused on abnormal behavior. By virtue of their medical training, psychiatrists are licensed to practice medicine and therefore are able to prescribe medication. Most psychiatrists are also trained in the use of psychosocial intervention.

Clinical psychology is concerned with the application of psychological science to the assessment and treatment of mental disorders. A clinical psychologist typically completes five years of graduate study in a department of psychology, as well as a one-year internship, before

Who provides help for people with mental disorders?

▼ Clinical psychologists perform many roles. Some provide direct clinical services. Many are involved in research, teaching, and various administrative activities.

receiving a doctoral degree. Clinical psychologists are trained in the use of psychological assessment procedures and in the use of psychotherapy. Within clinical psychology, there are two primary types of clinical training programs. One course of study, which leads to the Ph.D. (doctor of philosophy) degree, involves a traditional sequence of graduate training with major emphasis on research methods. The other approach, which culminates in a Psy.D. (doctor of psychology) degree, places greater emphasis on practical skills of assessment and treatment and does not require an independent research project for the dissertation. One can also obtain a Ph.D. degree in counseling psychology, a more applied field that focuses on training, assessment, and therapy.

Social work is a third profession that is concerned with helping people to achieve an effective level of psychosocial functioning. Most practicing social workers have a master's degree in social work. In contrast to psychology and psychiatry, social work is based less on a body of scientific knowledge than on a commitment to action. Social work is practiced in a wide range of settings, from courts and prisons to schools and hospitals, as well as other social service agencies. The emphasis tends to be on social and cultural factors, such as the effects of poverty on the availability of educational and health services, rather than on individual differences in personality or psychopathology. Psychiatric social workers receive specialized training in the treatment of mental health problems.

Like social workers, professional counselors work in many different settings, ranging from schools and government agencies to mental health centers and private practice. Most are trained at the master's degree level, and the emphasis of their activity is also on providing direct service. Marriage and family therapy (MFT) is a multidisciplinary field in which professionals are trained to provide psychotherapy. Most MFTs are trained at the master's level, and many hold a degree in social work, counseling, or psychology as well. Although the theoretical orientation is focused on couples and family issues, approximately half of the people treated by MFTs are seen in individual psychotherapy. Psychiatric nursing is a rapidly growing field. Training for this profession typically involves a bachelor's degree in nursing plus graduate level training (at least a master's degree) in the treatment of mental health problems.

Another approach to mental health services that is expanding rapidly in size and influence is psychosocial rehabilitation (PSR). Professionals in this area work in crisis, residential, and case management programs for people with severe forms of disorder, such as schizophrenia. PSR workers teach people practical, day-to-day skills that are necessary for living in the community, thereby reducing the need for long-term hospitalization and minimizing the level of disability experienced by their clients. Graduate training is not required for most PSR positions; three out of four people providing PSR services have either a high school education or a bachelor's degree.

It is difficult to say with certainty what the mental health professions will be like in the future. Boundaries between professions change as a function of progress in the development of therapeutic procedures, economic pressures, legislative action, and courtroom decisions. This has been particularly true in the field of mental health, where enormous changes have taken place over the past few decades (Scheffler, Ivey, & Garrett, 1998). Reform is currently being driven by the pervasive influence of managed care, which refers to the way that services are financed. For example, health insurance companies typically place restrictions on the types of services that will be reimbursed, as well as the specific professionals who can provide them. Managed care places a high priority on cost containment and the evaluation of treatment effectiveness. Legislative issues that determine the scope of clinical practice are also very important. Many psychologists are pursuing the right to prescribe medication (Robiner et al., 2003; Welsh, 2003). Decisions regarding this issue will also have a dramatic impact on the boundaries that separate the mental health professions. Ongoing conflicts over the increasing price of health care, priorities for treatment, and access to services suggest that debates over the rights and privileges of patients and their therapists will intensify in coming years.

One thing is certain about the future of the mental health professions: There will always be a demand for people who are trained to help those suffering from abnormal behavior. Many people experience mental disorders. Unfortunately, most of those who are in need do not get help. Among people in the United States who have an active mental disorder, only 20 percent received treatment for their problems (Kessler et al., 1994).

Many factors may account for this fact. Some people who qualify for a diagnosis may not be so impaired as to seek treatment; others, as we shall see, may not recognize their disorder. In some cases, treatment may not be available, the person may not have the time or resources to obtain treatment, or the person may have tried treatments in the past that failed (see Getting Help at the end of this chapter.)

PSYCHOPATHOLOGY IN HISTORICAL CONTEXT

Throughout history, many other societies have held very different views of the problems that we consider to be mental disorders. Before leaving this introductory chapter, we must begin to place contemporary approaches to psychopathology in historical perspective.

The search for explanations of the causes of abnormal behavior dates to ancient times, as do conflicting opinions about the etiology of emotional disorders. References to abnormal behavior have been found in ancient accounts from Chinese, Hebrew, and Egyptian societies. Many of these records attribute abnormal behavior to the disfavor of the gods or the mischief of demons. In fact, abnormal behavior continues to be attributed to demons in some preliterate societies today.

The Greek Tradition in Medicine

More earthly and less supernatural accounts of the etiology of psychopathology can be traced to the Greek physician Hippocrates (460–377 B.C.), who ridiculed demonological accounts of illness and insanity. Instead, Hippocrates hypothesized that abnormal behavior, like other forms of disease, had natural causes. Health depended on maintaining a natural balance within the body, specifically a balance of four body fluids (which were also known as the four humors): blood, phlegm, black bile, and yellow bile. Hippocrates argued that various types of disorder, including psychopathology, resulted from either an excess or a deficiency of one of these four fluids. The specifics of Hippocrates' theories obviously have little value today, but his systematic attempt to uncover natural, biological explanations for all types of illness represented an enor-

THE LEECH'S CHAMBER.

▲ This 16-century illustration shows sick people going to the doctor who attempts to cure their problems by extracting blood from them using a leech. The rationale for such treatment procedures was to restore the proper balance of bodily fluids.

mously important departure from previous ways of thinking.

The Hippocratic perspective dominated medical thought in Western countries until the middle of the nineteenth century (Golub, 1994). People trained in the Hippocratic tradition viewed "disease" as a unitary concept. In other words, physicians (and others who were given responsibility for healing people who were disturbed or suffering) did not distinguish between mental disorders and other types of illness. All problems were considered to be the result of an imbalance of body fluids, and treatment procedures were designed in an attempt to restore the ideal balance. These were often called "heroic" treatments because they were drastic (and frequently painful) attempts to quickly reverse the course of an illness. They involved bloodletting (intentionally cutting the person to reduce the amount of blood in the body) and purging (the induction of vomiting), as well as the use of heat and cold. These practices continued to be part of standard medical treatments well into the nineteenth century (Starr, 1982).

The Creation of the Asylum

In Europe during the Middle Ages, "lunatics" and "idiots," as the mentally ill and mentally retarded were commonly called, aroused little interest and were given marginal care. Most people lived in rural settings and made their living through agricultural activities. Disturbed behavior was considered to be the responsibility of the family rather than the community or the state. Many people were kept at home by their families, and others roamed freely as beggars. Mentally disturbed people who were violent or appeared dangerous often were imprisoned with criminals. Those who could not subsist on their own were placed in almshouses for the poor.

In the 1600s and 1700s, "insane asylums" were established to house the mentally disturbed. Several factors changed the way that society viewed people with mental disorders and reinforced the relatively new belief that the community as a whole should be responsible for their care (Grob, 1994). Perhaps most important was a change in economic, demographic, and social conditions. Consider, for example, the situation in the United States at the beginning of the nineteenth century. The period between 1790 and 1850 saw rapid population growth and the rise of large cities. The increased urbanization of the American population was accompanied by a shift from an agricultural to an industrial economy. Lunatic asylums—the original mental hospitals—were created to serve heavily populated cities and to assume responsibilities that had previously been performed by individual families.

Early asylums were little more than human warehouses, but as the nineteenth century began, the moral treatment movement led to improved conditions in at least some mental hospitals. Founded on a basic respect for human dignity and the belief that humanistic care would help to relieve mental illness, moral treatment reform efforts were instituted by leading mental health professionals of the day, such as Benjamin Rush in the United States, Phillipe Pinel in France, and William Tuke in England. Rather than simply confining mental patients, moral treatment offered support, care, and a degree of freedom. Belief in the importance of reason and the potential benefits of science played an important role in the moral treatment movement. In contrast to the fatalistic, supernatural explanations that had prevailed during the Middle Ages, these reformers touted an optimistic view, arguing that mental disorders could be treated successfully.

Many of the large mental institutions in the United States were built in the nineteenth century as a result of the philosophy of moral treatment. In the middle of the 1800s, the mental health advocate Dorothea Dix was a leader in this movement. Dix argued that treating the mentally ill in hospitals was both more humane and more economical than caring for them haphazardly in their communities, and she urged that special facilities be built to house mental patients. Dix and like-minded reformers were successful in their efforts. In 1830, there were only four public mental hospitals in the United States that housed a combined total of fewer than 200 patients. By 1880, there were 75 public mental hospitals, with a total population of more than 35,000 residents (Torrey, 1988).

The creation of large institutions for the treatment of mental patients led to the development of a new profession—psychiatry. By the middle of the 1800s, superintendents of asylums for the insane were almost always physicians who had experience in the care of people with severe mental disorders. The Association of Medical Superintendents of American Institutions for the Insane (AMSAII), which later became the American Psychiatric Association (APA), was founded in 1844. The large patient populations within these institutions provided an opportunity for these men to observe various types of psychopathology over an extended period of time. They soon began to publish their ideas regarding the causes of these conditions, and they also experimented with new treatment methods (Grob, 1994).

Worcester Lunatic Hospital: A Model Institution

In 1833, the state of Massachusetts opened a publicly supported asylum for lunatics, a term used at the time to describe people with mental disorders, in Worcester. Samuel Woodward, the asylum's first superintendent, also became the first president of the AMSAII. Woodward became very well known throughout the United States and Europe because of his claims that mental disorders could be cured just like other types of disease. We will describe this institution and its superintendent briefly because, in many ways, it became a model for psychiatric care on which other nineteenth-century hospitals were built.

Woodward's ideas about the causes of disorder represented a combination of physical and moral considerations. Moral factors focused on the person's lifestyle. Violations of "natural" or conventional behavior could presumably cause mental disorders. Judgments regarding the nature of these violations were based on the prevailing middle-class, Protestant standards that were held by Woodward and his peers, who were almost invariably well educated, white males. After treating several hundred patients during his first 10 years at the Worcester asylum, Woodward argued that at least half of the cases could be traced to immoral behavior, improper living conditions, and exposure to unnatural stresses. Specific examples included intemperance (heavy drinking), masturbation, overwork, domestic difficulties, excessive ambition, faulty education, personal disappointment, marital problems, excessive religious enthusiasm, jealousy, and pride (Grob, 1994). The remaining cases were attributed to physical causes, such as poor health or a blow to the head.

Treatment at the Worcester Lunatic Hospital included a blend of physical and moral procedures. If mental disorders were often caused by improper behavior and difficult life circumstances, presumably they could be cured by moving the person to a more appropriate and therapeutic environment, the asylum. Moral treatment focused on efforts to reeducate the patient, fostering the development of self-control that would allow the person to return to a "healthy" lifestyle. Procedures included occupational therapy, religious exercises, and recreation. Mechanical restraints were employed only when considered necessary.

Moral treatments were combined with a mixture of physical procedures. These included standard heroic interventions, such as bleeding and purging, which the asylum superintendents had learned as part of their medical training. For example, some symptoms were thought to be produced by inflammation of the brain, and it was believed that bleeding would restore the natural balance of fluids. Woodward and his colleagues also employed various kinds of drugs. Patients who were excited, agitated, or violent were often treated with opium or morphine. Depressed patients were given laxatives.

Woodward claimed that "no disease, of equal severity, can be treated with greater success than insanity, if the remedies are applied sufficiently early." He reported that the recovery rates at the Worcester hospital varied from 82 percent to 91 percent between 1833 and 1845. His reports were embraced and endorsed by other members of the young psychiatric profession. They fueled enthusiasm for establishing more large public hospitals, thus aiding the efforts of Dorothea Dix and other advocates for public support of mental health treatment.

▲ The Massachusetts Lunatic Asylum (as it appeared in 1835) was the first large state mental institution in the United States.

From the collection of the Worcester Historical Museum, Worcester, Massachusetts.

Lessons from the History of Psychopathology

The invention and expansion of public mental hospitals set in motion a process of systematic observation and scientific inquiry that led directly to our current system of mental health care. The creation of psychiatry as a professional group, committed to treating and understanding psychopathology, laid the foundation for expanded public concern and financial resources for solving the problems of mental disorders.

There are, of course, many aspects of nineteenth-century psychiatry that, in retrospect, seem to have been naive or misguided. To take only one example, it seems silly to have thought that masturbation would cause mental disorders. In fact, masturbation is now taught and encouraged as part of treatment for certain types of sexual dysfunction (see Chapter 12). The obvious cultural biases that influenced the etiological hypotheses of Woodward and his colleagues seem quite unreasonable today. But, of course, our own values and beliefs influence the ways in which we define, think about, and treat mental disorders. Mental disorders cannot be defined in a cultural vacuum or in a completely objective fashion. The best we can do is to be aware of the problem of bias and include a variety of cultural and social perspectives in thinking about and defining the issues (Manson, 1994).

The other lesson that we can learn from history involves the importance of scientific research. Viewed from the perspective of contemporary care, we can easily be skeptical of Samuel Woodward's claims regarding the

What was the rationale for moral treatment programs?

phenomenal success of treatment at the Worcester asylum. No one today believes that 90 percent of seriously disturbed, psychotic patients can be cured by currently available forms of treatment. Therefore, it is preposterous to assume that such astounding success might have been achieved at the Worcester Lunatic Hospital. During the nineteenth century, physicians were not trained in scientific research methods. Their optimistic statements about treatment outcome were accepted, in large part, on the basis of their professional authority. Clearly, Woodward's enthusiastic assertions should have been evaluated with more stringent, scientific methods.

Unfortunately, the type of naive acceptance that met Woodward's idealistic claims has become a regrettable tradition. For the past 150 years, mental health professionals and the public alike have repeatedly embraced new treatment procedures that have been hailed as cures for mental disorders. Perhaps most notorious was a group of somatic (bodily) treatment procedures that was introduced during the 1920s and 1930s (Valenstein, 1986). They included inducing fever, insulin comas, and lobotomy, a crude form of brain surgery (see Table 1–3). These dramatic procedures, which have subsequently proved to be ineffective, were accepted with the same enthusiasm that greeted the invention of large public institutions in nineteenth-century America. Thousands of patients were subjected to these procedures, which remained widespread until the early 1950s, when more effective pharmacological treatments were discovered. The history of psychopathology teaches us that people who claim that a new form of treatment is effective should be expected to prove it scientifically (see Research Methods).

METHODS FOR THE SCIENTIFIC STUDY OF MENTAL DISORDERS

This book will provide you with an introduction to the scientific study of psychopathology. The application of science to questions regarding abnormal behavior carries with it the implicit assumption that these problems can be studied systematically and objectively. Such a systematic and objective study is the basis for finding order in the frequently chaotic and puzzling world of mental disorders. This order will eventually allow us to understand the processes by which abnormal behaviors are created and maintained.

Clinical scientists adopt an attitude of open minded skepticism, tempered by an appreciation for the research methods that are used to collect empirical data. They formulate specific hypotheses, test them, and then refine them based on the results of these tests. For example, suppose you formulated the hypothesis that people who are depressed will improve if they eat more than a certain amount of chocolate every day. This hypothesis could be tested in a number of ways, using the methods discussed throughout this book. In order to get the most from it, you may have to set aside—at least temporarily—personal beliefs that you have already acquired about mental disorders. Try to adopt an objective, skeptical attitude. We hope to pique your curiosity and share with you the satisfaction, as well as perhaps some of the frustration, of searching for answers to questions about complex behavior problems.

TABLE 1–3 Somatic Treatments Introduced and Widely Employed in the 1920s and 1930s

NAME	PROCEDURE	ORIGINAL RATIONALE
Fever therapy	Blood from people with malaria was injected into psychiatric patients so that they would develop a fever.	Observation that symptoms sometimes disappeared in patients who became ill with typhoid fever
Insulin coma therapy	Insulin was injected into psychiatric patients to lower the sugar content of the blood and induce a hypoglycemic state and deep coma.	Observed mental changes among some diabetic drug addicts who were treated with insulin
Lobotomy	A sharp knife was inserted through a hole that was bored in the patient's skull, severing nerve fibers connecting the frontal lobes to the rest of the brain.	Observation that the same surgical procedure with chimpanzees led to a reduction in the display of negative emotion during stress

Note: Lack of critical evaluation of these procedures is belied by the unusual honors bestowed upon their inventors. Julius Wagner-Jauregg, an Austrian psychiatrist, was awarded a Nobel Prize in 1927 for his work in developing fever therapy. Egaz Moniz, a Portuguese psychiatrist, was awarded a Nobel Prize in 1946 for introduction of the lobotomy.

The Uses and Limitations of Case Studies

We have already presented one source of information regarding mental disorders: the **case study,** an in-depth look at the symptoms and circumstances surrounding one person's mental disturbance. For many people, our initial ideas about the nature and potential causes of abnormal behavior are shaped by personal experience with a close friend or family member who has struggled with a psychological disorder. We use a number of case studies in this book to illustrate the symptoms of psychopathology and to raise questions about their development. Therefore,

we should consider the ways in which case studies can be helpful in the study of psychopathology, as well as some of their limitations.

A case study presents a description of the problems experienced by one particular person. Detailed case studies can provide an exhaustive catalog of the symptoms that the person displayed, the manner in which these symptoms emerged, the developmental and family history that preceded the onset of the disorder, and whatever response the person may have shown to treatment efforts. This material often forms the basis for hypotheses about the causes of a person's problems. For example, based on Mary's case, one might speculate that depression plays a role in

RESEARCH METHODS Who Must Provide Scientific Evidence?

Scientists have established a basic and extremely important rule for making and testing any new hypothesis: The scientist who makes a new prediction must prove it to be true. Scientists are not obligated to disprove other researchers' assertions. Until a hypothesis is supported by empirical evidence, the community of scientists assumes that the new prediction is false.

The concepts of the experimental hypothesis and the null hypothesis are central to understanding this essential rule of science. An **experimental hypothesis** is any new prediction, such as the idea that eating chocolate can alleviate depression, made by an investigator. Researchers must adopt and state their experimental hypothesis in both correlational studies and experiments (discussed in Research Methods in Chapters 2 and 3). In all scientific research, the **null hypothesis** is the alternative to the experimental hypothesis. The null hypothesis always predicts that the experimental hypothesis is not true, for example, that eating chocolate does not make depressed people feel better. The rules of science dictate that scientists must assume that the null hypothesis holds until research contradicts it. That is, the burden of proof falls on the scientist who makes a new prediction, who offers an experimental hypothesis.

These rules of science are analogous to rules about the burden of proof that have been adopted in trial courts. In U.S. courtrooms, the law assumes that a defendant is innocent until proven guilty. Defendants do not need to prove their innocence; rather, prosecutors need to prove the defendant's guilt. Thus the null hypothesis is analogous to the assumption of innocence, and the

burden of proof in science falls on any scientist who challenges the null hypothesis, just as it falls on the prosecutor in a court trial.

These rules in science and in law serve important purposes. Both are conservative principles designed to protect the field from false assertions. Our legal philosophy is that "it is better to let 10 guilty people go free than to punish 1 innocent person." Scientists adopt a similar philosophy—that false "scientific evidence" is more dangerous than undetected knowledge. Because of these safeguards, we can be reasonably confident when an experimental hypothesis is supported or when a defendant is found guilty.

Some advertisements claim the null hypothesis: "No other drug has been proven to be more effective." Don't they have a burden to prove that their drug is more effective than the others?

We can easily apply these concepts and rules to claims that were made for the effectiveness of treatment methods such as lobotomy. In this example, the experimental hypothesis is that severing the nerve fibers that connect the frontal lobes to other areas of the brain will result in a significant decrease in psychotic symptoms. The null hypothesis is that this treatment is no more effective than having no treatment at all. According to the rules of science, a clinician who claims to have discovered a new treatment must prove that it

is true. Scientists are not obligated to prove that the assertion is false, because the null hypothesis holds until it is rejected.

The value of this conservative approach is obvious when we consider the needless suffering and permanent neurological dysfunction that was ultimately inflicted upon thousands of patients who were given lobotomies or subjected to fevers and comas during the 1940s (Valenstein, 1986). Had surgeons assumed that lobotomies did not work, many patients' brains would have been left intact. Similar conclusions can be drawn about less invasive procedures, such as institutionalization, medication, and psychotherapy. These treatments are also associated with costs, which range from financial considerations—certainly important in today's health care environment—to the disappointment brought about by false hopes. In all these cases, clinicians who provide mental health services should be required to demonstrate scientifically that their treatment procedures are effective (Dawes, 1994; McFall, 2001).

There is one more similarity between the rules of science and the rules of the courtroom. Courtroom verdicts do not lead to a judgment that the defendant is "innocent," but only to a decision that she or he is "not guilty." In theory, the possibility remains that a defendant who is found "not guilty" did indeed commit a crime. Similarly, scientific research does not lead to the conclusion that the null hypothesis is true. Scientists never prove the null hypothesis; they only fail to reject it. The reason for this position is that the philosophy of knowledge, epistemology, tells us that it is impossible ever to prove that an experimental hypothesis is false in every circumstance.

eating disorders. Case studies are especially important sources of information about conditions that have not received much attention in the literature and for problems that are relatively unusual. Multiple personality disorder and transsexualism are examples of disorders that are so infrequent that it is difficult to find groups of patients for the purpose of research studies. Much of what we know about these conditions is based on descriptions of individual patients.

Case studies also have several drawbacks. The most obvious limitation of case studies is that they can be viewed from many different perspectives. Any case can be interpreted in several ways, and competing explanations may be equally plausible. Consider, for example, the life of Jane Addams, an extremely influential social activist during the early years of the twentieth century. She founded a program to serve poor people in Chicago, promoted the assimilation of immigrants into middle-class life, and for these efforts was awarded the Nobel Peace Prize in 1931. As a young adult, Addams suffered through an 8-year period of profound depression. Some historians have argued that the foundation of her mood disorder was formed in a long-standing conflict with her father over her hopes to pursue a professional career—something that was discouraged among women at the time (Diliberto, 1999). His sudden death seemed to trigger the onset of her symptoms. Of course, many other factors might also have been involved. Her mother died when she was 2 years old. The impact of this tragic experience was intensified by subsequent losses, including the death of her older sister.

Heredity may also have played a role in the origins of Addams's depression. Her brother suffered from a mental disorder, including severe bouts of depression, and was treated at psychiatric hospitals throughout his adult life. Speculation of this sort is intriguing, particularly in the case of a woman who played such an important role in the history of the United States. But we must remember that case studies are not conclusive. Jane Addams's experience does not indicate conclusively whether the loss of a parent can increase a person's vulnerability to depression, and it does not prove that genetic factors are involved in the transmission of this disorder. These questions must be resolved through scientific investigation.

The other main limitation of case studies is that it is risky to draw general conclusions about a disorder from a single example. How can we know that this individual is representative of the disorder as a whole? Are his or her experiences typical for people with this disorder? Again, hypotheses generated on the basis of the single case must be tested in research with larger, more representative samples of patients.

Clinical Research Methods

The importance of the search for new information about mental disorders has inspired us to build another special feature into this textbook. Each chapter includes a Research Methods feature that explains one particular research issue in some detail. The Research Methods feature in this chapter, for example, is concerned with the null hypothesis, the need to consider not just that your hypothesis may be true, but also that it may be false. A list of the issues addressed in Research Methods throughout this textbook appears in Table 1–4. They are arranged to progress from some of the more basic research methods and issues, such as correlational and experimental designs, toward more complex issues, such as gene identification and heritability.

We decided to discuss methodological issues in small sections throughout the book, for two primary reasons. First, the problems raised by research methods are often complex and challenging. Some students find it difficult to digest and comprehend an entire chapter on research methods in one chunk, especially at the beginning of a book. Thus we have broken it down into more

▼ Many people lead successful lives and make important contributions to society in spite of their struggles with mental disorder. Jane Addams (1860–1935), who won the Nobel Peace Prize for her work in social justice, suffered through extended periods of profound depression as a young woman.

manageable bites. Second, and perhaps more important, the methods we discuss generally make more sense and are easier to understand when they are presented in the context of a clinical question that they can help answer. Our discussions of research methods are, therefore, introduced while we are explaining contemporary views of particular clinical problems.

Research findings are not the end of the road, either. The fact that someone has managed to collect and present data on a particular topic does not mean that the data are useful. We want you to learn about the problems of designing and interpreting research studies so that you will become a more critical consumer of scientific evidence. If you do not have a background in research design or quantitative methods, the Research Methods features will familiarize you with the procedures that psychologists use to test their hypotheses. If you have already had an introductory course in methodology, they will show you how these problems are handled in research on abnormal behavior.

TABLE 1–4 List of Research Methods Featured in This Book

CHAPTER	TOPIC
1	Who Must Provide Scientific Evidence?
2	Correlations: Does Psychology Make You Smarter?
3	The Experimental Method: Does Therapy Work?
4	Reliability: Agreement Regarding Diagnostic Decisions
5	Analogue Studies: Do Rats Get Depressed, and Why?
6	Statistical Significance: When Differences Matter
7	Retrospective Reports: Remembering the Past
8	Longitudinal Studies: Lives Over Time
9	Cross-Cultural Comparisons: The Importance of Context
10	Psychotherapy Placebos: Controlling for Expectations
11	Studies of People at Risk for Disorders
12	Hypothetical Constructs: What Is Sexual Arousal?
13	Comparison Groups: What Is Normal?
14	Finding Genes That Cause Behavioral Problems
15	Central Tendency and Variability: What Do IQ Scores Mean?
16	Samples: How to Select the People We Study
17	Heritability: Genes and the Environment
18	Base Rates and Prediction: Justice Blackmun's Error

GETTING HELP

Many students take an abnormal psychology class, in part, to understand more about their own problems or the problems of friends or family members. If you are considering whether you want to get help for yourself or for someone you know, these Getting Help sections should give you a head start in finding good therapists and effective treatments.

Of course, psychology is not just about problems. If you are wondering if you need help, if you are just curious about the problems people can have, or even if you are skeptical or disinterested, you will definitely learn more about yourself and others from this course and by studying psychology in general. That is what makes the subject so fascinating! But when the topic is abnormal psychology, you should be warned in advance about two risks.

The first is the "medical student's syndrome." As medical students learn about new illnesses, they often "develop" the symptoms of each successive disease they study. The same thing can happen when studying abnormal psychology. In fact, because many symptoms of emotional disorders share much in common with everyday experiences, students of abnormal psychology are even more likely to "discover" symptoms in themselves or others. ("Gee, I think maybe I have an anxiety disorder." "He is so self-absorbed; he has a personality disorder.") We all are frightened about experiencing illness and abnormality, and this fear can make us suggestible. So try to prepare yourself for bouts of the medical student's syndrome. And remember that it is normal to experience mild versions of many of the symptoms you will read about in this text.

Our second warning is much more serious. If you are genuinely concerned about your own problems or those of a loved one, you probably have or will consult various "self-help" resources—books, Web sites, or perhaps groups online or off-line. Do not accept uncritically the treatment programs they may suggest. You probably know that not everything you hear or read is true, and psychological advice is no exception.

Misleading, inaccurate, or simply wrong information is a particular problem in abnormal psychology for three reasons. First, to be honest, as you will learn throughout this course, psychological scientists simply do not know the causes of or absolutely effective treatments for many emotional problems. Second, people who have emotional problems, and those who have loved ones who have emotional problems, often are desperate to find a cure. Third, some well-meaning—and some unscrupulous—people will provide authoritative-sounding "answers" that really are theories, speculations, or distortions.

How can you know what information is accurate and what information is inaccurate? We have worked hard to bring you the most recent scientific information in this text. In addition to the detailed information we present in each chapter, we give you practical tips including recommended self-help books and Web sites in these Getting Help sections in each chapter. Two general resources you might want to explore now are Martin Seligman's book, *What You Can Change and What You Can't*, and the homepage of the National Institute of Mental Health: www.nimh.nih.gov. But we don't want you to rely only on this text or other authorities. We want you to rely on your own critical thinking skills, especially when it comes to getting help for yourself or someone you care about. Remember this: There is an army of scientists out there trying to solve the problems of emotional disorders, because, like us, they want to help. Breakthrough treatments that really are breakthrough treatments will not be kept secret. They will be announced on the front page of newspapers, not in obscure books or remote Web sites.

■ SUMMARY

Mental disorders are quite common. At least 50 percent of all men and women will experience a serious form of abnormal behavior, such as depression, alcoholism, or schizophrenia, at some point during their lives. Just as each of us is likely to be affected by medical problems at some point, it is also not surprising that we, or someone we love, will have to cope with a disorder of the mind.

One of our goals in this chapter is to make you more familiar with certain symptoms of **psychopathology.** We have described two relatively common forms of mental disorder: schizophrenia and bulimia nervosa. Schizophrenia is a severe form of mental disorder, a **psychosis,** in which the person is out of touch with reality. Bulimia nervosa is an eating disorder that involves recurrent episodes in which the person cannot control what (or how much) he or she eats. These episodes of binge eating are followed by efforts to prevent weight gain, such as self-induced vomiting. These and many other types of mental disorders are described in greater detail in subsequent chapters of this book.

Mental disorders are defined in terms of typical signs and symptoms rather than identifiable causal factors. A group of symptoms that appear together and are assumed to represent a specific type of disorder is called a **syndrome.** There are no definitive psychological or biological tests that can be used to confirm the presence of psychopathology. At present, the diagnosis of mental disorders depends on observations of the person's behavior and descriptions of personal experience.

No one has been able to provide a universally accepted definition of abnormal behavior. Statistical infrequency and subjective distress cannot be used for this purpose because not all infrequent behaviors are pathological, and because some people who exhibit abnormal behaviors do not have insight into their conditions. One useful approach defines mental disorders in terms of **harmful dysfunction.** The official classification system, DSM-IV-TR, defines mental disorders as a group of persistent maladaptive behaviors that result in personal distress or impaired functioning.

Various forms of voluntary social deviance and efforts to express individuality are excluded from the DSM-IV-TR definition of mental disorders. Political and religious actions, and the beliefs on which they are based, are not considered to be forms of abnormal behavior, even when they seem unusual to many other people. We must recognize, however, that the process of defining psychopathology is still influenced by **culture.**

The scientific study of the frequency and distribution of disorders within a population is known as **epidemiology.** Some severe forms of abnormal behavior, such as schizophrenia, have been observed in virtually every society that has been studied by social scientists. There are also forms of psychopathology—including eating disorders—for which substantial cross-cultural differences have been found. These epidemiological patterns may provide important clues that will help identify factors that influence the causes of mental disorders.

Some of the best information that is currently available on the epidemiology of mental disorders in the United States was collected in a study called the National Comorbidity Survey Replication (NCS-R). According to data from this project, the lifetime prevalence for at least one type of mental disorder was relatively high, with 46 percent of adults reporting at least one mental disorder at some point in their lives. Epidemiological studies have found significant gender differences for several types of mental disorders, including anxiety disorders, mood disorders, and alcoholism. Although a very large number of people experience a mental disorder at some time during their lives, severe disorders tend to be concentrated in a smaller segment of the population that is characterized by a high rate of **comorbidity.** The global burden of mental disorders is substantial. They are responsible for 47 percent of all disability in economically developed countries, like the United States, and 28 percent of all disability worldwide.

Many forms of specialized training prepare people to provide professional help to those who suffer from mental disorders. Psychiatry is a branch of medicine that is concerned with the study and treatment of mental disorders. A **psychiatrist** is licensed to practice medicine and is therefore able to prescribe medication. A **clinical psychologist** has received graduate training in the use of assessment procedures and psychotherapy. Most psychologists also have extensive knowledge regarding research methods, and their training prepares them for the integration of science and practice. Many other professions are also actively involved in the delivery of mental health services. These include social workers, professional counselors, and psychiatric nurses.

Throughout history, many societies have held different ideas about the problems that we consider to be mental disorders. Asylums were created in Europe and the United States during the 1600s and 1700s to house people who were mentally disturbed. Although the earliest asylums were little more than human warehouses, the moral treatment movement led to improved conditions in some mental hospitals. The existence of large institutions for mental patients led to the development of psychiatry as a profession. These physicians, who served as the superintendents of asylums, soon began to develop systems for describing, classifying, and treating people with various types of mental disorder. Their efforts led to the use of scientific methods to test these new ideas.

Scientific methods must be employed in the search for knowledge about mental disorders. A person who proposes a new theory about the causes of a form of psychopathology, or someone who advocates a new treatment procedure, should be expected to prove these claims with scientific evidence. The burden of proof falls on the clinical scientist who offers a new prediction, such as the claim that a particular kind of therapy is effective. In other words, the **null hypothesis** (the alternative to the **experimental hypothesis**) is assumed to be true until it is contradicted by systematic data. Individual **case studies** do not provide conclusive evidence about the causes of, or treatments for, mental disorders.

THE BIG PICTURE   CRITICAL THINKING REVIEW

Why is this book about "us" and not "them"?

Mental disorders are likely to touch all of us, or someone we love, at some point during our lives. (SEE PAGE 2)

What is the difference between normal and abnormal behavior?

While the line between normal and abnormal is not always obvious, several important considerations help to clarify the distinction. (SEE PAGES 6–8)

How does culture influence the definition of mental disorders?

Social and political forces influence the extent to which certain kinds of experience are considered to be pathological. (SEE PAGES 9–10)

How does the impact of mental disorders compare to that of other health problems?

Mental disorders are responsible for almost half of all disability in economically developed countries, ranking second in total

disease burden behind cardiovascular disease. (SEE PAGES 13–14)

Who provides help for people with mental disorders?

Many different forms of training can prepare people for professional careers in the delivery of mental health services. (SEE PAGES 15–16)

Why don't case studies provide conclusive evidence regarding the nature of mental disorders?

While we often find stories about a single person's life to be compelling, many different interpretations are possible for any case. (SEE PAGES 21–22)

Why do scientific methods play such an important role in psychology's approach to the study of mental disorders?

The hallmark of psychology as an academic discipline is the use of rigorous scientific methods to test the validity of alternative hypotheses regarding issues such as the causes and treatment of mental disorders. (SEE PAGES 22–23)

■ KEY TERMS

abnormal psychology **3**	culture **9**	harmful dysfunction **7**	prevalence **12**	psychosis **4**
case study **21**	epidemiology **11**	incidence **12**	psychiatry **15**	social work **15**
clinical psychology **15**	experimental hypothesis **20**	null hypothesis **20**	psychopathology **3**	syndrome **5**
comorbidity **13**				

CAUSES OF ABNORMAL BEHAVIOR

What causes abnormal behavior? We all would like an answer to this question. People—and their loved ones—suffering from emotional problems may be desperate for one. And some "experts" will offer a ready response. They point the finger of blame at the trauma of abuse, poor parenting, a "broken brain," or a dozen other handy explanations. Unfortunately, there is a big problem here: The simple accounts are almost certainly wrong. The truth is that psychological scientists do not yet know what causes most emotional disorders. In this chapter, we discuss "hot leads" in psychology's detective work on this important mystery, but at the outset you should know this: A conspiracy of biological, psychological, and social influences, not a lone culprit, appears to be responsible for causing most emotional problems.

OVERVIEW

You may be distressed to read that the cause, or *etiology*, of most abnormal behavior remains a mystery. In fact, you may have read or heard some popular story proclaiming something like, "Depression Found in the Brain!" Our reaction to such a breathless headline is, "Where did you expect to find depression—in your foot?" We *knew* depression was in the brain, and it *is* exciting that neuroscientists are identifying specific brain regions and chemicals involved in mental illnesses. But unfortunately, scientists still cannot tell when a "broken brain" causes depression (or virtually any other mental disorder), or when a difficult experience causes changes in the brain (that we experience as depression). In other words, popular accounts typically are oversimplified—and misleading—stories about the causes of abnormal behavior. They "solve" the mystery because that makes a good, reassuring narrative.

Some scientists also claim to have solved the mystery of abnormal behavior. Throughout much of the twentieth century, many psychologists vowed allegiance to one of four broad theories purporting to explain the etiology of psychological disorders—the biological, psychodynamic, cognitive behavioral, and humanistic paradigms. A **paradigm** is a set of shared assumptions that includes both the substance of a theory and beliefs about how scientists should collect data and test the theory. Thus, the four paradigms disagreed not only about what causes abnormal behavior, but also about how to study it. Returning to our mystery metaphor, the paradigms not only picked different suspects out of the lineup, but they also argued for different ways of proving guilt or innocence!

Most psychologists now recognize that abnormal behavior is caused by a combination of biological, psychological, and social factors (Kendler & Prescott, 2006; Rutter & Rutter, 1993). Biological contributions to abnormal behavior range from imbalanced brain chemistry to genetic predispositions. Psychological contributions range from troubled emotions to distorted thinking. Social and cultural contributions range from conflict in family relationships to gender and racial bias. Recognizing that biological, psychological, and social factors all

▲ Horrific events like the senselesss killing of 32 people at Virginia Tech make us desperate to know, "Why"? Unfortunately, most abnormal behavior defies easy explanation.

contribute to abnormal behavior, contemporary psychological scientists are guided by the **biopsychosocial model,** an effort to integrate research on these various contributions to causing mental disorders.

In this chapter, we briefly review the four paradigms and explain how integrated approaches have emerged to replace them. We also introduce a number of biological, psychological, and social processes that appear to contribute to emotional problems. In later chapters, we return to these concepts when discussing specific psychological disorders. As we do in every chapter, we begin our investigation with a case study. Most cases, including the following one, come from our own therapy files.

CASE **STUDY** Meghan's Many Hardships

At the age of 14, Meghan B. attempted to end her life by taking approximately 20 Tylenol® capsules. Meghan took the pills after an explosive fight with her mother over Meghan's grades and a boy she was dating. Meghan was in her room when she impulsively took the pills, but shortly afterward she told her mother what she had done. Her parents rushed Meghan to the emergency room, where her vital signs were closely monitored. As the crisis was coming to an end, Meghan's parents agreed that she should be hospitalized to make sure that she was safe and to begin to treat her problems.

Meghan talked freely during the 30 days she spent on the adolescent unit of a private psychiatric hospital. Most of her complaints focused on her mother. Meghan insisted that her mother was always "in her face," telling her what to do and when and how to do it. Her father was "great," but he was too busy with his job as a chemical engineer to spend much time with her.

Meghan also had longstanding problems in school. She barely maintained a C average despite considerable efforts to do better. Meghan said she didn't care about school, and her mother's insistence that she could do much better was a major source of conflict between them. Meghan also complained that she had few friends, either in or outside of school. She described her classmates as "straight," and said she had no interest in them. Meghan was obviously angry as she described her family, school, and friends, but she also seemed sad. She often denounced herself as

"stupid," and she cried about being a "reject" when discussing why no friends, including her boyfriend, came to see her at the hospital.

Mrs. B. provided details on the history of Meghan's problems. Mr. and Mrs. B. could not have children of their own, and they adopted Meghan when she was 2 years old. According to the adoption agency, Meghan's birth mother was 16 years old when she had the baby. Meghan's biological mother was a drug user, and she haphazardly left the baby in the care of friends and relatives for weeks at a time. Little was known about Meghan's biological father except that he had had some trouble with the law. Meghan's mother had known him only briefly.

When Meghan was 14 months old, her pediatrician reported her mother to a child abuse protection agency after noting bruises on Meghan's thighs and hips.

After a six-month legal investigation, Meghan's mother agreed to give her up for adoption. Meghan came to live with Mr. and Mrs. B. shortly thereafter.

Mrs. B. was eager to give Meghan all the love she had missed and happily doted on her daughter. Mr. B. also was a loving father, but like Meghan, Mrs. B. noted that he was rarely at home. Everything seemed fine with Meghan until first grade, when teachers began to complain about her. She disrupted the classroom with her restlessness, and she did not complete her

schoolwork. In second grade, a school psychologist suggested that Meghan was a "hyperactive" child who also had a learning disability. Her pediatrician recommended medication as a treatment. Mrs. B. was horrified by the thought of medication or of sending Meghan to a "resource room" for part of the school day. Instead, she decided to redouble her efforts at parenting.

Mrs. B. succeeded in getting Meghan through elementary school in reasonably good shape. Meghan's grades and classroom behavior remained acceptable as long as Mrs. B. consulted repeatedly with the school. Mrs. B. noted with bitterness, however, that the one problem that she could not solve was Meghan's friendships. The daughters of Mrs. B.'s friends and neighbors were well behaved and excellent students. Meghan did not fit in, and she never got invited to play with the other girls.

Mrs. B. was obviously sad when discussing Meghan's past, but she became agitated and angry when discussing the present. She was very concerned about Meghan, but she wondered out loud if the suicide attempt had been manipulative. Mrs. B. said that she had had major conflicts with Meghan ever since Meghan started middle school at the age of 12. Meghan would no longer work with her mother on her homework for the usual two hours each night. In addition, Meghan began arguing about everything from picking up her room to her boyfriend, an 18 year old whom Mrs. B. abhorred. Mrs. B. complained that she did not understand what had happened to her daughter. She clearly stated, however, that whatever it was, she would fix it.

What was causing Meghan's problems? Her case study suggests many possibilites. Some difficulties seem to be a reaction to a mother whose attentiveness at age 8 seems intrusive at age 14. We also could trace some of her troubles to anger over her failures in school or to rejection by her peers. However, Meghan's problems seem bigger than this. Surely she was affected by the physical abuse, inconsistent love, and chaotic living arrangements during the first, critical years of her life, but could those distant events account for her current problems? What about biological contributions? Did her birth mother's drug abuse affect Meghan as a developing fetus? Was Meghan a healthy, full-term newborn? Given her biological parents' history of troubled behavior, could Meghan's problems be partly genetic? Unfortu-

nately, we do not have ready answers to these questions, but we can tell you how psychological scientists are seeking to answer them.

BRIEF HISTORICAL PERSPECTIVE: TWENTIETH-CENTURY PARADIGMS

The search for explanations of the causes of abnormal behavior dates to ancient times. As we discussed in Chapter 1, many of the traditions begun by Hippocrates died away after the fall of the Roman Empire. Systematic, naturalistic accounts of mental illness were kept alive in Arab cultures (Grob, 1994), but the emphasis on objectivity and careful observation faded in

Europe. The rudiments of the scientific method were rediscovered during the Renaissance (approximately A.D. 1300–1600), but the scientific method was not applied to the study of abnormal behavior until much later. In fact, advances in the scientific understanding of abnormal behavior were not made until the nineteenth and early twentieth centuries, when three major events occurred. One was the discovery of the cause of general paresis, a severe mental disorder that has a deteriorating course and eventually ends in death. The second was the writing of Sigmund Freud, a thinker who had a profound influence not only on the field of abnormal psychology, but also on Western society as a whole. The third was the creation of a new academic discipline called psychology.

The Biological Paradigm

The *biological paradigm* looks for biological abnormalities that might cause abnormal behavior, for example, brain diseases, brain injuries, or genetic disorders. The search for a biological cause is not random but is guided by the careful observation of symptoms. If a common core of symptoms can be identified, this leads to a (typically imperfect) new diagnosis for some hypothesized disorder. With time, testing, and often with a good deal of luck, the diagnosis is refined to become increasingly accurate. If a specific cause can eventually be identified, the discovery leads to an even more sophisticated diagnosis, one that reveals a precise cause.

The story of the discovery of the cause of *general paresis* (general paralysis), a severe physical and mental disorder, offers a remarkably successful and historically important example of the biological paradigm. We now know that general paresis is caused by *syphilis,* a sexually transmitted disease, but its discovery was the result of over a century of research—some good and some bad. In 1798, John Haslam, a British physician, distinguished general paresis from other forms of "lunacy" based on its symptoms, which include delusions of grandeur, cognitive impairment (dementia), and progressive paralysis. (General paresis also has an unremitting course and ends in death after many years.) The diagnosis inspired a search for the cause of the new disorder, but it took scientists more than 100 years to solve the mystery.

The breakthrough began with the recognition that many people with general paresis had contracted syphilis earlier in their lives. At first, however, researchers questioned whether syphilis alone caused general paresis. For example, the French syphilis expert Jean Fournier concluded in an 1894 study that only 65 percent of patients with general paresis reported a history of syphilis. How could syphilis cause general paresis if a third of patients never contracted the sexually transmitted disease? But three years later, Austrian-German psychiatrist Richard von Kraft Ebbing demonstrated that Fournier's statistic was wrong. When he attempted to inoculate patients with general paresis against syphilis, no one became infected—which should have occurred when the inoculation exposed them to a mild form of the disease. There could be only one explanation: *All* of them had been infected with syphilis previously.

After the turn of the twentieth century, the spirochete that causes syphilis was discovered. Postmortem examination of the brains of paretic patients subsequently proved that the infection had invaded and destroyed parts of the central nervous system. In 1910, Paul Ehrlich, a German microbiologist, developed arsphenamine, an arsenic-containing chemical that destroyed the spirochete and prevented general paresis. Unfortunately, the drug worked only if the patient was treated in the early stages of infection. Later, scientists learned that syphilis could be cured by another new discovery, penicillin—the first antibiotic. As a result, general paresis was virtually eliminated when antibiotics became widely available after the end of World War II.

The slow but dramatic discovery of the cause of general paresis gave hope that scientists would soon discover biological causes for other mental disorders. To date, however, specific biological causes have been identified for only some cognitive disorders (see Chapter 14) and about half of all cases of mental retardation (see Chapter 15). Will the future bring similar discoveries for depression, bipolar disorder, schizophrenia, perhaps even substance abuse? Some scientists expect that it will. They hope to identify specific genes and brain processes that cause these disorders. Others believe that we will never discover a single cause, because so many factors are involved in the development of psychological disorders (Kendler & Prescott, 2006).

We agree more with the second group of scientists than the first. Specific biological causes, many genetic, probably will be discovered for some small percentage of mental disorders. To cite one interesting possibility, an inherited condition that can produce tumors on the adrenal gland, spur adrenaline production, and thereby increase violent behavior may have contributed to the famous feud between the Hatfields and McCoys—at least according to popular media articles that suggest the problem is common among McCoys (Associated Press, April 6, 2007). Perhaps. But despite dramatic increases in our understanding of genetics and of the brain, we expect the great majority of cases of abnormal behavior to defy simple explanation. Most mental illnesses apparently are caused by a combination of risk factors. Like heart disease and cancer, most mental disorders appear to be "lifestyle diseases" that result from the combination of biological, psychological, and social influences.

The Psychodynamic Paradigm

The *psychodynamic paradigm,* an outgrowth of the writings of Sigmund Freud (1856–1939), asserts that abnormal behavior is caused by unconscious mental conflicts that have roots in early childhood experience. Freud was trained as a neurologist, but experiences early in his career convinced him that abnormal behavior is caused by mental events that occur outside of conscious awareness.

Freud was trained in Paris by Jean Charcot (1825–1893), a neurologist who successfully used hypnosis to treat *hysteria.* Hysteria is characterized by unusual physical symptoms in the absence of physical impairment. For example, "hysterical

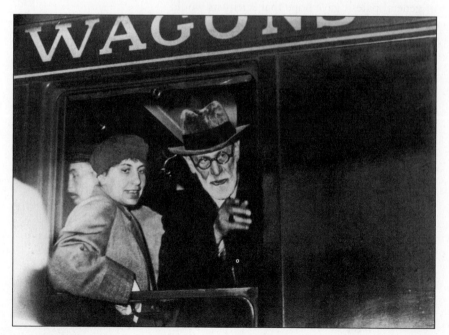

▼ Sigmund Freud with his daughter, Anna.

blindness" is the inability to see, but the blindness is not caused by an organic dysfunction. In fact, the afflicted individual may recover sight after resolving an emotional problem.

Freud observed that hysterical patients did not fake their symptoms. They also did not consciously associate the symptoms with emotional distress. Freud suggested, instead, that their psychological conflicts were unconsciously "converted" into physical symptoms. (In fact, experts now use the term *conversion disorder* to refer to what used to be called hysteria.) The peculiar problem of hysteria led Freud to believe that many memories, motivations, and protective psychological processes are unconscious, and this basic assumption was the impetus for his elaborate **psychoanalytic theory.** The term *psychoanalytic theory* refers specifically to Freud's theorizing; the broader term *psychodynamic theory* includes not only Freudian theory, but also the revisions of his followers, which we discuss further in Chapter 3.

Psychoanalytic theory is complicated and historically important, so we describe it in some detail here. You should know, however, that college students today are much more likely to learn about Freud's ideas in English departments than in psychology courses! Eighty-six percent of classes on psychoanalysis on U.S. campuses are taught *outside* of psychology departments (Shulman & Redmond, in press). Why? The theory is a rich source of theorizing—and weak on science.

Psychoanalytic theory divides the mind into three parts: the id, the ego, and the superego. The **id** is present at birth and houses biological drives, such as hunger, as well as two key psychological drives: sex and aggression. In Freudian theory, the id operates according to the *pleasure principle*— the impulses of the id seek immediate gratification and create discomfort or unrest until they are satisfied. Thus, in Freud's view, sexual or aggressive urges are akin to biological urges, like hunger.

The **ego** is the part of the personality that must deal with the realities of the world as it attempts to fulfill id impulses as well as perform other functions. Thus the ego operates on the *reality principle.* According to Freud, the ego begins to develop in the first year of life, and it continues to evolve, particularly during the preschool years. Unlike id impulses, which are primarily unconscious, much of the ego resides in conscious awareness.

The third part of the personality is the **superego,** which is roughly equivalent to your conscience. The superego contains societal standards of behavior, particularly rules that children learn from trying to be like their parents in their preschool years. Freud viewed the superego's rules as efforts to govern the id's sexual and aggressive impulses, with the ego mediating between the two. Freud called conflict between the superego and the ego *moral anxiety,* and conflict between the id and the ego *neurotic anxiety.*

Freud suggested that the ego protects itself from anxiety by utilizing various **defense mechanisms,** unconscious self-deceptions that reduce conscious anxiety by distorting anxiety-producing memories, emotions, and impulses. For example, the defense of *projection* turns the tables psychologically. When you use projection, you project your own feelings on to someone else: "I'm not mad at you. You're mad at me!" A list of some of the more familiar defenses can be found in Table 2–1. Many of these terms are now a part of everyday language, testimony to Freud's influence on Western culture.

Freud viewed early childhood experiences, especially related to forbidden topics, as shaping personality and emotional health. In his theory of *psychosexual development,* in fact, Freud argued that each stage of development is defined by a sexual conflict (see Table 2–5 on p. 54). For example, the *Oedipal conflict* centers on boys' forbidden sexual desire for their mothers. Because these impulses are impossible and overwhelming, Freud argued that boys resolve the dilemma by becoming like their mothers' spouse: They *identify* with their fathers. Freud hypothesized that girls, unlike boys, do not desire their opposite gender parent sexually. Instead, girls confront the *Electra complex,* yearning for something their fathers have and they are "missing"—a penis. This is the Freudian notion of "penis envy."

It is not difficult to criticize these ideas as farfetched, overly sexualized, and blatantly sexist. We also can (and do) criticize psychoanalytic theory for being vague and largely untestable. Still, Freud offered many innovative ideas, for example, that much mental processing occurs outside of conscious awareness, a hypothesis that *is* being tested in contemporary research (Weston, 1998). Some psychoanalysts insist on interpreting Freud literally. We believe, however, that Freud would have criticized such unchanging interpretations. After all, he often revised his own ideas. In this spirit, we view Freud's ideas as broad metaphors that are more valuable in the abstract than in their specifics.

The Cognitive Behavioral Paradigm

The *cognitive behavioral paradigm* views abnormal behavior—and normal behavior—as a product of learning. Like the biological and psychodynamic paradigms, the foundations of the cognitive behavioral paradigm can be traced to the nineteenth century, specifically to 1879, when Wilhelm Wundt (1842–1920) began the science of psychology at the University of Leipzig. Wundt's substantive contributions to psychology were limited, but he made a profound

TABLE 2–I	Some Freudian Defense Mechanisms
DENIAL	Insistence that an experience, memory, or need did not occur or does not exist. For example, you completely block a painful experience from your memory.
DISPLACEMENT	Feelings or actions are transferred from one person or object to another that is less threatening. For example, you kick your dog when you are upset with your boss.
PROJECTION	Attributing one's own feelings or thoughts to other people. For example, a husband argues that his wife is angry at him when, in fact, he is angry at her.
RATIONALIZATION	Intellectually justifying a feeling or event. For example, after not getting the offer, you decide that a job you applied for was not the one you really wanted.
REACTION FORMATION	Converting a painful or unacceptable feeling into its opposite. For example, you "hate" a former lover, but underneath it all you still really love that person.
REPRESSION	Suppressing threatening material from consciousness but without denial. For example, you "forget" about an embarrassing experience.
SUBLIMATION	Diverting id impulses into constructive and acceptable outlets. For example, you study hard to get good grades rather than giving in to desires for immediate pleasure.

and lasting contribution by introducing the scientific study of psychological phenomena, especially learning.

The two most prominent early contributors to learning theory and research were the Russian physiologist Ivan Pavlov (1849–1936) and the U.S. psychologist B. F. Skinner (1904–1990). These psychological scientists articulated, respectively, the principles of classical conditioning and operant conditioning—concepts that continue to be central to contemporary learning theory.

In his famous experiment, Pavlov (1928) rang a bell when he fed meat powder to dogs. After repeated trials, the sound of the bell alone elicited the salivation produced by the sight of food. This renowned experiment illustrates Pavlov's theory of classical conditioning. **Classical conditioning** is learning through association, and it involves four key components. There is an *unconditioned stimulus* (the meat powder), a stimulus that automatically produces the *unconditioned response* (salivation). A *conditioned stimulus* (the bell) is a neutral stimulus that, when repeatedly paired with an unconditioned stimulus, comes to produce a *conditioned response* (salivation). Finally, **extinction** occurs once a conditioned stimulus no longer is paired with an unconditioned stimulus. Eventually, the conditioned stimulus no longer elicits the conditioned response.

Skinner's (1953) principle of **operant conditioning** asserts that learned behavior is a function of its consequences. Specifically, behavior increases if it is rewarded, and it decreases if it is punished. In his numerous studies of rats and pigeons in his famous "Skinner box," Skinner identified four different, crucial consequences of behavior. *Positive reinforcement* is when the *onset* of a stimulus *increases* the frequency of behavior (for example, you get paid for your work). *Negative reinforcement* is when the *cessation* of a stimulus *increases* the frequency of behavior (you get up to turn off your alarm clock). *Punishment* is when the *onset* of a stimulus *decreases* the frequency of behavior (you spend less money after your parents scold you); and *response cost* is when the *cessation* of a stimulus *decreases* the frequency of behavior (you come home on time after getting grounded). *Extinction* results from ending the association between a behavior and its consequences, similar to the concept of extinction in classical conditioning.

The U.S. psychologist John B. Watson (1878–1958) was an influential proponent of applying learning theory to human behavior. Watson argued for *behaviorism,* suggesting that observable behavior was the only appropriate subject matter for the science of psychology, because, he argued, thoughts and emotions cannot be measured objectively. However, very important subsequent research, including therapies we discuss in Chapter 3, showed the importance of cognitive processes in learning. Thus, "cognitive" joined "behavioral." True to their historical roots, cognitive behavior therapists value and have promoted psychological research in many areas of abnormal psychology.

The Humanistic Paradigm

The *humanistic paradigm* argues that the human behavior is the product of *free will,* the view that we control, choose, and are responsible for our actions. In many respects, this stance is a reaction against *determinism,* the scientific assumption that human behavior is caused by potentially knowable factors (a position held by the other paradigms). Because free will, by definition, is not predictable, it is impossible to determine the causes of abnormal behavior according to the humanistic paradigm. For this reason, the approach perhaps is best considered an alternative philosophy, not as an alternative psychological theory. Major advocates of the humanistic paradigm included Abraham Maslow (1908–1970), Fritz Perls (1893–1970), and Carl Rogers (1902–1987). Rogers did not completely reject research. As we discuss in Chapter 3, in fact, he began an important line of investigation on the process of psychotherapy.

▼ Pavlov in his classical conditioning laboratory.

The humanistic paradigm is also distinguished by its explicitly positive view of human nature. They blame abnormal behavior on society, not on the individual, whom they see as inherently good (see Table 2–2). The term *humanistic* is appealing, and we should be clear about this: All psychologists are humanists in the sense that their ultimate goal is to improve the human condition.

The Problem with Paradigms

The influential historian and philosopher Thomas Kuhn (1962) noted that the assumptions made by paradigms can both direct and misdirect scientists. Paradigms can tell us where and how to find answers, but sometimes the apparent guidance can be a hindrance. The idea that a paradigm can be either enlightening or blinding can be illustrated by a brain teaser. Try to solve the following enigma, written by Lord Byron, before looking ahead for the answer:

I'm not in earth, nor the sun,
nor the moon.
You may search all the sky—
I'm not there.
In the morning and evening—
though not at noon,
You may plainly perceive me,
for like a balloon,
I am suspended in air.
Though disease may possess me,
and sickness and pain,
I am never in sorrow nor gloom;
Though in wit and wisdom
I equally reign
I am the heart of all sin and have
long lived in vain;
Yet I ne'er shall be found in the tomb.

What is this poem about? The topic of this rhyme is not the soul or ghosts. It is not life or shadows, or a dozen other possibilities that may have occurred to you. Rather, the topic is the letter *i* (suspended in a*i*r, the heart of all s*i*n). Why is the puzzle so difficult to solve? Because most people assume that the solution lies in the content of the poem, not in its form. This illustrates that the assumptions made by a paradigm can act as blinders; they can lead us to overlook what otherwise might be obvious. However, paradigms also can open up new perspectives. For example, now that you have been able to adopt a new "paradigm"—to focus on the form, not the

How are old paradigms too narrow?

◀ The android, Data, from *StarTrek: The Next Generation*. Are free will (and emotion) uniquely human qualities?

TOPIC	BIOLOGICAL	PSYCHODYNAMIC	COGNITIVE BEHAVIORAL	HUMANISTIC
Inborn human nature	Competitive, but some altruism	Aggressive, sexual	Neutral—a blank slate	Basic goodness
Cause of abnormality	Genes, neurochemistry, physical damage	Early childhood experiences	Social learning	Frustrations of society
Type of treatment	Medication, other somatic therapies	Psychodynamic therapy	Cognitive behavior therapy	Nondirective therapy
Paradigmatic focus	Bodily functions and structures	Unconscious mind	Observable behavior	Free will

TABLE 2–2 Comparison of Biological, Psychodynamic, Cognitive Behavioral, and Humanistic Paradigms

content of words—you can easily solve the following puzzle:

> The beginning of eternity, the end
> of time and space,
> The beginning of every end, the end
> of every place.

The now obvious answer is the letter *e*.

Like your initial approach to the brain teaser, the four paradigms make assumptions about the causes of abnormal psychology that can be too narrow. The biological paradigm can overemphasize the *medical model,* the analogy between physical and psychological illnesses. The psychodynamic paradigm can be unyielding in focusing on childhood and the unconscious, even in the face of current life difficulties. The cognitive behavioral paradigm can overlook the rich social, and biological, context of human behavior. Finally, the humanistic approach can be antiscientific. In short, each paradigm has weaknesses—and strengths. As in the word puzzles, the trick is to know when to use what strategy.

SYSTEMS THEORY

The Austrian biologist and philosopher of science Ludwig von Bertalanffy (1901–1972) is the "father" of **systems theory,** an integrative approach to science that has revolutionized many disciplines including engineering, computer science, biology, philosophy, and increasingly psychology

▼ Systems theory takes a holistic view of the enviroment, and of human behavior.

(Gottesman & Hanson, in press; Hinde, 1992; Richardson, 2000). Because it embraces multiple influences on behavior, you can think of systems theory as a synonym for the biopsychosocial model. However, systems theory also includes several key concepts that deserve elaboration.

Holism

A central principle of systems theory is *holism,* the idea that the whole is more than the sum of its parts. Holism is a familiar but important concept. A water molecule is more than the sum of two hydrogen atoms and one oxygen atom. Holistic medicine views human beings as more than their disease. Similarly, the approach views the whole of abnormal behavior as more than the sum of chemical reactions in the brain.

Reductionism We can better appreciate the principle of holism if we contrast it with its scientific counterpoint, reductionism. **Reductionism** understands problems by focusing on smaller and smaller units, viewing the smallest possible unit as the true or ultimate cause. For example, when depression is linked with the depletion of certain chemicals in the brain, reductionists view brain chemistry as *the* cause of depression. Systems theory reminds us, however, that difficult experiences can and do cause the changes in brain chemistry that may lead to depression (Kagan, 2007).

Part of our concern is cause and effect—does a "chemical imbalance in the brain" cause depression or does depression cause a chemical imbalance in the brain (see Research Methods). But our broader concern is with *levels of analysis,* an idea we find easiest to illustrate with a far-out example. Assume for a moment that three Martian scientists are sent to Earth to discover what causes those metallic vehicles to speed across the planet's landmass. One Martian reports that the vehicles (called "automobiles," the ecologist discovers) move at different speeds based on the width of the black paths on which they are set, whether the paths are straight or curved, and the presence of a something called "radar traps." A second Martian, a psychologist, disagrees, noting that the speed of automobiles is determined by the age, gender, and mood of the individual who sits behind the wheel. A third scientist, a reductionist, laughs at the other two. The Martian physicist notes that the speed of automobiles

RESEARCH METHODS

Correlations: Does a Psychology Major Make You Smarter?

The correlational study and *the experiment* (see Chapter 3) are two basic and essential research methods. In a **correlational study,** the relation between two factors (their co-relation) is studied systematically. For example, you might hypothesize that psychology majors learn more about research methods than biology majors. To support this hypothesis, you might simply argue your point, or you could rely on case studies—"I know more research than my roommate, and she's a biology major!"

If you were to conduct a correlational study, you would collect a large sample of both psychology and biology majors and compare them on an objective measure of knowledge of research methods. You would then use statistics to test whether research knowledge is correlated with academic major.

An important statistic for measuring how strongly two factors are related is the **correlation coefficient.** The correlation coefficient is a number that always ranges between −1.00 and +1.00. If all psychology majors got 100 percent correct on your test of research methods and all biology majors got 0 percent correct, the correlation between academic major and research knowledge would be 1.00. If all psychology and biology majors got 50 percent of the items correct, the correlation between major and knowledge would be zero. Two factors are more strongly correlated when a correlation coefficient has a higher absolute value, regardless of whether the sign is positive or negative.

Positive correlations (from 0.01 to 1.00) indicate that as one factor goes up, the other factor also goes up. For example, height and weight are positively correlated, as are years of education and employment income. Taller people weigh more; educated people earn more money. *Negative correlations* (from −1.00 to −0.01) indicate that, as one number gets bigger, the other number gets smaller. For example, your course load and your free time are negatively correlated. The more courses you take, the less free time you have.

Why does correlation not mean causation?

In this chapter, we discuss many factors that are correlated with and *might* cause psychological problems. Levels of neurotransmitters are positively correlated with some emotional problems (they are elevated in comparison to normal), and they are negatively correlated with other types of emotional problems (they are depleted in comparison to normal). However, you should always remember that *correlation does not mean causation*. This is true for the correlation between major and research knowledge and for the correlation between neurotransmitters and mental health (Kagan, 2007).

We might want to conclude that X causes Y—that depleted neurotransmitters cause de-

pression. A correlation *may* result from causation, but there are always two alternative explanations: reverse causality and third variables. **Reverse causality** indicates that causation could be operating in the opposite direction: Y could be causing X. Depression could be causing the depletion of neurotransmitters. The **third variable** problem indicates that a correlation between any two variables might be explained by their joint relation with some unmeasured factor—a third variable. For example, stress might cause both depression *and* the depletion of neurotransmitters.

So if you found that psychology majors know more about research methods, could you conclude that majoring in psychology *caused* this result? No! People who know more about research methods to begin with might become psychology majors (reverse causality). Or more intelligent people might both major in psychology and learn more about research methods (third variable).

As we discuss in Chapter 3, the experiment *does* allow scientists to determine cause and effect. However, it often is impractical or unethical to conduct experiments on psychological problems, while correlational studies can be conducted with far fewer practical or ethical concerns. Thus the correlational method has the weakness that correlation does not mean causation, but the strength that it can be used to study many real-life circumstances.

---

ultimately is caused by a chemical process that occurs inside an outdated machine, the internal combustion engine. The process involves oxygen, fuel, and heat, and results in mechanical energy.

Some laypeople and some scientists seem to believe that the most reductionistic accounts *are* ultimate causes (Uttal, 2001). The Martian example illustrates, however, that the most reductionistic, or *molecular,* explanation is no more (or less) accurate than the most general, or *molar,* one.

Levels of Analysis The Martian example also illustrates a key tenet of systems theory. Psychologists may focus on different—but not necessarily inconsistent—*levels of analysis* in trying to

understand the causes of abnormal behavior. Biological, psychological, and social views of abnormal behavior each use a different "lens": One is a microscope, another a magnifying glass, and the third a telescope. No one "lens" is "right." The lenses are just different, and each has value for different purposes.

Like Russian *matreska* dolls, accounts at different levels of analysis are nested one inside the other. In fact, we can order all academic disciplines according to their level of analysis (see Table 2–3). Within psychology and across disciplines, systems theory strives to understand both the parts and the whole.

Can two explanations of abnormal behavior both be accurate?

TABLE 2–3   Ordering Academic Disciplines by Level of Analysis

LEVEL OF ANALYSIS	ACADEMIC DISCIPLINE
Beyond Earth	Astronomy
Supranational	Ecology, economics
National	Government, political science
Organizations	Organizational science
Groups	Sociology
Organisms	Psychology, ethology, zoology
Organs	Cardiology, neurology
Cells	Cellular biology
Biochemicals	Biochemistry
Chemicals	Chemistry, physical chemistry
Atoms	Physics
Subatomic particles	Subatomic physics
Abstract systems	Mathematics, philosophy

Source: Based on G. E. Schwartz, 1982, "Testing the Biopsychosocial Model: The Ultimate Challenge Facing Behavioral Medicine," *Journal of Consulting and Clinical Psychology, 50,* pp. 1040–1053.

Causality

Human beings are not very patient with complicated explanations of causality. (You may feel this way yourself at this point.) Our orderly minds want to pinpoint a single causal culprit. We want to know *the* cause of cancer, *the* cause of heart disease, and *the* cause of mental illness.

But a question might help to unhinge you from this understandable human search for

► Like car accidents, mental illnesses have many causes, not one.

simplicity: What is *the* cause of automobile accidents? Of course, automobile accidents have many different causes: excessive speed, drunk drivers, slippery roads, and worn tires. It would be fruitless to search for *the* cause of automobile accidents. But much like the discovery of the cause of general paresis, we hope that scientists will discover *the* cause of every dreaded physical and mental disorder.

True, even complicated problems sometimes have a simple cause. Some car accidents are caused by a single factor such as faulty brakes or the driver's falling asleep at the wheel. Similarly, scientists may eventually discover a specific biological, psychological, or social cause for some emotional problems. More commonly, however, psychological disorders, like car accidents, appear to result from a conspiracy of causes, not a lone culprit.

Equifinality and Multifinality This frustrating fact is formalized in the systems theory principle, *equifinality,* the view that there are many routes to the same destination (or disorder). In fact, we use the term *multiple pathways* as a synonym for equifinality. Both terms highlight that the same disorder may have several different causes.

Equifinality has a mirror concept, the principle of *multifinality,* which says that the same event can lead to different outcomes. For example, the principle of multifinality tells us that not all childhood experiences lead to the same adult outcomes. Not all abused children grow up with the same problems later in life. In fact, not all abused children *have* psychological problems as adults. Throughout the text, you will repeatedly see examples of the principle of multifinality, because the human psyche is indeed a very complex system.

Reciprocal Causality Reciprocal **causality,** the idea that causality operates in both directions, is another important concept from systems theory. Reciprocal causality stands in contrast to *linear causality,* which paints causation as a one-way street, for example, the experimenter teaches a rat to press the bar in a Skinner box. B. F. Skinner himself recognized that operant conditioning experiments actually involve reciprocal causality (Skinner, 1956). As Skinner's own cartoon on the next page illustrates, the experimenter teaches rats to press the bar, but the rats also "teach" the experimenter to feed them! Another important example: Parents (try to) teach their children to behave in a certain ways, but children's reactions also teach parents to change their behavior (Bell, 1968).

The Diathesis-Stress Model The *diathesis-stress model* is a common if somewhat simplified way of describing multiple influences on abnormal behavior. A **diathesis** is a predisposition toward developing a disorder, for example, an inherited tendency toward depression. A **stress** is a difficult experience, for example, the loss of a loved one through an unexpected death. The diathesis-stress model suggests that mental disorders develop only when a stress is added on top of a predisposition; neither a diathesis nor a stress alone is sufficient to cause a disorder (Zuckerman, 1999).

Although it is a useful simplification, the diathesis-stress model does not imply that disorders are caused by the combination of only two risk factors, a diathesis and a stress. **Risk factors** are events or circumstances that are correlated with an increased likelihood or risk of a disorder and potentially contribute to causing the disorder. As we have noted, mental disorders appear to be produced by the combination of *many* different biological, psychological, and social risk factors.

Developmental Psychopathology

Because people change over time, knowledge of normal development is essential to understanding psychopathology. **Developmental psychopathology** is a new approach to abnormal psychology that emphasizes the importance of *developmental norms*—age-graded averages—to understanding influences on (and the definition of) abnormal behavior (Rutter & Garmezy, 1983). Developmental norms tell us that a full-blown temper tantrum is normal at 2 years of age, for example, but that kicking and screaming to get one's own way is abnormal at the age of 22. Development does not end at the age of 22, however, as predictable changes in both psychological and social experiences occur throughout adult life. Recognizing this, we devote an entire chapter (Chapter 17) to discussing the normal but psychologically trying changes that result from developmental transitions during adult life.

We also discuss the development of abnormal behavior itself. Many psychological disorders follow unique developmental patterns. Sometimes there is a characteristic **premorbid history,** a pattern of behavior that precedes the onset of the disorder. A disorder may also have a predictable course, or **prognosis,** for the future. By discussing the premorbid adjustment and the

"Boy, have I got this guy conditioned! Every time I press the bar down he drops a piece of food."

course of different psychological disorders, we hope to present abnormal behavior as a moving picture of development and not just as a diagnostic snapshot.

We divide the remainder of this chapter into sections on biological, psychological, and social factors in the development of psychopathology. This material reviews basic information relevant to our more specific discussions of the causes of abnormal behavior in subsequent chapters.

BIOLOGICAL FACTORS

We begin our discussion of biological factors affecting mental functioning by considering the smallest anatomic unit within the nervous system, the neuron or nerve cell. Next, we consider the major brain structures and current knowledge of their primary behavioral functions. We then turn to psychophysiology, the effect of psychological experience on the functioning of various body systems. Finally, we consider the broadest of all biological influences, the effect of genes on behavior.

In considering biological influences, it is helpful to note the distinction between the study of biological structures and of biological functions. The field of *anatomy* is concerned with the study of biological structures, and the field of *physiology* investigates biological functions. *Neuroanatomy* and *neurophysiology* are subspecialties within these broader fields that focus specifically on brain structures and brain functions. The study of neuroanatomy and neurophysiology is the domain of an exciting, multidisciplinary field of research called *neuroscience.*

AUTISM

XAVIER

"He is now talking, which was a blessing." On your CD-ROM menu, select "Autism" and click on "Autism: Xavier."

As you watch the video, observe Xavier's communication struggles and odd behavior, and keep in mind that he is functioning pretty well in comparison to many children with autism.

The Neuron and Neurotransmitters

Billions of tiny nerve cells—**neurons**—form the basic building blocks of the brain. Each neuron has four major anatomic components: the soma, or cell body, the dendrites, the axon, and the

axon terminal (see Figure 2–1). The *soma*—the cell body and largest part of the neuron—is where most of the neuron's metabolism and maintenance are controlled and performed. The *dendrites* branch out from the soma; they serve the primary function of receiving messages from other cells. The *axon* is the trunk of the neuron. Messages are transmitted down the axon toward other cells. Finally, the *axon terminal* is the end of the axon, where messages are sent out to other neurons.

Within each neuron, information is transmitted as a change in electrical potential that moves from the dendrites and cell body, along the axon, toward the axon terminal. The axon terminal is separated from other cells by a **synapse,** a small gap filled with fluid. Neurons typically have synapses with thousands of other cells (see Figure 2–2).

Unlike the electrical communication within a neuron, information is transmitted chemically across a synapse to other neurons. The axon terminal contains *vesicles* containing chemical substances called **neurotransmitters,** which are released into the synapse and are received at the **receptors** on the dendrites or soma of another neuron. Different receptor sites are more or less responsive to particular neurotransmitters. Dozens of different chemical compounds serve as neurotransmitters in the brain. *Serotonin* and *dopamine* are two that are known to be particularly important for abnormal behavior. Both can be altered by medication. You should know, however, that a single neurotransmitter is unlikely to be responsible for a given disorder.

Not all neurotransmitters cross the synapse and reach the receptors on another neuron. The process of **reuptake,** or reabsorption, captures some neurotransmitters in the synapse and returns the chemical substances to the axon terminal. The neurotransmitter then is reused in subsequent neural transmission.

In addition to the neurotransmitters, a second type of chemical affects communication in the brain. *Neuromodulators* are chemicals that can influence communication among many neurons by affecting the functioning of neurotransmitters. Neuromodulators often affect regions of the brain that are quite distant from where they were released. This occurs, for example, when stress causes the adrenal gland to release hormones that affect many aspects of brain functioning (as we discuss shortly).

The Neuron

FIGURE 2–1   The anatomic structure of the neuron, or nerve cell.

Source: Figure 1.1, p. 6 from *Human Neuropsychology,* 2nd ed., by Brian Kolb and Ian Q. Whislaw. © 1980, 1985 by W.H. Freeman and Company. Reprinted by permission of W. H. Freeman and Company.

Synaptic Transmission

Axon terminal
Vesicles
Neuro-transmitters
Receptors
Reabsorption
Synapse

FIGURE 2–2   When an electrical nerve impulse reaches the end of a neuron, synaptic vesicles release neurotransmitters into the synapse. The chemical transmission between cells is complete when neurotransmitters travel to receptor sites on another neuron.

Source: Keith Kasnot, © National Geographic Image Collection.

Neurotransmitters and Psychopathology

Scientists have found that disruptions in the functioning of various neurotransmitters are present among some people with mental disorders. An oversupply of certain neurotransmitters is found in some mental disorders, an undersupply in other cases, and disturbances in reuptake in other psychological problems. In addition, the density and/or sensitivity of receptors have been implicated as playing a role in some forms of abnormal behavior.

Much research linking mental disorders with neurotransmitters has investigated how drugs alter brain chemistry and affect the symptoms of a disorder. For example, medications that alleviate some of the symptoms of schizophrenia block receptors sensitive to the neurotransmitter *dopamine*. This suggests that abnormalities in the dopamine system may be involved in schizophrenia (see Chapter 13). Evidence that effective treatments for depression inhibit the reuptake of the *serotonin* links a depletion of that neurotransmitter to mood disorders (see Chapter 5). As we discuss in the appropriate chapters, however, several neurotransmitters are likely to be involved in these and other mental disorders. Consistent with our discussion of levels of analysis, moreover, a biochemical difference does not mean that these problems are caused by "a chemical imbalance in the brain," even though many people, including many mental health professionals, mistakenly leap to this conclusion (see box on Mind–Body Dualism).

MIND–BODY DUALISM

Advances in neuroscience are exciting, but the excitement can lead to some sloppy thinking. One big problem is that some people mistakenly conclude that, because neurophysiological functioning is correlated with a psychological problem, this means that there is something wrong in the brain. Certain regions of the brain "light up" with depression. This means that depression is a "brain disease," right? Medications that affect brain chemistry lessen symptoms of depression. This means depression is caused by a "chemical imbalance in the brain," right? Wrong—on both counts.

Are some psychological experiences separate from biology?

Much of this sloppy thinking can be traced to the logical error formally known as **dualism,** the mistaken view that the mind and body are somehow separable. This wrong-headed reasoning has a long and *un*distinguished history. Dualism dates to the French philosopher René Descartes (1596–1650), who attempted to balance the dominant religious views of his times with emerging scientific reasoning. Descartes recognized the importance of human biology, but he wanted to elevate human spirituality beyond the brain. To balance scientific and religious beliefs, he argued that many human experiences result from brain function, but higher spiritual thoughts and feelings somehow exist apart from the body. Descartes argued for a distinction—a dualism—between mind and body. But he was wrong. No psychological experience exists apart from biology. Computer software cannot run without computer hardware, and *no* psychological experience runs independently from the hardware of the brain (Valenstein, 1998).

Even love has a biochemical explanation, a fact that Calvin ponders in the accompanying cartoon. If you are unpersuaded by Calvin, you may be convinced by a study. Images of married women's brains show bigger responses to threat when a woman holds a stranger's hand instead of her husband's. Brain images also show a bigger response to threat when women are holding hands with husbands to whom they are less happily married (Coan, Schaefer, & Davidson, 2006). Love will still be love (we hope) even after scientists identify the "chemical imbalance" that explains it. And as with love, just because certain parts of the brain "light up" when people suffer from a psychological problem, this does not necessarily mean that they have a "broken brain."

CALVIN AND HOBBES © 1993 Watterson. Reprinted with permission of UNIVERSAL PRESS SYNDICATE. All rights reserved.

Major Brain Structures

Neuroanatomists divide the brain into three subdivisions: the hindbrain, the midbrain, and the forebrain (see Figure 2–3 on pages 42–43). Basic bodily functions are regulated by the structures of the *hindbrain,* which include the medulla, pons, and cerebellum. The *medulla* controls various bodily functions involved in sustaining life, including heart rate, blood pressure, and respiration. The *pons* serves various functions in regulating stages of sleep. The *cerebellum* serves as a control center in helping to coordinate physical movements. The cerebellum receives information on body movements and integrates this feedback with directives from higher brain structures about desired actions. Few forms of abnormal behavior are identified with disturbances in the hindbrain, because the hindbrain's primary role is limited to supervising these basic physical functions.

The *midbrain* also is involved in the control of some motor activities, especially those related to fighting and sex. Much of the reticular activating system is located in the midbrain, although it extends into the pons and medulla as well. The *reticular activating system* regulates sleeping and waking. Damage to areas of the midbrain can cause extreme disturbances in sexual behavior, aggressiveness, and sleep, but such abnormalities typically result from specific and unusual brain traumas or tumors.

Most of the human brain consists of the *forebrain.* The forebrain evolved more recently than the hindbrain and midbrain and, therefore, is the site of most sensory, emotional, and cognitive processes. These higher mental processes of the forebrain are linked with the midbrain and hindbrain by the **limbic system.** The limbic system is made up of a variety of different brain structures that are central to the regulation of emotion and basic learning processes. Two of the most important components of the limbic system are the thalamus and the hypothalamus. The *thalamus* is involved in receiving and integrating sensory information from both the sense organs and higher brain structures. The **hypothalamus** also plays a role in sensation, but its more important functions are behavioral ones. The hypothalamus controls basic biological urges, such as eating, drinking, and sexual activity. Much of the functioning of the autonomic nervous system (which we discuss shortly) is also directed by the hypothalamus.

Cerebral Hemispheres

Most of the forebrain is composed of the two **cerebral hemispheres.** Many brain functions are **lateralized,** so that one hemisphere serves a specialized role as the site of specific cognitive and emotional activities. In general, the *left cerebral hemisphere* is involved in language and related functions, and the *right cerebral hemisphere* is involved in spatial organization and analysis. The lateralization and localization of certain brain functions often make it possible to pinpoint brain damage based solely on behavioral difficulties.

The two cerebral hemispheres are connected by the *corpus callosum,* which is involved in coordinating the different functions that are performed by the left and the right hemispheres of the brain. When we view a cross section of the forebrain, four connected chambers, or **ventricles,** become apparent. The ventricles are filled with cerebrospinal fluid, and they become enlarged in some psychological and neurological disorders.

The **cerebral cortex** is the uneven surface area of the brain that lies just underneath the skull. It is the site of the control and integration of sophisticated memory, sensory, and motor functions. The cerebral cortex is divided into four lobes (see Figure 2–3). The *frontal lobe,*

▶ This cross-sectional image of the brain shows the ventricles, four connected chambers that are filled with cerebrospinal fluid.

located just behind the forehead, is involved in controlling a number of complex functions, including reasoning, planning, emotion, speech, and movement. The *parietal lobe,* located at the top and back of the head, receives and integrates sensory information and also plays a role in spatial reasoning. The *temporal lobe,* located beneath much of the frontal and parietal lobes, processes sound and smell, regulates emotions, and is involved in some aspects of learning, memory, and language. Finally, the *occipital lobe,* located behind the temporal lobe, receives and interprets visual information.

Major Brain Structures and Psychopathology

The brain is incredibly complex, and scientists are only beginning to understand the subtle reciprocal relationships between various anatomic structures and functions. At present, only the most severe mental disorders have clearly been linked to abnormalities in neuroanatomy. In most cases, brain damage is extensive. For example, during a *stroke,* blood vessels in the brain rupture, cutting off the supply of oxygen to parts of the brain and thereby killing surrounding brain tissue. This in turn disrupts the functioning of nearby healthy neurons because the brain cannot remove the dead tissue (see Figure 2–3). Tangles of neurons are found in patients with *Alzheimer's disease,* but the damage can be identified only during postmortem autopsies (see Figure 2–3). In patients with schizophrenia, the ventricles of the brain are enlarged, and asymmetries are also found in other brain structures (see Figure 2–3).

Still, research on the brain holds great promise. Neuroscientists have made dramatic breakthroughs in observing the anatomic structure of the living brain and in recording some of its global physiological processes. These imaging procedures are now being used to study psychological disorders ranging from schizophrenia to learning disabilities; they are discussed in Chapter 4, along with other methods of psychological assessment.

At present, new brain imaging techniques are more exciting technically than practically for identifying biological causes of mental disorders. However, scientific advances frequently follow the development of new instruments. There is every reason to hope that brain imaging techniques will greatly improve our understanding of both normal and abnormal brain structure and function.

Psychophysiology

Psychophysiology is the study of changes in the functioning of the body that result from psychological experiences. Some of these reactions are familiar. Psychophysiological responses include a pounding heart, a flushed face, tears, sexual excitement, and numerous other reactions. Such responses reflect a person's psychological state, particularly the degree and perhaps the type of their emotional arousal.

Endocrine System Psychophysiological arousal results from the activity of two different communication systems within the body, the endocrine system and the nervous system. The **endocrine system** is a collection of glands found at various locations throughout the body. Its major components include the ovaries or testes and the pituitary, thyroid, and adrenal glands (see Figure 2–4 on page 44). Endocrine glands produce psychophysiological responses by releasing **hormones** into the bloodstream—chemical substances that affect the functioning of distant body systems and sometimes act as neuromodulators. The endocrine system regulates some aspects of normal development, particularly physical growth and sexual development. Parts of the endocrine system, particularly the adrenal glands, also are activated by stress and help prepare the body to respond to an emergency.

Certain abnormalities in the functioning of the endocrine system are known to cause psychological symptoms. For example, in *hyperthyroidism,* also known as *Graves' disease,* the thyroid gland secretes too much of the hormone thyroxin, causing restlessness, agitation, and anxiety. Recent research on depression also suggests that endocrine functioning sometimes may be involved in the etiology of this disorder.

Autonomic Nervous System The more familiar and basic system of communication within the body is the *nervous system.* The human nervous system is divided into the *central nervous system,* which includes the brain and the spinal cord, and the peripheral nervous system. The *peripheral nervous system* includes all connections that stem from the central nervous system and innervate the body's muscles, sensory systems, and organs.

The peripheral nervous system itself has two subdivisions. The voluntary *somatic nervous system* governs muscular control, and the involuntary

The Healthy Brain

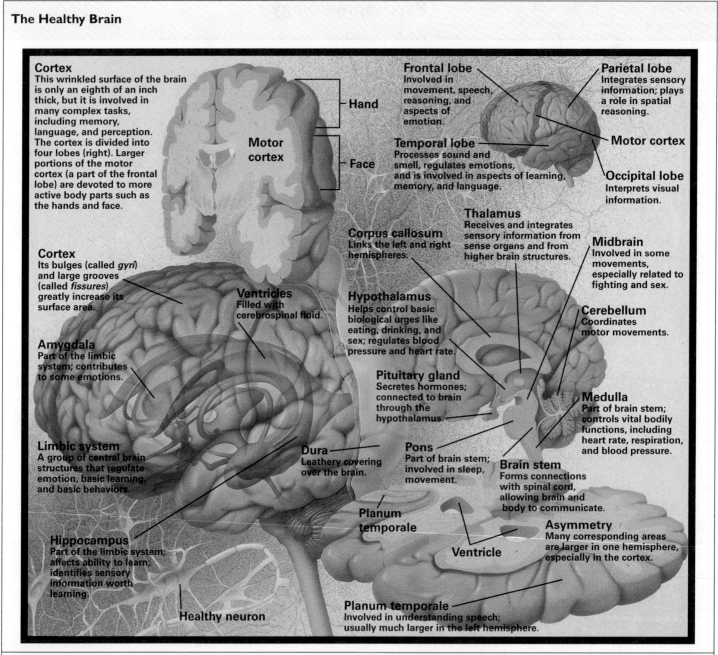

Cortex
This wrinkled surface of the brain is only an eighth of an inch thick, but it is involved in many complex tasks, including memory, language, and perception. The cortex is divided into four lobes (right). Larger portions of the motor cortex (a part of the frontal lobe) are devoted to more active body parts such as the hands and face.

Cortex
Its bulges (called *gyri*) and large grooves (called *fissures*) greatly increase its surface area.

Amygdala
Part of the limbic system; contributes to some emotions.

Limbic system
A group of central brain structures that regulate emotion, basic learning, and basic behaviors.

Hippocampus
Part of the limbic system; affects ability to learn; identifies sensory information worth learning.

Healthy neuron

Hand

Motor cortex

Face

Ventricles
Filled with cerebrospinal fluid.

Dura
Leathery covering over the brain.

Planum temporale

Ventricle

Planum temporale
Involved in understanding speech; usually much larger in the left hemisphere.

Corpus callosum
Links the left and right hemispheres.

Hypothalamus
Helps control basic biological urges like eating, drinking, and sex; regulates blood pressure and heart rate.

Pituitary gland
Secretes hormones; connected to brain through the hypothalamus.

Pons
Part of brain stem; involved in sleep, movement.

Frontal lobe
Involved in movement, speech, reasoning, and aspects of emotion.

Temporal lobe
Processes sound and smell, regulates emotions, and is involved in aspects of learning, memory, and language.

Thalamus
Receives and integrates sensory information from sense organs and from higher brain structures.

Parietal lobe
Integrates sensory information; plays a role in spatial reasoning.

Motor cortex

Occipital lobe
Interprets visual information.

Midbrain
Involved in some movements, especially related to fighting and sex.

Cerebellum
Coordinates motor movements.

Medulla
Part of brain stem; controls vital bodily functions, including heart rate, respiration, and blood pressure.

Brain stem
Forms connections with spinal cord, allowing brain and body to communicate.

Asymmetry
Many corresponding areas are larger in one hemisphere, especially in the cortex.

FIGURE 2–3   Scientists are only beginning to discover how the healthy brain performs its complex functions. You should view this complex figure as a rough road map that will be redrawn repeatedly. Like a road map, you should not try to memorize the figure, but use it as a guide. You will appreciate more and more detail as you return to examine it repeatedly. Despite the continuing mysteries, increasingly sophisticated tools have allowed researchers to identify more and more of the functions performed by different areas of the brain. For example, the four lobes of the brain's cortex play very different roles in thought, emotion, sensation, and motor movement (see top right of figure). Still, our incomplete knowledge of the healthy brain limits our understanding of brain abnormalities.

autonomic nervous system regulates the functions of various body organs, such as the heart and stomach. The somatic nervous system controls intentional or voluntary actions like scratching your nose. The autonomic nervous system is responsible for psychophysiological reactions—responses that occur with little or no conscious control.

The autonomic nervous system can be subdivided into two branches, the sympathetic and parasympathetic nervous systems. In general, the *sympathetic nervous system* controls activities asso-

The Unhealthy Brain

Stroke and the Motor Cortex
A stroke commonly disrupts voluntary movement on one side of the body. The stroke shown at the right has affected the face and hand.

Hand

Face

Umbra

Penumbra

STROKE

Umbra

Penumbra

Blockage

Blood

Diseased carotid artery

Middle cerebral artery

ALZHEIMER'S DISEASE

Atrophied tissue

"Senile plaque"

Tangle

Diseased neuron

Beta amyloid protein

SCHIZOPHRENIA

Ventricles
Larger than normal in schizophrenia.

Planum temporale
May be larger in right hemisphere in schizophrenia, unlike normal asymmetry.

Planum temporale

Scientists have identified clear brain abnormalities only for some severe mental disorders. A stroke is caused by loss of blood supply to a region of the brain, and it kills off nearby cells (see Chapter 14.) Cells die rapidly near the center of the damaged tissue, the umbra. Cells die less rapidly in the periphery, the penumbra, and may be saved by future medical advances. Alzheimer's disease is a severe cognitive disorder associated with aging (see Chapter 14) that is characterized by atrophied brain tissue, "senile plaques" (caused by clumps of beta amyloid protein), and tangles of diseased or dead neurons. Schizophrenia is a very serious psychotic illness (see Chapter 13) that remains a mystery as a brain disorder, despite some promising leads. For example, among people with schizophrenia the ventricles often are enlarged, and asymmetries in the planum temporale may be reversed.

Source: Keith Kasnot, © National Geographic Image Collection.

ciated with increased arousal and energy expenditure, and the *parasympathetic nervous system* controls the slowing of arousal and energy conservation. Thus the two branches work somewhat in opposition to each other as a means of maintaining homeostasis.

Psychophysiology and Psychopathology
Psychophysiological overarousal and underarousal both can contribute to abnormal behavior. For example, overactivity of the autonomic nervous system (a pounding heart and sweaty hands) has been linked with excessive anxiety. In contrast,

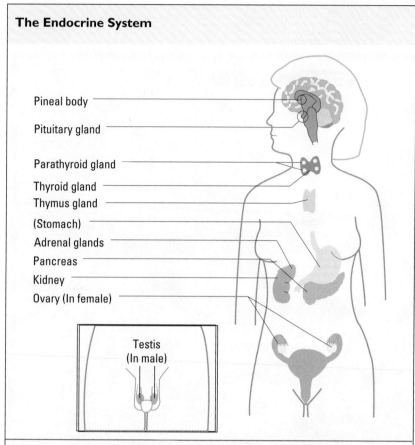

The Endocrine System

Pineal body

Pituitary gland

Parathyroid gland

Thyroid gland

Thymus gland

(Stomach)

Adrenal glands

Pancreas

Kidney

Ovary (In female)

Testis
(In male)

FIGURE 2–4 The glands that comprise the endocrine system, which affects physical and psychophysiological responses through the release of hormones into the blood-stream.

Source: John G. Seamon and Douglas T. Kenrick, 1994, *Psychology*, 2nd ed., Upper Saddle River, NJ: Prentice Hall, p. 67.

chronic autonomic underarousal may explain some of the indifference to social rules and the failure to learn from punishment found in antisocial personality disorder. Psychophysiological assessment also is important, because it can be a useful way of objectively measuring reactions to psychological events, as we discuss in Chapter 4.

Behavior Genetics

Genes are ultramicroscopic units of DNA that carry information about heredity. Genes are located on **chromosomes,** chainlike structures found in the nucleus of cells. Humans normally have 23 pairs of chromosomes.

The field of *genetics* identifies specific genes and their hereditary functions, often focusing at the level of molecules. Geneticists typically have training in biochemistry, not psychology. **Behavior genetics** is a much broader approach that studies genetic influences on the evolution and development of normal and abnormal behavior (Rutter et al., 2001). Behavior geneticists study various human characteristics, often in an attempt to discover if the behavior is more or less strongly affected by genes. However, many experts in genetics and behavior genetics are working together today in the hope of identifying specific genes involved in shaping normal and abnormal behavior (Kendler & Prescott, 2006; Plomin & Crabbe, 2000).

Dominant and Recessive Inheritance One of the most important principles of genetics is the distinction between genotype and phenotype. A **genotype** is an individual's actual genetic structure. Advances in human genetics—the entire human genome has now been mapped—have allowed scientists to determine more and more aspects of genetic structure. Still, it is impossible to observe much of an individual's genotype directly. Instead, what we observe is the **phenotype,** the expression of a given genotype. It usually is impossible to infer a precise genotype from a given phenotype, because phenotypes, but not genotypes, are influenced by the environment. And different genotypes can produce similar phenotypes, as Austrian monk Gregor Mendel (1822–1884) discovered in his famous studies of garden peas.

Genes have alternative forms known as *alleles. Dominant/recessive inheritance* occurs when a trait is caused by a single or *autosomal* gene that has only two alleles (for example, A and *a*) and only one *locus,* a specific location on a chromosome. This is the pattern found in Mendel's peas. The gene for color had only two alleles, A (yellow, dominant) and *a* (green, recessive). Thus, three genotypes are possible: AA, *a*A (or A*a*), and *aa.* Because A is dominant over *a,* however, both AA and *a*A plants will have yellow color, while *aa* plants will be green. Thus, although three genotypes are possible, only two phenotypes are observed: yellow and green. Figure 2–5 shows the patterns of inheritance for dominant and recessive disorders.

Polygenic Inheritance

Dominant/recessive inheritance causes some rare forms of mental retardation (Plomin, DeFries, & McClearn, 1990; Thapar et al., 1994), but most mental disorders are not caused by a single gene—if they have genetic causes at all. Instead, they are **polygenic,** that is, they are influenced by more than one gene (Gottesman, 1991).

Polygenic inheritance has an important effect on the distribution of traits. In contrast to the categorically different phenotypes produced by a single gene (for example, yellow versus green; see the top panel in Figure 2–6), polygenic inheritance produces characteristics that differ by a matter of degree (for example, height). In fact, the distribution of a phenotype in the population begins to resemble the normal distribution as more genes are involved in determining the trait (see the bottom panel in Figure 2–6). This distinction between categories and degrees might seem a bit abstract, so let's bring it down to earth with a familiar example. Test score averages differ by degree. Letter grades represent different categories. And the difference can be important, as you know if you ever ended up with an 89.9 average—and got a "B" for a letter grade.

Most mental disorders appear to be polygenic (and also are influenced by the environment). This holds important implications for how we think about genes and disorders. It is easy to think of emotional problems in terms of categories: A young woman either is depressed or not. It's also easy to think of genes in terms of dominant and recessive inheritance: She has "the gene for" depression. However, both easy assumptions are wrong.

As best we can tell, there is no "gene for" depression or most any other known mental disorder. Instead, there appear to be *multiple* genes involved in the risk for different mental disorders, just as multiple genes affect height. And just like height, this means there is no clear genetic basis for drawing the line—the *threshold*—between normal and abnormal. People can be "*really* short," "not really short," "kind of short," and so on. Similarly, because mental disorders are influenced by multiple genes, people can be "*really* depressed," "not really depressed, "kind of depressed," and so on.

Family Incidence Studies Behavior geneticists have developed important methods for studying genetic contributions to behavior, including family incidence studies, twin studies, and adoption studies. Family incidence studies ask whether diseases "run in families." Investigators identify normal and ill **probands,** or index cases, and tabulate the frequency with which other members of their families suffer from the

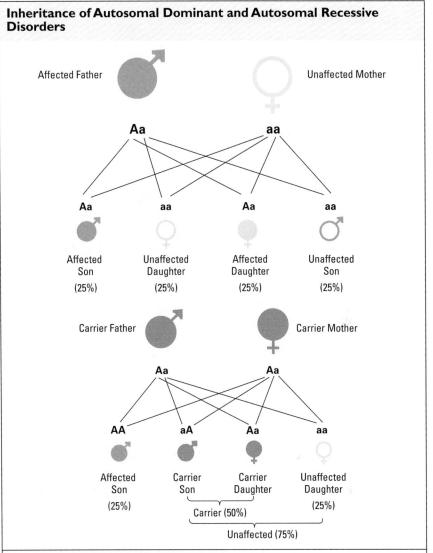

Inheritance of Autosomal Dominant and Autosomal Recessive Disorders

FIGURE 2–5 Patterns of transmission from parents to children for autosomal dominant (top figure) and autosomal recessive disorders (bottom figure). Note that the disorder is either present or absent for both patterns of inheritance.

Source: Based on S.V. Garaone, M.T. Tsuang, and D.W. Tsuang, 1999, *Genetics of Mental Disorders.* New York: Guilford.

same disorder. If a higher prevalence of illness is found in the family of an ill proband, this is consistent with genetic causation. The finding also is consistent with environmental causation, however, because families share environments as well as genes. For this reason, no firm conclusions about the relative role of genes or the environment can be reached from family incidence studies alone.

Twin Studies Studies of twins, in contrast, can provide strong evidence about genetic and environmental contributions to a disorder.

How do twin studies show that genes—and experience—matter?

Single Gene and Polygenetic Inheritance

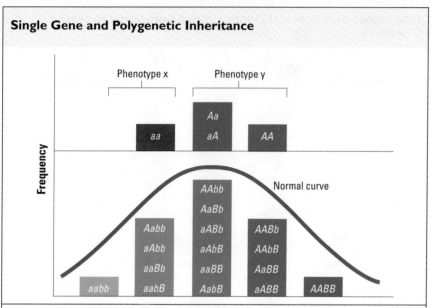

FIGURE 2–6 Single genes produce phenotypes that differ qualitatively, as illustrated in the top panel. Multiple genes produce phenotypes that differ quantitatively. As more genes are involved (only two in this illustration), the distribution of traits approximates the normal curve, as illustrated in the bottom panel.

Monozygotic (MZ) twins are *identical*. One egg is fertilized by one sperm, and thus MZ twins have identical genotypes. **Dizygotic (DZ) twins** are *fraternal*. These twins are produced from two eggs and two sperm. Thus, like all siblings, DZ twins share an average of 50 percent of their genes, whereas MZ twins share 100 percent of their genes. Of course, most MZ and DZ twin pairs are raised in the same family. Thus MZ and DZ twins differ in their genetic similarity, but they are alike in their environmental experiences.

Comparisons between MZ and DZ twin pairs thus shed light on genetic and environmental contributions. The key comparison involves determining the **concordance rate** of the two sets of twins, specifically whether MZ twins are more alike than DZ twins are alike. A twin pair is *concordant* when both twins either have the same disorder or are free from the disorder, for example, both suffer from schizophrenia. The twin pair is discordant when one twin has the disorder but the other does not, for example, one twin has schizophrenia but the co-twin does not.

If we assume that the environmental effects on a disorder are the same for DZ twin pairs as they are for MZ twin pairs, then any differences between the concordance rates for MZ and DZ twins must be caused by genetics. If a disorder is purely genetic, for example, scientists should find a concordance rate of 100 percent for MZ twins (who are genetically identical) and 50 percent for DZ twins (who share half of the same genes on average) (see Table 2–4).

In contrast, similar concordance rates for MZ and DZ twins suggest environmental causes. Environmental causes are implicated regardless of whether the concordance rates for MZ and DZ twins are both 0 percent, both 100 percent, or both anywhere in between. However, the level of concordance does provide information about the nature of the environmental contribution. *High* concordance rates for both MZ and DZ twins point to the etiological role of the **shared environment,** the experiences the two twins share in common, for example, growing up in poverty. If the shared environment explained *all* of the variance in a trait, the concordance rate would 100 percent for both MZ and DZ twins. They would be alike because both MZ and DZ twins share the same environment (see Table 2–4).

What causal effect is implied by similar but *low* concordance rates for both MZ and DZ pairs? In this case, the culprit is the **nonshared environment,** experiences unique to one twin, for example, your boyfriend or girlfriend. In this case, genetic causes are again ruled out, because MZ twins are no higher than DZ twins. And shared environmental causes are ruled out by low concordance rates. If the nonshared environment explained *all* of the variance in a trait, the concordance rate would be 0 percent for both MZ and DZ twins (see Table 2–4). In real research, of course, nothing is perfect. Twin studies provide useful estimates of the role played by genes, the shared environment, and the nonshared environment by yielding data in between the perfect scenarios summarized in Table 2-4.

Twin studies often indicate that genes have a substantial influence on mental disorders. Somewhat surprising, behavior genetic research also indicates that many environmental influences

TABLE 2–4   Twin Studies: Implications of Different Findings

CONCORDANCE FOR CONCORDANCE	SUPPORTS INFLUENCE OF	PERFECT CASE[1]
MZ > DZ	Genes	MZ = 100%; DZ = 50%
MZ = DZ; both high	Shared environment	MZ = 100%; DZ = 100%
MZ = DZ; both low	Nonshared environment	MZ = 0%; DZ = 0%

[1]The identified influence explains everything in the perfect case. Actual concordance rates almost always fall between these extremes, thus providing an index of the relative contributions of genes, the shared environment, and/or the nonshared environment.

appear to be nonshared. However, the logic of twin studies depends on the assumption that the environment affects DZ twins in the same way that it influences MZ twins. If MZ twins have more similar personalities than DZ twins, MZs may seek similar environments and get more similar responses from the environment. If so, then higher concordance rates for MZ twins might result from more similar environmental experiences and not from more similar genetic endowments.

Adoption Studies This is one reason why behavior genetic researchers also conduct adoption studies. In this research design, people who were adopted as infants are compared with their biological versus their adoptive relatives (usually their parents) in terms of concordance for a disorder. If concordance is higher for biological than for adoptive relatives, then genetic factors are involved, because adopted children share their biological relatives' genes but not their environment. On the other hand, if children are more similar to their adoptive than to their biological relatives, then environment is causal, because adopted children share their adoptive relatives' environment but not their genes.

The logic of the adoption design might be clearer if we think about the case of the adopted girl, Meghan, from the beginning of this chapter. Genetic influences are implicated if Meghan develops problems similar to her biological, but not adoptive, parents. On the other hand, environmental influences are causal if Meghan develops problems more similar to her adoptive than their biological parents.

Adoption studies have some potential problems, for example, the fact that adoption placement is selective. Still, you can be confident in the findings of behavior genetic researchers when adoption and twin studies produce similar results (Kendler & Prescott, 2006).

Misinterpreting Behavior Genetics Findings
Behavior genetic research is powerful, but unfortunately, people often misinterpret it (Kagan, 2007; Rutter, Moffitt, & Caspi, 2006). One serious misinterpretation is that a psychological disorder is inevitable if it is genetic. Genetic influences on abnormal behavior are *predispositions,* increased risks, not *predestinations*—inevitabilities. And because concordance rates are almost always well below 100 percent for MZ twins, we know that

the *environment* contributes to the development—or prevention—of mental disorders (Faraone, Tsuang, & Tsuang, 1999).

It also is wrong to think that genetic characteristics cannot be modified. Even in cases where mental retardation has a known genetic cause, environmental experiences such as dietary restrictions or rich, early intellectual stimulation can lead to substantial increases in IQ (Turkheimer, 1991). In short, the conclusion "It's genetic" does not mean, "It's inevitable" or "It's hopeless." Nature and nurture are not separate influences on behavior. Nature and nurture always work together (Li, 2003).

Finally, behavior genetic findings do not tell us what genetic mechanism is at work. When we read that a disorder is "genetic," we tend to think there is "a gene for" depression, alcoholism, or hyperactivity, but this too is wrong. Think about this. Criminal behavior also is "genetic," as is divorce and political affiliation. For these behaviors, concordance rates are higher for MZ than for DZ twins. But no one thinks (we hope) that people have a "crime gene," a "divorce gene," or a "Republican gene." Behavior genetic studies tell us that genes are important, but they reveal nothing about the genetic mechanism. For criminal behavior, perhaps people inherit an underaroused autonomic nervous system, which makes them less fearful and therefore less likely to learn from punishment. This is a *long* way from having a "crime gene." The point is that you need to think about behavior genetic research more deeply than, "it's genetic."

Genetics and Psychopathology Genes have very broad influences on abnormal—and normal—behavior. Still, we doubt that specific genetic causes will be discovered for most mental disorders. Why? Scientists have collared a single gene culprit responsible for a few, rare forms of mental disorder, and we expect some more to be identified. However, we are unlikely to find a gene for depression, for eating disorders, or for most forms of psychopathology. Most mental disorders appear to be caused by multiple genes (they are polygenic) and multiple environmental events. In short, you should recognize pervasive genetic influences on behavior, but also think critically and beyond familiar models of dominant and recessive inheritance. In fact, you should be skeptical of anyone who claims to have found "the" cause of any mental disorder (see Critical Thinking Matters).

CRITICAL THINKING MATTERS

Do Vaccinations Cause Autism?

In 1998, the highly reputable British journal *Lancet* published a study by Dr. Andrew Wakefield and a dozen co-authors (1998). The authors speculated that the measles/mumps/rubella (MMR) vaccination might be responsible for 12 cases of autism they diagnosed. *Autism* is a severe psychological disorder that begins very early in life and is marked by extreme problems with communication, social interaction, and stereotyped behavior (see Chapter 15). The researchers did not analyze any scientific data, or study children who were vaccinated but did not develop autism. In fact, a skeptical editorial was published with the article and questioned its validity (Chen & DeStefano, 1998).

None of these limitations prevented a tsunami of concerns and assertions about vaccinations causing autism. Warnings spread on television, radio, in print, and especially over the Internet. The U.S. Congress held hearings. The National Institutes of Health funded new research. Many parents refused to vaccinate their children. This worried public health officials. Measles, mumps, and rubella are serious illnesses, and the MMR vaccination not only protects the vaccinated child but also helps keep these highly contagious diseases from spreading.

Is there any scientific support for Dr. Wakefield's speculation? No. One Danish study of a *half million* children found no differences in the rate of autism between children who did and did not receive the MMR vaccine containing the supposed autism-causing agent, *thimerosal* (Hviid et al., 2003), as did a major study in the United Kingdom (Chen, Landau, & Sham, 2004) and two in Japan (Honda et al., 2005; Uchiyama et al., 2007). If this does not make you skeptical, consider this: Ten of the original 13 co-authors of the 1998 paper retracted their speculation (*New York Times*, March 4, 2004).

Misinformation, fear, and anger still abound even after public retractions and negative re-

sults for hundreds of thousands of children (versus speculations about 12). Search the Internet, and you will find many vehement, if unscientific, assertions that MMR causes autism. It's fine to hypothesize, but it's more important to be skeptical—to doubt not only other people's theories but your own too. And with so much "scientific" information available on the Internet and elsewhere, it's important for you to be skeptical, not only in psychology class but also in evaluating all kinds of information. We want you to think critically in abnormal psychology and in life.

Why are scientists skeptics?

And here's another reason to think critically. As we were revising this chapter, a federal compensation court awarded money to the parents of Hannah Poling who was diagnosed with autism (*New York Times*, March 8, 2008). The money came from a fund designated for people hurt by vaccines. The fund was created in 1988 in response to fears about neurological damage caused by the diphtheria-pertussis-tetanus (DPT) vaccine, fears that most experts conclude were false (Sugarman, 2007). Still, lawyers convinced some juries that DPT caused the damage, and resulting legal costs led manufacturers to stop making DPT. When the last manufacturer threatened to halt production, the U.S. government created the fund, fearing devastating public health consequences if children were no longer vaccinated (Sugarman, 2007).

The Poling incident is fueling new fears about vaccines causing autism—and who knows what future juries will decide—but consider this: Hannah's behavior deteriorated rapidly around the time she was vaccinated. However, she also had a rare disorder of the mitochondria, the energy factories of cells.

Problems due to mitochondrial disorders often surface only following a severe infection. An expert witness claimed that this is what happened to Hannah as a result of her multiple vaccinations, a claim that leading vaccine scientists note has no basis in science. Vaccines, in fact, can *protect* people with mitochondrial disorders by warding off serious infection (*New York Times*, March 31, 2008).

We cannot know what courts will decide in the 5,000 *pending* legal cases alleging that MMR causes autism. Yet, we do know that legal rulings are *not* scientific evidence. Ultimately, the law is about convincing a judge or jury that some alleged fact is true; scientists must prove facts publicly and repeatedly. And while we are on the topic of legal action, here's another one: At the same time the Poling case went public, Dr. Andrew Wakefield and two colleagues were being investigated by Britain's General Medical Council. One charge among several is that, at the time of publishing his case studies, Wakefield failed to disclose receiving substantial financial support from lawyers who were suing manufactuers of the MMR vaccine (Sugarman, 2007).

It is far easier to create false fears than to dispel them. On April 4, 2008, the Web site of the National Institute of Child Health and Human Development read: "To date there is no definite, scientific proof that any vaccine or combination of vaccines can cause autism." If you are paranoid about vaccinations, you can focus on the "to date" and "definite" qualifications. Yet science can *never* prove the negative. (Prove that those Martian scientists we discussed earlier did *not* write this textbook. *You* just can't see them!) This is why the burden of proof rests upon any scientist who offers a hypothesis. If we speculate that vaccinations cause autism—or Martians write textbooks—we need to prove the validity of our assertion. You do not need to prove us wrong. Until we can show that our hypothesis is true, the community of scientists assumes it is false. Critical thinking *matters*.

Genes and the Environment Before turning to psychological and social factors, we need to introduce two key concepts about how genes and the environment work together. The first is **gene–environment interaction,** the widely accepted idea that a combination of a genetic risk

and an environmental stress causes emotional disorders (Moffitt et al., 2006; see Figure 2-7).

The second concept is **gene–environment correlation,** the fact that people's experience often is correlated with their genetic makeup (Rutter, Moffitt, & Caspi, 2006). We explore this important concept further when discussing marital status and psychopathology later in this chapter. For now, you should ponder this important fact: Experience is *not* random. Anxious parents can give children "anxious" genes *and* an anxious upbringing. Girls who get pregnant as teenagers differ in many ways from women who delay pregnancy until their 30s, including in ways that are affected by genes (e.g., age at first menarche, intelligence, personality). Skydivers surely differ from flight phobics in terms of thrill seeking, a genetically influenced personality characteristic. The point is that skydiving, teen pregnancy, anxious parenting, and hundreds of other experiences are not random. Our experience is correlated with our genetic makeup; there is a gene–environment correlation.

PSYCHOLOGICAL FACTORS

We must begin our overview of psychological factors in emotional disorders on a humbling note: Psychology does not have a widely accepted theory of *personality,* the essential traits that, taken as a whole, describe human behavior. We are faced with the task of trying to explain abnormal behavior without a good understanding of normal behavior! This is a huge limitation, akin to chemistry without a periodic table of the elements or biology without a classification of living things. As a result, any listing of the psychological factors involved in mental disorders, including our own, is necessarily incomplete and likely to be controversial. Still, we can organize many psychological factors affecting mental health into five categories: (1) human nature and temperament; (2) emotion; (3) learning and cognition; (4) our sense of self; and (5) human development.

Human Nature and Temperament

What are our basic psychological motivations—both those that we share with other animals and others that are uniquely human? Freud's answer to this question was that we have two basic drives, sex and aggression. In contrast, Watson suggested that we come into the world as blank slates—there is no human nature apart from our common experi-

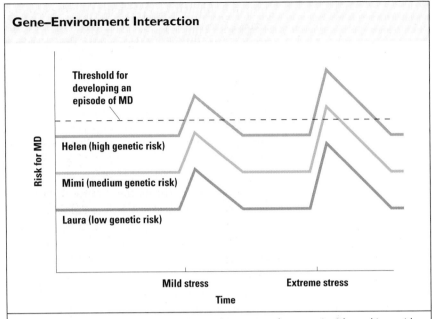

Gene–Environment Interaction

FIGURE 2–7 A gene–environment interaction occurs when genetic risk combines with environmental stress to produce a mental disorder. Note how different combinations of genetic risk and stress severity cross the threshold for disorder.

Source: K. S. Kendler and C.A. Prescott, 2006, *Genes, Environment, and Psychopathology: Understanding the Causes of Psychiatric and Substance Use Disorders.* New York: Guilford, p. 187.

ence. Today, psychologists are revisiting questions about the nature of human nature in a new, exciting, and controversial field of study called evolutionary psychology.

> *How is human nature basic to understanding abnormal behavior?*

Evolutionary Psychology Evolutionary psychology is the application of the principles of evolution to our understanding of the animal and human mind. Behavior geneticists study how genes influence *individual differences,* or how people are different from one another. Evolutionary psychology, studies *species-typical characteristics*—genetically influenced characteristics that people share as a part of human nature. Evolutionary psychologists assume that animal and human psychology, like animal and human anatomy, have evolved genetically based on two broad principles of evolution, natural selection and sexual selection.

Natural selection is the process through which successful inherited adaptations to environmental problems become more common over successive generations of offspring. The adaptation is selected by evolution, because it increases *inclusive fitness,* the reproductive success of those who have the adaptation, their offspring, and/or their kin. For example, the large human brain, with its particularly large cerebral cortex, presumably was selected across evolutionary history. The adaptations that a larger brain enabled (e.g., the use of tools for survival and weapons for defense) increased the survival and reproductive success of early humans with larger brains, as well as that of their offspring and kin. *Sexual selection* improves inclusive fitness through increased access to mates and mating. Mating access can be increased by successful *intra*sexual competition, for example, a dominant male limits the mating opportunities of other males; or by successful *inter*sexual selection, for example, a more brightly colored bird attracts more members of the opposite sex (Gaulin & McBurney, 2001; Larsen & Buss, 2002).

Evolutionary psychology seeks to understand how evolution shaped human behavior. Among other things, the approach actually seeks to answer the age-old question, *What is human nature?* As we noted, psychologists do not agree about the nature of human nature, but two qualities that belong at the top of anyone's list are: the need to form close relationships and the competition for dominance.

Attachment Theory The theoretical writings of British psychiatrist John Bowlby (1907–1990) greatly influenced psychologists' views about the

human need to form close relationships. Bowlby was trained in psychoanalysis, but he rejected Freudian theory and placed the need to form close relationships at the core of his view of development (Bowlby, 1969). The heart of Bowlby's theory was the observation that infants form **attachments** early in life—special and selective bonds with their caregivers.

Bowlby based his approach, known as *attachment theory,* on findings from *ethology,* the study of animal behavior. Ethologists documented that close relationships develop between infants and caregivers in many species of animals. In some species, selective relationships develop in the first hours or days of life, a process called *imprinting.* Human attachments are far more flexible and slow to develop. Still, human infants and toddlers, like many animal offspring, develop selective bonds to caregivers early in life. You can readily observe this: Ducklings swim in line behind their mother; toddlers explore the world in an irregular orbit around a parent. These bonds, together with displays of distress when separated, keep infant and parent in close proximity. From an evolutionary standpoint, proximity has survival value, because parents protect their offspring from danger. Thus, attachment behavior is an inborn characteristic, a product of natural selection.

Bowlby's writings were theoretical, but psychological research supports many aspects of attachment theory. Particularly relevant to the development of abnormal behavior is research on *insecure* or *anxious attachments,* uncertain or ambivalent parent–child relationships that are a product of inconsistent and unresponsive parenting during the first year of life (Ainsworth et al., 1979). Anxious attachments can make children mistrustful, dependent, and/or rejecting in subsequent relationships, a pattern that may continue into adult life. Attachment difficulties can be overcome (Rutter & Rutter, 1993), but as we discuss throughout the text, research shows that supportive relationships promote mental health throughout the life span.

▶ A Japanese macaque monkey and her one-month-old baby. Strong bonds between infants and caregivers are found across many species. Disruptions in human attachments may contribute to abnormal behavior.

Dominance The development of attachments, or more generally of *affiliation* with other members of the same species, is one of the two broad categories of social behaviors studied by ethologists. The second is **dominance,** the hierarchical ordering of a social group into more and less privileged members. Dominance hierarchies are easily observed in human as well as other animal social groups. From the perspective of evolutionary psychology, dominance competition is basic to sexual selection, and therefore a prime candidate on our short list of species-typical human qualities.

In research on abnormal behavior, dominance often is an implicit rather than explicit focus. For example, a strong internal sense of control and effectiveness is widely viewed as basic to positive mental health. And it is widely accepted that the best parents are *authoritative* (Maccoby & Martin, 1983), that is, they are both warmly responsive to children (thereby encouraging secure attachments) and firm in discipline (thereby maintaining parental authority).

Additional social motivations, as well as cognitive ones, belong on psychology's "periodic table." Still, we are confident that attachment and dominance will rank high on the final list of psychological elements. We think Freud would agree. We view Freud's basic drives, sex and aggression, as metaphors for the broader qualities of affiliation and dominance.

Temperament One of the most important areas of research on individual differences in personality is the study of **temperament,** characteristic styles of relating to the world. Researchers generally agree that temperament consists of five dimensions (McAdams & Pals, 2006). The "big five" are (1) openness to experience—imaginative and curious versus shallow and imperceptive; (2) conscientiousness—organized and reliable versus careless and negligent; (3) extraversion—active and talkative versus passive and reserved; (4) agreeableness—trusting and kind versus hostile and selfish; and (5) neuroticism—nervous and moody versus calm and pleasant. The acronym OCEAN, which uses the first letter of each term, will help you to remember "the big five."

Individual differences in temperament may play a role in a number of psychological disorders, especially personality disorders and child behavior problems. Still, you should view temperamental contributions to personality from a systems perspective. The critical issue is the *goodness of fit* between a child's biologically based temperament and the psychological and social environments. For example, a "difficult" temperament increases the risk for child behavior problems, but parenting determines whether the difficult behavior grows worse or is controlled (Rothbart, 2007).

▲ Evolution shapes behavior in animals and humans. Do humans compete for dominance, perhaps in more subtle ways than these stags compete?

"It's not you—it's natural selection."

▲ The cartoon pokes fun at intersexual selection and perhaps suggests a new break up line.

Emotions

Emotions, internal feeling states, are essential to human experience and to our understanding of mental disorders. But we have hundreds of words for different feelings in the English language. What emotions are most essential? Researchers have used statistical analysis to reduce our lexicon of feelings to six basic emotions:

▶ Emotions often come to us without intention, effort, or desire, as illustrated by Halle Berry while accepting her Oscar for best actress for her role in *Monster's Ball*.

- Love
- Joy
- Surprise
- Anger
- Sadness
- Fear

This list can be pared further into two categories, positive emotion (the left column) and negative emotion (the right column). Of course, negative emotions are most relevant to abnormal psychology, and we have separate chapters that focus primarily on sadness (Chapter 5) and fear (Chapter 6). We consider anger in relation to a number of disorders.

Emotions come to us without intention, effort, or desire, and as we have seen, emotions are controlled primarily by subcortical brain structures. Thus, our feelings are more "basic" or primitive than our thoughts, which are controlled by the cerebral cortex, a more recent product of evolution (Buck, 1999). Cognition can regulate emotion, but we cannot wholly control our feelings intellectually (Panksepp, 1998). This fact often becomes an issue in treating abnormal behavior, as people often want to but cannot easily change their emotions.

Learning and Cognition

Emotions, motivations, and temperamental styles can be modified, at least to some degree, by learning. Earlier, we discussed classical and operant conditioning, two modes of learning that are essential to the development of normal and abnormal behavior. We know, for example, that classical conditioning can create new fears, and antisocial behavior can be maintained by positive reinforcement.

Modeling A third learning mechanism described by the U.S. psychologist Albert Bandura of Stanford University is **modeling** or learning through imitation, a process that you surely have observed many times. A particular concern for the development of abnormal behavior is when parents or other important adults model dysfunctional behavior for children, for example, excessive drinking.

Cognition and Social Cognition Cognitive psychologists study other, more complex learning mechanisms such as attention, information processing, and memory. In doing so, cognitive psychologists often draw analogies between human thinking and computers, but the "human computer" apparently is programmed in ways that make decision making more efficient but less objective (Kahneman, 2003). That is, we routinely make cognitive errors not because we reason wrongly, but because we use shorthand calculations (*heuristics*) that require little effort and typically are accurate enough—but sometimes are way off the mark.

Cognitive psychology has profoundly affected thinking about the cause of mental disorders, as has the parallel field of *social cognition*—the study of how humans process information about the social world. The important concept of attribution illustrates this approach. **Attributions** are perceived causes, that is, people's *beliefs* about cause–effect relations. Attributions reveal that people are "intuitive scientists." We routinely draw shorthand conclusions about causality instead of examining things scientifically. If your girlfriend gets mad at you for "ditching" her at a party, for example, you are unlikely to examine her feelings objectively. Instead, you attribute her anger to some reasonable cause, perhaps her tendency to cling to you. Intuitive judgments are efficient because they require little cognitive effort, but research shows that attributions often are inaccurate (Wilson, 2002).

Interestingly, one cognitive theory suggests that automatic and distorted perceptions of reality cause people to become depressed (Beck et al., 1979). For example, people prone to depression may conclude that they are inadequate based on a single unpleasant experience. A successful treatment based on this theory encourages depressed people to be more scientific and less intuitive in evaluating conclusions about themselves (see Chapter 5). One controversy, however, is whether depressed people actually see the world all too accurately. Perhaps nondepressed people are the ones who make routine cognitive errors by seeing the world, and themselves, in an unrealistically positive light (Taylor et al., 2003).

The Sense of Self

We share emotions and motivations with other animals, and we share some information-processing strategies with computers. Perhaps our sense of self is uniquely human. The exact definition of self can be elusive, however, both in psychological theory—and personally.

One influential conceptualization is Erik Erikson's (1968) concept of **identity,** an integrated sense of individuality, wholeness, and continuity. Erikson viewed identity as the product of the adolescent's struggle to answer the question "Who am I?" As we discuss in Chapter 17, Erikson urged young people to take some time and try out new values and roles before adopting a single, enduring identity.

Other theorists argue that we do not have one identity but many "selves." The psychologist George Kelly (1905–1966), for example, emphasized the identities linked with the different roles that people play in life. These include obvious roles like being a daughter, a student, and a friend, as well as less obvious roles, like being a "caretaker," a "jock," or "the quiet one." Kelly argued that people develop many different role identities, various senses of self corresponding with actual life roles. A related, contemporary theory is that people have multiple *relational selves,* unique actions and identities linked with different significant relationships (Chen, Boucher, & Tapias, 2006).

The idea that children and adults must develop **self-control**—internal rules for guiding appropriate behavior—is an important concept in research on abnormal behavior. Self-control is learned through the process of *socialization,* where parents, teachers, and peers use discipline, praise, and their own example to teach children prosocial behavior and set limits on their antisocial behavior. Over time, these standards are *internalized*—that is, the external rules become internal regulations. The result is self-control.

Self-esteem, valuing one's abilities, is another important and sometimes controversial aspect of our sense of self. The concept of self-esteem has been derided recently, partly in reaction to misguided school programs that urged raising children's self-esteem as a cure to everything from school dropout to teen pregnancy (Swann, Chang-Schneider, & McClarty, 2007). High self-esteem can be as much a product of success as a cause of it; raising children's self-esteem in isola-

▲ Brain imaging shows deterioration caused by frontotemporal lobar degeneration after just 15 months. The ability to self-reflect often is lost as a result of the disease.

tion of actual achievement produces little benefit (Baumeister et al., 2003). Similarly, low self-esteem can result from psychological problems rather than a cause of them.

One final note: Our sense of self may be uniquely human, but there still is no dualism between mind and body. Like all psychological experiences, our sense of self is represented in the brain. In fact, much of the human sense of self apparently is localized in the frontal lobe. A terrible form of degenerative brain disease rapidly damages the front lobe and causes patients to lose much self-reflection and self-control (Levenson & Miller, 2007).

Stages of Development

Development, or how people grow and change, is of basic importance to normal and abnormal psychology. A key developmental concept is that psychological growth can be characterized by various **developmental stages**—periods of time marked by age and/or social tasks during which children or adults face common social and emotional challenges. Two prominent theories that divided development into stages are Freud's theory of psycho*sexual* development and Erikson's theory of psycho*social* development. Freud highlighted the child's internal struggles with sexuality as marking the various stages of development. In contrast, Erikson emphasized social tasks and the conflicts involved in meeting the demands of the external world. Importantly and in contrast to Freud, Erikson also suggested that development does not end with adolescence; rather, he proposed that development continues throughout the life span.

The key tasks, ages, and defining events of these two stage theories are summarized in Table 2–5. In addition to noting differences between the theories, you should observe that both theorists use similar ages to denote the

TABLE 2–5   Freud's and Erikson's Stage Theories of Development

AGE[1]	0–1½	1–3	2–6	5–12	11–20	18–30	25–70	65 ON
FREUD	ORAL	ANAL	PHALLIC	LATENCY	GENITAL			
	Oral gratification through breast feeding. Meeting one's own needs.	Learning control over environment and inner needs through toilet training.	Sexual rivalry with opposite-gender parent. Oedipal conflicts, penis envy, identification.	Not a stage, as psychosexual development is dormant during these ages.	Mature sexuality and formation of mutual heterosexual relationships.			
ERIKSON	BASIC TRUST VS. BASIC MISTRUST	AUTONOMY VS. SHAME AND DOUBT	INITIATIVE VS. GUILT	INDUSTRY VS. INFERIORITY	IDENTITY VS. ROLE CONFUSION	INTIMACY VS. SELF-ABSORPTION	GENERATIVITY VS. STAGNATION	INTEGRITY VS. DESPAIR
	Developing basic trust in self and others through feeding and caretaking.	Gaining a sense of competence through success in toileting and mastering environment.	Gaining parental approval for initiative rather than guilt over inadequacy.	Curiosity and eagerness to learn leads to a sense of competence or inadequacy.	Identity crisis is a struggle to answer question, "Who am I?"	Aloneness of young adult resolved by forming friendships and a lasting intimate relationship.	Success in work but especially in raising the next generation, or failure to be productive.	Satisfaction with the life one lived rather than despair over lost opportunities.

[1]Ages are approximate, as indicated by overlap in age ranges.

beginning and end of developmental stages of childhood. Other theorists also have suggested that key developmental transitions occur around the ages of 1, 6, and 12, as these ages are key times of change for children.

Developmental transitions mark the end of one developmental stage and the beginning of a new one, for example, the end of childhood and the beginning of adolescence. Developmental transitions often are a time of turmoil. As routine functioning changes, we are forced to learn new ways of thinking, feeling, and acting. Because of this, we devote Chapter 17 to a discussion of difficult developmental transitions, emotionally challenging times that often are linked to psychological struggles.

SOCIAL FACTORS

Social factors are the broadest level of analysis for understanding contributions to abnormal behavior. Potential influences are numerous, including interpersonal relationships, societal institutions, and cultural values. In our necessarily selective overview, we focus on several key examples including intimate relationships, gender roles, ethnicity, poverty, and social values.

Social perspectives emphasize that abnormal behavior can be influenced by *social roles,* behavior that, like a role in a play, is shaped by social "scripts." In fact *labeling theory* asserts that emotional disorders themselves are the enactment of prescribed social roles (Rosenhan, 1973). Labeling theory suggests that people's actions conform to the expectations created by the label, a process termed *the self-fulfilling prophecy.* For example, when an elementary school boy is labeled "a troublemaker," both he and his teachers may act in ways that make the label come true.

There is little doubt that expectations affect behavior, but labeling alone offers a limited understanding of much abnormal behavior. For example, how could labeling someone "schizophrenic" cause severe hallucinations, delusions, and life disruptions? The roles we play in life—including roles shaped by gender, race, social class, and culture—help to shape who we become. But psychopathology is much more than the expectations a label creates.

Relationships and Psychopathology

Researchers consistently find that relationship problems, particularly conflict and anger in close relationships, are associated with various emotional disorders (Beach, Wamboldt, & Kaslow, 2006; Miklowitz, Otto, & Frank, 2007). We need to wonder, however, do troubled relationships cause abnormal behavior, or do an individual's psychological problems cause relationship difficulties?

Marital Status and Psychopathology The association between marital status and psychopathology is a good example of the cause–effect dilemma. The demographics of the U.S. family have changed greatly over the last few decades. Cohabitation before marriage is frequent, many children are born outside of marriage, and almost half of all marriages end in divorce (Bramlett & Mosher, 2001). In part because of the uncertainty created by these rapid changes, researchers have carefully studied the psychological consequences of alternative family structures for children and adults.

Marital status and psychological problems clearly are *correlated.* Children and adults from divorced or never-married families have somewhat more psychological problems than people from always-married families (Amato, 2001; Emery, 1999; Waite & Gallagher, 2000; Whisman, Sheldon, & Goering, 2000). But does marital status *cause* these problems? Behavior geneticists have found that personality characteristics that are genetically influenced contribute to marital disruption (McGue & Lykken, 1992). Could a parent's genes, not their marital status, also influence children's behavior? This is an example of a *gene–environment correlation,* discussed earlier. Children's genetic makeup is correlated with their experience of growing up in a disrupted family, because an increased risk for both is passed to children by their parents.

In an exciting innovation, researchers now are using twins to control for gene–environment correlations, comparing twins (or their children) who *differ* in terms of some major life experience (Rutter, 2007). For example, if we find that an MZ twin who gets divorced has more psychological problems than his co-twin who remains married, and get the same result across many pairs of twins, we know that the difference is *not* due to genes. We also know that the difference is

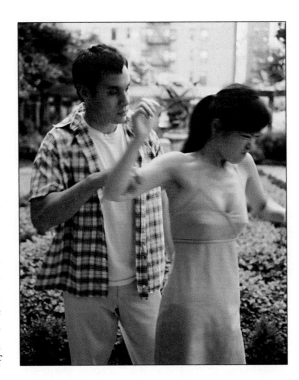

◀ Intimate relationships can be a source of great social support or emotional distress.

not caused by childrearing or other experiences that twins share. Why? Identical twins have identical genes and grow up in the same families. Any difference between them therefore must be caused by the nonshared environment, their unique experiences, one of which is divorce in the present example. In fact, new twin research suggests that divorce is a cause of some psychological problems both in children (D'Onofrio et al., 2007) and adults (Spotts, Lichtenstein, & Pederson, 2005).

Social Relationships Research also shows that a good relationship with someone *outside* of the family is associated with better mental health among children (Landis, Gaylord-Harden, & Malinowski, 2007; Werner & Smith, 1992) and adults (Birditt & Antonucci, 2007; Reis, Collins, & Berscheid, 2000). A few things are critical about this **social support**—the emotional and practical assistance received from others. Significantly, one close relationship can provide as much support as many relationships. The greatest risk comes from having *no* social support. In addition, it is much worse to be actively rejected than to be neglected. Especially among children, it is far worse to be "liked least" than not to be "liked most" by your peers (Coie & Kupersmidt, 1983).

Once again, the association between abnormal behavior and the lack of supportive relationships may have several causes. In some circumstances, peer rejection may cause emotional difficulties. Being an outcast surely causes much distress. In other cases, the lack of a close relationship may be a consequence of psychopathology. Psychologically disturbed people can be socially awkward. Finally, social support may help still other people to cope more successfully with preexisting emotional problems.

Gender and Gender Roles

How can gender roles influence abnormal behavior?

Gender and **gender roles,** expectations regarding the appropriate behavior of males or females, can dramatically affect our behavior. One common distinction argues that women are more *relational,* or oriented toward others, whereas men are more *instrumental,* or oriented toward action and achievement (Gilligan, 1982). Whether such differences really exist—and, if they do, what causes them—is open to debate. Some gender differences are determined by genetics and hormones, but socially prescribed gender roles also exert a strong influence on our behavior (Maccoby, 1998).

Gender roles may influence the development, expression, or consequences of psychopathology. Some theorists suggest, for example, that women's traditional roles foster dependency and helplessness, which accounts for the considerably higher rates of depression among women. Others argue that gender roles may not cause abnormal behavior, but they do influence how psychopathology is expressed. For example, social expectations may allow women to become depressed when confronted with adversity, whereas men's roles dictate that they "carry on" or perhaps sooth their inner turmoil with alcohol or drugs.

Some believe that *androgyny*—the possession of both "female" and "male" gender-role characteristics—is the answer to the problems associated with being either overly "feminine" or overly "masculine." Others embrace traditional gender roles. Our goal is not to address such conflicting values. Instead, we consider gender differences in the prevalence of various psychological disorders throughout the text. When appropriate, we interpret this evidence in terms of the roles played by men and women.

Prejudice, Poverty, and Society

Prejudice and poverty are broad social influences on psychological well-being in the United States today. We consider these two factors together because they are so commonly linked in American life. In 2000, 10.3 percent of white families with children were living below the poverty level, compared with 24.9 percent of black families and 22.9 percent of Latino families. Race and poverty also are closely linked to marital status. Among married African American families with children, 6.3 percent lived in poverty, in comparison to 41.0 percent of families headed by a single mother. Among whites the comparable poverty rates were 5.8 percent married versus 27.5 percent single mother, and 16.9 percent married versus 41.4 percent single mother for Hispanics (U.S. Census Bureau, 2002).

An increased risk for psychological disorders is associated with prejudice and poverty, although the separate consequences of race and poverty need to be disentangled. Poverty is linked with many stressors, including gruesome traumas (Evans, 2004). For example, one researcher found that 12 percent of school aged children living in a Washington, D.C. neighborhood reported having seen a dead body in the streets outside their homes (Richters, 1993). Poverty also increases exposure to chemical toxins, such as to the lead found in old, chipped paint and automotive exhaust fumes (Evans, 2004). When ingested at toxic levels, lead can damage the central nervous system.

The conditions of poverty affect a disproportionate number of African Americans, but the experiences of American blacks and whites differ in

▼ Socially prescribed gender roles exert a strong influence on our behavior and perhaps on the development, expression, and consequences of psychopathology.

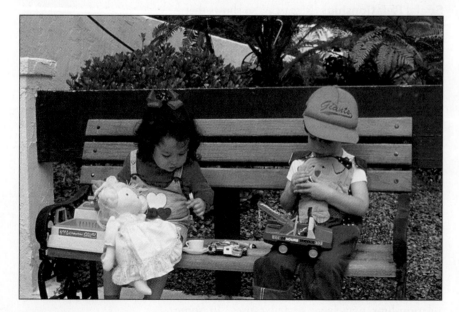

many ways. African Americans have endured a history of slavery and discrimination, and racial prejudices undermine physical and mental health (Clark et al., 1999). Of course, African Americans are not the only targets of prejudice. For example, extensive evidence links the prejudice experienced by gays and lesbians to an increased risk for mental health problems (Meyer, 2003).

Even more broadly, we recognize that society and culture influence abnormal behavior. Our lives, our education, and even our science are deeply embedded within our culture. Societal practices, beliefs, and values help to shape the definition of abnormal behavior and the scientific enterprise that attempts to uncover its roots.

GETTING HELP

The problems that you study in abnormal psychology can touch your life in a very personal way. At one time or another, you, someone in your family, or one of your close friends likely will experience a serious psychological problem. If so, we hope you will seek and find meaningful help. What can you do if you think you may want to get help?

A good place to start is to talk frankly with someone you trust—a friend, a family member, a mental health professional, maybe a professor. Taking this step can be difficult, but you surely will be relieved once you have opened up a little. In fact, this may be the end of your search for help. With the aid of a little perspective, you may be reassured that what you thought were "crazy" feelings or concerns really are pretty normal.

Normal? Yes. We mean it when we say that there is not a high wall dividing normal from abnormal behavior. Negative emotions are part of everyday life. Most of us experience mild to moderate levels of anxiety, sadness, and anger fairly often. In fact, these emotions often are adaptive. These feelings can energize us to cope with the challenges in our lives. So, maybe all you really need is the understanding and perspective of a caring friend or relative, or of an objective third party.

Recognizing where you are in your life also may help you to achieve a little perspective. The late teens and early twenties—the age of many people taking this class—is frequently a time of uncertainty and self-doubt. It is quite common for young people to question their goals, beliefs, values, friendships, sexuality, family relationships, and almost everything else. If this sounds like you, you may want to read ahead in Chapter 17, which discusses many of the challenges of the transition to adult life. You also may want to look at this chapter if you are a nontraditional student, because we

also discuss many other common, but trying, developmental transitions throughout the adult life span. Times of change and challenge can be very exciting, but they also can be very distressing and lonely.

What should you do if you did not feel better after talking with someone you trust? We suggest that you consider consulting a mental health professional. This is a good next step whether you think you are suffering from a psychological problem, are not sure, or simply want help with some normal but distressing life experience. We know that there can be a stigma about seeing "a shrink," but we strongly believe that the stigma is wrong. Mental health problems are incredibly common, and a therapist, or maybe your family doctor, can offer you an informed perspective and some good treatment alternatives. We give suggestions about how to go about finding a reliable mental health professional in the Getting Help section of Chapter 3.

■ SUMMARY

The **biological, psychodynamic, cognitive behavioral,** and **humanistic** approaches to understanding the causes of abnormal behavior are alternative **paradigms,** and not just alternative theories. Biological approaches emphasize causes that occur "within the skin." Psychodynamic theory highlights unconscious processes and detailed case histories. Cognitive behavioral viewpoints focus on observable, learned behavior. Finally, the humanistic paradigm argues that behavior is not determined but, instead, is a product of free will.

None of these broad paradigms offers the "right" explanation of abnormal behavior, which is best understood in terms of the **biopsychosocial model,** the combination of different biological, psychological, and social factors. **Systems theory** is a way of integrating biological, psychological, and social contributions to abnormal behavior. Its central principle is **holism,** the idea that the whole is more than the sum of its parts—a scientific counterpoint to **reductionism.**

Biological factors in abnormal behavior begin with the **neuron,** or nerve cell. Communication between neurons occurs when the axon terminals release chemical substances called **neurotransmitters** into the **synapse** between nerve cells. Disrupted communication among neurons, particularly disruptions in the functioning of various neurotransmitters, is involved in several types of abnormal behavior, although you should be cautioned against mind–body dualism.

Neuroanatomists commonly divide the brain into three subdivisions: the hindbrain, the midbrain, and the forebrain. The forebrain is the location of most sensory, emotional, and cognitive processes. Most of the forebrain is composed of the two cerebral hemispheres, and many brain functions are lateralized, so that each hemisphere is the site of specific cognitive and emotional activities. Finally, the cerebral cortex is the uneven surface area of the brain that lies just underneath the skull. It is the site of the control and integration of sophisticated memory, sensory, and motor functions. Because of the rudimentary state of our knowledge about the brain, only the most severe mental disorders have been clearly linked with abnormalities in neuroanatomy. In most of these cases, brain damage is extensive and obvious.

Psychophysiology involves changes in the functioning of the body that result from psychological experiences. Psychophysiological arousal is caused by two different communication systems within the body: the **endocrine system** and the nervous system. Endocrine glands release **hormones** into the bloodstream that regulate some aspects of normal development as well as some responses to stress. The autonomic nervous system is the part of the central nervous system that is responsible for psychophysiological reactions. It has two branches, the sympathetic and the parasympathetic nervous systems. In general, the sympathetic nervous system controls arousal, and the parasympathetic nervous system controls energy conservation.

Behavior genetics is the study of genetic influences on the development of behavior. Most forms of abnormal behavior are **polygenic,** that is, they are caused by more than one **gene.** Comparisons of **monozygotic (MZ)** and **dizygotic (DZ)** twins can yield information about genetic contributions to behavior, as can adoption studies. The fact that a psychological disorder has a genetic component does not mean that the disorder will inevitably appear; genetically influenced behavior also is affected by the environment. Few single genes directly affect abnormal behavior; thus genetic effects probably occur at some more basic level—for example, by affecting psychophysiological arousal.

Psychology has not developed a list of its core components. Some promise toward this goal is offered by **evolutionary psychology,** the application of the principles of evolution to our understanding of the animal and human minds. Evolutionary psychologists assume that animal and human psychology have evolved based on natural selection and sexual selection. Two basic psychological motivations seen in humans and other animals are the formation of **attachments** and competition for **dominance. Emotion** drives these basic motivations. **Temperament** is an individual's characteristic style of relating to the world, and researchers agree on the "big five" dimensions of temperament.

Learning mechanisms include **classical conditioning, operant conditioning, modeling,** and human cognition, and they contribute to both normal and abnormal behavior. The sense of self is a uniquely human quality that also may play a role in causing emotional problems. The idea of **developmental stages** not only charts the course of normal development, against which abnormal behavior must be compared, but it highlights the important issue of developmental transitions.

Social roles influence the definition and development of psychopathology. Evidence links abnormal behavior with distressed or conflicted family relationships, and **social support** from people other than family members can be an important buffer against stress. **Gender roles** may influence the development, expression, or consequences of psychopathology. Race and poverty also are broad social influences on psychological well-being in the United States today.

THE BIG PICTURE CRITICAL THINKING REVIEW

How are old paradigms too narrow?

Brain teasers illustrate how paradigms can enlighten—or blind—us when trying to understand what causes abnormal behavior. (SEE PAGE 33)

Can two explanations of abnormal behavior both be accurate?

Like Russian matreska dolls, different explanations of abnormal behavior at different levels of analysis are nested one inside the other. (SEE PAGE 35)

How is human nature basic to understanding abnormal behavior?

Trying to explain abnormal behavior without a theory of normal behavior is like biology without a classification of living things. (SEE PAGE 49)

How can gender roles influence abnormal behavior?

Androgyny—the possession of both "female" and "male" gender-role characteristics—may be the answer to the problems associated with gender roles. (SEE PAGE 56)

Why does correlation not mean causation?

If psychology majors know more than biology majors, this may not mean that majoring in psychology *caused* this. (SEE PAGE 35)

Are some psychological experiences separate from biology?

Software cannot run without a computer, and no psychological experience runs independently from the hardware of the brain. (SEE PAGE 39)

■ KEY TERMS

attachments 50
attributions 52
autonomic nervous system 42
behavior genetics 44
biopsychosocial model 27
cerebral cortex 40
cerebral hemispheres 40
chromosomes 44
classical conditioning 32
concordance rate 46
correlational study 35
correlation coefficient 35
defense mechanisms 31

developmental psychopathology 37
developmental stages 53
diathesis 37
dizygotic (DZ) twins 46
dominance 50
dualism 39
ego 30
emotions 51
endocrine system 41
evolutionary psychology 49
extinction 32
gender roles 56
genes 44

gene–environment correlation 48
gene–environment interaction 48
genotype 44
hormones 41
hypothalamus 40
id 30
identity 53
lateralized 40
limbic system 40
modeling 52
monozygotic (MZ) twins 46
neurons 38

neurotransmitters 38
nonshared environment 46
operant conditioning 32
paradigm 27
phenotype 44
polygenic 45
premorbid history 37
probands 45
prognosis 37
psychoanalytic theory 30
psychophysiology 41
receptors 38
reciprocal causality 36
reductionism 34

reuptake 38
reverse causality 35
risk factors 37
self-control 53
shared environment 46
social support 55
stress 37
superego 30
synapse 38
systems theory 34
temperament 51
third variable 35
ventricles 40

TREATMENT OF PSYCHOLOGICAL DISORDERS

Many people seek psychological help when battling bulimia, depression, anxiety, or other mental disorders. Others consult a professional when struggling in their relationships, or searching for a happier, more meaningful life. Can psychological treatment help in any of these circumstances? Does it matter if you see a psychiatrist, clinical psychologist, social worker, or counselor? Should you look for someone who specializes in the problem needing treatment? Should medication be a part of therapy? What should you expect a therapist to do and say? How can "talking" help? Psychological concerns touch on most of our lives at some point in time, and many people turn to mental health professionals—perhaps in desperation—for answers to these kinds of searching questions.

OVERVIEW

What can help? Few questions in abnormal psychology are more important than this one. We use psychological science to begin to answer this essential question in this chapter. However, we continue to ask, "What helps?" throughout the text, because research shows that different treatments work better for different disorders (Barlow, 2008; Nathan & Gorman, 2007).

One treatment that can help is **psychotherapy,** the use of psychological techniques and the therapist–client relationship to produce emotional, cognitive, and behavior change. We can define psychotherapy generally, but it can be a challenge to be more specific. One big complication is that adherents to different paradigms offer very different treatments (Prochaska & Norcross, 2006). Mental health professionals often ask one another, "What is your theoretical orientation?" The answer is supposed to be "biological," "psychodynamic," "cognitive behavioral," or "humanistic," an indication of the therapist's preferred treatment approach.

Today, however, most mental health professionals describe themselves as **eclectic,** meaning they use different treatments for different disorders (Bechtoldt et al., 2001). We embrace the eclectic approach, as long as clinicians use research to select the most effective treatment (Chambless & Ollendick, 2000). That is, the practice of psychotherapy must be *evidencedbased.* In this chapter, we focus on evidence based both on the *outcome* of therapy, or how well a treatment works, and the *process* of therapy, or what makes therapy work (Kazdin, 2008).

Evidence-based treatment is the practical—and scientific—approach to therapy. Unfortunately, some therapists fail to educate their clients about evidence-based treatments, and there is an even bigger problem: Most people with psychological problems do not get *any* help. Eighty-seven percent of people with a diagnosable mental disorder have *not* received treatment in the past year, including many people with common, serious, and treatable disturbances (Howard et al., 1996; see Figure 3–1).

We introduce the treatment of psychological disorders with a case study. As you read the following case, think about what might be wrong

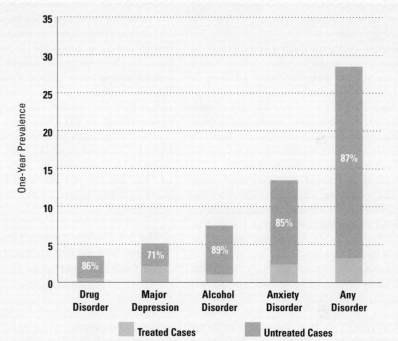

One-Year Prevalence of Selected Psychological Disorders and the Percentage of Treated and Untreated Cases

FIGURE 3–1 Data from the Epidemiologic Catchment Area study indicate that most diagnosed cases of common mental disorders did not receive treatment by a mental health professional in the past year.

Source: K. I. Howard, T. A. Cornille, J. S. Lyons, J. T. Vessey, R. J. Lueger, & S. M. Saunders, 1996, Patterns of Service Utilization, *Archives of General Psychiatry, 53,* 696–703.

with this young woman and what might help her. After the case, we discuss how different therapists might treat the same client using a biological, psychodynamic, cognitive behavioral, or humanistic approach.

CASE **STUDY** Why Is Frances Depressed?

Frances, a 23-year-old woman, sought psychotherapy for depression. She said she had been depressed for almost three years, with periods of relative happiness or deeper despair. When she came into therapy, her depression was severe. She had little appetite and had lost 10 pounds over the previous six weeks, and her erratic sleeping patterns were worse than usual. She awoke around 2 or 3 A.M. every night, tossed in bed for several hours, and finally fell asleep again near dawn.

Frances reported feeling profoundly depressed about herself, her new marriage, and life in general. She freely admitted to frequent thoughts of suicide. She once sat in her bathroom holding a razor blade for over an hour, contemplating whether to slash her wrists. But she decided she could never commit the act. Now, she often wished she were dead, but she felt that she "lacked the courage" to take her own life.

Frances also noted that she found herself without motivation. She withdrew from her husband and the few friends she had, and she frequently called in sick at work when she felt blue. Frances's reports of depression were underscored by her careless dress, frequent bouts of crying, and slowed speech and body movements.

Frances reported that she had experienced a happy childhood. She had not known depression until the current episode began in her senior year in college. At first, she convinced herself that she was only suffering from "senior year syndrome." She wasn't sure what to do with her life. Secretly, she longed to move to New York

and finally break out and do something exciting. But when she told her parents about her plans, her mother begged Frances to return home. She insisted that the two of them needed to have fun together again after four long years with Frances away at college. After graduation, Frances returned home to live with her parents.

It was shortly after moving home that Frances realized that her difficulties were much more serious than she had thought. She found herself intermittently screaming at her anxious and doting mother and being "super-nice" to her after feeling guilty about losing her temper. Frances described her mother as "a saint." Frances thought that her erratic behavior toward her mother was all her fault. Her mother apparently agreed. In Frances's mind, she was a failure as a daughter.

Frances described both her mother and her father as loving and giving, but some of her comments about them were far from glowing. She said she was her mother's best friend. When asked if her mother was her best friend, Frances began to cry.

She felt like her mother's infant, her parent, or even her husband, but not her friend and certainly not like her grown daughter.

Frances had little to say about her father. She pictured him drinking beer, eating meals, and falling asleep in front of the television.

Throughout the time she lived at home, Frances's depression only seemed to deepen.

After a year of living with her parents, she married her high school sweetheart. Frances felt pressured to get married. Both her future husband and her mother insisted that it was time for her to settle down and start a family. At the time, she had hoped that marriage would be the solution to her problems. The excitement of the wedding added to this hope. But after the marriage, Frances said that things were worse—if that were possible. Still, she insisted that her marriage problems were all her fault.

Frances's husband was a young accountant who reminded Frances of her father. He didn't drink but spent most of his brief time at home working or reading in his study. She said they had little communication, and she felt no warmth in her marriage. Her husband often was angry and sullen, but Frances said she couldn't blame him for feeling that way. His problem was being married to her. She wanted to love him, but she never had. She was a failure as a wife. She was a failure in life.

The theme of self-blame pervaded Frances's descriptions of her family. She repeatedly noted that, despite their flaws, her parents and her husband were good and loving people. She was the one with the problem. She had everything that she could hope for, yet she was unhappy. One reason she wanted to die was to ease the burden on them. How could they be happy when they had to put up with her foul moods? When she talked about these things, however, Frances's tone of voice often sounded more angry than depressed.

Frances and the Four Paradigms

How might Frances's problems be viewed differently through the lens of each of the four paradigms? Biological, psychodynamic, cognitive behavioral, and humanistic therapists all would note her depressed mood, self-blame, and troubled relationships. However, therapists working within these different paradigms would approach treatment and evaluate Frances in very different ways (see Table 3–1).

Biological therapies approach mental illness by drawing an analogy with physical illness. Thus, a biologically oriented psychiatrist or psychologist would focus first on making a diagnosis

of Frances's problems. This would not be difficult, because Frances's symptoms paint a clear picture of depression. The therapist also would take note of Frances's description of her father, who seems chronically depressed. Perhaps a genetic predisposition toward depression runs in her family.

A biologically oriented therapist would sympathize with Frances's interpersonal problems but would not blame either Frances or her family for their troubles. Rather, the therapist would blame something that neither Frances nor her family members could control: depression. It is exhausting to deal with someone who is constantly agitated and depressed. In the end, the therapist might explain that depression is caused by a

TABLE 3–1	Comparison of Biological, Psychodynamic, Behavioral, and Humanistic Treatments			
TOPIC	BIOLOGICAL	PSYCHODYNAMIC	COGNITIVE BEHAVIORAL	HUMANISTIC
Goal of treatment	Alter biology to relieve psychological distress	Gain insight into defenses/unconscious motivations	Learn more adaptive behaviors/cognitions	Increase emotional awareness
Primary method	Diagnosis, medication	Interpretation of defenses	Instruction, guided learning, homework	Empathy, support, exploring emotions
Role of therapist	Active, directive, diagnostician	Passive, nondirective, interpreter (may be aloof)	Active, directive, nonjudgmental, teacher	Passive, nondirective, warm, supporter
Length of treatment	Brief, with occasional follow-up visits	Usually long term; some new short-term treatments	Short term, with later "booster" sessions	Varies; length not typically structured

chemical imbalance in the brain, recommend medication, and schedule follow-up appointments to monitor the effects of the medication on Frances's mood.

A psychodynamic therapist would also note Frances's depression but likely would focus on her *defensive style*. The therapist might view Frances's justification of her parents' and husband's behavior as a form of *rationalization*. The therapist would also see a pattern of *denial* in Frances's refusal to acknowledge the imperfections of her loved ones and their failure to fulfill her needs. When Frances says that she is a burden on her family, a psychodynamic therapist might wonder if she was *projecting* onto them her own sense of feeling burdened by her mother's demands and her husband's indifference.

A psychodynamic therapist probably would not challenge Frances's defenses early in therapy but instead begin by exploring her past and her hopes, feelings, and frustrations. The therapist might encourage Frances to talk about whatever she wanted to discuss. The goal would be to illuminate Frances's unconscious motivations, internal conflicts, and defenses to the therapist and, over time, to Frances herself. Eventually, the psychodynamic therapist would confront Frances's defenses in order to help her gain *insight* into her hidden resentment toward her mother, longing for a relationship with her father, and unfulfilled fantasies about marriage.

A cognitive behavior therapist might note many of the same issues in Frances's life but would approach treatment quite differently. Rather than focusing on defense mechanisms, the therapist would hone in on Frances's cognitive and behavioral patterns. Frances's self-blame—her pattern of attributing all of her interpersonal difficulties to herself—would be seen as a cognitive error. Her withdrawal from pleasing activities and her apparent unassertiveness also might be seen as contributing to her depression. In comparison to a psychodynamic therapist, a cognitive behavior therapist would be far more directive in discussing these topics. For example, he or she would tell Frances that her thinking was distorted and her cognitive errors were contributing to her depression.

The therapist would go on to make direct suggestions with the goal of teaching Frances new ways of thinking, acting, and feeling. The therapist might encourage Frances to blame others appropriately, not just herself, for relationship problems and urge her to try out new ways of relating to her mother, father, and husband. The therapist would want Frances to play an active role in this learning process by completing *homework*—activities that continued her treatment outside the therapy, for example, monitoring conflicts with her family to see if she really was always at fault. A cognitive behavior therapist would expect Frances's depressed mood to begin to lift once she learned to assert herself and no longer blame herself for everything that went wrong in her life.

A humanistic therapist would also note Frances's depression, her self-blame, and her unsatisfactory relationships with loved ones. A more prominent focus, however, would be her lack of emotional genuineness—her inability to "be herself" with other people and within herself. The therapist would almost certainly explore Frances's tendency to bury her true feelings. The goal would be to help Frances recognize how she *really* feels and to make life choices based on her heightened emotional awareness.

In conducting therapy, the humanistic therapist would be nondirective in terms of specific topics for discussion but would continually focus on emotional issues. Initially, the therapist might simply empathize with Frances's feelings of sadness, loneliness, and isolation. Over time, he or she might suggest that Frances had other feelings that she did not express, including frustration and guilt over her mother's controlling yet dependent style, and anger at her husband's and her father's self-centeredness. The humanistic therapist would tell Frances that her feelings were legitimate and might encourage Frances to "own" her feelings. The therapist would not directly encourage Frances to act differently but expect Frances to make changes in her life as a result of her increased emotional awareness.

These approaches to treating Frances are very different, but you may wonder if a therapist could use the best aspects of each one. In fact, psychologists often integrate elements of different approaches when working to find more effective treatments. One straightforward example is when psychotherapy is combined with medication (Otto, Smits, & Reese, 2005). Before considering how different approaches can be integrated, however, we first need to elaborate on their theoretical differences.

Brief Historical Perspective

We can trace the roots of the treatment of psychological disorders to two healing traditions: the spiritual/religious tradition and the naturalistic/scientific tradition (Frank, 1973). The spiritual/religious tradition is an ancient one that attributes both physical and mental ailments to supernatural forces. For example, archaeologists have unearthed skulls that lead them to believe that ancient tribal healers performed a primitive form of surgery to treat mental disorders. *Trephining* involved chipping a hole through the unfortunate sufferer's skull with a crude stone tool. Presumably, the purpose was to allow evil spirits to escape.

Other examples throughout history and across cultures show how people have believed that demons cause abnormal behavior and attempted exorcism to treat it. Until the seventeenth century, many cases of mental disturbance in Europe and in the American colonies were attributed to witchcraft (Neuge-

bauer, 1979). Those suspected of being witches were put through painful tests that they often could not pass. One examination was to dunk the suspected witch under water. The only way to pass the test—to be found not to be a witch—was to drown!

The spiritual/religious tradition produced bizarre explanations and treatments, but the influence of belief and ritual is no joke. Believing is a powerful part of healing. Later in the chapter, we prove this when we explore the *placebo effect,* scientifically documented changes in mental and physical disease that are produced by a mere sugar pill. More generally, spiritual beliefs help people cope with all sorts of life difficulties. The power of shared beliefs also calls attention to the essential role of ethnicity and culture in therapy. Gays and lesbians (Eubanks-Carter, Burckell, & Goldfried, 2005) and some members of minority groups may see therapy as ineffective, intrusive, or threatening unless it is sensitive to their unique experiences and culture (see Ethnic Minorities in Psychotherapy).

Naturalistic/scientific approaches to helping also have ancient roots. Hippocrates recommended treatments such as rest, exercise, and a healthy diet (see Chapter 1). In the 1600s, "insane asylums" were developed based on the hope that rest and isolation would alleviate mental disturbances. Although the beginnings of scientific approaches can be traced to ancient times, the biological, psychodynamic, cognitive behavioral, and humanistic paradigms did not fully emerge until the nineteenth and early twentieth centuries.

BIOLOGICAL TREATMENTS

General paresis is an example not only of the hope of the biological approach to etiology and treatment but also of the medical model of research (see Chapter 2). First, a diagnosis is developed and refined. Second, clues about causes are put together like pieces of a puzzle to form a picture of the specific etiology of the disease. Third, scientists experiment with various treatments for preventing or curing the disorder until they find an effective treatment. These are far from simple tasks, of course, as shown by the century it took to diagnose general paresis, discover syphilis as its cause, and develop antibiotics as a treatment for the disease.

ETHNIC MINORITIES IN PSYCHOTHERAPY

Treating people from diverse backgrounds is a major challenge for psychologists. Among the dozens of ethnic groups in the United States, the most numerous are African Americans, Latinos, Asian Americans, and Native Americans. In fact, over 25 percent of Americans today are ethnic minorities, and minorities will outnumber whites by the middle of the twenty-first century. Despite the numbers, mainstream psychotherapy does not adequately meet the mental health needs of minority group members (Casas, 1995; Hwang, 2006; Neighbors et al., 2007; Vasquez, 2007).

One concern is that mental health professionals recognize both commonalities and diversity in the values and experiences of ethnic minorities. For example, most immigrants came to the United States voluntarily; Native Americans, however, were driven from their homeland and confined to reservations. African Americans share a common history of racism but differ widely based on socioeconomic status, religion, and region of upbringing. Latinos share the Spanish language but may be black or white and have diverse origins in Mexico, the Caribbean, and Central and South America. Asian Americans share cultural traditions, for example, the value of collectivism over individualism, but differ greatly in language, country, and experiences with industrialization (Surgeon General, 2001).

A second concern is recognizing that many problems faced by ethnic minorities stem from social and cultural experiences and not individual psychological problems (Comas-Diaz, 2000). All ethnic minorities face the challenge of *acculturation*, the process of learning or adopting the cultural patterns of the majority group (Casas, 1995; Sue, 1998). Acculturation is a political goal of the American "melting pot." However, language, ethnic values, and social customs may be undermined or even derided by the majority culture. African Americans and Native Americans have faced particularly difficult challenges in acculturation.

The process of acculturation affects the individual as well as the group. Acculturation challenges *ethnic identity,* minority members' understanding of self in terms of their own culture. Atkinson, Morten, and Sue (1993) proposed a five-stage model of the development of ethnic identity: (1) *conformity,* a time of self-deprecation and discrimination; (2) *dissonance,* a period of conflict between self-deprecation and appreciation of one's ethnicity; (3) *resistance and immersion,* a stage of self-appreciation and ethnocentrism, accompanied by depreciation of the majority group; (4) *introspection,* a phase of questioning the basis of self-appreciation, as well as the basis for depreciation of the majority group; and (5) *synergetic articulation and awareness,* including both self-appreciation and appreciation of the basis for majority group values. Researchers have infrequently studied this model of ethnic identity development, but it provides a helpful framework for understanding the individual's struggle with acculturation (Casas, 1995).

How can acculturation affect therapy with minorities?

Research on psychotherapy with members of ethnic minority groups is limited. Some

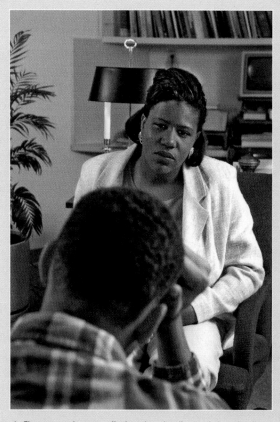

▲ Therapy may be more effective when the client and therapist share a similar cultural background.

evidence suggests that psychotherapy may be more effective when client and therapist share a similar cultural background and when the treatment is tailored to the specific culture (Hwang, 2006; Leong, 2007). Therapy also may be more effective when therapists are trained to be sensitive to minority issues (Hall, 2001; Parks, 2003). What is most clear, however, is the need to study and adapt psychotherapy to meet the needs of ethnic minority group members.

Unlike the single bacterial infection that causes general paresis, most mental disorders appear to be caused by many factors. As a result, scientists often search for biological treatments without knowing a disorder's specific cause. These treatments focus on *symptom alleviation,* reducing the dysfunctional symptoms of a disorder but not eliminating its root cause (Valenstein, 1998).

Experimentation has produced mixed results in the biological treatment of emotional problems. Early and ineffective biological treatments included bleeding, forced hot baths, the use of various physical restraints, and the surgical removal of sexual organs. Happily, numerous medications, many of which are very effective for symptom alleviation, have been discovered since the 1950s, and particularly since the 1980s. Before discussing these new drugs, we briefly consider two biological treatments with controversial histories: electroconvulsive therapy and psychosurgery.

Electroconvulsive Therapy

Electroconvulsive therapy (ECT) involves deliberately inducing a seizure by passing electricity through the brain. The technique was developed in 1938 by Ugo Cerletti and Lucio Bini, two Italian physicians who were seeking a treatment for schizophrenia. At the time, schizophrenia was erroneously thought to be rare among people who had epilepsy. This led to speculation that epileptic seizures somehow prevented the disorder. Cerletti and Bini discovered a means of inducing seizures at will when visiting a slaughterhouse. There they observed electric current being passed through the brains of animals, which produced a convulsion and unconsciousness. Shortly thereafter, the two physicians began to use a modified electroconvulsive technique as an experimental treatment for schizophrenia.

Typically, ECT involves a series of 6 to 12 sessions over the course of a few weeks. Approximately 100 volts of electric current is passed through a patient's brain in order to cause a convulsion, although the current needed to produce a convulsion varies. In *bilateral ECT,* electrodes are placed on the left and right temples, and the current passes through both brain hemispheres. In *unilateral ECT,* the current is passed through only one side of the brain, the nondominant hemisphere. Unilateral ECT produces less *retrograde amnesia*—loss of memory of past events, a disturbing side effect of ECT (Lisanby et al., 2000). Unfortunately, unilateral ECT is less effective than bilateral ECT. Similarly, low-dose ECT (just enough current to produce a seizure) is less effective but causes fewer memory impairments than high-dose ECT (2.5 or more times the minimal current) (Sackheim et al., 2000; UK ECT Review Group, 2003). Thus, effectiveness must be weighed against increased side effects.

Books and movies like *One Flew Over the Cuckoo's Nest* show how ECT was misused in the middle of the twentieth century. Today, however, ECT is used cautiously and less frequently, and it is an effective treatment for depression (but not for its original purpose, schizophrenia; UK ECT Review Group, 2003). Side effects can be serious and can include memory loss and even death in rare cases. Still, ECT can be very useful in treating severe depressions, especially when patients do not respond to other treatments.

Psychosurgery

Psychosurgery, the surgical destruction of specific regions of the brain, is another biological treatment with a checkered history. Egas Moniz (1874–1953), a Portuguese neurologist, introduced psychosurgery in 1935. He performed a procedure called *prefrontal lobotomy,* irrevocably severing the frontal lobes of the brain. In 1949, Moniz won a Nobel Prize for his work, and thousands of prefrontal lobotomies were performed around the world—between 10,000 and 20,000 in the United States alone.

Sadly, prefrontal lobotomy was subsequently discredited. It has limited benefits and causes frequent, often severe, side effects, including excessive tranquility, emotional unresponsiveness, and even death. Ironically, Moniz himself was shot and paralyzed by one of his lobotomized patients, a sad testament to the unpredictable outcome of the procedure.

Prefrontal lobotomies are a thing of the past, but today very precise psychosurgeries may be used to treat severe affective or anxiety disorders—when all other treatments have failed. For example, *cingulotomy,* lesioning pinpointed regions of the cingulate cortex, may help very severe cases of obsessive–compulsive disorder (Mashour, Walker, & Martuza, 2005). Still, the irreversibility of brain damage makes psychosurgery a very rarely used

▼ American neuroligist Walter Freeman perfomed almost 3,500 lobotomies, often severing the frontal lobes by knocking an instrument through the back of the eye socket. Today, lobotomy is completely discredited, but refined neurosurgery may play a role in treating severe disorders that do not respond to other treatments.

procedure. Perhaps the future will bring effective refinements in psychosurgery and other direct brain treatments (Dougherty & Rauch, 2007).

Psychopharmacology

The most promising biological treatment is **psychopharmacology**—the use of medications to treat psychological disturbances. In recent years, scientists have developed new medications that have increasingly specific effects on emotional states and mental disorders (see Table 3–2).

There are many **psychotropic medications,** chemical substances that affect psychological state. Some psychotropic medications produce rapid changes in thinking, mood, and behavior. Traditional antianxiety agents have effects that become apparent soon after the medication is taken. Others, such as antidepressant medications, have more subtle influences that build up gradually over time. Still other psychotropic drugs affect people with mental disorders very differently from the way they affect someone who is functioning normally. Antipsychotic medications help to eliminate delusions and hallucinations among people suffering from schizophrenia, but the same medications would disorient most people and send them into a long, groggy sleep.

Do psychotropic drugs cure underlying causes or only alleviate symptoms?

◄ Prozac, the first of a new generation of antidepressants called SSRIs, has been taken by more than 40 million people worldwide.

TABLE 3–2 Major Categories of Medications for Treating Psychological Disorders

THERAPEUTIC USE	CHEMICAL STRUCTURE OR PSYCHOPHARMACOLOGIC ACTION	EXAMPLE	
		Generic Name	*Trade Name*
Antipsychotics (also called major tranquilizers or neuroleptics)	Phenothiazines	Chlorpromazine	Thorazine
	Thioxanthenes	Thiothixene	Navane
	Butyrophenones	Haloperidol	Haldol
	Rauwolfia alkaloids	Reserpine	Sandril
	Atypical neuroleptics	Clozapine	Clozaril
Antidepressants	Tricyclic antidepressants (TCAs)	Amitriptyline	Elavil
	Monoamine oxidase inhibitors (MAOIs)	Phenelzine	Nardil
	Selective serotonin reuptake inhibitor (SSRI)	Fluoxetine	Prozac
	Atypical antidepressants	Bupropion	Wellbutrin
Psychomotor stimulants	Amphetamines	Dextroamphetamine	Dexedrine
	Other	Methylphenidate	Ritalin
Antimanic	Metallic element	Lithium carbonate	Eskalith
	Anticonvulsants	Carbamazepine	Tegretol
Antianxiety (also called minor tranquilizers)	Benzodiazepines	Diazepam	Valium
	Triazolobenzodiazepine	Alprazolam	Xanax
Sedative hypnotic	Barbiturates	Phenobarbital	
	Benzodiazepines	Triazolam	Halcion
Antipanic	Benzodiazepines	Alprazolam	Xanax
	SSRIs	Paroxetine	Paxil
Antiobsessional	TCA	Clomipramine	Anafranil
	SSRIs	Fluvoxamine	Luvox

The growth of psychopharmacology is evident in the expanding development and use of psychotropic medications. Prescriptions of psychostimulants, used to treat inattentive and hyperactive behavior, tripled for preschoolers during the 1990s (Zito et al., 2000). Early in the 1990s, the antidepressant medication Prozac outsold *every* prescription medication, including all medications used to treat physical ailments. Today, fully 11 percent of American women and 5 percent of American men are taking an antidepressant (Barber, 2008).

We review evidence on particular psychotropic medications in each relevant chapter. For now, you should note a few general points. First, medication often is an effective and safe treatment for many mental disorders. Second, psychotropic medications do not cure underlying causes, but symptom alleviation is extremely important. Where would we be without pain relievers, another medication that only offers symptom relief? Third, many psychotropic drugs must be taken for long periods of time. Because the medications do not produce a cure, patients may need to keep taking the drug—for months, years, or sometimes for a lifetime. Fourth, all medications have side effects, some of which are very unpleasant. Partly for this reason, many patients do not take their medication as prescribed, and they may experience a relapse as a result. Finally, we share the concern that people, perhaps especially Americans, sometimes look to medication to solve problems that ultimately are psychological or interpersonal (Barber, 2008).

PSYCHODYNAMIC PSYCHOTHERAPIES

An early influence on the psychodynamic approach to therapy was Joseph Breuer (1842–1925), who used hypnosis to induce troubled patients to talk freely about problems in their lives. Upon awakening from a hypnotic trance, many patients reported relief from their symptoms. Breuer attributed their improvement to *catharsis,* the release of previously unexpressed feelings, pent up emotion that Breuer assumed was responsible for his patients' psychological problems. A visual metaphor for catharsis is the sudden release of steam through the whistle of a teapot.

Freudian Psychoanalysis

Breuer's collaborator, Sigmund Freud (1856–1939), adopted the hypnotic method for a time, but he soon concluded that hypnosis was not necessary to encourage open expression. Instead, Freud simply told his patients to speak freely about whatever thoughts crossed their mind. This method, called **free association,** became a cornerstone of Freud's famous treatment, **psychoanalysis.**

Unlike Breuer, Freud did not see catharsis as an end in itself. The true benefit of free association, in Freud's view, was that it revealed aspects of the unconscious mind. Freud found clues to his patients' unconscious desires in their unedited speech. Freud also believed that dreaming (defenses presumably are weaker in dreams) and slips of the tongue (now called Freudian slips, for example, saying "sin" when you meant to say "sex") provided especially revealing information about the unconscious. Thus, according to Freud, free association, dreams, and slips of the tongue are valuable because they are "windows into the unconscious."

Psychoanalytic Techniques Freud saw the psychoanalyst's first task as discovering unconscious conflicts that lie behind psychological difficulties. In order to overcome their problems, however, patients must come to share the psychoanalyst's understanding of these conflicts. They must achieve what Freud called **insight,** bringing formerly unconscious material into conscious awareness. Freud asserted that insight is sufficient for curing psychological disorders.

The analyst's main tool for promoting insight is **interpretation.** In offering an interpretation, the analyst suggests hidden meanings to patients' accounts of their life. Typically, interpretations relate to past experiences, especially experiences with loved ones. Recall from Chapter 2, however, that Freud viewed the defense mechanisms as keeping intrapsychic conflicts from conscious awareness. Thus, psychoanalysts must overcome defenses like reaction formation as patients resist their interpretations. ("Hate my mother? My mother is a *saint!*"). Timing is everything in overcoming such *resistance.* The patient must be on the verge of discovering the hidden meaning himself or herself; otherwise, the interpretation will be rejected. For example, return to the case history and consider the dilemma of convincing Frances that deep resentment lies beneath her professed love for her mother. Given her long history of subjugating her own needs to those of her mother, Frances would be unlikely to accept such an interpretation if it were made too early in her treatment.

One essential element in probing the unconscious mind is *therapeutic neutrality,* maintaining a distant stance toward the patient in order to minimize the therapist's personal influence. The classical psychoanalyst "sits behind the patient where the patient cannot see him. He tries to create, as far as possible, a controlled laboratory situation in which the individual peculiarities of the analyst shall play as little role as possible in stimulating the patient's reactions" (Alexander & French, 1946, p. 83).

The analyst's distant stance is thought to encourage **transference,** the process whereby patients transfer their feelings about some key figure in their life onto the shadowy figure of the analyst. For psychoanalysis to succeed, the analyst must not respond to transference in a manner that the patient views as critical or threatening. Analysts also must avoid reacting to their patients in the same way as key figures in their life, for example, by responding to Frances's helplessness by becoming overprotective (like her mother). Finally, psychoanalysts must guard against *countertransference,* or letting their own feelings influence their responses to their patients. Instead, the analyst's job is to maintain therapeutic neutrality and offer interpretations that will promote insight about the transference. For example, "You seem frustrated that I won't tell you what to do. I wonder if you have come to expect authority figures to solve your problems for you."

Insight into the transference relationship presumably helps patients understand how and why they are relating to the analyst in the same dysfunctional manner in which they related to a loved one. This awareness creates a new understanding both of past relationships and of unconscious motivations in present relationships. For example, consider a transference that might develop between Frances and a psychoanalyst. Frances might have trouble accepting a therapeutic relationship in which she was receiving care instead of giving it. She might, therefore, try to get the analyst to reveal personal problems, or perhaps she would bring gifts to her therapist. The therapist's polite refusal of Frances's attempts at caretaking might cause Frances to feel hurt, rejected, and, eventually, angry. As therapy proceeded, these actions could be interpreted as reflecting Frances's style of relating to her mother and her tendency to deny her own needs.

A common misconception about psychoanalysis is that the ultimate goal of insight is to rid the patient of all defenses. This is not the case. According to Freud, defenses are essential for the functioning of a healthy personality. Thus, rather than ridding the patient of defenses, one goal of psychoanalysis is to replace them. Defenses such as denial and projection are confronted because they distort reality dramatically, whereas "healthier" defenses, such as rationalization and sublimation, are left unchallenged. A second goal of psychoanalysis is to help patients become more aware of their basic needs or drives so that they may find socially and psychologically appropriate outlets for them. A goal for Frances, for example, would be to admit that anger is a legitimate and acceptable part of her personality.

The Decline of Freudian Psychoanalysis In traditional psychoanalysis, patients meet with their analyst for an hour several times each week. These sessions often go on for years. Because psychoanalysis requires substantial time, expense, and self-exploration, it is accessible only to people who are relatively well functioning, introspective, and financially secure. Moreover, very little research has been conducted on its effectiveness. For these reasons, you should view psychoanalysis more as a process for people seeking self-understanding than as a treatment for emotional disorders.

Although psychoanalysis has declined greatly, the approach spawned numerous variations broadly referred to as **psychodynamic psychotherapy.** Psychodynamic psychotherapists often are more engaged and directive, and treatment may be relatively brief in comparison to psychoanalysis.

How is insight obtained in psychodynamic therapy?

"Why do <u>you</u> think you cross the road?"

Ego Analysis

Ego analysis originated in the work of a number of therapists trained in psychoanalysis, but who developed somewhat different theories and techniques. Whereas Freud emphasized the role of the id, these new theorists focused much more on the ego. The major function of the ego, according to Freudian theory, is to mediate between the conflicting impulses of the id and the superego (see Chapter 2). Of equal importance to ego analysts, however, is the ego's role in dealing with reality. Ego analysts, therefore, are concerned with unconscious motivations, but they also consider the patient's dealings with the external world.

The patient's past and present interpersonal relationships are of greatest importance according to Harry Stack Sullivan (1892–1949), an influential ego analyst. He suggested that many characteristics of the personality could be conceptualized in interpersonal rather than intrapsychic terms. Sullivan saw two basic dimensions of relationships. Interpersonal power ranges from dominance to submission. Interpersonal closeness ranges from love to hate. In looking at Frances's relationships, Sullivan might say that she was both overly submissive and perhaps unloved, since she busily met others needs while ignoring her own.

Other influential ego analysts include Erik Erikson (1902–1994) and Karen Horney (1885–1952). Horney's (1939) lasting contribution was her view that people have conflicting ego needs: to move toward, against, and away from others. Essentially, Horney argued that there are competing human needs for closeness, for dominance, and for autonomy. In her view, the key to a healthy personality is finding a balance among the three styles of relating to others. Pause and consider these three needs in relation to Frances. You should be able to identify her conflicts between Horney's three needs.

We introduced Erikson's stage theory of development in Chapter 2. As with other ego analysts, Erikson focused on the interpersonal context, as evident in his emphasis on the psycho*social* stages of development. Importantly, Erikson also argued that an individual's personality is not fixed by early experience but develops as a result of predictable psychosocial conflicts throughout the life span.

John Bowlby's (1907–1991) *attachment theory* perhaps has had the greatest effect on contemporary thought about interpersonal influences on psychopathology (see Chapter 2). Unlike Freud, Bowlby elevated the need for close relationships to a primary human characteristic. From an attachment theory perspective, people are inherently social beings. Our hunger to form close relationships is not so different from our hunger for food, as both reflect a basic human need.

Psychodynamic Psychotherapy

Many different approaches to psychotherapy have been developed based on the theories of Sullivan, Horney, Erikson, Bowlby, and other ego analysts. All these approaches seek to uncover hidden motivations and emphasize the importance of insight. However, psychodynamic psychotherapists are much more actively involved with their patients. They are more ready to direct the patient's recollections, to focus on current life circumstances, and to offer interpretations quickly and directly. Most psychodynamic psychotherapists are also much more "human" in conducting therapy. They may be distant and reflective at times, but they also are willing to offer appropriate emotional support.

Short-term psychodynamic psychotherapy is a form of treatment that uses many psychoanalytic techniques. Therapeutic neutrality is typically maintained, and transference remains a central issue, but the short-term psychodynamic therapist actively focuses on a particular emotional issue rather than relying on free association. The short-term approach has gained attention because it typically is limited to 25 or fewer sessions and therefore is less expensive and more amenable to research (Luborsky, Barber, & Beutler, 1993). Research generally supports Freud's observation that psychodynamic therapy is ineffective in treating more severe disorders, although it may be helpful with milder problems (Luborsky et al., 1993).

COGNITIVE BEHAVIOR THERAPY

Cognitive behavior therapy (CBT) involves using various research-based techniques to help troubled clients learn new ways of thinking, acting, and feeling. The approach contrasts sharply with psychodynamic therapy. CBT encourages collaborative therapist–client relationships, a focus on the present, direct efforts to change problems, and the use of different, empirically supported treatments.

The beginnings of CBT can be traced to John B. Watson's (1878–1958) **behaviorism,** the view that the appropriate focus of psychological study is observable behavior. Watson viewed the therapist as a teacher and the goal of treatment as providing new, more appropriate learning experiences. Early behavior therapists relied heavily on animal learning principles, particularly Pavlov's classical conditioning and Skinner's operant conditioning. Today, CBT incorporates many learning principles based on cognitive psychology. Thus, the term "cognitive behavior therapy" has largely replaced the older term "behavior therapy."

Unlike psychoanalysis, CBT is not based on an elaborate theory about human personality. Rather,

CBT is a practical approach oriented to changing behavior rather than trying to understand the dynamics of personality. One of the most important aspects of CBT is its embrace of empirical evaluation. Cognitive behavior therapists have asked, "What works?" in hundreds of treatment outcome studies that use the *experimental method* (see Research Methods). The answers include a variety of different treatments for different problems.

> *How is the cognitive behavior therapist like a teacher?*

RESEARCH METHODS

The Experimental Method: Does Therapy *Cause* Improvement?

How can researchers discover whether therapy *causes* improved psychological functioning? They must use the **experimental method,** a scientific procedure that allows researchers to determine cause and effect. The experiment has four essential features.

The first is a **hypothesis**—the experimenter's prediction about cause and effect. For example, a researcher might predict that in comparison to no treatment at all, cognitive behavior therapy will reduce symptoms of depression.

The second feature of the experiment is the **independent variable,** a variable controlled and carefully manipulated by the experimenter. The independent variable might be whether patients receive therapy or no treatment at all. People who receive an active treatment belong to the **experimental group**. Those who receive no treatment belong to the **control group**.

The third feature is **random assignment,** ensuring that each participant has a statistically equal chance of receiving different levels of the independent variable. Flipping a coin is one of many ways of randomly assigning participants to experimental or control groups. Random assignment ensures that the members of the experimental and control groups did not differ *before* they began the experiment. If people could choose whether they receive psychotherapy or nontreatment, for example, researchers could not know whether any differences obtained between the groups were caused by the treatment or by characteristics that led people to pick one treatment or no treatment. Random assignment guards against such possibilities.

The fourth feature is the measurement of the **dependent variable,** the outcome that is hypothesized to vary according to manipula-

tions in the independent variable. The outcome *depends* on the experimental manipulation—thus the term "dependent variable." Symptoms are commonly measured dependent variables in psychotherapy outcome research.

> *What is the major strength and major weakness of the experimental method?*

Statistical tests establish whether the independent variable has reliably changed the dependent variable, or whether the outcomes are a result of chance. A finding is considered to be **statistically significant** if it occurs by chance in fewer than 1 out of 20 experiments. That is, the probability of a chance outcome is less than 5 percent, a specification that is often written as $p < 05$. A statistically significant result is not the same as a *clinically significant* finding. A treatment may cause changes in symptoms, but the changes may be too small to make a meaningful difference in the patient's life. Whether therapy works can be studied using the experimental method, because researchers can control whether or not someone receives a particular treatment. However, completely controlling the independent variable—treatment—is a challenge. Some people drop out of treatment, and others seek additional help outside of the experiment. Therapists might individualize psychotherapy instead of treating everyone, or patients might not take a medication being studied. These are only a few of the many ways in which the independent variable can be *confounded* with other factors. Confounds threaten the *internal validity* of an experiment, whether the experiment accurately links changes in the dependent variable to changes

in the independent variable. If the independent variable is confounded with other factors, we can no longer accurately determine cause and effect. The confound, not the independent variable, may have changed the dependent variable.

External validity refers to whether the findings of an experiment generalize to other circumstances. Experiments require a degree of artificiality in order to give the experimenter maximum control. Therapy might last for exactly 10 sessions, and therapists might follow a prescribed script. These rules strengthen the experiment's internal validity, but they can compromise its external validity. In the real world, the length and nature of treatment often are tailored to the individual client's needs. Scientists and practitioners can, and often do, raise questions about the external validity of psychotherapy outcome research—whether the findings generalize to the real world.

The ability to demonstrate causation is a powerful strength of the experiment. (Recall that in Chapter 2 we introduced the *correlational method* but concluded that correlation does not mean causation.) The experimental method is limited, however, because many important variables cannot be manipulated practically or ethically in real life. Researchers can randomly assign clients to different treatments, but we cannot, for example, randomly assign children to live with abusive parents to test hypotheses about the consequences of abuse! This is why you must understand the strengths and the limitations of both the correlational and the experimental methods. Psychologists seek to understand cause and effect, but ethical and practical concerns often prohibit researchers from using the experimental method.

Systematic Desensitization

Joseph Wolpe (1915–1997), a South African psychiatrist whose research focused on eliminating phobias, developed an early and influential treatment used by cognitive behavior therapists. Wolpe (1958) assumed that at least some phobias were learned through classical conditioning. He reasoned that if fears could be learned, they could be unlearned. The key was to break the association between stimulus and response.

The technique Wolpe developed is called **systematic desensitization,** a technique for eliminating fears that has three key elements. The first is relaxation training using *progressive muscle relaxation,* a method of inducing a calm state by tightening and then relaxing all the major muscle groups. The second is constructing a *hierarchy of fears* ranging from very mild to very intense, a ranking that allows clients to confront their fears gradually. The third part is the *learning process,* maintaining relaxation while confronting ever-increasing fears. Wolpe had his clients confront fears in their imagination. Thus systematic desensitization involves imagining increasingly fearful events while simultaneously maintaining a state of relaxation.

Systematic desensitization has been studied extensively; in fact, the technique can be credited with spurring psychotherapy outcome research in general. Evidence shows that it can be an effective treatment for fears and phobias, but classical conditioning may not be the only reason it works. Other "active ingredients" in systematic desensiti-

zation may include the extinction of the fear, no longer reinforcing avoidance, increased self-confidence, or benefits flowing from a supportive relationship.

Other Exposure Therapies

Many factors contribute to effective systematic desensitization, but most investigators agree that *exposure* ultimately is the key to fear reduction: In order to conquer your fears, you must confront them (Barlow, Raffa, & Cohen, 2002). In addition to systematic desensitization, other exposure therapies include *in vivo desensitization,* gradually confronting fears in real life while simultaneously maintaining a state of relaxation. *Flooding,* in contrast, involves confronting fears at full intensity. Someone who was afraid of heights might be brought to the top of the CN Tower in Toronto (the world's tallest freestanding structure) in a quick and dramatic attempt to extinguish fear.

Aversion Therapy

The goal in **aversion therapy** is the use of classical conditioning to create, not eliminate, an unpleasant response. The technique is used primarily in treating substance use disorders such as alcoholism and cigarette smoking. For example, one form of aversion therapy pairs the sight, smell, and taste of alcohol with severe nausea produced artificially by a drug.

Not surprisingly, aversion therapy is controversial precisely because of its aversive nature. Moreover, it is not clear whether aversion therapy is effective (Finney & Moos, 2002). Aversion treatments often achieve short-term success, but relapse rates are high. Everyday life offers the substance abuser the opportunity, and perhaps the motivation, to desensitize himself or herself to the classically conditioned responses learned in aversion therapy.

Contingency Management

Contingency management is an operant conditioning technique that directly changes rewards and punishments for identified behaviors. A *contingency* is the relationship between a behavior and its consequences; contingency management involves changing this relationship. The goal of contingency management is to reward desirable

▼ Children must get back on their bikes to get over the fear of another fall. Cognitive behavior therapists take a similar, practical approach; exposure is the key to overcoming anxiety.

behavior systematically and to extinguish or punish undesirable behavior. In order to achieve this goal, the therapist must control relevant rewards and punishments. Thus, contingency management is used primarily in circumstances where the therapist has considerable direct or indirect control over the client's environment, such as in institutional settings or when children are brought for treatment by their parents.

The **token economy** is an example of contingency management that has been adopted in many institutional settings. In a token economy, desired and undesired behaviors are clearly identified, contingencies are defined, behavior is carefully monitored, and rewards or punishments are given according to the rules of the token economy. For example, in a group home for juvenile offenders, a token economy may specify that residents earn tokens for completing schoolwork and household chores, and lose tokens for arguing or fighting. Each resident's behavior is monitored and recorded, and tokens are "paid" accordingly. The key to the success of the program is that tokens can be exchanged for rewards desired by the residents—for example, going out unescorted on a Saturday night.

Research shows that contingency management successfully changes behavior for diverse problems such as institutionalized clients with schizophrenia (Paul & Lentz, 1977) and juvenile offenders in group homes (Phillips et al., 1973). However, improvements often do not generalize to real-life situations where the therapist cannot control rewards and punishments. A psychologist can set up clear and consistent contingencies for a juvenile living in a group home, but it may be impossible to alter the rewards and punishments the teenager encounters when he or she returns to live with a chaotic family or delinquent peers (Emery & Marholin, 1977). Sadly, in the real world a troubled adolescent's positive behavior may be ignored, his undesirable behavior may be rewarded, and punishment can be inconsistent or long delayed.

Social Skills Training

The goal of **social skills training** is to teach clients new ways of behaving that are both desirable and likely to be rewarded in everyday life. Two commonly taught skills are assertiveness and social problem solving.

The goal of *assertiveness training* is to teach clients to be direct about their feelings and wishes.

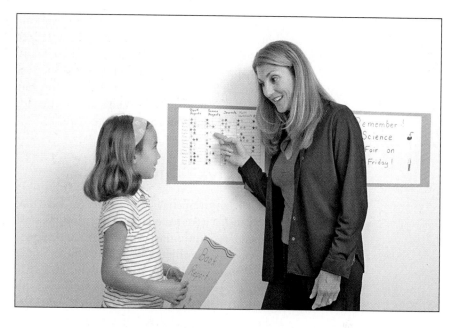

The training may involve different levels of detail, from learning to make eye contact to asking a boss for a raise. In teaching assertiveness, therapists frequently use *role playing,* an improvisational acting technique that allows clients to rehearse new social skills. Clients try out new ways of acting as the therapist assumes the role of some person in their life. For example, a cognitive behavior therapist might assume the role of Frances's mother, and ask Frances to express some of her frustration to her "mother" during a role play.

Social problem solving is a multistep process that has been used to teach children and adults ways to go about solving a variety of life's problems. The first step involves defining the problem in detail, breaking a complex difficulty into smaller, more manageable pieces. "Brainstorming" is the second step. In order to encourage creativity, therapists ask clients to come up with as many alternative solutions as they can imagine—even wild and crazy options—without evaluating these alternatives. The third step involves carefully evaluating these options. Finally, the best solution is chosen and implemented, and its success is evaluated objectively. If the option does not work, the entire process can be repeated until an effective solution is found.

▲ "Star charts" and similar systems help parents and teachers to be systematic in monitoring and rewarding children for behaving well, while ignoring or mildly punishing misbehavior.

HYPOCHONDRIASIS

HENRY

"I hear snickering in the background, 'Oh, it's him again.'"

Henry on hypochondriasis, see *Speaking Out: Case Studies in Abnormal Psychology*. Look for Henry's nonverbal behavior and apparent nonchalance about his problems.

It is difficult to draw general conclusions about the effectiveness of social skills training because the technique has been applied to many specific problems with varying degrees of success. Clients can learn new social skills in therapy, but it is less clear whether these skills are used effectively in real life (Mueser & Bellack, 2007).

Cognitive Techniques

All the cognitive behavior therapies we have discussed so far have foundations in either classical or operant conditioning. More recent techniques are rooted in cognitive psychology. One example is *attribution retraining,* based on the idea that people are "intuitive scientists" who are constantly drawing conclusions about the causes of events in their lives. These perceived causes, which may or may not be objectively accurate, are called *attributions.* Attribution retraining involves changing attributions, often by asking clients to abandon intuitive strategies. Instead, clients are instructed in more scientific methods, such as objectively testing hypotheses about themselves and others. For example, first-year college students often attribute their "blues" to their own failings. If they carefully observe the reactions of other first-year students, however, they may be persuaded to adopt a more accurate causal explanation: The first year of college can be trying, lonely, and stressful (Wilson & Linville, 1982).

Self-instruction training is another cognitive technique that is often used with children. In Meichenbaum's (1977) self-instruction training, the adult first models an appropriate behavior while saying the self-instruction aloud. Next, the child is asked to repeat the action and also to say the self-instruction aloud. Following this, the child repeats the task while whispering the self-instructions. Finally, the child does the task while repeating the instructions silently. This procedure is designed as a structured way of developing *internalization,* helping children to learn internal controls over their behavior.

Beck's Cognitive Therapy

CBT has been strongly influenced by the clinical work of Aaron Beck (1976). Beck's **cognitive therapy** was developed specifically as a treatment for depression (Beck et al., 1979). Beck suggested that depression is caused by errors in thinking.

These distortions lead depressed people to draw incorrect, negative conclusions about themselves, conclusions that create and maintain depression. Simply put, Beck hypothesized that depressed people see the world through gray-colored glasses (as opposed to the rose-colored variety). According to his analysis, this negative filter makes the world appear much bleaker than it really is.

Beck's cognitive therapy challenges cognitive errors, often by having clients analyze their thoughts more carefully (Beck et al., 1979). For example, a cognitive therapist might ask Frances to keep a record of her various family conflicts, including a brief description of the dispute, her thoughts in the moment, and her feelings that followed. The cognitive therapist might help Frances use this information to challenge her tendency to engage in "black and white" (all bad or all good) thinking about her relationships. "Yes, your mother got angry, but does the fact that you didn't meet her expectations really mean that she *hates* you and you are a complete failure and totally worthless?"

Rational–Emotive Therapy

Albert Ellis's (1913–2007) **rational–emotive therapy (RET)** is also designed to challenge cognitive distortions. According to Ellis (1962), emotional disorders are caused by *irrational beliefs,* absolute, unrealistic views of the world, such as "Everyone must love me all the time." The rational–emotive therapist searches for a client's irrational beliefs, points out the impossibility of fulfilling them, and uses any and every opportunity to persuade the client to adopt more realistic beliefs. Rational–emotive therapy shares concepts and techniques in common with Beck's approach. A major difference, however, is that rational–emotive therapists directly challenge the client's beliefs during therapy (Ellis, 1962). For example, a rational–emotive therapist might strongly challenge Frances's desire to make her mother happy with a sharp comment like, "That's impossible! That's irrational!"

"Third-Wave" CBT

Recent years have witnessed a "third wave" of CBT, following the first wave (based on operant and classical conditioning), and the second (cognitive therapies; Hayes, 2004). Third-wave CBT treatments focus on broad, abstract principles such as acceptance, mindfulness, values, and relationships (Ost, 2008). For example, *dialectical behavior therapy,* a treatment for borderline personality disorder (see Chapter 9), includes an emphasis on "mindfulness," increased awareness of your feelings, thoughts, and motivations (Linehan, 1993). *Acceptance and commitment therapy,* a values-oriented approach used in treating a variety of disorders and problems, encourages accepting oneself as well as making appropriate changes (Hayes, 2004). Empirical support is not as strong for third-wave CBT as it is for other forms of CBT, but importantly, the treatments are being evaluated systematically (Ost, 2008).

Integration and Research

Increasingly what defines CBT is a commitment to research, not to a particular form of therapy, as evidenced by the growing number of techniques called cognitive behavior therapy. cognitive behavior therapists increasingly embrace *any* treatment—as long as it is proven effective. In the future, we envision CBT becoming *the* eclectic approach to therapy, comprised of whatever treatments work.

HUMANISTIC THERAPIES

Humanistic psychotherapy developed as a "third force" in psychotherapy, a counterpoint to both psychodynamic and cognitive behavior therapy. Humanistic psychologists see both approaches as ignoring what is most essential about being human: making choices and shaping our own future. To be human is to be responsible for your own life—and for finding meaning in it. From this perspective, therapy cannot solve problems for you. Therapy can only help you to solve your own problems, to make better choices in your life (Rogers, 1951).

The key to making better choices is increased *emotional awareness.* Humanistic therapists encourage people to recognize and experience their true feelings. Like psychodynamic therapy, this involves "uncovering" hidden emotions; thus, both treatments strive to promote insight. Yet, humanistic therapists are more concerned with how people feel rather than why they are feeling that way. And like CBT, humanistic therapy focuses primarily on the present.

Humanists view the therapist–client relationship as *the* method for encouraging change.

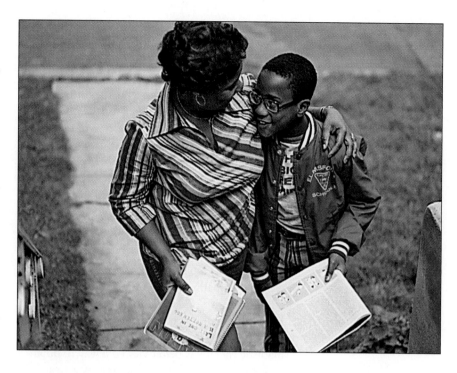

▲ Warmth is a vital aspect of relationships with family and friends. Social support also is instrumental to the therapy relationship.

Other approaches also see the therapy relationship as important but view it as a way to make the real treatment—insight or behavior change—more effective. In humanistic therapy, the relationship *is* the treatment.

Client-Centered Therapy

Carl Rogers (1902–1987) and his *client-centered therapy* epitomize this focus on the therapy relationship. Rogers (1951) viewed three qualities as essential in a therapist: warmth, genuineness, and particularly **empathy,** emotional understanding. Empathy involves putting yourself in someone else's shoes and conveying your understanding of that person's feelings and perspectives. Therapists show empathy by reflecting their client's feelings and, at a deeper level, by anticipating emotions their clients have not yet expressed.

Rogers encouraged appropriate therapist *self-disclosure,* intentionally revealing some of the therapist's own, similar feelings and experiences as a way of showing empathy and helping clients to better understand themselves. And because emotional understanding can grow out of many life experiences, not just from professional training, Rogers felt that client-centered therapists need not be professionals. They could be ordinary people who had faced life difficulties similar to those of their clients.

Client-centered therapists do not act as "experts," pretending to know more about people than they know about themselves. Rather, they strive to share genuinely in another human's experience. Rogers felt that client-centered therapists must demonstrate *unconditional positive regard*, valuing clients for who they are and not judging them. Out of respect for the client's humanity, client-centered therapists avoid directing the therapy process; they are *nondirective*. Rogers believed that, if clients can experience and accept themselves, they will be able to resolve their own problems.

A Means, Not an End?

Rogers (1951) took a strong stand. He asserted that warmth, empathy, and genuineness were necessary and sufficient conditions for therapeutic change. Few have studied whether humanistic therapy effectively changes abnormal behavior. Perhaps humanistic therapy is better viewed a way to obtain a new emotional understanding, not as a treatment for specific mental disorders (Pascual-Leone & Greenberg, 2007).

> *Why are humanistic therapy techniques a means, not an end, in therapy?*

Despite the lack of outcome research, a lasting legacy of Rogers and his colleagues is a commitment to psychotherapy *process* research. Process research shows that the therapeutic alliance or bond between a therapist and client is crucial to the success of therapy (Baldwin, Wampold, & Imel, 2007). A therapist's caring, concern, and respect for the individual are important to the success of *all* psychological treatments.

RESEARCH ON PSYCHOTHERAPY

Now that we have described psychotherapy, we can begin to ask some questions about it. Many people claim not to "believe" in psychotherapy. Is their skepticism well founded? Does psychotherapy work? And if therapy is helpful, what approach works best?

Researchers often disagree, sometimes vehemently, about the answers to these questions. Based on the evidence we discuss in the following sections, however, we reach four major conclusions about psychotherapy. First, psychotherapy *outcome* research shows that psychotherapy *does* work—for many people and for many problems. Second, psychotherapy *process* research indicates that most approaches to psychotherapy share key "active ingredients" (e.g., a supportive therapist–client relationship). Third, different treatments are more or less effective for different disorders. Fourth, some "treatments" are complete shams that not only do not help but may well harm (see Critical Thinking Matters and Table 3–3).

Does Psychotherapy Work?

Psychotherapy outcome research examines the outcome, or result, of psychotherapy—its effectiveness for relieving symptoms, eliminating disorders, and/or improving life functioning. Hundreds of studies have compared the outcome of psychotherapy with alternative treatments or with no treatment at all. In order to summarize findings across all of these studies, psychologists often use a statistical technique called **meta-analysis,** a statistical procedure that allows researchers to combine the results from different studies in a standardized way. Meta-analysis creates a common currency for research findings, similar to converting different numbers of euros, yen, rubles, yuan, and so on into dollar amounts.

Meta-analysis indicates that the average benefit of psychotherapy is .85 standard deviation units (Smith & Glass, 1977). We describe the mathematical meaning of the *standard deviation*

TABLE 3–3 Therapies That May Harm		
NAME	**BRIEF DESCRIPTION**	**POTENTIAL HARM**
Critical incident stress Debriefing	"Processing" trauma soon after the experience	Increased risk for posttraumatic stress symptoms
Scared straight	Seasoned inmates scare youth about consequences of criminality	Increased conduct problems
Facilitated communication	Facilitator helps impaired individual type on keyboard	False accusations of child abuse
Rebirthing therapy	Wrapped tightly in sheets while group resists struggle to be "reborn"	Physical injury, death
Recovered memories	Encouragement to "recover" memories of trauma	Creation of false memories
Boot camps	Delinquent youth sent to military style camp	Increased conduct problems
DARE programs	Preadolescent children educated about danger of drugs	Increased substance use

Source: Adapted from S. O. Lilienfeld, 2007, "Psychological Treatments That Cause Harm," *Perspectives on Psychological Science, 2*, pp. 53–70.

CRITICAL THINKING MATTERS

Are All Therapies Created Equal?

Research demonstrates that, in general, psychotherapy "works." Evidence also shows that different approaches to therapy contain "common factors" that contribute to their success. Does this mean that all therapies are equally effective? No way!

Contemporary research shows that specific treatments are more or less effective for specific disorders (DeRubeis, Brotman, & Gibbons, 2005; Nathan & Gorman, 2007). Because of this, we strongly believe that therapists are ethically obligated to inform their clients about the effectiveness of alternative treatments. We also believe that there is a long list of "therapies" that professionals *never* should offer as a treatment for *any* emotional problem.

Many so-called treatments are, to be blunt, hoaxes. The list of phony therapies has grown in recent years, as susceptible members of the public seem to have lost faith in science and instead placed their hopes in "alternative" therapies. The problem has led several scientifically minded psychologists to debunk various fake therapies (e.g., Lilienfeld, Lynn, & Lohr, 2003; Singer & Lalich, 1996). Among the most dubious of treatments are

- "Rebirthing therapy," a technique that purports to free people from deep-seated emotional problems by teaching them to breathe using their diaphragm instead of their chest.

- "Primal therapy," where patients overcome the trauma of their own birth by learning the appropriate way to scream and thereby release destructive emotions.
- "Attunement-enhancing, shame-reducing, attachment therapy," which involves holding a child firmly and encouraging her rage and despair, as a way of getting the child to talk about trauma.
- "Alien abduction therapy," which helps people to cope with the various mental disorders caused by being abducted by aliens. (We're not making this up!)
- "Facilitated communication," a technique in which a facilitator helps someone with impaired communication to speak by "assisting" his or her typing on a keyboard.

Are some psychological "treatments" really hoaxes?

We hope that these treatments strike you as completely outlandish. They are. To see just how far some "experts" are willing to go with their outrageous claims, you might do a Web search on these and other "alternative" therapies.

The treatments may be silly, but they have a very serious effect. The desperation of people suffering from mental disorders, and their loved ones, can lead them to be duped into trying sham treatments—and perhaps missing out on legitimate ones. For example, facilitated communication was so widely promoted as a treatment for autism in the 1990s that legitimate scientists, and a panel of experts appointed by the American Psychological Association, had to spend valuable time proving that the technique does *not* work. We detail the troubling story of facilitated communication in Chapter 15, but here's a hint how it works: Ever hear of the Ouija board?

Scientists cannot debunk every hare-brained idea offered by misguided or deceptive "therapists," nor should they have to. Recall that the burden of proof falls on the shoulders of anyone who claims that alien abductions cause mental disorders. Until proven true, we reject such claims. And proof requires objective, replicable evidence—not case studies, testimonials, or films produced by advocates of some technique.

Outlandish therapies—and seemingly legitimate but ineffective treatments—would cause fewer problems if two things happened. First, mental health professions need to take a strong stand and endorse clear standards of care for treating various mental disorders. Second, the public—you—needs to think critically. Hone your inquiring skepticism. Don't be duped by self-anointed experts, case studies, or sensational media stories, however believable they may seem.

---

in Research Methods in Chapter 15. For now, you can begin to appreciate the finding by comparing psychotherapy with other interventions. Nine months of reading instruction leads to a smaller, .67 standard deviation unit increase in reading achievement among elementary school children. Many well-accepted medical treatments have very small effect sizes. For example, chemotherapy has about a .10 effect size in reducing mortality following breast cancer (Lipsey & Wilson, 1993).

The .85 standard deviation statistic also indicates that the average client who receives therapy is better off than 80 percent of untreated persons (see Figure 3–2). The .85 standard deviation change also indicates that roughly two-thirds of clients improve significantly with psychotherapy, while about one-third of people who receive no treatment improve over time. Thus, we can conclude that therapy "works," but with a very important qualification: Many benefits of psychotherapy diminish in the year or two after treatment ends (Westen & Bradley, 2005).

Improvement Without Treatment? Many psychologists accept that about two-thirds of clients improve, at least in the short term, as a result of psychotherapy. Some skeptics have suggested, however, that a high percentage of emotional disorders have a *spontaneous remission,* that is, they improve without any treatment at all. In fact, the British psychologist Hans Eysenck (1916–1997) famously concluded that psychotherapy was totally ineffective for this very reason. Eysenck

Meta-Analysis of Psychotherapy Outcomes

.85 SD

Control group
Psychotherapy group

80th percentile of control group

FIGURE 3–2   The average effect of psychotherapy has been found to be .85 standard deviation units. This means that the average client who receives therapy functions better than 80 percent of untreated controls (shaded area).

Adapted from M. L. Smith, G. V. Glass, and T. I. Miller, 1980, *The Benefits of Psychotherapy,* Baltimore: Johns Hopkins University Press.

(1952/1992) agreed that therapy helps about two out of three people. The problem, he claimed, is that two-thirds of people also improve *without* treatment.

Was Eysenck right? This simple question turns out to be not so straightforward to answer. Consider a basic experiment. Clients seeking therapy are randomly assigned to receive either psychotherapy or no treatment at all. People in the *no-treatment control group* might be put on a waiting list, with the promise that they will receive therapy in the future. But people on a waiting list are likely to seek counseling and advice from family members, friends, religious leaders, or maybe a different professional. If we find that their problems improve 6 months later, is this spontaneous remission or a result of *informal* psychological help?

Informal counseling often is helpful, as you surely know from your own life experiences. In fact, researchers have found that as many as one-half of people seeking psychotherapy improve as a result of simply having unstructured conversations with a professional (Lambert & Bergin, 1994). Thus, some experts argue that so-called no-treatment controls actually receive some form of treatment. Other experts assert that "just talking" is hardly psychotherapy. Should we consider informal counseling to be part of psychotherapy, or is "just talking" merely a placebo?

In what ways are placebo effects relevant to psychotherapy process and outcome?

The Placebo Effect   In medicine, *placebos* are pills that are pharmacologically inert; they have no medicinal value. More broadly, placebos are any type of treatment that contains no known active ingredients for the condition at hand. But the absence of active ingredients does not prevent placebos from healing. The **placebo effect,** the powerful healing produced by inert treatments, has been documented widely in psychotherapy, psychopharmacology, dentistry, optometry, cardiovascular disease, cancer treatment, and even surgery (Baskin et al., 2003). The recipient's belief in a treatment, and expectation of improvement, are responsible for much of what works in psychological—and physical—treatments. Consider this: A recent study found that full-price placebos (costing $2.50 per pill) produced significantly more pain relief than "discount" placebos (costing $.10 per pill) (Waber et al., 2008).

Some view the placebo effect as a mere nuisance. This is understandable, because a goal of science is to identify *active ingredients*—treatments that are more than placebos (Baskin et al., 2003). But we can also view the placebo effect itself as a treatment—one that heals psychologically. Of course, psychotherapy also heals psychologically. Viewed in this light, the placebo effect is something to study, not dismiss. Ironically, psychotherapy research must identify the "active ingredients" in placebos! In fact, a recent study showed that the passage of time (spontaneous remission), a healing ritual (acupuncture in this study), and therapist–client relationship all contributed to heightening the placebo effect. The most effective placebo contained all three "active ingredients" (Kaptchuk et al., 2008). Furthermore, neuroscientists have found that placebos actually decrease the brain's response to pain; the placebo effect produces real changes in experience, not just decreased reporting of pain (Wager, 2005). We do need to understand the placebo effect, as well as devise treatments to surpass it.

Placebo Control Groups   In order to identify active ingredients *beyond* the placebo effect, medical investigators routinely include *placebo control groups* in their studies—patients intentionally are given treatments that contain no active ingredients, for example, sugar pills. But there is another complication: The *doctor's* expectations also can influence a treatment's effectiveness. To control for this second effect, medical scientists use **double-blind studies,** investigations where neither the physician nor the patient knows whether the pill is real or a placebo.

Unfortunately, there is no way to construct a double-blind study of psychotherapy. You can disguise a pill, but you cannot disguise psychotherapy. Therapists know when a treatment is the real thing or a placebo—"just talk." Does this matter? Yes. Research shows that a therapist's "allegiance" to one form of therapy or another has a powerful influence on whether it is effective (see The Allegiance Effect). Because it is impossible to conduct double-blind studies, more and more psychotherapy research is involving competitions between rival "teams" of therapists, each believing in their own, unique treatment (Klein, 1999). This does not eliminate the placebo effect, but it should make the placebo effect similar for the rival treatments.

So after all of these considerations, what is our "bottom line" about improvement without treatment? Our best estimate still is that about one-third of people improve without treatment. Thus psychotherapy does, indeed, work for many people and many problems.

Efficacy and Effectiveness Tightly controlled experiments provide important information about the *efficacy* of psychotherapy, that is, whether the treatment *can* work under prescribed circumstances. However, such studies provide little information about the *effectiveness* of the treatment—whether the therapy *does* work in

the real world. In the real world, therapies are not assigned at random; therapists vary the type and length of treatment, and clients commonly have multiple problems (Nathan, Stuart, & Dolan, 2000; Stirman et al., 2003; Weston, Novotny, & Thompson-Brenner, 2004). How does psychotherapy fare under these circumstances?

Studies on the effectiveness of psychotherapy attempt to answer this question. For example, the magazine *Consumer Reports* (1995, November) surveyed nearly 3,000 readers who had seen a mental health professional in the past three years, and the respondents generally rated psychotherapy highly. Among the major findings:

- Of the 426 people who were feeling "very poor" at the beginning of treatment, 87 percent reported feeling "very good," "good," or at least "so-so" when they were surveyed.
- Clients of psychologists, psychiatrists, and social workers reported no differences in treatment outcome, but all three professions were rated more effective than marriage counselors.
- People who received psychotherapy alone reported no more or less improvement than people who received psychotherapy plus medication (Seligman, 1995).

Because the *Consumer Reports* study was correlational, we cannot draw conclusions about

THE ALLEGIANCE EFFECT

The **allegiance effect** is the tendency for researchers to find that their favorite treatment—the one to which they hold allegiance—is the most effective (Luborsky et al., 1999). In comparing psychodynamic therapy and cognitive behavior therapy, for example, researchers allied with cognitive behavior therapy tend to find that treatment to be more effective. In contrast, researchers allied with psychodynamic therapy, tend to find *that* treatment to be more effective. In fact, according to a meta-analysis of 29 studies (Luborsky et al., 1999) .69 percent of the variance in the effectiveness of one treatment over another was explained by allegiance effects.

What causes allegiance effects? In discussing the double-blind study, we already

suggested one influence: the therapist's expectations contribute to a treatment's effectiveness. Other, less subtle influences also contribute to the allegiance effect (Luborsky et al., 1999). When designing a study, researchers probably pick a weak rival alternative treatment. This may or may not be intentional, but investigators, of course, want their preferred approach to "win."

Another not so subtle contribution may be that investigators are more likely to publish research papers when their findings are consistent with their hypotheses (Luborsky et al., 1999). For example, a researcher allied with psychodynamic therapy might quickly publish the findings demonstrating the superiority of that treatment but be more reluctant to

publish results favoring cognitive behavior therapy! This is called the *file drawer problem*. We know the results of published studies; we can only guess about the results of research sitting in someone's file drawer. The file drawer problem is not necessarily deliberate. Instead, researchers may be genuinely puzzled by, or just not believe, results that contradict their hypotheses.

Finally, sometimes allegiance may not *cause* biased results, but instead be an *effect* of convincing findings (Luborsky et al., 1999). That is, researchers may ally with the treatment they find to be most effective. We would be delighted if this circumstance fully explained the allegiance effect, but we doubt that this is so.

causation. For example, perhaps people who had good experiences in therapy were more likely to complete the survey than were people who had bad experiences. Still, like other research, the *Consumer Reports* study suggests that psychotherapy helps many people in the real world, not just in the laboratory.

When Does Psychotherapy Work? What predicts when psychotherapy is more or less likely to be effective? The most important predictor is the nature of a client's problems—the diagnosis. For this reason, we discuss research on specific treatments for specific disorders in every chapter throughout the text. Here, we consider two of the many other predictors of treatment outcome: the length of treatment and the client's background characteristics.

If therapy is going to be effective, it usually works pretty fast. As Figure 3–3 indicates, improvement is greatest in the first several months of treatment. Improvement continues with longer term therapy, but at a notably slower rate (Howard et al., 1986), although there is some debate about how long it takes for therapy to work best (Seligman, 1995). Unfortunately, the average client sees a therapist for only five sessions, because so many people drop out of treatment early (Hansen, Lambert, & Forman, 2002). Clearly, there are practi-

cal, economic, and empirical reasons to keep treatment brief—or at least relatively brief.

Clients' background characteristics also predict outcome in psychotherapy. The acronym YAVIS was coined to indicate that clients improve more in psychotherapy when they are "young, attractive, verbal, intelligent, and successful." This finding has caused considerable concern, for it seems to indicate that psychotherapy works best for the most advantaged members of our society. Another concern is that men are considerably less likely than women to seek therapy. The masculine role seems to discourage appropriate help seeking (Addis & Mahalik, 2003).

Psychotherapy Process Research

If psychotherapy can be effective, just how does it work? This is the question asked by *psychotherapy process research,* an approach that examines what aspects of the therapist–client interaction account for better outcomes (Doss, 2004; Kazdin, 2008; Norcross & Hill, 2004).

Common Factors One historically important type of psychotherapy process research compared psychodynamic, cognitive behavioral, and human-

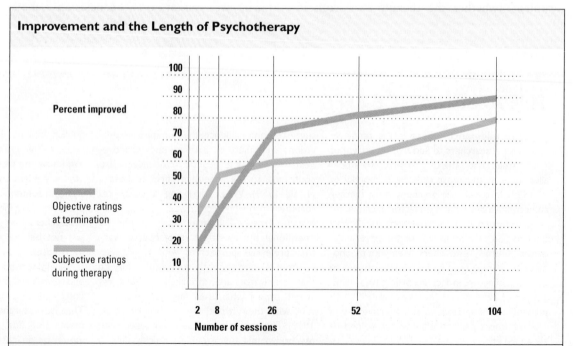

Improvement and the Length of Psychotherapy

Percent improved

Objective ratings at termination

Subjective ratings during therapy

Number of sessions

FIGURE 3–3 Most improvement occurs early in psychotherapy, suggesting that relatively short-term treatments may be cost effective.

Source: K. J. Howard, S. M. Kopta, M. S. Krause, and D. E. Orlinsky, 1986, "The Dose–Effect Relationship in Psychotherapy," *American Psychologist, 41,* pp. 159–164. © 1996 by American Psychological Association. Reprinted by permission of D. E. Orlinsky.

istic treatments. The central question was: Do these different psychotherapies share *common factors* that help make them effective?

The answer is a qualified "yes" according to a classic study by Sloane and colleagues (1975). In this study, 90 patients who had moderate difficulties with anxiety, depression, or similar problems were assigned at random to receive either psychodynamic psychotherapy, behavior therapy, or no treatment. The different therapies were delivered by six therapists, all of whom were highly experienced in their preferred form of treatment. Both treatments lasted for an average of 14 sessions. To ensure that the treatments were offered as planned, the differences between the two therapies were clearly defined (see Table 3–4), and tape recordings of the fifth sessions were coded so the actual treatments could be compared.

The two therapies clearly differed. Behavior therapists talked about as often as their clients talked, gave specific advice, and directed much of the course of therapy. In contrast, psychodynamic therapists talked only one-third as often as their clients, refused to answer specific questions, and followed their clients' lead during the session. Psychodynamic therapists focused more on feelings, their underlying causes, and techniques such as free association. Behavior therapists focused on specific behaviors, ways of changing them, and techniques such as systematic desensitization.

What did the very different treatments have in common? Perhaps more than you would expect. Surprisingly, behavior therapists and psychodynamic therapists offered the same number of interpretations. And the clients' ratings of therapist warmth, empathy, and genuineness predicted successful outcome in both treatment groups. Clients also rated their relationship with their therapists as the single most important aspect of both behavior therapy and psychodynamic psychotherapy. Finally, although behavior therapy was more effective in a few instances, there were no differences in treatment outcome between the two groups (Sloane et al., 1975).

Psychotherapies *are* more effective when they contain "active ingredients" for treating a particular disorder. This is particularly true when the disorder is more severe (Stevens, Hynan, & Allen, 2000). Nevertheless, much of the effectiveness of different forms of psychotherapy is explained by common factors (Norcross & Hill, 2004; Wampold, 2007). An analogy may help you to understand why this is so. Baseball and soccer differ

greatly, but participating in some sport, any sport, may be more important to children's development than whether they play basketball or lacrosse, ice skate or do gymnastics (see Table 3–5).

Therapy as Social Support As we have said, Carl Rogers was right—in part. Research shows that a positive therapist–client relationship predicts positive outcomes across approaches to treatment (Baldwin, Wampold, & Imel, 2007). Significantly, however, *clients'* ratings of supportiveness predict outcome better than objective indicators. A supportive relationship is not defined simply by a therapist's behavior but also by a therapist's behavior in relation to a particular client. Some people, probably most, feel understood when a therapist makes empathic statements; others are more comfortable with a more detached therapist (Beutler et al., 1991).

TABLE 3–4 Definitions of Psychotherapy and Behavior Therapy

TECHNIQUE	PSYCHOTHERAPY	BEHAVIOR THERAPY
Specific advice	Given infrequently	Given frequently
Transference interpretation	May be given	Avoided
Resistance interpretation	Used	Not used
Dreams	Interested and encouraged	Disinterested
Level of anxiety	Maintained when possible	Diminished when possible
Relaxation training	Only indirect	Directly undertaken
Desensitization	Only indirect	Directly undertaken
Assertion training	Indirectly encouraged	Directly encouraged
Report of symptoms	Discouraged	Encouraged
Childhood memories	Explored	Historical interest only

Source: "Differences in Technique in Behavior Therapy and Psychotherapy," as adapted from R. B. Sloane, F. R. Staples, A. H. Cristo, N. J. Yorkston, and K. Whipple, 1975, *Psychotherapy versus Behavior Therapy,* Cambridge, MA: Harvard University Press, pp. 237–240.

TABLE 3–5 Common Factors in Effective Brief Psychotherapies

1. Treatment is offered soon after the problem is identified.
2. Assessment of the problem is rapid and occurs early in treatment.
3. A therapeutic alliance is established quickly, and it is used to encourage change in the client.
4. Therapy is designed to be time limited, and the therapist uses this to encourage rapid progress.
5. The goals of therapy are limited to a few specified areas.
6. The therapist is directive in managing the treatment sessions.
7. Therapy is focused on a specific theme.
8. The client is encouraged to express strong emotions or troubling experiences.
9. A flexible approach is taken in the choice of treatment techniques.

Source: Adapted from M. P. Koss and J. M. Butcher, 1986, "Research on Brief Psychotherapy," in S. L. Garfield and A. E. Bergin, Eds., *Handbook of Psychotherapy and Behavior Change,* 3rd ed, New York: Wiley, pp. 627–670.

"You haven't a clue what I'm talking about, do you?"

What are some common factors across different approaches to therapy?

Social support is a big part of therapy, but warmth, empathy, and genuineness are a quality of the *relationship,* not just the therapist.

Therapy as Social Influence Psychotherapy is a process of social influence not just social support. Even Carl Rogers, the advocate of nondirective therapy, directed his clients. Audiotapes indicate that Rogers was more likely to empathize with certain types of statements than others (Truax & Carkhuff, 1967). He responded to his clients conditionally and thereby directed therapy subtly.

Jerome Frank, an American trained both in psychology and psychiatry, argued that, in fact, psychotherapy is a process of persuasion—persuading clients to make beneficial changes in their emotional life. Frank (1973) highlighted a gentle aspect of persuasion in therapy—instilling hope. People seek professional help when they have been unable to solve their own problems, when they have lost hope. Frank saw therapy as a chance to instill new hope, and in so doing, helping people to make the changes they have been struggling to make (Frank, 1973).

Process research clearly demonstrates the therapist's social influence. For example, evidence shows that clients tend to adopt beliefs similar to their therapists. In fact, treatment is more effective when, over time, clients' beliefs become more similar to those of their therapists (Beutler et al., 1991; Kelly, 1990). Positive outcomes are more likely when the new beliefs relate directly to psychotherapy—for example, the importance of expressing emotions—than when they reflect broader values (Beutler et al., 1994).

Recognition of the therapist's social influence raises questions about values in psychotherapy.

Psychotherapy is not value free. There are values inherent in the nature of therapy itself—for example, the belief that talking is good. Moreover, the values of individual therapists about such topics as love, marriage, work, and family necessarily influence clients. Like the rest of the human race, psychotherapists cannot transcend their own beliefs and values. All we can do is recognize our biases and inform our clients about them.

COUPLES, FAMILY, AND GROUP THERAPY

Medication and psychotherapy treat problems by changing the individual. Consistent with the systems perspective, professionals also can treat individual problems by changing social circumstances. Consider the case of Frances. Medication or therapy might improve her troubled family relationships, but improving her relationships with her parents and husband also might alleviate Frances's depression. Some would argue, in fact, that Frances and women like her become depressed precisely because of the roles women are expected to play in families and in society. In this section, we briefly consider treatments for couples and families, group therapy, and efforts at preventing emotional disorders through social change.

Couples Therapy

Couples therapy involves seeing intimate partners together in therapy. This approach is sometimes called *marital therapy* or *marriage counseling,* but the reference to couples captures the range of partners

"She said, 'I'll go if you go,' and I said, 'I'll go if you go,' and here we are."

who may seek treatment together. Dating pairs, prospective mates, live-in partners, and gay and lesbian couples also may seek couples therapy.

The goal of couples therapy typically is to improve the relationship, and not to treat the individual. However, couples treatment also may be used to help both partners function more adequately when one member suffers from a psychological problem. In treating relationships, all couples therapists focus on resolving conflicts and promoting mutual satisfaction. Couples therapists do not tell their clients what compromises they should accept or how they should change their relationship. Instead, they typically help partners improve their *communication* and *negotiation* skills (Emery, in press; Gurman & Jacobson, 2002; Jacobson & Christensen, 1996).

How does this work? A couples therapist might, for example, suggest that Frances had a problem with "mind reading" in her marriage. Without ever telling him, Frances hopes (or expects) her husband to know what she wants. She might want more attention, but she never asks for it—she wants him to "figure it out for himself." The therapist would point out that no one can read another person's mind; instead, partners need to communicate their wishes directly (Gottman, 1997). This may sound simple, but learning to be direct can be tricky for many people. Frances may feel selfish when making requests, or perhaps she wants to be "surprised" with her husband's attention. She may think that his attention is less meaningful if she asks for it.

Another component of most couples therapies is negotiation or *conflict resolution*. Negotiation is the art of give and take. Effective negotiation defines problems clearly, considers a wide range of solutions, uncovers hidden agendas (unstated concerns), and experiments with alternative solutions. These strategies are similar to the social problem-solving model discussed earlier, an approach that has been effectively applied to with couples (Emery, in press). Politeness also is an essential component of effective negotiation, and setting clear ground rules can facilitate polite communication. Examples of ground rules include not raising your voice, not interrupting the other person, and speaking about your own feelings—that is, not telling your partner how he or she feels (Emery, in press; Gottman et al., 1976).

Research shows that couples therapy can improve satisfaction in marriages (Baucom & Epstein, 1990; Gurman & Jacobson, 2002). However, questions remain about the long-term effectiveness of couples therapy, the relative efficacy of alternative approaches to couples therapy, and the role of couples therapy in the context of societal views about marriage and gender roles (Alexander, Holtzworth-Munroe, & Jameson, 1994).

Couples therapy also has been used in the treatment of specific disorders, including depression, anxiety, substance abuse, and child behavior problems. This typically is done either as a supplement or an alternative to individual therapy. Couples therapy, alone or combined with individual treatment, often is more effective than individual therapy alone (Beach, Sandeen, & O'Leary, 1990; Jacobson, Holtzworth-Munroe, & Schmaling, 1989).

Family Therapy

Family therapy might include two, three, or more family members in a treatment designed to improve communication, negotiate conflicts, and perhaps change family relationships and roles. Like couples therapy, family therapy has the general goal of improving relationships. Some forms of family therapy also focus on resolving specific conflicts, such as disputes between adolescents and their parents. *Parent management training* is an approach that teaches parents new skills for rearing troubled children (Patterson, 1982). Other types of family therapy are designed to educate families about how best to cope with the serious psychopathology of one family member.

There are many different styles of family therapy, but most share an emphasis on systems

▼ Family therapists attempt to improve mental health by altering family relationships.

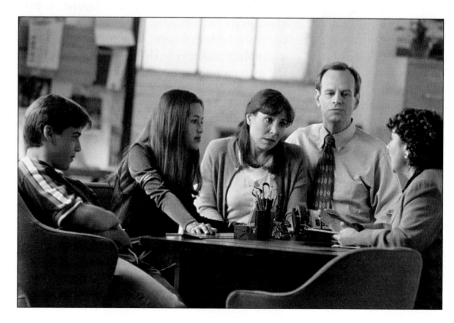

theory (Gurman & Jacobson, 2002). In applying systems theory, family therapists emphasize interdependence among family members and the importance of viewing the individual within the family system. For example, family systems therapists often call attention to the pattern of *alliances* or strategic loyalties among family members. In well-functioning families, the primary alliance is between the two parents, even when the parents do not live together. In contrast, dysfunctional families often have alliances that cross generations—that is, "teams" that include one parent and some or all of the children opposing the other parent or another child. Like a poorly organized business, families function inadequately when their leaders fail to cooperate. Thus, a common goal in systems approaches to family therapy is to strengthen the alliance between the parents, to get parents to work together and not against each other (Emery, 1992).

Group Therapy

Group therapy involves treating several people facing similar emotional problems or life issues. Therapy groups may be as small as 3 or 4 people or as large as 20 or more. Group therapy has numerous variations and targets for treatment, and here we can highlight only a few facets of the group approach.

Psychoeducational groups teach specific psychological information or life skills. The term *psychoeducational* aptly conveys the goals of this type of group. Teaching is the primary mode of treatment, but the content of the "course" is psychological. For example, assertiveness might be taught in a group format. In other circumstances, a common disorder such as an eating disorder, not a common treatment, is the reason for group membership.

There are two basic reasons for offering therapy in a psychoeducational group instead of in individual psychotherapy. Less expense is one obvious justification. A second is the support, encouragement, and practice that group members can offer one another. Many people who have psychological problems feel isolated, alone, and sometimes "weird." The simple act of coming to a group can be part of the therapeutic process. Learning that you are not alone with your problems can be a powerful experience that is one of the unique "active ingredients" in group therapy.

In *experiential group therapy*, in fact, the relationships group members form are the primary mode of treatment. For example, group members might be encouraged to look beyond one another's "façades"—to reveal secrets about themselves or otherwise to break down the barriers that we all erect in relationships. Group members, in turn, can offer one another feedback and support. In an *encounter group*, group members may question self-disclosure when it is "phony" but support more honest appraisals of oneself. Such experiential groups typically include members who are well functioning and who view the group as an opportunity for personal growth. Little research has been conducted on the effectiveness of this type of group.

Self-help groups bring together people who face a common problem and who seek to help themselves and each other by sharing information and experiences. Self-help groups are very popular—including Internet-based groups (Taylor & Luce, 2003). The potential organizing topics are as numerous as the problems life throws at us. Technically, self-help groups are not therapy groups, because typically a professional does not lead them. If there is a leader, it may be someone who already has faced the particular problem, perhaps a former group member.

Prevention

Social influences on psychopathology extend far beyond interpersonal relationships. Social institutions, school, and work environments are important contributors to mental health, as are such broad societal concerns as poverty, racism, and sexism. Of course, the goal of improving society is hardly the exclusive domain of psychologists. Still, *community psychology* is one approach within clinical psychology that attempts to improve individual well-being by promoting social change (Wandersman & Florin, 2003).

The concept of prevention is an important consideration in promoting social change. Community psychologists often distinguish among three levels of prevention. **Primary prevention** tries to improve the environment in order to prevent new cases of a mental disorder from developing. The goal of primary prevention is to promote wellness, not just treat illness. Efforts at primary prevention range from offering prenatal care to impoverished pregnant women, to teaching schoolchildren about the dangers of drug abuse.

Secondary prevention focuses on the early detection of emotional problems in the hope of preventing them from becoming more serious and difficult to treat. The screening of "at-risk" schoolchildren is one example of an effort at secondary prevention. Crisis centers and hotlines are other examples of attempts to detect and treat problems before they become more serious.

Finally, **tertiary prevention** may involve any of the treatments discussed in this chapter, because the intervention occurs after the illness has been identified. In addition to providing treatment, however, tertiary prevention also attempts to address some of the adverse, indirect consequences of mental illness. Helping the chronically mentally ill to find adequate housing and employment is an example of a tertiary prevention effort.

No one can doubt the importance of prevention, whether directed toward biological, psychological, or social causes of abnormal behavior. Unfortunately, many prevention efforts face an insurmountable obstacle: We simply do not know the specific cause of most psychological disorders. Prevention efforts directed at broader social change face another obstacle that also seems insurmountable at times. Social problems like poverty, racism, and sexism defy easy remedies. We do not wish to blame the victim of social injustice, but blaming the system can be equally problematic. Each individual must take personal responsibility for changing his or her own life, even as we collectively work to shape a world that promotes mental health.

SPECIFIC TREATMENTS FOR SPECIFIC DISORDERS

Psychotherapy began with treatments based solely in theory and case histories. It progressed as researchers documented the superiority of psychotherapy over no treatment at all. Contemporary researchers are advancing knowledge by studying factors common to all therapies. The ultimate goal of treatment research, however, is to identify therapies that have specific active ingredients for treating specific disorders (Nathan & Gorman, 2007). Consistent with this goal, in subsequent chapters we discuss only treatments that either are promising or have proved to be effective for alleviating the symptoms of the disorder at hand.

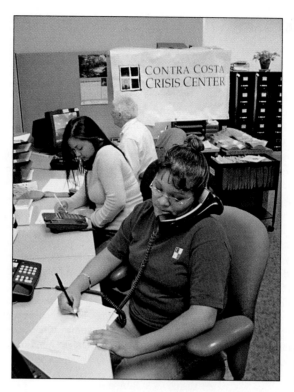

◄ Telephone hotlines are an example of secondary prevention, trying to detect and treat emotional problems early, before they get more serious.

We strongly believe that the client's problems, not the therapist's "theoretical orientation," should determine the choice of treatment. For many emotional problems, enough scientific evidence exists to identify the treatment of choice or at least to rule out some less effective forms of therapy. In these cases, we feel very strongly that mental health professionals must inform their clients about research and treatment alternatives. If a therapist is not skilled in offering the most effective approach, he or she should offer to refer the client to someone with specialized training.

For other emotional problems, researchers have not yet identified a clear treatment of choice, but this does not mean that "anything goes." Rather, more experimental therapies must be acknowledged as experimental, and the rationale for the approach must be clear to both the therapist and the client.

The identification of effective treatments for specific disorders is necessary if clinical psychology is to fulfill its scientific promise. Even as we explore new evidence-based treatments, however, we must remember that humanism—and research—point to the central importance of a human relationship in effective psychotherapy. After all, individual people, not diagnostic categories, seek treatment for psychological disorders.

What are the different levels for trying to prevent mental disorders?

GETTING HELP

How can you find the right therapist for yourself, a friend, or a family member? Our basic advice is to be a good consumer. Find out more about the nature of the psychological problem and about treatments that work. You will find a lot of useful information in later chapters on treatments for specific disorders, including the Getting Help sections, where we make a lot of practical suggestions.

As a good consumer, you also should think carefully about what type of treatment you think you prefer and whom you prefer to see. A good "fit" between you and your therapist is an important part of effective therapy. For example, you may be more or less comfortable seeing a man or a woman. Many therapists offer, or even expect you to have, an initial interview before deciding about beginning therapy with them. If you are not com-

fortable with a particular therapist, you should feel free to shop around until you find one who not only offers well-supported treatments, but also who seems to understand you well. In fact, you may want to consult briefly with a few professionals before starting therapy, so you can pick the one who seems best for you.

People from a lot of different professional backgrounds offer psychotherapy. The person usually is more important than the profession, but we recommend that you see a professional from one of the three major mental health professions—a clinical psychologist, a psychiatrist, or a clinical social worker.

If you feel you may need medication, your family physician may be willing to prescribe antidepressants or some other commonly used medications. You might need to talk to a psychiatrist, a physician specializing in mental

illnesses, if your family physician is uncomfortable offering you a particular type of medication or if you would prefer to talk with a physician who is trained as a therapist.

If you are considering psychotherapy, read about different types of therapy, particularly those that research shows to be more helpful for certain disorders. In addition to consulting the relevant Getting Help and treatment sections of Chapters 5 through 17, you might also want to explore some self-help books or resources on the Internet. You will need to continue to be a good consumer when consulting these sources, however, as there is a lot of conflicting and inaccurate information about psychological problems and their treatment. A good starting point might be the Web site of the National Institute of Mental Health, which contains a lot of useful, up-to-date information on disorders and treatments.

■ SUMMARY

The various forms of **psychotherapy** can be roughly classified into four broad groups. Biological approaches primarily use **psychopharmacology,** medication that has psychological effects, but **ECT** and **psychosurgery** may also be useful treatments in unusual circumstances. **Psychodynamic psychotherapies** encourage the exploration of the past in order to obtain **insight** into unconscious motivations. **Cognitive behavior therapy** focuses on present experience in helping clients overcome maladaptive behaviors and learn adaptive ones. **Humanistic psychotherapy** offers clients warmth, **empathy,** and unconditional positive regard in helping them to heighten emotional awareness and make life choices. More therapists say they are **eclectic,** using different treatments for different disorders and different clients, than say they adhere to any one of these approaches.

Psychotherapy outcome research indicates that therapy "works," but we cannot adequately understand its efficacy without considering

how we define therapy and the **placebo effect.** The **allegiance effect** also is very important to interpreting psychotherapy research, as researchers tend to find that their preferred treatment is most effective. Psychotherapy process research highlights the components that contribute to making different treatments effective, particularly aspects of the therapist–client relationship.

Interventions for psychological problems may be directed toward biological, psychological, or social systems. **Couples therapy, family therapy,** and **group therapy** all focus on changing relationships, not just individuals. Various prevention efforts attempt to change dysfunctional aspects of the broader society. The future of psychotherapy research involves developing specific treatments for specific disorders, while continuing to recognize and better understand the nonspecific factors that are essential to the special relationship that develops in psychotherapy.

THE BIG PICTURE   CRITICAL THINKING REVIEW

How can acculturation affect therapy with minorities?

Acculturation can undermine minority values and customs and challenge the individual's ethnic identity. (SEE PAGE 65)

How is insight obtained in psychodynamic therapy?

The analyst's main tool for promoting insight is interpretation, suggesting hidden meanings to patients' accounts of their life. (SEE PAGE 69)

What is the major strength and major weakness of the experimental method?

The experimental method can prove causation, but it is limited because many variables cannot be manipulated practically or ethically in real life. (SEE PAGE 71)

Why are humanistic therapy techniques a means, not an end, in therapy?

A therapist's caring, concern, and respect for the individual are important to the success of *all* psychological treatments. (SEE PAGE 76)

Are some psychological "treatments" really hoaxes?

Desperation can lead people into being duped into trying sham treatments—and missing out on legitimate ones. (SEE PAGE 77)

In what ways are placebo effects relevant to psychotherapy process and outcome?

The placebo effect is something to study, not just control for, because placebos work psychologically. (SEE PAGE 78)

■ KEY TERMS

allegiance effect **79**
aversion therapy **72**
behaviorism **70**
cognitive behavior therapy **70**
cognitive therapy **74**
control group **71**
couples therapy **82**
dependent variable **71**
double-blind study **78**

eclectic **61**
electroconvulsive therapy (ECT) **66**
empathy **75**
experimental group **71**
experimental method **71**
family therapy **83**
free association **68**
group therapy **84**

humanistic psychotherapy **75**
hypothesis **71**
independent variable **71**
insight **68**
interpretation **68**
meta-analysis **76**
placebo effect **78**
primary prevention **84**
psychoanalysis **68**

psychodynamic psychotherapy **69**
psychopharmacology **67**
psychosurgery **66**
psychotherapy **60**
psychotropic medications **67**
random assignment **71**
rational–emotive therapy (RET) **74**

secondary prevention **85**
social skills training **73**
statistically significant **71**
systematic desensitization **72**
tertiary prevention **85**
therapeutic alliance **76**
token economy **73**
transference **69**

CLASSIFICATION AND ASSESSMENT OF ABNORMAL BEHAVIOR

Imagine that you are a therapist who has begun to interview a new patient. She tells you that she has had trouble falling asleep for the past few weeks. She has become increasingly frustrated and depressed, in part because she is always so tired when she goes to work in the morning. Your job is to figure out how to help this woman. How serious is her problem? What else do you need to know? What questions should you ask and how should you collect the information? The process of gathering this information is called **assessment.** You will want to use data from your assessment to compare her experiences with those of other patients whom you have treated (or read about). Are there any similarities that might help you know what to expect in terms of the likely origins of her problems, how long they will last, and the kinds of treatment that might be most helpful? In order to make those comparisons, you will need a kind of psychological road map to guide your search for additional information. This road map is known as a *classification system*—a list of various types of problems and their associated symptoms. This chapter will describe the classification system that has been developed to describe various forms of abnormal behavior. It will also summarize the different kinds of assessment tools that psychologists use.

OVERVIEW

One important part of the assessment process is making a diagnostic decision based on the categories in the official classification system that describes mental disorders. **Diagnosis** refers to the identification or recognition of a disorder on the basis of its characteristic symptoms. In the field of mental health, a clinician assigns a diagnosis if the person's behavior meets the specific criteria for a particular type of disorder, such as schizophrenia or major depressive disorder. This decision is important because it tells the clinician that the person's problems are similar to those that have been experienced by some other people. The diagnosis enables the clinician to refer to the base of knowledge that has accumulated with regard to the disorder. For example, it will provide clues about associated symptoms and treatments that are most likely to be effective. To formulate a comprehensive treatment plan, the clinician utilizes the person's diagnosis plus many other types of information that we will discuss in this chapter.

In some fields, diagnosis refers to *causal* analysis. If your car doesn't start, you expect that your mechanic's "diagnosis" will explain the origins of the problem. Has the battery lost its charge? Is the fuel line blocked? Is the ignition switch dead? In this situation, the "diagnosis" leads directly to the problem's solution. In the field of psychopathology, assigning a diagnosis does not mean that we understand the etiology of the person's problem (see Chapter 2). Specific etiologies have not been identified for mental disorders. Psychologists can't "look under the hood" in the same way that a mechanic can examine a car. In the case of a mental disorder, assigning a diagnostic label simply identifies the nature of the problem without implying exactly how the problem came into existence.

Our consideration of the assessment enterprise and diagnostic issues will begin with an example from our own clinical experience. In the following pages we will describe Michael, a young man who found himself thinking and acting in ways that he could not seem to control. This case study illustrates the kinds of decisions that psychologists have to make about ways to collect and interpret information used in diagnosis and assessment.

CASE **STUDY** Obsessions, Compulsions, and Other Unusual Behaviors

Michael was an only child who lived with his mother and father. He was 16 years old, a little younger than most of the other boys in the 11th grade, and he looked even younger. From an academic point of view, Michael was an average student, but he was not a typical teenager in terms of social behavior. He felt alienated from other boys, and he was extremely anxious when he talked to girls. He despised everything about school. His life at home was also unpleasant. Michael and his parents argued frequently, especially Michael and his father.

One awful incident summed up Michael's bitter feelings about school. As a sophomore, he decided to join the track team. Michael was clumsy and not athletic. When he worked out with the other long-distance runners, he soon became the brunt of their jokes. One day, a belligerent teammate forced Michael to take off his clothes and run naked to a shelter in the park. When he got there, Michael found an old pair of shorts, which he put on and wore back to the locker room. The experience was humiliating. Later that night, Michael started to worry about those shorts. Who had left them in the park? Were they dirty? Had he been exposed to some horrible disease? Michael quit the track team the next day, but he couldn't put the experience out of his mind.

In the following year, Michael became more and more consumed by anxiety. He was obsessed about "contamination," which he imagined to be spreading from his books and school clothes to the furniture and other objects in his house. When the clothes that he had worn to school rubbed against a chair or a wall at home, he felt as though that spot had become contaminated. He didn't believe this was literally true; it was more like a reminder by association. When he touched something that he had used at school, he was more likely to think of school. That triggered unpleasant thoughts and the negative emotions with which they were associated (anger, fear, sadness).

Michael tried in various ways to minimize the spread of contamination. For example, he took a shower and changed his clothes every evening at 6 o'clock immediately after he finished his homework.

After this "cleansing ritual" he was careful to avoid touching his books or dirty clothes as well as anything that they had touched.

If he bumped into one of the contaminated objects by accident, he went into the bathroom and washed his hands. Michael washed his hands 10 or 15 times in a typical evening. He paced back and forth watching television without sitting down so that he would not touch contaminated furniture.

Whenever he was not in school, Michael preferred to be alone at home, playing games on his computer. He did not enjoy sports, music, or outdoor activities. The only literature that interested him was fantasy and science fiction. *Dungeons and Dragons* was the only game that held his attention. He read extensively about the magical powers of fantastic characters and spent hours dreaming up new variations on themes described in books about this imaginary realm. When Michael talked about the *Dungeons and Dragons* characters and their adventures, his speech would sometimes become vague and difficult to follow. Other students at Michael's school shared his interest in *Dungeons and Dragons,* but he didn't want to play the game with them. Michael said he was different from the other students. He expressed contempt for other teenagers, as well as for the city in which he lived.

Michael and his parents had been working with a family therapist for more than two years. Although the level of interpersonal conflict in the family had been reduced, Michael's anxiety seemed to be getting worse. He had become even more isolated from other boys his own age and had become quite suspicious about their motives. He often felt that they were talking about him, and that they were planning to do something else in order to humiliate him.

His worries about contamination had become almost unbearable to his parents, who were deeply confused and frustrated by his behavior. They knew that he was socially isolated and extremely unhappy. They believed that he would never be able to resume a more normal pattern of development until he gave up these "silly" ideas. Michael's fears disrupted his parents' own activities in several ways. They weren't allowed to touch him or his things after being in certain rooms of the house. His peculiar movements and persistent washing were troublesome to them. Michael's father usually worked at home, and he and Michael quarreled frequently, especially when Michael ran water in the bathroom next to his father's study.

Michael and his mother had always been very close. He was quite dependent on her, and she was devoted to him. They spent a lot of time together while his father was working. His mother had begun to find it difficult to be close to Michael. He shunned physical contact. When she touched him, he sometimes cringed and withdrew. Once in a while he would shriek, reminding her that she was contaminated by her contact with chairs and other objects like his laundry. Recently, Michael had also become aloof intellectually. His mother felt that he was shutting her out, as he seemed to withdraw further into his fantasy world of *Dungeons and Dragons* and his obsessive thoughts about contamination.

After learning about Michael's problems, his worries about contamination, his efforts to avoid contamination, and his fear of being with other people, his therapist would be faced with several important decisions. One involves the level of analysis at which she should think about the problem. Is this primarily Michael's problem, or should she consider this problem in terms of all members of the family? One possibility is that Michael has a psychological disorder that is disrupting the life of his family. It may be the other way around, however. Perhaps the family system as a whole is dysfunctional, and Michael's problems are only one symptom of this dysfunction.

Another set of choices involves the type of data that his therapist will use to describe Michael's behavior. What kinds of information should be collected? The therapist can consider several sources of data. One is Michael's own report, which can be obtained in an interview or through the use of questionnaires. Another is the report of his parents. The therapist may also decide to employ psychological tests.

In conducting an assessment and arriving at a diagnosis, one question the therapist must ask is whether Michael's abnormal behavior is similar to problems that have been exhibited by other people. She would want to know if Michael's symptoms fall into a pattern that has been documented by many other mental health professionals. Rather than reinventing the wheel each time a new patient walks into her office, the therapist can use a classification system to streamline the diagnostic process. The classification system serves as a common language among therapists, giving them a form of professional "shorthand" that enables them to discuss issues with colleagues. Because different disorders sometimes respond to different forms of treatment, the distinctions can be very important. In the next section we will review the development and modification of classification systems for abnormal behavior.

BASIC ISSUES IN CLASSIFICATION

A **classification system** is used to subdivide or organize a set of objects. The objects of classification can be inanimate things, such as CDs, rocks, or books; living organisms, such as plants, insects, or primates; or abstract concepts, such as numbers, religions, or historical periods. Formal classification systems are essential for the collection and communication of knowledge in all sciences and professions.

There are many ways to subdivide any given class of objects. Classification systems can be based on different principles (Bowker & Star, 1999). Some systems are based on descriptive similarities. For example, both a diamond and a ruby may be considered jewels because they are valuable stones. Other systems are based on less obvious characteristics, such as structural similarities. A diamond and a piece of coal, for example, may belong together because they are both made of carbon.

The point is simple: Classification systems can be based on various principles, and their value will depend primarily on the purpose for which they were developed. Different classification systems are not necessarily right or wrong; they are simply more or less useful. In the following section we will consider several fundamental principles that affect all attempts to develop a useful classification or typology of human behavior.

Categories Versus Dimensions

Classification is often based on "yes or no" decisions. After a category has been defined, an object is either a member of the category or it is not. A **categorical approach to classification** assumes that distinctions among members of different categories are qualitative. In other words, the differences reflect a difference in kind (quality) rather than a difference in amount (quantity). In the classification of living organisms, for example, we usually consider species to be qualitatively distinct; they are different kinds of living organisms. Human beings are different from other primates; an organism is either human or it is not. Many medical conditions are categorical. Infection is one clear example. A person is either infected with a particular virus, or he is not. It doesn't make sense to talk about whether someone is partially infected or almost infected.

▲ Taxonomy is the science of arranging living organisms into groups. Humans and dolphins belong to the same "class" (mammals) because they share certain characteristics (are warm-blooded, nourish their young, and have body hair).

Although categorically based classification systems are often useful, they are not the only kind of system that can be used to organize information systematically. As an alternative, scientists often employ a **dimensional approach to classification**—that is, one that describes the objects of classification in terms of continuous dimensions. Rather than assuming that an object either has or does not have a particular property, it may be useful to focus on a specific characteristic and determine *how much* of that characteristic the object exhibits. This kind of system is based on an ordered sequence or on quantitative measurements rather than on qualitative judgments (Kraemer, 2008).

For example, in the case of intellectual ability, psychologists have developed sophisticated measurement procedures. Rather than asking whether or not a particular person is intelligent (a "yes or no" judgment), the psychologist sets out to determine how much intelligence the person exhibits on a particular set of tasks. This process allows scientists to record subtle distinctions that would be lost if they were forced to make all-or-none decisions.

From Description to Theory

The development of scientific classification systems typically proceeds in an orderly fashion over a period of several years. The initial stages, which focus on simple descriptions or observations, are followed by more advanced theoretical stages. At the latter point, greater emphasis is placed on scientific concepts that explain causal relationships among objects. In the study of many medical disorders, this progression begins with an emphasis on the description of specific symptoms that cluster together and follow a predictable course over time. The systematic collection of more information regarding this syndrome may then lead to the discovery of causal factors.

Clinical scientists hope that similar progress will be made in the field of psychopathology (Murphy, 2006). Mental disorders are currently classified on the basis of their descriptive features or symptoms because specific causal mechanisms have not yet been discovered. While we may eventually develop a more sophisticated, theoretically based understanding of certain disorders, this does not necessarily mean we will ever know the precise causes of disorders or that it will be possible to develop a classification system based entirely on causal explanations (Kendler, 2006). In fact, the most likely explanations for mental disorders involve complex interactions of psychological, biological, and social systems (see Chapter 2).

CLASSIFYING ABNORMAL BEHAVIOR

We need a classification system for abnormal behavior for two primary reasons. First, a classification system is useful to clinicians, who must match their clients' problems with the form of intervention that is most likely to be effective. Second, a classification system must be used in the search for new knowledge. The history of medicine is filled with examples of problems that were recognized long before they could be treated successfully. The classification of a specific set of symptoms has often laid the foundation for research that eventually identified a cure or a way of preventing the disorder.

Why do we need a system to classify abnormal behaviors?

Brief Historical Perspective

Currently, two diagnostic systems for mental disorders are widely recognized. One—the *Diagnostic and Statistical Manual* (DSM)—is published by the American Psychiatric Association. The other—the *International Classification of Diseases* (ICD)—is published by the World Health Organization. Both systems were developed shortly after World War II, and both have been revised several times. Because the American diagnostic manual is now in its fourth edition, it is called DSM-IV-TR. The "TR" stands for "text revision" and refers to the fact that some of the background material provided in the manual was updated in 2000. The World Health Organization's manual is in its tenth edition and is therefore known as ICD-10.

During the 1950s and 1960s, psychiatric classification systems were widely criticized. One major criticism focused on the lack of consistency in diagnostic decisions (Nathan & Langenbucher, 2003). Independent clinicians frequently disagreed with one another about the use of diagnostic categories as they were listed in the first two editions of the American classification system, DSM-I and DSM-II. Objections were also raised from philosophical, sociological, and political points of view. For example, some critics charged that diagnostic categories in psychiatry would be more appropriately viewed as "problems in living" than as medical disorders (Szasz, 1963). Others were concerned about self-fulfilling prophesies. In other words, once a psychiatric label had been assigned, the person so labeled might be motivated to continue behaving in ways that were expected from someone who is mentally disturbed (see Labels and Stigma on page 93). For all these reasons, many mental health professionals paid less and less attention to the formal process of diagnosis during these years.

Renewed interest in the value of psychiatric classification grew steadily during the 1970s, culminating in the publication of the third edition of the DSM in 1980. This version of the manual represented a major turning point in the history of psychiatric classification (Jablensky, 1999). The committee that produced the new manual was firmly committed to producing a classification system based on clinical description rather than on theories of psychopathology that had not been empirically validated. This principle led to an emphasis on the use of specific, detailed criterion sets for each disorder.

The revisions introduced in 1980 have been retained and strengthened in both DSM-IV-TR and ICD-10. The two manuals are very similar in most respects. Deliberate attempts were made to coordinate the production of DSM-IV-TR and ICD-10. Most of the categories listed in the manuals are identical, and the criteria for specific disorders are usually similar.

LABELS AND STIGMA

What does it mean to be labeled with a psychiatric diagnosis? Labeling theory is a perspective on mental disorders that is primarily concerned with the social context in which abnormal behavior occurs and the ways in which other people respond to this behavior. It assigns relatively little importance to specific behaviors as symptoms of a disorder that resides within the person. Labeling theory is primarily concerned with the social factors that determine whether a person will be given a psychiatric diagnosis rather than the psychological or biological reasons for the abnormal behaviors. In other words, it is concerned with events that take place after a person has behaved in an unusual way rather than with factors that might explain the original appearance of the behavior itself.

Labeling theory assumes that it is useful to think of mental disorders as being maladaptive social roles. The process of diagnostic labeling is the most important factor in establishing that role for a particular person (Scheff, 1984). The symptoms of mental disorders are viewed as violations of social expectations that most people take for granted: showing too much emotion, not showing enough emotion, or talking too much or in strange ways. A person who breaks these unwritten rules runs the risk of being labeled as mentally disturbed.

According to labeling theory, the probability that a person will receive a diagnosis is determined by several factors. These include the severity of the unusual behavior and its visibility, as well as the tolerance level of the community. The most important considerations are the social status of the person who violates social expectations and the social distance between that person and mental health professionals. People from disadvantaged groups, such as racial and sexual minorities and women, are presumably more likely to be labeled than are white males.

The merits and limitations of labeling theory have been hotly debated. The theory has inspired research on a number of important questions. Some studies have found that people from lower status groups, including racial minorities, are indeed more likely to be assigned severe diagnoses (Phelan & Link, 1999). On the other hand, it would also be an exaggeration to say that the social status of the patient is the most important factor influencing the diagnos-

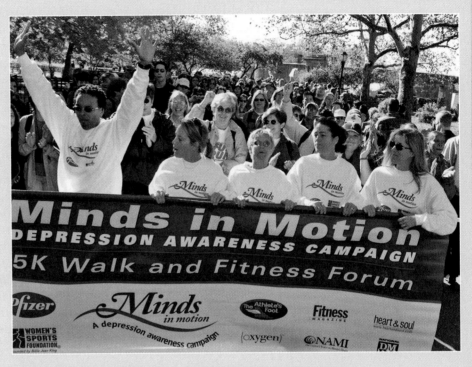

▲ Efforts to promote awareness of depression help to combat negative images of people with mental disorders.

tic process. In fact, clinicians' diagnostic decisions are determined primarily by the form and severity of the patient's symptoms rather than by such factors as gender, race, and social class (Gove, 1990; Ruscio, 2004).

> *Can diagnostic labels have a negative impact on a person's life? How do these effects compare to the positive consequences of receiving a diagnosis?*

Another focus of the debate regarding labeling theory is the issue of **stigma** and the negative effects of labeling. Stigma refers to a stamp or label that sets the person apart from others, connects the person to undesirable features, and leads others to reject the person. Labeling theory notes that negative attitudes toward mental disorders prevent patients from obtaining jobs, finding housing, and forming new relationships. Various kinds of empirical evidence support the conclusion that a psychiatric label can have a harmful impact on a person's life. Negative attitudes are

associated with many types of mental disorder, such as alcoholism, schizophrenia, and sexual disorders. When a person becomes a psychiatric patient, the person expects to be devalued and discriminated against (Couture & Penn, 2003; Kroska & Harkness, 2006). These expectations could cause the person to behave in strained and defensive ways, which may in turn lead others to reject him or her.

Labeling theory has drawn needed attention to several important problems associated with the classification of mental disorders, but it does not provide an adequate explanation for abnormal behavior. It is clearly an exaggeration to think of mental disorders as nothing more than social roles. Many factors other than the reactions of other people contribute to the development and maintenance of abnormal behavior. Furthermore, a diagnosis of mental illness can have positive consequences, such as encouraging access to effective treatment. Many patients and their family members are relieved to learn that their problems are similar to those experienced by other people and that help may be available. The effects of diagnostic labeling are not always harmful.

The DSM-IV-TR System

More than 200 specific diagnostic categories are described in DSM-IV-TR. These are arranged under 18 primary headings. A complete list appears inside the back cover of this book. Disorders that present similar kinds of symptoms are grouped together. For example, conditions that include a prominent display of anxiety are listed under "Anxiety Disorders," and conditions that involve a depressed mood are listed under "Mood Disorders."

The manual lists specific criteria for each diagnostic category. We can illustrate the ways in which these criteria are used by examining the diagnostic decisions that would be considered in Michael's case. The criteria for obsessive–compulsive disorder (OCD) are listed in Table 4–1. Michael would meet all of the criteria in "A" for both obsessions and compulsions. His repetitive hand-washing rituals were performed in response to obsessive thoughts regarding contamination. Consistent with criterion "B," Michael admitted that these concerns were irrational. He also meets criterion "C" in that these rituals were time consuming and interfered with his family's routine. His relationships with friends were severely limited because he refused to invite them to his house, fearing that they would spread contamination.

For various types of disorder, the duration of the problem is considered as well as the clinical picture. For example, criterion "C" for OCD specifies that the patient's compulsive rituals must take more than one hour each day to perform.

In addition to the inclusion criteria, symptoms that must be present, many disorders are also defined in terms of certain exclusion criteria. In other words, the diagnosis can be ruled out if certain conditions prevail. For example, in the case of OCD, the diagnosis would not be made if the symptoms occurred only during the course of another disorder, such as a person with alcoholism being preoccupied with thoughts of obtaining another drink (criterion "D").

The DSM-IV-TR employs a *multiaxial classification system;* that is, the person is rated on five separate axes. Each axis is concerned with a

---

TABLE 4–1 DSM-IV-TR Criteria for Obsessive–Compulsive Disorder

A. Either obsessions or compulsions:

Obsessions as defined by (1), (2), (3), and (4):

1. Recurrent and persistent thoughts, impulses, or images that are experienced, at some time during the disturbance, as intrusive and inappropriate, and that cause marked anxiety or distress
2. The thoughts, impulses, or images are not simply excessive worries about real-life problems
3. The person attempts to ignore or suppress thoughts, impulses, or images or to neutralize them with some other thought or action
4. The person recognizes that the obsessional thoughts, impulses, or images are a product of his or her own mind (not imposed from without as in thought insertion)

Compulsions as defined by (1) and (2):

1. Repetitive behaviors (such as hand washing, ordering, checking) or mental acts (such as praying, counting, repeating words silently) that the person feels driven to perform in response to an obsession, or according to rules that must be applied rigidly
2. The behaviors or mental acts are aimed at preventing or reducing distress or preventing some dreaded event or situation; however, these behaviors or mental acts either are not connected in a realistic way with what they are designed to neutralize or prevent, or are clearly excessive

B. At some point during the course of the disorder, the person has recognized that the obsessions or compulsions are excessive or unreasonable.

C. The obsessions or compulsions cause marked distress; are time-consuming (take more than one hour a day); or significantly interfere with the person's normal routine, occupational (or academic) functioning, or usual social activities or relationships with others.

D. If another Axis I disorder is present, the content of the obsessions or compulsions is not restricted to it (for example, preoccupation with food in the presence of an Eating Disorder; preoccupation with drugs in the presence of a Substance Use Disorder; or guilty ruminations in the presence of Major Depressive Disorder).

Source: Reprinted with permission from the *Diagnostic and Statistical Manual of Mental Disorders,* Fourth Edition, Text Revision. Copyright © 2000 by the American Psychiatric Association.

different domain of information. Two are concerned with diagnostic categories and the other three provide for the collection of additional relevant data. The rationale for this approach is that to manage individual cases, the clinician must consider several important factors besides specific symptoms. These supplementary factors include the environment in which the person is living, aspects of the person's health that might affect psychological functions, and fluctuations in the overall level of the person's adjustment.

The first two axes are concerned with clinical disorders that are defined largely in terms of symptomatic behaviors. Most diagnoses appear on Axis I, which includes conditions, such as OCD, schizophrenia, and mood disorders. Many of the diagnoses described on Axis I are characterized by episodic periods of psychological turmoil. Axis II is concerned with more stable, long-standing problems, such as personality disorders and mental retardation. The separation of disorders on Axis I and Axis II is designed to draw attention to long-standing conditions, such as a paranoid or dependent personality style, that might be overlooked in the presence of a more dramatic symptomatic picture, such as the hallucinations and delusions frequently found in schizophrenia. A person can be assigned more than one diagnosis on either Axis I or Axis II (or on both axes) if he or she meets criteria for more than one disorder.

Michael would receive a diagnosis of obsessive–compulsive disorder on Axis I. His obsessions and compulsions were, in fact, his most obvious symptoms. On Axis II, Michael would also be coded as meeting criteria for schizotypal personality disorder (see Chapter 9). This judgment depends on a consideration of his long-standing, relatively rigid patterns of interacting with other people and his inability to adjust to the changing requirements of different people and situations. For example, he was suspicious of other people's motives, he did not have any close friends in whom he could confide, and he was very anxious in social situations because he was afraid that other people might take advantage of him. These are important considerations for a therapist who wants to plan a treatment program for Michael, but they are relatively subtle considerations in comparison to the obsessions and compulsions, which were currently the primary source of conflict with his parents.

Axis III is concerned with general medical conditions that are outside the realm of psychopathology but may be relevant to either the causes of the patient's abnormal behavior or the ways in which it might be treated. Examples include thyroid conditions, which may lead to symptoms of psychosis, and diabetes in children, which is sometimes associated with conduct disorders. The presence of chronic medical conditions does predict worse outcomes for certain kinds of mental disorders, especially depression (Saavedra et al., 2001). In Michael's case, there were no known physical disorders that were relevant to his psychological problems.

Axis IV is concerned with psychosocial and environmental problems that may affect the diagnosis or treatment of a mental disorder. Michael's therapist noted the presence of three psychosocial problems: frequent arguments within the family, social isolation, and discord with classmates at school. Note that stressful circumstances may be the products as well as the causes of mental disorders. In Michael's case, for example, many of the family's arguments were precipitated by his hand-washing rituals. In deciding whether to list social stresses on Axis IV, psychologists need not determine whether the stresses primarily arose from or contributed to the condition. They are all listed if they are relevant to treatment planning, and these were all important considerations in Michael's case.

Finally, Axis V provides for a global rating of adaptive functioning. This rating is made on a scale of 1 to 100, with higher numbers representing better levels of adjustment. The scale applies to psychological, social, and occupational functioning. This information is considered useful because it draws attention to recent changes in the patient's condition and because it provides a balanced view of the patient's strengths as well as his or her weaknesses. Michael's psychologist assigned a rating of 50 for his current level of functioning. Michael was performing at an adequate level academically, but his social life was clearly impaired as a consequence of his rituals.

◀ Axis IV calls for information about life events that may have an impact on diagnosis or treatment. This 7-year-old boy is drawing a picture of his friends who were killed by a bomb in Afghanistan.

Culture and Classification

DSM-IV-TR addresses the relation between cultural issues and the diagnosis of psychopathology in two principal ways. First, the manual encourages clinicians to consider the influence of cultural factors in both the expression and recognition of symptoms of mental disorders. People express extreme emotions in ways that are shaped by the traditions of their families and other social groups to which they belong. Intense, public displays of anger or grief might be expected in one culture but considered signs of disturbance in another. Interpretations of emotional distress and other symptoms of disorder are influenced by the explanations that a person's culture assigns to such experiences. Religious beliefs, social roles, and sexual identities all play an important part in constructing meanings that are assigned to these phenomena (Hwang et al., 2008). The accuracy and utility of a clinical diagnosis depend on more than a simple count of the symptoms that appear to be present. They also hinge on the clinician's ability to consider the cultural context in which the problem appeared. This is a particularly challenging task when the clinician and the person with the problem do not share the same cultural background.

The diagnostic manual attempts to sensitize clinicians to cultural issues by including a glossary of **culture-bound syndromes.** These are patterns of erratic or unusual thinking and behavior that have been identified in diverse societies around the world and do not fit easily into the other diagnostic categories that are listed in the main body of DSM-IV-TR. They are called "culture-bound" because they are considered to be unique to particular societies, particularly in non-Western or developing countries. Their appearance is easily recognized and understood to be a form of abnormal behavior by members of certain cultures, but they do not conform to typical patterns of mental disorder seen in the United States or Europe. Culture-bound syndromes have also been called *idioms of distress.* In other words, they represent a manner of expressing negative emotion that is unique to a particular culture and cannot be easily translated or understood in terms of its individual parts.

One syndrome of this type is a phenomenon known as *ataques de nervios,* which has been observed most extensively among people from Puerto Rico and other Caribbean countries (Guarnaccia, 1996; San Miguel et al., 2006). Descriptions of this experience include four dimensions, in which the essential theme is loss of control—an inability to interrupt the dramatic sequence of emotion and behavior. These dimensions include emotional expressions (an explosion of screaming and crying, coupled with overwhelming feelings of anxiety, depression, and anger), bodily sensations (including trembling, heart palpitations, weakness, fatigue, headache, and convulsions), actions and behaviors (dramatic, forceful gestures that include aggression toward others, suicidal thoughts or gestures, and trouble eating or sleeping), and alterations in consciousness (marked feelings of "not being one's usual self," accompanied by fainting, loss of consciousness, dizziness, and feelings of being outside of one's body).

The frequency and duration of *ataques de nervios* vary from one person to the next. An episode typically lasts less than an hour, but some last more than a day. When the *ataque* is over, the person may be unable to remember what occurred. The person usually returns quickly to his or her previous level of functioning, often feeling better or relieved.

Ataques are typically provoked by situations that disrupt or threaten the person's social world, especially the family. Many *ataques* occur shortly after the person learns unexpectedly that a close family member has died. Others result from an imminent divorce or after a serious conflict with a child. Women are primarily responsible for maintaining the integrity of the family in this culture, and they are also more likely than men to experience *ataques de nervios.* Puerto Rican women from poor and working-class families define themselves largely in terms of their success in building and maintaining a cohesive family life. When this social role is threatened, an *ataque* may result. This response to threat or conflict—an outburst of powerful, uncontrolled negative emotion—expresses suffering while simultaneously providing a means for coping with the threat. It serves to signal the woman's distress to important other people and to rally needed sources of social support.

What is the relation between culture-bound syndromes and the formal categories listed in DSM-IV-TR? The answer is unclear and also varies from one syndrome to the next. Are they similar problems that are simply given different names in other cultures? Probably not, at least not in most instances (Guarnaccia & Pincay, 2008). In some cases, people who exhibit behavior that would fit the definition of a culture-bound syndrome would also qualify for a DSM-IV-TR diagnosis, if they were diagnosed by a clinician trained in the use of that manual. But everyone who displays the culture-bound syndrome would not meet criteria for a DSM-IV-TR disorder, and of those who do, not all would receive the same DSM-IV-TR diagnosis.

The glossary on culture-bound syndromes has been praised as a significant advance toward integrating cultural considerations into the classification system (Lopez & Guarnaccia, 2000). It has also been criticized for its ambiguity. The most difficult conceptual issue involves the boundary between culture-bound syndromes and categories found elsewhere in the diagnostic manual. Some critics have argued that they should be fully integrated, without trying to establish a distinction (Hughes, 1998). Others have noted that if culturally unique disorders must be listed separately from other, "mainstream" conditions, then certain disorders now listed in the main body of the manual—especially eating disorders, such as bulimia—should actually be listed as culture-bound syndromes. Like *ataques de nervios,* bulimia nervosa is a condition that is found primarily among a limited number of cultures (Keel & Klump, 2003). The difference is that bulimia is found in *our* culture—people living in Western or developed countries—rather than in other cultures. Dissociative amnesia—the inability to recall important personal information regarding a traumatic event—also resembles culture-bound syndromes because it appears to be experienced only by people living in modern, developed cultures (Pope et al., 2007).

Thinking about this distinction helps to place the more familiar diagnostic categories in perspective and shows how our own culture has shaped our views of abnormal behavior. We must not be misled into thinking that culture shapes only conditions that appear to be exotic in faraway lands; culture shapes various facets of all disorders. Though it is imperfect, the glossary of culture-bound syndromes does serve to make clinicians more aware of the extent to which their own views of what is normal and abnormal have been shaped by the values and experiences of their own culture (Mezzich et al., 2001).

EVALUATING CLASSIFICATION SYSTEMS

The *Diagnostic and Statistical Manual* is an evolving document produced by the American Psychiatric Association. DSM-IV was pub-lished in 1994, and discussions regarding the next edition began in 1999. *DSM-V* is currently scheduled to appear in 2012. Information about progress on this revision process and the people who are guiding it can be obtained on a Web site for DSM-V (www. psych.org/dsmv.asp). Decisions about changes in the diagnostic manual will be made by a task force that is composed of 28 experts on the classification and diagnosis of mental disorders. Several work groups were appointed and each will examine one of the major diagnostic categories, such as anxiety disorders, mood disorders, psychotic disorders, and so on. The work groups will make recommendations to the task force on the basis of reviews of the existing literature and analyses of extensive issue-focused field trials. It seems likely that DSM-V will include a number of important changes, but it is too early to know exactly what form they will take. The important thing to understand is that the official classification system for mental disorders is revised on a regular basis and that the process is guided by research evidence.

How can we evaluate a system like DSM-IV-TR? Is it a useful classification system? Utility can be measured in terms of two principal criteria: reliability and validity.

Reliability

Reliability refers to the consistency of measurements, including diagnostic decisions. If a diagnostic category is to be useful, it will have to be

How is bulimia nervosa similar to culture-bound syndromes?

▼ Just as judges sometimes disagree in their assessment of evidence presented during a trial, psychologists and psychiatrists do not always agree on how various disorders should be diagnosed. Of course, both judges and mental health professionals attempt to be reliable (consistent) in their judgments.

used consistently. One important form of reliability, known as interrater reliability, refers to agreement among clinicians. Suppose, for example, that two psychologists interview the same patient and that each psychologist independently assigns a diagnosis using DSM-IV-TR. If both psychologists decide that the patient fits the criteria for a major depressive disorder, they have used the def-

inition of that category consistently. Of course, one or two cases would not provide a sufficient test of the reliability of a diagnostic category. The real question is whether the clinicians would agree with each other over a large series of patients. The process of collecting and interpreting information regarding the reliability of diagnosing mental disorders is discussed in Research Methods.

RESEARCH METHODS

Reliability:
Agreement Regarding Diagnostic Decisions

Several formal procedures have been developed to evaluate diagnostic reliability. Most studies of psychiatric diagnosis in the past 40 years have employed a measure known as kappa. Instead of measuring the simple proportion of agreement between clinicians, kappa indicates the proportion of agreement that occurred above and beyond that which would have occurred by chance. Negative values of kappa indicate that the rate of agreement was less than that which would have been expected by chance in this particular sample of people. Thus kappa of zero indicates chance agreement, and a kappa of 1.0 indicates perfect agreement between raters.

How should we interpret the kappa statistic? There is no easy answer to this question (Kirk & Kutchins, 1992). It would be unrealistic to expect perfect consistency, especially in view of the relatively modest reliability of some other types of diagnostic decisions that are made in medical practice (Garb et al., 2002; Meyer et al., 2001). On the other hand, it isn't very encouraging simply to find that the level of agreement among clinicians is somewhat better than chance. We expect more than that from a diagnostic system, especially when it is used as a basis for treatment decisions. One convention suggests that kappa values of .70 or higher indicate relatively good agreement. Values of kappa below .40 are often interpreted as indicating poor agreement.

The reliability of many diagnostic categories has improved since the publication of DSM-III, in part, because of more detailed diagnostic criteria for specific disorders. Still, most studies also indicate that there is considerable room for improvement. The reliability of some diagnostic categories remains well below acceptable standards. Consider, for example, evidence from field trials that were conducted by

the World Health Organization when ICD-10 was being prepared (Sartorius et al., 1993). Data were collected at more than 100 clinical centers in 39 countries around the world. Each person was interviewed separately by two clinicians who independently arrived at a diagnosis. Kappa values for several of the diagnostic categories are presented in Table 4–2.

> ### Are psychiatric diagnoses made consistently by different clinicians?

The reliability data in Table 4–2 are organized according to major headings (such as anxiety disorders), which are then subdivided into more specific forms (such as obsessive–compulsive disorder). Note that kappa values for major headings are, in most cases, higher than those for specific subtypes. This pattern indicates that clinicians are more likely to agree on the general category into which an individual's problems fall than they are on the specific nature of those problems. To understand this process, imagine that you and a friend try to identify types of automobiles as they pass on the street. You might find it relatively easy to agree that a particular vehicle is a minivan, but you might have more trouble deciding whether it is the specific type of minivan made by Chrysler, Ford, or Toyota.

On the standard of .70 or higher, good agreement was found for many specific categories, especially obsessive–compulsive disorder, bipolar mood disorder, and paranoid schizophrenia. For some other categories, such as phobic disorder and depressive episode, diagnostic reliability was acceptable, while clearly leaving room for improvement. Reliability for generalized anxiety disorder was only fair, and the reliability for diagnosing personality disor-

TABLE 4–2	Reliability for Diagnoses of Several Types of Mental Disorder
DISORDER	**KAPPA**
SCHIZOPHRENIC DISORDERS	**.82**
Paranoid schizophrenia	.73
Catatonic schizophrenia	.39
Hebephrenic schizophrenia	.43
ANXIETY DISORDERS	**.74**
Phobic disorder	.63
Obsessive–compulsive disorder	.81
Generalized anxiety disorder	.48
MOOD DISORDERS	**.77**
Manic episode	.69
Depressive episode	.66
Bipolar mood disorder	.81
PERSONALITY DISORDERS	**.47**
Schizotypal*	.37
Histrionic	.12
Dependent	.33
SUBSTANCE USE DISORDERS	**.80**
Alcohol dependence	.70
Opioid dependence	.77

*In ICD-10, schizotypal disorder is grouped with Schizophrenic Disorders rather than with Personality Disorders. We list it here for consistency with DSM-IV.

Source: Based on the World Health Organization's field trial for ICD-10 (see Sartorius et al., 1993).

ders was very low. This evidence suggests that we should not accept uncritically the assumption that the diagnostic categories in DSM-IV-TR and ICD-10 are always used reliably (Kirk & Kutchins, 1992).

Validity

The most important issue in the evaluation of a diagnostic category is whether it is *useful* (Kendell & Jablensky, 2003). By knowing that a person fits into a particular group or class, do we learn anything meaningful about that person? For example, if a person fits the diagnostic criteria for schizophrenia, is that person likely to improve when he or she is given antipsychotic medication? Or is that person likely to have a less satisfactory level of social adjustment in five years than a person who meets diagnostic criteria for bipolar mood disorder? Does the diagnosis tell us anything about the factors or circumstances that might have contributed to the onset of this problem? These questions are concerned with the validity of the diagnostic category. The term **validity** refers to the meaning or importance of a measurement—in this case, a diagnostic decision (Rounsaville et al., 2002). Importance is not an all-or-none phenomenon; it is a quantitative issue. Diagnostic categories are more or less useful, and their validity (or utility) can be determined in several ways.

Validity is, in a sense, a reflection of the success that has been achieved in understanding the nature of a disorder. Have important facts been discovered? Systematic studies aimed at establishing the validity of a disorder may proceed in a sequence of phases (Robins & Guze, 1989), such as those listed in Table 4–3. After a clinical description has been established, diagnostic categories are refined and validated through this process of scientific exploration. It should be emphasized, however, that the sequence listed in Table 4–3 represents an ideal scenario. Relatively few, if any, of the disorders listed in DSM-IV-TR are supported by an extensive set of research evidence supporting all these points. Clinical scientists have not identified "points of rarity" between related syndromes (McGuffin & Farmer, 2005). For most disorders, the evidence regarding long-term outcome and treatment response varies considerably from one person to the next. You should not assume that the types of studies listed in Table 4–3 have all provided unequivocal support for the validity of the disorders listed in DSM-IV-TR.

It may be helpful to think of different forms of validity in terms of their relationship in time with the appearance of symptoms of the disorder. *Etiological validity* is concerned with factors that contribute to the onset of the disorder. These are things that have happened in the past. Was the disorder regularly triggered by a specific set of events or circumstances? Did it run in families? The ultimate question with regard to etiological validity is whether there are any specific causal factors that are regularly, and perhaps uniquely, associated with this disorder. If we know that a person exhibits the symptoms of the disorder, do we in turn learn anything about the circumstances that originally led to the onset of the problem?

Concurrent validity is concerned with the present time and with correlations between the disorder and other symptoms, circumstances, and test procedures. Is the disorder currently associated with any other types of behavior, such as performance on psychological tests? Do precise measures of biological variables, such as brain structure and function, distinguish reliably between people who have the disorder and those who do not? Clinical studies that are aimed at developing a more precise description of a disorder also fall into this type of validity.

Predictive validity is concerned with the future and with the stability of the problem over time. Will it be persistent? If it is short lived, how long will an episode last? Will the disorder have a predictable outcome? Do people with this problem typically improve if they are given a specific type of medication or a particular form of psychotherapy? The overall validity of a diagnostic category depends on the body of evidence that accumulates as scientists seek answers to these questions.

What is the difference between reliability and validity?

TABLE 4–3 Types of Studies Used to Validate Clinical Syndromes

Identification and description of the syndrome, either by clinical intuition or by statistical analyses.

Demonstration of boundaries or "points of rarity" between related syndromes.

Follow-up studies establishing a distinctive course or outcome.

Therapeutic trials establishing a distinctive treatment response.

Family studies establishing that the syndrome "breeds true."

Demonstration of association with some more fundamental abnormality—psychological, biochemical, or molecular.

Source: Adapted from R. E. Kendell, 1989, "Clinical Validity," *Psychological Medicine, 19,* 47.

The list of categories included in DSM-IV-TR is based on the results of research studies as well as clinical experience. Some disorders are based on a much more extensive foundation of evidence than others. Each time the manual is revised, new categories are added and old categories are dropped, presumably because they are not sufficiently useful. Up to the present time, clinicians have been more willing to include new categories than to drop old ones. It is difficult to know when we would decide that a particular diagnostic category is not valid. At what point in the accumulation of knowledge are clinical scientists willing to conclude that a category is of no use and to recommend that the search for more information should be abandoned? This is a difficult question that the authors of DSM-V will need to confront. The situation regarding validity and psychiatric diagnosis is an evolving process, with more evidence being added on a regular basis.

Unresolved Questions

Several important issues are being addressed as systematic information is collected about the diagnostic categories in DSM-IV-TR. As we saw in Chapter 1, one fundamental question that applies to every disorder involves the boundary between normal and abnormal behavior. The definitions that are included in the present version of the manual are often vague with regard to this threshold (Widiger & Clark, 2000). Many definitions rely on the requirement that a particular set of symptoms causes "clinically significant distress or impairment in social or occupational functioning." Unfortunately, these concepts are not defined specifically. Mental health professionals must rely on their own subjective judgment to decide how distressed or how impaired a person must be by his or her symptoms in order to qualify for a diagnosis. These concepts are not defined in the manual, and measurement tools are not provided.

Cutoff points for the number of features that are required for a diagnosis also affect the boundary between normal and abnormal behavior. The cutoffs listed in DSM-IV-TR were often chosen with little empirical justification. Future research should determine optimal thresholds for each disorder. For example, in the case of schizotypal personality disorder, the disorder is defined in terms of a set of nine typical symptoms, such as "odd thinking and speech," "suspiciousness or paranoid ideation," and "excessive social anxiety." The present cutoff point holds that the person must exhibit five out of the nine features in order to pass the diagnostic threshold. But are any of the features unnecessary or redundant? In that case, the list could be shortened to eight criteria. Should one or more of the features be given special weight? Are they all equally important? These questions will have to be answered by investigators who explore the validity of each individual diagnostic category.

Specific time periods are also used in the definition of various disorders. The length of time is often based on a relatively arbitrary choice. For example, in the case of schizophrenia, DSM-IV-TR requires that the person exhibit symptoms for at least six months before the diagnosis can be made. An episode of major depression must last at least two weeks. A panic attack must develop abruptly and reach its peak within 10 minutes. The usefulness of these boundaries for the duration of symptoms and disorders is an important topic for future empirical studies.

Problems and Limitations of the DSM-IV-TR System

Although DSM-IV-TR is a clear improvement over earlier versions of APA's classification system, the manual has been criticized extensively, often with good reason (Houts, 2002). Some clinicians have emphasized conceptual issues. They argue that the syndromes defined in DSM-IV-TR may not represent the most useful ways to think about psychological problems, either in terms of planning current treatments or in terms of designing programs of research. Widespread acceptance of DSM-IV-TR may hinder the consideration of promising alternative classification systems. For example, it might be better to focus on individual symptoms rather than on groups of symptoms.

These critics pose such questions as, Should we design treatments for people who exhibit distorted, negative ways of thinking about themselves, regardless of whether their symptoms happen to involve a mixture of depression, anxiety, or some other pattern of negative emotion or interpersonal conflict? The answer is, We don't know. It would certainly be premature to cut off consideration of these alternatives just because they address problems in a way that deviates from the official diagnostic manual. In our current state of uncertainty, diversity of opinion should be encouraged, particularly if it is grounded in cautious skepticism and supported by rigorous scientific inquiry (Horwitz, 2002).

From an empirical point of view, DSM-IV-TR is hampered by a number of problems that suggest that it does not classify clinical problems into syndromes in the simplest and most beneficial way (Kendell, 2002; Widiger & Clark, 2000). One of the thorniest issues involves **comorbidity,** which is defined as the simultaneous appearance of two or more disorders in the same person. Comorbidity rates are very high for mental disorders as they are defined in the DSM system. For example, in the National Comorbidity Survey, among those people who qualified for at least one diagnosis at some point during their lifetime, 56 percent met the criteria for two or more disorders (Kessler, 1995). A small subgroup, 14 percent of the sample, actually met the diagnostic criteria for three or more lifetime disorders. That group of people accounted for almost 90 percent of the severe disorders in the study.

There are several ways to interpret comorbidity (Krueger, 2002). Some people may independently develop two separate conditions. In other cases, the presence of one disorder may lead to the onset of another. Unsuccessful attempts to struggle with prolonged alcohol dependence, for example, might lead a person to become depressed. Neither of these alternatives creates conceptual problems for DSMIV-TR. Unfortunately, the very high rate of comorbidity suggests that these explanations account for a small proportion of overlap between categories.

The real problem associated with comorbidity arises when a person with a mixed pattern of symptoms, usually of a severe nature, simultaneously meets the criteria for more than one disorder. Consider, for example, a client who was treated by one of the authors of this text. This man experienced a large number of diffuse problems associated with anxiety, depression, and interpersonal difficulties. According to the DSM-IV-TR system, he would have met the criteria for major depressive disorder, generalized anxiety disorder, and obsessive–compulsive disorder, as well as three types of personality disorder listed on Axis II. It might be said, therefore, that he suffered from at least six types of mental disorder. But is that really helpful? Is it the best way to think about his problems? Would it be more accurate to say that he had a complicated set of interrelated problems

that were associated with worrying, rumination, and the regulation of high levels of negative emotion, and that these problems constituted one complex and severe type of disorder?

The comorbidity issue is related to another limitation of DSM-IV-TR: the failure to make better use of information regarding the course of mental disorders over time. More than 100 years ago, when schizophrenia and bipolar mood disorder were originally described, the distinction between them was based heavily on observations regarding their long-term course. Unfortunately, most disorders listed in DSM-IV-TR are defined largely in terms of snapshots of symptoms at particular points in time. Diagnostic decisions are seldom based on a comprehensive analysis of the way that a person's problems evolve over time. If someone meets the criteria for more than one disorder, does it matter which one came first? Is there a predictable pattern in which certain disorders follow the onset of others? What is the nature of the connection between childhood disorders and adult problems? Our knowledge of mental disorders would be greatly enriched if greater emphasis were placed on questions regarding lifespan development (Buka & Gilman, 2002).

These issues must be considered by clinicians when they use the DSM-IV-TR system. Attempts to provide solutions to these problems and limitations will ensure that the classification system will continue to be revised. As before, these changes will be driven by the interaction of clinical experience and empirical evidence.

How could the DSM-IV-TR system be improved?

▼ The manifestations of mental disorders may change over the life span. In his later life, Uncle Junior (in *The Sopranos*) showed many features of antisocial personality disorder, but they focused more on deceit and lack of empathy than on violence and aggression.

BASIC ISSUES IN ASSESSMENT

Up to this point, we have discussed the development and use of classification systems. But we haven't talked about the way in which a psychologist might collect the information that is necessary to arrive at a diagnostic decision. Furthermore, we have looked at the problem only in relatively general terms. The diagnostic decision is one useful piece of information. It is not, however, a systematic picture of the specific person's situation. It is only a starting point. In the following section we extend our discussion to consider methods of collecting information. In so doing, we discuss a broad range of data that may be useful in understanding psychopathological behavior.

Purposes of Clinical Assessment

To appreciate the importance and complexity of assessment procedures, let's go back to the example of Michael. When Michael and his parents initially approached the psychologist, they were clearly upset. But the nature of the problem, in terms of Michael's behavior and the family as a whole, was not clearly defined. Before he could attempt to help this family, the psychologist had to collect more information. He needed to know more about the range and frequency of Michael's obsessions and compulsions, including when they began, how often he experienced these problems, and the factors that made them better or worse. He also needed to know whether there

▶ Diagnostic interviews provide an opportunity to make detailed inquiries about a person's subjective experience while also observing his or her behavior.

were other problems, such as depression or delusional beliefs, that might either explain these responses or interfere with their treatment. In addition, he had to learn how Michael got along with classmates, how he was doing in school, and how his parents responded when he behaved strangely. Was his behavior, at least in part, a response to environmental circumstances? How would the family support (or interfere with) the therapist's attempts to help him change? The psychologist needed to address Michael's current situation in terms of several different facets of his behavior.

Psychological assessment is the process of collecting and interpreting information that will be used to understand another person. Numerous data-gathering techniques can be used in this process. Several of these procedures are described in the following pages. We must remember, however, not to confuse the process of assessment with this list of techniques. Assessment procedures are tools that can be used in many ways. They cannot be used in an intellectual vacuum. The person who conducts the assessment must adopt a theoretical perspective regarding the nature of the disorders that are being considered and the causal processes that are involved in their origins (see Chapter 2). Interviews can be used to collect all sorts of information for all sorts of reasons. Psychological tests can be interpreted in many different ways. The value of assessment procedures can be determined only in the context of a specific purpose (McFall, 2005).

Assessment procedures can be used for several purposes. Perhaps most obvious is the need to describe the nature of the person's principal problem. This goal typically involves making a diagnosis. The clinician must collect information to support the diagnostic decision and to rule out alternative explanations for the symptoms. Assessment procedures are also used for making predictions, planning treatments, and evaluating treatments. The practical importance of predictions should be obvious: Many crucial decisions are based on psychologists' attempts to determine the probability of future events. Will a person engage in violent behavior? Can a person make rational decisions? Is a parent able to care for his or her children? Assessment is also commonly used to evaluate the likelihood that a particular form of treatment will be helpful for a specific patient and to provide guideposts by which the effectiveness of treatment programs

▲ Every assessment device has its own strengths and weaknesses. Each presents a somewhat different perspective on the person.

can be measured. Different assessment procedures are likely to be employed for different purposes. Those that are useful in one situation may not be helpful in another.

Assumptions About Consistency of Behavior

Assessment involves the collection of specific samples of a person's behavior. These samples may include things that the person says during an interview, responses that the person makes on a psychological test, or things that the person does while being observed. None of these would be important if we assumed that they were isolated events. They are useful to the extent that they represent examples of the ways in which the person will feel or behave in other situations. Psychologists, therefore, must be concerned about the consistency of behavior across time and situations. They want to know if they can *generalize,* or draw inferences about the person's behavior in the natural environment on the basis of the samples of behavior that are obtained in their assess-

ment. If the client is depressed at this moment, how did she feel one week ago, and how will she feel tomorrow? In other words, is this a persistent phenomenon, or is it a temporary state? If a child is anxious and unable to pay attention in the psychologist's office, will he also exhibit these problems in his classroom? And how will he behave on the playground?

Psychologists typically seek out more than one source of information when conducting a formal assessment. Because we are trying to compose a broad, integrated picture of the person's adjustment, we must collect information from several sources and then attempt to integrate these data. Each piece of information may be considered to be one sample of the person's behavior. One way of evaluating the possible meaning or importance of this information is to consider the consistency across sources. Do the conclusions drawn on the basis of a diagnostic interview agree with those that are suggested by a psychological test? Do the psychologist's observations of the client's behavior and the client's self-report agree with observations that are reported by parents or teachers?

Evaluating the Usefulness of Assessment Procedures

The same criteria that are used to evaluate diagnostic categories are used to evaluate the usefulness of assessment procedures: reliability and validity. We have already discussed interrater reliability with regard to diagnostic decisions. In the case of assessment procedures, reliability can refer to various types of consistency. For example, the consistency of measurements over time is known as test–retest reliability. Will a person receive the same score if an assessment procedure is repeated at two different points in time? The internal consistency of items within a test is known as split-half reliability. If a test with many items measures a specific trait or ability, and if the items are divided in half, will the person's scores on the two halves agree with each other? Assessment procedures must be reliable if they are to be useful in either clinical practice or research.

The validity of an assessment procedure refers to its meaning or importance (Meyer et al., 2001). Is the person's score on this test or procedure actually a reflection of the trait or ability that the test was designed to measure? And does the score tell us anything useful about the person's behavior in other situations? Knowing that the person has achieved a particular score on this evaluation, can we make meaningful predictions about the person's responses to other tests, or about his or her behavior in future situations? These are all questions about the validity of an assessment procedure. In general, the more consistent the information provided by different assessment procedures, the more valid each procedure is considered to be (see Critical Thinking Matters).

Cultural differences present an important challenge to the validity of assessment procedures. It is often difficult to understand the thoughts and behaviors of people from a cultural background that is different from our own. Measurement procedures that were constructed for one group may be misleading when they are applied to people from another culture. Language, religion, gender roles, beliefs about health and illness, and attitudes toward the family can all have an important impact on the ways in which psychological problems are experienced and expressed. These factors must be taken into consideration when psychologists collect information about the nature of a specific person's problems. Interviews, observational procedures, and personality tests must be carefully evaluated for cross-cultural validity (Padilla, 2001). Unfortunately, this issue has often been overlooked in treatment planning and in psychopathology research. We should not assume that a questionnaire developed in one culture will necessarily be useful in another. Investigators must demonstrate empirically that it measures the same thing in both groups.

PSYCHOLOGICAL ASSESSMENT PROCEDURES

Our purpose in the rest of this chapter is to outline a range of assessment procedures. This is a selective sampling of measures rather than an exhaustive review. We begin our discussion with psychological assessment procedures, ranging from interviews to various kinds of psychological tests. The last section of this chapter is concerned with biological assessment procedures that tap neurological and biochemical events that are associated with mental disorders.

"Person variables" are typically the first things that come to mind when we think about the assessment of psychopathology. What did the person do or say? How does the person feel about his or her current situation? What skills and abilities does the person possess, and are there any important cognitive or social deficits that should be taken into consideration? These questions about the individual person can be addressed through a number of procedures, including interviews, observations, and various types of self-report instruments and psychological tests.

Interviews

Often, the best way to find out about someone is to talk with that person directly. The clinical interview is the most commonly used procedure in psychological assessment. Most of the categories that are defined in DSM-IV-TR are based on information that can be collected in an interview. These data are typically supplemented by information that is obtained from official records (previous hospital admissions, school reports, court files) and interviews with other informants (for example, family members), but the clients' own direct descriptions of their problems are the primary basis for diagnostic decisions. Except for mental retardation, none of the diagnostic categories in DSM-IV-TR is defined in terms of psychological or biological tests.

CRITICAL THINKING MATTERS

The Barnum Effect and Assessment Feedback

Lots of people believe that psychologists can read minds. Unfortunately, assessment procedures used by psychologists do not provide a magic window into the psyche. Many procedures have been developed to collect information about human behavior and clinical problems. Each has its own strengths and weaknesses. None is infallible.

If psychologists do make errors, why do people often accept the results of their assessments uncritically? In a classic essay, Paul Meehl (1973) described a problem that he called the *Barnum Effect,* after P. T. Barnum, the brilliant and shameless promoter who founded the circus called "The Greatest Show on Earth." The Barnum effect refers to the practice of saying things about a specific person that are true of virtually all people. For example, imagine that the psychologist working with Michael had conducted a formal psychological assessment and concluded that Michael had ambivalent feelings about his parents, that he was sometimes lacking in self-confidence, or that his ex-

pectations were sometimes unrealistic. People often accept such vague or superficial statements as being meaningful comments about themselves, failing to understand that vague generalizations like these apply to almost everyone. Clearly, psychological assessment should be held to a higher standard. Diagnostic decisions and clinical judgments should contain meaningful, specific information.

Should we always trust clinical judgments?

What can we do to improve the validity of psychological assessments? One important step is to recognize their fallibility. Like everyone else, clinical psychologists are prone to a variety of cognitive biases and errors in decision making (Garb, 2005). Under conditions of uncertainty, they use mental shortcuts to make clinical judgments. For example, they pay too much attention to information that confirms

their initial impressions, and they tend to ignore information that is inconsistent with these impressions. They can be unduly influenced by vivid, individual cases that come readily to mind and sometimes fail to consider more important evidence based on data from large samples. The impact of these cognitive biases might be minimized if clinicians would deliberately consider alternative hypotheses (such as a diagnosis other than their first impression) and then consider evidence that would either support or disconfirm that possibility.

If you think about it for a moment, you probably will realize that these are common errors in human thinking, not just in assessments made by psychologists. As you study abnormal psychology, you probably pay more attention to information that is consistent with your own ideas and are overly influenced by dramatic case studies. Critical thinking—careful, objective reasoning and evaluation—is the best safeguard against these tendencies for you and for professional psychologists.

Interviews provide an opportunity to ask people for their own descriptions of their problems. Many of the symptoms of psychopathology are subjective, and an interview can provide a detailed analysis of these problems. Consider, for example, Michael's problems with anxiety. The unrelenting fear and revulsion that he experienced at school were the central feature of his problem. His obsessive thoughts of contamination were private events that could only be known to the psychologist on the basis of Michael's self-report, which was quite compelling. His family could observe Michael's peculiar habits with regard to arranging his schoolbooks, changing his clothes, and washing his hands, but the significance of these behaviors to Michael was not immediately apparent without the knowledge that they were based on an attempt to control or neutralize his anxiety-provoking images of taunting classmates.

Interviews also allow clinicians to observe important features of a person's appearance and nonverbal behavior. In Michael's case, the psychologist noticed during the initial interview that the skin on Michael's hands and lower arms was red and chafed from excessive scrubbing. He was neatly

dressed but seemed especially self-conscious about his hair and glasses, which he adjusted repeatedly. Michael was reluctant to make eye contact, and his speech was soft and hesitant. His obvious discomfort in this social situation was consistent with his own descriptions of the anxiety that he felt during interactions with peers. It was also interesting to note that Michael became visibly agitated when discussing particular subjects, such as the incident with his track team. At these points in the interview, he would fidget restlessly in his seat and clasp his arms closely around his sides. His speech became more rapid, and he began to stutter a bit. On one occasion, he found it impossible to sit still, and he began to pace quickly back and forth across the psychologist's office. These nonverbal aspects of Michael's behavior provided useful information about the nature of his distress.

my psych lab VIDEO CASE

DEPRESSION/DELIBERATE SELF HARM

SARAH

"I would be asked later 'well how did these cuts get here' and I would know that I had done it, but I wouldn't remember how I had done it or with what."

Watch the video "Depression/Deliberate Self Harm: Sarah" on MyPsychLab. Notice how the interviewer uses a flexible sequence of questions to elicit a compelling description of the subjective experiences associated with Sarah's cutting behavior.

Structured Interviews Assessment interviews vary with regard to the amount of structure that is imposed by the clinician. Some are relatively open ended, or nondirective. In this type of interview, the clinician follows the train of thought supplied by the client. One goal of nondirective interviews is to help people clarify their subjective feelings and to provide general empathic support for whatever they may decide to do about their problems. In contrast to this open-ended style, some interviews follow a more specific question-and-answer format. Structured interviews, in which the clinician must ask each patient a specific list of detailed questions, are frequently employed for collecting information that will be used to make diagnostic decisions and to rate the extent to which a person is impaired by psychopathology.

Several different structured interviews have been developed for the purpose of making psychiatric diagnoses in large-scale epidemiological and cross-national studies (Segal, 1997). Investiga-

tors reasoned that the reliability of their diagnostic decisions would improve if they could ensure that clinicians always made a consistent effort to ask the same questions when they interviewed patients. Other forms of structured diagnostic interviews have been designed for use in the diagnosis of specific types of problems, such as personality disorders, anxiety disorders, dissociative disorders, and the behavior problems of children.

Structured interviews list a series of specific questions that lead to a detailed description of the person's behavior and experiences. As an example, consider the Structured Interview for DSM-IV-TR Personality Disorders (SIDP-IV; Pfohl, Blum, & Zimmerman, 1995), which could have been used as part of the assessment process in Michael's situation. The SIDP is a widely adopted semistructured interview that covers all of the DSM-IV-TR personality disorder categories. Selected questions from the SIDP-IV are presented in Table 4–4. We have included in this table some

---

TABLE 4–4 Sample Interview Questions for the Assessment of Schizotypal Personality Disorder

SOCIAL RELATIONSHIPS

This set of questions concerns the way you think and act in situations that involve other people. Remember that I'm interested in the way you are when you are your usual self.

DSM Diagnostic Criterion: Excessive social anxiety that does not diminish with familiarity and tends to be associated with paranoid fears rather than negative judgments about self.

> Question: "Do you generally feel nervous or anxious around people?"
> (IF YES, ask follow-up questions): "How bad does it get?" "Do you get nervous around people because you worry about what they might be up to?" "Are you less nervous after you get to know people better?"

PERCEPTION OF OTHERS

The questions in this section ask about experiences you may have had with other people.

DSM Diagnostic Criterion: Suspects, without sufficient basis, that others are exploiting, harming, or deceiving him or her

> Question: "Have you had experiences where people who pretended to be your friends took advantage of you?"
> (IF YES, follow-up questions): "What happened?" "How often has this happened?"
> Question: "Are you good at spotting someone who is trying to deceive or con you?"
> (IF YES, follow-up questions): "Can you give me some examples?"

DSM Diagnostic Criterion: Ideas of reference (the belief that irrelevant or harmless events refer to the person directly or have special personal significance for him or her)

> Question: "Have you ever found that people around you seem to be talking in general, but then you realize their comments are really meant for you?"
> (IF YES, follow-up question): "How do you know they're talking about you?"
> Question: "Have you felt like someone in charge changed the rules specifically because of you, but they wouldn't admit it?"
> Question: "Do you sometimes feel like strangers on the street are looking at you and talking about you?"
> (IF YES, follow-up question): "Why do you think they notice you in particular?"

Source: Reprinted with permission from the *Structured Interview for DSM-IV Personality* (SIDP-IV) by Bruce Pfohl, Nancee Blum, and Mark Zimmerman (1997), Washington, D.C.: American Psychiatric Press.

of the questions that are specifically relevant to a diagnosis of schizotypal personality disorder.

Structured interview schedules provide a systematic framework for the collection of important diagnostic information, but they don't eliminate the need for an experienced clinician. If the interviewer is not able to establish a comfortable rapport with the client, then the interview might not elicit useful information. Furthermore, it is difficult to specify in advance all the questions that should be asked in a diagnostic interview. The client's responses to questions may require clarification. The interviewer must determine when it is necessary to probe further and in what ways to probe. Having lists of specific questions and clear definitions of diagnostic criteria will make the clinician's job easier, but clinical judgment remains an important ingredient in the diagnostic interview.

Advantages The clinical interview is the primary tool employed by clinical psychologists in the assessment of psychopathology. Several features of interviews account for this popularity, including the following issues:

1. The interviewer can control the interaction and can probe further when necessary.
2. By observing the patient's nonverbal behavior, the interviewer can try to detect areas of resistance. In that sense, the validity of the information may be enhanced.
3. An interview can provide a lot of information in a short period of time. It can cover past events and many different settings.

Limitations Several limitations in the use of clinical interviews as part of the assessment process must be kept in mind. These include the following considerations:

1. Some patients may be unable or unwilling to provide a rational account of their problems. This may be particularly true of young children, who have not developed verbal skills, as well as some psychotic and demented patients who are unable to speak coherently.
2. People may be reluctant to admit experiences that are embarrassing or frightening. They may feel that they should report to the interviewer only those feelings and behaviors that are socially desirable. Negative stereotypes about people with mental disorders interfere with an open and honest discussion of a person's problems.

3. Information provided by the client is necessarily filtered through the client's eyes. It is a subjective account and may be influenced or distorted by errors in memory and by selective perception.
4. Interviewers can influence their clients' accounts by the ways in which they phrase their questions and respond to the clients' responses.

Why do clinical interviews sometimes provide limited or distorted results?

Observational Procedures

In addition to the information that we gain from what people are willing to tell us during interviews, we can also learn a lot by watching their behavior. Observational skills play an important part in most assessment procedures. Sometimes the things that we observe confirm the person's self-report, and at other times the person's overt behavior appears to be at odds with what he or she says. A juvenile delinquent might express in words his regret at having injured a classmate, but his smile and the twinkle in his eye may raise doubts about the sincerity of his statement. In situations such as this, we must reconcile information that is obtained from different sources. The picture that emerges of another person's adjustment is greatly enriched when data collected from interviews are supplemented by observations of the person's behavior.

Observational procedures may be either informal or formal. Informal observations are

▼ Direct observation can provide one of the most useful sources of information about a person's behavior. In this case, the children and their teacher are being observed from behind a one-way mirror in order to minimize reactivity, the effect that the observer's presence might have on their behavior.

primarily qualitative. The clinician observes the person's behavior and the environment in which it occurs without attempting to record the frequency or intensity of specific responses. Michael's case illustrates the value of informal observations in the natural environment. When the therapist visited Michael and his parents at their home, he learned that his ritualistic behaviors were more extreme than Michael had originally described. This was useful, but not particularly surprising, as patients with OCD are often reluctant to describe in an interview the full extent of their compulsive behavior. The therapist also learned that the parents themselves were quite concerned with rules and order. Everything in their home was highly polished and in its place. This observation helped the therapist understand the extent to which Michael's parents might contribute to, or reinforce, his rigid adherence to a strict set of rules.

Although observations are often conducted in the natural environment, there are times when it is useful to observe the person's behavior in a situation that the psychologist can arrange and control. Sometimes it isn't possible to observe the person's behavior in the natural environment because the behavior in question occurs infrequently or at times when an observer cannot be present; at other times the environment is inaccessible; and sometimes the behavior that is of interest is inherently a private act. In these cases, the psychologist may arrange to observe the person's behavior in a situation that in some ways approximates the real environment. These artificial situations may also allow for more careful measurements of the person's problem than could be accomplished in a more complex situation.

In the case of obsessive–compulsive behavior, this approach might involve asking the person deliberately to touch an object that would ordinarily trigger ritualistic behaviors. The therapist might collect a set of objects that Michael would not want to touch, such as a school book, a pair of old track shorts, and the knob of a door leading to the laundry room. It would be useful to know specifically which objects he would touch, the degree of discomfort that he experienced when touching them, and the length of time that he was able to wait before washing his hands after touching these objects. This information could also be used as an index of change as treatment progressed.

Rating Scales Various types of procedures can be used to provide quantitative assessments of a person's behavior that are based on observations.

One alternative is to use a **rating scale** in which the observer is asked to make judgments that place the person somewhere along a dimension. For example, a clinician might observe a person's behavior for an extended period of time and then complete a set of ratings that are concerned with dimensions such as the extent to which the person exhibits compulsive ritualistic behaviors.

Ratings can also be made on the basis of information collected during an interview. The Yale-Brown Obsessive Compulsive Scale (Y-BOCS; Goodman et al., 1989; Woody, Steketee, & Chambless, 1995) is an example of an interview-based rating scale that is used extensively in the evaluation of people with problems like Michael's. The interviewer asks the person a series of specific questions about the nature of their experience with obsessive thoughts and compulsive behaviors. For example, "How much of your time is occupied by obsessive thoughts?" Using a scale that ranges from 0 (none) to 4 (extreme), the interviewer then assigns a rating on several dimensions such as "time spent occupied by obsessive thoughts," "interference due to obsessive thoughts," "distress associated with obsessive thoughts," and "resistance against obsessions." The composite rating—the total across all the items in the scale—can be used as an index of the severity of the disorder.

Rating scales provide abstract descriptions of a person's behavior rather than a specific record of exactly what the person has done. They require social judgments on the part of the observer, who must compare this person's behavior with an ideal view of other people. How does this person compare to someone who has never experienced any difficulties in this particular area? How does the person compare to the most severely disturbed patients? The value of these judgments depends on the experience of the person who makes the ratings. They are useful to the extent that the observer is able to synthesize accurately the information that has been collected and then rate the frequency or severity of the problem relative to the behavior of other people.

Behavioral Coding Systems Another approach to quantifying observational data depends on recording the person's actual activities. Rather than making judgments about where the person falls on a particular dimension, **behavioral coding systems** focus on the frequency of specific behavioral events (Furr & Funder, 2007). This type of observation, therefore, requires fewer inferences on the part of the observer. Because they require extensive time and training, behavioral coding systems are used more frequently in research studies than in clinical settings. Coding systems can be used with observations that are made in the person's natural environment as well as with those that are performed in artificial, or contrived, situations that are specifically designed to elicit the problem behavior under circumstances in which it can be observed precisely. In some cases, the observations are made directly by a therapist, and at other times the information is provided by people who have a better opportunity to see the person's behavior in the natural environment, including teachers, parents, spouse, and peers.

Some approaches to systematic observation can be relatively simple. Consider, once again, the case of Michael. After the psychologist had conducted several interviews with Michael and his family, he asked Michael's mother to participate in the assessment process by making detailed observations of his hand washing over a period of several nights. The mother was given a set of forms—one for each day—that could be used to record each incident, the time at which it occurred, and the circumstances that preceded the washing. The day was divided into 30-minute intervals starting at 6:30 A.M., when Michael got out of bed, and ending at 10:30 P.M., when he usually went to sleep. On each line (one for each time interval), his mother indicated whether he had washed his hands, what had been going on just prior to washing, and how anxious (on a scale from 1 to 100) Michael felt at the time that he washed.

Some adult clients are able to complete this kind of record by keeping track of their own behavior—a procedure known as *self-monitoring*. In this case, Michael's mother was asked to help because she was considered a more accurate observer than Michael and because Michael did not want to touch the form that would be used to record these observations. He believed that it was contaminated because it had touched his school clothes, which he wore to the therapy session.

Two weeks of observations were examined prior to the start of Michael's treatment. They indicated several things, including the times of the day when Michael was most active with his washing rituals (between 6 and 9 P.M.) and those specific objects and areas in the house that were most likely to trigger a washing incident. This information helped the therapist plan the treatment procedure, which would depend on approaching Michael's problem at the level that could most easily be handled and moving toward those situations that were the most difficult for him. The observations provided by Michael's mother were also used to mark his progress after treatment began.

Advantages Observational measures, including rating scales and behavioral coding systems, can provide a useful supplement to information that is typically collected in an interview format. Their advantage lies primarily in the fact that they can provide a more direct source of information than interviews can, because clinicians observe behavior directly rather than relying on patients' self-reports. Specific types of observational measures have distinct advantages:

1. Rating scales are primarily useful as an overall index of symptom severity or functional impairment.
2. Behavioral coding systems provide detailed information about the person's behavior in a particular situation.

Limitations Observations are sometimes considered to be similar to photographs: They provide a more direct or realistic view of behavior than do people's recollections of their actions and feelings. But just as the quality of a photograph is influenced by the quality of the camera, the film, and the process that is used to develop it, the value of observational data depends on the procedures that are used to collect them. Thus, observations have a number of limitations:

1. Observational procedures can be time-consuming and therefore expensive. Raters usually require extensive training before they can use a detailed behavioral coding system.
2. Observers can make errors. Their perception may be biased, just as the inferences of an interviewer may be biased. The reliability of ratings as well as behavioral coding must be monitored.
3. People may alter their behavior, either intentionally or unintentionally, when they know that they are being observed—a phenomenon known as **reactivity.** For example, a person who is asked to count the number of times that he washes his hands may wash less frequently than he does when he is not keeping track.

> *When would it be most important to collect behavioral observations rather than relying on self-report measures?*

"Here they come—act infantile."

4. Observational measures tell us only about the particular situation that was selected to be observed. We don't know if the person will behave in a similar way elsewhere or at a different time, unless we extend the scope of our observations.

5. There are some aspects of psychopathology that cannot be observed by anyone other than the person who has the problem. This is especially true for subjective experiences, such as guilt or low self-esteem.

Personality Tests and Self-Report Inventories

Personality tests are another important source of information about an individual's adjustment. Tests provide an opportunity to collect samples of a person's behavior in a standardized situation. The person who is being tested is presented with some kind of standard stimuli. The stimuli may be specific questions that can be answered true or false. They might be problems that require solutions, or they can be completely ambiguous inkblots. Exactly the same stimuli are used every time that the test is given. In that way, the clinician can be sure that differences in performance can be interpreted as differences in abilities or traits rather than differences in the testing situation.

Personality Inventories Because of their structure, **personality inventories** are sometimes referred to as "objective tests." They consist of a series of straightforward statements; the person being tested is typically required to indicate whether each statement is true or false in relation to himself or herself. Several types of personality inventories are widely used. Some are designed to identify personality traits in a normal population, and others focus more specifically on psychological problems. We have chosen to focus on the most extensively used personality inventory—the *Minnesota Multiphasic Personality Inventory* (MMPI)—to illustrate the characteristics of these tests as assessment devices.

The original version of the MMPI was developed in the 1940s at the University of Minnesota. For the past 50 years, it has been the most widely used psychological test. Thousands of research articles have been published on the MMPI. The inventory was revised several years ago, and it is currently known as the MMPI-2 (Butcher & Williams, 2000).

The MMPI-2 is based on a series of more than 500 statements that cover topics ranging from physical complaints and psychological states to occupational preferences and social attitudes. Examples are statements such as, "I sometimes keep on at a thing until others lose their patience with me"; "My feelings are easily hurt"; and "There are persons who are trying to steal my thoughts and ideas." After reading each statement, the person is instructed to indicate whether it is true or false. Scoring of the MMPI-2 is objective. After the responses to all questions are totaled, the person receives a numerical score on each of 10 clinical scales as well as four validity scales.

Before considering the possible clinical significance of a person's MMPI-2 profile, the psychologist will examine a number of validity scales, which reflect the patient's attitude toward the test and the openness and consistency with which the questions were answered. The L (Lie) Scale is sensitive to unsophisticated attempts to avoid answering in a frank and honest manner. For example, one statement on this scale says, "At times I feel like swearing." Although this is perhaps not an admirable trait, virtually all normal subjects indicate that the item is true. Subjects who indicate that the item is false (does not apply to them) receive 1 point on the L scale. Several responses of this sort would result in an elevated score on the scale and would indicate that the person's overall test results should not be interpreted as a true reflection of his or her feelings. Other validity scales reflect tendencies to exaggerate problems, carelessness in completing the questions, and unusual defensiveness.

If the profile is considered valid, the process of interpretation will be directed toward the 10 clinical scales, which are described in Table 4–5. Some of these scales carry rather obvious meaning, whereas others are associated with a more general or mixed pattern of symptoms. For example, Scale 2 (Depression) is a relatively straightforward index of degree of depression. Scale 7 (Psychasthenia), in contrast, is more complex and is based on items that measure anxiety, insecurity, and excessive doubt. There are many different ways to obtain an elevated score on any of the clinical scales, because each scale is composed of many items. Even the more obvious scales can indicate several different types of problems. Therefore, the pattern of scale scores is more important than the elevation of any particular scale.

Rather than depending only on their own experience and clinical judgment, which may be subject to various sorts of bias and inconsistency, many clinicians analyze the results of a specific test on the basis of an explicit set of rules that are derived from empirical research (Greene, 2006). This is known as an **actuarial interpretation.** We can illustrate this process using Michael's profile. The profile is first described in terms of the pattern of scale scores, beginning with the highest and proceeding to the lowest. Those that are elevated above a scale score of 70 are most important, and interpretations are sometimes based on the "high-point pair." Following this procedure, Michael's profile could be coded as a 2–0; that is, his highest scores were on Scales 2 and 0. The clinician then looks up this specific configuration of scores in a kind of MMPI-2 "cookbook" to see what sort of descriptive characteristics apply. One cookbook offers the following statement about adolescents (mostly 14 and 15 years old) who fit the 2–0/0–2 code type:

> Eighty-seven percent of the 2–0/0–2s express feelings of inferiority to their therapists. They say that they are not good-looking, that they are afraid to speak up in class, and that they feel awkward when they meet people or try to make a date (91 percent of high 2–0/0–2s). Their therapists see the 2–0/0–2s as anxious, fearful, timid, withdrawn, and inhibited. They are depressed, and very vulnerable to threat. The 2–0/0–2 adolescents are overcontrolled; they cannot let go, even when it would be appropriate for them to do so. They are afraid of emotional involvement with others and, in fact, seem to have little need for such affiliation. These adolescents are viewed by their psychotherapists as schizoid; they think and associate in unusual ways and spend a good deal of time in personal fantasy and daydreaming. They are serious young people who tend to anticipate problems and difficulties. Indeed, they are prone toward obsessional thinking and are compulsively meticulous.
>
> (Marks, Seeman, & Haller, 1974, p. 201)

Several comments must be made about this statement. First, nothing is certain. Actuarial descriptions are probability statements. They indicate that a certain proportion of the people who produce this pattern of scores will be associated with a certain characteristic or behavior. If 87 percent of the adolescents who produce this code type

TABLE 4–5	**Clinical Scales for the MMPI**	
SCALE NUMBER	**SCALE NAME**	**INTERPRETATION OF HIGH SCORES**
1	Hypochondriasis	Excessive bodily concern; somatic symptoms
2	Depression	Depressed; pessimistic; irritable; demanding
3	Hysteria	Physical symptoms that cannnot be traced to a medicall illness; self-centered; demands attention
4	Psychopathic Deviate	Asocial or antisocial; rebellious; impulsive, poor judgment
5	Masculinity–Femininity	For men: aesthetic interests For women: assertive; competitive; self-confident
6	Paranoia	Suspicious, sensitive; resentful; rigid; may be frankly psychotic
7	Psychasthenia	Anxious; worried; obsessive; lacks self-confidence; problems in decision making
8	Schizophrenia	May have thinking disturbance, withdrawn; feels alienated and unaccepted
9	Hypomania	Excessive activity; lacks direction; low frustration tolerance; friendly
0	Social-Introversion	Socially introverted; shy; sensitive; overcontrolled; conforming

Why is the MMPI-2 sometimes called an objective personality test?

express feelings of inferiority, 13 percent do not. Many aspects of this description apply to Michael's current adjustment, but they don't all fit. The MMPI must be used in conjunction with other assessment procedures. The accuracy of actuarial statements can be verified through interviews with the person or through direct observations of his or her behavior.

Advantages The MMPI-2 has several advantages in comparison to interviews and observational procedures. In clinical practice, it is seldom used by itself, but, for the following reasons, it can serve as a useful supplement to other methods of collecting information.

1. The MMPI-2 provides information about the person's test-taking attitude, which alerts the clinician to the possibility that clients are careless, defensive, or exaggerating their problems.
2. The MMPI-2 covers a wide range of problems in a direct and efficient manner. It would take a clinician several hours to go over all these topics using an interview format.
3. Because the MMPI-2 is scored objectively, the initial description of the person's adjustment is not influenced by the clinician's subjective impression of the client.
4. The MMPI-2 can be interpreted in an actuarial fashion, using extensive banks of information regarding people who respond to items in a particular way.

Limitations The MMPI-2 also has some limitations. Some of its limitations derive from the fact that it has been used for many years, and the ways in which different forms of psychopathology are viewed have changed over time.

1. The utility of the traditional clinical scales (see Table 4–5) has been questioned, especially with regard to their ability to discriminate between different types of mental disorder. Restructured clinical scales have been developed in order to address these problems, but the new scales remain controversial (Nichols, 2006).
2. The test depends on the person's ability to read and respond to written statements. Some people cannot complete the rather extensive list of questions. These include many people who are acutely psychotic, intellectually impaired, or poorly educated.

3. Specific data are not always available for a particular profile. Many patients' test results do not meet criteria for a particular code type with which extensive data are associated. Therefore, actuarial interpretation is not really possible for these profiles.
4. Some studies have found that profile types are not stable over time. It is not clear whether this instability should be interpreted as lack of reliability or as sensitivity to change in the person's level of adjustment.

Projective Personality Tests

In **projective tests,** the person is presented with a series of ambiguous stimuli. The best known projective test, introduced in 1921 by Hermann Rorschach (1884–1922), a Swiss psychiatrist, is based on the use of inkblots. The Rorschach test consists of a series of 10 inkblots. Five contain various shades of gray on a white background, and five contain elements of color. The person is asked to look at each card and indicate what it looks like or what it appears to be. There are, of course, no correct answers. The instructions are intentionally vague in order to avoid influencing the person's responses through subtle suggestions.

Projective techniques such as the Rorschach test were originally based on psychodynamic assumptions about the nature of personality and psychopathology. Considerable emphasis was placed on the importance of unconscious motivations—conflicts and impulses of which the person is largely unaware. In other words, people being tested presumably project hidden desires and conflicts when they try to describe or explain the cards. In so doing, they may reveal things about themselves of which they are not consciously aware or that they might not be willing to admit if they were asked directly. The cards are not designed or chosen to be realistic or representational; they presumably look like whatever the person wants them to look like.

Michael did not actually complete any projective personality tests. We can illustrate the way in which these tests might have been used in his case, however, by considering a man who had been given a diagnosis of obsessive–compulsive disorder on Axis I, as well as showing evidence of two types of personality disorder, dependent and schizotypal features. This patient was 22 years old, unemployed, and living with his mother. His father had died in an accident four years earlier. Like Michael, this man was bothered by intrusive thoughts of contamination, and he frequently engaged in compulsive washing (Hurt, Reznikoff, & Clarkin, 1991). His responses to the cards on the Rorschach frequently mentioned emotional distress ("a man screaming"), interpersonal conflict ("two women fighting over something"), and war ("two mushrooms of a nuclear bomb cloud"). He did not incorporate color into any of his responses to the cards.

The original procedures for scoring the Rorschach were largely impressionistic and placed considerable emphasis on the content of the person's response. Responses given in the example above might be taken to suggest a number of important themes. Aggression and violence are obvious possibilities. Perhaps the man was repressing feelings of hostility, as indicated by his frequent references to war and conflict. These themes were coupled with a guarded approach to emotional reactions, which is presumably reflected by his avoidance of color. The psychologist might have wondered whether the man felt guilty about something, such as his father's death. This kind of interpretation, which depends heavily on symbolism and clinical inference, provides intriguing material for the clinician to puzzle over. Unfortunately, the reliability and validity of this intuitive type of scoring procedure are very low (Garb et al., 2005).

When we ponder the utility of these interpretations, we should also keep in mind the relative efficiency of projective testing procedures. Did the test tell us anything that we didn't already know or that we couldn't have learned in a more straightforward manner? The clinician might learn about a client's feelings of anger or guilt by using a clinical interview, which is often a more direct and efficient way of collecting information.

More recent approaches to the use of projective tests view the person's descriptions of the cards as a sample of his or her perceptual and cognitive styles. The psychologist John Exner has developed an objective scoring procedure for the Rorschach that is based primarily on the form rather than the content of the subject's responses (Exner, 1993, 1999). According to Exner's system, interpretation of the test depends on the way in which the descriptions take into account the shapes and colors on the cards. Does the person see movement in the card? Does she focus on tiny details, or does she base her descriptions on global impressions of the entire form of the inkblot? These and many other considerations contribute to the overall interpretation of the Rorschach test. The reliability of this scoring system is better than would be achieved by informal,

THE FAR SIDE®   BY GARY LARSON

"It's just a simple Rorschach inkblot test, Mr. Bromwell, so just calm down and tell me what each one suggests to you."

impressionistic procedures. The validity of the scores, however, remains open to question (Hunsley & Bailey, 2001; Wood et al., 2003).

There are many different types of projective tests. Some employ stimuli that are somewhat less ambiguous than the inkblots in the Rorschach. The Thematic Apperception Test (TAT), for example, consists of a series of drawings that depict human figures in various ambiguous situations. Most of the cards portray more than one person. The figures and their poses tend to elicit stories with themes of sadness and violence. The person is asked to describe the identities of the people in the cards and to make up a story about what is happening. These stories presumably reflect the person's own ways of perceiving reality.

◄ Projective tests require a person to respond to ambiguous stimuli. Here, a woman is taking the Thematic Apperception Test (TAT), in which she will be asked to make up a story about a series of drawings of people.

Advantages The advantages of projective tests center on the fact that the tests are interesting to give and interpret, and they sometimes provide a way to talk to people who are otherwise reluctant or unable to discuss their problems. Projective tests are more appealing to psychologists who adopt a psychodynamic view of personality and psychopathology because such tests are believed to reflect unconscious conflicts and motivations. Some specific advantages are listed below.

1. Some people may feel more comfortable talking in an unstructured situation than they would if they were required to participate in a structured interview or to complete the lengthy MMPI.
2. Projective tests can provide an interesting source of information regarding the person's unique view of the world, and they can be a useful supplement to information obtained with other assessment tools (Weiner, 2000).
3. To whatever extent a person's relationships with other people are governed by unconscious cognitive and emotional events, projective tests may provide information that cannot be obtained through direct interviewing methods or observational procedures (Meyer & Archer, 2001; Stricker & Gold, 1999).

Limitations There are many serious problems with the use of projective tests. The popularity of projective tests has declined considerably since the 1970s, even in clinical settings, primarily because research studies have found little evidence to support their reliability and validity (Garb et al., 2005).

1. Lack of standardization in administration and scoring is a serious problem, even though Exner's system for the Rorschach has made some improvements in that regard.
2. Little information is available on which to base comparisons to normal adults or children.
3. Some projective procedures, such as the Rorschach, can be very time consuming, particularly if the person's responses are scored with a standardized procedure such as Exner's system.
4. The reliability of scoring and interpretation tends to be low.
5. Information regarding the validity of projective tests is primarily negative.

BIOLOGICAL ASSESSMENT PROCEDURES

Clinicians have developed a number of techniques for measuring the association between biological systems and abnormal behavior. These techniques are seldom used in clinical practice (at least for the diagnosis of psychopathology), but they have been employed extensively in research settings, and it seems possible that they will one day become an important source of information on individual patients.

Brain Imaging Techniques

The past three decades have seen a tremendous explosion of information and technology in the neurosciences. We now understand in considerable detail how neurons in the central nervous system communicate with one another, and scientists have invented sophisticated methods to create images of the living human brain (Bremner, 2005). Some of these procedures provide static pictures of various brain structures at rest, just as an X ray provides a photographic image of a bone or some other organ of the body. Studies of this type are typically concerned with the size of various parts of the brain. For example, many studies have compared the average size of the lateral ventricles—large chambers filled with cerebrospinal fluid—in groups of patients with schizophrenia and normal comparison groups. Other methods can be used to create dynamic images of brain functions—reflecting the rate of activity in various parts of the brain—while a person is performing different tasks. These functional images allow scientists to examine which parts of the brain are involved in various kinds of events, such as perception, memory, language, and emotional experience. They may also allow us to learn whether specific areas or pathways in the brain are uniquely associated with specific types of mental disorders.

Precise measures of brain structure can be obtained with *magnetic resonance imaging* (MRI). In MRI, images are generated using a strong magnetic field rather than X rays (Posner & DiGirolamo, 2000). A large magnet in the scanner causes chemical elements in specific brain regions to emit distinctive radio signals. Both computerized tomography (CT) scanning and MRI can provide a static image of specific brain structures. MRI provides more detailed images than CT scans and is able to identify smaller parts of the brain. For this reason, and because it lends itself more easily to the creation of three-dimensional pictures of the brain, MRI has replaced CT scanning in most research facilities.

In addition to structural MRI, which provides a static view of brain structures, advances in the neurosciences have also produced techniques that create images of brain functions (Raichle, 2001). *Positron emission tomography* (PET) is one scanning technique that can be used to create functional brain images (Wahl, 2002). This procedure is much more expensive than the other imaging techniques because it requires a nuclear cyclotron to produce special radioactive elements. PET scans are capable of providing relatively detailed images of the brain. In addition, they can reflect changes in brain activity as the person responds to the demands of various tasks.

The newest and most exciting method of imaging brain functions involves *functional MRI* (fMRI). When neurons are activated, their metabolism increases and they require increased blood flow to supply them with oxygen. The magnetic properties of blood change as a function of the level of oxygen that it is carrying. In fMRI, a series of images is acquired in rapid succession. Small differences in signal intensity from one image to the next provide a measure of moment-to-moment changes in the amount of oxygen in blood flowing to specific areas of the brain. While other functional imaging procedures such as PET are only able to measure activities that are sustained over a period of several minutes, fMRI is able to identify changes in brain activity that lasts less than a second (Huettel, Song, & McCarthy, 2004).

Functional brain imaging procedures have been used extensively to study possible neurological underpinnings of various types of mental disorder. For example, in the case of obsessive–compulsive disorder (OCD), studies using PET and fMRI have suggested that symptoms of OCD are associated with multiple brain regions, including the caudate nucleus (one part of the basal ganglia, which are also illustrated in Figure 14–3 on page 447), the orbital prefrontal cortex, and the anterior cingulate cortex (located on the medial surface of the frontal lobe). These pathways are illustrated in Figure 4–1. They seem to be overly active in people with OCD, especially when the person is confronted with stimuli that provoke his or her obsessions (Husted et al., 2006; Menzies et al., 2008).

These results are intriguing because they suggest that certain regions and circuits in the brain

▲ Positron emission topography (PET scan) can provide useful images of dynamic brain functions. Areas that appear red or yellow indicate areas of the brain that are active (consuming the labeled glucose molecules), whereas those that are blue or green are relatively inactive. Different areas of the brain become active depending on whether the person is at rest or engaged in particular activities when the image is created.

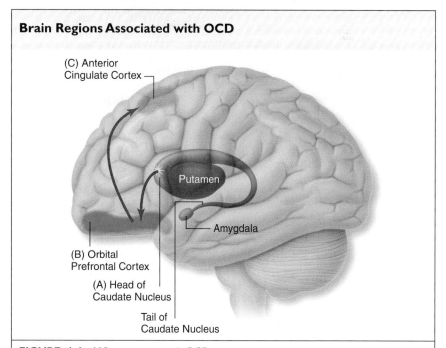

Brain Regions Associated with OCD

(C) Anterior Cingulate Cortex

Putamen

Amygdala

(B) Orbital Prefrontal Cortex

(A) Head of Caudate Nucleus

Tail of Caudate Nucleus

FIGURE 4–1   When a person with OCD experiences symptoms, an increase in neural activity is seen in the caudate (A), which triggers the urge to "do something," through the orbital prefrontal cortex (B), which gives the feeling that "something is wrong," and back through the anterior cingulated cortex (C), which keeps attention fixed on the feeling of unease.

Source: R. Carter, 1998, *Mapping the Mind,* Berkeley: University of California Press, illustrations by Malcolm Godwin. Copyright © 1998 by Moonrunner Design Ltd. Reprinted by permission of Malcolm Godwin, Moonrunner Design, Ltd.

▲ This view of Earth from space shows hot spots on the Earth's surface at night, an indication of areas of heavier population. Imaging techniques like fMRI offer views of the brain that are similarly fascinating—and similarly lacking in resolution, detail, and meaning.

may somehow be associated with the presence of obsessive–compulsive symptoms. We must emphasize, however, that the results of such imaging procedures are not useful diagnostically with regard to an individual person. In other words, some people with OCD do not exhibit increased metabolism rates in the caudate or the anterior cingulate cortex, and some people who do not have OCD do show increased levels of activity in these brain regions.

Advantages Brain imaging techniques provide detailed information regarding the structure of brain areas and activity levels in the brain that are associated with the performance of particular tasks. They have important uses, primarily as research tools:

1. In clinical practice, imaging techniques can be used to rule out various neurological conditions that might explain behavioral or cognitive deficits. These include such conditions as brain tumors and vascular disease.

2. Procedures such as fMRI and PET can help research investigators explore the relation between brain functions and specific mental disorders. This type of information will be considered in several chapters later in this book.

Limitations Brain imaging procedures are used extensively in the study and assessment of neurological disorders. In the field of psychopathology, they are currently research tools and have little clinical importance outside the assessment and treatment of disorders such as Alzheimer's disease (see Chapter 14). Some of the major limitations are listed below.

1. Norms have not been established for any of these measures. It is not possible to use brain imaging procedures for diagnostic purposes.

2. These procedures are relatively expensive—especially PET scans and fMRI—and some procedures must be used cautiously because the patient may be exposed to radioactive substances.

3. We should not assume that all cognitive processes, emotional experiences, or mental disorders are necessarily linked to activity (or the absence of activity) in a specific area of the brain. Scientists are still debating the extent to which these experiences are localized within the brain (Uttal, 2001).

Psychophysiological Assessment

Changes in physiological response systems, such as heart rate, respiration rate, and skin conductance, can provide useful information regarding a person's psychological adjustment. The basic components of the human nervous system (reviewed in Chapter 2) include the central nervous system (CNS) and the peripheral nervous system (PNS). The PNS is divided into two parts: the somatic nervous system and the autonomic nervous system. The somatic nervous system is responsible for communication between the brain and external sense receptors, as well as regulation of voluntary muscle movements. The autonomic nervous system is responsible for body processes that occur without conscious awareness, such as heart rate. It maintains equilibrium in the internal environment.

The autonomic nervous system is highly reactive to environmental events and can provide useful information about a person's internal states, such as emotion (Keller, Hicks, & Miller, 2000). Recording procedures have been developed to measure variables such as respiration rate, heart rate, and skin conductance. As the person becomes aroused, activity levels change in these systems. Psychophysiological measures can, therefore, provide sensitive indices of the person's internal state.

It must be emphasized, however, that all these measures do not act together. The concept of general arousal was abandoned many years ago (for example, see Lacey, 1967). If several physiological responses are measured at the same time, they may not all demonstrate the same strength, or even direction, of response. Moreover, physiological measures frequently disagree with the person's own subjective report. Therefore, as with other assessment procedures, physiological recordings should be used in conjunction with other measures. They represent supplements to, rather than substitutes for, the other types of measures that we have already considered.

Psychophysiological measurements have been used extensively in the assessment of anxiety disorders. Consider Michael's case. He was afraid to touch contaminated objects in his house. If he had been forced to do so, it is likely that his heart rate would have increased dramatically (Yartz & Hawk, 2001). Psychophysiological events of this sort can be monitored precisely. To the extent that the clinician might be in need of information that would confirm data from other sources (observation, self-report) or that could be used to measure changes in the person's response to particular stimuli in the environment, physiological measurements may be very useful.

Advantages Physiological procedures are not used frequently in clinical settings, but they are used extensively in research on psychopathology. These tools have several advantages in comparison to other assessment procedures (Drobes, Stritzke, & Coffey, 2000).

1. Psychophysiological recording procedures do not depend on self-report and, therefore, may be less subject to voluntary control. People may be less able to make the assessment show what they want it to show.

2. Some of these measures can be obtained while the subject is sleeping or while the subject is actively engaged in some other activity.

Limitations In addition to the fact that they require relatively sophisticated equipment and a technician who is trained in their use, physiological measures have a number of drawbacks.

1. The recording equipment and electrodes may be frightening or intimidating to some people. These emotional responses can skew results.
2. There are generally low correlations between different autonomic response systems. It is not wise to select arbitrarily one specific physiological measure, such as heart rate, and assume that it is a direct index of arousal.
3. Physiological reactivity and the stability of physiological response systems vary from person to person. The measures may be informative for some people but not for others.
4. Physiological responses can be influenced by many other factors. Some are person variables, such as age and medication, as well as psychological factors, such as being self-conscious or fearing loss of control. Other important considerations are situational variables, such as extraneous noise and electrical activity.

Why are brain imaging procedures not used for the diagnosis of mental disorders?

GETTING HELP

Only one in five people who needs treatment actually gets it. There are several reasons for this unfortunate state of events. One is lack of information. If you don't recognize the presence of a serious problem, you won't seek help. You will get care more promptly and make better treatment choices if you understand your problems. One consideration is the extent to which your experiences resemble the formal diagnostic terms used by mental health professionals. Allen Frances, chairperson of the DSM-IV-TR Taskforce, and Michael First have written a useful book called *Your Mental Health: A Layman's Guide to the Psychiatrist's Bible.* This primer for consumers of mental health services covers many types of adult and childhood disorders. Each chapter includes a concise, readable description of the typical symptoms and course of the disorder, followed by a discussion designed to help you

decide whether your problems warrant professional help ("Am I okay?"). Finally, the authors review treatment options and where to go for help for each of the problems.

Even after they recognize the presence of a serious problem, some people are reluctant to seek help; they fear there is a stigma attached to "mental problems" despite the fact that seeking therapy is now commonplace. Negative stereotypes regarding mental disorders persist. We hope that you will not allow these distorted views to delay or interfere with efforts to improve your life. If you have concerns about this issue, it may help to read about stigma and mental health, a problem that has been addressed by Rosalynn Carter, a leading advocate on behalf of people with mental disorders and wife of former president Jimmy Carter. Her book, *Helping Someone with Mental Illness,* contains an excellent discussion of these issues. The Carter Cen-

ter is actively involved in issues that affect public policies regarding mental disorders. The URL for their Web page is www.cartercenter.org. It also contains information relevant to the struggle to correct biased and inaccurate views of people with mental disorders.

We can all help eliminate discrimination against those who suffer from (or have recovered from) mental disorders. Advice for positive action is presented on several Web sites, including the National Mental Health Associations' "Stigma Watch" homepage. This site includes, for example, a sample letter that can be mailed to legislators as well as instructions that encourage people to report media events that depict mental disorders in an unfair light. People will find it easier to seek help when they no longer need to worry about the potential effects of distorted, negative views of their problems.

■ SUMMARY

Formal **classification systems** for mental disorders have been developed in order to facilitate communication, research, and treatment planning. The current official system published by the American Psychiatric Association is the fourth edition of the *Diagnostic and Statistical Manual of Mental Disorders,* or DSM-IV-TR. It is based on a **categorical approach to classification** and typically employs specific inclusion and exclusion criteria to define each disorder. The categories that are defined in DSM-IV-TR are based primarily on descriptive principles rather than on theoretical knowledge regarding the etiology of the disorders. Five axes are included in this system. Axes I and II are employed for describing mental disorders (personality disorders and mental retardation on Axis II). The remaining three axes are concerned with supplementary information that may also be useful in treatment planning.

Cultural factors play an important role in both the expression and recognition of symptoms of mental disorders. The accuracy and utility of a clinical diagnosis depend on the clinician's ability to consider the cultural context in which the problem appeared. DSM-IV-TR includes a glossary of **culture-bound syndromes,** such as amok. These patterns of erratic or unusual thinking and behavior do not fit easily into the other categories that are listed in the main body of the diagnostic manual.

The usefulness of a classification system depends on several criteria, especially **reliability** and **validity.** The reliability of many categories in DSM seems to have improved with the introduction of specific inclusion criteria and exclusion criteria. Nevertheless, serious questions remain about this issue. The reliability of some categories, such as the personality disorders, is still marginal in many studies. Reliability is also likely to be diminished in clinical settings where clinicians are not experts in a particular disorder and reliability is not being monitored. The validity of most categories is still under active investigation.

The general process of collecting and interpreting information is called **assessment.** Many different assessment tools can be used to generate information systematically. Interviews, observations, and tests are among the most frequently used procedures. Assessments can be directed toward biological, psychological, and social systems. In many cases, information is collected and integrated across more than one system, but it is never possible to learn everything about a particular person. Choices have to be made, and some information must be excluded from the analysis.

Psychological assessment procedures systems are typically based on a combination of interviews, observations, and self-report inventories. Structured diagnostic interviews are used extensively in conjunction with the DSM-IV-TR classification system. They can also form the basis for ratings of the person's adjustment on a number of dimensions. Interviews can be used to collect additional information that is relevant to planning treatment. Their main advantage is their flexibility. Their primary limitation lies in the inability or unwillingness of some clients to provide a rational description of their own problems, as well as the subjective factors that influence the clinician's interpretation of data collected in an interview.

Personality inventories, like the MMPI, offer several advantages as supplements to interviews and observations. They can be scored objectively, they often contain validity scales that reflect the person's attitude and test-taking set, and they can be interpreted in reference to well-established standards for people with and without specific types of adjustment problems. Some psychologists use **projective personality tests,** like the Rorschach, to acquire information that might not be obtained from direct interviews or observations. Unfortunately, research studies have found little evidence to support the reliability and validity of projective tests. The continued use of these tests is, therefore, controversial.

Many different tools are used in biological assessment procedures that are used in an effort to advance our knowledge of mental disorders. These include brain imaging techniques, such as MRI and PET scans, as well as psychophysiological recording procedures. Biological assessment procedures are used extensively in research studies. They do not have diagnostic value in clinical situations, except for the purpose of ruling out certain conditions, such as brain tumors and vascular disease.

THE BIG PICTURE CRITICAL THINKING REVIEW

Why do we need a system to classify abnormal behavior?

Classification systems provide a way for scientists and clinicians to organize information and communicate with each other and with patients regarding the nature of mental disorders. (SEE PAGE 92)

Should disorders that are unique to our own culture be considered *culture-bound* syndromes?

In the same way that *ataques de nervios* is a behavioral phenomenon associated with the culture of Puerto Rico, bulimia seems to be uniquely associated with Western culture and is closely linked to its values regarding beauty. (SEE PAGE 97)

What is the difference between reliability and validity?

The fact that two people agree on assigning a specific diagnosis does not necessarily imply that it is meaningful. (SEE PAGES 97–99)

How could the DSM-IV-TR classification system be improved?

Committees working on the next version of the diagnostic manual (DSM-V) will pay greater attention to the dimensional nature of abnormal behaviors while attempting to clarify the boundaries between mental disorders and normal behavior. (SEE PAGE 101)

Why do clinical interviews sometimes provide limited or distorted results?

Some people are either unwilling or unable to provide an accurate account of their problems. (SEE PAGE 107)

Why is the MMPI-2 sometimes called an objective personality test?

The person's responses to test items are scored according to an explicit set of rules that are based on empirical research and interpreted using actuarial predictions. (SEE PAGE 110)

Why are brain imaging procedures not used for the diagnosis of mental disorders?

They are currently best seen as research tools. No unique patterns of brain structure or function have been found that consistently and accurately identify people with specific mental disorders. (SEE PAGE 116)

■ KEY TERMS

actuarial interpretation **111**
assessment **88**
behavioral coding system **108**
categorical approach to classification **91**
classification system **101**
comorbidity **96**
culture-bound syndrome **96**
diagnosis **89**
dimensional approach to classification **91**
personality inventory **110**
projective tests **102**
rating scale **108**
reactivity **109**
reliability **97**
stigma **93**
validity **99**

MOOD DISORDERS AND SUICIDE

Sadness may be the price that we pay for attachments to other people. Losses are inevitable, and we all endure the pain that comes with them. Beyond relatively short-lived feelings of grief and sorrow, prolonged sadness can grow into something much more debilitating. Everyone's life contains the potential for despair. Some people are able to work their ways through it, but others become overwhelmed. When it reaches higher levels of intensity and begins to interfere with a person's ability to function and enjoy life, a low mood is known as clinical depression. In this chapter we will consider emotional disorders that involve prolonged periods of severe depression.

OVERVIEW

If one measures disability in terms of years lived with severe impairments, major depression is the leading cause of disability worldwide (Moussavi et al., 2007). The magnitude of the problem is truly staggering. Depression accounts for more almost 10 percent of all disability (see Table 5–1). Experts predict that it will become an even greater problem by the year 2020. Younger generations are experiencing higher rates of depression than their predecessors, and those who become depressed are doing so at an earlier age.

Psychopathologists use several terms to describe problems that are associated with emotional response systems. This language can become confusing because most of us already use these words in our everyday vocabulary. Thus we must define these terms as they are used in psychopathology so that our discussion will be clear. *Emotion* refers to a state of arousal that is defined by subjective states of feeling, such as sadness, anger, and disgust. Emotions are often accompanied by physiological changes, such as changes in heart rate and respiration rate. **Affect** refers to the pattern of observable behaviors, such as facial expression, that are associated with these subjective feelings. People also express affect through the pitch of their voices and

TABLE 5-1	Leading Causes of Disability Worldwide as Measured by Years of Life Lived with a Disability
	PROPORTION OF TOTAL YEARS LIVED WITH DISABILITY
ALL CAUSES	
1. Depression	9.4
2. Hearing loss	5.5
3. Cataracts	5.2
4. Osteoarthritis	3.2
5. Vision disorders	3.1
6. Cerebrovascular disease	2.7
7. Dementia	2.6
8. Perinatal conditions	2.5
9. Alcohol-use disorders	2.5
10. Chronic obstructive pulmonary disease	2.1

Source: From "Depression is Very Disabling" by G. Andrews and N. Titov, The Lancet, 370 (2007), 808–809. Copyright © 2007 by Elsevier. Reprinted by permission of Elsevier.

point at which "feeling down or blue" crosses a line and becomes depression. One experience shades gradually into the next. The transition has been described by Andrew Solomon (2001) in *The Noonday Demon,* an eloquent book in which he documents his own struggles with depression:

> Depression starts out insipid, fogs the days into a dull color, weakens ordinary actions until their clear shapes are obscured by the effort they require, leaves you tired and bored and self-obsessed—but you get through all that. Not happily, perhaps, but you can get through. No one has ever been able to define the collapse point that marks major depression, but when you get there, there's not much mistaking it. (p. 17)

People who are in a severely depressed mood describe the feeling as overwhelming, suffocating, or numbing. In the syndrome of depression, which is also called **clinical depression,** a depressed mood is accompanied by several other symptoms, such as fatigue, loss of energy, difficulty in sleeping, and changes in appetite. Clinical depression also involves a variety of changes in thinking and overt behavior. The person may experience cognitive symptoms, such as extreme guilt, feelings of worthlessness, concentration problems, and thoughts of suicide. Behavioral symptoms may range from constant pacing and fidgeting to extreme inactivity. Throughout the rest of this chapter, we will use the term **depression** to refer to the clinical syndrome rather than the mood.

Mania, the flip side of depression, also involves a disturbance in mood that is accompanied by additional symptoms. **Euphoria,** or elated mood, is the opposite emotional state from a

with their hand and body movements. **Mood** refers to a pervasive and sustained emotional response that, in its extreme form, can color the person's perception of the world (APA, 2000). The disorders discussed in this chapter are primarily associated with two specific moods: depression and elation.

Depression can refer either to a mood or to a *clinical syndrome,* a combination of emotional, cognitive, and behavioral symptoms. The feelings associated with a **depressed mood** often include disappointment and despair. Although sadness is a universal experience, profound depression is not. No one has been able to identify the exact depressed mood. It is characterized by an exaggerated feeling of physical and emotional well-being (APA, 2000). Manic symptoms that frequently accompany an elated mood include inflated self-esteem, decreased need for sleep, distractibility, pressure to keep talking, and the subjective feeling of thoughts racing through the person's head faster than they can be spoken. Mania is, therefore, a syndrome in the same sense that clinical depression is a syndrome.

Mood disorders are defined in terms of *episodes*—discrete periods of time in which the person's behavior is dominated by either a depressed or manic mood. Unfortunately, most people with a mood disorder experience more than one episode. The following case studies illustrate the way that numerous symptoms combine to form syndromes that are used to define mood dis-

orders. They also provide examples of the two primary types of mood disorders: (1) those in which the person experiences only episodes of depression, known as **unipolar mood disorder;** and (2) those in which the person experiences episodes of mania as well as depression, known as **bipolar mood disorder.** Episodes of depression are defined by the same symptoms, regardless of whether the person's disorder is unipolar or bipolar in nature. A small number of patients have only manic episodes with no evidence of depression; they are included in the bipolar category. Years ago, bipolar mood disorder was known as *manic–depressive disorder.* Although this term has been replaced in the official diagnostic manual, some clinicians still prefer to use it because it offers a more direct description of the patient's experience.

CASE **STUDY** An Attorney's Major Depressive Episode

Cathy was a 31-year-old attorney who had been promoted to the rank of partner the previous year and was considered one of the brightest, most promising young members of her firm. In spite of her apparent success, she was plagued by doubts about her own abilities and was convinced that she was unworthy of her promotion. Cathy decided to seek treatment because she was profoundly miserable. Beyond being depressed, she felt numb. She had been feeling unusually fatigued and irritable for several months, but her mood took a serious swing for the worse after one of the firm's clients, for whom Cathy was primarily responsible, decided to switch to another firm. Although the decision was clearly based on factors that were beyond her control, Cathy blamed herself. She interpreted this event as a reflection of her professional incompetence, in spite of the fact that virtually all of her other clients had praised her work and the senior partners in her firm had given her consistently positive reviews.

Cathy had always looked forward to going to the office, and she truly enjoyed her work. After she lost this client, however, going to work had seemed like an overwhelming burden. She found it impossible to concentrate and instead brooded about her own incompetence. Soon she started calling in sick. She began to spend her time sitting in bed staring at the television screen, without paying attention to any program, and she never left her apartment. She felt lethargic all the time, but she wasn't sleeping well. Her appetite disappeared. Her best friend tried repeatedly to get in touch with her, but Cathy wouldn't return her calls. She listened passively as her friend left messages on the answering machine. She just didn't feel like doing anything or talking to anyone.

Life has lost its interest and meaning. I've failed at my job and failed in my relationships. I deserve to be alone.

Cathy considered her social life to be a disaster, and it didn't seem to be getting any better. She had been separated from her husband for 5 years, and her most recent boyfriend had started dating another woman. She had tried desperately for several weeks to force herself to be active, but eventually she stopped caring. The situation seemed completely hopeless. Although she had often gone to parties with other members of her law firm, she usually felt as though she didn't fit in. Everyone else seemed to be part of a couple, and Cathy was usually on her own. Other people didn't appreciate the depth of her loneliness. Sometimes it seemed to Cathy that she would be better off dead. She spent a good deal of time brooding about suicide, but she feared that if she tried to harm herself she might make things worse than they already were.

Cathy's problems would be classified as a unipolar mood disorder because she had experienced at least one episode of major depression and she had never had a manic episode. Her experience provides a framework in which we can discuss the difference between normal sadness and clinical depression. Some important con-

siderations regarding this distinction are listed in Table 5–2. They include the extent to which the low mood remains consistent over an extended period of time as well as the inability to occasionally enjoy activities that would otherwise provide some relief from feeling down or blue. Distractions such as watching television or talking on the phone with a friend had lost their ability to make Cathy feel any better. Her mood had deteriorated shortly after one of her clients switched to another firm. The intensity of her depression was clearly way out of proportion to the event that seemed to trigger it (departure of a client to another firm). She had withdrawn from other people and was no longer able to work or to participate in any kind of social activity. The onset of her depression was accompanied by a number of other symptoms, including feelings of guilt, lack of energy, and difficulty sleeping. Finally, the quality of her mood was more than just a feeling of sadness; she was so profoundly miserable that she felt numb. For all of these reasons, Cathy's problems would fit the description of major depression.

Our next case illustrates the symptoms of mania, which often appear after a person has already experienced at least one episode of depression. People who experience episodes of both depression and mania are given a diagnosis of bipolar mood disorder. The symptoms of a full-blown

manic episode are not subtle. People who are manic typically have terrible judgment and may get into considerable trouble as a result of their disorder. The central feature of mania is a persistently elevated or irritable mood that lasts for at least one week.

TABLE 5–2 Important Considerations in Distinguishing Clinical Depression from Normal Sadness

1. The mood change is pervasive across situations and persistent over time. The person's mood does not improve, even temporarily, when he or she engages in activities that are usually experienced as pleasant.
2. The mood change may occur in the absence of any precipitating events, or it may be completely out of proportion to the person's circumstances.
3. The depressed mood is accompanied by impaired ability to function in usual social and occupational roles. Even simple activities become overwhelmingly difficult.
4. The change in mood is accompanied by a cluster of additional signs and symptoms, including cognitive, somatic, and behavioral features.
5. The nature or quality of the mood change may be different from that associated with normal sadness. It may feel "strange," like being engulfed by a black cloud or sunk in a dark hole.

What is the difference between clinical depression and a low mood?

CASE **STUDY** Debbie's Manic Episode

Debbie, a 21-year-old single woman, was admitted to a psychiatric hospital in the midst of a manic episode. She had been in psychotherapy for depression for several months while she was in high school but had not received any type of treatment since then. After she completed two semesters at a community college, Debbie found a well-paying job in the advertising office of a local newspaper, where she had been working for 2 years.

Debbie's manic episode could be traced to experiences that began 3 or 4 months prior to her admission to the hospital. Debbie had been feeling unusually good for several weeks. At first she didn't think anything was wrong. In fact, her impression was quite the opposite. Everything seemed to be going right for her. Her energy level was up, and she felt a renewed confidence in herself and her relationships with other people, especially with her boyfriend, who had recently moved to a distant city. Debbie initially welcomed these feelings, especially because she had been so lethargic and also tended to be reserved with people.

One day when she was feeling particularly exhilarated, Debbie impulsively quit her job and went to visit her boyfriend. Giving up her job

without careful consideration and with no prospect for alternative employment was the first indication that Debbie's judgment was becoming impaired. Although she left home with only enough money to pay for her airplane ticket, she stayed for several weeks, mostly engaged in leisure activities. It was during this time that she started having trouble sleeping. The quality of her mood also began to change. It was less often cheerful and frequently irritable. She was extremely impatient and would become furious if her boyfriend disagreed with her. On one occasion, they had a loud and heated argument in the parking lot of his apartment complex. She took off her blouse and angrily refused to put it on again in spite of his demands and the presence of several interested bystanders. Shortly after the fight, she packed her clothes and hitchhiked back home.

After returning to her parents' home, Debbie argued with them almost continuously for several days. Her moods shifted constantly. One moment she would be bubbling with enthusiasm, gleefully throwing herself into new and exciting activities. If her plans were thwarted, she would fly into a rage. She phoned an exclusive tennis club to arrange for private lessons, which she

obviously could not afford, especially now that she was unemployed. Her mother interrupted the call and canceled the lessons. Debbie left the house in a fury and set off to hitch a ride to the tennis club. She was picked up by two unknown men, who persuaded her to accompany them to a party rather than go to the club. By the time they arrived at the party, her mood was once again euphoric. She stayed at the party all night and had intercourse with three men whom she had never met before.

The following day, Debbie borrowed money from a friend and took a train home. Another argument ensued when she arrived at home. Debbie struck her father and took the family car. Angry and frightened by her apparently irrational behavior, her parents phoned the police, who found her and brought her home. When another argument broke out, even more hostile than the first, the police took Debbie to their precinct office, where she was interviewed by a psychiatrist. Her attitude was flippant, and her language was abusive and obscene. On the basis of her clearly irrational and violent mood, as well as her marked impairment in judgment, the psychiatrist arranged for her to be committed to a psychiatric hospital.

"I am a psychic therapist, filled with the healing powers of the universe. I see things so clearly and deeply, and I must share this knowledge with everyone else."

Debbie's behavior on the ward was belligerent, provocative, and demanding. Although she hadn't slept a total of more than 4 hours in the previous 3 days, she claimed to be bursting with energy. She behaved seductively toward some of the male patients, sitting on their laps, kissing them, and occasionally unfastening her clothing. Although her speech was coherent, it was rapid and pressured. She expressed several grandiose ideas, including the boast that she was an Olympic swimmer and that she was a premed student in college. She had no insight into the severity of her mental condition. Failing to recognize that her judgment was impaired, she insisted that she had been brought to the ward so that she could help the other patients.

SYMPTOMS

The cases of Cathy and Debbie illustrate many of the most important symptoms and signs of mood disorders, which can be divided into four general areas: emotional symptoms, cognitive symptoms, somatic symptoms, and behavioral symptoms. Episodes of major depression and mania typically involve all four kinds of symptoms.

Emotional Symptoms

We all experience negative emotions, such as sadness, fear, and anger. These reactions usually last only a few moments, and they serve a useful purpose in our lives, particularly in our relationships with other people. Emotional reactions serve as signals to other people about our current feelings and needs. They also coordinate our responses to changes in the immediate environment.

Depressed, or **dysphoric** (unpleasant), mood is the most common and obvious symptom of depression. Most people who are depressed describe themselves as feeling utterly gloomy, dejected, or despondent. The severity of a depressed mood can reach painful and overwhelming proportions. Andrew Solomon (2001) has described the progression from sadness to severe depression in the following ways:

> I returned, not long ago, to a wood in which I had played as a child and saw an oak, a hundred years dignified, in whose shade I used to play with my brother. In twenty years, a huge vine had attached itself to this confident tree and had nearly smothered it. It was hard to say where the tree left off and the vine began. The vine had twisted itself so entirely around the scaffolding of tree branches that its leaves seemed from a distance to be the leaves of the tree; only up close could you see how few living oak branches were left. I empathized with that tree. My depression had grown on me as that vine had conquered the oak; it had been a sucking thing that had wrapped itself around me, ugly and more alive than I. (p. 18)

In contrast to the unpleasant feelings associated with clinical depression, manic patients like Debbie experience periods of inexplicable and unbounded joy known as euphoria. Debbie felt extremely optimistic and cheerful—"on top of the world"—in spite of the fact that her inappropriate behavior had made a shambles of her current life circumstances. In bipolar mood disorders, periods of elated mood tend to alternate with phases of depression.

Kay Jamison, professor of psychiatry at Johns Hopkins University School of Medicine, has written an eloquent and moving description of her own experiences with mania and depression.

> My manias, at least in their early and mild forms, were absolutely intoxicating states that gave rise to great personal pleasure, an incomparable flow of thoughts, and a ceaseless energy that allowed the translation of new ideas into papers and projects. (1995, pp. 5–6)

Unfortunately, as these feelings become more intense and prolonged, they can become ruinous. It may not be clear when the person's experience

▼ The quality of a depressed mood is often different from the sadness that might arise from an event such as the loss of a loved one. Some depressed people say that they feel like they are drowning or suffocating.

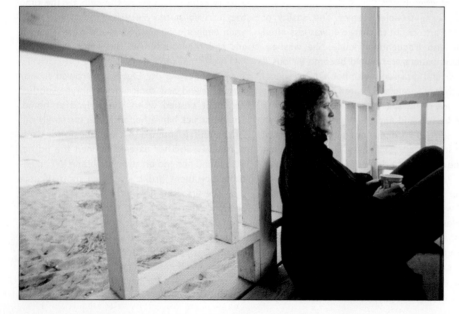

crosses the unmarked boundary between being productive and energetic to being out of control and self-destructive. Jamison described this subtle transition in the following way:

> There is a particular kind of pain, elation, loneliness, and terror involved in this kind of madness. When you're high it's tremendous. The ideas and feelings are fast and frequent like shooting stars, and you follow them until you find better and brighter ones. Shyness goes, the right words and gestures are suddenly there, the power to captivate others a felt certainty. There are interests found in uninteresting people. Sensuality is pervasive, and the desire to seduce and be seduced irresistible. Feelings of ease, intensity, power, well-being, financial omnipotence, and euphoria pervade one's marrow. But, somewhere, this changes. The fast ideas are far too fast, and there are far too many; overwhelming confusion replaces clarity. Memory goes. Humor and absorption on friends' faces are replaced by fear and concern. Everything previously moving with the grain is now against—you are irritable, angry, frightened, uncontrollable, and enmeshed totally in the blackest caves of the mind. (p. 67)

Many depressed and manic patients are irritable. Their anger may be directed either at themselves or at others, and frequently at both. Even when they are cheerful, people in a manic episode, like Debbie, are easily provoked to anger. Debbie became extremely argumentative and abusive, particularly when people challenged her grandiose statements about herself and her inappropriate judgment.

Anxiety is also common among people with mood disorders, just as depression is a common feature of some anxiety disorders (see Chapter 6). Two out of every three depressed patients also report feeling anxious (Rivas-Vasquez et al., 2004). People who are depressed are sometimes apprehensive, fearing that matters will become worse than they already are or that others will discover their inadequacy. They sometimes report that they are chronically tense and unable to relax.

Cognitive Symptoms

In addition to changes in the way people feel, mood disorders also involve changes in the way people think about themselves and their surroundings. People who are clinically depressed frequently note that their thinking is slowed down, that they have trouble concentrating, and

that they are easily distracted. Cathy's ability to concentrate was so disturbed that she became unable to work. She had extreme difficulty making even the simplest decisions. After she started staying home, she sat in front of the television set but was unable to pay attention to the content of even the simplest programs.

Guilt and worthlessness are common preoccupations. Depressed patients blame themselves for things that have gone wrong, regardless of whether they are in fact responsible. They focus considerable attention on the most negative features of themselves, their environments, and the future—a combination known as the "depressive triad" (Beck, 1967).

In contrast to the cognitive slowness associated with depression, manic patients commonly report that their thoughts are speeded up. Ideas flash through their minds faster than they can articulate their thoughts. Manic patients can also be easily distracted, responding to seemingly random stimuli in a completely uninterpretable and incoherent fashion. Grandiosity and inflated self-esteem are also characteristic features of mania.

Many people experience self-destructive ideas and impulses when they are depressed. Interest in suicide usually develops gradually and may begin with the vague sense that life is not worth living. Such feelings may follow directly from the overwhelming fatigue and loss of pleasure that typically accompany a seriously depressed mood. In addition, feelings of guilt and failure can lead depressed people to consider killing themselves. Over a period of time, depressed people may come to believe that they would be better off

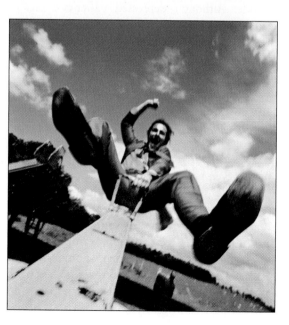

◀ Manic episodes are associated with euphoria as well as boundless energy and enthusiasm.

dead or that their family would function more successfully and happily without them. Preoccupation with such thoughts then leads to specific plans and may culminate in a suicide attempt.

Somatic Symptoms

The **somatic symptoms** of mood disorders are related to basic physiological or bodily functions. They include fatigue, aches and pains, and serious changes in appetite and sleep patterns. People, like Cathy, who are clinically depressed often report feeling tired all the time. The simplest tasks, which she had previously taken for granted, seemed to require an overwhelming effort. Taking a shower, brushing her teeth, and getting dressed in the morning became virtually impossible.

Sleeping problems are also common, particularly trouble getting to sleep. This disturbance frequently goes hand in hand with cognitive difficulties mentioned earlier. Worried about her endless problems and unable to relax, Cathy found that she would toss and turn for hours before finally falling asleep. Some people also report having difficulty staying asleep throughout the night, and they awaken 2 or more hours before the usual time. Early-morning waking is often associated with particularly severe depression. A less common symptom is for a depressed individual to spend more time sleeping than usual.

In the midst of a manic episode, a person is likely to experience a drastic reduction in the need for sleep. Some patients report that reduced sleep is one of the earliest signs of the onset of an episode. Although depressed patients typically feel exhausted when they cannot sleep, a person in a manic episode will probably be bursting with energy in spite of the lack of rest.

Depressed people frequently experience a change in appetite. Although some patients report that they eat more than usual, most reduce the amount that they eat; some may eat next to nothing. Food just doesn't taste good any more. Depressed people can also lose a great deal of weight, even without trying to diet.

People who are severely depressed commonly lose their interest in various types of activities that are otherwise sources of pleasure and fulfillment. One common example is a loss of sexual desire. Depressed people are less likely to initiate sexual activity, and they are less likely to enjoy sex if their partners can persuade them to participate.

Various ill-defined somatic complaints can also accompany mood disorders. Some patients complain of frequent headaches and muscular aches and pains. These concerns may develop into a preoccupation with bodily functions and fear of disease.

Behavioral Symptoms

The symptoms of mood disorders also include changes in the things that people do and the rate at which they do them. The term **psychomotor retardation** refers to several features of behavior that may accompany the onset of serious depression. The most obvious behavioral symptom of depression is slowed movement. Patients may walk and talk as if they are in slow motion. Others become completely immobile and may stop speaking altogether. Some depressed patients pause for very extended periods, perhaps several minutes, before answering a question.

In marked contrast to periods when they are depressed, manic patients are typically gregarious and energetic. Debbie's behavior provided many examples, even after her admission to the psychiatric hospital. Her flirtatious and provocative behavior on the ward was clearly inappropriate. She found it impossible to sit still for more than a moment or two. Virtually everything was interesting to her, and she was easily distracted, flitting from one idea or project to the next. Like other manic patients, Debbie was full of plans that were pursued in a rather indiscriminate fashion.

Other Problems Commonly Associated with Depression

Many people with mood disorders suffer from some clinical problems that are not typically considered symptoms of depression. Within the field of psychopathology, the simultaneous manifestation of a mood disorder and other syndromes is referred to as comorbidity, suggesting that the person exhibits symptoms of more than one underlying disorder. The greatest overlap is with anxiety disorders. Among people who meet the diagnostic criteria for major depression at some point during their lives, 60 percent also qualify for a diagnosis of at least one anxiety disorder (Kessler, Merikangas, & Wang, 2007).

Alcoholism and depression are also closely related phenomena. Many people who are depressed also drink heavily, and many people who are dependent on alcohol—approximately 40 percent—have experienced major depression at some point during their lives (Swendsen & Merikangas, 2000). The order of onset for the depression and alcoholism varies from one person to the next. Some people become depressed after they develop a drinking problem; others begin drinking after being depressed. There is also an association between these disorders within families. Alcohol abuse is common among the immediate families of patients with mood disorders. Eating disorders and anxiety disorders are also more common among first-degree relatives of depressed patients than among people in the general population.

DIAGNOSIS

Psychopathologists have proposed hundreds of systems for describing and classifying mood disorders. In the following section we will describe briefly some of the historical figures who played a prominent role in the development of classification systems (Berrios, 1992). This discussion should help place our description of the current diagnostic system, DSM-IV-TR, in perspective.

Brief Historical Perspective

Although written descriptions of clinical depression can be traced to ancient times, the first widely accepted classification system was proposed by the German physician Emil Kraepelin (1921). Kraepelin divided the major forms of mental disorder into two categories: *dementia praecox,* which we now know as schizophrenia (see Chapter 13), and *manic–depressive psychosis.* He based the distinction on age of onset, clinical symptoms, and the course of the disorder (its progress over time). The manic–depressive category included all depressive syndromes, regardless of whether the patients exhibited manic and depressive episodes or simply depression. In comparison to dementia praecox, manic–depression typically showed an episodic, recurrent course with a relatively good prognosis. Kraepelin observed that most manic-depressive patients returned to a normal level of functioning between episodes of depression or mania.

Despite the widespread acceptance and influence of Kraepelin's diagnostic system, many alternative approaches have been proposed. Two primary issues have been central in the debate regarding definitions of mood disorders. First, should these disorders be defined in a broad or a narrow fashion? A narrow approach to the definition of depression would focus on the most severely disturbed people—those whose depressed mood seems to be completely unrelated to any precipitating events, is entirely pervasive, and completely debilitating. A broader approach to definition would include milder forms of depression. Some recent critics have argued that the current diagnostic system has expanded the definition of depression to include normal sadness because it does not *exclude* reactions to a wide array of negative events, such as betrayal by a romantic partner or failing to reach an important life goal (Horwitz & Wakefield, 2007). This issue is, of course, a question about the validity of this diagnostic category (see Chapter 4). Is depression necessarily "normal" if it follows a stressful event? The resolution of this debate will depend on a consideration of research evidence (Zisook & Kendler, 2007).

The second issue regarding the diagnosis of mood disorders concerns heterogeneity. All depressed patients do not have exactly the same set of symptoms, the same pattern of onset, or the same course over time. Some patients have manic episodes, whereas others experience only depression. Some exhibit psychotic symptoms, such as delusions and hallucinations, in addition to their symptoms of mood disorder; others do not. In some cases, the person's depression is apparently a

> *Should normal sadness or grief following a loss ever be considered a disorder?*

▼ Bereavement is part of normal human experience. A clinical diagnosis would not be made following the loss of a loved one unless symptoms persist for more than two months or include marked functional impairment.

reaction to specific life events, whereas in others the mood disorder seems to come out of nowhere. Are these qualitatively distinct forms of mood disorder, or are they different expressions of the same underlying problem? Is the distinction among the different types simply one of severity?

Contemporary Diagnostic Systems

The DSM-IV-TR approach to classifying mood disorders recognizes several subtypes of depression, placing special emphasis on the distinction between unipolar and bipolar disorders. The overall scheme includes two types of unipolar mood disorder and three types of bipolar mood disorder.

Unipolar Disorders The unipolar disorders include two specific types: major depressive disorder and dysthymia. In order to meet the criteria for major depressive disorder, a person must experience at least one major depressive episode in the absence of any history of manic episodes. Table 5–3 lists the DSM-IV-TR criteria for a major depressive episode. Although some people experience a single, isolated episode of major depression followed by complete recovery, most cases of unipolar depression follow an intermittent course with repeated episodes.

Dysthymia differs from major depression in terms of both severity and duration. Dysthymia represents a chronic mild depressive condition that has been present for many years. In order to fulfill DSM-IV-TR criteria for this disorder, the person must, over a period of at least 2 years, exhibit a depressed mood for most of the day on more days than not. Two or more of the following symptoms must also be present:

1. Poor appetite or overeating
2. Insomnia or hypersomnia
3. Low energy or fatigue
4. Low self-esteem
5. Poor concentration or difficulty making decisions
6. Feelings of hopelessness

These symptoms must not be absent for more than 2 months at a time during the 2-year period. If at any time during the initial 2 years the person met criteria for a major depressive episode, the diagnosis would be major depression rather than dysthymia. As in the case of major depressive disorder, the presence of a manic episode would rule out a diagnosis of dysthymia.

The distinction between major depressive disorder and dysthymia is somewhat artificial because both sets of symptoms are frequently seen in the same person. In such cases, rather than thinking of

---

TABLE 5–3 Symptoms Listed in DSM-IV-TR for Major Depressive Episode

Five or more of the following symptoms have been present during the same 2-week period and represent a change from previous functioning; at least one of the symptoms is either (1) depressed mood, or (2) loss of interest or pleasure.

1. Depressed mood most of the day, nearly every day, as indicated either by subjective report (for example, feels sad or empty) or observation made by others (for example, appears tearful). Note: in children and adolescents, can be irritable mood.
2. Markedly diminished interest or pleasure in all, or almost all, activities most of the day, nearly every day.
3. Significant weight loss when not dieting or weight gain (for example, a change of more than 5 percent of body weight in a month), or decrease or increase in appetite nearly every day. Note: in children, consider failure to make expected weight gains.
4. Insomnia or hypersomnia nearly every day.
5. Psychomotor agitation or retardation nearly every day (observable by others).
6. Fatigue or loss of energy nearly every day.
7. Feelings of worthlessness or excessive or inappropriate guilt nearly every day (not merely self reproach or guilt about being sick).
8. Diminished ability to think or concentrate, or indecisiveness, nearly every day.
9. Recurrent thoughts of death (not just fear of dying), recurrent suicidal ideation without a specific plan, or a suicide attempt or a specific plan for committing suicide.

Source: Reprinted with permission from the *Diagnostic and Statistical Manual of Mental Disorders,* Fourth Edition, Text Revision. Copyright © 2000 by the American Psychiatric Association.

them as separate disorders, it is more appropriate to consider them as two aspects of the same disorder, which waxes and wanes over time. Some experts have argued that chronic depression is a single, broadly conceived disorder that can be expressed in many different combinations of symptoms over time (McCullough et al., 2003).

Bipolar Disorders All three types of bipolar disorders involve manic or hypomanic episodes. Table 5–4 lists the DSM-IV criteria for a manic episode. The mood disturbance must be severe enough to interfere with occupational or social functioning. A person who has experienced at least one manic episode would be assigned a diagnosis of *bipolar I disorder*. The vast majority of patients with this disorder have episodes of major depression in addition to manic episodes.

Some patients experience episodes of increased energy that are not sufficiently severe to qualify as full-blown mania. These episodes are called **hypomania.** A person who has experienced at least one major depressive episode, at least one hypomanic episode, and no full-blown manic episodes would be assigned a diagnosis of *bipolar II disorder*. The symptoms used in DSM-IV-TR to identify a hypomanic episode are the same as those used for manic episode (at least three of the seven symptoms listed in Table 5–4). The differences between manic and hypomanic episodes involve duration and severity. The symptoms need to be present for a minimum of only 4 days to meet the threshold for a hypomanic episode (as opposed to 1 week for a manic episode). The mood change in a hypomanic

episode must be noticeable to others, but the disturbance must not be severe enough to impair social or occupational functioning or to require hospitalization.

Cyclothymia is considered by DSM-IV-TR to be a chronic but less severe form of bipolar disorder. It is, therefore, the bipolar equivalent of dysthymia. In order to meet criteria for cyclothymia, the person must experience numerous hypomanic episodes and numerous periods of depression (or loss of interest or pleasure) during a period of 2 years. There must be no history of major depressive episodes and no clear evidence of a manic episode during the first 2 years of the disturbance.

Further Descriptions and Subtypes DSM-IV-TR includes several additional ways of describing subtypes of the mood disorders. These are based on two considerations: (1) more specific descriptions of symptoms that were present during the most recent episode of depression (known as *episode specifiers*) and (2) more extensive descriptions of the pattern that the disorder follows over time (known as *course specifiers*). These distinctions may provide a useful way to subdivide depressed patients, who certainly present a heterogenous set of problems. On the other hand, the validity of these subtypes is open

BIPOLAR MOOD DISORDER WITH PSYCHOTIC FEATURES
ANN

"I felt very tense, like my mind was racing; that I was making unusual connections; that I couldn't sleep at night."

Watch the video "Bipolar Mood Disorder with Psychotic Features: Ann" on MyPsych-Lab. Although Ann's manic episodes were associated with increased productivity, they also led to serious occupational and social problems.

TABLE 5–4	Symptoms Listed in DSM-IV-TR for Manic Episode

A. A distinct period of abnormally and persistently elevated, expansive, or irritable mood, lasting at least 1 week (or any duration if hospitalization is necessary).

B. During the period of mood disturbance, three or more of the following symptoms have persisted (four if the mood is only irritable) and have been present to a significant degree:

1. Inflated self-esteem or grandiosity.
2. Decreased need for sleep—for example, feels rested after only 3 hours of sleep.
3. More talkative than usual, or pressure to keep talking.
4. Flight of ideas or subjective experience that thoughts are racing.
5. Distractibility—that is, attention too easily drawn to unimportant or irrelevant external stimuli.
6. Increase in goal-directed activity (either socially, at work or school, or sexually) or psychomotor agitation.
7. Excessive involvement in pleasurable activities that have a high potential for painful consequences—for example, the person engages in unrestrained buying sprees, sexual indiscretions, or foolish business investments.

Source: Reprinted with permission from the *Diagnostic and Statistical Manual of Mental Disorders*, Fourth Edition, Text Revision. Copyright © 2000 by the American Psychiatric Association.

to question, especially those based on episode specifiers. Long-term follow-up studies suggest that a patient's subtype diagnosis is likely to change over repeated episodes (Angst, Sellaro, & Merikangas, 2000).

One episode specifier allows the clinician to describe a major depressive episode as having melancholic features. **Melancholia** is a term that is used to describe a particularly severe type of depression. Some experts believe that melancholia represents a subtype of depression that is caused by different factors than those that are responsible for other forms of depression (Leventhal & Rehm, 2005). The presence of melancholic features may also indicate that the person is likely to have a good response to biological forms of treatment, such as antidepressant medication and electroconvulsive therapy (Taylor & Fink, 2008).

In order to meet the DSM-IV-TR criteria for melancholic features, a depressed patient must either (1) lose the feeling of pleasure associated with all, or almost all, activities or (2) lose the capacity to feel better—even temporarily—when something good happens. The person must also exhibit at least three of the following: (1) The depressed mood feels distinctly different from the depression a person would feel after the death of a loved one; (2) the depression is most often worst in the morning; (3) the person awakens early, at least 2 hours before usual; (4) marked psychomotor retardation or agitation; (5) significant loss of appetite or weight loss; and (6) excessive or inappropriate guilt.

Another episode specifier allows the clinician to indicate the presence of *psychotic features*—hallucinations or delusions—during the most recent episode of depression or mania. The psychotic features can be either consistent or inconsistent with the patient's mood. For example, if a depressed man reports hearing voices that tell him he is a worthless human being who deserves to suffer for his sins, the hallucinations would be considered "mood congruent psychotic features." Depressed patients who exhibit psychotic features are more likely to require hospitalization and treatment with a combination of antidepressant and antipsychotic medication (Parker et al., 1997).

Another episode specifier applies to women who become depressed or manic following pregnancy. A major depressive or manic episode can be specified as having a *postpartum onset* if it begins within 4 weeks after childbirth. Because the woman must meet the full criteria for an episode of major depression or mania, this category does not include minor periods of postpartum "blues," which are relatively common (Seyfried & Marcus, 2003).

The DSM-IV-TR course specifiers for mood disorders allow clinicians to describe further the pattern and sequence of episodes, as well as the person's adjustment between episodes. For example, the course of a bipolar disorder can be specified as *rapid cycling* if the person experiences at least four episodes of major depression, mania, or hypomania within a 12-month period. Patients whose disorder follows this problematic course are likely to show a poor response to treatment and are at greater risk than other types of bipolar patients to attempt suicide (Coryell et al., 2003).

A mood disorder (either unipolar or bipolar) is described as following a seasonal pattern if, over a period of time, there is a regular relationship between the onset of a person's episodes and particular times of the year. The most typical seasonal pattern is one in which the person becomes depressed in the fall or winter, followed by a full recovery in the following spring or summer.

Researchers refer to a mood disorder in which the onset of episodes is regularly associated

▶ In a book about her struggle with postpartum depression, actress Brooke Shields described problems in forming a bond with her infant daughter.

with changes in seasons as **seasonal affective disorder.**[1] The episodes most commonly occur in winter, presumably in response to fewer hours of sunlight. Seasonal depression is usually characterized by somatic symptoms, such as overeating, carbohydrate craving, weight gain, fatigue, and sleeping more than usual. Among outpatients who have a history of at least three major depressive episodes, approximately one out of six will meet criteria for the seasonal pattern (Westrin & Lam, 2007). Most patients with seasonal affective disorder have a unipolar disorder.

COURSE AND OUTCOME

To describe the typical sequence over time and outcome of mood disorders, it is useful to consider unipolar and bipolar disorders separately. Most studies point to clear-cut differences between these two conditions in terms of age of onset and prognosis.

Unipolar Disorders

People with unipolar mood disorders typically have their first episode in their early thirties; the average age of onset is 32 (Kessler et al., 2007). The length of episodes varies widely. DSM-IV-TR sets the minimum duration at 2 weeks, but they can last much longer. Most unipolar patients will have at least two depressive episodes. The mean number of lifetime episodes is five or six.

The results of long-term follow-up studies of treated patients indicate that major depressive disorder is frequently a chronic and recurrent condition in which episodes of severe symptoms may alternate with periods of full or partial recovery (Thase, 2003). When a person's symptoms are diminished or improved, the disorder is considered to be in **remission,** or a period of recovery. **Relapse** is a return of active symptoms in a person who has recovered from a previous episode. These phases of the disorder are represented schematically in Figure 5–1.

Approximately half of all unipolar patients recover within 6 months of the beginning of an episode. After recovery from an episode of major

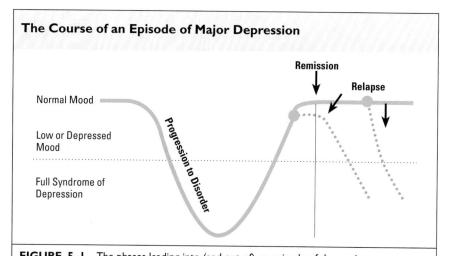

FIGURE 5–1 The phases leading into (and out of) an episode of depression.

Source: E. Frank, H. A. Swartz, and D. J. Kupfer, 2000, "Interpersonal and Social Rhythm Therapy: Managing the Chaos of Bipolar Disorder," *Biological Psychiatry, 48,* pp. 593–604. Copyright © 2000 by Society for Biological Psychiatry. Reprinted by permission of Elsevier, Ltd.

depression, the risk of relapse goes down as the period of remission increases. In other words, the longer the person remains free of depression, the better his or her chance of avoiding relapse (Hart, Craighead, & Craighead, 2001).

Bipolar Disorders

Onset of bipolar mood disorders usually occurs between the ages of 18 and 22 years, which is younger than the average age of onset for unipolar disorders. The first episode is just as likely to be manic as depressive. The average duration of a manic episode runs between 2 and 3 months. The onset of a manic episode is not always sudden. Jamison noted, for example:

> I did not wake up one day to find myself mad. Life should be so simple. Rather, I gradually became aware that my life and mind were going at an ever faster and faster clip until finally, over the course of my first summer on the faculty, they both had spun wildly and absolutely out of control. But the acceleration from quick thought to chaos was a slow and beautifully seductive one. (p. 68)

How do unipolar and bipolar disorders differ with regard to age of onset and sequence over time?

The long-term course of bipolar disorders is most often intermittent (Cuellar et al., 2005). Most patients have more than one episode, and bipolar patients tend to have more episodes than unipolar patients. The length of

---

[1]"Affect" and "mood" are sometimes used interchangeably in psychiatric terminology. Depression and mania were called "affective disorders" in DSM-III.

intervals between episodes is difficult to predict. The long-term prognosis is mixed for patients with bipolar mood disorder. Although some patients recover and function very well, others experience continued impairment. Several studies that have followed bipolar patients over periods of up to 10 years have found that approximately half of the people are able to achieve a sustained recovery from the disorder. On the other hand, many patients remain chronically disabled.

FREQUENCY

Several studies provide detailed information regarding the frequency of mood disorders in various countries around the world (Kessler, Merikangas, & Wang, 2007; Waraich et al., 2004). Some are based on information collected from nonclinical samples of men and women by investigators using structured diagnostic interviews. In other words, the people who participated in these studies did not have to be in treatment at a hospital or clinic in order to be identified as being depressed. These studies are particularly important because large numbers of people experience serious depression without wanting or being able to seek professional help. Data based exclusively on treatment records would underestimate the magnitude of the problem.

Incidence and Prevalence

Unipolar depression is one of the most common forms of psychopathology. In a representative sample of more than 9,000 people who were interviewed for the National Comorbidity Survey Replication (NCS-R), approximately 16 percent suffered from major depressive disorder at some point during their lives. Lifetime risk for dysthmia was approximately 3 percent. The lifetime risk for bipolar I and II disorders combined was close to 4 percent. Taken together, unipolar disorders are much more common than bipolar disorders. The ratio of unipolar to bipolar disorders is at least 5:1 (Kessler et al., 2005).

Because the NCS-R study identified a representative sample of community residents rather than patients already in treatment, it provides some insight regarding the proportion of depressed people who seek professional help for their problems. Slightly more than 20 percent of those people who met diagnostic criteria for a mood disorder in the past 12 months had received adequate treatment during that same time period. These data indicate that a substantial proportion of people who are clinically depressed do not receive professional treatment for their disorders. Finding ways to help these people represents an important challenge for psychologists and psychiatrists who treat mood disorders (Wittchen, Holsboer, & Jacobi, 2001).

Risk for Mood Disorders Across the Life Span

Age is an important consideration in the epidemiology of mood disorders. Some readers might expect that the prevalence of depression would be higher among older people than among younger people. This was, in fact, what many clinicians expected prior to large-scale epidemiological investigations, such as the NCS-R. This belief may stem from the casual observation that many older people experience brief episodic states of acute unhappiness, often precipitated by changes in status (for example, retirement, relocation) and loss of significant others (for example, children moving away, deaths of friends and relatives). But brief episodes of sadness and grief are not the same thing as clinical depression.

Although many people mistakenly identify depression with the elderly, data from the NCS-R project suggest that mood disorders actually are most frequent among young and middle-aged adults. These data are illustrated in Figure 5–2.

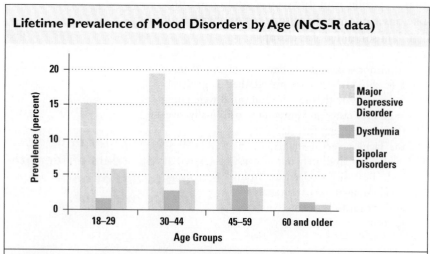

FIGURE 5–2 Lifetime prevalence of major depression, dysthymia, and bipolar disorder in a representative community sample.

Source: From Kessler et al. (2005), "Lifetime Prevalence and Age-of-Onset Distributions of DSM-IV Disorders in the National Comorbidity Survey Replication", *Archives of General Psychiatry, 62,* 593–602. Copyright © 2005. Reprinted by permission of American Medical Association.

Prevalence rates for major depressive disorder, dysthymia, and bipolar disorder were all significantly lower for people over the age of 60.

Several explanations have been offered for this pattern. One interpretation is based on the fact that elderly people are more likely to experience memory impairments (see Chapter 14). People who are in their sixties and seventies may have more trouble remembering, and therefore may fail to report, episodes of depression that occurred several months before the research interview is conducted. Also, because mood disorders are associated with increased mortality (for example, suicide), many severely depressed people might not have survived into old age. These are both plausible hypotheses that may have influenced the results of the NCS-R study. Nevertheless, the same pattern has been observed in several studies, and most investigators now believe that the effect is genuine: Clinical depression is less common among elderly people than it is among younger adults (Blazer, 2004).

The findings on age and depression also raise another important question: Has the frequency of depression increased in recent years? The answer is apparently yes. People born after World War II seem to be more likely to develop mood disorders than were people from previous generations. In fact, several studies have reported a consistent trend toward higher lifetime rates of depression in successively younger generations. The average age of onset for clinical depression also seems to be lower in people who were born more recently (Kessler et al., 2005; Wittchen, Knauper, & Kessler, 1994).

Gender Differences

Women are two or three times more vulnerable to depression than men are (Nolen-Hoeksema, 2002). This pattern has been reported in study after study, using samples of treated patients as well as community surveys, and regardless of the assessment procedures employed. The increased prevalence of depression among women is apparently limited to unipolar disorders. Gender differences are not typically observed for bipolar mood disorders.

Some observers have suggested that the high rates for unipolar mood disorders in women reflect shortcomings in the data collection process. Women simply might be more likely than men to seek treatment or to be labeled as being depressed. Another argument holds that culturally determined sanctions make it more difficult for men to admit to subjective feelings of distress such as hopelessness and despair. None of these alternatives has been substantiated by empirical evidence. Research studies clearly indicate that the higher prevalence of depression among women is genuine. Possible explanations for this gender difference have focused on a variety of factors, including sex hormones, stressful life events, and childhood adversity as well as response styles that are associated with gender roles (Hankin & Abramson, 2001; Kuehner, 2003). These issues are discussed later in this chapter.

Cross-Cultural Differences

Comparisons of emotional expression and emotional disorder across cultural boundaries encounter a number of methodological problems (see Research Methods in Chapter 9). One problem involves vocabulary. Each culture has its own ways of interpreting reality, including different styles of expressing or communicating symptoms of physical and emotional disorder. Words and concepts that are used to describe illness behaviors in one culture might not exist in other cultures. For example, some African cultures have

PEARSON mypsychlab VIDEO CASE

MAJOR DEPRESSION

EVERETT

"You feel absolute worthlessness. You feel there is no hope for the future."

Watch the video "Major Depression: Everett" on MyPsychLab. Notice the importance and persistence of the negative way in which he views himself and his abilities.

▼ Contrary to popular views, older people are actually less likely to be depressed than are younger people. Some subgroups of elderly people, however, are at high risk for depression.

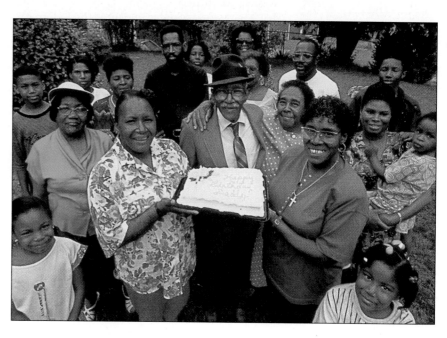

only one word for both anger and sadness. Interesting adaptations are, therefore, required to translate questions that are supposed to tap experiences such as anxiety and depression. One investigation, which employed a British interview schedule that had been translated into Yoruba—a language spoken in Nigeria—used the phrase "the heart goes weak" to represent depression (Leff, 1988). Our own diagnostic categories have been developed within a specific cultural setting; they are not culture-free and are not necessarily any more reasonable than the ways in which other cultures describe and categorize their own behavioral and emotional disorders (Lavender et al., 2006; Manson & Kleinman, 1998).

In what way are the symptoms of depression different in China?

Cross-cultural differences have been confirmed by a number of research projects that have examined cultural variations in symptoms among depressed patients in different countries. These studies report comparable overall frequencies of mood disorders in various parts of the world, but the specific type of symptom expressed by the patients varies from one culture to the next. In Chinese patients, depression is more likely to be described in terms of somatic symptoms, such as sleeping problems, headaches, and loss of energy (Kleinman, 2004). Depressed patients in Europe and North America are more likely to express feelings of guilt and suicidal ideas (Kirmayer, 2001).

These cross-cultural comparisons suggest that, at its most basic level, clinical depression is a universal phenomenon that is not limited to Western or urban societies. They also indicate that a person's cultural experiences, including linguistic, educational, and social factors, may play an important role in shaping the manner in which he or she expresses and copes with the anguish of depression. Cross-cultural variations should also be kept in mind when clinicians attempt to identify central or defining features of depression. We will return to this point later in the chapter when we discuss the rationale behind studies that rely on animal models of depression.

CAUSES

In the next few pages we turn our attention to current speculation and knowledge about causes of mood disorders. Discussions of this topic must keep in mind the relatively high prevalence of these problems. Major depression is a severely disabling condition that affects at least 16 percent of the population, usually appearing during young adulthood when the person would be expected to be most active and productive. Why hasn't this problem been eliminated through the process of natural selection? Evolutionary theorists suggest that it is because, in addition to being painful and disruptive to a person's life, mild to moderate symptoms of depression may serve a useful purpose (Gilbert, 2006; Price et al., 2004). This argument is focused on those situations in which depression represents a temporary response to circumstances in the person's environment. As we will see, many episodes of depression do seem to be triggered by stressful life events and harsh social circumstances. An evolutionary perspective would hold that the symptoms of depression—slowing down, loss of motivation, withdrawal from other people—may represent a response system that helps the person disengage from a situation that is not going well (Nesse, 1999). For example, someone who is involved in an unsuccessful marriage may eventually become depressed, withdraw, and reconsider the long-term benefits of investing further time and resources in a relationship that is likely to remain unrewarding. At low levels and over brief periods of time, depressed mood may help us refocus our motivations and it may help us to conserve and redirect our energy in response to experiences of loss and defeat.

Psychological explanations for mood disorders focus on individual differences, and they are primarily concerned with the most severe and disabling forms of depression. Following difficult and challenging experiences, why do some people develop major depression and others do not? What factors are responsible for a relatively drastic failure of the psychological and biological systems that regulate mood? A disorder that is as common as depression must have many causes rather than one.

Our consideration of etiological factors is organized around different levels of analysis. We will consider social, psychological, and biological mechanisms that are involved in the onset and maintenance of mood disorders. This organization should help you appreciate the complementary nature of these analyses. After we have considered the impact of stressful life events on mood, we will discuss psychological factors, such as cognitive biases, that shape a person's response to stress. Then we will review what is known about hormones and brain activities that coordinate our responses to environmental stressors.

Social Factors

It should not be surprising that much of the literature on depression focuses on interpersonal loss and separation. From birth to death, our lives are intertwined with those of other people. We are fundamentally social organisms, and we feel sad when someone close to us dies. Similar feelings occasionally follow major disappointments, such as failure to win acceptance to the school of our choice or being fired from a job. In these cases, rather than losing other people, some clinicians have suggested that we may be losing "social roles" or ways in which we think about ourselves. Clues to the causes of depression may be found in studying these experiences of normal sadness. The onset and maintenance of clinical depression clearly involves a disruption or failure of the normal mechanisms that regulate the negative emotions following major losses.

Various theories of depression have been built around a consideration of the impact of stressful life events. Beginning around the turn of the twentieth century, psychodynamic theories emphasized the central role played by interpersonal relationships and loss of significant others in setting the stage for depression as well as in bringing about a depressive episode (Freud, 1917/1961). Freud's theory laid the intellectual foundation for many subsequent studies of psychological and social factors in the development and maintenance of unipolar depression. He focused interest on the possibility that stressful life events, such as the death of a close friend or family member, may precipitate the onset of mood disorders. Freud was also interested in the observation that some people who become depressed are extremely dependent on other people for the maintenance of their self-esteem. This hypothesis anticipated subsequent studies of social skills in depression and the importance of interpersonal relationships over the course of mood disorders.

Stressful Life Events and Unipolar Disorders
Several investigations have explored the relationships between stressful life events and the development of unipolar mood disorders. Do people who become clinically depressed actually experience an increased number of stressful life events? The answer is yes. The experience of stressful life events is associated with an increased probability that a person will become depressed. This correlation has been demonstrated many times (Hammen, 2005; Monroe & Harkness, 2005).

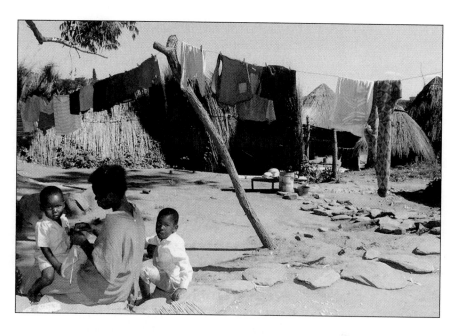

▲ A series of studies comparing the life experiences of women in six communities—including Harare, Zimbabwe—found that the greater the frequency of severe events, the higher the prevalence of depression.

Investigators have faced difficult methodological issues in order to interpret the strong relationship between stressful life events and the onset of depression. One particularly troublesome problem involves the direction of the relationship between life events and mood disorders. For example, being fired from a job might lead a person to become depressed. On the other hand, the onset of a depressive episode, with its associated difficulties in energy and concentration, could easily affect the person's job performance and lead to being fired. Therefore, if depressed people experience more stressful events, what is the direction of effect? Does failure lead to depression, or does depression lead to failure?

By using prospective research designs, in which subjects are followed over time, investigators have been able to address the question of cause and effect (see Research Methods in Chapter 8). Prospective studies have found that stressful life events are useful in predicting the subsequent onset of unipolar depression (Brown, 2002; Monroe & Harkness, 2005). This evidence supports the argument that, in many cases, stressful life events contribute to (and are not merely consequences of) the onset of mood disorders.

Although many kinds of negative events are associated with depression, a special class of circumstances—those involving major losses of important people or roles—seems to play a crucial role in precipitating unipolar depression, especially a person's first lifetime episode. This conclusion is based, in large part, on a series of

Do negative life events cause depression? Or does depression lead to negative events?

studies reported by George Brown, a sociologist, and Tirril Harris, a clinical psychologist, both at Guy's, King's, and St. Thomas' School of Medicine (University of London in England). Their studies have compared the living circumstances and life experiences of depressed and nondepressed women, regardless of whether they are receiving treatment for their problems. Brown and Harris (1978) found that "severe" events—those that are particularly threatening and have long-term consequences for the woman's adjustment—increase the probability that a woman will become depressed. On the other hand, the ordinary hassles and difficulties of everyday living (events that are not severe) do not seem to lead to the onset of depression (Monroe & Simons, 1991).

Severe events increase the probability of depression, but most women who experience a severe event do not become depressed. What is the difference between the circumstances of women who become depressed after a severe event and those who do not? Brown and his colleagues believe that depression is more likely to occur when severe life events are associated with feelings of humiliation, entrapment, and defeat (Brown, 1998; 2002). An example of a humiliating event

would be a woman learning unexpectedly of her husband's long-standing infidelity. An example of an event fitting the entrapment theme would be a woman receiving official notification that her application to move out of appalling housing conditions had been denied. These data point to a particularly powerful relationship between the onset of depression and certain kinds of stressful life events. The likelihood that a woman will become depressed is especially high if she experiences a severe event that would be expected to lead to a sense of being devalued as a person or trapped with no way toward a brighter future (Kendler et al., 2003).

Comparisons among different populations can shed further light on the relation between severe life events and the etiology of depression. Brown (1998) repeated his study with women living in six different populations in Europe and Africa. Some of these are impoverished urban regions, such as a township in Harare, Zimbabwe, and others are rural. In each sample, Brown found that severe life events preceded the onset of most depressive episodes. He also found very large differences among these communities in terms of their overall prevalence of depression. These differences varied directly in proportion to the frequency with which their women experienced severe life events; communities with the highest rates of severe events produced the highest prevalence of major depression (see Figure 5–3). This pattern suggests that variations in the overall prevalence of depression are driven in large part by social factors that influence the frequency of stress in the community.

Social Factors and Bipolar Disorders Most investigations of stressful life events have been concerned with unipolar depression. Less attention has been paid to bipolar mood disorders, but some have found that the weeks preceding the onset of a manic episode are marked by an increased frequency of stressful life events (Hlastala et al., 2000; Johnson & Kizer, 2002). The kinds of events that precede the onset of mania tend to be different from those that lead to depression. While the latter include primarily negative experiences involving loss and low self-esteem, the former include schedule-disrupting events (such as loss of sleep) as well as goal attainment events. Some patients experience an increase in manic symptoms after they have achieved a significant goal toward which they had been working (Johnson et al., 2000). Examples of this kind of goal

Severe Life Events and Prevalence of Depression

FIGURE 5–3 Yearly rate of irregular or disruptive severe events per 100 women in six populations and prevalence of cases of depression in the same year.

Source: G. W. Brown, 1998, "Genetic and Population Perspectives on Life Events and Depression," *Social Psychiatry and Psychiatric Epidemiology, 33,* pp. 363–372. Copyright © 1998 by Springer-Verlag. Reprinted by permission of Springer-Verlag.

attainment event would be a major job promotion, being accepted to a competitive professional school program, or the blossoming of a new romantic relationship. These exhilarating experiences, coupled with the person's ongoing problems with emotion regulation, may contribute to a spiral of positive emotion and excess activity that culminates in a full-blown manic episode.

Aversive patterns of emotional expression and communication within the family can also have a negative impact on the adjustment of people with bipolar mood disorders. Longitudinal studies of bipolar patients have focused on the relation between frequency of relapse and the emotional climate within their families. Patients living with family members who are hostile toward or critical of the patient are more likely to relapse shortly after being discharged from the hospital (Miklowitz, Goldstein, & Neuchterlein, 1995). Furthermore, bipolar patients who have less social support are more likely to relapse and recover more slowly than patients with higher levels of social support (Cohen et al., 2004; Johnson et al., 1999). This evidence indicates that the course of bipolar mood disorder can be influenced by the social environment in which the person is living.

Psychological Factors

Severe events are clearly related to the onset of depression, but they do not provide a complete account of who will become depressed. Many people who do not become depressed also experience severe events. Presumably those who become depressed are somehow more vulnerable to the effects of stress. Several psychological factors may contribute to a person's vulnerability to stressful life events. In the following pages, we will consider two principal areas that have received attention in the research literature: cognitive factors and social skills.

Cognitive Vulnerability Cognitive theories concerning the origins of unipolar depression are based on the recognition that humans are not only social organisms; they are also thinking organisms, and the ways in which people perceive, think about, and remember events in their world can have an important influence on the way that they feel. Two people may react very differently to the same event, in large part because they may

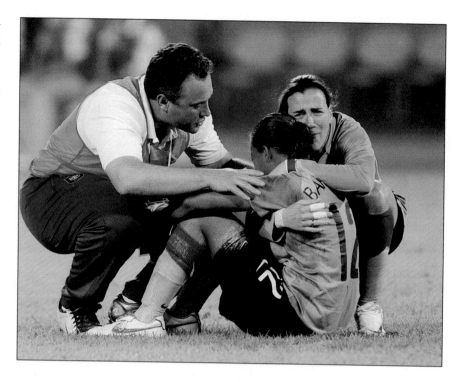

interpret the event differently. Cognitive theories about vulnerability to depression have typically focused on the ways in which people respond to negative experiences involving loss, failure, and disappointment (Alloy et al., 2006; Mathews & MacLeod, 2005).

Aaron Beck, a psychiatrist at the University of Pennsylvania, has been the most influential proponent of a cognitive view of depression (see Beck, 1974; Clark, Beck, & Alford, 1999). Beck began with a primary interest in the things that depressed people say, particularly their self-critical thoughts and their extremely pessimistic views of their environment. According to the cognitive perspective, these pervasive and persistent negative thoughts play a central role in the onset of depression when they are activated by the experience of a negative life event.

Various types of distortions, errors, and biases are characteristic of the thinking of depressed people. One is the tendency to assign global, personal meaning to experiences of failure. An example might be a person who has been turned down after he tried out for a competitive sports team and says to himself, "This proves that I am a failure" rather than acknowledging that many talented people were being considered, that only a few people could be retained, and difficult decisions had to be made by the coach. Another cognitive distortion associated with depression is the tendency to overgeneralize conclusions about the self based on negative experiences. Following the

▲ After losing an important game, an athlete who is prone to depression might think to herself, "It was my fault." "I fail at everything." "Things will never improve."

example raised above, the person might also say to himself, "The fact that I was cut from the team shows that I am also going to fail at everything else." A third type of cognitive error involves drawing arbitrary inferences about the self in the absence of supporting evidence (often in spite of contradictory evidence). In this regard, consider a player who is a member of an athletic team. If they lose a game and the coach is upset, the player might arbitrarily decide that the loss was his fault and the coach doesn't like him, even though nothing about his performance was particularly instrumental with regard to the team's performance in the game. The final type of cognitive bias related to depression is the tendency to recall selectively events with negative consequences and to exaggerate the importance of negative events while simultaneously discounting the significance of positive events. For example, suppose that an athlete is looking back over her experiences during the course of an entire season. She would be more likely to feel depressed about her performance if she tends to dwell on the mistakes that she made and the games that they lost rather than emphasizing the positive contributions that she made and the successes that she shared with her teammates.

How do these self-defeating biases lead to the onset of depression? According to Beck's theory, cognitive distortions combine to form a general pattern or cognitive **schema** that guides the ways in which people perceive and interpret events in their environment. Schemas are described as enduring and highly organized representations of prior experience. Although schemas may be latent—that is, not prominently represented in the person's conscious awareness at any given point in time—they are presumably reactivated when the person experiences a similar event. Depressive schemas increase the probability that the person will overreact to similar stressful events in the future.

A similar view of cognitive vulnerability to depression has been described in terms of hopelessness (Alloy et al., 2004). Hopelessness refers to the person's negative expectations about future events and the associated belief that these events cannot be controlled. According to this view, de-

Why do some people become depressed after stressful life events while others do not?

pression is associated with the expectation that desirable events probably will not occur or that aversive events probably will occur regardless of what the person does. Following a negative life event, the probability that the person will become depressed is a function of the explanations and importance that the person ascribes to these events. These explanations are known as *causal attributions*.

Some people tend to explain negative events in terms of internal, stable, global factors. This pattern has been called a depressogenicattributional style. For example, after failing an important exam, someone who uses this cognitive style would probably think that her poor performance was the result of her own inadequacies (internal), which she has recognized for a long time and which will persist into the future (stable), and which also are responsible for her failure in many other important tasks, both academic and otherwise (global). As in Beck's description of negative schemas, attributional style is not considered to be a sufficient cause of depression. It does represent an important predisposition to depression, however, to the extent that people with a generalized depressogenicattributional style are more likely to develop hopelessness if they experience a negative life event.

Several studies have demonstrated that cognitive distortions are indeed more common among depressed people than among people who are not depressed. Furthermore, attributional style is useful in predicting people's responses to negative events (Alloy et al., 2004; Metalsky et al., 1993). Prospective studies have identified persistent biases toward memory for negative information among people who later become depressed (Gotlib & Neubauer, 2000). Thus, there is substantial empirical support for the role of cognitive factors as a form of vulnerability to depression.

Interpersonal Factors and Social Behavior
Several investigators have suggested that, in addition to how we think about negative or stressful experiences, the ways in which we actually respond to these events may also influence the probability that we will become depressed. In other words, it's not just how you think about an event or circumstance, but the things that you actually do that will determine its eventual outcome. How does the depressed person cope with stressful events and respond to other people? What types of responses does the patient elicit from others? What are the extent and form of social resources that are available to help support the person during a crisis?

Some depressed people create difficult circumstances that increase the level of stress in their lives. In other words, the relationship between stressful life events and depression runs in both directions. For example, in comparison to women who are not depressed and women with other medical disorders, unipolar depressed women generate higher levels of stress, especially in the context of interpersonal relationships (Coyne, Thompson, & Palmer, 2002; Hammen, 2005; Harkness et al., 1999). Maladaptive tactics for coping with marital distress are important factors in this process. For example, when involved in a serious disagreement with a spouse, a depressed person might express escalating complaints and hostile, provocative comments rather than trying to work toward a solution to the conflict. This dynamic process leads to an escalation of stress.

Response Styles and Gender Another perspective on the development of depression has emphasized response styles, which represent a slightly different aspect of coping behavior. This approach has been developed in an effort to explain gender differences in the frequency of depression. The manner in which a person responds to the onset of a depressed mood seems to influence the duration and the severity of the mood (Nolen-Hoeksema, 1994, 2000). Two different response styles have been emphasized in this work. Some people respond to feelings of depression by turning their attention inward, contemplating the causes and implications of their sadness. This is called a *ruminative style*. Writing in a diary or talking extensively with a friend about how one feels are indications of a ruminative style. Other people employ a *distracting style* to divert themselves from their unpleasant mood. They work on hobbies, play sports, or otherwise become involved in activities that draw their attention away from symptoms of depression.

The first hypothesis of the response styles model is that people who engage in ruminative responses have longer and more severe episodes of depression than do people who engage in distracting responses. The second hypothesis is that women are more likely to employ a ruminative style in response to depression, whereas men are more likely to employ a distracting style. Because the ruminative style leads to episodes of greater duration and intensity, women are more susceptible to depression than are men.

Integration of Cognitive and Interpersonal Factors The factors that we have considered in the preceding pages almost certainly work in combination rather than individually. We do not need to decide whether cognitive vulnerabilities

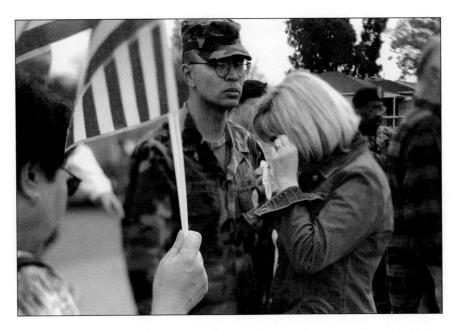

▲ Separation from a spouse during a war can be extremely stressful. Whether or not the person becomes depressed is influenced by cognitive events as well as interpersonal skills that are used to cope with this difficult situation.

are somehow more or less important than interpersonal behaviors because they are undoubtedly different sides of the same coin. The development of depression must be understood in terms of several stages: vulnerability, onset, and maintenance. Cognitive factors and interpersonal skills play an important role within each stage (Gotlib & Hammen, 1992; Alloy et al., 2006).

Vulnerability to depression is influenced by experiences during childhood, including events such as being repeatedly neglected or harshly criticized by parents. Negative ways of thinking about the world and dysfunctional interpersonal skills are presumably learned early in life (Ingram & Ritter, 2000). As the child grows up, the combination of biased cognitive schemas and deficits in interpersonal skills then affects his or her social environment in several ways: It increases the likelihood that the person will enter problematic relationships; it diminishes the person's ability to resolve conflict after it occurs; and it minimizes the person's ability to solicit support and assistance from other people (Hammen & Garber, 2001).

The onset of depression is most often triggered by life events and circumstances. The stressful life events that precipitate an episode frequently grow out of difficult personal and family relationships. The impact of these experiences depends on the meanings that people assign to them. People become depressed when they interpret events in a way that diminishes their sense of self-worth. Persistent interpersonal and cognitive problems also serve to maintain a depressed mood over an extended period of time and help it escalate to clinical proportions.

Biological Factors

We have considered a number of social and psychological factors that contribute to the etiology of mood disorders. Biological factors are also influential in the regulation of mood. Various studies suggest that genetic factors are somehow involved in unipolar and bipolar disorders, that hormonal abnormalities are regularly associated with depression, and that depression is associated with abnormalities in the activation of specific regions of the brain.

Genetics   Genetic factors are clearly involved in the transmission of mood disorders (Leonardo & Hen, 2006). Studies that support this conclusion also suggest that bipolar disorders are much more heritable than unipolar disorders.

Twin Studies   The comparison of monozygotic (MZ) and dizygotic (DZ) twin pairs provides one test of the possible influence of genetic factors (see Chapter 2). Several twin studies of mood disorders have reported higher concordance rates among MZ than among DZ twins (Kendler & Prescott, 2006; McGuffin et al., 2003).

One classic study used national twin and psychiatric registers in Denmark to identify 110 pairs of same-sex twins in which at least one member was diagnosed as having a mood disorder (Bertelson, Harvald & Hause, 1977). The concordance rates for bipolar disorders in MZ and DZ twins were .69 and .19, respectively. For unipolar disorders, concordance rates for MZ and DZ twins were .54 and .24, respectively. The fact that the concordance rates were significantly higher for MZ than for DZ twins indicates that genetic factors are involved in the transmission of both bipolar and unipolar mood disorders. The fact that the difference between the MZ and DZ rate was somewhat higher for bipolar than for unipolar disorders may suggest that genes play a more important role in bipolar disorders than in unipolar disorders. Similar patterns of MZ and DZ concordance rates have been reported subsequently from twin studies of mood disorders conducted in Sweden (Torgersen, 1986) and in England (McGuffin, et al., 1996).

Twin studies also tell us that environmental factors influence the expression of a genetically determined vulnerability to depression. The best evidence for the influence of nongenetic factors is the concordance rates in MZ twins, which consistently fall short of 100 percent. If genes told the whole story, MZ twins would always be concordant. Mathematical analyses have been used to estimate the relative contributions of genetic and environmental events to the etiology of mood disorders. The results of these analyses are expressed in terms of *heritability*, which can range from 0 percent (meaning that genetic factors are not involved) to 100 percent (meaning that genetic factors alone are responsible for the development of the trait in question) (see Research Methods in Chapter 17). These analyses indicate that genetic factors are particularly influential in bipolar mood disorders, for which the heritability estimate is 80 percent. Genes and environment contribute about equally to the etiology of major depressive disorder, in which the heritability estimate is close to 50 percent. The genetic contribution may be relatively minor for dysthymia or neurotic depression, where the heritability estimate is only 10 percent (Katz & McGuffin, 1993).

Mode of Transmission and Linkage Studies
The family and twin studies indicate that genetic factors play an important role in the development of mood disorders. They have not, however, established the operation of a particular mode of inheritance. It is difficult to identify specific genes involved in complex behavioral disorders because there is no straightforward pattern of inheritance. Most investigators view mood disorders as being polygenic—that is, they are influenced by several different genes—and each of these genes on its own only changes risk for the disorder by a small amount.

Several groups of investigators have searched for evidence of chromosomal linkage between the locus of a known gene and the locus for a gene that is responsible for mood disorders. Two loci are said to be linked when they occupy positions that are close together on the same chromosome. Linkage is usually detected by examining the degree of association between two or more traits within specific families (see Research Methods in Chapter 14).

Linkage studies have been focused on both bipolar and unipolar mood disorders. With the introduction of new gene-mapping techniques, our knowledge in this area is expanding dramatically but the results remain inconclusive. Many findings have been reported, but specific genes and genetic risk factors have not been confirmed (Kato, 2007). Preliminary reports of linkage to regions on various chromosomes have often failed to replicate when they were tested by investigators in different laboratories.

The possibility of detecting linkage to known traits is very exciting. This knowledge might eventually enable mental health professionals to identify people who are vulnerable to a disorder before the onset of overt symptoms. At the same time, however, two important cautions must be kept in mind regarding the complexity of the search for causes of mood disorders. One problem involves genetic heterogeneity. Within the general population, there may be more than one locus that contributes to the development of depression. Mood disorders may be linked to one marker within a certain extended family and to an entirely different marker in another family (Detera-Wadleigh & McMahon, 2004). Second, we also know that the environment plays an important role in the development of mood disorders. The onset of a mood disorders is determined by a combination of genetic and environmental risk factors that the individual experiences.

Genetic Risk and Sensitivity to Stress

How do genetic factors and stressful life events interact to bring about depression? The combined effects of genetic and environmental factors has been evaluated by incorporating the measurement of stressful life events into a standard twin design. One such study employed a large sample of female same-sex twins in a study of unipolar mood disorder (Kendler & Prescott, 2006). The twins were divided into four groups, based on levels of genetic risk. They were also divided into those who had experienced a severe life event during the follow-up period and those who had not. The negative impact of severe events was much higher among those women who were also at greater genetic risk for unipolar depression. Therefore the effects of the environment and genetic factors are not independent. Genetic factors apparently control the person's sensitivity to environmental events.

Another important demonstration of this phenomenon was based on new genetic techniques that allow investigators to identify specific genes (Caspi et al., 2003). This investigation focused on the serotonin transporter (5-HTT) gene, which has been studied because several drugs that are used to treat depression have a direct impact on this particular neurotransmitter (see page 146). There are two alleles (long and short) for one particular region of the 5-HTT gene: The short allele ("s") is associated with reduced efficiency of neural transmission in serotonin pathways. People who are homozygous for the "s" allele of the 5-HTT gene are at a particularly high risk for becoming clinically depressed if they experience stressful life events (see Figure 5–4). In the absence of increased stress, the presence of this gene does not increase the person's risk for depression. Both factors seem to be necessary.

The Neuroendocrine System Various kinds of central nervous system events are associated with the connection between stressful life events and major depression. In the following sections, we will consider evidence regarding hormones and specific regions of the brain. These are the biological phenomena that are closely associated with the social and psychological factors that we have described thus far. Cognitive and emotional events are implemented in these events (Miller & Keller, 2000). They are part of the process by which the brain communicates with the rest of the body and mobilizes activities in response to changes in the external environment.

The endocrine system plays an important role in regulating a person's response to stress. Endocrine glands, such as the pituitary, thyroid, and adrenal glands, are located at various sites throughout the body (see Figure 2–4). In response to signals from the brain, these glands secrete hormones into the bloodstream. One important pathway in the endocrine system that may be

How do genetic factors and stressful life events interact to cause depression?

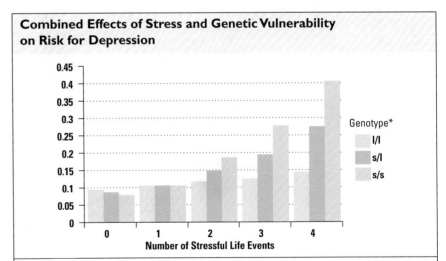

Combined Effects of Stress and Genetic Vulnerability on Risk for Depression

FIGURE 5–4 Probability of onset of major depressive episode as a function of genotype for the serotonin transporter gene.

*The short ("s") allele is associated with lower efficiency compared to the long ("l") allele.

Source: A. Caspi, K. Sugden, T. E. Moffitt, A. Taylor, I. W. Craig, H. Harrington, J. McClay, J. Mill, J. Martin, A. Braithwaite, and R. Poulton, 2003, "Influence of Life Stress on Depression: Moderation by a Polymorphism in the 5-HTT Gene," *Science, 301*, pp. 386–389. Copyright © 2003 by American Association for the Advancement of Science. Reprinted by permission of the publisher.

closely related to the etiology of mood disorders is called the *hypothalamic–pituitary–adrenal (HPA) axis*. When the person detects a threat in the environment, the hypothalamus signals the pituitary gland to secrete a hormone called ACTH, which in turn modulates secretion of hormones, such as cortisol, from the adrenal glands into the bloodstream. Increased levels of cortisol help the person to prepare to respond to the threat by increasing alertness and delivering more fuel to muscles while also decreasing interest in other activities that might interfere with self-protection (such as sleeping and eating). This system is illustrated in Figure 5–5.

An association between the HPA axis and depression is indicated by evidence regarding the *dexamethasone suppression test* (DST), which has been used extensively to study endocrine dysfunction in patients with mood disorders (Nemeroff, 1998). Dexamethasone is a potent synthetic hormone. People who have taken a test dose of dexamethasone normally show a suppression of cortisol secretion because the hypothalamus is fooled into thinking that there is already enough cortisol circulating in the system. Some depressed people show a different response: Approximately half of depressed patients show a failure of suppression in response to the DST. After their symptoms have improved, most of these patients exhibit a normal response on the DST. This pattern is consistent with the hypothesis that a dysfunction of the HPA axis may be involved in the development or maintenance of clinical depression, at least for some people (Stone et al., 2008; Whybrow, 1997).

In what ways might endocrine problems be related to other etiological factors? Several possibilities exist. In terms of the specific link between the endocrine system and the central nervous system, overproduction of cortisol may lead to changes in brain structure and function. At a more general level, hormone regulation may provide a process through which stressful life events interact with a genetically determined predisposition to mood disorder. Stress causes the release of adrenal steroids, such as cortisol, and steroid hormones play an active role in regulating the expression of genes (Gotlib et al., 2008).

Brain Imaging Studies The newest tools in the search for biological underpinnings of mood disorders are those that allow scientists to create detailed images of brain structures and to monitor ongoing brain functions in living patients (see Chapter 4 for a description of these procedures). The brain circuits that are involved in the experience and control of emotion are complex, centering primarily on the limbic system and its connections to the prefrontal cortex and the anterior cingulate cortex. Brain imaging studies indicate that severe depression is often associated with abnormal patterns of activity as well as structural changes in various brain regions (Davidson et al., 2002; Gotlib & Hamilton, 2008). Some of these areas of the brain are illustrated in Figure 5–6. See Figure 2–3 for illustrations of the amygdala, hippocampus, and other structures involved in the limbic system.

Abnormal patterns of activation in regions of the prefrontal cortex (PFC) are often found in association with depression. This evidence has been collected using functional brain imaging procedures, such as PET and fMRI. Some areas show *decreased activity*, especially the dorsolateral prefrontal cortex on the left side of the brain. This area of the PFC is involved in planning that

Hormonal System Known as the Hypothalamic–Pituitary–Adrenal (HPA) Axis

HYPOTHALAMUS
CRF
ANTERIOR PITUITARY GLAND
STRESS
ACTH
ADRENAL GLAND
CORTISOL
INHIBITORY SIGNAL
BLOODSTREAM
PHYSIOLOGICAL CHANGES SUPPORTING "FIGHT OR FLIGHT" RESPONSES

Effects of CRF Application to Brain in Animals	
DECREASED	INCREASED
Eating	Restless activity in familiar environments
Sleeping	Withdrawal in unfamiliar environments
Reproductive activity	

FIGURE 5–5 The hypothalamic-pituitary-adrenal axis is activated in response to stress.
Source: Adapted from Nemeroff, C. (1998). The neurobiology of depression. *Scientific American. 278,* 28–35

is guided by the anticipation of emotion. A person who has a deficit of this type might have motivational problems, such as an inability to work toward a pleasurable goal. Other areas of the PFC have been found to show *abnormally elevated* levels of activity in depressed people. These include the orbital PFC and the ventromedial PFC, areas of the brain that are important for determining a person's responses to reward and punishment. More specifically, the orbital PFC inhibits inappropriate behaviors and helps the person ignore immediate rewards while working toward long-term goals. The ventromedial PFC is involved in the experience of emotion and the process of assigning meaning to perceptions. Overactivity in these regions of the brain might be associated with the prolonged experience of negative emotion.

The anterior cingulate cortex (ACC) provides a connection between the functions of attention and emotion. It allows us to focus on subjective feelings and to consider the relation between our emotions and our behavior. For example, the ACC is activated when a person has been frustrated in the pursuit of a goal, or when he or she experiences an emotion, such as sadness, in a situation where it was not expected. People suffering from major depressive disorder typically show decreased activation of the ACC (Davidson et al., 2002). A reduction in ACC activity might be reflected in a failure to appreciate the maladaptive nature of prolonged negative emotions and a reduced ability to engage in more adaptive behaviors that might help to resolve the person's problems.

The amygdala (see Figure 5–6), almond-sized nuclei near the tip of the hippocampus on each side of the brain, appear to be an important part of the neural circuit involved in emotion (Whybrow, 1997). They are extensively connected to the hypothalamus. This system is responsible for monitoring the emotional significance of information that is processed by the brain and regulating social interactions. Functional imaging studies have identified elevated levels of resting blood flow and glucose metabolism in the amygdala among patients with major depressive disorder and bipolar mood disorder (Drevets, 2002). Higher metabolism rates are associated with more severe levels of depression. Patients who respond positively to treatment show a normalization of amygdala metabolism.

It is tempting to infer from this pattern that the increased activity reflected in images of the amygdala represents, at the neurochemical level of

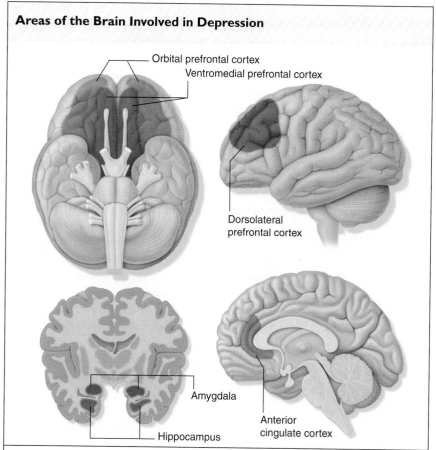

Areas of the Brain Involved in Depression

FIGURE 5–6 Brain regions involved in emotion and mood disorders.
Source: After R. J. Davidson et al., 2002, "Depression: Perspectives from Affective Neuroscience," *Annual Review of Psychology, 53*, p. 575.

analysis, a reflection of the distorted cognitive functions that have been described by clinical psychologists in association with depression (Gotlib & Hamilton, 2008). Of course, this kind of speculation will need to be tested using more detailed research strategies in which specific cognitive processes are measured while brain activities are recorded in depressed and nondepressed people.

How could the amygdala be related to problems in mood regulation?

Neurotransmitters Communication and coordination of information within and between areas of the brain depend on neurotransmitters, chemicals that bridge the gaps between individual neurons (see Chapter 2). Over the past several decades, scientists have gathered a great deal of information concerning the neurochemical underpinnings of depression and mania (Delgado & Moreno, 2006). Our knowledge in this area began with the accidental discovery, during the 1950s, of several drugs that have the ability to alter people's moods. The development of antidepressant drugs stimulated research on several specific neurotransmitters that have been shown to be responsible for their effects. Most notable among these are serotonin, norepinephrine, and dopamine. Each neurotransmitter works in a broad set of pathways connecting fairly specific brain locations.

Serotonin is the chemical messenger that is enhanced by medications such as Prozac. It has a profound effect on a person's mood, with higher levels being associated with feelings of serenity and optimism. Serotonin also plays an important role in areas of the brain that regulate sleep and appetite. Serotonin pathways include connections involving the amygdala, the hypothalamus, and areas of the cortex. The beneficial effects of drugs like Prozac (see the section on treatment of depression) provide the most convincing evidence for the argument that some type of malfunction in serotonin pathways is involved in the etiology of depression.

We know that the relation between neurotransmitters and depression is complex, and the specific mechanisms are not well understood. There may be more than 100 different neurotransmitters in the central nervous system, and each neurotransmitter is associated with several types of postsynaptic receptors. It seems unlikely that a heterogeneous disorder like depression, which involves a dysregulation of many cognitive and emotional functions, will be linked to only one type of chemical messenger or only one loop in the brain's circuitry. Current theories tend to emphasize the interactive effects of several neurotransmitter systems, including serotonin, norepinephrine, dopamine, and neuropeptides (short chains of amino acids that exist in the brain and appear to modulate the activity of the classic neurotransmitters) (Stockmeier, 2003; Thase, Ripu, & Howland, 2002).

Interaction of Social, Psychological, and Biological Factors

We have considered a variety of social, psychological, and biological factors that appear to be related to the causes of mood disorders. How can these factors be combined or integrated? One type of research that illustrates this point has employed an animal model of depression (see Research Methods). When laboratory animals are exposed to uncontrollable stress (such as a 15-minute forced swim in cold water from which they cannot escape), they frequently exhibit behavioral symptoms that are similar to (yet obviously not the same as) those seen in depressed humans (Kalueff, Wheaton, & Murphy, 2007; Lanfumey et al., 2008). The animals develop deficits in motor activity, sleep, and eating behaviors. This type of stress-induced depression in laboratory rats produces various temporary effects on neurotransmitters, including changes in the concentration of norepinephrine, serotonin, and dopamine in the specific regions of the limbic system and the frontal cortex. Rats that show these neurochemical consequences following exposure to stress exhibit signs of depression. If the neurotransmitters are not depleted, the rats do not appear to be depressed. Furthermore, administering antidepressant drugs to these animals has been shown to reverse or prevent the behavioral effects of uncontrollable stress. Selective breeding experiments have been able to produce subtypes of rats that differ in their response to behavioral challenges (such as the forced swim test), as well as in their response to antidepressant medication (Ressler & Mayberg, 2007).

This animal model illustrates the need to consider the interaction between biological and psychological phenomena. The data on stress-induced depression in rats suggest that neurochemical processes may be reactions to environmental events, such as uncontrollable stress in rats or severe life events in people. Psychological and biological explanations of depression are complementary views of the same process, differing primarily in terms of their level of analysis.

▼ Rats wearing "water wings" in a forced swim test. One (left) shows vigorous motor activity while the other (right) shows passive behavior (floating without limb movement) that is considered an analogue for depression.

RESEARCH METHODS Analogue Studies: Do Rats Get Depressed, and Why?

Many questions about the etiology of psychopathology cannot be addressed using highly controlled laboratory studies with human subjects. For example, does prolonged exposure to uncontrollable stress cause anxiety disorders? This kind of issue has been addressed using correlational studies with people who have the disorders in question, but experiments on these issues cannot be done with human subjects. For important ethical reasons, investigators cannot randomly assign people to endure conditions that are hypothesized to produce full-blown disorders like clinical depression. The best alternative is often to study a condition that is similar, or analogous, to the clinical disorder in question. Investigations of this type are called **analogue studies** because they focus on behaviors that resemble mental disorders—or isolated features of mental disorders—that appear in the natural environment.

Many analogue studies depend on the use of animal models of psychopathology, which have provided important insights regarding the etiology of conditions such as anxiety, depression, and schizophrenia (Kalueff et al., 2007). In the 1960s, Harry Harlow's research demonstrated that rhesus monkey infants develop despair responses after separation from their mothers. The somatic symptoms exhibited by these monkeys—facial and vocal displays of sadness and dismay, social withdrawal, changes in appetite and sleep, and psychomotor retardation—were remarkably similar to many symptoms of clinical depression in humans.

Why do some investigators study "depression" in animals?

This social separation model of depression has been used to explore several important variables that may be involved in mood disorders. For example, infant monkeys who have extensive experience with peers and other adults are less likely to become depressed following separation from their mothers. The skills that they learn through social exploration apparently allow them to cope more successfully with stress. The social separation model has also been used to explore neurochemical factors and mood disorders. Drug companies have used the model to evaluate the antidepressant effects of new drugs.

Some clinicians have argued that mental disorders like depression cannot be modeled in a laboratory setting, especially using animals as subjects. Cognitive symptoms—such as Beck's depressive triad—cannot be measured with animals. Do monkeys feel guilty? Can rats experience hopelessness or suicidal ideas? But these symptoms are not necessarily the most central features of the disorder. Cross-cultural studies have shown that in some non-Western societies somatic symptoms are the most prominent symptoms of depression. Many of these aspects of mood disorder are seen in animals. The value of any analogue study hinges, in large part, on the extent to which the analogue condition is similar to the actual clinical disorder. Some models are more compelling than others.

Analogue studies have one important advantage over other types of research design in psychopathology: They can employ an experimental procedure. Therefore the investigator can draw strong inferences about cause and effect. The main disadvantage of analogue studies involves the extent to which the results of a particular investigation can be generalized to situations outside the laboratory. If a particular set of circumstances produced a set of maladaptive behaviors in the laboratory, is it reasonable to assume that similar mechanisms produce the actual clinical disorder in the natural environment? In actual practice, questions about the etiology of disorders like depression will probably depend on converging evidence generated from the use of many different research designs.

TREATMENT

Several procedures, both psychosocial and biological, have proved to be useful in the treatment of mood disorders. In the following pages we will examine some of the more prominent contemporary approaches to the treatment of unipolar and bipolar mood disorders, as well as the research evidence on their usefulness.

Unipolar Disorders

Most psychological approaches to the treatment of depression owe some debt to psychodynamic procedures and Freud's emphasis on the importance of interpersonal relationships. According to Freud's view, the primary goal of therapy should be to help the patient understand and express the hostility and frustration that are being directed against the self. These negative emotions are presumably rooted in dysfunctional relationships with other people. Freud also placed considerable emphasis on the apparently irrational beliefs that depressed people hold about themselves and their world. These cognitive factors are also emphasized by cognitive therapists.

Cognitive Therapy The cognitive model assumes that emotional dysfunction is influenced by the negative ways in which people interpret events in their environments and the things that they say to themselves about those experiences. Based on the assumption that depression will be relieved if these maladaptive schemas are changed, cognitive therapists focus on helping their patients replace self-defeating thoughts with more rational self-statements (Dobson, 2008; Garratt et al., 2007).

A specific example may help illustrate this process. Consider the case of Cathy, the depressed attorney whom we introduced at the beginning of the chapter. Cathy focused a great deal of attention on relatively minor negative events at work, blaming herself for anything other than a perfect performance. Her therapist helped her to recognize that she was engaging in a pattern of cognitive distortion that Beck has labeled "selective abstraction." Taking a detail out of context, she would invariably ignore those aspects of her performance that refuted the conclusion that she was professionally incompetent. Her therapist helped her overcome these tendencies by teaching her to question her conclusions and to develop more objective ways of evaluating her experiences.

Cathy also tended to think about herself in absolute and unvarying terms. During the course of therapy, she learned to recognize this pattern and to substitute more flexible self-statements. Instead of saying to herself, "I am a hopeless introvert and will never be able to change," she learned to substitute, "I am less comfortable in social situations than some other people, but I can learn to be more confident."

The cognitive approach to treatment shares many features with behavioral approaches to intervention. Cognitive therapists are active and directive in their interactions with clients, and they focus most of their attention on their clients' current experience. They also assume that people have conscious access to cognitive events: Our thinking may not always be rational, but we can discuss private thoughts and feelings. Another important aspect of the cognitive approach to treatment, and a characteristic that it shares with the behavioral perspective, is a serious commitment to the empirical evaluation of the efficacy of treatment programs. Several studies have found that cognitive therapy is effective in the treatment of nonpsychotic, unipolar depression (Hollon, Stewart, & Strunk, 2006).

Interpersonal Therapy Interpersonal therapy is another contemporary approach to the psychological treatment of depression (Bleiberg & Markowitz, 2008; Weissman, Markowitz, & Klerman, 2000). It is focused primarily on current relationships, especially those involving family members. The therapist helps the patient develop a better understanding of the interpersonal problems that presumably give rise to depression and attempts to improve the patient's relationships

with other people by building communication and problem-solving skills. Therapy sessions often include nondirective discussions of social difficulties and unexpressed or unacknowledged negative emotions, as well as role playing to practice specific social skills.

Antidepressant Medications The types of medication that are used most frequently in the treatment of unipolar mood disorders fall intofour general categories: selective serotonin reuptake inhibitors (SSRIs), tricyclics (TCAs), monoamine oxidase inhibitors (MAO-Is), and "other," more recently developed drugs. Among patients who respond positively to antidepressant medication, improvement is typically evident within 4 to 6 weeks, and the current episode is often resolved within 12 weeks (De-Paulo & Horvitz, 2002; Schulberg et al., 1999). Medication is usually continued for at least 6 to 12 months after the patient has entered remission in order to reduce the chance of relapse.

Selective Serotonin Reuptake Inhibitors The **selective serotonin reuptake inhibitors (SSRIs)** were developed in the early 1980s and are now the most frequently used form of antidepressant medication, accounting for more than 80 percent of all prescriptions written for that purpose (Hirschfeld, 2001). Unlike the original forms of antidepressant medication, which were discovered by accident, SSRIs were synthesized in the laboratories of pharmaceutical companies on the basis of theoretical speculation regarding the role of serotonin in the etiology of mood disorders. There are many specific types of SSRIs (see Table 5–5). Controlled outcome studies indicate that Prozac and other SSRIs are about as effective as traditional forms of antidepressant medication (Kroenke et al., 2001).

The SSRIs inhibit the reuptake of serotonin into the presynaptic nerve ending and thus promote neurotransmission in serotonin pathways by increasing the amount of serotonin in the synaptic cleft. They are called "selective" because they seem to have little if any effect on the uptake of norepinephrine and dopamine. Nevertheless, the SSRIs are not entirely selective, in the sense that some of them do block reuptake of other neurotransmitters. They also vary in the potency with which they block serotonin reuptake. Their effectiveness in treating depression does not seem to be directly related to either the extent to which a particular SSRI is selective with regard to serotonin or its potency in blocking serotonin reuptake (Pallanti & Sandner, 2007).

The SSRIs are typically considered to be easier to use than other antidepressant drugs. They also have fewer side effects (such as constipation and drowsiness), and they are less dangerous in the event of an overdose. This does not mean, of course, that they are completely without side effects (see Critical Thinking Matters on page 148). Some patients experience nausea, headaches, and sleep disturbances, but these symptoms are usually mild and short term. The most troublesome side effects associated with SSRIs are sexual dysfunction and weight gain (Sussman & Ginsberg, 1998). The rate of decreased sexual desire and orgasmic dysfunction may be as high as 50 percent among both men and women taking SSRIs. Weight changes in response to SSRIs vary in relation to length of treatment. Many patients experience an initial weight loss, but most regain this weight after 6 months. Those who continue to take the medication may gain an average of 20 pounds.

TABLE 5–5 Medications for Unipolar Mood Disorders

DRUG CLASS	GENERIC NAME (TRADE NAME)	MODE OF ACTION
Selective serotonin Reuptake inhibitors (SSRI)	Fluoxetine (Prozac) Paroxetine (Paxil) Sertraline (Zoloft) Citalopram (Celexa) Fluvoxamine (Luvox)	Block 5-HT reuptake
Tricyclic antidepressants (TCA)	Amitriptyline (Elavil) Clomipramine (Anafranil) Imipramine (Tofranil)	Block reuptake of 5-HT and norepinephrine
Monoamine oxidase inhibitors (MAO-Is)	Phenelzine (Nardil)	Deactivate enzyme that breaks down monoamines
Other antidepressants	Trazodone (Desyrel)	Block 5-HT reuptake and block 5-HT receptors
	Buproprion (Wellbutrin)	Block norepinephrine and dopamine reuptake
	Venlafaxine (Effexor)	Block reuptake of 5-HT and norepinephrine

Note: 5-HT is serotonin.

Tricyclics The **tricyclics (TCAs),** such as imipramine (Tofranil) and amitriptyline (Elavil), have been in relatively widespread use since the 1950s, but their use has declined since the introduction of the SSRIs because they have more side effects. Common reactions include blurred vision, constipation, drowsiness, and a drop in blood pressure. The TCAs affect brain functions by blocking the uptake of neurotransmitters (especially norepinephrine) from the synapse. Several controlled double-blind studies indicate that TCAs benefit many depressed patients, although improvements might not be evident until 2 or 3 weeks after the beginning of treatment (Schatzberg, 1999; Thase, 2006). The several different kinds of tricyclic medication vary in potency and side effects, but they are generally equal in terms of effectiveness. Comparisons of TCAs and SSRIs indicate that they are approximately equal in terms of success rates, with positive responses being shown by 50 to 60 percent of depressed patients (Schulberg et al., 1999).

Monoamine Oxidase Inhibitors The antidepressant effects of **monoamine oxidase inhibitors (MAO-Is),** such as phenelzine (Nardil), were discovered at about the same time as those of the tricyclic drugs. These drugs have not been used as extensively as tricyclics, however, primarily for two reasons. First, patients who use MAO-Is and also consume foods containing large amounts of the compound tyramine, such as cheese and chocolate, often develop high blood pressure. Second, some early empirical evaluations of antidepressant medications suggest that MAO-Is are not as effective as tricyclics.

"I think the dosage needs adjusting. I'm not nearly as happy as the people in the ads."

CRITICAL THINKING MATTERS

Do Antidepressant Drugs Cause Violent Behavior?

Extensive media attention has been devoted to the suggestion that some of the SSRIs can increase the risk of violent and suicidal behavior. Several dramatic cases have been discussed at great length. One example is Chris Pittman, who was found guilty in 2005 of killing his paternal grandparents with a shotgun when he was 12 years old. No one questioned the basic facts of the case. Pittman admitted that he blasted his grandparents with a shotgun while they were sleeping. He then set their house on fire and fled the area. After he was caught, his defense team mounted what some court observers called the *Zoloft defense*, claiming that the murders were triggered by the boy's reaction to antidepressant medication that he had been taking for several days before the murders (see Chapter 18 for a discussion of the insanity defense). Prosecutors argued, on the other hand, that he killed his grandparents because he was angry after they disciplined him for fighting with a younger student on the school bus earlier that day. In other words, his motivation did not involve a mental disorder or a reaction to medication. Pittman was tried as an adult, convicted by a jury, and sentenced to 30 years in prison.

Tragic public cases such as this one generate strong opinions on both sides. Magazines and Web sites are filled with warnings about the dangers of treating children and adolescents with SSRIs, some more extreme than others. Many psychiatrists have responded by noting the beneficial effects that antidepressant medication can have for young people. Clearly parents should be warned about negative side-effects that are sometimes associated with drugs like Zoloft, but should they be frightened to the point that they avoid using one of the most effective forms of treatment for mood disorders? Critical thinking must prevail.

> *Are people taking Zoloft more likely to be violent than other people suffering from mood disorders?*

One important issue in this on going debate is the need for empirical evidence. Do SSRIs cause a significant increase in the risk of violence and suicide? Millions of people take antidepressant medication. Many depressed people commit suicide, in spite of the best efforts to treat their condition. The fact that one person committed suicide or any other violent crime while taking a specific drug does not provide convincing evidence that the drug *caused* the person to engage in that behavior. The question is whether people taking Zoloft are more likely to be suicidal or violent than other (similarly) depressed people who are being given another form of treatment. The data suggest that SSRI treatment does not increase risk of suicidal behavior, but the issue has not been closed entirely (Breggin, 2004; Gibbons et al., 2007). In the absence of better evidence, the U.S. Food and Drug Administration (FDA) requires that a warning be printed on the label when Zoloft (and some other SSRIs) are prescribed for children, including the following statement:

> Families and caregivers of pediatric patients being treated with antidepressants ... should be alerted about the need to monitor patients for the emergence of agitation, irritability, unusual changes in behavior, and the other symptoms described above, as well as the emergence of suicidality.

The legal implications of these findings remain ambiguous. Most forms of antidepressant medication are capable of triggering manic episodes in people who are depressed (Goldberg & Truman, 2003), and the symptoms of mania sometimes include hostility and aggression. Does that mean that SSRIs can *cause* someone to become homicidal or suicidal? When people come out of a period of depression and their mood is lifting, they also experience an increase in energy. For many years, experts have recognized that this period of time can be especially dangerous for people who have harbored serious thoughts of violence. If they decide to act on those impulses, is it the pill's fault? Is the person no longer responsible for his or her behavior?

While the public does need to be warned about side effects that can be associated with medication, it is also irresponsible to exaggerate or distort that evidence. People who are frightened do not make well-informed decisions. In fact, the risks of medication side effects must be balanced against the risks associated with failing to treat a potentially lethal condition such as depression. (Brent, 2004)

More recent studies have shown that MAO inhibitors are indeed useful in the treatment of depressed patients (Thase, 2006). They can be used safely when the patient avoids foods such as cheese, beer, and red wine. In addition, MAO-Is are now widely used in the treatment of certain anxiety disorders, especially agoraphobia and panic attacks (see Chapter 6).

The Efficacy of Psychotherapy and Medication Considerable time and energy have been devoted to the evaluation of psychological and pharmacological treatments for depression. The bottom line in this lengthy debate—based on extensive reviews of the research literature—is that cognitive therapy and antidepressant medication are both effective forms of treatment for people who suffer from unipolar depression (Hollon, Thase, & Markowitz, 2002). This is true for people with major depressive disorder as well as dysthymia. In actual practice, many experts recommend treatment with a combination of psychotherapy and medication (Kupfer & Frank, 2001; Simon et al., 2006).

Carefully controlled treatment outcome studies indicate that medication and psychotherapy are approximately equivalent in the treatment of people who are chronically depressed. Either form of treatment is a reasonable choice for people suffering from unipolar depression. Recent evidence indicates that the combination of psychotherapy and antidepressant medication often leads more quickly to a remission of symptoms than either form of treatment alone (Manber et al., 2008).

Bipolar Disorders

Treatment of bipolar mood disorders has also focused on the combined use of medication and psychotherapy. A variety of mood stabilizing drugs are employed with bipolar patients. They are used to help people recover from episodes of mania and depression and also on a long-term maintenance basis to reduce the frequency of future episodes (Geddes et al., 2004). Antidepressant medications are sometimes used, usually in combination with a mood stabilizer, for the treatment of bipolar patients (Fountoulakis et al., 2008). Clinicians must be cautious, however, because antidepressants can sometimes trigger a switch from depression into a hypomanic or manic episode.

Lithium In 1949, the Australian psychiatrist John Cade discovered that the salt *lithium carbonate* was effective in treating bipolar mood disorders. An extensive literature indicates that lithium carbonate is an effective form of treatment in the alleviation of manic episodes, and it remains the first choice for treating bipolar disorders. It is also useful in the treatment of bipolar patients who are experiencing a depressive episode. Perhaps most importantly, bipolar patients who continue to take lithium between episodes are significantly less likely to experience a relapse (Bauer & Mitchner, 2004).

Unfortunately, there are also some limitations associated with the use of lithium. Many bipolar patients, perhaps 40 percent, do not improve when they take lithium (Mendlewicz, Souery, & Rivelli, 1999). Nonresponse is particularly common among rapid cycling patients, those who exhibit a mixture of manic and depressed symptoms, and those with comorbid alcohol abuse. Compliance with medication is also a frequent problem; at least half the people for whom lithium is prescribed either fail to take it regularly or stop taking it against their psychiatrist's advice. The main reasons that patients give for discontinuing lithium involve its negative side effects, including nausea, memory problems, weight gain, and impaired coordination.

Anticonvulsant Medications Often, bipolar patients who do not respond to lithium are prescribed anticonvulsant drugs, particularly carbamazepine (Tegretol) or valproic acid (Depakene) (Walden et al., 1998). Outcome data suggest that slightly more than 50 percent of bipolar patients respond positively to these drugs. Like lithium, carbamazepine and valproic acid can be useful in reducing the frequency and severity of relapse, and they can be used to treat acute manic episodes. Valproic acid may be more effective than lithium for the treatment of rapid cycling bipolar patients and those with mixed symptoms of mania and depression in a single episode (Gadde & Krishnan, 1997). Common side effects include gastrointestinal distress (nausea, vomiting, and diarrhea) and sedation.

Psychotherapy Although medication is the most important method of treatment for bipolar disorders, psychotherapy can be an effective supplement to biological intervention. Both cognitive therapy and interpersonal therapy have been adapted for use with bipolar disorders. Cognitive therapy can address the patient's reactions to stressful life events as well as his or her reservations about taking medication (Craighead & Miklowitz, 2000).

A variation on interpersonal therapy, known as "interpersonal and social rhythm therapy" has been developed for use with bipolar patients (Frank, 2005). It is based on the recognition that a repeated episode of either mania or depression is often precipitated by one of the following factors: stressful life events, disruptions in social rhythms (the times of day in which the person works, sleeps, and so on), and failure to take medication. Special emphasis is placed on monitoring the interaction between symptoms (especially the onset of hypomanic or manic episodes) and social interactions. Therapists help patients learn to lead more orderly lives, especially with regard to sleep–wake cycles, and to resolve interpersonal problems effectively. Regulation of sleep and work patterns is also important. This therapy program is employed in combination with the long-term use of mood stabilizing medication.

Current evidence indicates that the combination of psychotherapy and medication for the treatment of bipolar disorder is more beneficial than medication alone (Miklowitz et al., 2007). There is an obvious need for more extensive research on the effectiveness of various types of psychosocial treatment for bipolar mood disorders.

Electroconvulsive Therapy

The procedure known as electroconvulsive therapy (or ECT) has proved beneficial for many patients suffering from unipolar or bipolar mood disorders (see Chapter 3 for a review of the background of ECT). Electroconvulsive therapy is typically administered in an inpatient setting and consists of a series of treatments given three times a week for 2 to 7 weeks (Abrams, 2002). Many patients show a dramatic improvement after six to eight sessions, but some require more. In current clinical practice, muscle relaxants are always administered before a patient receives ECT. This procedure has eliminated bone fractures and dislocations that were unfortunate side effects of techniques used many years ago. The electrodes can be placed either bilaterally (on both sides of the head) or unilaterally (at the front and back of the skull on one side of the patient's head). Unilateral placement on the nondominant hemisphere (the right side of the head for right-handed people) may minimize the amount of postseizure memory impairment, but it may also be less effective.

Although how ECT works remains largely a mystery, empirical studies have demonstrated that it is an effective form of treatment for severely depressed patients (Khalid et al., 2008). Reservations regarding the use of ECT center around widely publicized, although infrequent, cases of pervasive and persistent memory loss. Reviews of the research evidence indicate that ECT-induced changes in memory and other cognitive functions are almost always short-lived, and ECT does not

induce loss of neurons or other changes in brain structure (Lisanby, 2007).

No one denies that ECT is an invasive procedure that should usually be reserved for patients who have been resistant to other forms of intervention, such as medication and cognitive therapy. Nevertheless, it remains a viable and legitimate alternative for some severely depressed patients, especially those who are so suicidal that they require constant supervision to prevent them from harming themselves. As always, the risks of treatment must be carefully weighed against those associated with allowing the disorder to follow its natural course.

Seasonal Mood Disorders

The observation that changes in seasons can help bring on episodes of mood disorder leads to the relatively obvious implication that some patients might respond to manipulations of the natural environment. For centuries, physicians have prescribed changes in climate for their depressed clients (Wehr, 1989). The prominent French psychiatrist Jean Esquirol (1772–1840) reportedly advised a patient whose depression appeared when the days grew shorter to move from Belgium to Italy during the winter.

Modern light therapy was introduced in the 1980s (Rosenthal, 1998). Typical treatment involves exposure to bright (2,500 lux), broad-spectrum light for 1 to 2 hours every day. Some patients also respond positively to shorter periods (30 minutes) of high-intensity (10,000 lux) light (Hill, 1992). This high-intensity light is roughly equivalent to the amount of light that would be generated by a 750-watt spotlight focused on a surface 1 square meter in area. The light source—most often a rectangular box containing fluorescent ceiling fixtures—must be placed close to the patient at eye level. Improvement in the person's mood is often seen within 2 to 5 days.

Outcome studies have found that light therapy is an effective form of treatment for seasonal affective disorder, with outcome being roughly equivalent to the use of standard antidepressant medication (Lam et al., 2006). The combination of light therapy with cognitive therapy may be more effective than either form of treatment alone (Rohan et al., 2007). Many patients with seasonal affective disorders do respond well to light therapy, and it is considered by many clinicians to be a useful approach to this disorder. It is

▼ Electroconvulsive therapy is an effective form of treatment for severely depressed patients. It should be considered for people who do not improve with psychotherapy or antidepressant medication.

not exactly clear why or how light therapy works, but the process may help the body to normalize circadian rhythms, which regulate processes such as hormone secretion (Whybrow, 1997).

SUICIDE

BRIEF CASE **STUDY**
An Admiral's Suicide

Admiral Jeremy (Mike) Boorda was the highest ranking officer in the U.S. Navy when, at the age of 56, he committed suicide (Thomas, 1996). He was married and the father of four children. Boorda was the first person in the history of the navy to rise from the enlisted ranks to become chief of naval operations. Although his record of leadership was widely admired by both fellow officers and prominent politicians, he had recently been the subject of journalistic scrutiny. Questions had been raised about whether Boorda had legitimately earned two medals that he displayed on his uniform for several years (small Vs that are awarded to people who have shown valor in combat). These public symbols of heroism are a source of considerable status, especially among professional military people. Boorda had stopped wearing the medals after the issue was initially raised, but some members of the media had decided to pursue the issue further. On the morning of his death, Boorda was told that reporters from *Newsweek* magazine wanted to ask him some more questions about his justification for wearing these medals. He never met with them. Telling other officers that he was going home for lunch, Boorda went home and shot himself in the chest with a .38 revolver.

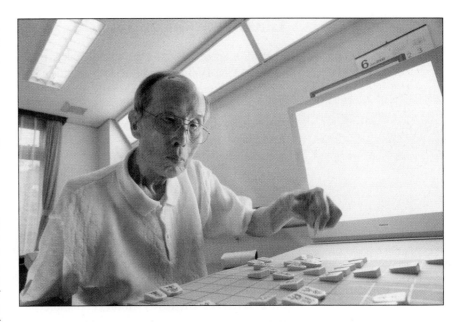

▲ This man is receiving light therapy for the treatment of seasonal affective disorder.

Why would such a successful person choose to end his own life? Suicide is an extremely personal, private, and complicated act. We will never know exactly why Admiral Boorda killed himself, but the circumstances surrounding his death are consistent with a number of facts about suicide. The highest rate of suicide in the United States is found among white males over the age of 50. Within this group, men who have been occupationally successful are more likely to commit suicide, especially if that success is threatened or lost. Notes that the admiral left for his wife and for navy personnel indicated that he could no longer face the public dishonor that might result from *Newsweek*'s investigation. Escape from psychological suffering is often a significant motive in suicide. Did Boorda commit suicide primarily to end his own subjective distress? Or was his death intended to avoid bringing disgrace to the navy, which had been plagued

by other scandals in recent years? When he was appointed chief of naval operations, several months before his death, it had been hoped that he would restore morale and improve public confidence in the navy. The *Newsweek* probe threatened to negate all of those efforts. Did his death represent a personal sacrifice for the military service that he loved and to which he had devoted 40 years of his life? These difficult questions illustrate the challenges faced by clinicians, who must try to understand suicide so that they can more effectively prevent it.

Aides said that Admiral Boorda did not show any signs of being depressed, even on the morning that he died. Nor were there any indications of substance abuse or other mental disorders. In this respect, Boorda's situation was unusual. Although many people who commit suicide do not appear to be depressed, and psychopathology doesn't explain all suicidal behavior, there is undoubtedly a strong relationship between depression and self-destructive acts. The available evidence suggests that at least 50 percent of all suicides occur as a result of, or in the context of, a primary mood disorder (Jamison, 1999). Moreover, the risk of completed suicide is much higher among people who are clinically depressed than it is among people in the general population. Follow-up studies consistently indicate that 15 to 20 percent of all patients with mood disorders will eventually kill themselves (Clark & Goebel-Fabbri, 1999). Thus it seems reasonable to conclude that there is a relatively close link between suicide and depression.

Classification of Suicide

Common sense tells us that suicide takes many forms. DSM-IV-TR does not address this issue; rather, it lists *suicidal ideation* (thoughts of suicide) only as a symptom of mood disorders. Clinicians and social scientists have proposed a number of systems for classifying subtypes of suicide, based on speculation regarding different motives for ending one's own life. Therefore, in contrast to the principles that were followed in creating DSM-IV-TR, classification systems for suicide are based on causal theories rather than descriptive factors.

The most influential system for classifying suicide was originally proposed in 1897 by Emile Durkheim (1858–1917), a French sociologist who is one of the most important figures in the history of sociology (Coser, 1977). In order to appreciate the nature of this system, you must understand Durkheim's approach to studying social problems. Durkheim was interested in "social facts," such as religious groups and political parties, rather than the psychological or biological features of particular individuals. His scientific studies were aimed at clarifying the social context in which human problems appear, and they were based on the assumption that human passions and ambition are controlled by the moral and social structures of society. One of his most important scientific endeavors was a comparison of suicide rates among various religious and occupational groups.

In his book *Suicide,* Durkheim (1897/1951) argued that the rate of suicide within a group or a society would increase if levels of social integration and regulation are either excessively low or excessively high. He identified four different types of suicide, which are distinguished by the social circumstances in which the person is living:

- *Egoistic suicide* (diminished integration) occurs when people become relatively detached from society and when they feel that their existence is meaningless. Egoistic suicide is presumably more common among groups such as people who have been divorced and people who are suffering from mental disorders. The predominant emotions associated with egoistic suicide are depression and apathy.
- *Altruistic suicide* (excessive integration) occurs when the rules of the social group dictate that the person must sacrifice his or her own life for the sake of others. One example is the former practice in some Native American tribes of elderly persons voluntarily going off by themselves to die after they felt they had become a burden to others.
- *Anomic suicide* (diminished regulation) occurs following a sudden breakdown in social order or a disruption of the norms that govern people's behavior. Anomic suicide explains increased suicide rates that occur following an economic or political crisis or among people who are adjusting to the unexpected loss of a social or occupational role. The typical feelings associated with *anomie* (a term coined by Durkheim, which literally means "without a name") are anger, disappointment, and exasperation.
- *Fatalistic suicide* (excessive regulation) occurs when the circumstances under which a person lives become unbearable. A slave, for example, might choose to commit suicide in order to escape from the horrible nature of his or her existence. This type of suicide was mentioned only briefly by Durkheim, who thought that it was extremely uncommon.

Durkheim believed that egoistic and anomic suicide were the most common types of suicide in Western industrial societies. Although he distinguished between these two dominant forms, he recognized that they were interconnected and could operate together. Some people may become victims of both diminished integration and ineffective regulation.

Durkheim's system for classifying types of suicide has remained influential, but it does have some limitations (Leenaars, 2004; Stack, 2004). For example, it does not explain why one person commits suicide while other members of the same

▼ Distinctions among Durkheim's types of suicide can be difficult to make. Do the motives of suicide bombers reflect a breakdown of social order? Or does their violent behavior represent a personal sacrifice for the sake of their society?

group do not. All the people in the group are subject to the same social structures. Another problem with Durkheim's system is that the different types of suicide overlap and may, in some cases, be difficult to distinguish. If the system is used to describe individual cases of suicide, such as that of Admiral Boorda, would clinicians be likely to agree on these subtypes? We are not aware of any attempts to evaluate the reliability of such judgments, but it might be quite low.

Nonsuicidal Self-Injury Some people deliberately harm themselves without trying to end their own lives. The most frequent forms of nonsuicidal self-injurious behaviors involve cutting, burning, or scratching the skin, usually in a place where the wounds and resulting scars can easily be concealed from others (Levenkron, 2006). Nonsuicidal self-injury must be distinguished from fashion trends, such as piercing and tattooing. People get tattoos and pierce various parts of their bodies with ornaments and jewelry because the effect on their appearance is considered stylish or distinctive. These activities are accomplished in spite of the initial pain that the person must endure. In contrast, people who engage in nonsuicidal self-injury do it because the pain serves a useful purpose for them and regardless of its impact on their appearance.

This problem can take many different forms and be associated with various kinds of mental disorder. Deliberate self-harm is listed in DSM-IV-TR as one of the symptoms of borderline personality disorder (see Chapter 9), but it also occurs among people suffering from other disorders, especially substance use disorders, eating disorders, depression, and posttraumatic stress disorder. Approximately 4 percent of people in the general population report that they have engaged in nonsuicidal self-injurious behaviors, and many of them would not qualify for the diagnosis of any specific disorder (Klonsky et al., 2003; Nock & Kessler, 2006). Sometimes, deliberate self-harm is itself the primary problem.

Why do some people deliberately hurt themselves, often disfiguring their own bodies? Several different explanations have been reported (Klonsky, 2007). For some people, cutting is a way to punish the self and is a reflection of frustration and anger. In other cases, the person uses self-inflicted pain in an effort to combat extended periods of dissociation and feelings of emptiness that accompany the absence of family members and friends. But the most commonly reported mechanism suggests that self-injury becomes a maladaptive way to

▲ Self-injury is often a maladaptive way to regulate intense, negative emotions.

regulate intense, negative emotional states. Episodes of self-injurious behavior are typically preceded by strong feelings of anxiety, anger, frustration, or sadness. These emotions are quickly diminished once the cutting has begun, and the person experiences relief. The final phase of the sequence involves the experience of shame or guilt when the episode is completed and the person reflects on what they have done.

Frequency of Suicide

In the United States and Canada, the annual rate of completed suicide across all age groups has averaged between 10 and 12 people per 100,000 population for several years (Goldsmith, 2001). More than 30,000 people in the United States kill themselves every year. Suicide rates vary as a function of many factors, including age, gender, and socioeconomic status (see Figure 5–7 on page 154). The suicide rate increased among adolescents from the 1970s through the mid 1990s, corresponding to an increase in the prevalence of depression and a decrease in the average age of onset for depression. Rates among other age groups either fell or remained steady. Suicide has become the third leading cause of death for people between the ages of 15 and 24, and it is the eighth leading cause of death in the general population (Kochanek et al., 2004).

Why do some people decide to end their own lives?

Suicide attempts are much more common than are completed suicides. The ratio of attempts to completed suicides in the general population is approximately 10 to 1; among adolescents, the ratio is closer to 100 to 1 (Hendin, 1995). There are important gender differences in rates of attempted suicide versus rates of completed suicide. Females aged 15 to 19 years make three times as many suicide attempts as males. Completion rates, however, are four times higher among males (Spirito & Esposito-Smythers, 2006). The difference in fatalities may be due, in part, to the methods employed. Men and boys are more likely to use violent and lethal methods such as firearms and hanging, whereas women and girls are more likely to take an overdose of drugs, which may allow time for discovery and interventions by other people.

The risk of successful suicide is highest among older people. Suicide rates have increased among young adults in recent years, but the highest rates are still found among older people, especially older white men. Although suicide attempts are most common among younger people, with most being made by those younger than 30, the proportion of suicide attempts that end in death is particularly high among the elderly. It is not clear whether this pattern should be attributed to a difference in method or to decreased physical resilience. Rates of suicide in the United States—broken down by age, race, and gender—are illustrated in Figure 5–7. In 1991, more than 70 percent of all suicides were committed by white men, with the highest rate being among those over the age of 80. The pattern for women is somewhat different. Their risk for suicide increases steadily with age until midlife and then tends to level off.

Causes of Suicide

Many factors contribute to suicidal behavior. In the following discussion, we consider some of the variables that operate at the level of the individual person—psychological and biological considerations—and are associated with suicidal behavior. We also summarize some contemporary research on social factors that are related to suicide.

Psychological Factors Many experts have argued that psychological events lie at the core of suicidal behavior (Joiner, 2005). Social factors may set the stage for self-destructive acts, but events taking place within the person's mind are most immediately responsible for determining whether a particular individual will attempt to end his or her own life. Prominent among these events are intense emotional distress and hopelessness. An outline of several psychological variables that are commonly associated with suicide is presented in Common Elements of Suicide.

The interpersonal-psychological theory of suicidal behavior maintains that suicidal behavior represents an attempt to escape from unbearable psychological pain (Joiner, 2005; Schneidman, 1996). According to this perspective, psychological pain is produced by prolonged frustration of psychological needs. Most important are the needs for affiliation and competence. People who view themselves as having failed in these domains—those who are low in belongingness or high in burdensomeness—will experience intense negative emotional states, such as shame, guilt, anger, and grief. For some people, suicide appears to offer a solution or a way to end their intolerable distress.

The desire to die is linked closely to social isolation and the belief that one has become a burden to others. But most people who experience these problems do not go on to attempt suicide. That action requires that the desire to end one's own life must be accompanied by the ability to enact lethal self-injury. Fear of death is one of our strongest emotions and self-preservation is a very powerful motive. Fortunately, these

Suicide Rates Across the Lifespan

Black women · Black men
White women · White men

Rates per 100,000

5-year age groups

FIGURE 5–7 Suicide rates per 100,000 population by 5-year group, race, and gender, United States 1991.

Source: Figure, p. 25, "Suicide Rates Across the Lifespan" in "Epidemiology of Suicidal Behavior" by E. K. Moscicki, SUICIDE AND LIFE-THREATENING BEHAVIOR, pp. 22-35. Copyright © 1995. Reprinted by permission of Guilford Publications, Inc.

COMMON ELEMENTS OF SUICIDE

Most people who kill themselves are suffering from some form of mental disorder, such as depression, substance dependence, or schizophrenia (Jamison, 1999). No single explanation can account for all self-destructive behavior. Edwin Schneidman (1996), a clinical psychologist who is a leading authority on suicide, described 10 characteristics commonly associated with completed suicide. Schneidman's list includes features that occur most frequently and may help us understand many cases of suicide:

1. The common purpose of suicide is to seek a solution. Suicide is not a pointless or random act. To people who think about ending their own lives, suicide represents an answer to an otherwise insoluble problem or a way out of some unbearable dilemma. It is a choice that is somehow preferable to another set of dreaded circumstances, emotional distress, or disability, which the person fears more than death. Attraction to suicide as a potential solution may be increased by a family history of similar behavior. If someone else whom the person admired or cared for has committed suicide, then the person is more likely to do so.

2. The common goal of suicide is cessation of consciousness. People who commit suicide seek the end of conscious experience, which to them has become an endless stream of distressing thoughts with which they are preoccupied. Suicide offers oblivion.

3. The common stimulus (or information input) in suicide is unbearable psychological pain. Excruciating negative emotions—including shame, guilt, anger, fear, and sadness—frequently serve as the foundation for self-destructive behavior. These emotions may arise from any number of sources.

4. The common stressor in suicide is frustrated psychological needs. People with high standards and expectations are especially vulnerable to ideas of suicide when progress toward these goals is suddenly frustrated. People who attribute failure or disappointment to their own shortcomings may come to view themselves as worthless, incompetent, or unlovable. Family turmoil is an especially important source of frustration to adolescents. Occupational and interpersonal difficulties frequently precipitate suicide among adults. For example, rates of suicide increase during periods of high unemployment.

5. The common emotion in suicide is hopelessness-helplessness. A pervasive sense of hopelessness, defined in terms of pessimistic expectations about the future, is even more important than other forms of negative emotion, such as anger and depression, in predicting suicidal behavior. The suicidal person is convinced that absolutely nothing can be done to improve his or her situation; no one can help.

Why is it difficult for a suicidal person to consider different solutions to their problems?

6. The common cognitive state in suicide is ambivalence. Most people who contemplate suicide, including those who eventually kill themselves, have ambivalent feelings about this decision. They are sincere in their desire to die, but they simultaneously wish that they could find another way out of their dilemma.

7. The common perceptual state in suicide is constriction. Suicidal thoughts and plans are frequently associated with a rigid and narrow pattern of cognitive activity that is analogous to tunnel vision. The suicidal person is temporarily unable or unwilling to engage in effective problem-solving behaviors and may see his or her options in extreme, all-or-nothing terms. As Schneidman points out, slogans such as "death before dishonor" may have a certain emotional appeal, but they do not provide a sensible basis for making decisions about how to lead one's life.

8. The common action in suicide is escape. Suicide provides a definitive way to escape from intolerable circumstances, which include painful self-awareness (Baumeister, 1990).

9. The common interpersonal act in suicide is communication of intention. One of the most harmful myths about suicide is the notion that people who really want to kill themselves don't talk about it. Most people who commit suicide have told other people about their plans. Many have made previous suicidal gestures. Schneidman estimates that in at least 80 percent of committed suicides, the people provide verbal or behavioral clues that indicate clearly their lethal intentions.

10. The common pattern in suicide is consistency of lifelong styles. During crises that precipitate suicidal thoughts, people generally employ the same coping responses that they have used throughout their lives. For example, people who have refused to ask for help in the past are likely to persist in that pattern, increasing their sense of isolation.

instincts protect most people in their worst emotional moments. The second component of the interpersonal-psychological theory holds that people who make lethal suicide attempts often work their way up to the act gradually (Joiner, 2005). This process may involve repeated nonsuicidal self-injurious behaviors, which allow the person to habituate to pain and fear of death. Previous suicide attempts, those that do not result in death, may also set the stage for a final lethal attempt. The interpersonal-psychological theory holds that death by suicide requires a combination of both the desire to die and the ability to inflict lethal harm to the self, which is frequently acquired through previous experience. Research evidence provides considerable support for this proposal (Van Orden et al., 2008).

Biological Factors Studies of the connection between neurotransmitters and suicide have focused primarily on reduced levels of serotonin, which might be related to poor impulse control as well as increased levels of violent and aggressive behavior (Currier & Mann, 2008; Joiner, Brown, & Wingate, 2005). Analogue studies with animals have found that lesions resulting in serotonin dysfunction lead to increases in aggression and failure to inhibit responses that were previously punished. Difficulty in regulating serotonin systems has been found among people who attempted suicide, and it has also been found among people who have shown other types of violent and aggressive behavior.

Twin studies and adoption studies have found that genetic factors are involved in the transmission of major mood disorders. Do genes contribute to the risk for suicide indirectly by increasing the risk for mental disorders, such as depression, schizophrenia, and substance abuse? Or is there a more direct contribution of genetic factors to self-destructive behavior? The answer appears to be yes. Genes associated with various neurotransmitter systems, especially serotonin, influence the development of impulsive personality characteristics, and suicide appears to be an especially likely outcome when a person inherits a predisposition to both psychopathology and impulsive or violent behavior. Genetic factors moderate the impact of environmental factors,

▶ Actress Margaux Hemingway killed herself in 1996 at the age of 41 by taking an overdose of a sedative. She was the fifth person in her family to commit suicide. Her grandfather, Ernest Hemingway, had committed suicide 35 years earlier.

such as stressful life events and childhood abuse, on suicidal behavior (Brezo et al., 2008).

Social Factors Durkheim (1897/1951) believed that suicide rates had increased during the nineteenth century because of an erosion of the influence of traditional sources of social integration and regulation, such as the church and the family. Social structures do represent one important consideration with regard to suicide (Stockard & O'Brien, 2002). For example, religious affiliation is significantly related to suicide rates. The active social networks encouraged by some church communities can become an important source of emotional support during difficult times, protecting the person from the potential influence of self-destructive impulses.

Social policies regulating access to firearms, especially handguns, also have an effect on suicide rates. Guns are a particularly lethal method of suicide, accounting for more than 60 percent of the 30,000 deaths that occur in the United States each year (Hendin, 1995). In states and countries with restrictive gun laws, the suicide rate usually drops, particularly among adolescents (Brent & Bridge, 2003; Kapusta et al., 2007). Of course, people who have definitely decided to end their own lives inevitably find a way to accomplish that goal, but many people who attempt suicide are ambivalent in their intent. Many attempts are made impulsively. Ready access to guns increases the chance that a person who does engage in an impulsive suicide attempt will die, because gunshot wounds are very likely to be fatal.

Prominent television and newspaper coverage of suicidal deaths, especially those of well-known celebrities, can have disastrous consequences by unintentionally encouraging other people to kill themselves (Cheng et al., 2007). Young people are especially vulnerable to this effect, which is sometimes called contagious suicide or a suicide cluster. There was, for example, an increase in rates of suicide in both the United States and England in the months immediately after Marilyn Monroe committed suicide. Imitation of this sort may represent a misdirected attempt to lend meaning to a person's life through association with the death of a celebrity. It might also be inspired by the attention that results with increased media coverage that invariably follows in the wake of multiple or sequential suicides. Descriptions of someone else's death may simply reduce some people's resistance to impulsive action.

Treatment of Suicidal People

Efforts to avoid the tragic consequences of suicidal behavior can be organized at several levels. One approach would focus on social structures that affect an entire society. Durkheim's theory of suicide, for example, indicates that the social structure of a society influences suicide rates. The social factors that we have just considered suggest some changes that could be made in contemporary Western societies in an effort to reduce the frequency of suicide. For example, more restrictive gun control laws might minimize access to the most lethal method of self-destruction. More cautious reporting by the media of suicidal deaths might reduce the probability of cluster suicides. These are, of course, controversial decisions, in which many other considerations play an important role. The media, for example, are motivated to report stories in a way that will maximize their popularity with the public. And many people oppose gun control legislation for reasons that have nothing to do with suicide rates. Therefore, it may be unrealistic to hope that these measures, aimed broadly at the level of an entire population, would be implemented widely. Most treatment programs that are concerned with suicidal behavior have been directed toward individual persons and their families.

Crisis Centers and Hotlines Many communities have established crisis centers and telephone hotlines to provide support for people who are distraught and contemplating suicide. The purpose of these programs is typically viewed in terms of suicide prevention. Sponsored by various agencies, including community mental health centers, hospitals, and religious groups, these services are often staffed by nonprofessionals, frequently volunteers. They offer 24-hour-a-day access to people who have been trained to provide verbal support for those who are in the midst of a crisis and who may have nowhere else to turn. Rather than provide ongoing treatment, most crisis centers and hotlines help the person through the immediate crisis and then refer him or her to mental health professionals.

Public and professional enthusiasm for suicide prevention centers peaked during the 1960s and 1970s. Unfortunately, data that were reported in the 1970s and 1980s did not support optimistic claims that these centers were "saving lives." Em-

◀ Elizabeth Shin was a 19 year-old student at MIT when she committed suicide. Her parents filed a lawsuit against the university, claiming that school officials could have prevented her death. This case involves several very difficult issues, including confidentiality (whether therapists can tell parents about such problems).

pirical studies showed that suicide rates do not differ in comparisons of similar communities that either have or do not have suicide prevention programs. Availability of crisis centers and hotlines does not seem to reduce suicide rates in communities (Brown et al., 2007; Lester, 2002).

Why don't hotlines reduce suicide rates? The challenges faced by these programs are enormous. Think about the characteristics of people who are driven to contemplate suicide. They are often socially isolated, feeling hopeless, and unable to consider alternative solutions. Many people with the most lethal suicidal ideation will not call a hotline or visit a drop-in crisis center. In fact, most clients of suicide prevention centers are young women; most suicides are committed by elderly men. The primary problem faced by suicide prevention programs is this: The people who they are trying to serve are, by definition, very difficult to reach.

It might be hard to justify the continued existence of crisis centers and hotlines if they are viewed solely in terms of suicide prevention. Only a small proportion of people who call hotlines are seriously suicidal. Most are people who are experiencing serious difficulties and who need to talk to someone about those problems. The value of contact with these individuals should not be underestimated. Crisis centers and hotlines provide support and assistance to very large numbers of people in distress. These services are undoubtedly valuable in their own right, even if serious questions remain about their impact on suicide rates.

Psychotherapy Psychological interventions with people who are suicidal can take many forms. These include all the standard approaches to psychotherapy, such as cognitive, behavioral, psychoanalytic, and family therapy. The research evidence indicates that cognitive behavior therapy does lead to a significant reduction in suicidal behavior, at least over short- and medium-term follow-up periods (Tarrier et al., 2008). Psychological treatments can address underlying problems that set the stage for the person's current problems. Additional treatment guidelines are also dictated by the threat of suicide. The following recommendations cover special considerations that are particularly important when clients have expressed a serious intent to harm themselves (adapted from Berman & Jobes, 1994):

1. *Reduce lethality.* The most important task is to reduce the person's experience of psychological pain from which the person is seeking escape. At a more concrete level, this also involves reducing access to means that could be used to commit suicide, such as guns and pills.

2. *Negotiate agreements.* Therapists frequently ask clients who have threatened to kill themselves to sign a contract, in which the client agrees to postpone self-destructive behavior for at least a short period of time. This kind of written agreement typically includes the client's consent to contact the therapist directly before engaging in any lethal actions. Of course, these agreements can be broken, but they may provide brakes to inhibit impulsive actions. The process of negotiating the agreement can also help the clinician to determine the severity of the client's suicidal intentions.

3. *Provide support.* It is often useful to make concrete arrangements for social support during a suicidal crisis. Friends and family members are alerted and asked to be available so that the person is not alone. The presence of others allows the person to discuss his or her problems (if he or she chooses to do so) and also provides supervision that may inhibit dangerous behaviors.

4. *Replace tunnel vision with a broader perspective.* People who are seriously contemplating suicide are typically unable to consider alternative solutions to their problems. Death may strike others as an irrational choice, but to people contemplating suicide, in the midst of the crisis, it seems perfectly logical. The therapist must help potential suicide victims develop or recover a more flexible and adaptive pattern of problem solving.

Medication Treatment of mental disorders, especially depression and schizophrenia, is usually the most important element of intervention with suicidal clients. The use of various types of medication is often an important part of these treatment efforts. Antidepressant drugs are frequently given to patients who are clinically depressed, and antipsychotic medication is useful with those who meet the diagnostic criteria for schizophrenia (see Chapter 13).

Considerable attention has been devoted recently to the use of selective serotonin reuptake inhibitors (SSRIs), such as fluvoxamine (Luvox) and fluoxetine (Prozac), because of the link between suicide and serotonin disregulation. Extensive clinical reports suggest that the use of SSRIs in treating depression actually lowers suicide rates (Gibbons et al., 2007). It should also be noted, however, that placebo-controlled outcome studies have not addressed this specific question. Furthermore, cases have been reported in which treatment with SSRIs has been followed by the development of new suicidal ideation (King, Segman, & Anderson, 1994). This pattern suggests that the relation between serotonin and suicide is neither direct nor simple and that caution is warranted in the use of SSRIs in treating suicidal clients (see Critical Thinking Matters on page 148).

Involuntary Hospitalization People who appear to be on the brink of committing suicide are often hospitalized, either with their permission or involuntarily (see Chapter 18 for a discussion of the legal issues involved in this process). The primary consideration in such cases is safety. In many cases, commitment to a hospital may be the best way to prevent people from harming themselves. The person's behavior can be monitored continuously, access to methods of harming oneself can be minimized (though perhaps not entirely eliminated), and various types of treatment can be provided by the hospital's professional staff.

GETTING HELP

The distinction between severe depression and the ups and downs of everyday life provides an important guide to the need for treatment. If you have been seriously depressed for several weeks and if depression is interfering with your ability to function, you should seek professional help. Fortunately, you have already taken the first step toward improvement. By reading this chapter, you can learn to recognize the symptoms of mood disorders.

Several effective forms of treatment are available for mood disorders. The first step in getting help is to find someone with whom you can talk. This might be your family physician, someone at your school's counseling center, or a therapist in private practice. It is important that you feel comfortable with the person you choose and with the form of treatment that she or he will provide.

Depression is not uncommon, but people who are depressed often feel lonely and alienated. A number of good books may help make it easier for you to find the right treatment for yourself. Various forms of treatment, including antidepressant medication, are described in *Understanding Depression: What We Know and What You Can Do About It* (2002) by Raymond De-Paulo. Self-help books may be useful to people whose depression has not reached severe proportions. The cognitive approach to therapy is described with exceptional clarity in *Feeling Good: The New Mood Therapy* (1999), by David Burns, a psychiatrist who has worked extensively with Aaron Beck. Helpful information regarding bipolar mood disorder can be found in *The Bipolar Disorder Survival Guide* (2002) by David Miklowitz.

People who are depressed need support and encouragement to seek treatment. Families and friends of depressed people find themselves in a very difficult and challenging situation. Mood disorders interfere with the person's ability to get along with other people and deplete his or her energy and motivation for seeking treatment. If they don't follow through with therapy or make noticeable improvements after several sessions, their friends can easily become discouraged or frustrated. Don't feel guilty if your efforts appear to go unrewarded. And don't blame the depressed person if he or she doesn't get better right away. Mood disorders are serious problems that require professional help. More detailed advice for families and friends can be found in a useful book entitled *How You Can Survive When They're Depressed: Living and Coping with Depression Fallout* by Anne Sheffield (1998).

■ SUMMARY

Mood disorders are defined in terms of emotional, cognitive, behavioral, and **somatic symptoms.** In addition to a feeling of pervasive despair or gloom, people experiencing an episode of major **depression** are likely to show a variety of symptoms, such as diminished interest in their normal activities, changes in appetite and sleep, fatigue, and problems in concentration. In contrast, a person in a manic episode feels elated and energetic. Manic patients also exhibit related symptoms, such as inflated self-esteem, rapid speech, and poor judgment.

DSM-IV-TR lists two major categories of mood disorders. People with **unipolar mood disorders** experience only episodes of depression. People with **bipolar mood disorders** experience episodes of **mania,** which are most often interspersed with episodes of depression. There are two specific types of unipolar mood disorder in DSM-IV-TR. Major depressive disorder is diagnosed if the person has experienced at least one episode of major depression without any periods of mania. **Dysthymia** is a less severe, chronic form of depression in which the person has been depressed for at least 2 years without a major depressive episode.

A person who has experienced at least one manic episode would receive a diagnosis of bipolar I disorder, regardless of whether he or she has ever had an episode of depression. One episode of major depression combined with evidence of at least one period of **hypomania** would qualify for a diagnosis of bipolar II disorder. **Cyclothymia** is a less severe, chronic form of bipolar mood disorder in which the person has experienced numerous periods of hypomania interspersed with periods of depressed mood.

The validity of the distinction between unipolar and bipolar mood disorders is supported by several types of evidence. Bipolar disorders tend to have an earlier age of onset and a worse prognosis than unipolar disorders.

Mood disorders are among the most common forms of psychopathology. Epidemiological studies have found that the lifetime risk for major depressive disorder is approximately 16 percent and the lifetime risk for dysthymic disorder is approximately 3 percent. Rates for both of these disorders are two or three times higher among women than among men. The lifetime risk for bipolar I and II disorders combined is close to 4 percent. Women and men are equally likely to develop bipolar mood disorder. The prevalence of depression appears to be increasing, with people born after World War II being more likely to become clinically depressed than people born in earlier generations.

The causes of mood disorders can be traced to the combined effects of social, psychological, and biological factors. Social factors include primarily the influence of stressful life events, especially severe losses that are associated with significant people or significant roles. Some studies show that people who are clinically depressed help to create some of the stressful events that they experience, especially those involving interpersonal relationships.

Two types of psychological factors play an important role in the development of mood disorders: cognitive responses to disappointment and failure and interpersonal skills. Cognitive theories are primarily concerned with the way in which depressed people experience a severe event. Beck's **schema** model places principal emphasis on cognitive distortions or the erroneous ways in which some people think about themselves and their environments. The **hopelessness** model holds that depression is associated with the expectation that desirable events will not occur or aversive events will occur regardless of what the person does. Furthermore, people will be more likely to become depressed if they attribute negative events to internal, stable, global factors.

Interpersonal theories focus on the ways in which individuals respond to people and events in their environments. Depressed people behave in ways that have a negative impact on other people. In this way they contribute to the stressful nature of their social environment. Coping behaviors may help to explain gender differences in the prevalence of unipolar depression. A ruminative style, in which the person's attention is turned inward, may be associated with longer and more severe episodes of depression. Women may be more likely than men to employ a ruminative style of response to the onset of a depressed mood.

Twin studies indicate that genetic factors play an important role in the etiology of both unipolar and bipolar mood disorders. They also indicate that genetic factors may play a stronger role in the development of bipolar than unipolar disorders. Genes may contribute to the development of depression directly through an effect on the central nervous system and indirectly by influencing the person's sensitivity to environmental events, such as severe stress. The mode of genetic transmission in mood disorders has not been identified. Linkage studies may help to find these pathways and could allow clinical scientists to identify individuals who are genetically predisposed to depression.

Neurochemical messengers in the brain also play a role in the regulation of mood and the etiology of mood disorders. Current thinking is focused on serotonin, norepinephrine, and dopamine, although many other neurotransmitter substances may also be involved in depression. Evidence regarding the long-term effects of antidepressant medications points to the interactive effects of multiple neurotransmitter systems.

Several types of psychological and biological treatment have been shown to be effective for mood disorders. Two types of psychotherapy, cognitive therapy and interpersonal therapy, are beneficial for unipolar and dysthymic patients. Three types of antidepressant medication are also useful in the treatment of major depressive disorder: **selective serotonin reuptake inhibitors, tricyclic antidepressants,** and **monoamine oxidase inhibitors.** Medication and psychotherapy are frequently used together. Outcome studies do not consistently favor either psychological or psychopharmacologic treatment.

Three other types of biological treatment are beneficial for specific types of mood disorder. Lithium carbonate and certain anticonvulsant drugs are useful for patients with bipolar mood disorders. Electroconvulsive therapy has been shown to be effective in the treatment of certain depressed patients, and it may be especially useful for patients who are severely suicidal or have failed to respond to other types of treatment. Light therapy seems to be effective for managing seasonal affective disorders.

People commit suicide for many different reasons. Most people who kill themselves are suffering some form of mental disorder, such as depression, substance abuse, or schizophrenia. For some people, suicide represents an escape from unbearable negative emotions, which are often the associated with social isolation and the perception of being a burden to others. Suicidal ideas are often accompanied by narrow patterns of perception and cognitive activity that make suicide seem like a reasonable solution to an otherwise unbearable dilemma. Serotonin dysfunction and genetic factors seem to contribute to the etiology of suicidal behavior. Social factors that have been studied in relation to suicide include religious affiliation, gun control laws, and media coverage of suicidal deaths. Efforts to prevent suicide include the use of hotlines and crisis centers, as well as the provision of psychotherapy and medication for people who are willing or able to seek professional treatment.

THE BIG PICTURE CRITICAL THINKING REVIEW

What is the difference between clinical depression and a low mood?

There is not an obvious marker to identify when sadness crosses over to serious depression, but several considerations help clinicians identify the disorder. These include duration of the depressed mood, presence of associated symptoms, and an inability to occasionally enjoy activities that would otherwise provide some relief from feeling down or blue. (SEE PAGE 123)

Are there different kinds of depression?

The easy (and short) answer is "yes." Many systems have been proposed to identify meaningful subtypes of mood disorder. The most obvious distinction is between unipolar and bipolar mood disorders. (SEE PAGES 128–129)

How do unipolar and bipolar disorders differ with regard to age of onset and sequence over time?

The age of onset and course of these disorders varies from one person to the next, but—on average—bipolar disorders have an earlier age of onset and bipolar patients typically experience more episodes over their lifetime. (SEE PAGES 131–132)

Are we more likely to experience depression as we get older?

Although many people mistakenly identify depression with the elderly, epidemiological studies have shown that mood disorders actually are most frequent among young and middle-aged adults. (SEE PAGES 132–133)

Do negative life events cause depression? Or does depression lead to negative events?

It works both ways. Major life events increase the probability that a person will become depressed, and people who are depressed can also generate higher levels of stress in their own lives. (SEE PAGES 135–136)

Why do some people become depressed after stressful life events while others do not?

Part of the answer depends on how a person interprets the event. Do they exaggerate the importance of the negative event, blowing it out of proportion? (SEE PAGE 138)

How do genetic factors and stressful life events interact to cause depression?

People who inherit certain genetic risk factors (such as having two short alleles for the serotonin transporter gene) are more likely than other people to become depressed following severe stress. (SEE PAGE 141)

How could the amygdala be related to problems in mood regulation?

The amygdala are involved in monitoring the emotional significance of events in the environment. High levels of amygdala activation in depressed people may reflect maladaptive cognitive factors. (SEE PAGE 143)

Why do some people want to end their own lives?

The desire to die is linked closely to social isolation and the belief that one has become a burden to others. (SEE PAGES 154–155)

■ KEY TERMS

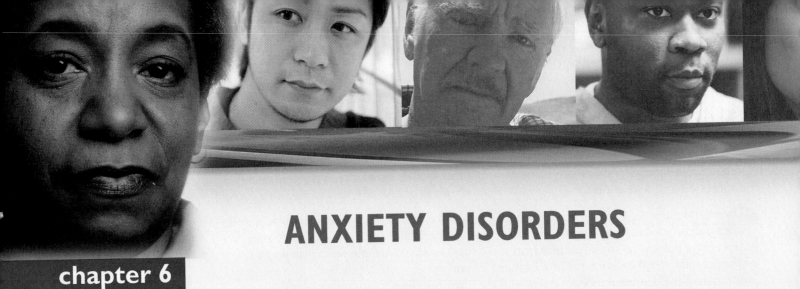

ANXIETY DISORDERS

Fear and anxiety play important roles in all of our lives. Fear helps us avoid danger in our immediate environment. Have you ever jumped out of the street to avoid a car that was unexpectedly rushing toward you? Or run away from an animal with a menacing growl? The sudden burst of fear that you experienced allowed you to react immediately. Anxiety is focused on the future rather than the immediate present. It helps us anticipate and prepare for important events. Remember when you called someone for the first time, performed at a musical recital, or spoke up in class? If you felt anxious in the time leading up to this event, you may have also noticed that your heart was pounding, your mouth was dry, and you were breathing faster. These are some of the physical signs of anxiety. Anxiety may be unpleasant, but it is often adaptive; we would have trouble organizing our lives if it were eliminated completely. Unfortunately, anxiety can also disrupt our lives. There are many ways in which anxiety can become maladaptive. It is often a question of degree rather than kind. We can worry too much, feel anxious too often, or be afraid at inappropriate times. In this chapter we will explore many of the important distinctions that psychologists make among phenomena such as fear, anxiety, worry, and panic. We will discuss the ways in which these experiences can become maladaptive and the ways in which the problems can be treated. In the next chapter, we will consider one other specific form of anxiety, known as posttraumatic stress disorder.

OVERVIEW

Taken together, the various forms of anxiety disorders—including phobias, obsessions, compulsions, and extreme worry—represent the most common type of abnormal behavior. The National Comorbidity Survey Replication (NCS-R) found that 18 percent of adults in the U.S. population have at least one type of anxiety disorder in any given year (Kessler et al., 2005). This figure was higher than the 1-year prevalence rates that were observed for mood disorders (10 percent) and substance use disorders (4 percent). Anxiety disorders lead to significant social and occupational impairment and a reduced quality of life (Olatunji et al., 2007).

Anxiety disorders share several important similarities with mood disorders. From a descriptive point of view, both categories are defined in terms of negative emotional responses. Feelings such as guilt, worry, and anger frequently accompany anxiety and depression. Many patients who are anxious are also depressed, and, similarly, many patients who are depressed are also anxious (Kessler et al., 2008; Shankman & Klein, 2003).

The close relationship between symptoms of anxiety and those for depression suggests that these disorders may share common causal features. In fact, stressful life events seem to play a role in the onset of both depression and anxiety. Cognitive factors are also important in both types of problems. From a biological point of view, certain brain regions and a number of neurotransmitters are involved in the etiology of anxiety disorders as well as mood disorders (Ressler & Mayberg, 2007).

The following case study illustrates the kinds of symptoms that are included under the heading of anxiety disorders. You should notice the overlap among different features of anxiety disorders, including panic, worry, avoidance, and a variety of alarming physical sensations. This narrative was written by Johanna Schneller (1988), a freelance writer who has been treated for panic disorder. *Agoraphobia* refers to an exaggerated fear of being in situations from which escape might be difficult, such as being caught in a traffic jam on a bridge or in a tunnel.

CASE **STUDY** A Writer's Panic Disorder with Agoraphobia

My heart was really pounding now, and I felt short of breath, as if wheels were rolling across my chest. I was terrified of what was happening to me. Would I be able to get home?

Three years have passed since my first panic attack struck, but even now I can close my eyes and see the small super-market where it happened. I can feel the shoppers in their heavy coats jostling me with their plastic baskets, and once again my stomach starts to drop away.

"It was November. I had just moved to New York City and completed a long search for a job and an apartment. The air felt close in that checkout line, and black fuzz crept into the corners of my vision. Afraid of fainting, I began to count the number of shoppers ahead of me, then the number of purchases they had. The overhead lights seemed to grow brighter. The cash register made pinging sounds that hurt my ears. Even the edges of the checkout counter looked cold and sharp. Suddenly I became nauseated, dizzy. My vertigo intensified, separating me from everyone else in the store, as if I were looking up from underwater. And then I got hot, the kind of hot you feel when the blood seems to rush to your cheeks and drain from your head at the same time.

"My heart was really pounding now, and I felt short of breath, as if wheels were rolling across my chest. I was terrified of what was happening to me. Would I be able to get home? I tried to talk myself down, to convince myself that if I could just stay in line and act as if nothing was happening, these symptoms would go away. Then I decided I wasn't going to faint—I was going to start screaming. The distance to the door looked vast and the seconds were crawling by, but somehow I managed to stay in the checkout line, pay for my bag of groceries and get outside, where I sat on a bench, gulping air. The whole episode had taken ten minutes. I was exhausted.

"At home, I tried to analyze what had happened to me. The experience had been terrifying, but because I felt safe in my kitchen, I tried to laugh the whole thing off—really, it seemed ridiculous, freaking out in a supermarket. I decided it was an isolated incident; I was all right, and I was going to forget it ever happened.

"Two weeks later, as I sat in a movie theater, the uncomfortable buzz began to envelop me again. But the symptoms set in faster this time. I mumbled something to my friends about feeling sick as I clambered over them. It was minutes before I caught my breath, hours before I calmed down completely.

"A month full of scattered attacks passed before they started rolling in like Sunday evenings, at least once a week. I tried to find a pattern: They always hit in crowded places, places difficult to escape. My whole body felt threatened, primed to run during an attack. Ironically, my attacks were invisible to anyone near me unless they knew what to look for—clenched neck muscles, restless eyes, a shifting from foot to foot—and I was afraid to talk to anyone about them, to perhaps hear something I wouldn't want to hear. What if I had a brain tumor? And I was embarrassed, as if it were my fault that I felt out of control. But then one night I had an attack alone in my bed—the only place I had felt safe. I gave in and called a doctor.

"As the weeks passed and the attacks wore on, I began to think maybe I was crazy. I was having attacks in public so often I became afraid to leave my house. I had one on the subway while traveling to work almost every morning but, luckily, never panicked on the job. Instead, I usually lost control in situations where I most wanted to relax: on weekend trips, or while visiting friends. I felt responsible for ruining other people's good time. One attack occurred while I was in a tiny boat deep sea fishing with my family; another hit when I was on a weekend canoe trip with my boyfriend. I also suffered a terrifying attack while on my way to see friends, stuck in traffic, merging into a tunnel near Boston's Logan Airport, with no exit ramp or emergency lane in sight.

"I began declining offers I wanted to accept: All I could think was, 'What if I panic in the middle of nowhere?' The times I did force myself to go out, I sat near the doors of restaurants, in aisle seats at movie theaters, near the bathroom at parties. For some reason, I always felt safe in bathrooms, as if whatever happened to me there would at least be easy to clean up.

"On days when I didn't have an actual attack, I could feel one looming like a shadow over my shoulder; this impending panic was almost worse than the real thing. By remembering old episodes, I brought on new ones, and each seemed to pull me closer to a vision I had of my mind snapping cleanly in half, like a stalk of celery."

Johanna's description of her problems raises a number of interesting questions, to which we will return later in the chapter. Was it just a coincidence that her first attack occurred shortly after the difficult experience of moving to a new city, starting a new job, and finding a new apartment? Could the stress of those experiences have contributed to the onset of her disorder? Was there a pattern to her attacks? Why did she feel safe in some situations and not in others? She mentions feeling out of control, as if she were responsible for her attacks. Could she really bring on another attack by remembering one from the past?

the private terrors that she endured, she was able to carry on most aspects of her life.

In addition to these general considerations, the diagnosis of anxiety disorders depends on several specific types of symptoms, which we discuss in the following sections. We begin with the nature of anxiety, which should be distinguished from more discrete emotional responses, like fear and panic.

SYMPTOMS

People with anxiety disorders share a preoccupation with, or persistent avoidance of, thoughts or situations that provoke fear or anxiety. Anxiety disorders frequently have a negative impact on various aspects of a person's life. Johanna found that anxiety and its associated problems constrained both her ability to work and her social relationships. Most people who knew Johanna probably did not know that she suffered from a mental disorder. In spite of

Anxiety

Like depression, the term *anxiety* can refer to either a mood or a syndrome. Here, we use the term to refer to a mood. Specific syndromes associated with anxiety disorders are discussed later in the chapter.

Anxious mood is often defined in contrast to the specific emotion of fear, which is more easily understood. **Fear** is experienced in the face of real, immediate danger. It usually builds quickly in intensity and helps organize the person's behavioral responses to threats from the environment (escaping or fighting back). Classic studies of fear among normal adults have often focused on people in combat situations, such as airplane crews during bombing missions over Germany in World War II (Rachman, 1991). In contrast to fear, **anxiety** involves a more general or diffuse emotional reaction—beyond simple fear—that is out of proportion to threats from the environment (Barlow, 2004). Rather than being directed toward the person's present circumstances, anxiety is associated with the anticipation of future problems.

Anxiety can be adaptive at low levels, because it serves as a signal that the person must prepare for an upcoming event. When you think about final exams, for example, you may become somewhat anxious. That emotional response may help to initiate and sustain your efforts to study. In contrast, high levels of anxiety become incapacitating by disrupting concentration and performance.

A pervasively anxious mood is often associated with pessimistic thoughts and feelings ("If something bad happens, I probably won't be able to control it"). The person's attention turns inward, focusing on negative emotions and self-evaluation ("Now I'm so upset that I'll never be able to concentrate during the exam!") rather than on the organization or rehearsal of adaptive responses that might be useful in coping with negative events. Taken together, these factors can be used to define maladaptive anxiety, or what David Barlow, a psychologist at Boston University, has called *anxious apprehension,* which consists of (1) high levels of diffuse negative emotion, (2) a sense of uncontrollability, and (3) a shift in attention to a primary self-focus or a state of self-preoccupation (Barlow, 2004).

Excessive Worry

Worrying is a cognitive activity that is associated with anxiety. In recent years psychologists have studied this phenomenon carefully because they consider it to be critical in the subclassification of anxiety disorders (DSM-IV-TR). **Worry** can be defined as a relatively uncontrollable sequence of negative, emotional thoughts that are concerned with possible future threats or danger. This sequence of worrisome thoughts is usually self-initiated or provoked by a specific experience or ongoing difficulties in the person's daily life. When excessive worriers are asked to describe their thoughts, they emphasize the predominance of verbal, linguistic material rather than images

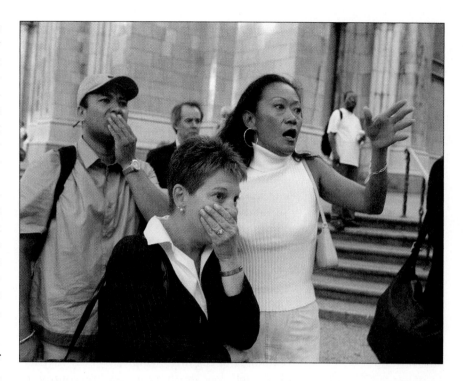

▲ People react with fear as they look toward the World Trade Center on September 11, 2001. Fear is a response to immediate danger, while anxiety is concerned with events that might happen in the future.

(Borkovec, Alcaine, & Behar, 2004). In other words, worriers are preoccupied with "self-talk" rather than unpleasant visual images.

Because everyone worries at least a little, you might wonder whether it is possible to distinguish between pathological and normal worry. The answer is yes, but there is not a clear line that divides the two kinds of experience. The distinction hinges on quantity—how often the person worries and about how many different topics the person worries. It also depends on the quality of worrisome thought. Excessive worriers are more likely than other people to report that the content of their thoughts is negative, that they have less control over the content and direction of their thoughts, and that in comparison to other adults, their worries are less realistic (Zebb & Beck, 1998).

Panic Attacks

A **panic attack** is a sudden, overwhelming experience of terror or fright, like the attack that was experienced by Johanna as she waited in the checkout line. Whereas anxiety involves a blend of several negative emotions, panic is more focused. Some clinicians think of panic as a normal fear response that is

PANIC DISORDER

JERRY

"I couldn't be in one place, a movie or a church—things would be closing in on me, and I would have to get up and leave."

Watch the video "Panic Disorder: Jerry" on MyPsychLab. Pay careful attention to the description of his first panic attack, which occurred while he was driving a car on the interstate.

triggered at an inappropriate time (Barlow, Brown, & Craske, 1994). In that sense, panic is a "false alarm." Descriptively, panic can be distinguished from anxiety in two other respects: It is more intense, and it has a sudden onset.

Panic attacks are defined largely in terms of a list of somatic or physical sensations, ranging from heart palpitations, sweating, and trembling to nausea, dizziness, and chills. Table 6–1 lists the DSM-IV-TR criteria for a panic attack. A person must experience at least 4 of these 13 symptoms in order for the experience to qualify as a full-blown panic attack. The symptoms must develop suddenly and reach a peak intensity within 10 minutes. The actual numbers and combinations of panic symptoms vary from one person to the next, and they may also change over time within the same person.

Why is a panic attack sometimes called a "false alarm"?

People undergoing a panic attack also report a number of cognitive symptoms. They may feel as though they are about to die, lose control, or go crazy. Some clinicians believe that the misinterpretation of bodily sensations lies at the core of panic disorder. Patients may interpret heart palpitations as evidence of an impending heart attack, or racing thoughts as evidence that they are about to lose their minds.

Panic attacks are further described in terms of the situations in which they occur, as well as the person's expectations about their occurrence. An attack is said to be expected, or *cued*, if it occurs only in the presence of a particular stimulus. For example, someone who is afraid of public speaking might have a cued panic attack if forced to give a speech in front of a large group of people. Unexpected panic attacks, like Johanna's experience in the grocery checkout line, appear without warning or expectation, as if "out of the blue."

Is there a typical pattern for panic attacks in the natural environment? In one descriptive study, panic disorder patients kept daily diaries describing panic experiences, and they also wore an ambulatory heart rate/physical activity recorder (Margraf et al., 1987). The average (mean) number of panic attacks among these patients was slightly less than one per day, but the number varied considerably across patients. Expected and unexpected panic attacks were experienced in roughly equivalent proportions. Unexpected attacks occurred most frequently at home, whereas situational attacks occurred most frequently in the car, usually while driving on freeways. The timing of unexpected attacks was evenly distributed across the day and night hours, with some occurring while the patient was asleep or trying to fall asleep. The results of this study and several others indicate that the symptoms and timing of panic attacks can vary widely from one patient to the next (Uhlenhuth et al., 2006).

Phobias

In contrast to both diffuse anxiety, which represents a blend of negative emotions, and panic attacks, which are frequently unexpected, **phobias** are persistent, irrational, narrowly defined fears that are associated with a specific object or situa-

---

TABLE 6–1   Diagnostic Criteria for Panic Attack in DSM-IV-TR

A discrete period of intense fear or discomfort, in which four (or more) of the following symptoms developed abruptly and reached a peak within 10 minutes:

1. Palpitations, pounding heart, or accelerated heart rate
2. Sweating
3. Trembling or shaking
4. Sensations of shortness of breath or smothering
5. Feeling of choking
6. Chest pain or discomfort
7. Nausea or abdominal distress
8. Feeling dizzy, unsteady, lightheaded, or faint
9. Derealization (feelings of unreality) or depersonalization (being detached from oneself)
10. Fear of losing control or going crazy
11. Fear of dying
12. Paresthesias (numbness or tingling sensations)
13. Chills or hot flushes

Source: Reprinted with permission from the *Diagnostic and Statistical Manual of Mental Disorders,* Fourth Edition, Text Revision. Copyright © 2000 by the American Psychiatric Association.

tion. Avoidance is an important component of the definition of phobias. A fear is not considered phobic unless the person avoids contact with the source of the fear or experiences intense anxiety in the presence of the stimulus. Phobias are also irrational or unreasonable. Avoiding only snakes that are poisonous or only guns that are loaded would not be considered phobic.

The most straightforward type of phobia involves fear of specific objects or situations. Different types of specific phobias have traditionally been named according to the Greek words for these objects. Examples of typical specific phobias include fear of heights (acrophobia), fear of enclosed spaces (claustrophobia), fear of small animals (zoophobia), fear of blood (hemophobia), and fear of flying on airplanes (aerophobia).

Some people experience marked fear when they are forced to engage in certain activities, such as public speaking, initiating a conversation, eating in restaurants, or using public rest rooms, which might involve being observed or evaluated by other people. Attempts to avoid these feared situations cause serious impairment in the person's social and occupational activities. For example, one young man who was treated by one of the authors of this text was afraid of urinating in public rest rooms. He planned his daily schedule with great care so that he would always be near a rest room with a locking door. Consequently, he was unable to attend movies or eat in restaurants unless they happened to have single-person rest rooms that he could lock from the inside.

The most complex and incapacitating form of phobic disorder is **agoraphobia,** which literally means "fear of the marketplace (or places of assembly)" and is usually described as fear of public spaces. The case of Johanna provides a brief description of the types of problems experienced by a person suffering from agoraphobia. The fear usually becomes more intense as the distance between the person and his or her familiar surroundings increases, or as avenues of escape are closed off. In that sense, agoraphobia is somewhat different from the other phobias because it is not so much a fear of being close to one specific object or situation (for example, animals, public speaking) as it is of being separated from signals associated with safety.

Typical situations that cause problems include crowded streets and shops, enclosed places like theaters and churches, traveling on public transportation, and driving an automobile on bridges, in tunnels, or on crowded expressways. In any of these

THE FAR SIDE®   BY GARY LARSON

Math phobic's nightmare

situations, the presence of a trusted friend may help the person with agoraphobia feel more comfortable. In the most extreme form of the disorder, agoraphobic patients are unable to venture away from their own homes. Some people with agoraphobia are able to visit public places (for example, shopping malls, theaters) but may remain near exits or aisles so that their escape cannot be easily blocked.

The uncomfortable sensations experienced by people with agoraphobia are similar to those that have already been described for other anxiety

▼ People with agoraphobia are afraid of crowded places from which they might not be able to escape. They also frequently experience panic attacks that are not cued by particular environmental circumstances.

disorders. They range from vague feelings of apprehension to specific physical sensations and full-blown panic attacks. People with agoraphobia are frequently afraid that they will experience an "attack" of these symptoms that will be either incapacitating or embarrassing, and that help will not be available to them. Many patients report that they are afraid of becoming dizzy, fainting, losing bladder or bowel control, or having heart problems. In some cases, previous experiences of this sort may have triggered persistent fear of repeated episodes.

Some clinicians have suggested that "fear of fear" is the central feature of agoraphobia (e.g., Goldstein & Chambless, 1978; Smits et al., 2004). The crucial event that triggers subsequent fears is often a terrifying, unexpected panic attack, which is why the two forms of anxiety disorder often occur in combination, as in Johanna's case. Following such an experience, the person may become acutely aware of all internal bodily sensations that may signal the onset of another attack. Fear of losing control of these internal experiences then leads, paradoxically, to a further increase in anxiety. This concept has been expanded to include fear of various strong emotions, including anger and depression as well as anxiety (Williams, Chambless, & Ahrens, 1997).

Obsessions and Compulsions

Obsessions are repetitive, unwanted, intrusive cognitive events that may take the form of thoughts or images or impulses. They intrude suddenly into consciousness and lead to an increase in subjective anxiety. Obsessive thinking can be distinguished from worry in two primary ways: (1) Obsessions are usually experienced as coming from "out of the blue," whereas worries are often triggered by problems in everyday living; and (2) the content of obsessions most often involves themes that are perceived as being socially unacceptable or horrific, such as sex, violence, and disease/contamination, whereas the content of worries tends to center around more acceptable, commonplace concerns, such as money and work (de Silva & Rachman, 2004).

Compulsions are repetitive behaviors or mental acts that are used to reduce anxiety. Examples include checking many times to be sure that a door is locked or repeating a silent prayer over and over again. These actions are considered by the person who performs them to be senseless or irrational. The person attempts to resist performing the compulsion but cannot. The following case study illustrates many of the most common features of obsessions and compulsions.

CASE **STUDY** Ed's Obsessive–Compulsive Disorder

Ed, a 38-year-old lawyer, lived with his wife, Phyllis. Most aspects of Ed's life were going well, except for the anxiety-provoking thoughts that lurked beneath his relatively easygoing exterior. One focus of Ed's anxiety was handwriting. He became so tense that his eyes hurt whenever he was forced to write. Feeling exhausted and overwhelmed, Ed avoided writing whenever possible. The problem seemed utterly ridiculous to him, but he couldn't rid himself of his obsessive thoughts.

Sinister meanings had somehow become linked in Ed's imagination to the way in which letters and numbers were formed. The worst letters were P and T (the first letters in "Phyllis" and in "Tim," his younger brother's name). "Improperly" formed letters reminded Ed of violent acts, especially decapitation and strangulation.

If the parts of a letter, such as the two lines in the letter T, were not connected, an image of a head that was not attached to its body might pop into his mind.

Closed loops reminded him of suffocation, like a person whose throat had been clamped shut. These images were associated with people whose names began with the malformed letter. As a result of these concerns, Ed's handwriting had become extremely awkward and difficult to read.

These writing problems made it very difficult for Ed to complete his work, especially when he was under time pressure. In one particularly upsetting incident, Ed was responsible for completing an important official form that had to be mailed that day. He came to a section in which he needed to write a capital P and became concerned that he hadn't done it properly. The loop seemed to be closed, which meant that Phyllis might be strangled! He tore up the first copy and filled it out again. When it was finally done to his satisfaction, Ed sealed the form in an envelope and put it in the box for outgoing mail. After returning to his desk, he was suddenly overwhelmed by the feeling that he had indeed made a mistake with that P. If he allowed the form to be mailed, the evil image would be associated forever with his wife. Consumed by fear, Ed rushed

back to the mailbox, tore up the envelope, and started a new form. Twenty minutes later, he had the form filled out and back in the mailbox. Then the cycle repeated itself. Each time, Ed became more distraught and frustrated, until he eventually felt that he was going to lose his mind.

In addition to his problems with writing, Ed was also afraid of axes. He would not touch an ax, or even get close to one. Any situation in which he could possibly encounter an ax made him extremely uncomfortable. He refused to shop in hardware stores because they sell axes, and he would not visit museums because their exhibits often contain artifacts such as medieval armor. His fear of axes was quite specific. Ed wasn't afraid of knives, guns, or swords.

One frightening experience seemed to trigger the pervasive anxiety that had plagued Ed for 20 years. When he was 17 years old, some friends persuaded Ed to try smoking marijuana. They told him that it would make him feel high—relaxed, sociable, and perhaps a bit giddy. Unfortunately, Ed didn't react to the drug in the same way that the others had. The physical effects seemed to be the same, but his psychological reaction was entirely different. After sharing two joints with his friends, Ed began to feel lightheaded. Then things around him began to seem unreal, as though he were watching himself and his friends in a movie. The intensity of these feelings escalated rapidly, and panic took over. Frightening thoughts raced through his head. Was he losing his mind? When would it stop? This experience lasted about 2 hours.

The marijuana incident had an immediate and lasting impact. Ed became preoccupied with a fear of accidentally ingesting any kind of mind-altering drug, especially LSD. Every spot on his skin or clothing seemed as though it might be a microscopic quantity of this hallucinogen. He felt compelled to clean his hands and clothes repeatedly to avoid contamination. Intellectually, Ed knew that these concerns were silly. How could a tiny spot on his hand be LSD? It didn't make any sense, but he couldn't keep the thought out of his mind.

The most horrifying aspect of the drug experience was the sensation of being totally out of control of his actions and emotions. The fear of returning to that state haunted Ed. He struggled to resist impulses that he had never noticed before, such as the temptation to shout obscenities aloud in church. He also began to worry that he might hurt his younger brother. He resisted the impulses with all his might. He never acted on them, but they pervaded his consciousness and absorbed his mental energy.

The thoughts were so persistent and unshakable that Ed began to wonder if he might, in fact, be a pathological killer. Could he be as deranged and evil as Richard Speck, who had brutally murdered eight nurses in a Chicago apartment building in 1966? Ed spent many hours reading articles about Speck and other mass murderers. The number 8 came to have special meaning to him because of the number of Speck's victims. Over time, Ed's fears and worries became focused on numbers and letters. The violent images and impulses became a less prominent part of his everyday life, but the writing difficulties escalated proportionately.

Ed's thoughts about violence and death illustrate the anxiety-provoking nature of obsessions. It is not just the intrusive quality of the thought, but also the unwanted nature of the thought that makes it an obsession. Some scientists and artists, for example, have reported experiencing intrusive thoughts or inspirational ideas that appear in an unexpected, involuntary way, but these thoughts are not unwanted. Obsessions are unwelcome, anxiety-provoking thoughts. They are also nonsensical; they may seem silly or "crazy." In spite of the recognition that these thoughts do not make sense, the person with full blown obsessions is unable to ignore or dismiss them.

Examples of typical obsessive thoughts include the following: "Did I kill the old lady?" "Christ was a bastard!" "Am I a sexual pervert?" Examples of obsessive impulses include "I might expose my genitals in public," "I am about to shout obscenities in public," "I feel I might strangle a child." Obsessional images might include mutilated corpses, decomposing fetuses, or a family member being involved in a serious car accident. Although obsessive impulses are accompanied by a compelling sense of reality, obsessive people seldom act upon these impulses.

Most normal people experience obsessions in one form or another. Between 80 and 90 percent of normal subjects report having had intrusive, unacceptable thoughts or impulses that are similar in many ways to those experienced by patients being treated for obsessive–compulsive disorder (Rachman & de Silva, 1978; Salkovskis & Harrison, 1984). These include impulses to hurt other people, impulses to do something dangerous, and thoughts of accidents or disease. In contrast to the obsessions described by people who are not in treatment, those experienced by clinical patients occur more frequently, last longer, and are associated with higher levels of discomfort than normal obsessions. Clinical obsessions are also resisted more strongly, and patients report more difficulty dismissing their unwanted thoughts and impulses. Research evidence suggests that obsessions are relatively common, and that clinical obsessions differ from normal obsessions in degree rather than in nature. Similarities and continuities have also been observed between clinical compulsions and rituals that are commonly performed by people who do not qualify for a diagnosis of obsessive–compulsive disorder (Muris, Merckelbach, & Clavan, 1997).

Ed's constricted style of forming letters and his habitual pattern of going back to check and correct his writing illustrate the way in which compulsions are used to reduce anxiety. If he did not engage in these ritualistic behaviors, he would become extremely uncomfortable. His concern about someone being strangled or decapitated if the letters were not properly formed was not delusional, because he readily acknowledged that this was a "silly" idea. Nevertheless, he couldn't shake the obsessive idea that some dreadful event would occur if he was not excruciatingly careful about his writing. He felt as though he had to act, even though he knew that his obsessive thought was irrational. This paradox is extremely frustrating to obsessive–compulsive patients, and it is one of the most common and interesting aspects of the disorder.

Compulsions reduce anxiety, but they do not produce pleasure. Thus some behaviors, such as

What is the difference between normal and abnormal obsessions?

gambling and drug use, that people describe as being "compulsive" are not considered true compulsions according to this definition.

Although some clinicians have argued that compulsive rituals are associated with a complete loss of voluntary control, it is more accurate to view the problem in terms of *diminished control.* For example, Ed could occasionally manage to resist the urge to write in his compulsive style; the behavior was not totally automatic. But whenever he did not engage in this ritualistic behavior, his subjective level of distress increased dramatically, and within a short period of time he returned to the compulsive writing style.

The two most common forms of compulsive behavior are cleaning and checking. The case of Michael, presented in Chapter 4, provides an example of a person with compulsive cleaning rituals. Compulsive cleaning is often associated with an irrational fear of contamination, and in that respect it bears a strong resemblance to certain phobias (Rachman & Hodgson, 1980). There are passive as well as active features of compulsive cleaning. Compulsive cleaners, like Michael, go out of their way to avoid contact with dirt, germs, and other sources of contamination. Then, when they believe that they have come into contact with a source of contamination, they engage in ritualistic cleaning behavior, such as washing their hands, taking showers, cleaning kitchen counters, and so on. These rituals typically involve a large number of repetitions. Some people may wash their hands 50 times a day, taking several minutes to scrub their hands up to the elbow with industrial-strength cleanser. Others take showers that last 2 or 3 hours in which they wash each part of their body in a fixed order, needing to repeat the scrubbing motion an exact number of times.

Compulsive checking frequently represents an attempt to ensure the person's safety or the safety and health of a friend or family member. The person checks things, such as the stove or the lock on a door, over and over in an attempt to prevent the occurrence of an imagined unpleasant or disastrous event (for example, an accident, a burglary, or an assault).

DIAGNOSIS

To understand the way in which anxiety disorders are currently classified, we must briefly consider the ways in which they have been described in previous classification systems. This general set of emotional problems was the topic of considerable diagnostic controversy throughout the twentieth century and continues into the twenty-first.

Brief Historical Perspective

Anxiety and abnormal fears did not play a prominent role in the psychiatric classification systems that began to emerge in Europe during the second half of the nineteenth century (see Chapter 4). Anxiety disorders were probably left out of these descriptions because the authors were primarily superintendents of large asylums. Their patients were people who were psychotic (see Chapter 1) or so out of touch with reality that they could no longer reside in the larger community (Jablensky, 1985; Klerman, 1990a). People with anxiety problems seldom came to the attention of psychiatrists during the nineteenth century because very few cases of anxiety disorder require institutionalization.

Freud and his followers were responsible for some of the first extensive clinical descriptions of pathological anxiety states. Working primarily with patients who were not hospitalized, Freud had an opportunity to treat and study a variety of anxiety-related problems. He described cases of phobia, generalized anxiety, and obsessive–compulsive behavior. The form of specific symptoms (a phobia as compared to a compulsion) was considered to be less important than the underlying causes, which were presumably similar.

Freud's psychological explanations for the origins of anxiety disorders were extremely influential throughout the twentieth century (Josephs, 1994). Freud focused primarily on the importance of mental conflicts and innate biological impulses (primarily sexual and aggressive instincts) in the etiology of anxiety (see Chapter 2). This perspective played a central role in the way that anxiety disorders were classified in early versions of the DSM. They were grouped with several other types of problems under the general heading of **neurosis,** a term used to describe persistent emotional disturbances, such as anxiety and depression, in which the person is aware of the nature of the problem. Neurotic disorders are distinguished from psychotic disorders, in which the person is often out of touch with reality and unaware of the nature of his or her problems (see Chapter 1).

The basic outline of Freud's theory of anxiety hinges on the notion that the person's ego can experience a small amount of anxiety as a signal indicating that an instinctual impulse that has previously been associated with punishment and disapproval is about to be acted on. This usually means that the person is going to do something aggressive or sexual that is considered inappropriate. Signal anxiety triggers the use of ego defenses—primarily repression—that prevent conscious recognition of the forbidden impulse, inhibit its expression, and thereby reduce the person's anxiety. When the system works as it should, anxiety is adaptive, and the person's behavior is regulated to conform with social expectations.

Unfortunately, people can still experience pathological levels of anxiety if the system is overwhelmed. Traumatic events or circumstances can lead to extreme levels of free-floating anxiety. The ego is then forced to resort to additional defensive maneuvers that can produce symptoms such as phobias and compulsions. The specific form of overt symptoms is determined by the defense mechanisms that are employed by the ego, but the underlying process is presumably the same across all of the anxiety neuroses.

Freud's conceptual model for the anxiety neuroses incorporated several important features, including the importance of biologically based impulses, learning experiences based on interactions with other people, and cognitive (or intrapsychic) events that play an important role in mediating between current and past experience. It was firmly grounded in Freud's observations of his own patients' experiences and the process of their treatment with psychoanalysis. Although it served as a useful stimulus to future clinicians and identified many important factors in the etiology of anxiety disorders, his model suffered from a number of weaknesses. Perhaps the major problem was that of measurement. Because Freud's ideas were based on unconscious mental processes that could not be measured directly, his theory of anxiety could not be tested empirically.

Contemporary Classification

The DSM-IV-TR (APA, 2000) approach to classifying anxiety disorders is based primarily on descriptive features, rather than etiological hypotheses and recognizes several specific subtypes. They include panic disorder, three types of phobic disorders, obsessive–compulsive disorder, and generalized anxiety disorder, as well as posttraumatic stress disorder (PTSD) and acute stress disorder.

We will discuss PTSD and acute stress disorder in Chapter 7. The manual also describes problems with anxiety that appear in children, specifically separation anxiety disorder and school refusal. These problems will be discussed in Chapter 16.

Panic Disorder To meet the diagnostic criteria for **panic disorder,** a person must experience recurrent, unexpected panic attacks. At least one of the attacks must have been followed by a period of 1 month or more in which the person has either persistent concern about having additional attacks, worry about the implications of the attack or its consequences, or a significant change in behavior related to the attacks. Panic disorder is divided into two subtypes, depending on the presence or absence of agoraphobia.

Agoraphobia DSM-IV-TR defines agoraphobia in terms of anxiety about being in situations from which escape might be either difficult or embarrassing. This approach is based on the view that agoraphobia is typically a complication that follows upon the experience of panic attacks (Frances, First, & Pincus, 1995). Avoidance and distress are important elements of the definition. In order to meet the DSM-IV-TR criteria, the person must either avoid agoraphobic situations, such as traveling away from his or her own home; endure the experience with great distress; or insist on being accompanied by another person who can provide some comfort or security. In most cases, the person avoids a wide variety of situations rather than just one specific type of situation. People who fit this description of agoraphobia without meeting the criteria for panic disorder would be assigned a diagnosis of agoraphobia without history of panic disorder.

Specific Phobia A *specific phobia* is defined in DSM-IV-TR as "a marked and persistent fear that is excessive or unreasonable, cued by the presence or anticipation of a specific object or situation." Frequently observed types of specific phobia include fear of heights, small animals (such as spiders, bugs, mice, snakes, or bats), tunnels or bridges, storms, illness and injury (including blood), being in a closed place (such as a very small room), and being on certain kinds of public transportation (such as airplanes, buses, or elevators). Exposure to the phobic stimulus must be followed by an immediate fear response. Furthermore, the person must appreciate the fact that the fear is excessive or unreasonable, and the

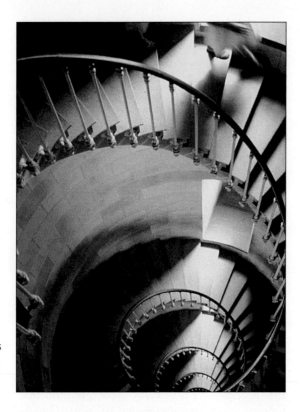

▶ Specific phobias are irrational fears associated with specific situations that the person avoids. Acrophobia is the name given to fear of heights.

person must avoid the phobic situation. DSM-IV-TR also provides a severity threshold: The avoidance or distress associated with the phobia must interfere significantly with the person's normal activities or relationships with others.

Social Phobia The DSM-IV-TR definition of **social phobia** is almost identical to that for specific phobia, but it includes the additional element of performance. A person with a social phobia is afraid of (and avoids) social situations. These situations fall into two broad headings: doing something in front of unfamiliar people (performance anxiety) and interpersonal interactions (such as dating and parties). Fear of being humiliated or embarrassed presumably lies at the heart of the person's discomfort. Some people have a circumscribed form of social phobia that is focused on one particular type of situation. Examples include giving a speech, playing a musical instrument, urinating in a public rest room, or eating in a restaurant. For these people, the feared task could be completed easily if they were able to do it privately. In other cases, the fear is more generalized, and the person is in-

tensely anxious in almost any situation that involves social interaction. This type of person might be described as being extremely shy. The extensive overlap between generalized social phobia and avoidant personality disorder (see Chapter 10) has created some confusion and has been the topic of numerous research studies (Hofmann, Heinrichs, & Moscovitch, 2004).

Generalized Anxiety Disorder Excessive anxiety and worry are the primary symptoms of **generalized anxiety disorder (GAD).** The person must have trouble controlling these worries, and the worries must lead to significant distress or impairment in occupational or social functioning. The worry must occur more days than not for a period of at least 6 months, and it must be about a number of different events or activities. In order to distinguish GAD from other forms of anxiety disorder, DSM-IV-TR notes that the person's worries should not be focused on having a panic attack (as in panic disorder), being embarrassed in public (as in social phobia), or being contaminated (as in obsessive–compulsive disorder). Finally, the person's worries and free-floating anxiety must be accompanied by at least three of the following symptoms: (1) restlessness or feeling keyed up or on edge, (2) being easily fatigued, (3) difficulty concentrating or mind going blank, (4) irritability, (5) muscle tension, and (6) sleep disturbance.

Generalized anxiety disorder remains one of the most controversial anxiety disorders, for several reasons. The diagnostic reliability of GAD is often substantially lower than that for other types of anxiety disorder (Chorpita, Brown, & Barlow, 1998). It also has the highest degree of overlap with the other anxiety disorders. The validity of GAD as a separate diagnostic category is, therefore, open to question. Some experts have suggested that it might be more useful to think of GAD as a trait or a vulnerability factor that sets the stage for later development of other specific types of anxiety disorder, such as panic disorder, social phobia, or obsessive–compulsive disorder (Brown, Barlow, & Liebowitz, 1994). On the other hand, findings have also been reported which indicate that GAD is an important, independent type of anxiety disorder (Kessler, Keller, & Wittchen, 2001). We will discuss some of this evidence in our consideration of genetic factors.

Obsessive–Compulsive Disorder DSM-IV-TR defines obsessive–compulsive disorder (OCD) in

PEARSON
mypsych lab **VIDEO CASE**

SOCIAL PHOBIA

STEVE

"I imagine that people are watching me. They are watching me stumble in my efforts...."

Watch the video "Social Phobia: Steve" on MyPsychLab. What is his worst fear when he is talking to another person at a party?

terms of the presence of either obsessions or compulsions. Most people who meet the criteria for this disorder actually exhibit both of these symptoms. The person must recognize that the obsessions or compulsions are excessive or unreasonable. The diagnostic manual specifies further that these thoughts must not be simply excessive worries about real problems. Intrusive thoughts about overdue bills, for example, would not qualify as obsessions. The DSM-IV-TR definition also requires that the person must attempt to ignore, suppress, or neutralize the unwanted thoughts or impulses.

The line of demarcation between compulsive rituals and normal behavior is often difficult to define. How many times should a person wash her hands in a day? How long should a shower last? Is it reasonable to check more than one time to be sure that the door is locked or the alarm clock is set? DSM-IV-TR has established an arbitrary threshold which holds that rituals become compulsive if they cause marked distress, take more than an hour per day to perform, or interfere with normal occupational and social functioning.

"Lumpers" and "Splitters"

Experts who classify mental disorders can be described informally as belonging to one of two groups, "lumpers" and "splitters" (Mack et al., 1994; Wittchen et al., 2001). Lumpers argue that anxiety is a generalized condition or set of symptoms without any special subdivisions. Splitters distinguish among a number of conditions, each of which is presumed to have its own etiology. During the first half of the twentieth century, psychiatrists tended to adopt a generalized position with regard to anxiety disorders (see Jablensky, 1985). In other words, they lumped together the various anxiety disorders. The DSM-IV-TR system splits them into many separate disorders.

Although it is currently not a popular position, a reasonable argument can still be made in favor of a more unified approach to the classification of anxiety disorders (Haslam, 2003; Nesse, 1999). Consider, for example, the cases of Ed in this chapter and Michael in Chapter 4. Both exhibited a relatively wide range of anxiety symptoms. The high rate of comorbidity among anxiety disorders suggests that these cases are not unusual. Should Ed be considered to have both a phobic disorder (fear of axes) and an obsessive–

◀ Obsessive thoughts about contamination can trigger ritualistic cleaning behaviors that take many hours to perform.

compulsive disorder? Or are these diverse symptoms best viewed as manifestations of the same anxiety disorder? These are questions about the validity of diagnostic categories (see Chapter 4). Decisions regarding the breadth or specificity of anxiety disorders will ultimately depend on evidence from many areas. Do phobias and OCD show distinct, separate patterns in family studies? Do they respond to different types of treatment? Can we distinguish between them in terms of typical patterns of onset and course? Definitive answers are not yet available. Future research efforts are needed to address these issues.

Course and Outcome

Anxiety disorders are often chronic conditions. Long-term follow-up studies focused on clinical populations indicate that many people continue to experience symptoms of anxiety and associated social and occupational impairment many years after their problems are initially recognized. On the other hand, some people do recover completely. The most general conclusion, therefore, is that the long-term outcome for anxiety disorders is mixed and somewhat unpredictable (Tyrer, Sievewright, & Johnson, 2004; Yonkers et al., 2003).

Most people with these disorders continue to have significant problems for many years (Rubio & Lopez-Ibor, 2007). The frequency and intensity of panic attacks tend to decrease as people reach middle age, but agoraphobic avoidance typically remains stable. The nature of the most prominent symptoms may also evolve over time. In patients

What is the expected long-term outcome for people with anxiety disorders?

with GAD, worries may be replaced by complaints about physical symptoms. Worse outcomes tend to be associated with a younger age of onset and lack of appropriate treatment.

The long-term course of obsessive–compulsive disorder also follows a pattern of improvement mixed with some persistent symptoms. One remarkable study has reported outcome information for a sample of 144 patients with severe OCD who were assessed at two follow-up intervals: first about 5 years after they were initially treated at a psychiatric hospital and then again more than 40 years later (Skoog & Skoog, 1999). The data are interesting both because of the very long follow-up interval and because the patients were initially treated between 1947 and 1953, well before the introduction of modern pharmacological and psychological treatments for the disorder. The results are summarized in Figure 6–1. Slightly less than 30 percent of the patients were rated as being recovered at the first follow-up interval. By the time of the 40-year follow-up, almost 50 percent of the patients

were considered to show either full recovery or recovery with subclinical symptoms. More than 80 percent of the patients showed improved levels of functioning if we also count people who continued to exhibit some clinical symptoms. Nevertheless, half of the patients in this sample exhibited symptoms of OCD for more than 30 years. This study shows that although many patients do improve, OCD is a chronic disorder for many people.

FREQUENCY

Some epidemiological studies focus exclusively on treated cases of a disorder, but that strategy can provide a distorted view of the distribution of the disorder within the general population. Many factors can influence whether a person decides to seek treatment. Some cases are less severe than others. Some people treat themselves without consulting a mental health professional. Some people are suspicious of medical facilities, and others are concerned about what people will think of them if they are treated for a mental disorder. Of course, people with agoraphobia are extremely reluctant to leave their homes for any reason. This issue has been a special problem in epidemiological studies of anxiety disorders. Only about 25 percent of people who qualify for a diagnosis of anxiety disorder ever seek psychological treatment. Therefore our estimates of the frequency and severity of these problems must be based on community surveys.

Prevalence

The National Comorbidity Survey Replication (NCS-R), which included approximately 9,000 people aged 18 and older throughout the United States, found that anxiety disorders are more common than any other form of mental disorder (Kessler et al., 2005). Specific phobias are the most common type of anxiety disorder, with a 1-year prevalence of about 9 percent of the adult population (men and women combined). Social phobia is almost as common, with a 1-year prevalence of 7 percent. Panic disorder and GAD both affect approximately 3 percent of the population. Obsessive–compulsive disorder and agoraphobia without panic both affect another 1 percent of the population.

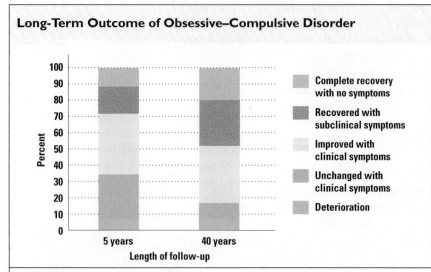

Long-Term Outcome of Obsessive–Compulsive Disorder

Legend:
- Complete recovery with no symptoms
- Recovered with subclinical symptoms
- Improved with clinical symptoms
- Unchanged with clinical symptoms
- Deterioration

X-axis: 5 years, 40 years — Length of follow-up
Y-axis: Percent

FIGURE 6–1 Changes in clinical severity for 144 patients with OCD measured 5 years and 40 years after hospitalization.

Source: G. Skoog and I. Skoog, 1999, "A 40-year Follow-up of Patients with Obsessive–Compulsive Disorder," *Archives of General Psychiatry,* 56, pp.121–127. Copyright © 1999. Reprinted by permission of American Medical Association.

Comorbidity

The symptoms of various anxiety disorders overlap considerably. Many people who experience panic attacks develop phobic avoidance, and many people with obsessive thoughts would also be considered chronic worriers. One study found that 50 percent of people who met the criteria for one anxiety disorder also met the criteria for at least one other form of anxiety disorder or mood disorder (Brown & Barlow, 1992).

Both anxiety and depression are based on emotional distress, so it is not surprising that considerable overlap also exists between anxiety disorders and mood disorders (Kessler et al., 2008; Regier et al., 1998). Approximately 60 percent of people who receive a primary diagnosis of major depression also qualify for a secondary diagnosis of some type of anxiety disorder. This extensive overlap raises interesting questions about the relation between these general diagnostic categories. Do people who meet the criteria for both depression and an anxiety disorder really suffer from two distinct syndromes? Or should we think about the existence of three types of disorder: "pure" anxiety disorders, "pure" mood disorders, and a third type of disorder that represents a mixture of anxiety and depression? Reasonable arguments have been made on both sides of this debate, which remains unresolved (Das-Munshi et al., 2008; Schmidt et al., 2007).

Substance dependence is another problem that is frequently associated with anxiety disorders. People who have an anxiety disorder are about three times more likely to have an alcohol use disorder than are people without an anxiety disorder (Grant et al., 2004). In situations such as these, questions of cause and effect are not clear. Did the person use alcohol in an attempt to reduce heightened anxiety, or did he or she become anxious after drinking excessively? Prospective studies conclude that it works both ways. One study found that among first-year college students, the presence of an anxiety disorder increased by four times the risk for later onset of heavy drinking problems. Conversely, the presence of alcohol dependence among first-year college students caused a similar increase in the probability that the person would later develop a new anxiety disorder (Kushner, Sher, & Erickson, 1999).

Gender Differences

There are significant gender differences in lifetime prevalence for several types of anxiety disorders. Furthermore, among people who suffer

▲ Heavy drinkers are more likely than other people to develop anxiety disorders, and people who are highly anxious are more likely to start to drink heavily.

from an anxiety disorder, relapse rates are higher for women than for men. The gender difference in prevalence is particularly large for specific phobias, where women are three times as likely as men to experience the disorder. Women are about twice as likely as men to experience panic disorder, agoraphobia (without panic disorder), and generalized anxiety disorder. Social phobia is also more common among women than among men, but the difference is not as striking as it is for other types of phobia. The only type of anxiety disorder for which there does not appear to be a significant gender difference is OCD (Torres et al., 2006).

The significant gender differences in the prevalence and course of anxiety disorders must be interpreted in the light of etiological theories, which are considered in the next section. Several explanations remain plausible. Psychological speculation has focused on such factors as gender differences in child-rearing practices or differences in the way in which men and women respond to stressful life events. Gender differences in hormone functions or neurotransmitter activities in the brain may also be responsible (Altemus, 2006).

Anxiety Across the Life Span

Prevalence rates for anxiety disorders have been found to be lower when people over the age of 60 are compared to younger adults (Kessler et al., 2005). On the other hand, the gradual reduction in anxiety that has been observed among middle-aged adults may reverse itself later in life. Anxiety may increase as people move into their 70s and 80s (O'Connor, 2006; Teachman, 2006). Increased anxiety among the elderly may be due to problems associated with loneliness, increased dependency, declining physical and cognitive capacities, and changes in social and economic conditions.

Most elderly people with an anxiety disorder have had the symptoms for many years. It is relatively unusual for a person to develop a new case of panic disorder, specific phobia, social phobia, or obsessive–compulsive disorder at an advanced age. The only type of anxiety disorder that begins with any noticeable frequency in late life is agoraphobia (Barlow et al., 2003).

The diagnosis of anxiety disorders among elderly people is complicated by the need to consider factors such as medical illnesses and other physical impairments and limitations (Carmin, Pollard, & Gillock, 1999). Respiratory and cardiovascular problems may resemble the physiological symptoms of a panic attack. Hearing losses may lead to anxiety in interpersonal interactions. Subsequent avoidance might be inappropriately attributed to the onset of a social phobia. A frail elderly person who falls down on the street may become afraid to leave home alone, but this may be a reasonable concern rather than a symptom of agoraphobia. For reasons such as these, the diagnosis of anxiety disorders must be done with extra caution in elderly men and women.

Cross-Cultural Comparisons

People in different cultures express anxiety in different ways. As in the case of depression, people in nonwestern cultures are more likely to communicate their anxiety in the form of somatic complaints, such as "My chest hurts," "I can't breath," or "I'm tired and restless all the time" (Halbreich et al., 2007; Hoge et al., 2006). The primary focus of anxiety complaints also varies considerably across cultural boundaries. In other words, we need to consider the kinds of situations that provoke intense anxiety as well as the ways in which we recognize that a person is anxious. People in Western societies often experience anxiety in relation to their work performance, whereas in other societies people may be more concerned with family issues or religious experiences. In the Yoruba culture of Nigeria, for exam-

ple, anxiety is frequently associated with fertility and the health of family members (Good & Kleinman, 1985).

Anxiety disorders have been observed in preliterate as well as Westernized cultures. Of course, the same descriptive and diagnostic terms are not used in every culture, but the basic psychological phenomena appear to be similar (Draguns & Tanaka-Matsumi, 2003). Cultural anthropologists have recognized many different culture-bound syndromes that, in some cases, bear striking resemblance to anxiety disorders listed in DSM-IV-TR. The following example of "kayak angst" in an Inuit (Eskimo) hunter illustrates a similar point. The problem sounds a lot like panic disorder.

> Isak H., aged 34, [was a] hunter fisherman of mixed race from Nugatsiak. He had been quite well before. In 1939 he saw a kayak man drowned [sic] and was very much upset. In the summer of 1946, when he was paddling along in his kayak on a calm day with a soft backwash and bright sunshine he suddenly became terrified when looking down to the bottom of the sea. He seemed to feel the kayak filling with water, the point of the kayak being very distant and dim. His head felt queer and he took off his cap. His heart started beating rapidly and he trembled so violently that the kayak shook. Perspiration ran down his face, his heart seemed to turn over and his arms were heavy and numb. He made an effort to reach shore, he vomited, his bowels were loose and he had a strong desire to pass water. Next time he set out in his kayak the same symptoms occurred. He felt more and more terrified of crouching down in his kayak, and he finally gave up all attempts and stopped fishing by kayak.
>
> (Katschnig & Amering, 1990, pp. 77–78)

Very few epidemiological studies have attempted to collect cross-cultural data using standardized interviews and specific diagnostic criteria. One such study was conducted to evaluate specific drugs for the treatment of panic attacks (Cross-National Collaborative Panic Study, 1992). More than 1,000 patients were treated in 14 different countries in North America, Latin America, and Europe. Several interesting findings emerged from this study. Most important was the fact that panic disorder occurred in all the countries that were included in the study. The most prominent symptoms—choking or smothering, fear of dying, phobic avoidance—varied from one region to the next, but the overall prevalence rate appeared to be about the same.

CAUSES

Now that we have discussed the various symptoms associated with anxiety disorders and their distribution within the population, we can consider the origins of these disorders. How do these problems develop? Going back to the cases that were presented at the beginning of the chapter, what might account for the onset of Johanna's panic attacks? Why would Ed find himself plagued by violent images and compelled to form letters in a meticulous fashion?

Adaptive and Maladaptive Fears

Current theories regarding the causes of anxiety disorders often focus on the evolutionary significance of anxiety and fear. These emotional response systems are clearly adaptive in many situations. They mobilize responses that help the person survive in the face of both immediate dangers and long-range threats. An evolutionary perspective helps to explain why human beings are vulnerable to anxiety disorders, which can be viewed as problems that arise in the regulation of these necessary response systems (Hofmann, Moscovitch, & Heinrichs, 2004). The important question is not why we experience anxiety, but why it occasionally becomes maladaptive. When anxiety becomes excessive, or when intense fear is triggered at an inappropriate time or place, these response systems can become more harmful than helpful. In order to understand the development of anxiety disorders, we must consider a variety of psychological and biological systems that have evolved for the purpose of triggering and controlling these alarm responses.

Should we expect to find unique causal pathways associated with each of the types of anxiety disorder listed in DSM-IV-TR? This seems unlikely, particularly in light of the extensive overlap among the various subtypes. Should we expect that all the different types of anxiety disorders are produced by the same causes? This also seems unlikely.

Isaac Marks and Randolph Nesse (1994) have proposed a broad evolutionary perspective for the causes of anxiety disorders that suggests a middle ground between these two extremes. They suggest that generalized forms of anxiety probably evolved to help the person prepare for threats that could not be identified clearly. More specific forms of anxiety and fear probably evolved to provide more effective responses to certain types of danger. For example, fear of heights is associated with a freezing of muscles rather than running away, which could lead to a fall. Social threats are more likely to provoke responses such as shyness and embarrassment that may increase acceptance by other people by making the individual seem less threatening. Each type of anxiety disorder can be viewed as the dysregulation of a mechanism that evolved to deal with a particular kind of danger. This model leads us to expect that the etiological pathways leading to various forms of anxiety disorders may be partially distinct but not completely independent.

Social Factors

Stressful life events, particularly those involving danger and interpersonal conflict, can trigger the onset of certain kinds of anxiety disorders. For example, various aspects of parent–child relationships may leave some people more vulnerable to the development of anxiety disorders when they become adults. Taken together, the evidence bearing on these issues helps explain the relationship between, and the overlap among, anxiety disorders and mood disorders.

Stressful Life Events Common sense suggests that people who experience high stress levels are likely to develop negative emotional reactions, which can range from feeling "on edge" to the

> *Is there a unique causal pathway for each type of anxiety disorder?*

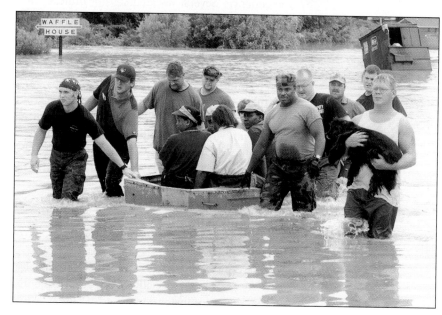

▼ Stressful life events that involve lack of personal security and serious danger—such as a flood—are often associated with the onset of anxiety disorders.

onset of full-blown panic attacks. In Chapter 5 we reviewed the literature concerning stressful life events and depression. Several investigations suggest that stressful life events can influence the onset of anxiety disorders as well as depression. Patients with anxiety disorders are more likely than other people to report having experienced a negative event in the months preceding the initial development of their symptoms (Kendler et al., 2003).

Why do some negative life events lead to depression while others lead to anxiety? The nature of the event may be an important factor in determining the type of mental disorder that appears (Updegraff & Taylor, 2000). People who develop an anxiety disorder are much more likely to have experienced an event involving danger (lack of security), whereas people who are depressed are more likely to have experienced a severe loss (lack of hope). Mixed cases frequently report both types of events (Rueter et al., 1999). In other words, different types of environmental stress may lead to different types of emotional symptoms. Those associated with insecurity, including severe disagreements with other people, and danger, seem to be mostly closely associated with anxiety disorders. Interpersonal conflicts, such as serious arguments with a partner, parents, or close friends, seem to be especially common prior to the onset of agoraphobia (Franklin & Andrews, 1989).

Childhood Adversity If recent dangers and conflicts can precipitate the full-blown symptoms of an anxiety disorder, do past experiences—those that took place years ago—set the stage for this experience? Several research studies indicate that they can (Harkness & Wildes, 2002; Levitan et al., 2003). Studies of these phenomena focus on measures of childhood adversity. This concept includes experiences such as maternal prenatal stress, multiple maternal partner changes, parental indifference (being neglected by parents), and physical abuse (being physically beaten or threatened with violence). Children who are exposed to higher levels of adversity are more likely to develop anxiety disorders later in their lives (Moffitt et al., 2007; Phillips et al., 2005).

Evidence regarding childhood adversity and the development of psychopathology points, once again, to similarities between depression and anxiety. Keep in mind that there is substantial overlap in these disorders; people who meet criteria for anxiety disorders, especially GAD, also frequently meet criteria for major depression. Those who are exposed to parental abuse, neglect, and violence are more vulnerable to the development of both anxiety disorders and major depression (Kessler et al., 2008; Lara & Klein, 1999). There does not seem to be a direct connection between particular forms of adverse environmental events and specific types of mental disorder.

Attachment Relationships and Separation Anxiety The evidence regarding childhood adversity is similar to another perspective on the origins of anxiety disorders that has been concerned with the infant's attachment relationship with caretakers. Attachment theory (see Chapter 2) integrates the psychodynamic perspective with field observations of primate behavior and with laboratory research with human infants. According to the British psychiatrist John Bowlby (1973, 1980), anxiety is an innate response to separation, or the threat of separation, from the caretaker. Those infants who are insecurely attached to their parents are presumably more likely to develop anxiety disorders, especially agoraphobia, when they become adults.

Several studies have found that people with a variety of anxiety disorders are more likely to have had attachment problems as children (Cassidy & Mohr, 2001; Lewinsohn et al., 2008). Anxious attachment as infants may make these individuals more vulnerable, once they are adults, to the threats that are contained in interpersonal conflict, for example, loss of a loved one if a marriage dissolves. This hypothesis fits nicely with the observation that interpersonal conflict is a relatively frequent triggering event for the onset of agoraphobic symptoms. There is also an interesting connection between attachment styles and childhood adversity. People who report childhood adversities involving interpersonal trauma (assault, abuse, neglect) are more likely to be insecurely attached, and they are also more vulnerable to depression and anxiety (Mickelson, Kessler, & Shaver, 1997).

Psychological Factors

Research suggests that stressful life events and childhood adversity contribute to the development of anxiety disorders. But what are the specific mechanisms that link these experiences to emotional difficulties, such as intense fears, panic attacks, and excessive worry? This question brings our discussion of causes to a different level of analysis. A number of psychological mechanisms undoubtedly play important roles in helping to shape the development and maintenance of anxiety disorders. They include learning processes and cognitive events.

Learning Processes Since the 1920s, experimental psychologists working in laboratory settings have been interested in the possibility that specific fears might be learned through classical (or Pavlovian) conditioning (Ayres, 1998). The central mechanism in the classical conditioning process is the association between an unconditioned stimulus (US) and a conditioned stimulus (CS). The US is able to elicit a strong unconditioned emotional response (UR), such as fear. Examples of potential USs are painfully loud and unexpected noises, the sight of dangerous animals, and sudden, intense pain. According to psychologists' original views of the classical conditioning process, the CS could be any neutral stimulus that happened to be present when an intense fear reaction was provoked. Through the process of association, the CS would subsequently elicit a conditioned response (CR), which was similar in quality to the original UR (see Chapter 2). This explanation for the development of specific phobias fits easily with common sense as well as with clinical experience. Many intense, persistent, irrational fears seem to develop after the person has experienced a traumatic event (Merckelbach, Muris, & Schouten, 1996).

Current views on the process by which fears are learned suggest that the process is guided by a *module,* or specialized circuit in the brain, that has been shaped by evolutionary pressures (Öhman & Mineka, 2001). Some psychologists have argued that the mind includes a very large number of prepared modules (specialized neural circuits) that serve particular adaptive functions, such as the recognition of faces and the perception of language (Pinker, 1997). These modules are designed to operate at maximal speed, are activated automatically, and perform without conscious awareness. They are also highly selective, in the sense that the module is particularly responsive to a narrow range of stimuli. Human beings seem to be prepared to develop intense, persistent fears only to a select set of objects or situations. Fear of these stimuli may have conferred a selective advantage upon those people—hundreds of thousands of years ago—who were able to develop fears and consequently avoid certain kinds of dangerous stimuli, such as heights, snakes, and storms. This is not to say

▲ Social phobias may involve prepared conditioning associated with faces that seem angry, critical, or rejecting.

that the fears are innate or present at birth, but rather that they can be learned and maintained very easily.

Many investigations have been conducted to test various facets of this **preparedness model** (Mineka & Oehlberg, 2008). The results of these studies support many features of the theory. For example, conditioned responses to fear-relevant stimuli (such as spiders and snakes) are more resistant to extinction than are those to fear-irrelevant stimuli (such as flowers). Furthermore, it is possible to develop conditioned fear responses after only one trial of learning.

The process of prepared conditioning may play an important role in the development of both social phobias and specific phobias. In specific phobias, the prepared stimuli are things like snakes, heights, storms, and small enclosed places. The prepared stimulus in social phobias might involve other people's faces. We are prepared to fear faces that appear angry, critical, or rejecting if they are directed toward us (Öhman, 1996). This process is presumably an evolutionary remnant of factors involved in establishing dominance hierarchies, which maintain social order among primates. Animals that are defeated in a dominance conflict are often allowed to remain as part of the group if they behave submissively. The responses of people with social phobias may be somewhat analogous, in the sense that they are afraid of directly facing, or being evaluated by, other people. When a performer makes eye contact with his or her audience, an association may develop very quickly between fear and angry or critical facial expressions.

If phobias are learned quickly and easily, why are they so hard to extinguish?

▶ Vicarious learning can influence the development of strong fear responses. Children who observe adults demonstrating strong emotional responses may be more likely to develop phobias.

We all learn many behaviors through imitation. Albert Bandura's early work on modeling, for example, demonstrated that children who observe a model hitting a doll are more likely to behave aggressively themselves when given the opportunity (see Chapter 2). Similar processes may also affect the development of intense fear, because some phobias develop in the absence of any direct experience with the feared object. People apparently learn to avoid certain stimuli if they observe other people showing a strong fear response to those stimuli (Poulton & Menzies, 2002). In other words, the traumatic event does not have to happen to you; it may be enough for you to witness a traumatic event happening to someone else or to watch someone else behave fearfully.

Learning experiences are clearly important in the origins of phobias, but their impact often depends on the existence of prepared associations between stimuli. Furthermore, vicarious learning is often as important as direct experience. The importance of the latter factor can be illustrated by considering the development of children's fears during the bombing of London in World War II. When civilian areas were subjected to prolonged and terrifying attacks, families sought safety in underground shelters. If intense fear could be conditioned to any originally neutral stimulus, most of the people subjected to this traumatic experience would develop specific phobic responses in association with whatever stimuli happened to be present during the worst moments of a raid (fear of tunnels, fear of the dark). In fact, it didn't work that way. Although people showed short-term emotional reactions, very few developed persistent, irrational phobic responses as a result of these terrifying experiences. Anecdotal evidence suggested that children were more likely to become fearful if they had observed their parents exhibiting strong emotional responses during the raids (Rachman, 1991).

Cognitive Factors Up to this point, we have talked about the importance of life events and specific learning experiences—variables that can be measured outside the organism. But cognitive events also play an important role as mediators between experience and response. Perceptions, memory, and attention all influence the ways that we react to events in our environments. It is now widely accepted that these cognitive factors play a crucial role in the development and maintenance of various types of anxiety disorders. We will focus on four aspects of this literature: perception of controllability and predictability, catastrophic misinterpretation (panic attacks), attentional biases and shifts in the focus of attention, and thought suppression.

Perception of Control There is an important relationship between anxiety and the perception of control. People who believe that they are able to control events in their environment are less likely to show symptoms of anxiety than are people who believe that they are helpless. This is, of course, part of the reason that the events of September 11, 2001, were so terrifying. The attack on the World Trade Center in New York City was beyond the control of its victims, who were going about their everyday activities.

An extensive body of evidence supports the conclusion that people who believe that they are less able to control events in their environment are more likely to develop global forms of anxiety (Andrews, 1996), as well as various specific types of anxiety disorder (Mineka & Zinbarg, 1998). Laboratory research indicates that feelings of lack of control contribute to the onset of panic attacks among patients with panic disorder. The perception of uncontrollability has also been linked to the submissive behavior frequently seen among people with social phobias as well as the chronic worries of people with generalized anxiety disorder.

Catastrophic Misinterpretation A somewhat different type of cognitive dysfunction has been described by David Clark, a psychologist at Oxford University in England. According to this view, panic disorder may be caused by the *catastrophic misinterpretation* of bodily sensations or perceived threat (Clark, 1986b, 1999). Although panic attacks can be precipitated by external stimuli, they are usually triggered by internal stimuli, such as bodily sensations, thoughts, or images. On the basis of past experience, these stimuli initiate an anxious mood, which leads to a variety of physiological sensations that typically accompany negative emotional reactions (changes in heart rate, respiration rate, dizziness, and so on). Anxious mood is accompanied by a narrowing of the person's attentional focus and an increased awareness of bodily sensations.

The crucial stage comes next, when the person misinterprets the bodily sensation as a catastrophic event. For example, a person who believes that there is something wrong with his heart might misinterpret a slight acceleration in heart rate as being a sign that he is about to have a heart attack. He might say to himself, "My heart will stop and I'll die!" This reaction ensures the continued operation of this feedback loop, with the misinterpretation enhancing the person's sense of threat, and so on, until the process spirals out of control. Thus both cognitive misinterpretation and biological reactions associated with the perception of threat are necessary for a panic attack to occur.

The person's automatic, negative thoughts may also lead him to engage in behaviors that are expected to increase his safety, when in fact they are counterproductive. For example, some people believe that they should take deep breaths or monitor their heart rate if they become aroused. This is actually incorrect information, and the alleged safety behaviors can further exaggerate the person's fear response.

Many research studies have found that the subjective experience of body sensations is, in fact, closely associated with maladaptive or catastrophic thoughts among patients with panic disorder (McNally, 1994). This connection by itself does not provide strong evidence for a *causal* link between catastrophic thoughts and the onset of panic attacks because catastrophic thoughts (such as fear of losing control and fear of dying) are, in fact, part of the definition of a panic attack (see Table 6–1). The theory is difficult to test (cannot be disproven) if there is no way to separate the measurement of catastrophic thoughts and the panic attack itself (Roth, Wilhelm, & Pettit, 2005).

Catastrophic misinterpretations cannot account for all instances of panic attacks. For example, patients with panic disorder sometimes experience panic attacks in their sleep (Craske & Rowe, 1997; Klein & Klein, 1989). How could that happen if the escalation to panic requires catastrophic misinterpretation of physical sensations, which presumably involves conscious cognitive processes? Clearly, other factors are also involved. One alternative explanation involves classical conditioning. The experience of an initial panic attack might lead to conditioned anxiety to cues associated with the first attack. These could be either internal bodily sensations or external stimuli. The conditioned anxiety might lower the person's threshold for subsequent panic attacks (Bouton, Mineka, & Barlow, 2001).

Attention to Threat and Biased Information Processing Earlier in this chapter we mentioned that anxiety involves negative thoughts and images anticipating some possible future danger. In recent years, several lines of research have converged to clarify the basic cognitive mechanisms involved in generalized anxiety disorder as well as panic disorder. Experts now believe that attention plays a crucial role in the onset of this process. People who are prone to excessive worrying and panic are unusually sensitive to cues that signal the existence of future threats (MacLeod et al., 2002; Teachman, Smith-Janik et al., 2007). They attend vigilantly to even fleeting signs of danger, especially when they are under stress. At such times, the recognition of danger cues triggers a maladaptive, self-perpetuating cycle of cognitive processes that can quickly spin out of control.

The threatening information that is generated in this process is presumably encoded in memory in the form of elaborate schemas, which are easily reactivated. The threat schemas of anxious people contain a high proportion of "what-if" questions, such as "What am I going to do if I don't do well in school this semester?" Once attention has been drawn to threatening cues, the performance of adaptive, problem-solving behaviors is disrupted,

▼ At first glance, this photo seems terrifying because the image looks like a shark. In fact, it's a dolphin, and once we know that, it seems less frightening. This is an example of the role played by cognitive factors in generating fear.

and the worrying cycle launches into a repetitive sequence in which the person rehearses anticipated events and searches for ways to avoid them. This process activates an additional series of "what-if" questions that quickly leads to a dramatic increase in negative affect (McLaughlin et al., 2007).

If worriers are preoccupied with the perception of threat cues and the rehearsal of dangerous scenarios but are unable to reach satisfactory solutions to their problems, why do they continue to engage in this vicious, maladaptive cycle? Thomas Borkovec, a clinical psychologist at Pennsylvania State University, and his students have studied the uncontrollable nature of the worry process. Two of Borkovec's conclusions are particularly important in explaining the self-perpetuating nature of worry: (1) Worry is an experience that is made up of "self-talk"—things that people say to themselves rather than visual images ("I'll never get all this work done!"). (2) Worry serves the function of avoiding unpleasant somatic activation through the suppression of imagery (Borkovec, Alcaine, & Behar, 2004). In other words, some people apparently continue to worry, even though it

Is it useful to struggle actively against unwanted thoughts?

is not productive, because worrying is reinforced by an immediate (though temporary) reduction in uncomfortable physiological sensations.

Attentional mechanisms also seem to be involved in the etiology and maintenance of social phobias. People who are capable of performing a particular task when they are alone (in practice) cannot perform it in front of an audience. Barlow (2004) has argued that this deterioration in skill is caused by anxious apprehension, which is similar to Borkovec's description of the process of worrying. The cycle is illustrated in Figure 6–2. An increase in negative affect presumably triggers a shift toward self-focused attention ("Oh, no, I'm getting really upset") and activates cognitive biases and threat schemas ("What if I make a mistake?"). The person becomes distracted by these thoughts, and performance deteriorates. In a sense, the person's fearful expectations become a self-fulfilling prophesy (Heerey & Kring, 2007).

Thought Suppression: Obsessive–Compulsive Disorder The cognitive model of worry or anxious apprehension places primary emphasis on the role of attentional processes. Worrying is unproductive and self-defeating in large part because it is associated with a focus on self-evaluation (fear of failure) and negative emotional responses rather than on external aspects of the problem and active coping behaviors. We may be consciously aware of these processes and simultaneously be unable to inhibit them. The struggle to control our thoughts often leads to a process known as *thought suppression,* an active attempt to stop thinking about something.

It seems simple to say, "Stop worrying," but it is virtually impossible for some people to do so. In fact, recent evidence suggests that trying to rid one's mind of a distressing or unwanted thought can have the unintended effect of making the thought more intrusive (Wegner, 1994). Thought suppression might actually increase, rather then decrease, the strong emotions associated with those thoughts. The bond between a thought and its associated emotion allows activation of one to result in the reinstatement of the other, a kind of dual pathway.

Obsessive–compulsive disorder may be related, in part, to the maladaptive consequences of attempts to suppress unwanted or threatening thoughts that the person has learned to see as being dangerous or forbidden (Abramowitz, Tolin, & Street, 2001; Purdon, 2004). Remember that obsessive thoughts are a common experience in the general population. They resemble "abnormal" obsessions in form and content. However, the obses-

Anxious Apprehension and Social Phobia

ANXIETY-PROVOKING SITUATION

↓

NEGATIVE AFFECT
including sense of uncontrollability

↓

ATTENTIONAL SHIFT
to self-evaluative focus → FURTHER INCREASE IN AROUSAL

DYSFUNCTIONAL PERFORMANCE

↓

COGNITIVE BIASES AND HYPERVIGILANCE
enhanced attention to threat cues

↓

ATTEMPTS TO COPE BY:

↓

AVOIDANCE
of situation

FIGURE 6–2 Processes involved in the generation of social anxiety.
Source: Adapted from D. H. Barlow, 2001, *Anxiety and Its disorders,* 2nd ed., New York: Guilford, p. 65.

sions of those in treatment for OCD are more intense and, perhaps most importantly, are more often strongly resisted and more difficult to dismiss. This resistance may be a key component in the association between emotional sensitivity and the development of troublesome obsessive thoughts. People who are vulnerable to the development of OCD apparently react strongly to events that trigger an emotional response. These individuals become aware of their exaggerated reactivity and find it unpleasant. In an effort to control their reaction, they attempt to resist or suppress the emotion (Campbell-Sills et al., 2006).

As a result of an individual's attempt to suppress strong emotion, a rebound effect may occur, culminating in a vicious cycle. Thoughts that are present during the instigation of such a cycle become robustly associated with the emotion and may become the content of an obsessive thought. This model may help to explain the episodic nature of obsessive–compulsive symptoms; relapse may be triggered by intense emotional episodes.

Biological Factors

Several pieces of evidence indicate that biological events play an important role in the development and maintenance of anxiety disorders. In the following pages we review the role of genetic factors, the connection between anxiety symptoms and specific regions in the brain, and the use of chemicals to induce symptoms of panic. These factors undoubtedly interact with the social and psychological variables that we have considered in the preceding sections.

Genetic Factors Some of the most useful information about the validity of anxiety disorders comes from studies aimed at identifying the influence of genetic factors. These data address the overlap, as well as the distinctions, among various types of anxiety disorder. They also shed additional light on the relationship between anxiety and depression.

Twin Studies Kenneth Kendler, a psychiatrist at the Medical College of Virginia, and his colleagues have studied anxiety disorders in large samples of twin pairs (Kendler & Prescott, 2006). The people who participated in this study were not psychiatric patients; they were living in the community and were identified through a statewide registry of twins. Diagnoses were assigned following structured diagnostic interviews conducted by the research team.

TABLE 6–2   Twin Concordance Rates for Specific Anxiety Disorders

DISORDER	MZ	DZ
Panic disorder	.24	.11
Agoraphobia	.23	.15
Social phobia	.24	.15
Animal phobia	.26	.11
Generalized anxiety disorder	.28	.17

Source: Data from the Virginia Twin Registry (Kendler et al., 1992a, 1992b).

Table 6–2 summarizes the results of Kendler's study with regard to several types of anxiety disorder. For each type, concordance rates were significantly higher for MZ twins than for DZ twins. Nevertheless, the MZ concordance rates were also relatively low (in comparison to MZ concordance rates for bipolar mood disorders, for example). Anxiety disorders appear to be modestly heritable, with genetic factors accounting for between 20 and 30 percent of the variance in the transmission of GAD. (See Research Methods in Chapter 16 for a discussion of heritability.)

Kendler and his colleagues have examined the influence of both genetic and environmental factors on the etiology of several kinds of anxiety disorder, including panic disorder, GAD, and phobias in these samples of twins (Hettema et al., 2005). Their analyses have led them to several important conclusions:

1. Genetic risk factors for these disorders are neither highly specific (a different set of genes being associated with each disorder) nor highly nonspecific (one common set of genes causing vulnerability for all disorders).
2. Two genetic factors have been identified: one associated with GAD, panic disorder, and agoraphobia, and the other with specific phobias.
3. Environmental risk factors that would be *unique* to individuals also play an important role in the etiology of all anxiety disorders. Environmental factors that would be *shared* by all members of a family do not seem to play an important role for many people.

Neurobiology Laboratory studies of fear conditioning in animals have identified specific pathways in the brain that are responsible for detecting and organizing a response to danger (LeDoux, 2000; Öhman & Mineka, 2003). The amygdala plays a central role in these circuits, which represent the biological underpinnings of the evolved fear module that we discussed earlier in connection with classical conditioning and phobias (see page 179). Scientists have discovered these pathways by monitoring and manipulating brain activities in animals that are participating in studies using classical conditioning to pair an originally neutral stimulus (the CS) with an aversive stimulus (the US). The results of these studies tell us *where* emotional responses, such as fear and panic, are located in terms of brain regions. They also begin to explain *how* they are produced. That knowledge, coupled with data regarding social and psychological factors, will help us understand *why* people experience problems such as irrational fears and panic attacks.

The brain circuits involved in fear conditioning are illustrated in Figure 6–3. This drawing uses the example of a person who has seen a dangerous

snake (Carter, 1999). Sensory information is projected to the thalamus, and from there it is directed to other brain areas for processing. Emotional stimuli follow two primary pathways, both of which lead to the amygdala. The first pathway (the red arrow) might be called a "shortcut" and represents the evolved fear module for conditioned fear. The message follows a direct connection between the thalamus and the amygdala, which is connected to the hypothalamus. Behavioral responses (such as the "fight or flight" response) are then activated and coordinated through projections from the hypothalamus to endocrine glands and the autonomic nervous system (see Chapter 2, as well as the discussion of the HPA axis in Chapter 5). Notice that this first pathway does not involve connections to cortical areas of the brain that might involve higher-level cognitive functions such as conscious memory or decision making. The amygdala does

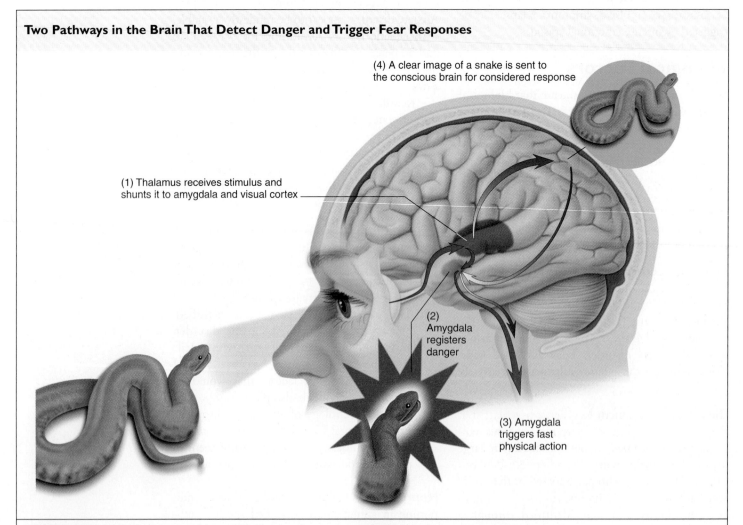

Two Pathways in the Brain That Detect Danger and Trigger Fear Responses

(4) A clear image of a snake is sent to the conscious brain for considered response

(1) Thalamus receives stimulus and shunts it to amygdala and visual cortex

(2) Amygdala registers danger

(3) Amygdala triggers fast physical action

FIGURE 6–3   (1) Evolved fear module, and (2) slower, indirect route through cortical processing areas.

Source: Illustrations from MAPPING THE MIND by R. Carter, illustrations by Malcolm Godwin. Copyright © 1998 by Moonrunner Design Ltd. Published by University of California Press. Reprinted by permission of Malcolm Godwin, Moonrunner Design, Ltd.

store unconscious, emotional memories—the kind that are generated through prepared learning.

A second, complementary path from the thalamus (the purple arrow) leads to the cortex and provides for a detailed, and comparatively slower, analysis of the information that has been detected. Using the example in Figure 6–3, information about the snake would be sent to the visual cortex. Once the pattern is recognized as a snake, the data would be integrated with additional information from memory about its emotional significance ("potentially dangerous"). This message would then be sent to the amygdala, which could, in turn, trigger an organized response to threat. This second pathway is longer and more complex than the first, and it will take longer to generate a response. The first pathway has presumably evolved because it is adaptive; it provides the organism with an alarm system that can be used to avoid immediate dangers in the environment. The fact that information can follow either path is consistent with the idea that some fear responses are "hardwired" (easily learned, difficult to extinguish, and mediated by unconscious processes) while others are dependent on higher-level analyses that involved thinking and reasoning.

A word of caution must be added when we consider the functions of these specific neural pathways. The fact that they are involved in processing fearful reactions does not mean that the amygdala and associated structures are exclusively dedicated to this particular purpose. Studies with animals have shown that artificial stimulation

CRITICAL THINKING MATTERS

Can a Strep Infection Trigger OCD in Children?

New hypotheses about the causes of mental disorders are usually based on clinical observations. These ideas are then evaluated in research studies designed to test their validity. Sometimes the data support the new idea, and sometimes they don't. During this period of evaluation, clinicians and scientists find themselves in a period of uncertainty, with some people embracing what they consider to be an important advance in knowledge while others provide skeptical criticism. Both groups need to think critically about relevant evidence.

This state of affairs is currently illustrated by a controversial proposal regarding the development of OCD in children. Clinical scientists at the National Institute of Mental Health, headed by psychiatrist Susan Swedo, suggested that, in some cases, symptoms of OCD develop suddenly following a strep infection. According to their hypothesis, antibodies that are triggered by the infection attack nerve cells in the basal ganglia of the brain (see Figure 4–1 on page 115). Swedo and her colleagues created a new term to use in diagnosing children with OCD who have a sudden onset and also test positive for a strep infection. They call the disorder *pediatric autoimmune neuropsychiatric disorders associated with streptococcal infection*, or PANDAS (Swedo & Grant, 2005). They recommend that a throat culture be given to any child who shows a sudden onset of symptoms of OCD. Children who test positive for strep are put on long-term antibiotics which are claimed, in some cases, to produce "miraculous results" (Anderson, 1996).

Can claims surrounding discovery of a new disorder be harmful?

Does the recognition of PANDAS represent a breakthrough discovery? Is it a valid diagnostic concept? Or is it a misguided hypothesis with potentially dangerous treatment implications? Reasonable people have taken both sides. The empirical evidence is certainly incomplete (da Rocha, Correa, & Teixeira, 2008; Singer & Loiselle, 2003), and some would say it is weak (Kurlan et al., 2008). Swedo and her colleagues have indeed described several cases that fit their profile. One of their papers described 109 cases in which the parents described a rapid onset of OCD symptoms (Swedo et al., 1998). Among these, 50 tested positive for strep. That leaves 59 rapid-onset cases that must have been triggered by some other, unknown factor. But even in the cases that did test positive, the existence of a strep infection does not prove that it was *causally* related to the OCD.

If 100 kids fall out of a tree and break their arms and we test them for strep, there's going to be a very high percentage of children who have evidence of recent infection. That doesn't mean strep is the reason they fell out of a tree.

(Shulman, quoted in Belkin, 2005).

Skeptics argue that, until more conclusive evidence is available to support the theory, we should assume that children who experience obsessions and compulsions are suffering from OCD, nothing more or less (Kurlan & Kaplan, 2004). Undue emphasis on the use of antibiotic treatment may lead parents to ignore more conventional treatments for the disorder. In fact, the combination of cognitive behavior therapy and SSRI medications has been shown to be effective for children with PANDAS-related OCD (Storch et al., 2006). Clinicians should also consider potential problems associated with the use of antibiotics as a form of treatment for children with OCD. Risks include the possibility of developing drug allergies and the promotion of antibiotic resistance.

While PANDAS is an intriguing hypothesis, remember that the burden of proof lies with those who propose new diagnostic categories or causal theories. Until it has been supported by *strong* empirical evidence, which is not yet the case with regard to PANDAS, the community of scientists assumes that the new hypothesis is false.

of the amygdala can produce different effects, depending in large part on the environmental context in which the animal is stimulated (Kagan, 1998). Anger, disgust, and sexual arousal are all emotional states that are associated with activity in pathways connecting the thalamus, the amygdala, and their projections to other brain areas. Fear responses are, therefore, only one of the many kinds of behavior associated with these circuits.

The brain regions that have been identified in studies of fear conditioning play an important role in phobic disorders and panic disorder (Etkin & Wager, 2007; Ninan & Dunlop, 2005). In the case of panic disorder, the fear module may be triggered at an inappropriate time. The sensitivity of this pathway is not the same in all people, and it is presumably influenced by genetic factors as well as hormone levels. Social and psychological factors that affect the threshold of the fear module include stressful life events and the development of separation anxiety during childhood (which increases the rate of panic disorder when these children become adults). The subcortical pathway between the thalamus and the amygdala may be responsible for the misinterpretation of sensory information, which then triggers the hypothalamus and activates a variety of autonomic processes (dramatic increases in respiration rate, heart rate, and so on). Some investigators have also speculated that this brain circuit may be associated with the biased attention to threat cues that has been demonstrated in patients with various types of anxiety disorder (Bishop, 2007).

The neurological foundations of OCD seem to involve regions of the brain that are different than those involved in other types of anxiety disorder (Bartz & Hollander, 2006). As we discussed in Chapter 4, obsessions and compulsions are associated with multiple brain regions, including the basal ganglia (a system that includes the caudate nucleus and the putamen), the orbital prefrontal cortex, and the anterior cingulate cortex (see Figure 4–1 on page 115). These circuits are overly active in people with OCD, especially when the person is confronted with stimuli that provoke his or her obsessions (Husted et al., 2006; Menzies et al., 2008).

Several different neurotransmitters are responsible for communication in the brain regions that regulate emotion. Their role in the development and maintenance of anxiety disorders has been examined in studies of animal models of anxiety (Pohl et al., 2007) as well as in studies of the impact of medications on human behavior (Kalueff

& Nutt, 2007). Perhaps most important with regard to the anxiety disorders are serotonin, norepinephrine, gamma-aminobutyric acid (GABA), and dopamine. Serotonin and GABA are inhibitory neurotransmitters that function to dampen stress responses. Pharmacological and environmental challenges that increase their availability lead to decreased levels of anxiety. Conversely, experiences that reduce levels of serotonin and GABA can provoke increases in fear and anxiety.

TREATMENT

Anxiety disorders are one of the areas of psychopathology in which clinical psychologists and psychiatrists are best prepared to improve the level of their clients' functioning (see Getting Help). We begin by describing procedures that were used in an effort to help Ed, the person with obsessive–compulsive disorder whose problems were described at the beginning of this chapter.

BRIEF CASE **STUDY**
Ed's Treatment

Ed's psychiatrist gave him a prescription for clomipramine (Anafranil), an antidepressant drug that is also used to treat people with severe obsessions. Weekly psychotherapy sessions continued as the dose was gradually increased. The medication had a beneficial impact after 4 weeks. Ed said that he had begun to feel as though he was trapped at the bottom of a well. After the medication, he no longer felt buried. His situation still wasn't great, but it no longer seemed hopeless or unbearable. He was also less intensely preoccupied by his obsessive violent images. They were still there, but they weren't as pressing. The drug had several annoying, though tolerable, side effects. His mouth felt dry, and he was occasionally a bit dizzy. He also noticed that he became tired more easily. Although Ed was no longer feeling seriously depressed, and the intensity of his obsessions was diminished, they had not disappeared, and he was now avoiding writing altogether.

Because the obsessions were still a problem, Ed's psychiatrist referred him to a psychologist who specialized in behavior therapy for anxiety disorders. He continued seeing the psychiatrist every other week for checks on his medication, which he continued to take. The new therapist told Ed that his fears of particular letters and numbers would be maintained as long as he avoided writing. Ed agreed to begin writing short essays every day, for a period of at least 30 minutes. The content could vary from day to day—anything that Ed felt like writing about—but he was encouraged to include the names of his wife and brother as often as possible. Furthermore, he was instructed to avoid his compulsive writing style, intentionally allowing the parts of letters to be separated or loops to be closed. At the beginning and end of each essay, Ed was required to record his anxiety level so that the therapist could monitor changes in his subjective discomfort. Over a period of 8 to 10 weeks, Ed's handwriting began to change. It was less of a struggle to get himself to write, and his handwriting became more legible.

The final aspect of behavioral treatment was concerned with his fear of axes. Ed and his therapist drew up a list of objects and situations related to axes, arranging them from those that were the least anxiety-provoking through those that were most frightening. They began with the least frightening. In their first exposure session, Ed agreed to meet with the psychologist while a relatively dull, wood-splitting maul was located in the adjoining room. Ed was initially quite anxious and distracted, but his anxiety diminished considerably before the end of their 2-hour meeting. Once that had been accomplished, the therapist helped him to confront progressively more difficult situations. These sessions were challenging and uncomfortable for Ed, but they allowed him to master his fears in an orderly fashion. By the end of the twelfth session of exposure, he was able to hold a sharp ax without fear.

Psychological Interventions

Psychoanalytic psychotherapy has been used to treat patients with anxiety disorders since Freud published his seminal papers at the turn of the twentieth century. The emphasis in this type of treatment is on fostering insight regarding the unconscious motives that presumably lie at the heart of the patient's symptoms, such as Ed's feelings about his brother. Although many therapists continue to employ this general strategy, it has not been shown to be effective in controlled outcome studies.

Systematic Desensitization and Interoceptive Exposure Like psychoanalysis, behavior therapy was initially developed for the purpose of treating anxiety disorders, especially specific phobias. The first widely adopted procedure was known as systematic desensitization (see Chapter 3). In desensitization, the client is first taught progressive muscle relaxation. Then the therapist constructs a hierarchy of feared stimuli, beginning with those items that provoke only small amounts of fear and progressing through items that are most frightening. Then, while the client is in a relaxed state, he or she imagines the lowest item on the hierarchy. The item is presented repeatedly until the person no longer experiences an increase in anxiety when thinking about the object or situation. This process is repeated several times as the client moves systematically up the hierarchy, sequentially confronting images of stimuli that were originally rated as being more frightening.

In the years since systematic desensitization was originally proposed, many different variations on this procedure have been employed. The crucial feature of the treatment involves systematic maintained exposure to the feared stimulus (McNally, 2007; Rachman, 2002). Positive outcomes have been reported, regardless of the specific manner in which exposure is accomplished. Some evidence indicates that direct ("in vivo") exposure works better than imaginal exposure. A few prolonged exposures can be as effective as a larger sequence of brief exposures. Another variation on exposure procedures, known as flooding, begins with the most frightening stimuli rather than working up gradually from the bottom of the hierarchy. All of these variations on the basic procedure have been shown to be effective in the treatment of phobic disorders. Several research studies have demonstrated that exposure therapy leads to clinically meaningful improvement when compared to placebo treatments. Positive results are typically maintained several months after the end of treatment (Barlow, Raffa, & Cohen, 2002). Exposure is often accomplished in the presence of the therapist, but the treatment can be just as effective when the client directs his or her own systematic exposure in the natural environment.

The treatment of panic disorder often includes two specific forms of exposure. One, *situational exposure,* is used to treat agoraphobic avoidance (Hahlweg et al., 2001). In this procedure, the person repeatedly confronts the situations that have previously been avoided. These often include crowded public places, such as shopping malls and theaters, as well as certain forms of transportation, such as buses and trains. *Interoceptive exposure,* the other form of exposure, is aimed at reducing the person's fear of internal, bodily sensations that are frequently associated with the onset of a panic attack, such as increased heart and respiration rate and dizziness. The process is accomplished by having the person engage in standardized exercises that are known to produce such physical sensations. These may include spinning in a swivel chair, running in place, breathing through a narrow straw, or voluntary hyperventilation, depending on the type of sensation that the person fears and avoids. Outcome studies indicate that interoceptive exposure is

Why is response prevention coupled with exposure in the treatment of OCD?

one of the most important ingredients in the psychological treatment of panic disorder (Barlow et al., 2002; Meuret et al., 2005).

Exposure and Response Prevention The most effective form of psychological treatment for obsessive–compulsive disorder combines prolonged exposure to the situation that increases the person's anxiety with prevention of the person's typical compulsive response (Abramowitz, 2006; Franklin & Foa, 2002). Neither component is effective by itself. The combination of exposure and response prevention is necessary because of the way in which people with obsessive–compulsive disorder use their compulsive rituals to reduce anxiety that is typically stimulated by the sudden appearance of an obsession. If the compulsive behavior is performed, exposure is effectively cut short.

Consider, for example, the treatment program employed with Ed. His obsessive thoughts and images, which centered around violence, were associated with handwriting. They were likely to pop into his mind when he noticed letters that were poorly formed. In an effort to control these thoughts, Ed wrote very carefully, and he corrected any letter that seemed a bit irregular. By the time he entered behavior therapy, Ed had avoided writing altogether for several months. The therapist arranged for him to begin writing short essays on a daily basis to be

▶ Exposure treatments can be administered in imagination or in the person's natural environment. This tarantula is not dangerous, and it is used in desensitization for people with spider phobias.

sure that he was exposed, for at least 30 minutes each day, to the situation that was most anxiety-provoking. He encouraged Ed to deliberately write letters that did not conform to his compulsive style. In their sessions, for example, Ed was also required to write long sequences of the letter T in which he deliberately failed to connect the two lines. He was not allowed to go back and correct this "mistake." The combination represents prolonged exposure to an anxiety-provoking stimulus and response prevention.

Controlled outcome studies indicate that this approach is effective with most OCD patients (Allen, 2006). After a few weeks of treatment with exposure and response prevention, most patients show improvements that are clinically important (see Research Methods). On the other hand, some patients (perhaps as many as 20 percent) do not respond positively to this form of treatment, and many continue to exhibit mild symptoms of the disorder after they have been successfully treated.

Relaxation and Breathing Retraining Behavior therapists have used relaxation procedures for many years. Relaxation training usually involves teaching the client alternately to tense and relax specific muscle groups while breathing slowly and deeply (Lehrer & Carr, 1997). This process is often described to the client as an active coping skill that can be learned through consistent practice and used to control anxiety and worry.

Outcome studies indicate that relaxation is a useful form of treatment for various forms of anxiety disorder. For example, applied relaxation and cognitive behavior therapy have been compared to nondirective psychotherapy for the treatment of patients with generalized anxiety disorder. Patients who received relaxation training and those who received cognitive therapy were more improved at the end of treatment than those who received only nondirective therapy (Borkovec et al., 2002; Siev & Chambless, 2007).

Breathing retraining is a procedure that involves education about the physiological effects of hyperventilation and practice in slow breathing techniques. It is often incorporated in treatments used for panic disorder (Barlow, 1997; Taylor, 2001). This process is similar to relaxation in the sense that relaxation exercises also include instructions in breathing control. The person learns to control his or her breathing

RESEARCH METHODS

Statistical Significance: When Differences Matter

Let's say that an outcome study reveals a statistical difference in the effectiveness of one form of treatment versus another form (or no treatment at all). Does this automatically mean that the difference is clinically significant? The answer is no. We can explain this point by using a hypothetical example. Imagine that you want to know whether exposure and response prevention are effective in the treatment of OCD. You could conduct a study, using an experimental design, in which 50 patients with OCD are randomly assigned to receive exposure and response prevention and another 50 patients—the control group—are not. The latter group might receive a placebo pill or nondirective supportive psychotherapy for purposes of comparison. Measures of obsessions and compulsions are collected before and after treatment for patients in both groups. Your hypothesis is that exposure treatment will lead to more improvement than will placebo or nondirective therapy. In contrast, the null hypothesis (see Research Methods in Chapter 1) holds that the two forms of treatment are not truly different. To conclude that exposure and response prevention is effective, you must reject the null hypothesis.

After collecting your data, you can use statistical tests to help you decide whether you can reject the null hypothesis. These tests assign a probability to that result, indicating how often we would find that result if there are not really differences between the two treatments. Psychologists have adopted the .05 level, meaning that if a difference occurs only by chance, you would find this difference less than 5 times out of every 100 times you repeated this experiment. Differences that exceed the .05 level, therefore, are assumed to reflect real differences between the variables rather than mere chance. Such results are said to be *statistically significant.*

> ## What is the difference between statistical significance and clinical importance?

Statistical significance should not be equated with clinical importance (Jacobson & Truax, 1991). It is possible for an investigator to find statistically significant differences between groups (and therefore reject the null hypothesis) on the basis of relatively trivial changes in the patients' adjustment. Consider the hypothetical example outlined above and suppose that you measured outcome in terms of a questionnaire for obsessions and compulsions whose scores could range from 0 (no symptoms) to 100 (highest score possible). Let's also assume that the average person without OCD gets a score of 50 on this questionnaire and that a score of 70 or higher is typically considered to indicate the presence of problems that are associated with a disruption of the person's social and occupational functioning. Both groups have a mean rating of 90 on the scale prior to treatment. At the end of treatment, the mean rating for the exposure group has dropped to 75, and the mean for the control group is now 85. If you have included enough subjects, and depending on the amount of variation among scores within each group, this difference might reach statistical significance. But is it clinically important? Probably not. The average patient in the exposure group still has a score above the cutoff for identifying meaningful levels of psychopathology and 25 points above the average for adults in the general population.

Clinical importance is sometimes measured in terms of the proportion of people in the treatment group whose outcome scores fall below a certain threshold of severity or within the range of scores that are produced by people without the disorder in question. In the case of OCD, people treated with exposure and response prevention do show levels of change that are considered clinically important as well as statistically significant (Abramowitz, 1998).

Clinical investigators should also consider the *kind* of changes that they expect to find as well as the *amount* of change. In addition to looking at changes in particular symptoms, such as a reduction in the frequency of compulsive behaviors, some clinical investigators also ask questions about the patient's quality of life (Gladis et al., 1999). These include an interest in the person's overall satisfaction as well as his or her ability to perform various social roles, at work, at school, or with friends and family. Therapists obviously hope that their patients will experience improvements in their overall quality of life and level of social adjustment when they are able to achieve a reduction in the severity of symptoms of mental disorders.

---

through repeated practice using the muscles of the diaphragm, rather than the chest, to take slow, deep breaths. Although breathing retraining appears to be a useful element in the treatment of panic disorder, the mechanisms involved are not entirely clear. A simple reduction in the frequency of hyperventilation is apparently not the main effect of breathing retraining. Some clinicians believe that the process works by enhancing relaxation or increasing the person's perception of control (Garssen, de Ruiter, & Van Dyck, 1992).

Cognitive Therapy Cognitive therapy is used extensively in the treatment of anxiety disorders. Cognitive treatment procedures for anxiety disorders are similar to those employed in the treatment of depression. Therapists help clients identify cognitions that are relevant to their problem; recognize the relation between these thoughts and maladaptive emotional responses (such as prolonged anxiety); examine the evidence that supports or contradicts these beliefs; and teach clients more useful ways of interpreting events in their environment (Schuyler, 1991).

In the case of anxiety disorders, cognitive therapy is usually accompanied by additional behavior therapy procedures. Barlow's approach to the treatment of panic disorder, for example, includes a cognitive component in addition to applied relaxation and exposure (Barlow, 1997). One aspect of the cognitive component involves an analysis of errors in the ways in which people think about situations in their lives. Typical examples of faulty logic include jumping to conclusions before considering all of the evidence, overgeneralizing ("That C in biology shows I'll never be a doctor"), all-or-none thinking (assuming that one mistake means total failure), and so on.

A second aspect of Barlow's cognitive component for panic patients is called *decatastrophisizing*. In this procedure, the therapist asks the client to imagine what would happen if his or her worst-case scenario actually happened. The same principles that are used in examining faulty logic are then applied to this situation. The therapist might say, "I don't think that you will fail the exam. But what would happen if you did fail the exam?" The client's initial reaction might be catastrophic ("I would die." "My parents would kill me." "I would flunk out of school."). Upon more careful analysis, however, the client might agree that these negative predictions actually represent gross exaggerations that are based on cognitive errors. Discussions in the therapy session are followed by extensive practice and homework assignments during the week. As one way of evaluating the accuracy of their own hypotheses, clients are encouraged to write down predictions that they make about specific situations and then keep track of the actual outcomes.

Several controlled outcome studies attest to the efficacy of cognitive therapy in the treatment of various types of anxiety disorder, including panic disorder, agoraphobia, social phobia, generalized anxiety disorder, and obsessive–compulsive disorder (Allen, 2006; Otto et al., 2004). Improvement in symptoms over time seems to be preceded by changes in cognitive processing. This observation provides support for the hypothesis that cognitive factors do play an important role in maintenance of these disorders (Hofmann, 2004; Teachman, Marker, & Smith-Janik, 2009).

Biological Interventions

Medication is the most effective and most commonly used biological approach to the treatment of anxiety disorders. Several types of drugs have been discovered to be useful. They are often used in conjunction with psychological treatment (Vanin, 2008).

Antianxiety Medications The most frequently used types of minor tranquilizers are from the class of drugs known as benzodiazepines, which includes diazepam (Valium) and alprazolam (Xanax). These drugs reduce many symptoms of anxiety, especially vigilance and subjective somatic sensations, such as increased muscle tension, palpitations, increased perspiration, and gastrointestinal distress. They have relatively less effect on a person's tendency toward worry and rumination. Benzodiazepines were the most widely prescribed form of psychiatric medication until the 1990s.

Benzodiazepines bind to specific receptor sites in the brain that are ordinarily associated with a neurotransmitter known as gamma-aminobutyric acid (GABA). Benzodiazepines, which enhance the activity of GABA neurons, are of two types, based on their rate of absorption and elimination from the body. Some, such as alprazolam and lorazepam (Ativan), are absorbed and eliminated quickly, whereas others, such as diazepam, are absorbed and eliminated slowly.

Benzodiazepines have been shown to be effective in the treatment of generalized anxiety disorders and social phobias (Ballenger, 2001; Benitez et al., 2008). Drug effects are most consistently evident early in treatment. The long-term effects of benzodiazepines (beyond 6 months of treatment) are not well established (Mahe & Balogh, 2000). They are not typically beneficial for patients with specific phobias or obsessive–compulsive disorder. Certain high-potency benzodiazepines are also useful for treating panic disorder (Spiegel & Bruce, 1997). Alprazolam (Xanax) is considered by some psychiatrists to be the drug of choice for patients with this condition because it produces clinical improvement more quickly than antidepressants.

Many patients with panic disorder and agoraphobia relapse if they discontinue taking medication (Marks et al., 1993). Exposure may be a preferable form of treatment for patients with a diagnosis of panic disorder with agoraphobia because of high relapse rates that have been observed after alprazolam is withdrawn.

Common side effects of benzodiazepines include sedation accompanied by mild psychomotor and cognitive impairments. These drugs can, for example, increase the risk of automobile accidents, because they interfere with motor skills. They can also lead to problems in attention and memory, especially among elderly patients.

The most serious adverse effect of benzodiazepines is their potential for addiction. Approximately 40 percent of people who use benzodiazepines for 6 months or more will exhibit symptoms of withdrawal if the medication is discontinued (Michelini et al., 1996). Withdrawal reactions include the reappearance of anxiety, somatic complaints, concentration problems, and sleep difficulties. They are most severe among patients who abruptly discontinue the use of benzodiazepines that are cleared quickly from the system, such as alprazolam. The risk for becoming dependent on benzodiazepines is greatest among people who have a history of abusing other substances, like alcohol.

Another class of antianxiety medication, known as the azapirones, includes drugs that work on entirely different neural pathways than the benzodiazepines (Cadieux, 1996). Rather than inhibiting the activity of GABA neurons, azapirones act on serotonin transmission. The azapirone that is used most frequently in clinical use is known as buspirone (BuSpar). Placebo-controlled outcome studies indicate that buspirone is effective in the treatment of generalized anxiety disorder (Davidson et al., 1999). Some clinicians believe that buspirone is preferable to the benzodiazepines because it does not cause drowsiness and does not interact with the effects of alcohol. The disadvantage is that patients do not experience relief from severe anxiety symptoms as quickly with buspirone as they do with benzodiazepines.

Antidepressant Medications The selective serotonin reuptake inhibitors (SSRIs), discussed in Chapter 5, have become the preferred form of medication for treating almost all forms of anxiety disorder. These include drugs such as fluoxetine (Prozac), fluvoxamine (Luvox), sertaline (Zoloft), and paroxetine (Paxil). Reviews of controlled outcome studies indicate that they are at least as effective as other, more traditional forms of antidepressants in reducing symptoms of various anxiety disorders (Anderson, 2006; Roy-Byrne & Cowley, 2002). They also have fewer unpleasant side effects, they are safer to use, and withdrawal reactions are less prominent when they are discontinued. Therefore, the SSRIs are now considered the first-line medication for treating

panic disorder, social phobia, and obsessive–compulsive disorder.

Imipramine (Tofranil), a tricyclic antidepressant medication, has been used for more than 40 years in the treatment of patients with panic disorder. A large number of double-blind, placebo-controlled studies indicate that it produces beneficial results (Jefferson, 1997; Mavissakalian & Ryan, 1998). Psychiatrists often prefer imipramine to antianxiety drugs for the treatment of panic disorder because patients are less likely to become dependent on the drug than they are to high-potency benzodiazepines like alprazolam.

The tricyclic antidepressants are used less frequently than the SSRIs because they produce several unpleasant side effects, including weight gain, dry mouth, and overstimulation (sometimes referred to as an "amphetamine-like" response). Some of the side effects (like feeling jittery, nervous, lightheaded, and having trouble sleeping) are upsetting to patients because they resemble symptoms of anxiety. Side effects often lead patients to discontinue treatment prematurely. In one study of patients who received long-term treatment with imipramine, 50 percent experienced distressing side effects, including 17 percent who found the effects intolerable (Noyes, Garvey, & Cook, 1989).

Clomipramine (Anafranil), another tricyclic antidepressant, has been used extensively in treating obsessive–compulsive disorder. Several placebo-controlled studies have shown clomipramine to be effective in treating OCD (Abramowitz, 1997; Kozak, Liebowitz, & Foa, 2000). One study found that more than 50 percent of the patients who received clomipramine improved to a level of normal functioning over a period of 10 weeks, compared to only 5 percent of the patients in a placebo group (Katz, DeVeaugh-Geiss, & Landau, 1990). Patients who continue to take the drug maintain the improvement, but relapse is common if medication is discontinued.

In actual practice, anxiety disorders are often treated with a combination of psychological and biological procedures. The selection of specific treatment components depends on the specific group of symptoms that the person exhibits. Table 6–3 summarizes various types of psychological treatment and specific types of medication that are effective with anxiety disorders. These are not the only types of treatment

Do psychological treatments have any advantages over medication for treatment of anxiety?

TABLE 6–3   Treatments of Choice for Anxiety Disorders

DISORDER	MEDICATION	EXAMPLE	PSYCHOLOGICAL TREATMENT
	DRUG CLASS	GENERIC NAME (TRADE NAME)	
Panic Disorder	SSRIs Benzodiazepines TCAs	Fluvoxamine (Luvox) Clonazepam (Klonopin) Imipramine (Tofranil)	Cognitive therapy Exposure (interoceptive) Breathing retraining
Agoraphobia	Benzodiazepines SSRIs TCAs	Lorazepam (Ativan) Sertraline (Zoloft) Imipramine (Tofranil)	Exposure (situational) Cognitive therapy
Generalized Anxiety Disorder	Benzodiazepines Azapirones	Alprazolam (Xanax) Buspirone (BuSpar)	Cognitive therapy Applied relaxation
Specific Phobias	Medication not usually recommended		Exposure *in vivo*
Social Phobia	SSRIs Benzodiazepines MAOIs	Paroxetine (Paxil) Clonazepam (Klonopin) Phenelzine (Nardil)	Exposure *in vivo* Cognitive therapy Social skills training
Obsessive–Compulsive Disorder	SSRIs TCAs	Fluoxetine (Prozac) Clomipramine (Anafranil)	Exposure plus response prevention Cognitive therapy

that are available, but they include those that have been subjected to empirical validation. The potential benefits and costs of combined treatment with medication and psychological procedures should be studied more carefully. Current evidence suggests that patients who receive both medication and psychotherapy may do better in the short run, but patients who receive only cognitive behavior therapy may do better in the long run because of difficulties that can be encountered when medication is discontinued (Otto et al., 2005).

GETTING HELP

Most people suffering from anxiety disorders can be treated successfully. Several forms of intervention are beneficial, primarily behavior therapy, cognitive therapy, and medication. If you plan to work with a professional therapist, do some research before you begin working with a specific person. Read about treatments that have been evaluated empirically, and look for someone who uses one of these procedures. Some excellent Internet sites may help you find the best therapist for you. Patient-run organizations have established support groups in many communities and share information about treatment alternatives. One outstanding example is the Anxiety Disorders Association of America. The URL for its Web site is www.adaa.org. It includes a consumer's guide to treatment alternatives that is organized by specific types of anxiety disorders. More detailed information about obsessive–compulsive disorder and related problems can be obtained from the Obsessive Compulsive Foundation, a not-for-profit organization composed of people with OCD, their families, and professionals. Its Web address is www.ocfoundation.org.

Some people may be able to make improvements on their own with the advice of a useful self-help book. There are a lot of good alternatives to choose from in the area of anxiety disorders. We recommend two books that describe a combination of cognitive and behavioral approaches to treatment. *Triumph over Fear* (1995), by Jerilyn Ross and Rosalynn Carter, describes the successful experiences of people who have recovered from various types of anxiety disorders, including phobias, panic, and generalized anxiety disorder. Practical, self-help strategies are also summarized in *Overcoming Panic, Anxiety, and Phobias: New Strategies to Free Yourself from Worry and Fear* (1996), written by Shirley Babior and Carol Goldman. This book includes simple instructions in progressive muscle relaxation, cognitive techniques to master anxiety, and exposure procedures for overcoming avoidance. Finally, more specific information about dealing with obsessive–compulsive disorder can be found in *Stop Obsessing: How to Overcome Your Obsessions and Compulsions* (2001), by Edna Foa and Reid Wilson.

■ SUMMARY

Anxiety disorders are defined in terms of a preoccupation with, or persistent avoidance of, thoughts or situations that provoke **fear** or anxiety. **Anxiety** involves a diffuse emotional reaction that is associated with the anticipation of future problems and is out of proportion to threats from the environment. A pervasive anxious mood is typically associated with pessimistic thoughts and feelings. The person's attention may also turn inward, focusing on negative emotions and self-evaluation rather than on the organization or rehearsal of adaptive responses that might be useful in coping with negative events.

A **panic attack** is a sudden, overwhelming experience of terror or fright. Panic attacks are defined largely in terms of a list of somatic sensations, ranging from heart palpitations, sweating, and trembling to nausea, dizziness, and chills.

Phobias are persistent and irrational narrowly defined fears that are associated with avoidance of a specific object or situation. The most complex and incapacitating form of phobic disorder is **agoraphobia,** which is usually described as fear of public spaces. It is not so much a fear of being close to one specific object or situation as it is a fear of being separated from signals associated with safety.

Obsessions are repetitive, unwanted, intrusive cognitive events that may take the form of thoughts or images or impulses. They intrude suddenly into consciousness and lead to an increase in subjective anxiety. **Compulsions** are repetitive behaviors, considered by the person to be senseless or irrational, that reduce the anxiety associated with obsessions. The person attempts to resist but cannot. The two most common forms of compulsive behavior are cleaning and checking.

DSM-IV-TR recognizes several specific subtypes of anxiety disorders: **panic disorders** (with or without agoraphobia), phobic disorders (specific phobia, social phobia, and agoraphobia without panic attacks), obsessive–compulsive disorder, and generalized anxiety disorder, as well as posttraumatic stress disorder and acute stress disorder.

The NCS-R study found that anxiety disorders are more common than any other form of mental disorder. Phobias are the most common type of anxiety disorder, with a 1-year prevalence of about 9 percent of the adult population, followed by social phobia (7 percent), generalized anxiety disorder (3 percent), and panic disorder (3 percent). Obsessive–compulsive disorder (1 percent) and agoraphobia without panic (1 percent) have the lowest 1-year prevalence rates. Women are more likely than men to experience specific phobias, social phobias, agoraphobia, panic disorder, and generalized anxiety disorder. Gender differences are less marked in obsessive–compulsive disorder. There is considerable overlap between anxiety disorders and other forms of psychopathology, especially depression and substance use disorders.

Causal explanations regarding the development and maintenance of anxiety disorders are based on the evolutionary significance of anxiety and fear. These emotions are most often adaptive, but they interfere with people's lives when they are too intense or are triggered at inappropriate times.

Many types of environmental events that can lead to depression are also involved in the development of pathological anxiety. Severe life events involving danger are most often associated with anxiety symptoms, while severe events involving loss are more often associated with depression. Various kinds of childhood adversity, including parental neglect and abuse, increase a person's risk for the later onset of an anxiety disorder.

The learning model explained the development of phobic disorders in terms of classical conditioning, or the pairing of fear with originally neutral stimuli that happen to be present during a traumatic experience. A modified learning view, known as the **preparedness model,** is based on recognition that there are biological constraints on the kinds of associations that members of a particular species are able to make. We may be prepared to develop intense, persistent fears only to a select set of objects or situations. People can apparently learn to avoid certain stimuli if they observe other people showing a strong fear response to those stimuli. Studies with infant monkeys support the preparedness model.

Cognitive theorists have argued that panic disorder is caused by the catastrophic misinterpretation of bodily sensations or perceived threat. This theory has the support of several research studies, but there are methodological problems associated with some of the studies. The cognitive theory of panic also has problems explaining some clinical observations regarding panic disorder, such as the fact that some patients experience panic attacks in their sleep.

People who are prone to excessive **worrying** are unusually sensitive to cues that signal the existence of future threats. The recognition of danger cues triggers a maladaptive, self-perpetuating cycle of cognitive processes that can quickly spin out of control. The threatening information that is generated in this process is presumably encoded in memory in the form of elaborate schemas that are easily reactivated. In comparison to the depressed person, who is convinced that failure will definitely occur, the anxious person is afraid of failure that may occur as a future event.

Twin studies indicate that genetic factors are involved in the etiology of several types of anxiety disorder, including panic disorder, generalized anxiety disorder, and social phobias. The influence of environmental events seems to be greatest in specific phobias.

Studies of fear conditioning in animals have identified specific pathways in the brain that are responsible for detecting and organizing a response to danger. The amygdala plays a central role in these circuits. Several other areas of the brain are also associated with anxiety and the symptoms of anxiety disorders.

Serotonin, norepinephrine, GABA, and dopamine are some of the neurotransmitters that are involved in the production of panic attacks. Many interacting neurotransmitter systems play a role in the etiology of anxiety disorders, and they are largely the same ones that are also involved in major depression.

Several psychological approaches to the treatment of anxiety disorders have been shown to be effective. These include the use of exposure and flooding in the treatment of phobic disorders, prolonged exposure and response prevention in the treatment of obsessive–compulsive disorders, and cognitive therapy in the treatment of panic disorder and GAD. Various types of medication are also effective treatments for anxiety disorders. These include benzodiazepines for generalized anxiety disorder, and selective serotonin reuptake inhibitors for obsessive–compulsive disorder, social phobia, and panic disorder.

THE BIG PICTURE CRITICAL THINKING REVIEW

Why is a panic attack sometimes called a "false alarm"?

Panic attacks resemble normal fear responses, but they are triggered at an inappropriate time (when the person is not confronted by an immediate source of danger). (SEE PAGES 165–166)

What is the difference between normal and abnormal obsessions?

Their content is similar (such as impulses to hurt other people). The differences hinge on duration, frequency, and the extent to which the person struggles against the obsessive thought. (SEE PAGE 169)

What is the expected long-term outcome for people with anxiety disorders?

Some people recover, but they are most often chronic conditions. (SEE PAGES 173–174)

Is there a unique causal pathway for each type of anxiety disorder?

Probably not. Studies of environmental events, genetic factors, and neurobiological mechanisms suggest that pathways leading to different types of anxiety disorder overlap to a considerable extent. (SEE PAGE 177)

If phobias are learned quickly and easily, why are they so hard to extinguish?

Because their development is guided by a "prepared module," which is presumably efficient, highly selective, and operating outside conscious awareness. (SEE PAGE 179)

Why is response prevention coupled with exposure in the treatment of OCD?

If the therapist did not prevent compulsive behaviors, a patient with OCD would use them to reduce anxiety that is stimulated by exposure to the obsession and the process would not be effective. (SEE PAGE 188)

Do psychological treatments have any advantages over medication for treatment of anxiety?

Yes. Problems with medication include various side effects, the potential for addiction (benzodiazepines), and increased risk of relapse following their discontinuation. (SEE PAGE 191)

■ KEY TERMS

agoraphobia **167**

anxiety **165**

compulsions **168**

fear **164**

generalized anxiety
   disorder (GAD) **172**

neurosis **170**

obsessions **168**

panic attack **165**

panic disorder **171**

phobias **166**

preparedness theory **179**

social phobia **172**

worry **165**

ACUTE AND POSTTRAUMATIC STRESS DISORDERS, DISSOCIATIVE DISORDERS, AND SOMATOFORM DISORDERS

A soldier experiences vivid flashbacks of combat long after returning to civilian life. A young woman discovers hidden parts of her personality that her therapist links to some long forgotten trauma. A middle-aged man finds his face divided in half with numbness, but the symptom must be psychological because it makes no neurological sense. Each of these cases apparently involves *unconscious mental processes,* information processing outside of conscious awareness. Anxiety, stress, and trauma seemingly are transformed, unconsciously, into a flashback, the splitting of consciousness, or a physical symptom. Do unconscious mental processes really affect people in such mysterious ways? What is the unconscious mind? How can we understand it?

OVERVIEW

We ask these questions in this chapter in the context of discussing traumatic stress disorders, dissociative disorders, and somatoform disorders. These psychological problems look very different but may share one important similarity: **dissociation**—the disruption of the normally integrated mental processes involved in memory, consciousness, identity, or perception (Spiegel &

Cardena, 1991). You should know from the outset that we are entering controversial territory in this chapter. Some psychologists view the unconscious mind as all powerful; others doubt its existence, or at least view unconscious mental processes as relatively unimportant. We approach the topic with both skepticism and curiosity. Especially given limited research, we are skeptical about problems that can be overdramatized. At the same time, we are captivated by unusual case studies that raise fascinating questions about their origin—and about how the mind works.

We begin by considering the least controversial and most studied problems, traumatic stress disorders. The DSM-IV-TR groups these diagnoses with anxiety disorders. We discuss traumatic stress disorders in a separate chapter, however, so we can consider them in detail and highlight their mixed symptoms of anxiety and dissociation.

ACUTE AND POSTTRAUMATIC STRESS DISORDERS

Stress is an inevitable, and in many ways a desirable, fact of everyday life. Some stressors, however, are so catastrophic and horrifying that they can cause serious psychological harm. Such **traumatic stress** is defined in DSM-IV-TR as an event that involves actual or threatened death or serious injury to self or others and creates intense feelings of fear, helplessness, or horror. Examples include rape, military combat, bombings, air-

plane crashes, earthquakes, major fires, and devastating automobile wrecks. In recent years, we know trauma all too well as a result of 9/11, school shootings, sexual assault, and the aftermath of combat in Iraq and Afghanistan.

It is normal for both survivors and witnesses to be greatly distressed by trauma. For some, however, the disturbance continues long after the trauma has ended. **Acute stress disorder (ASD)** occurs within 4 weeks after exposure to traumatic stress and is characterized by dissociative symptoms,

◄ A traumatized woman is covered in dust from the collapsing World Trade Center towers. Over 100,000 people directly witnessed the September 11 attacks on the World Trade Center and the Pentagon.

reexperiencing of the event, avoidance of reminders of the trauma, and marked anxiety or arousal. **Posttraumatic stress disorder (PTSD)** also is defined by symptoms of reexperiencing, avoidance, and arousal, but in PTSD the symptoms either are longer lasting or have a delayed onset. The following case study illustrates the horrors and lasting trauma of sexual assault.

CASE **STUDY** Sexual Assault and Stephanie's PTSD

One spring evening, Stephanie Cason, a bright, attractive, and well-adjusted 27-year-old graduate student, ran outside to investigate a fire in another building in her apartment complex. While watching the firemen, Stephanie chatted with a man who she assumed was a neighbor. After talking with a few other people, she returned to her apartment. The fire had caused a power outage, but Stephanie found her way upstairs and changed into her nightclothes. When she came back downstairs, she was startled by the man she had met outside. Without saying a word, he raised a tire iron and struck Stephanie across the top of her head—repeatedly—until she fell to the floor and stopped screaming. Stephanie was cut deeply and stunned by the vicious blows, but she attempted to resist as the man began to grab at her breasts and rip at her clothes. He began to mutter obscenities and told Stephanie he wanted to have sex with her. Stephanie thought, "He's going to kill me."

Somehow Stephanie managed to think clearly despite the blood pouring from her head. She "agreed" to have sex with her assailant but told him that she needed to "freshen up" first. Eventually, he let her go to "clean up." When Stephanie reached her bedroom, she shoved a bureau in front of the door and screamed frantically out the window for help. Her screams frightened her attacker, who tried to flee. But one of the firefighters tackled and captured him as he attempted to run away.

Stephanie saved herself from being raped, but she could not protect herself from the emotional fallout of her sexual assault. For days, eventually weeks and months, she felt intermittently terrified, dazed, and grateful to be alive. She replayed the horror of the evening in her mind repeatedly, and when she managed to fall asleep, she often was wakened by frightening nightmares. Stephanie was terrified to be alone, especially at night, but also at many times during the day. She relied on the unwavering support of her boyfriend and friends to stay nearby and help her cope.

Shortly after the assault, Stephanie sought help from a skilled clinical psychologist, but she fell into a depression despite the therapy. Antidepressant medication helped somewhat with her mood and lethargy, but for months she was hypervigilant—constantly on the lookout for new threats. She had difficulty concentrating and experienced intermittent feelings of numbness or unreality. In addition, she frequently reexperienced the images and emotions surrounding the dreaded event. She was able to resume her studies after about 3 months, and within 6 or 8 months she was working fairly regularly but with considerably less confidence and concentration than before. As the anniversary of her assault approached, Stephanie grew increasingly upset. The spring weather, usually a welcome change, reminded her of the terror of the previous spring. Her feelings of unreality returned. She had more flashbacks, reliving the dreaded night in her mind. The nightmares and fears of being alone reappeared. As the dreaded date passed, her reactions eased slowly. After about 2 or 3 months, she was able to renew her normal life—as normal as her life could be.

Stephanie found it painful but also helpful to talk about her assault with friends and, over time, more publicly. After the passing of the 1-year anniversary, she actually began to lecture about her experiences to classes and to women's groups. Lecturing gave her some relief, and more importantly, it gave her a sense that some good might come from her trauma. Stephanie also testified at the trial of her assailant, who was convicted and sent to prison for 20 years. Although she appeared strong in the courtroom, the trial renewed many of Stephanie's symptoms. She again relived the terror of the assault, avoided being alone at night, and became fearful and hypervigilant about dangers in her world.

Once her assailant was imprisoned, Stephanie felt a degree of resolution about the trauma. Still, she could not fully banish the demons. She again experienced intensely distressing episodes near the second and third anniversaries of the assault. And even at other times, Stephanie could unexpectedly fall victim to terror. For example, more than 3 years after the assault, her boyfriend (now her husband) silently entered her room after returning home unexpectedly one night. Frightened by his sudden appearance, Stephanie first screamed in terror, then sobbed in uncontrollable fear, and felt numb and unreal for several days afterwards.

Stephanie did not behave like a victim from the moment of the assault, throughout the trial, or in her public discussions of her trauma. But despite her strength, Stephanie could not prevent or control the recurrent terror of PTSD brought on by a violent sexual assault.

Symptoms of ASD and PTSD

The defining symptoms of both acute and posttraumatic stress disorder include (1) reexperiencing; (2) avoidance; and (3) persistent arousal or anxiety. Dissociative symptoms also are common in the immediate aftermath of a trauma and must be present to make a diagnosis of ASD, but not PTSD (Frances, First, & Pincus, 1995).

Reexperiencing Like Stephanie, survivors often *reexperience* trauma in various ways. Some people experience repeated, distressing images or thoughts of the incident. They visualize the trauma over and over, for example, or repeatedly question what they might have done differently. Others relive the trauma in horrifying dreams. Many people with ASD or PTSD have repeated and intrusive **flashbacks,** sudden memories during which the trauma is replayed in images or thoughts—often at full emotional intensity. In rare cases, reexperiencing occurs as a *dissociative state,* where the person feels and acts as if the trauma actually were recurring in the moment. A combat veteran in a dissociative state might act as if he is back in battle, and he may even take dangerous actions like gathering weapons or barricading himself in his residence. Typically, dissociative states are of short duration, but in unusual cases they can last for days.

Avoidance Marked or persistent avoidance of stimuli associated with the trauma is another symptom of ASD and PTSD. Trauma victims may attempt to avoid thoughts or feelings related to the event, or, like Stephanie, they may avoid people, places, or activities that remind them of the trauma. In PTSD, the avoidance also may manifest itself as a general *numbing of responsiveness*—emotions are dampened or even nonexistent. This synonym "emotional anesthesia" captures its essence. Emotional numbing can cause sufferers to withdraw from others, particularly from close relationships.

Arousal or Anxiety People suffering from ASD and PTSD also experience increased arousal and anxiety following the trauma, a symptom that, when it is more severe, predicts a worse prognosis (Schell, Marshall, & Jaycox, 2004). Examples of arousal and anxiety include Stephanie's hypervigilance in searching for dangers in her world, as well as restlessness, agitation, and irritability. A number of people with PTSD or ASD also have an *exaggerated startle response,* excessive fear reactions to unexpected stimuli, such as loud noises. These symptoms are why traumatic stress disorders are grouped with the anxiety disorders in DSM-IV-TR.

Dissociative Symptoms Acute stress disorder is characterized by explicit dissociative symptoms following trauma. Many people feel dazed, and act "spaced out." Others experience *depersonalization,* feeling cut off from themselves or their environment. They might feel "like a robot," for example, or as if they were sleepwalking. Still others experience *derealization,* a marked sense of unreality about yourself and the world around you. Immediately after September 11, for example, many people awoke wondering if the terrorist attacks had been only a nightmare—a sense of unreality that continued for days or

◄ Following trauma, many people have intrusive flashbacks, sudden memories during which the trauma is replayed in images and thoughts often at full emotional intensity.

longer. ASD also may be characterized by features of *dissociative amnesia,* the inability to recall important aspects of the traumatic experience (Harvey, Bryant, & Dang, 1998).

DSM-IV-TR lists a sense of numbing or detachment from others as a dissociative symptom that characterizes acute stress disorder. A very similar symptom is listed as an indicator of avoidance, not dissociation, in the diagnosis of PTSD (see Table 7–1). This discrepancy reflects some of the broader controversy about whether ASD and PTSD should be classified as dissociative disorders, anxiety disorders, or separately from both (van der Kolk & McFarlane, 1996).

Diagnosis of ASD and PTSD

Brief Historical Perspective Maladaptive reactions to trauma have long been of interest to the military, where "normal" performance is expected in the face of the trauma of combat. Historically, most of the military's concern has focused on battle dropout, that is, men who leave the field of action as a result of what has been called "shell shock" or "combat neurosis"

POSTTRAUMATIC STRESS DISORDER
BONNE

"I basically resigned myself to the fact that I was going to die."

Watch the video "Posttraumatic Stress Disorder: Bonnie" on MyPsychLab. As you watch the video, consider the terrible events Bonnie witnessed on 9/11. Her PTSD symptoms make sense. What treatments might help her recover?

TABLE 7–1   DSM-IV-TR Diagnostic Criteria for Posttraumatic Stress Disorder (PTSD)

A. The person has been exposed to a traumatic event in which both of the following were present:

1. The person experienced, witnessed, or was confronted with an event or events that involved actual or threatened death or serious injury, or a threat to the physical integrity of self or others.
2. The person's response involved intense fear, helplessness, or horror.

B. The traumatic event is persistently reexperienced in one (or more) of the following ways:

1. Recurrent and intrusive distressing recollections of the event including images, thoughts, or perceptions
2. Recurrent distressing dreams of the event
3. Acting or feeling as if the traumatic event were recurring
4. Intense psychological distress at exposure to internal or external cues that symbolize or resemble an aspect of the traumatic event
5. Physiologic reactivity upon exposure to internal or external cues that symbolize or resemble an aspect of the traumatic event

C. Persistent avoidance of stimuli associated with the trauma and numbing of general responsiveness (not present before the trauma), as indicated by three (or more) of the following:

1. Efforts to avoid thoughts, feelings, or conversations associated with the trauma
2. Efforts to avoid activities, places, or people that arouse recollections of the trauma
3. Inability to recall an important aspect of the trauma
4. Markedly diminished interest or participation in significant activities
5. Feeling of detachment or estrangement from others
6. Restricted range of affect
7. Sense of a foreshortened future

D. Persistent symptoms of increased arousal, as indicated by two (or more) of the following:

1. Difficulty falling or staying asleep
2. Irritability or outbursts of anger
3. Difficulty concentrating
4. Hypervigilance
5. Exaggerated startle response

E. Duration of the disturbance is more than 1 month

Specify if:
Acute: If duration of symptoms is less than 3 months
Chronic: If duration of symptoms is 3 months or more

Specify if:
With delayed onset: If onset of symptoms is at least 6 months after the stressor

Source: Reprinted with permission from the *Diagnostic and Statistical Manual of Mental Disorders,* Fourth Edition, Text Revision. Copyright © 2000 by the American Psychiatric Association.

(Jones et al., 2007). During the Vietnam War, however, battle dropout was less frequent than in earlier wars, but delayed reactions to combat were much more common (Figley, 1978). This change prompted much interest in PTSD, a condition first listed in the DSM in 1980.

Contemporary Classification The basic diagnostic criteria for PTSD—reexperiencing, avoidance, and arousal—have remained more or less the same in revisions of the DSM. However, two significant changes in the classification of traumatic stress disorders were made

with the publication of DSM-IV in 1994: Acute stress disorder was included as a separate diagnostic category, and the definition of trauma was altered.

Acute Stress Disorder

The diagnostic criteria for ASD and PTSD are essentially the same, except that ASD explicitly includes dissociative symptoms and lasts no longer than 4 weeks (see Table 7–2). PTSD must continue longer or have a delayed onset (see Table 7–1).

TABLE 7–2   DSM-IV-TR Diagnostic Criteria for Acute Stress Disorder (ASD)

A. The person has been exposed to a traumatic event in which both of the following were present:

1. The person experienced, witnessed, or was confronted with an event or events that involved actual or threatened death or serious injury, or a threat to the physical integrity of self or others.
2. The person's response involved intense fear, helplessness, or horror.

B. Either while experiencing or after experiencing the distressing event, the individual has three (or more) of the following dissociative symptoms:

1. A subjective sense of numbing, detachment, or absence of emotional responsiveness
2. A reduction in awareness of his or her surroundings (e.g., "being in a daze")
3. Derealization
4. Depersonalization
5. Dissociative amnesia (i.e., the inability to recall an important aspect of the trauma)

C. The traumatic event is persistently reexperienced in at least one of the following ways: recurrent images, thoughts, dreams, illusions, flashback episodes, or a sense of reliving the experience; or distress on exposure to reminders of the traumatic event.

D. Marked avoidance of stimuli that arouse recollections of the trauma (e.g., thoughts, feelings, conversations, activities, places, people).

E. Marked symptoms of anxiety or increased arousal (e.g., difficulty sleeping, irritability, poor concentration, hypervigilance, exaggerated startle response, motor restlessness).

F. The disturbance causes clinically significant distress or impairment in social, occupational, or other important areas of functioning or impairs the individual's ability to pursue some necessary task, such as obtaining necessary assistance or mobilizing personal resources by telling family members about the traumatic experience.

G. The disturbance lasts for a minimum of 2 days and a maximum of 4 weeks and occurs within 4 weeks of the traumatic event.

Source: Reprinted with permission from the *Diagnostic and Statistical Manual of Mental Disorders,* Fourth Edition, Text Revision. Copyright © 2000 by the American Psychiatric Association.

Not surprisingly, many people suffer from ASD after experiencing trauma, and the presence of ASD may predict future PTSD (Harvey & Bryant, 1998, 1999). Still, some experts wonder whether ASD really describes *normal* reactions to trauma and suggest that the diagnosis needs to be reformulated or dropped (Harvey & Bryant, 2002). The new classification was added to the DSM-IV without much research support. Why? The hope was that early intervention with ASD would prevent the development of PTSD (Frances et al., 1995, p. 263).

What Defines Trauma?

Earlier versions of DSM defined trauma as an event "outside the range of usual human experience." Unfortunately, many traumatic stressors are a *common* part of human experience. Thus, DSM-IV-TR defines trauma as (1) the experience of an event involving actual or threatened death or serious injury to self or others and (2) a response of intense fear, helplessness, or horror in

reaction to the event. One current controversy is whether PTSD can be caused by indirect exposure to trauma, such as seeing horrible scenes of 9/11 on television (Neria & Galea, 2007).

Different events all may be horrific, but different trauma also have unique psychological consequences. Thus, researchers study both common and unique reactions to traumatic events including combat (Monson et al., 2006), terrorism (Hobfoll, Canetli-Nisim, & Johnson, 2006), child sexual abuse (McDonagh et al., 2005), spouse abuse (Taft et al., 2005), children's coping with residential fires (Jones & Ollendick, 2002), and torture (Basoglu et al., 1997). We discuss some unique aspects of the trauma of sexual assault in the Trauma of Sexual Assault box.

The effect of exposure to disasters is a particular concern, because they commonly involve large numbers of people (Neria et al., 2007). For example, a random telephone survey of 1,008 residents living south of 110th Street in Manhattan

Why is trauma no longer defined as "outside of usual human experience"?

THE TRAUMA OF SEXUAL ASSAULT

Like many other traumas, sexual assault is all too common. Almost 10 percent of women report having been raped at least once in their lifetime, according to national surveys, and 12 percent report having been sexually molested (Kessler et al., 1995). Other evidence suggests a notably higher prevalence when the data include *acquaintance rapes,* assaults committed by people known to the victim (Goodman, Koss, & Russo, 1993).

Rape can be devastating physically, socially, and emotionally. Thirty-nine percent of rape victims are physically injured on parts of their bodies other than the genitals. A significant proportion of rape victims are infected with sexually transmitted diseases, and about 5 percent of rapes result in pregnancy (Goodman et al., 1993). Socially, sexual assault can undermine women's work, as well as their intimate relationships (Byrne et al., 1999).

Most victims of sexual assault show the symptoms of PTSD. Victims may reexperience the horrors of the assault; they may feel numbed in reacting to others, particularly sexual partners; they may avoid any potentially threatening situation; and they may maintain both autonomic hyperarousal and hypervigilance against possible victimization. Depression is also common. Sadness, crying, and

What is "secondary victimization"?

withdrawal from others often are coupled with sleep and appetite disturbances. Loss of interest in sex, insecurities about sexual identity, sexual dysfunction, and negative feelings toward men also are common (Goodman et al., 1993).

Many victims of sexual assault blame themselves, despite the fact that they are the victims. Women may wonder if they unwittingly encouraged their assailant, or chastise themselves for not being more cautious in avoiding dangerous circumstances. This irrational self-blame is abetted by cultural myths that women provoke rape or actually enjoy it. *Secondary victimization* is a growing concern, as insensitive legal, medical, and even mental health professionals can add to a rape victim's emotional burden. In fact, victims of acquaintance rape show increased symptoms of PTSD when they encounter victim-blaming behaviors from professionals who are supposed to help them (Campbell et al., 1999). Such findings may explain why as many as two-thirds of stranger rapes and four-fifths of acquaintance rapes are not reported to authorities.

---

on 9/11 found that, whether or not they directly witnessed the World Trade Center (WTC) attacks, 7.5 percent—equivalent to 67,000 people—suffered from PTSD one month later (Galea et al., 2002). This obviously is a huge public health issue, yet there are reasons for optimism too. Four months after the attacks the prevalence of PTSD among residents of the same area dropped to 1.7% and to 0.6% after 6 months (Galea et al., 2003). What protected the New Yorkers? We cannot know for certain, but key influences surely include the outpouring of support (McNally, Bryant, & Ehlers, 2003) and underestimated human resilience (Bonanno et al., 2006).

Disaster and Emergency Workers

September 11 also focused attention on how emergency workers cope with trauma. Firefighters, police, and paramedics must remain calm, but this does not make them immune to trauma's aftereffects. Five months after Hurricane Katrina in 2005, 22 percent of responding firefighters in New Orleans suffered from PTSD (CDC, 2006). In general, however, emergency workers are less than half as likely to develop PTSD as victims (Neria & Galea, 2007). Emergency workers are

protected by their training, preparation, and sense of purpose. More generally, *hardiness,* a sense of commitment, control, and challenge in facing stress, predicts lower risk for PTSD (Sutker et al., 1995). Still, emergency workers need education about the psychological effects of trauma on *them,* opportunities to express troubling emotions, and, in some cases, specialized psychological help.

Comorbidity

Many people with PTSD also suffer from another mental disorder. Comorbidity is high for depression, other anxiety disorders, and substance abuse (Brady, Back, & Coffey, 2004; Kessler et al., 1995). Other problems associated with PTSD include disturbing nightmares, physical symptoms like headaches and gastrointestinal problems, grief, and relationship difficulties (Cook et al., 2004). Anger—at others or at oneself—is another prominent issue (Orth & Wieland, 2006). A very important concern is increased suicide risk. One study found that 33 percent of rape survivors had thoughts of suicide, and 13 percent actually made a suicide attempt (Kilpatrick, Edmunds, & Seymour, 1992).

Differential diagnosis between ASD and PTSD and *adjustment disorder* is based on both the nature of the stressor and the type and severity of symptoms. Adjustment disorders (see Chapter 17) are caused by "normal" but painful stressors, such as losing a job, and they involve normal (if distressing) reactions to these events. As noted earlier, we expect ASD, PTSD, and adjustment disorders to be classified together as stress-related disorders in future revisions of the DSM.

Frequency of Trauma, PTSD, and ASD

Early studies suggested that PTSD was uncommon (e.g., Helzer, Robins, & McEvoy, 1987); however, more recent research documents that the prevalence of PTSD is high. The National Comorbidity Survey found that a prevalence rate of nearly 8 percent of people living in the United States, including about 10 percent of women and 5 percent of men (Kessler et al., 1995). A recent replication yielded a similar prevalence rate, 6.8% (Kessler et al., 2005).

What accounts for the increased incidence rates in more recent research? Much of the increase is due to the recognition that traumatic stressors are common, not rare. A study of a random sample of 2,181 adults living in the Detroit area found that almost 90 percent of the participants had experienced at least one traumatic stressor in their lifetime. About 9 percent of participants developed PTSD following a trauma (Breslau et al., 1998; see Figure 7–1). Similar rates of trauma and PTSD also are found in Mexico (Norris et al., 2003). Rape and assault clearly are among the very worst traumas, and they pose an especially high risk for PTSD (see Figure 7–1).

Women are especially likely to develop PTSD as a result of rape, while combat exposure is a major risk factor for PTSD among men (Breslau et al., 1991; Kessler et al., 1995; Prigerson, Maciejewski, & Rosenbeck, 2002). In general, however, women are more likely than men to develop PTSD following exposure to any trauma (Tolin & Foa, 2006). Children are especially vulnerable to trauma, with 20 percent to 40 percent developing PTSD (Neria & Galea, 2007). Minority group members are more likely to experience PTSD, in part because of their living conditions (Pole, Gone, & Kulkarni, 2008), and PTSD also is common among crime victims (Kilpatrick & Acierno, 2003). Still, the most common cause of PTSD is

Traumatic Events and the Risk for PTSD

	Experienced trauma	PTSD following trauma
Rape	5.4	49
Other sexual assault	6.2	23.7
Badly beaten up	11.4	31.9
Natural disaster	16.6	3.8
Mugged/threatened with weapon	25	8
Serious car crash	28	2.3
Witness killing/serious injury	29	7.3
Sudden unexpected death	60	14.3
Any trauma	89.6	9.2

100 80 60 40 20   0   10 20 30 40 50 60

FIGURE 7–1 Bars to the left of center indicate the percentage of adults who had experienced each trauma among a representative sample of 2,181 adults aged 18 to 45 and living in the Detroit area. Bars to the right of center indicate the percentage of adults who developed PTSD after exposure to the particular trauma.

Note: The prevalence of rape as reported in this study was lower than that reported in other studies. We assume that this statistic reflects only more violent rapes.

Source: From "Traumatic and Posttraumatic Stress Disorder in the Community: The 1996 Detroit Area Survey of Trauma" by N. Breslau, R. C. Kessler, H. D. Chilcoat, L. R. Schultz, G. C. Davis, and P. Andreski, *Archives of General Psychiatry*, (1998), 55, pp. 626-632. Copyright © 1998. Reprinted by permission of American Medical Association.

the sudden, unexpected death of a loved one. The risk for PTSD following the sudden death of a loved one is "only" about one in seven (Breslau et al., 1998). However, the high prevalence of unexpected death makes it the most common cause of PTSD (see Figure 7–1).

Risk for Trauma and PTSD Whether people get caught in events like September 11 or the Virginia Tech shootings is a matter of luck—good or bad. Many traumas, however, do not occur at random. Because they engage in more risky behavior, men, young people in their late teens and early 20s, people with a history of conduct disorders, and extroverts all are more likely to experience trauma. People who are anxious or who have a family history of mental illness also experience more trauma, but the reasons why are less clear. As noted, minorities and people with less education are more likely to live in dangerous environments and be exposed to more traumatic stress.

Is the experience of trauma random?

The development of PTSD following a trauma also is not random. Those who are "neurotic"—anxious and easily upset—are more likely to develop PTSD after a trauma, as are people with a family or personal history of mental disorder

(Breslau et al., 1991; Breslau, Davis, & Andreski, 1995; Breslau et al., 1998). People who developed PTSD following an earlier trauma, but not those who did not, also are at greater risk following a second trauma, suggesting a general susceptibility to trauma (Breslau, Peterson, & Schultz, 2008).

Course and Outcome People who suffer from ASD are more likely to develop PTSD subsequently (Bryant & Harvey, 2000). The prediction is far from perfect, raising questions about the prevention value of the diagnosis. Moreover, *subclinical* ASD—symptoms not severe or pervasive enough to meet diagnostic criteria—nevertheless increases the risk for PTSD (Harvey & Bryant, 1999). Three symptoms—numbing, depersonalization, and a sense of reliving the experience—are the best predictors of future PTSD (Bryant & Harvey, 2000).

Does trauma always cause PTSD?

The symptoms of PTSD generally diminish with time. The National Comorbidity Survey found that symptoms improved fairly rapidly during the first year, but more gradually over the next several years (see Figure 7–2). Symptoms diminished faster among people who received treatment, although treatment was not randomly assigned and may not have caused this. Importantly, over one-third of people still reported symptoms 10 years after the trauma, whether they were treated or not (Kessler et al., 1995).

These data show that PTSD can be chronic. In fact, one study found symptoms among many World War II prisoners of war—*40 years* after confinement. Only 30 percent of POWs who had suffered from PTSD (as diagnosed by retrospective report) were fully recovered, while 60 percent still had mild to moderate symptoms. Another 10 percent either showed no recovery or had a deteriorating course (Kluznik et al., 1986).

Causes of PTSD and ASD

By definition, trauma causes ASD and PTSD. Because not every traumatized person develops a disorder, however, trauma is a necessary but not a sufficient cause. What increases risk or resilience in the face of trauma?

Social Factors in ASD and PTSD Research on social factors and the risk for PTSD focuses primarily on (1) the nature of the trauma and the individual's level of exposure to it and (2) the availability of social support following the trauma. Victims of trauma are more likely to develop PTSD when the trauma is more intense, life-threatening, and involves greater exposure (Neria & Galea, 2007). For example, victims of attempted rape are more likely to develop PTSD if the rape is completed; if they are physically injured during the assault; and if they perceive the sexual assault as life-threatening (Kilpatrick et al., 1989). Similarly, PTSD is more prevalent in Vietnam veterans who were wounded, who were involved in the deaths of noncombatants, or who witnessed atrocities (Koenen et al., 2003; Oei, Lim, & Hennessy, 1990). A study of PTSD following September 11 found a greater prevalence among people who lived south of Canal Street, close to the World Trade Center (Galea et al., 2002).

As with less severe stressors, social support after a trauma can play a crucial role in alleviating long-term psychological damage. A lack of social support is thought to have contributed to the high prevalence of PTSD found among Vietnam veterans (Oei, Lim, & Hennessy, 1990). Rather than being praised as heroes, returning veterans often were treated with disdain. This made it difficult for many veterans to find meaning in their sacrifices, and likely increased their risk for PTSD. People who had little social support also were more likely to develop PTSD following September 11 (Galea et al., 2002).

A study of identical twins strongly supports the role of the environment in PTSD. Among 715 MZ twin pairs who were discordant for military service in Southeast Asia during the Vietnam War era, the

The Course of PTSD With and Without Treatment

Treatment (*n* = 266)
No treatment (*n* = 193)

Proportion of trauma victims reporting continued symptoms

Duration of symptoms, in months

FIGURE 7–2 The symptoms of PTSD decline over time but persist for 10 years among one-third of people. Treatment appears to hasten recovery, but this correlational finding may not mean causation.

Source: R. C. Kessler, A. Sonnega, E. Bromet, M. Hughes, and C. B. Nelson, 1995, "Posttraumatic Stress Disorder in the National Comorbidity Survey, *Archives of General Psychiatry, 52,* p. 1057. Copyright © 1995. Reprinted by permission of American Medical Association.

prevalence of PTSD was *nine times* higher for co-twins who served in Vietnam and experienced high levels of combat in comparison to their identical twin who did not serve (Goldberg et al., 1990).

Biological Factors in ASD and PTSD The same twin study also strongly points to biological factors in PTSD. In an analysis of more than 4,000 twin pairs, MZ twins had a higher concordance rate for exposure to combat than DZ twins. Following exposure, identical twins also had higher concordance rates for PTSD symptoms than fraternal twins (True et al., 1993). Importantly, genetic contributions differed across symptoms. Genes contributed most strongly to arousal/anxiety symptoms and least strongly to reexperiencing. Conversely, level of combat exposure predicted reexperiencing and avoidance but not arousal/anxiety (True et al., 1993).

Biological Effects of Exposure to Trauma

Does exposure to trauma have biological *consequences* as well as biological causes? People with PTSD show alterations in the functioning, and perhaps the structure, of the amygdala and hippocampus, findings consistent, respectively, with the experience of heightened fear reactivity and intrusive memories (Kolassa & Elbert, 2007). Other evidence links PTSD with general psychophysiological arousal, for example, an increased resting heart rate (Pole, 2007). Together, the pattern of biological findings suggests that the sympathetic nervous system is aroused and the fear response is sensitized in PTSD.

Does trauma damage the brain? Think critically. The differences in brain function and structure may reflect (1) damage caused by trauma, (2) normal biological adaptations to stress, or (3) preexisting differences (Newport & Nemeroff, 2000; Pitman, 1997). In support of the last possibility, a study of identical twins—including one Vietnam veteran with PTSD and his co-twin who neither served in Vietnam nor suffered from PTSD—found smaller than average hippocampus volume in *both* twins (Gilbertson et al., 2002). Similarly, twin research shows that preexisting differences account for IQ deficits that have been mistakenly attributed to brain damage owing to trauma (Gilbertson et al., 2006). Differences between people with and without PTSD are *correlations*. And even if assessed with exciting measures like fMRI, correlation still does not mean causation.

Psychological Factors in ASD and PTSD An important learning perspective on psychological contributions to PTSD is **two-factor theory,** which has two parts. First, classical conditioning *creates* fears when the terror of trauma is paired with the cues associated with it. Second, operant conditioning *maintains* avoidance by reducing fear (negative reinforcement). Avoidance also prevents the extinction of anxiety through exposure (Keane, Zimering, & Caddell, 1985). We can readily illustrate two-factor theory in Stephanie's case. Her fears of being alone at night—when she was attacked—are easy to trace to classical conditioning. Her avoidance was negatively reinforced (she felt far less anxious) when friends and family initially stayed with her at night. Stephanie's courage in confronting her fears—by eventually staying alone and in many other ways—also shows a needed step in overcoming PTSD.

Two-factor theory applies to everyone. What gives Stephanie and other people the courage to face their fears sooner or later? Research shows that the risk for PTSD following trauma depends upon cognitive factors such as preparedness, purpose, and blame. For example, pilots cope more successfully with helicopter crashes if they have training than if they have none, underscoring the importance of preparedness and control (Shalev, 1996). The importance of purpose comes from evidence that, despite greater physical suffering, political activists develop fewer psychological symptoms than nonactivists following torture (Basoglu et al., 1997). On the other hand, negative appraisals—the rape victim who blames herself or the driver who thinks he could have avoided an accident—are strongly tied to an increased risk for PTSD (Bryant & Guthrie, 2005; Halligan et al., 2003; McNally et al., 2003).

Some theories suggest that dissociation is an unconscious defense that helps victims cope with trauma (Oei, Lim, & Hennessy, 1990). However, research indicates that dissociation is associated with more not less PTSD (Ehlers, Mayou, & Bryant, 1998; Griffin, Resick, & Mechanic, 1997; Harvey, Bryant, & Dang, 1998). Among a sample of Israeli war trauma victims, for example, more dissociation reported within 1 week following a

PEARSON **mypsychlab** VIDEO CASE

POSTTRAUMATIC STRESS DISORDER
SARA

"I would wake up 37 times a night for the slightest noise, thinking this crazy person was going to come in and do something to me."

Watch the video "PostTraumatic Stress Disorder: Sara" on MyPsychLab. As you watch the video, listen for Sara's description of her PTSD symptoms: arousal, avoidance, and reexperiencing. Also consider ways in which the trauma of domestic violence is unique—for example, in the social isolation of the victim.

trauma predicted *more* severe PTSD 6 months later (Shalev et al., 1996).

Dissociation may not be adaptive, but most theorists agree that victims of trauma must, over time, find a balance between gradually facing their painful emotions while not being overwhelmed by them. The balancing act can be tricky, but it is essential. New York City college students had lower rates of PTSD following September 11 if they were better at enhancing *and* suppressing emotional expression (Bonanno et al., 2004). This is an example of what psychologist Edna Foa, a leading PTSD researcher, calls *emotional processing,* which involves three key stages. First, victims must engage emotionally with their traumatic memories. Second, victims need to find a way to articulate and organize their chaotic experience. Third, victims must come to believe that, despite the trauma, the world is not a terrible place (Foa & Riggs, 1995; Foa & Street, 2001; see Figure 7–3).

> **Is trauma by itself a sufficient cause of PTSD?**

This last step is similar to what other psychologists call *meaning making*—eventually finding some value or reason for having endured trauma (Ehlers & Clark, 2000). Meaning making is very personal and may involve religion, a renewed appreciation for life, or public service. Stephanie found meaning in her efforts to make others more aware of sexual assault. In the long run, many people actually report that trauma leads to growth (Park & Helgeson, 2006). *Posttraumatic growth,* positive changes resulting from trauma, is linked with less depression and more positive well-being, but also with more intrusive and avoidant thoughts (Helgeson, Reynolds, & Tomich, 2006). Finding meaning in trauma does not mean forgetting about it.

Integrating and Alternative Pathways Trauma always is a part of ASD and PTSD, but there still are alternative pathways to the disorders. Anyone might develop ASD or PTSD when exposed to a trauma of sufficient intensity. In other cases, trauma exacerbates or reveals a preexisting disorder. In most cases, however, trauma is a necessary but not a sufficient cause. ASD and PTSD develop as a result of a combination of factors, including personality characteristics that predate the trauma, exposure during the trauma, and emotional processing and social support afterwards (Ozer et al., 2003; Ozer & Weiss, 2004).

Prevention and Treatment of ASD and PTSD

We know that trauma precedes ASD and PTSD. This leads to a very important question: Can we prevent the disorders with early intervention?

Emergency Help for Trauma Victims Many experts hope that prevention is possible. In fact, the U.S. Federal Emergency Management Agency (FEMA) provides special funding to community mental health centers during disasters. Emergency treatments range from intensive individual counseling sessions with hurricane victims to group discussions with children following school violence (Litz, 2004). Approaches differ greatly, but offering immediate support to trauma victims is a common goal of all early interventions (McNally et al., 2003; Raphael et al., 1996).

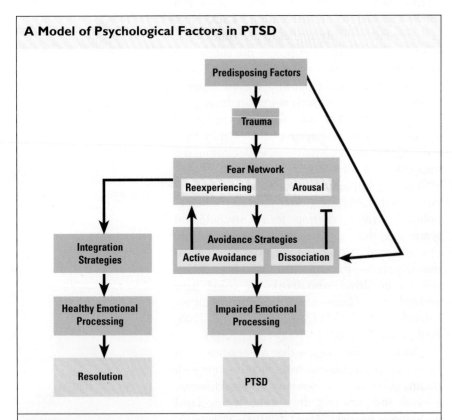

A Model of Psychological Factors in PTSD

FIGURE 7–3 Trauma victims may develop PTSD if they avoid their fears (by dissociation or active avoidance). In contrast, integrating the trauma into one's experience—and eventually finding meaning in the horror—leads to healthy emotional processing and resolution.

Source: Adapted from: R. A. Bryant & A. G. Harvey, 2000, *Acute Stress Disorder: A Handbook of Theory, Assessment, and Treatment,* Washington, DC: American Psychological Association, p. 38.

Perhaps the most widely used early intervention is **critical incident stress debriefing (CISD),** a single 1- to 5-hour group meeting offered 1 to 3 days following a disaster. CISD involves several phases where participants share their experiences and reactions, and group leaders offer education, assessment, and referral if necessary (Mitchell, 1982; Mitchell & Dyregrov, 1993). CISD is difficult to evaluate, since it is conducted in the midst of a crisis (Tuckey et al., 2007). Still, research provides *no* evidence that CISD prevents future PTSD (Bryant & Harvey, 2000; McNally et al., 2003), and some studies find that CISD is harmful (Lilienfeld, 2007). CISD may provoke too much emotion too soon after trauma. Clearly, there is a need to explore alternative prevention methods, including promising cognitive behavioral approaches (Neuner et al., 2004).

Since World War I, interventions with soldiers who drop out of combat have been based on the three principles of offering (1) immediate treatment in the (2) proximity of the battlefield with the (3) expectation of return to the front lines upon recovery (Jones, Thomas, & Ironside, 2007). The effectiveness of these treatment principles was not studied systematically until a 1982 evaluation of the Israeli army during the Lebanon war. Results indicated that 60 percent of soldiers treated near the front recovered sufficiently to return to battle within 72 hours. Soldiers who expected to return to the front experienced lower rates of PTSD than did those who did not expect to return to battle. In addition, soldiers who were treated on the front lines were less likely to develop PTSD subsequently compared to soldiers who were treated away from the battlefield (Oei, Lim, & Hennessy, 1990).

Former Mayor Rudolph Giuliani intuitively followed similar principles when, in the immediate aftermath of September 11, he regularly encouraged New Yorkers to grieve but also to go back to work, to go out, and to go on despite the horrors of the World Trade Center attacks. Such community-based efforts are more appealing, and perhaps more effective, than artificial debriefings. Consider this: Government agencies allocated over $150 million to pay for psychotherapy for New Yorkers in the wake of September 11, but $90 million remained unspent two years later (McNally et al., 2003).

Treatment of ASD Few studies of ASD treatment have been completed, which is not surpris-

ing since the diagnosis was developed only recently. Nevertheless, some research indicates that structured interventions with ASD *can* lead to the prevention of future PTSD. Unlike CISD, these treatments last longer and target the select group of trauma victims who meet ASD diagnostic criteria. The empirically backed ASD treatments are based on the principles of cognitive behavior therapy (described shortly), although they are briefer, involving five $1\frac{1}{2}$-hour sessions (Bryant et al., 2006; Bryant, Moulds, & Nixon, 2003).

Cognitive Behavior Therapy for PTSD While great sensitivity is required, the most effective treatment for PTSD is reexposure to trauma. One of the first studies of *prolonged exposure* asked rape victims to relive the trauma repeatedly over nine therapy sessions. While surely painful, exposure reduced PTSD symptoms more, over the long term, than three randomized alternatives, including relaxation/stress management, supportive counseling, and a wait list control group (Foa et al., 1991).

Depending on the client, the therapist, and the circumstances of the trauma, prolonged exposure might involve confronting feared situations in real life, in one's imagination, or by recounting events in therapy. One treatment, *imagery rehearsal therapy,* successfully reduces recurrent nightmares, a troubling problem frequently associated with PTSD. The exposure involves reliving nightmares while awake, but rewriting the nightmare script in any way the client wishes (Krakow et al., 2001).

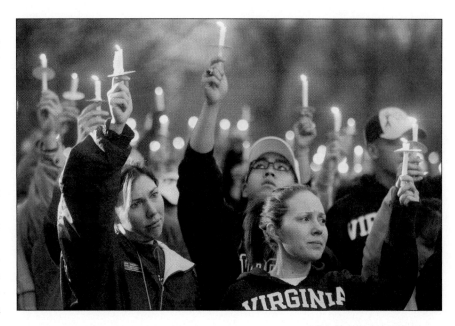

▲ Students gather for a vigil following the Virginia Tech shootings. For many, shared grief and support eases the pain of trauma and reduces the risk for PTSD.

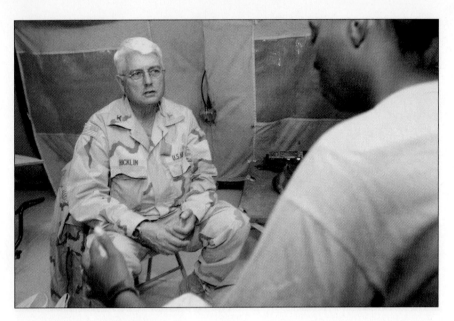

▲ A soldier in Iraq receiving counseling. Military personnel must routinely deal with the immediate and long-term effects of the trauma of combat.

effective (Bisson et al., 2007); however, prolonged exposure, not eye movements, again appears to be the "active ingredient" (Davidson & Parker, 2001).

Antidepressant Medication According to a consensus statement on the treatment of PTSD, antidepressants (SSRIs) and therapeutic reexposure are the two "first-line" therapies for PTSD (Ballenger et al., 2000). The effectiveness of SSRIs is likely at least partially due to the high comorbidity between PTSD and depression (Newport & Nemeroff, 2000). While antidepressants are helpful, traditional antianxiety medications are *not* effective in treating PTSD (Golier et al., 2007).

Prolonged exposure has now been used as a part of empirically supported treatments for PTSD following combat (Monson et al., 2006), childhood sex abuse (McDonagh et al., 2005), and assault (Foa et al., 2005) among other trauma. Other cognitive behavior therapy elements typically are included in treatment, for example, challenging maladaptive beliefs stemming from trauma such as, "No one cares" or "The world is hopeless." Still, exposure appears to be the key "active ingredient;" other CBT procedures do not add to its effectiveness (Foa et al., 2005). Nevertheless, we view prolonged exposure as the beginning, not the end, of the healing process. Emotional processing and meaning making are important to long-term adjustment to trauma, and require time and perspective, perhaps beyond what can be expected from therapy.

EMDR One final treatment for PTSD, *eye movement desensitization and reprocessing (EMDR)*, is a technique that has been greeted with considerable enthusiasm—and skepticism. Psychologist Francine Shapiro (1995) "discovered" that rapid back-and-forth eye movements reduced her own anxiety, so she tried the technique on her clients, who appeared to benefit from it. Why should this work? No one has a good theory why, which is the heart of the controversy (Keane et al., 2006). Still, Shapiro and other proponents use EMDR as a relaxation technique, while clients with PTSD simultaneously relive vivid images of trauma. A recent meta-analysis concluded that EMDR may be

DISSOCIATIVE DISORDERS

While dissociation in ASD and PTSD can be dramatic, the symptoms of **dissociative disorders**—characterized by persistent, maladaptive disruptions in the integration of memory, consciousness, or identity—verge on the unbelievable. They include psychologically produced amnesia, confused travel long distances from home (perhaps under a new identity), and the existence of two or more separate personalities in one person. Are these symptoms real? The answer is controversial. Some experts think dissociative disorders are phony, examples of nothing more than the power of suggestion. Others view them as real but rare problems. Still others believe dissociative disorders are misunderstood, overlooked, and prevalent. This controversy is about much more than dissociative disorders. It concerns the very nature of the human psyche.

In the past, dissociative disorders were of more interest to novelists than to scientists. You may be familiar with dramatic portrayals of *multiple personality disorder,* an old name for a dissociative disorder, in *Sybil* or *The Three Faces of Eve,* both of which were widely read books that became popular motion pictures. In recent years, however, psychological scientists have grown more interested in unconscious mental processes (Bargh & Morsella, 2008). Partially as a result, interest in dissociative disorders also has grown—without resolving basic controversies. We introduce these problems, and the debate, in the following case study.

CASE STUDY Dissociative Fugue—Dallae's Journey

Dallae disappeared mysteriously in the middle of final exams during her junior year at a California university. Her roommate last saw her studying for her organic chemistry exam. Dallae had been agitated that night. She kept bothering her roommate, who was cramming for the same exam, and left her room repeatedly. Dallae did not take the exam the next day. When she missed two more finals, her roommate contacted the authorities.

At first, the police suspected foul play, because it seemed unlikely that Dallae would leave college on her own. None of her personal possessions were missing; even her eyeglasses were still sitting on her desk. However, bank records indicated that Dallae withdrew all of her money from her bank account the day before the exam. Investigators also discovered that Dallae had told her parents that she had an A in organic chemistry. In fact, she was failing the course.

When the local police failed to locate Dallae, they contacted the FBI. After a 4-week investigation, they found Dallae in a college town on the East Coast. She had been brought to a hospital emergency room after she was found wandering the streets. She appeared confused and disoriented. She told the Emergency Room (ER) physician that her name was Dawn and that she had been living on the streets and sleeping in dormitory lounges. She said that she had just moved from the West Coast and had come to the town because she hoped to attend the university. She gave a vague account of other details of her life. For example, she could not say how she got to the East Coast.

Dallae allowed herself to be voluntarily admitted to the hospital's psychiatric unit. There she talked little and spent most of her time watching television. She told the staff that she was Vietnamese and had been adopted by American parents, but her stories remained vague and inconsistent. She said that she could not remember, but she was not upset by her memory impairment. A CAT scan and neuropsychological tests detected no physical abnormalities or deficits in short-term memory or motor functioning.

A hospital social worker contacted the local police about the disoriented young patient, and the police were able to identify Dallae from a missing persons report. The social worker contacted Dallae's parents, and her mother immediately flew east to see her. When her mother appeared at the hospital, Dallae did not recognize her. Her mother was greatly distressed by Dallae's indifference and noted other oddities and inconsistencies. For one thing, Dallae was not Vietnamese, and she was not adopted. She had grown up with her married parents, who were Korean immigrants. Her mother also noted that although Dallae was right-handed, she used her left hand to write a note at the hospital. Dallae's consistent use of her left hand was confirmed by the staff and by the neuropsychologist who had tested her.

Two nights after her mother arrived, Dallae's memories apparently returned. That night, she attempted suicide by slashing her wrists, but she was discovered by a hospital staff member, who quickly stopped the bleeding. Dallae was intermittently depressed and extremely agitated for the next several days, especially after seeing her mother. Although she would not talk at length, her conversation indicated that much of her memory was now intact, and she began using her right hand again.

During the next 2 weeks, Dallae gradually related details about her life to the psychologist who was treating her. Dallae had been a quiet and obedient girl all through her childhood. Her parents worked very hard, and had high ambitions for their three children. Dallae's older brother had an M.B.A. and was a successful young executive. Her older sister currently was editor of the law review at a prestigious law school. Throughout her life, her parents had told friends and relatives that Dallae would be a doctor one day.

During discussions with her therapist, Dallae began to talk more freely. She noted that she had been terrified to tell her parents about her grades and her lack of interest in medicine, especially her father. She cried at length when relating how he had struck her across the face during the previous Thanksgiving break, when she tried to tell him that she no longer wanted to study medicine.

After 6 weeks in the hospital, Dallae returned to California with her parents. Her memory was intact at the time of the discharge, except that she continued to have no recollection of her trip across the country or many of her days living on the streets. She was uncertain why she thought her name was Dawn, although she did mention being influenced by a television show she had seen about a Vietnamese child who had been adopted. At the time of Dallae's discharge, her depression had abated, and she was no longer actively suicidal. She reported being relieved at having told her mother about her feelings about medical school, but she remained very anxious about facing her father.

Dallae suffered from *dissociative fugue,* a rare disorder characterized by sudden, unplanned travel, the inability to remember details about the past, and confusion about identity or the assumption of a new identity. The travel is purposeful, despite the confusion and memory impairments. Dallae knew where she was going and provided at least a vague explanation about why. Dissociative fugue typically follows a traumatic event. It perhaps is most commonly observed among soldiers following a particularly gruesome battle.

Purposeful travel is the distinguishing symptom, but the core questions about fugue—and about all dissociative disorders—concern the split between conscious and unconscious psychological experience. How could Dallae be aware of the present but be unaware of her past? Why didn't all her memories return after she saw her mother? Could she be faking part or all of her "illness"? Key figures in the history of abnormal psychology have tried to answer such perplexing questions. In fact, attempts to explain these puzzling disorders led to theorizing about the existence of unconscious mental processes.

Hysteria and the Unconscious

Historically, dissociative disorders (and somatoform disorders, which we discuss shortly) were seen as forms of hysteria. In Greek, *hystera* means

▲ The French neurologist Jean Charcot (1825–1893) demonstrating a case of hysteria at the Salpetiere, a famous hospital in Paris.

"uterus," and the term **hysteria** reflects the ancient view that frustrated sexual desires, particularly a woman's desire to have a baby, cause the symptoms. Supposedly the uterus detached and moved about the body, causing a problem wherever it eventually lodged. Variations of this sexist view continued into the late nineteenth century, when many physicians erroneously believed that hysteria occurred only among women (Showalter, 1997).

Charcot, Freud, and Janet In the latter half of the nineteenth century, French neurologist Jean-Martin Charcot used hypnosis both to induce and treat hysteria. Charcot greatly influenced Sigmund Freud, who observed Charcot's hypnotic treatments early in his training. Charcot also strongly influenced Freud's contemporary and rival, Pierre Janet (1859–1947). Janet was a French philosophy professor who conducted psychological experiments on dissociation and who later trained as a physician in Charcot's clinic.

Both Janet and Freud were eager to explain hysteria, and both developed theories of unconscious mental processes to do so. Their theories differed sharply, however. Janet saw dissociation as an abnormal process. To him, detachment from conscious awareness occurred only as a part of psychopathology. In contrast, Freud considered dissociation to be normal, a routine means through which the ego defended itself against unacceptable unconscious thoughts. Freud saw dissociation and repression as similar processes, and, in fact, he often used the two terms interchangeably (Erdelyi, 1990; Perry & Laurence, 1984). Thus, Freud viewed dissociative and somatoform disorders as merely two of many expressions of unconscious conflict.

The two theorists criticized each other frequently. Janet thought that Freud greatly overstated the importance of the unconscious; Freud thought that Janet greatly underestimated it. Janet's work became increasingly obscure, however, as Freudian theory dominated the mental health professions throughout much of the twentieth century. As Freudian influences have declined in recent years, scholars have rediscovered Janet's contributions and his more narrow conception of dissociation and unconscious mental processes.

Psychological Science and the Unconscious
Today, psychological scientists generally agree that unconscious mental processes play a role in both normal and abnormal emotion and cognition (Bargh & Morsella, 2008). We remember a forgotten event, for example, without knowing how we accessed the memory. However, scientists debate the importance of unconscious mental events. Two cognitive scientists called the unconscious mind "dumb," not "smart" (Loftus & Klinger, 1992), that is, it is of limited importance to mental life. Others suggest elaborate models of unconscious mental processes—for example, that we have two systems of information processing: a rational system and an emotionally driven experiential system (Epstein, 1994). The *rational system* uses abstract, logical knowledge to solve complex problems over time. The *experiential system* uses intuitive knowledge to respond to problems immediately without the delay of thought. The unconscious experiential system is emotional, powerful, and often illogical (Epstein, 1994). Rationally, we might know that airplanes are safer than automobiles, for example, but emotionally, we are more likely to fear airplanes—especially in the wake of September 11.

In contrast to Freud, contemporary psychological scientists test hypotheses about unconscious mental processes using empirical research. In fact, scientists have created new techniques to study unconscious processes, for example, the distinction between explicit and implicit memory. *Explicit memory* is the conscious recollection of a past event. **Implicit memory** is indicated by changes in behavior apparently based on a memory of a prior event but with no conscious remembering of the event (Schacter, 1987). To illustrate the distinction, consider the problem of *prosopagnosia,* an impairment of face recognition that sometimes follows specific forms of brain damage. Patients with prosopagnosia have no explicit memory for faces, that is, they are unable to recognize people they know. However, they demonstrate the normal preference for viewing faces that are familiar, even though they claim that the face is *not* familiar (Farah, O'Reilly, & Vecera, 1993). Apparently, patients have an *implicit memory* for faces—that is, recognition occurs at some lower level of perception or consciousness. Such findings indicate a dissociation between conscious and unconscious cognitive processing.

Hypnosis: Altered State or Social Role?

The nature of **hypnosis,** in which subjects experience loss of control over their actions in response to suggestions from the hypnotist, is a topic of historical importance and contemporary debate about the unconscious mind. All agree that demonstrations of the power of hypnotic suggestion are impressive, and that different people are more or less susceptible to hypnosis. However, some experts assert that hypnosis is a dissociative experience, an altered state of consciousness. Others argue that hypnosis is merely a social role, a subject voluntarily complying with suggestions due to social expectations (Barnier, 2002; Kihlstrom, 1998b; Kirsch & Lynn, 1995, 1998; Woody & Sadler, 1998). Beware of concluding that hypnosis must be real and powerful because you have seen it at work in a group demonstration. Hypnotists select highly susceptible (or highly compliant!) participants from a large group for demonstration purposes. How? They usually give a small suggestion to the entire group, like closing your eyes and imagining that a helium balloon is tied to your hand. If your arm flies in the air, you're a candidate for coming on stage.

Symptoms of Dissociative Disorders

Like many ordinary cognitive processes, the extraordinary symptoms of dissociative disorders apparently involve mental processing outside of conscious awareness. Extreme cases of dissociation include a split in the functioning of the individual's entire sense of self. In *dissociative identity disorder (DID),* two or more personalities coexist within a single individual, and one or both of the personalities may be unaware of the existence of

the other. Unless we assume that the symptom is feigned, dissociative identity disorder demonstrates that the mind can function on multiple levels of consciousness.

Depersonalization is a less dramatic form of dissociation where people feel detached from themselves or their social or physical environment. Examples of depersonalization include feeling like a stranger in social interactions and out-of-body experiences—feelings of detachment from one's physical being, for example, the sensation of floating outside yourself and watching your actions as if you were another person.

Another dramatic example of dissociation is *amnesia*—the partial or complete loss of recall for particular events or for a particular period of time. Brain injury or disease can cause amnesia, but *psychogenic* (psychologically caused) amnesia results from traumatic stress or other severe emotional distress. Psychogenic amnesia may occur alone or in conjunction with other dissociative experiences. For example, in dissociative identity disorder one personality may not remember the actions, or even the existence, of another (Spiegel & Cardena, 1991).

Trauma and Dissociative Symptoms It is widely accepted that fugue and psychogenic amnesia are usually precipitated by trauma, thus providing another link between dissociative and traumatic stress disorders. The trauma usually is clear and sudden, and in most cases, psychological functioning rapidly returns to normal. Much more controversial is the role of trauma in dissociative identity disorder (DID). Some argue

Why are dissociative disorders so controversial?

▼ Hypnotized college students reacting to the suggestion that they are on a beach in Hawaii. Performance hypnotists produce such dramatic effects by selecting only highly suggestible subjects for their demonstrations.

CRITICAL THINKING MATTERS

Recovered Memories?

In 1990, George Franklin was convicted of the brutal murder of an 8-year-old girl. The crime occurred over 20 years earlier, and the major evidence was the "recovered memory" of Franklin's daughter Eileen. Eileen claimed she had witnessed her father commit the rape and murder, but dissociation pushed the memory into her unconscious mind. Twenty years later, according to the daughter, the memory returned. Eileen provided both verifiable and inconsistent accounts of the horrifying event. She recalled a smashed ring on her friend's finger as she raised her hand to protect herself from a blow with a rock. Records corroborated the incident. On the other hand, Eileen changed her story about the time of day of the murder and whether her sister was riding in the van with them. Based solely on his daughter's testimony, George Franklin was convicted in 1990. However, his conviction was overturned in 1995, and he was released from prison. A U.S. District Court judge ruled that the lower court erred in excluding evidence that Eileen could have learned details of the 1969 murder from newspaper articles. The prosecutor decided not to retry the case when Eileen's sister revealed they both were hypnotized before the first trial—a fact Eileen lied about—and Eileen accused her father of a second murder but DNA evidence cleared him.

Was Eileen's memory accurate or fiction? Our concern about so-called recovered memories extends well beyond the Franklin case. In the 1990s, as many as 25 percent of therapists said that recovering memories, particularly of sexual abuse, was an important part of their therapy with female clients (Poole et al., 1995). Popular books also have encouraged people to search for (create?) memories that they do not recall, for example, in *The Courage to Heal,* the authors state:

> You may think you don't have memories, but often as you begin to talk about what you do remember, there emerges a constellation of feelings, reactions, and recollections that add up to substantial information. To say "I was abused," you don't need the kind of recall that would stand up in a court of law.... Often the knowledge that you were abused starts with a tiny feeling, an intuition. It's important to trust that inner voice and work from there. Assume your feelings are valid. So far, no one we've talked to thought she might have been abused and then later discovered that she hadn't been.
>
> (Bass & Davis, 1988, p. 22)

Could such suggestions lead some people to create memories about events that never happened? Faced with accusations of past abuse, many parents say that misguided therapists have created false memories. In fact, the term, *false memory syndrome,* was coined to account for the implanting of false beliefs (Kihlstrom, 1998a).

Is memory always accurate?

Are recovered memories examples of dissociation or of the power of suggestion? Determining the truth in the individual case may be impossible. Still, research clearly shows that memories, even of highly dramatic events, can be inaccurate (Loftus, 2003, 2004). In one study, researchers interviewed people the day after the space shuttle *Challenger* exploded, and detailed how participants learned of the tragedy. Three years later, they asked the same people to remember what they were doing, and about one-third reported vivid and grossly inaccurate memories (Neisser & Harsch, 1992). In another study, researchers created false memories of "sliming" a first or second grade teacher (putting slime in the teacher's desk) among fully 65 percent of the participants. The key to the deception was using actual school photos to help participants to "remember" (Lindsay et al., 2004). Such research does do not prove that recovered memories of trauma are false (Gleaves et al., 2004). Still, the malleability of memory suggests many reasons for skepticism.

There certainly are good reasons to question the validity of "recovered memories" from early in life, since few people can report *any* accurate memories before age 3 or 4 (Loftus, 2003; 2004). The fact that people are especially likely to remember emotionally intense events is another reason to think critically about claims of recovered memories. Some documented victims of sexual abuse do not recall the experience many years later (Williams, 1994), but most do remember what happened (Goodman et al., 2003)—and many victims who do not remember were very young when they were abused. And, of course, documented cases of forgetting do not prove that undocumented cases of remembering are accurate.

Are some claims of recovered memories more accurate than others? A recent study found that memories that returned outside of therapy were more likely to be corroborated than memories "recovered" in therapy (Geraerts et al., 2007). Sadly, some patients with recovered memories apparently are victims of their therapists, not of abuse.

▲ Where were you when the World Trade Center towers collapsed? Researchers find that even powerful "flashbulb" memories of dramatic events often grow inaccurate over time.

that DID is linked with past, not present, trauma, particularly with chronic physical or sexual child abuse (Gleaves, 1996). Many psychological scientists are skeptical about this assertion, however, because information about childhood trauma is based solely on clients' reports—reports that may be distorted by many factors, including by a therapist's expectations (Kihlstrom, 2005; Lilienfeld et al., 1999). A related controversy concerns so-called **recovered memories,** dramatic recollections of long-ago traumatic experiences supposedly blocked from the conscious mind by dissociation (see Critical Thinking Matters box).

Diagnosis of Dissociative Disorders

Brief Historical Perspective For centuries, theorists considered dissociative and somatoform disorders as two forms of the same disorder—hysteria. However, the descriptive approach to classification introduced in DSM-III (1980), which continues today, led to placing the disorders into separate diagnostic categories. Consistent with DSM-IV-TR, we review the two problems separately, as their symptoms are very different. We discuss the problems in a single chapter, however, because of their historical relationship and because both apparently involve unconscious processes.

Contemporary Classification DSM-IV-TR distinguishes four major subtypes of dissociative disorders: dissociative fugue, dissociative amnesia, depersonalization disorder, and dissociative identity disorder. **Dissociative fugue** is characterized by sudden and unexpected travel away from home, an inability to recall details about the past, and confusion about identity or the assumption of a new identity. The case of Dallae is an example of dissociative fugue.

Dissociative amnesia involves a sudden inability to recall extensive and important personal information that exceeds normal forgetfulness. The memory loss in dissociative amnesia is not attributable to substance abuse, head trauma, or a cognitive disorder, such as Alzheimer's disease. As with fugue, dissociative amnesia typically has a sudden onset following trauma or extreme stress and an equally sudden recovery of memory. The most common form of amnesia in dissociative disorders is *selective amnesia*—patients do not lose all of their memory but instead cannot remember selected events and information, often related to a traumatic experience. In one study of 25 patients

in a dissociative disorders clinic, 76 percent had selective amnesia (Coons & Milstein, 1988, cited in Spiegel & Cardena, 1991). The following case study provides one dramatic account, based on an article written by David Grann for the *New York Times* (January 13, 2002).

BRIEF CASE **STUDY**
Amnesia for September 11

Kevin Shea, a firefighter for the Fire Department of New York, was one of the very few survivors rescued from the wreckage of the World Trade Center. On the evening of September 11, Shea was found buried under a pile of rubble, his thumb severed and his neck broken in three places. Fortunately, Shea was not paralyzed by his spinal injury, but, like his neck, Shea's memory was badly fractured.

Shea could remember his past and a few events from early on the day of September 11. For example, he could remember volunteering to help, even though he was off duty, and jumping on his firehouse's Engine 40 to rush downtown. As the engine approached the scene, he remembered seeing people falling from high floors of the towers. After this, however, Shea had no real memory of September 11, not until after he was hospitalized late in the day. For example, he had no memory of either tower collapsing, even though he was there at the horrifying, chaotic scene.

◀ Kevin Shea, a firefighter for the FDNY, received numerous injuries, including a broken vertebrae, working as a rescue worker during the World Trade Center attacks. Shea also suffered from amnesia, perhaps as a result of a blow to the head or perhaps from emotional causes.

Shea lost every member of his engine in the WTC rescue attempt. He became desperate to learn that he survived despite trying to save others and not because he instead focused on saving himself. Through diligent efforts in the months after September 11, he was able to piece together some evidence about what happened to him. Some details brought back fragments of his memory. For example, when another firefighter reminded him that they had embraced in the command center of the South Tower shortly before it collapsed, Shea remembered the event. However, no memories returned when Shea met another firefighter who himself was injured while trying to rescue Shea. No memories returned when Shea talked with yet another injured firefighter who rode in an ambulance with him after the rescue. No memories returned even when Shea was shown a photo of himself lying injured, almost unconscious, in the street near the South Tower, just moments before it collapsed.

It is unclear whether Shea suffered from dissociative amnesia due to the emotional trauma of the day, or whether his memory loss was caused by a blow to his head. Although by all accounts Kevin Shea was a hero, he had trouble convincing himself of the truth of this assessment, because he could not remember his own actions on September 11.

Depersonalization disorder, a less dramatic problem, is characterized by feelings of being detached from oneself, including such sensations as feeling as though you are living in a dream or floating above your body and watching yourself. Occasional depersonalization experiences like feelings of *déjà vu* are normal and are reported by about half the population. In depersonalization disorder, the symptoms are persistent or recurrent and cause marked personal distress. The onset of the disorder commonly follows a new or disturbing event, such as *drug use.* All depersonalization experiences are "as-if" feelings, not rigid, delusional beliefs. You *feel* as if you are in a dream; you don't really believe it. In fact, some experts question whether depersonalization should be considered a dissociative disorder, because it involves only limited splitting between conscious and unconscious mental processes, and no memory loss occurs (Spiegel & Cardena, 1991).

To many people, the most fascinating dissociative disorder is **dissociative identity disorder (DID),** a condition formerly known as **multiple personality disorder.** This unusual disorder is characterized by the existence of two or more distinct personalities in a single individual. At least two of these personalities repeatedly take control of the person's behavior, with at least some loss of recall between the personalities. The original personality especially is likely to have amnesia for

subsequent personalities, which may or may not be aware of other "alternates" (Aldridge-Morris, 1989). Recent case studies claim to have identified more and more alternate personalities in DID. The case of "Eve," published in 1957, identified 3 personalities; "Sybil" was reported to have 16 personalities in a 1973 best seller (the veracity of which has been questioned; Rieber, 1999); and some more recent cases have claimed to have a 100, even 1,000, alters. Not surprisingly, such claims have generated more debate about a diagnosis that already was controversial.

BRIEF CASE **STUDY**
The Three Faces of Eve

A famous case history multiple personality disorder is Thigpen and Cleckley's (1957) *The Three Faces of Eve,* which was made into a motion picture. Thigpen and Cleckley, two psychiatrists who treated the young woman, described Eve White as a young mother with a troubled marriage who sought psychotherapy for severe headaches, feelings of inertia, and "blackouts." Eve White was seen for several therapy sessions and was hypnotized during this time as a treatment for her amnesia. Then, during what proved to be a remarkable session, Eve White became agitated and complained of hearing an imaginary voice. As Thigpen and Cleckley wrote, "After a tense moment of silence, her hands dropped. There was a quick, reckless smile and, in a bright voice that sparkled, she said, 'Hi there, Doc!'" (p. 137). Eve Black had emerged—a carefree and flirtatious personality who insisted upon being called "Miss" and who scorned Eve White, the wife and mother.

Therapy with Eve White, Eve Black, and a third, more calm and mature personality, Jane, lasted over 2½ years. Thigpen used hypnosis to bring out the different personalities in an attempt to understand and reconcile them with one another. He eventually adopted the goal of fading out the two Eves and allowing Jane to take control.

▲ Chris Sizemore is "Eve," the patient from the book and movie *The Three Faces of Eve.* Sizemore is now cured and is an advocate for the mentally ill.

Therapy appeared to be successful. According to the psychiatrists' account, treatment ended with one integrated personality in control. This personality was much like Jane, but she decided to call herself "Mrs. Evelyn White."

The end of therapy with Thigpen and Cleckley was not the end of therapy for "Eve." Eve, whose real name is Chris Sizemore, claims to have had a total of 22 different personalities, some of which developed before her treatment with Thigpen and Cleckley and some of which developed afterward. The personalities always occurred in groups of three, and they always included a wife/mother image, a party girl, and a more normal, intellectual personality (Sizemore & Pittillo, 1977). Sizemore has written several books about her life, and as a well-functioning, unified personality, she has become a spokesperson for mental health concerns. In her book *A Mind of Her Own,* she offers the following observations on her personalities:

> Among these twenty-two alters, ten were poets, seven were artists, and one had taught tailoring. Today, I paint and write, but I cannot sew. Yet these alters were not moods or the result of role-playing. They were entities that were totally separate from the personality I was born to be, and am today. They were so different that their tones of voice changed. What's more, their facial expressions, appetites, tastes in clothes, handwritings, skills, and IQs were all different, too.
>
> (Sizemore, 1989, p. 9)

The case of Chris Sizemore dramatically illustrates the characteristics of dissociative identity disorder. Sizemore's words also foreshadow controversies about the condition. Some professionals argue that dissociative identity disorder is nothing more than role playing; others assert that multiple personalities are very real and very common.

Frequency of Dissociative Disorders

The prevalence of dissociative disorders is difficult to establish. The conditions generally are considered to be extremely rare. For example, only about 200 case histories of dissociative identity disorder were reported in the entire world literature prior to 1980 (Greaves, 1980). However, a small but vocal group of professionals has argued that many patients suffering from dissociative disorders are misdiagnosed as having schizophrenia, borderline personality disorder, depression, panic disorder, or substance abuse (Gleaves, 1996; Ross, Norton, & Wozney, 1989). One study conducted in Manitoba, Canada, claimed an unbelievably high prevalence: Over 10 percent of the general adult population suffers from a dissociative disorder—including 3 percent of adults with dissociative identity disorder (Ross, 1991). A later study by the

same author claimed that 40 percent of hospitalized psychiatric patients met DSM-IV-TR criteria for the diagnosis of a dissociative disorder (Ross, Duffy, & Ellason, 2002).

Clearly, either experts missed millions of cases of dissociative disorders for decades, or some advocates are overzealous in defining dissociative disorders. Research suggests many reasons to disbelieve claims that dissociative disorders are prevalent and overlooked (Kihlstrom, 2005; Waller & Ross, 1997):

1. Most cases of dissociative disorders are diagnosed by a handful of ardent advocates.
2. The frequency of the diagnosis of dissociative disorders in general and DID in particular increased rapidly after release of the very popular book and movie *Sybil.*
3. The number of personalities claimed to exist in cases of DID has grown rapidly, from a handful to 100 or more.
4. Dissociative disorders are rarely diagnosed outside of the United States and Canada; for example, only one unequivocal case of DID has been reported in Great Britain in the last 25 years (Casey, 2001).
5. The symptoms of dissociation in the most commonly used instruments like the Dissociative Experiences Questionnaire are far less dramatic than those found in dissociative disorders (see Table 7–3). The strange but familiar feeling of *déjà vu,* for example, is widely considered to be an experience of dissociation.

Why should you doubt claims that dissociative identity disorder is common?

TABLE 7–3 Sample Items from the Dissociative Experiences Questionnaire

- Some people find that sometimes they are listening to someone talk and they suddenly realize that they did not hear part or all of what was said.
- Some people have the experience of being in a familiar place but finding it strange and unfamiliar.
- Some people have the experience of finding themselves dressed in clothes that they don't remember putting on.
- Some people are told that they sometimes do not recognize friends or family members.
- Some people have the experience of feeling that their body does not seem to belong to them.
- Some people find that in one situation they may act so differently compared with another situation that they feel almost as if they were two different people.

Source: E. M. Bernstein and F. W. Putnam, 1986, "Development, Reliability, and Validity of a Dissociation Scale," *Journal of Nervous & Mental Disease, 174,* pp. 727–735. Copyright © 1986. Reprinted by permission of Lippincott Williams & Wilkins.

Disorder or Role Enactment? Some experts even doubt the very existence of dissociative identity disorder, arguing that DID is created by the power of suggestion (Mersky, 1992). The Canadian psychologist Nicholas Spanos (1942–1994) was a particularly outspoken critic, who argued that multiple personalities are caused by role playing. Spanos (1994) asserted that patients are influenced by their own and their therapists' goals and expectations about DID, and, like an actor who loses all perspective, they come to believe that the role is real.

To test his theory, Spanos and his colleagues conducted analogue experiments inspired by the case of Kenneth Bianchi, the infamous "Hillside Strangler." In 1979, Bianchi was charged with murdering two college women and was implicated in several other rape-murder cases where victims were left naked on the hillsides of Los Angeles. Considerable evidence supported Bianchi's guilt, but he reported frequent episodes of "blanking out," including an inability to remember events from the night that the murders were committed. At the request of his attorney, Bianchi was seen by a mental health expert, who hypnotized Bianchi and suggested to him, "I've talked a bit to Ken, but I think that perhaps there might be another part of Ken that I haven't talked to, another part that maybe

What is the basis of claims that multiple personalities are created by suggestion?

feels somewhat differently from the part I've talked to. And I would like to communicate with that other part" (Watkins, 1984). Bianchi responded that he was not Ken, but Steve. Steve knew of Ken, and he hated him. Steve also confessed to strangling "all of these girls."

Numerous experts who interviewed Bianchi disagreed about whether his apparent dissociative identity disorder was real or feigned. One was the psychologist and psychiatrist Martin Orne (1927–2000), an internationally recognized authority on hypnosis. Orne tested Bianchi by suggesting new symptoms to him. If Bianchi was faking, he might further the deception by developing the new symptoms. Orne suggested, for example, that if Bianchi really had dissociative identity disorder, he should have a third personality. Sure enough, a third personality, Billy, "emerged" when Bianchi was hypnotized (Orne, Dingers, & Orne, 1984). While hypnotized, Bianchi also followed Orne's suggestion to hallucinate that his attorney was in the room. Bianchi actually shook hands with the supposed hallucination—a very unusual behavior for someone under hypnosis. Orne concluded that Bianchi was indeed faking, and actually suffered from antisocial personality disorder (see Chapter 9). Bianchi's insanity defense failed, and he was found guilty of murder.

In testing his role theory, Spanos simulated procedures from the Bianchi case. In one study, undergraduate students played the role of the accused murderer and were randomly assigned to one of three conditions. In the "Bianchi" condition, the subjects were hypnotized, and the interviewer asked to communicate with their other part, just as Bianchi's interviewer had asked. Subjects assigned to the second "hidden part" condition also were hypnotized, but this time it was suggested that hypnosis could get behind the "wall" that hid inner thoughts and feelings from awareness. In the final condition, there was no hypnosis, and subjects simply were told that personality included "walls" between hidden thoughts and feelings.

When subsequently asked, "Who are you?" by the interviewer in the mock murder case, 81 percent of the subjects in the Bianchi condition gave a name different from the one assigned to them in the role play, as did 70 percent of the subjects in the hidden part condition. In contrast, only 31 percent of the subjects in the no-hypnosis condition gave a new name (Spanos, Weekes, & Bertrand, 1985). In a subsequent study, hypno-

"Would it be possible to speak with the personality that pays the bills?"

tized subjects also provided more "information" on exactly when in the past their alternate personalities had first emerged (Spanos et al., 1986).

These findings certainly raise the caution that the "symptoms" of DID can be induced by role playing and hypnosis (Lilienfeld et al., 1999). However, analogue studies cannot prove that role playing causes real cases of multiple personality (Gleaves, 1996). In fact, real patients show symptoms even on subtle measures where the "appropriate" answer is not obvious (Eich et al., 1997; Scroppo et al., 1998).

Given the current status of research, we reach some cautious conclusions. True dissociative disorders appear to be rare. Although some cases no doubt are misdiagnosed, a much greater problem is the creation of the diagnosis in the minds of clinicians and clients (Mersky, 1992; Piper, 1994; Showalter, 1997). At the same time, we do not doubt the existence of dissociative disorders.

Causes of Dissociative Disorders

Little systematic research has been conducted on the cause of dissociative disorders; thus, theory and outright speculation dominate. One exception is the widely held view that the disorders often are precipitated by trauma.

Psychological Factors in Dissociative Disorders There is little controversy that dissociative amnesia and fugue usually are precipitated by an obvious traumatic experience. What about DID? Many case studies suggest that multiple personalities develop in response to trauma, particularly the trauma of child abuse. In fact, some researchers have compiled large numbers of case studies from surveys of practitioners that support this view (Gleaves, 1996; Kluft, 1987; Putnam, Curoff et al., 1986; Scroppo et al., 1998; see Table 7–4).

When interpreting these findings, however, you should note that studies of the long-term consequences of child physical or sexual abuse find little evidence of dissociation or, indeed, of any consistent forms of psychopathology (Emery & Laumann-Billings, 1998; Rind, Tromovitch, & Bauserman, 1998). And case studies are based on patients' memories and clinicians' evaluations. They are not objective assessments of the past. Researchers have many concerns about the validity of such *retrospective reports*—evaluations of

TABLE 7–4 Correlates of Dissociative Identity Disorder in Two Surveys of Clinicians		
Item	**Ross**[1] *N = 236*	**Putnam**[2] *N = 100*
Average age	30.8	35.8
Percentage of females	87.7%	92.0%
Average years of treatment before diagnosis	6.7	6.8
Average number of personalities	15.7	13.3
Opposite-sex personality present	62.6%	53.0%
Amnesia between personalities	94.9%	98.0%
Past suicide attempt	72.0%	71.0%
History of child physical abuse	74.9%	75.0%
History of child sexual abuse	79.2%	83.9%

[1]Based on data from C. A. Ross, G. R. Norton, and K. Wozney, 1989, "Multiple Personality Disorder: An Analysis of 236 Cases," *Canadian Journal of Psychiatry, 34*, pp. 413–418.

[2]Based on data from F. W. Putnam, J. J. Curoff, et al., 1986, "The Clinical Phenomenology of Multiple Personality Disorder: Review of 100 Recent Cases," *Journal of Clinical Psychiatry, 47*, pp. 285–293.

the past from the vantage point of the present (see the Research Methods box). Memories may be selectively recalled, distorted, or even created to conform to a clinician's expectations (Kihlstrom, 2005).

If trauma is involved, how might it lead to the development of multiple personalities? One theory involves **state-dependent learning,** a process where learning that takes place in one state of affect or consciousness is best recalled in the same state of affect or consciousness (Bower, 1990). For example, when you are sad rather than happy, you more easily remember what happened when you were sad in the past. By extension, experiences that occur during a dissociated state may be most easily recalled within the same state of consciousness. Perhaps through the repeated experience of trauma, dissociation, and state-dependent learning, more complete and autonomous memories develop—ultimately leading to independent personalities (Braun, 1989).

Even if trauma contributes to dissociative disorders—and we are skeptical about trauma and DID, it clearly is not a sufficient cause. As we saw with ASD and PTSD, the vast majority of people who experience trauma do *not* develop a dissociative disorder. Thus, other factors must contribute to their development.

Biological Factors in Dissociative Disorders Little evidence or theory addresses the contribution of biological factors to dissociative

RESEARCH METHODS | Retrospective Reports: Remembering the Past

The topic of recovered memories has created particular controversy, but psychologists have long been skeptical about the accuracy of people's reports about the past. The concern is about the reliability and validity of **retrospective reports**— current recollections of past experiences, for example, events that occurred during childhood. Problems with retrospective reports are one of several reasons why investigators prefer prospective, longitudinal studies over retrospective research designs (see the Research Methods box in Chapter 8).

Concerns about retrospective reports focus on three particular issues (Brewin, Andrews, & Gotlib, 1993). First, normal memory often is inaccurate, particularly memory for events that occurred long ago and early in life. Second, memories of people with emotional problems may be particularly unreliable. Third, abnormal behavior may systematically bias memory; for example, memory processes may be "mood congruent." Depressed people may

tend to remember sad experiences, anxious people may better recall fearful events, and so on.

Why do researchers question retrospective reports?

Brewin, Andrews, and Gotlib (1993) revisited many of these concerns, but concluded that retrospective memories may be less flawed than some have suggested. The reviewers agreed that retrospective reports are often inaccurate. For example, only moderate correlations are found between children's and parents' reports about their past relationships, and, on average, children report more negative memories. At the same time, agreement between parents and children increases to an acceptable level for reports of specific, factual aspects of the past. Thus, memory for specific, important events in the family may be fairly re-

liable and valid, but people may "rewrite" their histories with regard to more global and subjective experiences.

Brewin, Andrews, and Gotlib (1993) also questioned the blanket assumption that psychopathology impairs memory. They found many flaws in research that supposedly demonstrated memory impairments for various psychological problems and concluded that, except for serious mental illness, there is no evidence for memory impairments associated with anxiety or depression. In particular, depressed people do not erroneously recall more than their share of negative events about the past.

Brewin and colleagues (1993) urge that retrospective reports should not be dismissed out of hand. Psychologists have many reasons to prefer prospective, longitudinal research designs over retrospective methods, but longitudinal research is expensive to conduct. Retrospective reports of specific events may be sufficiently reliable and valid to justify using them as an initial, less-expensive research method.

---

disorders (Kihlstrom, 2005). A preliminary twin study found no genetic contribution to dissociative symptoms, while the shared environment did contribute (Waller & Ross, 1997). However, evidence that biological factors can produce disso-

► Shirley Mason Ardell, the real "Sybil." Her case spurred an explosion in the diagnosis of dissociative identity disorder, and in the number of diagnosed "alters," but actual therapy tapes suggest that her therapist may have implanted Sybil's 16 personalities.

ciative symptoms is a reason to continue to search for biological contributions to dissociative disorders. Examples include the dramatic personality changes that sometimes accompany substance abuse and the amnesia found in cognitive disorders associated with aging. You should note, however, that a diagnosis of dissociative disorders is explicitly excluded in DSM-IV-TR if the dissociation occurs in conjunction with substance abuse or organic pathology.

Social Factors in Dissociative Disorders
Perhaps the most important theory about social contributions to dissociative disorders is that they are caused by **iatrogenesis,** the manufacture of a disorder by its treatment. Mersky (1992) reviewed classic case histories of dissociative identity disorder and concluded that many "cases" were created by the expectations of therapists. Mersky does not doubt the pain experienced by the patients in these cases. He argues, however, that the patients developed multiple personalities in response to their therapists' leading questions. Like Spanos (1994), Mersky argues that DID is a social role. Because of their susceptibility to suggestion, perhaps highly hypnotizable people are especially

likely to suffer iatrogenic effects in misguided therapy (Kihlstrom, Glisky, & Angiulo, 1994).

We believe that iatrogensis is the explanation for the explosion of DID cases diagnosed in the United States in the 1990s. However, evidence that DID can be diagnosed in the general population in Turkey (Akyuz et al., 1999), where there is no public awareness of the disorder, leads us to conclude that DID is a real but rare problem.

Treatment of Dissociative Disorders

Dating from the time of Janet and Freud, most treatments of dissociative disorders have focused on uncovering and recounting traumatic events. Presumably, the need for dissociation will disappear if the trauma can be expressed and accepted (Horevitz & Loewenstein, 1994). Many clinicians use hypnosis to help patients explore and relive traumatic events. However, no research supports the effectiveness of either *abreaction,* the emotional reliving of a past traumatic experiences, or hypnosis as a treatment for dissociative disorders (Horevitz & Loewenstein, 1994). Skeptics worry, in fact, that hypnosis may create dissociative symptoms or false memories of abuse (Casey, 2001).

The ultimate goal in treating DID is not to have one personality triumph over the others. Rather, the objective is to integrate the different personalities into a whole (Coons & Bowman, 2001; Ellason & Ross, 1997). Integration is not unlike the task we all face in reconciling our different roles in life into a coherent sense of self. Dallae, for example, needed to reconcile her role as a daughter, including her parents' expectations, together with her role as an independent young woman with her own desires, abilities, and acculturation experiences.

At this time, no systematic research has been conducted on the effectiveness of any treatment for dissociative disorders, let alone on the comparison of alternative treatments (Kihlstrom, 2005; Maldonado, Butler, & Spiegal, 2001). Antianxiety, antidepressant, and antipsychotic medications sometimes are used in treatment, but at best these medications reduce distress. They do not to cure the disorder (Horevitz & Loewenstein, 1994). Advances in treatment await a better understanding of the disorders and, more generally, of conscious and unconscious mental processes. In the meantime, you should view treatments championed for dissociative disorders—and the accuracy of the diagnosis itself—with a healthy dose of skepticism.

SOMATOFORM DISORDERS

In addition to dissociative disorders, hysteria included what we now know as **somatoform disorders**—unusual physical symptoms that occur in the absence of a known physical illness. There is no demonstrable physical cause for the symptoms of somatoform disorders. They are somatic (physical) in form only—thus their name.[1] We consider somatoform disorders together with dissociative disorders, because of their historical connection and because somatoform disorders involve a degree of dissociation. In some cases of somatoform disorder, the dissociation is relatively minor; in other cases, it is dramatic.

Are somatoform disorders real physical illnesses?

Symptoms of Somatoform Disorders

All somatoform disorders involve complaints about physical symptoms, but there is nothing physically wrong with the patient. Yet the symptoms are not feigned. The physical problem is very real in the mind, though not the body, of the sufferer.

The physical symptoms can take a number of different forms. In some dramatic cases, the symptom involves substantial impairment of a somatic system, particularly a sensory or muscular system. The patient will be unable to see, for example, or will report paralysis in one arm. In other cases, patients experience multiple physical symptoms rather than a single substantial impairment. These patients usually have numerous, constantly evolving complaints about such problems as chronic pain, upset stomach, and dizziness. Finally, some types of somatoform disorder are defined by a preoccupation with a particular part of the body or with fears about a particular illness. The patient may constantly worry that he or she has contracted some deadly disease, for example, and the anxiety persists despite negative medical tests and clear reassurance by a physician.

---

[1]The absence of demonstrable physical impairment distinguishes somatoform disorders from psychosomatic illnesses, stress-related physical disorders that do involve real, organic pathology (Chapter 8). In everyday language, we sometimes say, "His problems are psychosomatic" to indicate that an illness is "all in his head." However, somatoform disorders, not psychosomatic disorders, are the purely psychological problems.

Unnecessary Medical Treatment People with somatoform disorders typically do not bring their problems to the attention of a mental health professional. Instead, they repeatedly consult their physicians about their "physical" problems (Bass, Peveler, & House, 2001; Looper & Kirmayer, 2002). This often leads to unnecessary medical treatment. In one study, patients with *somatization disorder* had seen a health care provider more than six times, on average, during the previous 6 months. In addition, 25 percent of people with somatization disorder had been hospitalized in the past year, compared with 12 percent of the general population (Swartz et al., 1987). People with *body dysmorphic disorder* also receive excessive medical care. Three-quarters of patients with the disorder seek medical treatment, primarily dermatologic or surgical, but the medical procedures produce little benefit (Phillips et al., 2001).

Patients with somatoform disorders often complain about realistic physical symptoms that are difficult to evaluate objectively. Thus, physicians frequently do not recognize the psychological nature of the patients' problems, and they sometimes perform unnecessary medical procedures. For example, patients with somatoform disorders have surgery twice as often as people in the general population (Zoccolillo & Cloninger, 1986). In fact, some common surgical procedures are performed with startling frequency on patients with somatoform disorders. One research group concluded that, after discounting cancer surgeries, 27 percent of women undergoing a hysterectomy suffered from somatization disorder (Martin, Roberts, & Clayton, 1980).

Such data are distressing not only because of the risk to the patient but also because of the costs of unnecessary medical treatment. Estimates indicate that anywhere from 20 percent to 84 percent of patients who consult physicians do so for problems for which no organic cause can be found (Miller & Swartz, 1990). Such visits may account for as much as half of all ambulatory health care costs (Kellner, 1985). A variety of emotional problems can motivate people to consult their physicians, including the experience of trauma (Green et al., 1997), but much excessive health care utilization is specific to somatoform disorders. For example, patients with somatization disorder are three times more likely to consult physicians than are depressed patients (Morrison & Herbstein, 1988; Zoccolillo & Cloninger, 1986). In fact, health care expenditures for patients with somatization disorder are nine times the average annual per capita cost of medical treatment (Smith, Monson, & Ray, 1986).

Diagnosis of Somatoform Disorders

DSM-IV-TR lists five major subcategories of somatoform disorders: (1) conversion disorder, (2) somatization disorder, (3) hypochondriasis, (4) pain disorder, and (5) body dysmorphic disorder.

Conversion Disorder The symptoms of **conversion disorder,** a classic type of somatoform disorder, often mimic those found in neurological diseases, and they can be dramatic. "Hysterical" blindness and "hysterical" paralysis are examples of conversion symptoms. Although conversion disorders often resemble neurological impairments, they sometimes can be distinguished from these disorders because they make no anatomic sense. The patient may complain about anesthesia (or pain) in a way that does not correspond with the innervation of the body. In some facial anesthesias, for example, numbness ends at the middle of the face; but the nerves involved in sensation do not divide the face into equal halves (see Figure 7–4).

The term *conversion disorder* accurately conveys the central assumption of the diagnosis—the idea that psychological conflicts are converted into physical symptoms. This conversion captivated the attention of Charcot, Freud, and Janet and led them to develop theories about dissociation and unconscious mental processes. The following case from Janet's writings illustrates his view of "hysteria."

The Anatomy of Conversion Disorders

FIGURE 7–4 Conversion disorder symptoms may make no anatomical sense. As illustrated in this figure, pain insensitivity may be limited to one side of the face, but the nerves involved in pain sensation do not divide the face neatly in half.

Source: Adapted from D. M. Kaufman, 1985, *Clinical Neurology for Psychiatrists,* 2nd ed., p. 28, Orlando, FL. Grune & Stratton.

BRIEF CASE **STUDY**
Janet's Patient

A girl of 19 years of age suffered, at the time of her monthly period, convulsive and delirious attacks which lasted several days. Menstruation began normally, but a few hours after the commencement of the flow the patient complained of feeling very cold and had a characteristic shivering; menstruation was immediately arrested and delirium ensued. In the interval of these attacks the patient had paroxysms of terror with the hallucination of blood spreading out before her and also showed various permanent stigmata, among others anesthesia of the left side of the face with amaurosis of the left eye.

During a careful study of this patient's history, and particularly of the memories she had conserved of various experiences of her life, certain pertinent facts were ascertained. At the age of 13 she had attempted to arrest menstruation by plunging into a tub of cold water with resulting shivering and delirium; menstruation was immediately arrested and did not recur for several years; when it did reappear the disturbance I have just cited took place. Later on she had been terrified by seeing an old woman fall on the stairs and deluge the steps with her blood. At another time, when she was about 9 years old, she had been obliged to sleep with a child whose face, on the left side, was covered with scabs, and during the whole night she had experienced a feeling of intense disgust and horror (Janet, 1914/1915, pp. 3–4).

This case describes symptoms that are consistent with conversion disorder. The numbness on the left side of the face of Janet's young patient is a clear example of a conversion symptom. At the same time, we wonder about other aspects of this classic case. The frightening hallucinations of blood might suggest another diagnosis, perhaps psychotic depression or schizophrenia, with the conversion symptom as a secondary aspect of the case. Differential diagnosis was poor during the time of Charcot, Janet, and Freud, and we think that this might explain why conversion disorders were thought to be prevalent then but are rare today. A hundred years ago, many problems that might be diagnosed accurately today as either physical or psychological maladies probably were misdiagnosed as conversion disorders.

Somatization Disorder Today, a much more common somatoform disorder is **somatization disorder,** characterized by a history of multiple somatic complaints in the absence of organic impairments. The extent of the health concerns in somatization disorder is apparent from a cursory examination of the DSM-IV-TR diagnostic criteria. The patient must complain of at least *eight* physical symptoms. The complaints must involve multiple somatic systems, moreover, including symptoms of pain, gastrointestinal symptoms (for example, nausea and diarrhea), sexual symptoms (sexual dysfunction, menstrual difficulties), and pseudoneurologic symptoms (for example, double vision, numbness, or amnesia) (see Table 7–5).

Patients with somatization disorders sometimes present their symptoms in a *histrionic* manner—a

---

TABLE 7–5 DSM-IV-TR Diagnostic Criteria for Somatization Disorder

A. A history of many physical complaints beginning before age 30 that occur over a period of several years and result in treatment being sought or significant impairment in social, occupational, or other important areas of functioning.

B. Each of the following criteria must have been met, with individual symptoms occurring at any time during the course of the disturbance.

1. Four pain symptoms: A history of pain related to at least four different sites or functions (for example, head, abdomen, back, joints, extremities, chest, rectum, during menstruation, or sexual intercourse, or during urination)
2. Two gastrointestinal symptoms: A history of at least two gastrointestinal symptoms other than pain (for example, nausea, diarrhea, bloating, vomiting other than during pregnancy, or intolerance of several different foods)
3. One sexual symptom: A history of at least one sexual or reproductive symptom other than pain (for example, sexual indifference, erectile or ejaculatory dysfunction, irregular menses, excessive menstrual bleeding, vomiting throughout pregnancy)
4. One pseudoneurologic symptom: A history of at least one symptom or deficit suggesting a neurological disorder not limited to pain (conversion symptoms such as impaired coordination or balance, paralysis or localized weakness, difficulty swallowing or lump in throat, aphonia, urinary retention, hallucinations, loss of touch or pain sensation, double vision, blindness, deafness, seizures; dissociative symptoms such as amnesia; or loss of consciousness other than fainting)

Source: Reprinted with permission from the *Diagnostic and Statistical Manual of Mental Disorders,* Fourth Edition, Text Revision. Copyright © 2000 by the American Psychiatric Association.

vague but dramatic, self-centered, and seductive style. (Think Blanche DuBois in *Streetcar Named Desire*.) Patients also may exhibit *la belle indifference* ("beautiful indifference"), a flippant lack of concern about their symptoms. For example, a patient may list a long series of somatic complaints in an offhanded and cheerful manner. Although some experts view a histrionic style and la belle indifference as defining characteristics of somatization disorders, research indicates that they are found in only a minority of cases (Brown, 2004; Lipowski, 1988).

In contrast to stereotypes, somatization disorder is *not* more common among the aged, who consult health care professionals frequently because of chronic and real physical illnesses (National Institute of Mental Health, 1990). In fact, somatization disorder often begins in adolescence, and according to DSM-IV-TR criteria, must have an onset prior to the age of 30. The problem is sometimes referred to as *Briquet's syndrome,* in recognition of the French physician Pierre Briquet, who was among the first to call attention to the multiple somatic complaints found in some "hysterias" (National Institute of Mental Health, 1990).

Hypochondriasis Hypochondriasis is characterized by a fear or belief that one is suffering from a physical illness. Aspects of this mental disorder surely are familiar to you. The pejorative term *hypochondriac* is a part of everyday language. We all worry about our health, and even unrealistic worries sometimes are normal. Medical students often fear that they have contracted each new disease they encounter in their studies. Many students in abnormal psychology worry that each problem they read about is a perfect description of themselves.

► Some people suspect that Michael Jackson suffers from body dysmorphic disorder given his multiple plastic surgeries to change his appearance.

Hypochondriasis is much more serious than these normal and fleeting worries. The worries must last for at least 6 months according to DSM-IV-TR criteria. In addition, in hypochondriasis, a thorough medical evaluation or examination does not alleviate the fear of the disease. The person still worries that the illness may be emerging or that a test was overlooked. Still, the person with hypochondriasis is not delusional. For example, someone may worry excessively about contracting AIDS and therefore repeatedly go for blood tests. When faced with negative results, the person does not delusionally believe that he or she actually has contracted the illness. Instead, he persistently worries that the test was wrong or was taken too soon to detect the disease. Hypochondriasis is severe and preoccupying and often leads to substantial impairment in life functioning.

Pain Disorder As its name implies, **pain disorder** is characterized by preoccupation with pain. Although there is no objective way to evaluate pain, psychological factors are judged to be significant in creating or intensifying the chronic pain in pain disorder. Complaints seem excessive and apparently are motivated at least in part by psychological factors. For example, some pain disorder patients seem to relish the attention their illness brings to them. DSM-IV-TR distinguishes between pain disorder that occurs with associated problems in general medical conditions and pain disorder that appears in the absence of such problems. For example, low back pain that begins after a physical injury would be differentiated from back pain that cannot be traced to any physical cause.

As with other somatoform disorders, pain disorder can lead to the repeated, unnecessary use of medical treatments. People who experience chronic pain are at a particular risk for developing a dependence on minor tranquilizers or painkillers. The disorder also frequently disrupts social and occupational functioning.

Body Dysmorphic Disorder Body dysmorphic disorder is a different type of somatoform disorder in which the patient is preoccupied with some imagined defect in appearance. The preoccupation typically focuses on some facial feature, such as the nose or mouth, and in some cases may lead to repeated visits to a plastic surgeon. Preoccupation with the body part far exceeds normal worries about physical imperfections. The endless worry causes significant distress, and in extreme cases, it may interfere with work or social relationships.

U.S. researchers are just beginning to study body dysmorphic disorder, although the problem has received somewhat more attention among European and Asian mental health professionals. One controversy is whether the diagnosis should be grouped with other somatoform disorders. In Japan and Korea, body dysmorphic disorder is classified as a type of social phobia (Phillips, 1991). The following brief case history illustrates this unusual type of somatoform disorder.

BRIEF CASE **STUDY**
Body Dysmorphic Disorder

A 28-year-old single white man became preoccupied at the age of 18 with his minimally thinning hair. Despite reassurance from others that his hair loss was not noticeable, he worried about it for hours a day, becoming "deeply depressed," socially withdrawn, and unable to attend classes or do his schoolwork. Although he could acknowledge the excessiveness of his preoccupation, he was unable to stop it. He saw four dermatologists but was not comforted by their reassurances that his hair loss was minor and that treatment was unnecessary. The patient's preoccupation and subsequent depression have persisted for 10 years and have continued to interfere with his social life and work, to the extent that he avoids most social events and has been able to work only part-time as a baker. He only recently sought psychiatric referral, at the insistence of his girlfriend, who said his symptoms were ruining their relationship (Phillips, 1991, pp. 1138–1139).

Malingering and Factitious Disorder Somatoform disorders represent real *psychological* problems, even though the physical symptoms are not real. As such, somatoform disorders must be distinguished from **malingering,** pretending to have a physical illness in order to achieve some external gain, such as a disability payment. Because there is no objective way to test for somatoform disorders, detecting malingering is extremely difficult. Besides searching for an obvious reason for feigning an illness, one clue to malingering can be when a patient presents symptoms that are more, not less, dramatic.

A related diagnostic concern is **factitious disorder,** a feigned condition that, unlike malingering, is motivated primarily by a desire to assume the sick role rather than by a desire for external gain. People with factitious disorder pretend to be ill or make themselves appear to be ill, for example, by taking drugs to produce a rapid heart rate. They will undergo extensive and often painful medical procedures in order to garner attention from health care professionals. A rare, repetitive pattern of factitious disorder is some-times called *Munchausen syndrome,* named after Baron Karl Friedrich Hieronymus von Munchausen, an eighteenth-century writer known for his tendency to embellish the details of his life.

Frequency of Somatoform Disorders

No one knows how prevalent conversion disorders were during the time of Charcot, Janet, and Freud, but the literature of the period suggests that they were common (Shorter, 1992). Today, conversion disorders are rare, perhaps as infrequent as 50 cases per 100,000 population (Akagi & House, 2001). Ironically, the unusual disorders treated by Freud and Janet have been less enduring than the theories developed to explain them! The lower prevalence today may be a result of improved diagnostic practices—cases now are correctly diagnosed as real physical or psychological illnesses, or perhaps of Western society's greater acceptance of the expression of feelings (Shorter, 1992). A very different—and controversial—viewpoint is that conversion disorders *are* prevalent today, but they take the form of conditions like chronic fatigue syndrome, Gulf War syndrome, and similar puzzling maladies (Johnson, 2008; Showalter, 1997).

Most other somatoform disorders also appear to be relatively rare. For example, one study found a 0.7 percent prevalence of body dysmorphic disorder (Otto et al., 2001). Hypochondriasis also is quite rare, although less severe worrying about physical illness is quite common (Looper & Kirmayer, 2001). The lifetime prevalence of somatization disorder in the United States is only 0.13 percent (Miller & Swartz, 1990). However, like hypochondriacal worrying, physical complaints that do not meet all the diagnostic criteria for somatization disorder are very common (Ladwig et al., 2001). In one study, 11.6 percent of people suffered from four to six physical symptoms with no identifiable organic cause (fewer than the eight required for the diagnosis of somatization disorder) (Swartz et al., 1990). Indeed, a new diagnostic category, *multisomatoform disorder,* which requires only three physical symptoms—but chronic ones—has been proposed and likely will be included in DSM-V (Kroenke et al., 1997).

Gender, SES, and Culture With the exception of hypochondriasis, somatoform disorder is more common among women. This is particularly true of somatization disorder, which may be as much as 10 times more common among women than men (Swartz et al., 1990). Why

▲ Children often describe their nervousness in somatic terms, "My stomach hurts!" Cultural and historical differences in somatoform disorders sometimes are attributed to a similar lack of insight into emotion.

women? Some feminist writers attribute women's hysteria during the time of Freud and Janet to the sexual repression of the Victorian era. Today's disproportionate prevalence among women often is blamed on widespread sexual abuse. Feminist Elaine Showalter (1997) criticizes both of these views. Instead, she argues, "Women still suffer from hysterical symptoms not because we are essentially irrational or because we're all victims of abuse but because, like men, we are human beings who will convert feelings into symptoms when we are unable to speak" (p. 207).

In addition to gender, socioeconomic status and culture are thought to contribute to somatization disorder. In the United States, somatization is more common among lower socioeconomic groups and people with less than a high school education. It is four times more common among African Americans than among Americans of European heritage, and considerably higher in Puerto Rico than on the U.S. mainland (Canino et al., 1987). However, expected differences between industrialized and nonindustrialized countries were not found in a study sponsored by the World Health Organization. The one notable cultural difference was the high prevalence of somatization in Latin America (Gureje et al., 1997). Some speculate that this is due to a Latin view of emotional expression as a sign of weakness, while others hypothesize that it is due to the stigma associated with mental illness.

In addition to affecting prevalence, culture can influence when and how somatoform symptoms are experienced. An example is *hwa-byung,* a Korean folk syndrome that is attributed to unexpressed anger. (The open expression of anger is frowned upon in Korea.) The symptoms of hwa-byung include fatigue, insomnia, indigestion, and various aches and pains.

Comorbidity Somatoform disorders typically occur with other psychological problems, particularly depression and anxiety (Creed & Barsky, 2004; Otto et al., 2001; Smith et al., 2005). The link between depression and somatoform disorders has several possible explanations. Either condition may cause the other, or both could be caused by a third variable, such as life stress. One possibility that primary care physicians must consider carefully is that some patients may express depression indirectly through their somatic complaints (Lipowski, 1988).

There also are several possible explanations for the comorbidity between somatoform disorders and anxiety, including the fact that anxiety often is experienced physically and may be misreported in terms of physical symptoms (upset stomach, dizziness, weakness, sweating, dry mouth). A particular concern is the accurate, differential diagnosis of panic disorder. Some symptoms of panic, such as dizziness, numbness, and fears about dying, may be dismissed by physicians, or misdiagnosed as either hypochondriasis or somatization disorder (Lipowski, 1988).

Finally, somatization disorder has frequently been linked with *antisocial personality disorder,* a lifelong pattern of irresponsible behavior that involves habitual violations of social rules. The two disorders do not typically co-occur in the same individual, but they often are found in different members of the same family (Lilienfeld, 1992). Because antisocial personality disorder is far more common among men, while somatoform disorders have the opposite pattern, some have speculated that the two problems are flip sides of the same coin. Antisocial personality disorder may be the male expression of high negative emotion and the absence of inhibition, whereas somatization disorder is the female expression of the same characteristics (Lilienfeld, 1992).

Causes of Somatoform Disorders

Despite their historical and medical significance, surprisingly little systematic research has been conducted on somatoform disorders. Next, we integrate emerging findings with some theoretical considerations in the context of the biopsychosocial model.

Biological Factors—The Perils of Diagnosis by Exclusion An obvious—and potentially critical—biological consideration in somatoform disorders is the possibility of misdiagnosis. A patient may be incorrectly diagnosed as suffering from a somatoform disorder when, in fact, he or she actually has a real physical illness that is undetected or is perhaps unknown. The diagnosis of a somatoform disorder requires that there is no *known* organic cause of the symptom. This is very different from the positive identification of a psychological cause of the symptom.

This means that the identification of somatoform disorders involves a process called *diagnosis by exclusion.* The physical complaint is assumed to be a part of a somatoform disorder only when various known physical causes are ruled out. Indeed, many experts refer to somatoform disorders as "medically unexplained syndromes" (Johnson, 2008; Smith et al., 2005). The possibility always remains, however, that an incipient somatic disease has been overlooked. Some of the problems with diagnosis by exclusion can be appreciated by way of analogy. Consider the difference in certainty between two police lineups, one in which a victim positively identifies a criminal—"That's him!"—versus a second where the identification is made by ruling out alternatives—"It isn't him or him or him, so I guess it must be that one."

The possibility of misdiagnosis is more than a theoretical concern. Follow-up studies of patients diagnosed as suffering from conversion disorders show that somatic illnesses are later detected in some cases (Shalev & Munitz, 1986). Typically, a neurological disease such as epilepsy or multiple sclerosis is the eventual diagnosis. In one classic study, a *quarter* of patients diagnosed as having a conversion symptom later developed a neurological disease (Slater, 1965). Fortunately, recent research has found a much smaller percentage (5 percent or less) of undetected physical illnesses when following up cases of somatoform disorder several years later (Crimlisk et al., 1998; Schuepbach, Adler, & Sabbioni, 2002). We attribute the new findings to the improved detection of real physical illnesses and again wonder how many of the "hysterias" treated by Charcot, Freud, and Janet would be diagnosed as real physical conditions today.

Psychological Factors—Imagined or Real Trauma Initially, both Freud and Janet assumed that conversion disorders were caused by a traumatic experience. According to their reasoning, trauma overwhelmed normal coping efforts, and unconscious coping processes were called into action as a result. However, Freud later questioned the accuracy of his patients' reports of traumatic sexual abuse. Instead, he decided that their memories of trauma were fantasized, not real. This led

▲ Diagnosis by exclusion is like identifying a criminal by ruling out other suspects. "It isn't the guy in the flowered shirt, he didn't have a mustache, and the two guys on the left are too stocky. It must be the guy on the right." But the real criminal might not be in the lineup, and the real disease might go undetected when using diagnosis by exclusion.

him to develop his theory of childhood sexuality (Freud, 1924/1962). He came to view dissociation as protecting people from unacceptable sexual impulses, not from intolerable memories (Freud, 1924/1962). By extension, he saw conversion symptoms as expressions of intolerable unconscious conflicts. In Freud's terminology, this is the *primary gain* of the symptom. Ironically, some contemporary theorists have noted that, unfortunately, childhood sexual abuse is all too common and suggest that Freud's initial position may have been the accurate one.

Recent evidence does suggest that the somatization can be triggered by traumatic stress, but not necessarily by sexual abuse. Exposure to dead bodies, for example, has been tied to increased somatic symptoms. A study of 358 people who worked in the mortuary during the first Gulf War found an increase in somatization from before to after the experience. Somatic symptoms included faintness, pains in the chest, nausea, trouble breathing, hot or cold spells, numbness, and feeling weak. Importantly, somatization increased more among workers with greater exposure to death (see Figure 7–5). Although it is not clear why trauma leads to increased somatization, likely contributors include an increased awareness of one's own body, the somatic consequences of stress, and the expression of psychological distress through complaints about somatic symptoms.

Freud also suggested that hysterical symptoms could produce **secondary gain,** for example, avoiding work or responsibility or gaining attention and sympathy. This view has more support than Freud's ideas about primary gain, although cognitive behavior therapists call this process *reinforcement,* not secondary gain. In addition to positive reinforcement (extra attention) or negative reinforcement (avoidance of work),

> *What does it mean to say that somatoform disorder is "diagnosis by exclusion"?*

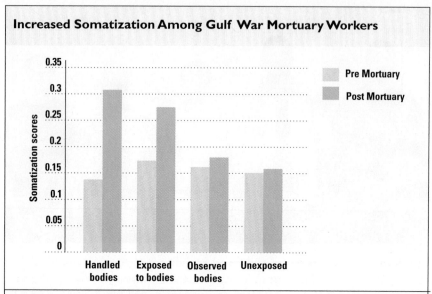

Increased Somatization Among Gulf War Mortuary Workers

FIGURE 7–5 Somatic complaints, including faintness, chest pains, nausea, trouble breathing, hot or cold spells, numbness, and feeling weak, increased from before to after exposure to dead among the first Gulf War mortuary workers. Workers exposed more directly to death showed a more notable increase in somatization.

Source: J. E. McCarroll, R. J. Ursano, C. S. Fullerton, X. Liu, and A. Lundy, 2002, "Somatic Symptoms in Gulf War Mortuary workers," *Psychosomatic Medicine, 64,* pp. 29–33. Copyright © 2002. Reprinted by permission of Lippincott Williams & Wilkins.

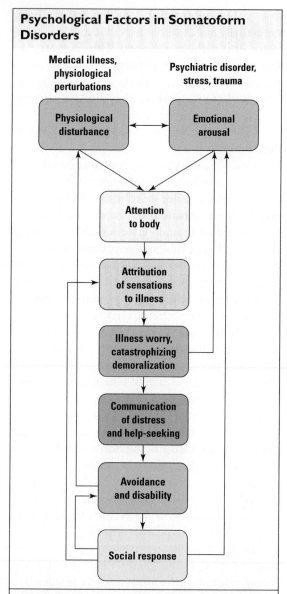

Psychological Factors in Somatoform Disorders

FIGURE 7–6 Minor physical symptoms may develop into a somatoform disorder when combined with emotional arousal, excessive attention to physical symptoms, misattributions, and other psychological tendencies and social reactions.

Source: Adapted from K. J. Looper and L. J. Kirmayer, 2002, "Behavioral Medicine Approaches to Somatoform Disorders," *Journal of Consulting and Clinical Psychology, 70,* pp. 810–827.

learning the sick role through modeling may contribute to somatoform disorders (Lipowski, 1988). Cognitive tendencies also may play a role, especially (1) a tendency to amplify somatic symptoms (Brown, 2004; Kirmayer, Robbins, & Paris, 1994); (2) *alexithymia*—a deficit in one's capacity to recognize and express the emotions signaled by physiological arousal (Bankier, Aigner, & Bach, 2001); (3) the misattribution of normal somatic symptoms (Brown, 2004; Rief, Hiller, & Margraf, 1998); and (4) memory biases (Pauli & Alpers, 2002). Figure 7–6 summarizes how these and other factors may contribute to the development of somatoform disorders.

Social Factors in Somatoform Disorders

A widely held social theory of somatoform disorders argues that, when people in certain cultures experience psychological distress, they describe and experience their emotions as physical symptoms. Why? The theory assumes that some cultures do not teach or allow open emotional expression. A simple analogy for this theory is a child who complains about an upset stomach, not fear of failure, before giving a piano recital. Presumably, increasing psychological sophistication in the West explains both a decline in somatoform disorders over time and a lower prevalence compared to other cultures today (Shorter, 1992). As noted earlier,

however, unusual physical illnesses may have been misdiagnosed as somatoform disorders 100 years ago, and the disorders do not appear to be more prevalent in nonindustrialized than industrialized countries.

Treatment of Somatoform Disorders

Charcot, Janet, and Freud encouraged their patients to recall and recount psychologically painful events as a way of treating conversion disorders. In the century or more since they refined their techniques, however, no systematic research was conducted on any "cathartic" therapies for somatoform disorders, or for that matter, on any treatment. While research is still limited, accumulating evidence indicates that cognitive behavior therapy can reduce physical symptoms in somatization disorder (Woolfolk et al., 2007), hypochondriasis (Clark et al., 1998), and body dysmorphic disorder (Rosen, Reiter, & Orosan, 1995).

The most extensive studies focus on pain disorders. Operant approaches to chronic pain alter contingencies that reward "pain behavior" and the sick role. The goal is to reward successful coping and life adaptation instead (Fordyce, 1976). Cognitive behavior therapy also uses cognitive restructuring to address the emotional and cognitive components of pain. Research demonstrates the effectiveness of both approaches in treating chronic lower back pain (Blanchard, 1994).

Antidepressants also may be helpful in treating somatoform disorders. SSRIs produce more improvement in comparison to placebo for body dysmorphic disorder (Phillips, Albertini, & Rasmussen, 2002) and pain disorder (Fishbain et al., 1998). Both medication and cognitive behavior therapy may be effective, in part, because the treatments alleviate the depression and anxiety that often are comorbid with somatoform disorders (Looper & Kirmayer, 2002; Simon, 2002).

One reason for the limited research on the psychological treatment of somatoform disorders is that primary care physicians treat most of these patients (Bass et al., 2001). Patients with somatoform disorders typically consult physicians about their ailments, and they often insist that their problems are physical despite negative test results. Such patients are likely to refuse a referral to a mental health professional. As a result, primary care physicians often must learn how to manage hypochondriasis, somatization disorder, and related problems in the medical setting.

This can be difficult. The absence of a clear physical problem can frustrate primary care physicians, who may be unsympathetic toward "hypochondriacs" when so many patients with "real" problems need medical treatment. Not surprisingly, such reactions weaken the physician–patient relationship, and this can intensify the problem. In fact, the major recommendation for the medical management of patients with somatization disorder is to establish a strong and consistent physician–patient relationship. Physicians are urged to schedule

GETTING HELP

The disorders discussed in this chapter are fascinating, and the controversies about them are intellectually exciting— unless you or someone you know is suffering from PTSD or a dissociative or somatoform disorder. In this case, the unusual symptoms can be extremely frightening, the lack of acceptance can be isolating, and the controversy surrounding the disorders can seem callous.

The controversies and limited scientific information make it difficult to make clear recommendations for getting help. However, you can review the treatment sections of the three categories of disorder to get some specifics on the best approaches based on current research. These treatments generally involve some type of cognitive behavior therapy and/or antidepressant medication.

We also can readily offer a strong suggestion: If you have been the victim of trauma, for example, rape, abuse, or disaster, or a victim or witness of some other form of violence, talk to someone about it. You may find it difficult to trust anyone, but trying to "forget about it" is

exactly the wrong thing to do. Confronting fear, embarrassment, or others' lack of understanding is far better than keeping it all inside. If you are not willing to consider therapy, start by confiding in a friend, a family member, even a stranger.

We are particularly concerned about the trauma of rape, including acquaintance rape, an all-too-frequent occurrence among college students. If you or someone you know has been raped, the first step may be to get to a hospital emergency room or to call the police. You also may want to contact a rape crisis center in your area. The Rape Abuse and Incest Network National hotline, (800)-656-4673, can provide you with the telephone number of the rape crisis center closest to you. You also may want to visit its Web site: http://www.rainn.org/ . A good self-help book on rape is *Free of the Shadows: Recovering from Sexual Violence,* by Caren Adams and Jennifer Fay.

There are many other resources available for victims of rape, disasters like September 11, and other types of trauma. If you are surfing the Web for information, we suggest that you begin your Internet exploration with the National

Institute of Mental Health. You will find much helpful information there, as well as links to other useful Web sites.

Another reason why we recommend that you begin with the NIMH Web site is that you need to be extremely cautious about information on PTSD and dissociative and somatoform disorders. The controversies discussed in this chapter are not just theoretical ones. There are many self-help resources—and professionals— who claim that one side or the other of a given controversy is fact, not theory or opinion. We urge you to be wary if a professional or resource fails to acknowledge the uncertain state of scientific information and the range of opinion about such things as the long-term consequences of childhood trauma, the prevalence of multiple personality disorder, or the nature of recovered memories. A dramatic illustration of the havoc that can be created by those who are supposed to help can be found in the book *Remembering Satan,* Lawrence Wright's journalistic account of the consequences of one episode of false "recovered memories" of satanic ritual abuse.

routine appointments with these patients every month or two and to conduct brief medical exams during this time (National Institute of Mental Health, 1990). This approach not only provides consistent emotional support and medical reassurance but also helps to reduce unnecessary medical care. Patients who feel misunderstood are likely to recruit a new, more understanding physician (National Institute of Mental Health, 1990). On the other hand, a physician who knows the patient can recognize the psychological origin of the physical complaints and order fewer unnecessary medical tests or treatments. At least one study documented the effectiveness of this management approach (Smith, Monson, & Ray, 1986).

■ SUMMARY

To some extent, all the disorders we consider in this chapter involve **dissociation,** the disruption of the normally integrated mental processes involved in memory or consciousness. Many of the disorders also are known or hypothesized to be reactions to **traumatic stress,** exposure to some event that involves actual or threatened death or serious injury to self or others and creates intense fear, helplessness, or horror.

Acute stress disorder (ASD) is a short-term reaction to trauma that is characterized by symptoms of dissociation, reexperiencing, avoidance, and increased anxiety or arousal. **Posttraumatic stress disorder (PTSD)** is characterized by very similar symptoms—reexperiencing, numbed responsiveness or avoidance, and increased autonomic arousal—but the symptoms either last for longer than 1 month or have a delayed onset. Trauma may be reexperienced as a **flashback**—a dissociative state in which the person relives the trauma in the moment. The diminished responsiveness sometimes is called emotional anesthesia. The increased arousal in ASD or PTSD may include excessive fear, anxiety, or irritability, as well as general psychophysiological arousal.

Trauma is distressingly common and often leads to PTSD, especially rape for women and combat exposure for men. More symptoms of ASD predict later PTSD, and the nature and level of exposure to a traumatic event, as well as social support after the occurrence of the trauma, are crucial to long-term adjustment. By definition, trauma is the central cause of PTSD, but other factors contribute to its development. Genetic factors increase the risk both for experiencing trauma and for developing PTSD following trauma. Key psychological contributions include **two-factor theory,** a combination of classical and operant conditioning, and **emotional processing,** which involves facing fear, diminishing its intensity, and coming to some new understanding about the trauma and its consequences.

Early intervention holds the hope of easing the pain of trauma, but data are lacking on the effectiveness of **critical incident stress debriefing** and other early interventions. Promising evidence suggests that treating acute stress disorder may reduce PTSD. Prolonged exposure is perhaps the least obvious but most important strategy for treatment for PTSD, which has a chronic course in about one-third of cases.

Dissociative disorders are characterized by persistent, maladaptive disruptions in the integration of memory, consciousness, or identity. **Somatoform disorders** are identified by unusual physical symptoms that occur in the absence of a known physical illness. Memories become inaccessible in dissociative disorders; psychological distress is converted into physical symptoms in somatoform disorders. Thus, these unusual emotional problems involve unconscious processes by definition, and they challenge psychological theorists to explain those psychological events that occur outside of awareness. Both Freud and Janet developed their influential theories about unconscious processes when attempting to explain these disorders.

Dissociative disorders include **dissociative fugue,** characterized by sudden and unexpected travel away from home, an inability to recall the past, and confusion about identity or the assumption of a new identity; **dissociative amnesia,** a sudden inability to recall extensive and important personal information that exceeds normal forgetfulness; **depersonalization disorder,** a less dramatic problem characterized by severe and persistent feelings of being detached from oneself; and **dissociative identity disorder (DID),** also known as **multiple personality disorder,** characterized by the existence of two or more distinct personalities in a single individual.

Although some suggest otherwise, dissociative disorders are rare. Some evidence links the conditions with traumatic experiences, particularly with child abuse, but we must be very cautious in drawing inferences from purported **recovered**

memories of past abuse, the sudden remembering of long forgotten traumatic experiences. Evidence is weak or nonexistent on other factors that may contribute to the development of dissociative disorders. Similarly, there is no systematic research on the treatment of dissociative disorders.

The term **conversion disorder** accurately conveys the central assumption of the diagnosis—the idea that psychological conflicts are converted into physical symptoms. **Somatization disorder** is characterized by a history of multiple, somatic complaints in the absence of organic impairments. **Hypochondriasis** is characterized by a fear or belief that the individual is suffering from a physical illness. **Pain disorder** is characterized by preoccupation with pain. Although there is no objective way to evaluate pain, psychological factors are judged to be significant in creating or exacerbating the chronic pain in pain disorder. In **body dysmorphic disorder** the patient is preoccupied with some imagined defect in appearance—a preoccupation that typically focuses on some facial feature, such as the nose or mouth.

True somatoform disorders are rare, although complaints about unexplained medical conditions are common and represent a significant proportion of medical care. Causes include the possible misdiagnosis of incipient neurological diseases as somatoform disorders; the experience of trauma; secondary gain or reinforcement for the sick role; cognitive factors, such as a tendency to amplify somatic symptoms; and alexithymia—a deficit in the individual's capacity to recognize and express the emotions signaled by physiological arousal. Cultural influences on somatoform disorders may be less prominent than previously thought. Cognitive behavior therapy and antidepressant medications are useful treatments for somatoform disorders, which also may require supportive medical management.

THE BIG PICTURE CRITICAL THINKING REVIEW

Why is trauma no longer defined as "outside of usual human experience"?

DSM III defined trauma as "outside the range of usual human experience," but trauma is a *common* part of human experience. (SEE PAGE 201)

Does trauma always cause PTSD?

Because not every traumatized person develops a disorder, trauma is a necessary, but not a sufficient cause. (SEE PAGE 204)

Why are dissociative disorders so controversial?

This controversy is about much more than dissociative disorders; it concerns the very nature of the human psyche. (SEE PAGE 211)

Is memory always accurate?

Research clearly shows that memories, even of highly dramatic events such as where you were during 9/11, can be inaccurate. (SEE PAGE 212)

What does it mean to say that somatoform disorder is "diagnosis by exclusion"?

Consider two police lineups, one where the victim says, "That's him!" and a second where the victim ponders, "It isn't him or him or him, so I guess it must be that one." (SEE PAGE 225)

■ KEY TERMS

acute stress disorder (ASD) **197**
body dysmorphic disorder **222**
conversion disorder **220**
critical incident stress debriefing (CISD) **207**

depersonalization disorder **214**
dissociation **196**
dissociative amnesia **213**
dissociative disorders **208**
dissociative fugue **213**
dissociative identity disorder (DID) **214**

factitious disorder **223**
flashbacks **199**
hypnosis **211**
hypochondriasis **222**
hysteria **210**
iatrogenesis **218**
implicit memory **210**
malingering **223**

multiple personality disorder **214**
pain disorder **222**
posttraumatic stress disorder (PTSD) **197**
recovered memories **213**
retrospective reports **218**
secondary gain **225**

somatization disorder **221**
somatoform disorders **219**
state-dependent learning **217**
traumatic stress **197**
two-factor theory **205**

STRESS AND PHYSICAL HEALTH

How do you feel when you are "stressed out"? Different people feel jittery, tired, down, preoccupied, vigilant, defeated, angry, sick, or just plain lousy. How do you cope? Some people try to eliminate stress by solving the problem; others calm themselves by writing or talking about the stress; and still other people distract themselves in healthy ways (exercise) or unhealthy ones (smoking, alcohol, or overeating). What are the consequences of stress and different ways of coping with it? Can stress *really* make you sick? How?

OVERVIEW

Scientists define **stress** as any challenging event that requires physiological, cognitive, or behavioral adaptation. Stress may involve minor, daily hassles, like taking an exam, or major events, such as going through a divorce. The most common daily stressors involve interpersonal arguments and tensions (Almeida, 2005). As we saw in Chapter 7, *traumatic stress* involves actual or threatened death or serious injury to oneself or others and a reaction of intense fear, helplessness, or horror. This chapter is about more normal stress, how we cope with it, and how stress affects our physical health.

Scientists once thought that stress contributed to only a few physical diseases, like ul-

cers, migraine headaches, hypertension (high blood pressure), asthma, and other *psychosomatic disorders,*[1] a term indicating that a disease is a product of both the *psyche* (mind) and the *soma* (body). Today, the term is outdated. Medical scientists now view *every* physical illness—from colds to cancer to AIDS—as a product of the interaction between the mind and body. Thus, there is no list of "psychosomatic disorders" in the DSM-IV-TR or elsewhere.

[1]In everyday language, we sometimes use the term *psychosomatic* to imply that an illness is imagined or not real. Unlike conversion disorders (Chapter 7), psychosomatic disorders involve very real physical damage or dysfunction.

This holistic view of health and disease has brought about major changes in medicine. Of particular note is the rapid development of **behavioral medicine,** a multidisciplinary field that includes both medical and mental health professionals who investigate psychological factors in the symptoms, cause, and treatment of physical illnesses. Psychologists who specialize in behavioral medicine often are called *health psychologists.*

Learning more adaptive ways of **coping,** responses aimed at diminishing the burden of stress, can limit the recurrence or improve the course of many physical illnesses (Lazarus, 2000; Snyder, 1999). In order to promote health, specialists in behavioral medicine therefore study and encourage healthy coping thorough stress management, proper diet, regular exercise, and avoidance of tobacco use. In treating diseases, behavioral medicine includes interventions such as educating parents of chronically ill children, teaching strategies for coping with chronic pain, and running support groups for people with terminal cancer.

In this chapter we discuss innovations in behavioral medicine and review evidence on the link between stress and some physical illnesses. In order to illustrate the challenges in studying stress, we also include an extended discussion of the number-one killer in the United States today, cardiovascular disease. We begin with a case study from our files.

CASE **STUDY** Bob Carter's Heart Attack

One Thursday afternoon, Bob Carter, a salesman for a beer and liquor wholesaler, was completing his route, calling on customers. Throughout the morning, he had felt a familiar discomfort in his chest and left arm. As had been happening on occasion for at least a year, that morning he experienced a few fleeting but sharp pains in the center and left side of his chest. This was followed by a dull ache in his chest and left shoulder and a feeling of congestion in the same areas. Breathing deeply made the pain worse, but Bob could manage it as long as he took shallow breaths. He continued on his route, alternately vowing to see a doctor soon and cursing his aging body.

After grabbing a hamburger for lunch, Bob called on a customer who was behind in his payments. At first, Bob shared a cigarette with the customer and chatted with him in a friendly way. He was a salesman, after all. Soon it was time to pressure him about the bill. As Bob raised his voice in anger, a crushing pain returned to his chest and radiated down his left arm. This was much worse than anything he had experienced before. The pain was so intense that Bob was unable to continue speaking. He slumped forward against the table, but with his right arm he waved away any attempt to help him. After sitting still for about 10 minutes, Bob was able to drag himself to his car and drive to his home 30 miles away. When his wife saw him shuffle into the house looking haggard and in obvious pain, she called for an ambulance. The Carters soon discovered that Bob had suffered a *myocardial infarction* (a heart attack).

Bob was 49 years old at the time. His home life was happy, but it also put a lot of pressures on him. His 24-year-old daughter was living at home while her husband was serving in combat duty overseas. Naturally, the entire family was anxious about the son-in-law's well-being. More stress came from Bob's 21-year-old daughter, who had just graduated from college and was getting married in 3 weeks. Finally, Bob's 19-year-old son was home from his first year of college, full of rebellion and ideas that challenged Bob's authority. There was no shortage of family stress.

Bob also put plenty of stress on himself. A former high school athlete, he had always been competitive and hard-driving. He wanted to be the best at whatever he did, and right now his goal was to be the best salesman in his company. Bob used his charm, humor, and some not-so-gentle pressure to sell his products, and it worked. But once he had become the best salesman in his wholesaling company, Bob wanted to be the best salesman for the producers whose products he sold. No matter what he accomplished, Bob drove himself hard to meet a new goal.

Bob maintained his drive and competitiveness from his youthful days as a star athlete, but he had not maintained his physical condition. The only exercise he got was playing golf, and he usually rode in a cart instead of walking the course. He was at least 30 pounds overweight, smoked a pack and a half of cigarettes a day, ate a lot of fatty red meat, and drank heavily. Bob was a good candidate for a heart attack.

Bob recuperated quickly in the hospital. He was tired and in considerable pain for a couple of days, but he was telling jokes before the end of a week. His cardiologist explained what had hap-

pened and gave Bob a stern lecture about changing his lifestyle. He wanted Bob to quit smoking, lose weight, cut down on his drinking, and gradually work himself back into shape with a careful program of exercise. He urged Bob to slow down at work and told him to quit worrying about his children—they were old enough to take care of themselves.

To underscore these messages, the cardiologist asked a psychologist from the hospital's behavioral medicine unit to consult with Bob. The psychologist reviewed information on coronary risk and gave Bob several pamphlets to read. The psychologist also explained that the hospital ran several programs that might interest Bob, including workshops on stress management, weight reduction, and exercise. Fees were minimal, because the hospital offered them as a community service. The psychologist also offered to talk

to Bob, because cardiac patients and their families sometimes have trouble adjusting to the sudden reminder of the patient's mortality. But Bob waved off the offer of assistance much as he had waved off help in the middle of his heart attack.

Bob was discharged from the hospital 10 days after being admitted. Against his doctor's advice, he walked his daughter down the aisle at her wedding the following weekend, and he was back to work within a month. At his 6-week checkup, Bob admitted that he was smoking again. His weight was unchanged, and his exercise and drinking were only a "little better." When the cardiologist chastised Bob, he promised to renew his efforts. However, he thought to himself that giving up these small pleasures would not make him live any longer, it would just seem that way. Clearly, one heart attack was not going to get Bob Carter to slow down.

The case of Bob Carter illustrates how stress can contribute to coronary heart disease, but it also raises a number of questions about the link. What is the physiological mechanism that transforms psychological stress into coronary risk? Is stress the problem, or is the real culprit the unhealthy behaviors that result from stress—smoking, drinking, and overeating? What is the role of personality in stress? Can someone like Bob change his lifestyle, and if so, does this lower the risk for future heart attacks? We consider these and related questions in this chapter. First, though, we need to consider more carefully exactly what we mean by "stress."

DEFINING STRESS

We define *stress* as a challenging event that requires physiological, cognitive, or behavioral adaptation. However, we need to examine this definition closely. Is stress the event itself? Some people would relax after becoming the top salesman, but Bob Carter viewed this achievement as another challenge. Perhaps stress should be defined in terms of the individual's reactions to an event. However, we want to learn if stress causes problems. If we define stress in terms of the reactions it causes, is this merely circular logic? In fact, scientists continue to debate whether stress is best defined as a life event itself or an *appraisal* of life events, the event plus the individual's reaction to it.

Stress as a Life Event

Researchers often define stress as a life event—a difficult circumstance regardless of the individual's reaction to it. An example that contributed greatly to the development of stress research, and is still widely used, is Holmes and Rahe's (1967) Social Readjustment Rating Scale (SRRS), a measure that assigns stress values to life events based on the judgments of a large group of normal adults. The SRRS views stressors that produce more *life change units* as causing more stress (see Table 8–1).

Ratings on the SRRS and similar instruments are correlated with a variety of physical illnesses (Dohrenwend, 2006; Miller, 1989). Critics note, however, that stress checklists (1) rely on retrospective reports; (2) contain stressors that do not apply to people of different ages and ethnic backgrounds (Contrada et al., 2001) (Is the SRRS a good measure of college student stress?); (3) treat both positive and negative events as stressors (Would you equate getting married with getting fired?); (4) fail to distinguish between short-lived and chronic stressors; and (5) most importantly, treat the same event as causing the same amount of stress for everyone (Is getting pregnant just as stressful for an unwed teenager and for a married couple who want a baby?).

Dohrenwend and colleagues (1990) demonstrated the importance of this last point. They found, for example, that an assault caused a *large* change for nearly 20 percent of respondents, but it caused *no* change for the same percentage of people (see Table 8–2). Because of this variability, many experts define stress as the combination of an event plus each individual's reaction to it.

TABLE 8–1   Change Caused by Different Life Events

LIFE EVENT	LIFE CHANGE UNITS	LIFE EVENT	LIFE CHANGE UNITS
Death of one's spouse	100	Son or daughter leaving home	29
Divorce	73	Trouble with in-laws	29
Marital separation	65	Outstanding personal achievement	28
Jail term	63	Wife beginning or stopping work	26
Death of a close family member	63	Beginning or ending school	26
Personal injury or illness	53	Change in living conditions	25
Marriage	50	Revision of personal habits	24
Being fired at work	47	Trouble with one's boss	23
Marital reconciliation	45	Change in work hours or conditions	20
Retirement	45	Change in residence	20
Change in the health of a family member	44	Change in schools	20
Pregnancy	40	Change in recreation	19
Sex difficulties	39	Change in church activities	19
Gain of a new family member	39	Change in social activities	18
Business readjustment	39	Mortgage or loan of less than $10,000	17
Change in one's financial state	38	Change in sleeping habits	16
Death of a close friend	37	Change in number of family get-togethers	15
Change to a different line of work	36	Change in eating habits	15
Change in number of arguments with one's spouse	35	Vacation	13
Mortgage over $10,000	31	Christmas	12
Foreclosure of a mortgage or loan	30	Minor violations of the law	11
Change in responsibilities at work	29		

The SRRS rates different stressors as causing more or less life change for people. More difficult stressors have a higher number of "life change units."

Source: From "The Social Readjustment Rating Scale" by T. H. Holmes and R. H. Rahe, Journal of *Psychosomatic Research*, (1967), 11. Copyright © 1967 by Elsevier, Inc. Reprinted by permission of Elsevier, Ltd.

TABLE 8–2   Different Reactions to the Same Life Event

TYPE OF EVENT	PERCENTAGE OF SUBJECTS REPORTING EACH AMOUNT OF CHANGE			
	LARGE	MODERATE	LITTLE	NONE
Serious physical illness	47.2%	27.8%	8.3%	16.7%
Relations with mate got worse	41.2	47.1	0.0	11.8
Relative died (not child/spouse)	8.3	8.3	29.2	54.2
Close friend died	5.3	15.8	29.8	49.1
Financial loss (not work related)	16.3	44.2	18.6	20.9
Assaulted	18.5	22.2	40.7	18.5
Broke up with a friend	0.0	26.1	37.0	37.0
Laid off	13.3	63.3	13.3	10.0
Had trouble with a boss	17.5	35.0	32.5	15.0
Got involved in a court case	9.5	9.5	28.6	52.4

Source: Adapted from B. P. Dohrenwend et al., 1990, "Measuring Life Events: The Problem of Variability Within Event Categories," *Stress Medicine*, 6, p. 182.

Stress as Appraisal of Life Events

One influential example is Richard Lazarus's (1966) definition of stress as the individual's *appraisal* of a challenging life event. An impending exam is stressful when you feel inadequately prepared, but not when you are confident. Lazarus also distinguished between people's *primary appraisal,* our evaluation of the challenge, threat, or harm posed by an event, and people's *secondary appraisal,* our assessment of our abilities and resources for coping with that event (Lazarus & Folkman, 1984). Thus, even if you feel unprepared, the impending exam causes less stress if you have the time and the ability to study.

The appraisal approach recognizes that the same event is more or less stressful for different people but runs the risk of circular reasoning. What is stress? Stress is an event that causes us to feel threatened and overwhelmed. What causes us to feel threatened and overwhelmed? Stress. Logically, such a definition would be a *tautology,* a redundant statement that means nothing. Stress is best defined as a life event plus its appraisal. Because of the potential tautology, however, researchers must carefully distinguish independent variables (stressors) from hypothesized dependent variables (adverse outcomes).

Are our evolved reactions to stress maladaptive in the face of modern stressors?

SYMPTOMS OF STRESS

Stress is a part of life. In fact, stress is an *adaptive* response to many aspects of living. If you had no stress response, you would not be motivated to jump out of the way of a cement truck barreling down on you, let alone to study for your exams!

The renowned American physiologist Walter Cannon (1871–1945), one of the first and foremost stress researchers, recognized the adaptive, evolutionary aspects of stress. Cannon (1935) viewed stress as the activation of the **fight or flight response,**[2] the reaction you witness when a cat is surprised by a barking dog. The cat can either

---

[2]Ethologists now view mammals' responses to threat as more nuanced: freeze–flight–fight–fright. Mammals' first response to threat is to freeze (hide); if that fails they flee; and fighting is the third option. Fright or *tonic immobility,* also known as "playing dead," is the final option when a threat is imminent and mortal. Future stress research surely will incorporate freeze–flight–fight–fright (Bracha et al., 2004), but we use the fight or flight dichotomy which dominates in current efforts.

scratch at the dog or flee to safety. The fight or flight response has obvious survival value. Cannon observed, however, that fight or flight is a *maladaptive* reaction to much stress in the modern world such as being reprimanded by your boss or giving a speech before a large audience. In other words, the human environment may have evolved more rapidly than our physiological reactions to it. (Some psychologists think that fight or flight is a *male* reaction to stress. See the Tend and Befriend box on page 236.)

Psychophysiological Responses to Stress

Physiologically, the fight or flight response activates the *sympathetic nervous system:* Your heart and respiration rates increase, blood pressure rises, your pupils dilate, blood sugar levels elevate, and your blood flow is redirected in preparation for muscular activity (Baum et al., 1987; Koranyi, 1989). These physiological reactions heighten attention, provide energy for quick action, and prepare the body for injury (Sapolsky, 1992, 2003). This physiological reaction is adaptive if a truck is headed your way, and presumably it also was an adaptive response to many threats over the course of human evolution. When your boss is yelling—or you worry that your boss *might* yell—the response only leaves your body racing and you feeling nervous and agitated.

Adrenal Hormones How does the stress response work physiologically? When a perceived threat registers in the cortex, it signals the *amygdala,* the brain structure primarily responsible for activating the stress response, which secretes *corticotrophin-releasing factor (CRF).* CRF stimulates the brainstem to activate the sympathetic nervous system. In response to the sympathetic arousal, the *adrenal glands* release two key hormones. One is *epinephrine* (commonly known as *adrenaline*), which acts as a neuromodulator and leads to the release of *norepinephrine* and more *epinephrine* into the bloodstream (see Figure 8–1). This familiar "rush of adrenaline" further activates the sympathetic nervous system.

The second key adrenal hormone is **cortisol,** often called the "stress hormone" because its release is so closely linked with stress. Cortisol has a less rapid action than adrenaline, yet it functions quickly to help the body make repairs in response to injury or infection. One function of cortisol is "containment" of pathogens in the body—the same function performed by the steroids that you may take for inflammation and skin irritation. Like externally administered steroids, however, cortisol can promote healing in the short run, but an excess of cortisol can harm the body by damaging the hippocampus, causing muscular atrophy, and producing hypertension (Song & Leonard, 2000; Yehuda, 2002).

The Physiology of the Stress Response

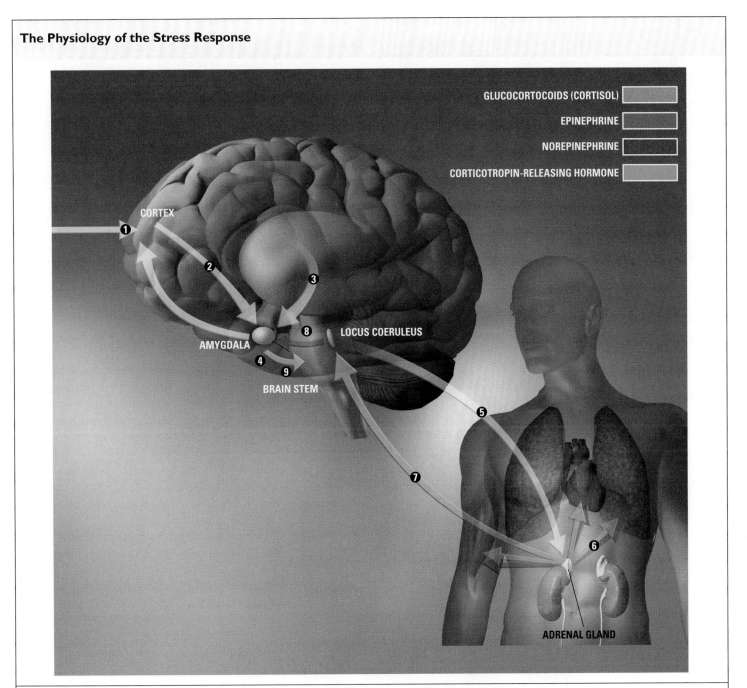

FIGURE 8–1 Stress pathways are diverse and involve many regions of the brain in feedback loops that can sometimes greatly amplify a response. The process—simplified somewhat in this diagram—begins when an actual or perceived threat activates the sensory and higher reasoning centers in the cortex (1). The cortex then sends a message to the amygdala, the principal mediator of the stress response (2). Separately, a preconscious signal may precipitate activity in the amygdala (3). The amygdala releases corticotropin-releasing hormone, which stimulates the brain stem (4) to activate the sympathetic nervous system via the spinal cord (5). In response, the adrenal glands produce the stress hormone epinephrine; a different pathway simultaneously triggers the adrenals to release glucocorticoids. The two types of hormones act on the muscle, heart, and lungs to prepare the body for "fight or flight" (6). If the stress becomes chronic, glucocorticoids induce the locus coeruleus (7) to release norepinephrine that communicates with the amygdala (8), leading to the production of more CRH (9)—and to ongoing reactivation of stress pathways.

Source: Figures by Alfred Kamajian from "Taming Stress" written by R. Sapolsky, *Scientific American, 286,* (September 2003), p. 89. Reproduced by permission of Alfred Kamajian.

TEND AND BEFRIEND: THE FEMALE ALTERNATIVE TO FIGHT OR FLIGHT?

Health psychologist Shelly Taylor and her colleagues (2000; 2006) suggest that fight or flight may be a particularly *male* response to stress. Females, particularly primate females, instead may **tend and befriend**. *Tending* involves caring for offspring, especially protecting them from harm. *Befriending* involves social affiliation, finding safety in numbers, and sharing resources.

Theoretically, the tend and befriend response, like fight or flight, is a product of evolution. Inclusive fitness may be increased by caretaking and blending into the environment in response to threat. Attachment is the mechanism hypothesized to underlie tending and befriending, but Taylor (2006) focuses on the benefits for the caretaker rather than the infant. She argues that evolution selected for caretaking tendencies in adult females.

> **How does tending and befriending differ from fight or flight?**

Taylor and her colleagues (2000) suggested that, unlike male aggression, female aggression is activated less by sympathetic nervous system arousal due to the lack of *testosterone* (the male sex hormone). This limits the female's fight response. Flight tendencies, in turn, are countered by *oxytocin* released by the pituitary and by the female sex hormone, *estrogen*. Theoretically, the result is the activation of the parasympathetic nervous system, which has a calming effect.

The tend and befriend hypotheses are speculative, but they focus attention on important issues, for example, including more females in studies of stress. Prior to 1995, males made up 83 percent of the participants in laboratory studies of stress. Critics might see sexism in Taylor assertions about female–male sex differences, but Taylor carefully acknowledges cultural influences on gender roles. And under the right conditions, or through learning, males may also respond to stress by tending and befriending.

Immune System Responses The release of cortisol and CRF also cause *immunosuppression,* the decreased production of immune agents. In fact, a whole field of study, **psychoneuroimmunology (PNI),** investigates the relation between stress and immune function (Adler, 2001; Song & Leonard, 2000). PNI research shows that particularly vulnerable to stress are *T cells,* one of the two major types of *lymphocytes,* white blood cells that fight off *antigens,* foreign substances like bacteria that invade the body. Decreased T cell production makes the body more susceptible to infectious diseases during times of stress (Adler, 2001; Song & Leonard, 2000).

Why would stress inhibit immune function? From an evolutionary perspective, *heightened* immune functioning might seem to better prepare the body for the infection that may follow injury. However, the immune response creates inflammation, maintains fever, and intensifies pain—all of which impair immediate action (Maier, Watkins, & Fleshner, 1994). Thus, immunosuppression may actually be an adaptive short-term reaction to stress.

Current evidence suggests a response to stress that is more nuanced than blanket immunosuppression. Short-term stressors and physical threats *enhance* immune responses that are quick, require little energy, and contain infection due to an injury. However, stress *impairs* immune responses that drain energy from the fight or flight response. Chronic stressors and losses (as opposed to threats) also create immunosupression (Segerstrom, 2007; Segerstrom & Miller, 2004).

Illness and Chronic Stress When repeated over time, physiological reactions to stress can leave you susceptible to illness. Cannon (1935) hypothesized this occurs because intense or chronic stress overwhelms the body's **homeostasis** (a term he coined), the tendency to return to a steady state of normal functioning. He suggested that, over time, the

▶ A white blood cell (microphage) reaches out to capture a bacterium.

prolonged arousal of the sympathetic nervous system eventually damages the body, because it no longer returns to its normal resting state.

Canadian physiologist Hans Selye (1907–1982), another very influential stress researcher, offered a different hypothesis based on his concept of the **general adaptation syndrome (GAS).** Seyle's GAS consists of three stages: alarm, resistance, and exhaustion. The stage of *alarm* occurs first and involves the mobilization of the body in reaction to threat. The stage of *resistance* comes next and is a period of time during which the body is physiologically activated and prepared to respond to the threat. *Exhaustion* is the final stage, and it occurs if the body's resources are depleted by chronic stress. Selye viewed the stage of exhaustion as the key in the development of physical illness from stress. At this stage, the body is damaged by continuous, failed attempts to reactivate the GAS (Selye, 1956).

Although similar, Selye's theory differs from Cannon's in important ways. An analogy for Cannon's theory is a car in which the engine continues to race instead of idling down after running fast. In contrast, an analogy for Selye's theory is a car that has run out of gas and is damaged because stress keeps turning the key, trying repeatedly and unsuccessfully to restart the engine.

Stress may create physical illness in both ways, but a third mechanism may be as important. Because the stress response uses so much energy, the body may not be able to perform many routine functions, such as storing energy or repairing injuries (Sapolsky, 1992). The result is greater susceptibility to illness. An automotive analogy for this third model is a car running constantly at such high speeds that the cooling and lubricant systems cannot keep up, making a breakdown likely.

Coping

People cope with stress in many ways, good and bad. Two very important, alternative strategies are problem-focused and emotion-focused coping (Lazarus & Folkman, 1984). **Problem-focused coping** involves attempts to change a stressor. If your job is stressful, you look for a new one. **Emotion-focused coping** is an attempt to alter internal distress. Before taking a big exam, you sit quietly and breathe deeply to calm yourself.

We all face a big problem in deciding how to cope: What will work? What if you are stressed out by poor grades in a difficult class? Should you re-

Calvin and Hobbes
by Bill Watterson

double your efforts, drop the course, or accept that this is not your best subject? Culturally, Americans prefer change over acceptance. Asian cultures, in contrast, emphasize acceptance over change. We think that flexibility is the key. There is much truth in Reinhold Niebuhr's (1951) "Serenity Prayer":

> God, give us the serenity to accept what cannot be changed;
> Give us the courage to change what should be changed;
> Give us the wisdom to distinguish one from the other.

Predictability and Control Of course, events are less stressful when we are better prepared to cope with them. Studies of animals and humans show that *predictability* and *control* both dramatically reduce stress. For example, when a flash of a light signals an impending shock, rats show a smaller stress response than when the shock is unsignaled (Sapolsky, 1992). The predictability apparently allows animals (and humans too) to begin to cope even before the onset of a stressor.

Animal research also shows the benefits of control. When they can stop a shock by pressing a bar, rats have a smaller stress response than when they have no control (Sapolsky, 1992). Even the *illusion* of control can help to alleviate stress. However, the perception of control *increases* stress when people believe they could have exercised control but failed to do so, or when they lose control over a formerly controllable stressor (Mineka & Kihlstrom, 1978). Control lessens stress when we have it, even when it is illusory, but failed attempts at control intensify stress.

Outlets for Frustration Physical activity also reduces physiological reactions to stress, even when the effort does not include problem-focused coping. For example, rats secrete less

TABLE 8–3 Coping Tendencies of Optimists and Pessimists

OPTIMISTS	PESSIMISTS
Information seeking	Suppression of thoughts
Active coping and planning	Giving up
Positive reframing	Self-distraction
Seeking benefit	Cognitive avoidance
Use of humor	Focus on distress
Acceptance	Overt denial

Source: From C. S. Carver and M.F. Scheier, 1999, "Optimism," in C. R. Snyder, Ed., *Coping: The Psychology of What Works*, p. 194. New York: Oxford University Press. Used by permission of Oxford University Press, Inc.

cortisol following an electric shock if they can attack another rat or run on a running wheel (Sapolsky, 1992). Sound like you at the gym—or dumping on your roommates? Having *outlets for frustration* does reduce stress.

Repression *Repression* is a generally maladaptive form of emotion-focused coping (Cramer, 2000; Somerfield & McCrae, 2000). Bob Carter kept his feelings bottled up. Did his repression contribute to his risk for a heart attack? Apparently. People who report positive mental health but whom clinicians judge to have emotional problems (so-called "defensive deniers") show greater psychophysiological reactions to stress (Shedler, Mayman, & Manis, 1993). On the flip side, stress is reduced when people talk about their stressful experiences (Pennebaker, 1990; Frattaroli, 2006; Harris, 2006).

Optimism In contrast to repression, **optimism** is a healthy coping style. Optimists have a positive attitude about dealing with stress, even when they cannot control it. Pessimists are defeated from the outset (see Table 8–3). Positive thinking is linked with better health habits and less illness (Carver & Scheier, 1999; Kubzansky et al., 2001; Shatte et al., 1999). Stress is taxing, but less so if we approach it optimistically (Folkman & Moskowitz, 2000; see the Critical Thinking Matters box).

CRITICAL THINKING MATTERS

Resilience

Popular culture, and much psychological research, tells us that stress is bad, something to be avoided. Stress will make us tense, irritable, and unhappy. Stress makes us sick.

Stress *can* make us more susceptible to illness, but a little critical thinking leads us to ask: Are we really so vulnerable to stress? After all, humans evolved in stressful, often dangerous environments. Evolution *must* have selected for successful strategies for coping with stress, not crumbling in the face of it. And stress is a part of everyday life, often a good part—a challenge. We typically expect to rise to the challenge of a sporting event, a difficult class, even a crisis in our lives. Does it make sense that humans are fragile in the face of stress?

The answer is "No" according to proponents of *positive psychology*, an approach that highlights human psychological strengths (Linley & Joseph, 2005). Positive psychologists instead see pervasive human **resilience,** the ability to cope successfully with the challenges of life, including very stressful ones. Most peo-

ple overcome not only normal stress but traumatic stress too. For example, most people do *not* develop PTSD following trauma; most people who have lost a loved one are *not* overcome by depression in their bereavement (Bonanno, 2004).

Are resilient people completely invulnerable to stress?

To be sure, successful coping is not the same as the absence of inner distress (Litz, 2005). One study found, for example, that among resilient young people whose parents divorced—college students doing well in school and free from emotional problems—nearly half still reported they had a harder childhood than most other kids. Almost one-third agreed that they sometimes wondered if their father even loved them (Laumann-Billings & Emery, 2000). These young people bounced back from the stress of their

parents' divorce, but the bounce apparently still hurt.

Even successful coping can be painful, but pain is not the same as pathology. In fact, not only are most people resilient, but also some people grow—they get stronger—as a result of facing the challenge of stress (Linley & Joseph, 2005). For example, bicyclist Lance Armstrong's battle with cancer only spurred him on to win after win in the Tour de France.

Resilience lies partly within the individual—for example, positive affect (even after controlling for absence of negative affect) is related to many indices of health (Cohen & Pressman, 2006). Resilience also is partly attributable to social support and other aspects of environments (Roisman, 2005). Whatever resilience is, it is a quality that most people possess in most circumstance. Stress can make us weaker, or it can make us stronger. While chronic, uncontrollable stress can break us down, most people find the strength they need to cope when confronted by stress.

Religion Surprisingly, psychologists have only recently begun to study the health benefits of religious coping (Hill & Pargament, 2003). Emerging evidence demonstrates, for example, that mortality risk is lower among those who attend church services, probably as a result of improved health behavior (Powell, Shahabi, & Thoresen, 2003). As another example, forgiveness, a religious and philosophical virtue, apparently also offers earthly benefits. Forgiveness has beneficial health effects (Witvliet, Ludwig, & Vander Laan, 2001).

Forgiveness is important, but research is shattering some misconceptions about religious coping, which is mistakenly thought to promote only acceptance of one's lot in life. A study of 200 Latinos with arthritis found that religion encouraged *active*, not passive, coping—and less pain, less depression, and improved psychological well-being (Abraído-Lanza, Vásquez, & Echeverría, 2004). Their religious beliefs apparently helped these Latino arthritis suffers to gain control *with* God, not to accept control *by* God (Pargament & Park, 1995).

Health Behavior

We have focused on the direct effects of stress and coping on health, but stress also contributes to illness *indirectly* by disrupting health behavior (Cohen & Williamson, 1991). **Health behavior** is any action that promotes good health. It includes healthy habits like a balanced diet, regular sleep, and exercise, as well as avoiding unhealthy activities like cigarette smoking, excessive alcohol consumption, and drug use. Poor health habits, not stress per se, may be responsible for much of the relation between stress and illness (Bogg & Roberts, 2004). Consider this: Basic and public health behaviors—personal hygiene, sanitation, and an adequate diet—are more responsible for our vastly increased health and life expectancy than are scientific advances like the discovery of penicillin (Ray, 2004).

Following Medical Advice One very important health behavior is following medical advice, something that as many as 93 percent of all patients *fail* to do fully (Taylor, 1990). This is a particular problem for illnesses like hypertension (high blood pressure) that usually have no obvious symptoms. Patients may discontinue their medication, for example, because it offers no

▲ Students taking the SAT exam. Stress is a fact of life.

noticeable relief, even though it may be controlling a dangerous underlying condition. Stress also can interfere with treatments that *do* affect symptoms. For example, family conflict makes children with insulin-dependent diabetes less likely to adhere to medical advice about exercise, diet, and testing blood sugars (Miller-Johnson et al., 1994).

What are some positive coping techniques?

Illness Behavior *Illness behavior*—behaving as if you are sick—also is stress related. Increased stress is correlated with such illness behaviors as making more frequent office visits to physicians or allowing chronic pain to interfere with everyday activities (Taylor, 1990). Effective coping involves ignoring of some physical discomfort and living life as normally as possible, particularly when coping with chronic illness.

▼ Even welcome life events, like graduation or marriage, can be stressful.

▲ The real-life Patch Adams inspired the film in which Robin Williams played the title role. Adams was a rebellious medical student in the 1960s who wanted to provide holistic care and instill optimism in his patients.

Social Support You may know that *social support* can encourage positive health behavior, but you may be unaware of its direct, physical benefits. Even stressed monkeys exhibit less immunosuppression when they interact more with other monkeys (Cohen et al., 1992), and stressed rabbits develop clogged arteries more slowly if they affiliate with other rabbits (McCabe et al., 2002). Increased social support in humans predicts improved immune, cardiovascular, and endocrine functioning (Schneiderman, Ironson, & Siegel, 2004; Uchino, Cacioppo, & Kiecolt-Glaser, 1996).

People seek social support in different ways, however, and cultural differences can be important too. For example, Asians and Asian Americans benefit from *implicit* social support such as focusing on valued social groups during times of stress. *Explicit* social support such as seeking advice and emotional solace does not buffer stress for Asians, whereas it does for European Americans (Taylor et al., 2007). And it may be better to give than to receive. *Providing* social support promotes good health at least as much as receiving it does (Brown et al., 2003).

Of all potential sources of social support, a good marriage can be critical (Kiecolt-Glaser & Newton, 2001). One fascinating study admitted 90 newlyweds to a hospital research ward where the couples discussed marital problems for 30 minutes. Partners who were hostile or negative during the discussion had more immunosuppression over the next 24 hours, and their blood pressure remained elevated too (Kiecolt-Glaser et al., 1993). And a follow-up study found that epinephrine levels during newlywed conflicts were 34 percent higher for couples who got divorced in the next 10 years (Kiecolt-Glaser et al., 2003). A conflicted marriage is bad for your health, and too much stress is bad for your marriage!

Illness as a Cause of Stress

Stress can cause illness, but illness also causes stress. For example, consider the effects of the diagnosis of insulin-dependent diabetes on a 10-year-old boy and his family. In order to maintain a normal range of blood sugar, the child and his parents must frequently test his blood sugar, adjust to giving and receiving one, two, or three injections of insulin daily, and carefully monitor exercise and diet because of their profound effect on blood sugar. In addition, the child and his family must somehow cope with the stigma of being "different." Finally, they have to learn to cope with the possibility of his suffering profound, long-term side effects from hyperglycemia (high blood sugar), including kidney dysfunction or blindness. As this example suggests, helping children, adults, and families cope with the stress of chronic illness is an important part of behavioral medicine (Martire & Schulz, 2007). And more generally, we need to recognize that relationship between stress, personality, and health is a complicated one. Figure 8–2 portrays four alternative explanations of their association (Smith, 2006).

DIAGNOSIS OF STRESS AND PHYSICAL ILLNESS

The DSM-IV-TR does not distinguish psychosomatic disorders from other physical illnesses. Yet, it was not so long ago that experts made incredible and inaccurate assertions about the origins of psychosomatic disorders.

Brief Historical Perspective

Psychosomatic disorders included a few illnesses, like asthma, in which stress and anxiety appeared important. The mothers of asthmatic children *looked* neurotic. They were always worried about their children having an attack (probably realistically). The psychoanalytic psychiatrists who dominated the field of psychosomatic medicine claimed they could identify specific causes of specific psychosomatic diseases based on characteristic personality profiles. For example, Franz

Alexander (1950), one of the most influential of the theorists, wrote:

> The crucial finding in ulcer patients is the frustration (external or internal) of passive, dependent, and love-demanding desires that cannot be gratified in normal relationships. Onset of illness occurs when the intensity of the patient's unsatisfied dependent cravings increases either because of external deprivation or because the patient defends against his cravings by assuming increased responsibilities.
>
> (Alexander, French, & Pollock, 1968, p. 16)

We hope this assertion strikes you as outlandish. It is. No research links personality directly related to physical symptoms, and there is no short list of psychosomatic disorders in the DSM.

Contemporary Approaches

In DSM-IV-TR virtually any physical illness can be coded on Axis III, *general medical conditions.* When a physical illness is the focus of treatment, the diagnosis of *psychological factors affecting medical condition* is used on Axis I (see Table 8–4). The diagnosis may be used for various psychological factors, including not only mental disorders but also psychological symptoms, personality traits, maladaptive health behaviors, or stress-related physiological responses.

DSM-IV-TR also has a separate axis for coding stressors, Axis IV, psychosocial and environmental problems. Earlier versions of DSM asked clinicians to rate the amount of stress using an approach similar to the SRRS, but this proved to be unreliable (Skodol et al., 1990). Now DSM-IV-TR simply asks clinicians to rate the presence or absence of difficulties within various categories like social, educational, or economic problems.

THE ROLE OF PSYCHOLOGICAL FACTORS IN SOME FAMILIAR ILLNESSES

At the beginning of the twentieth century, infectious diseases, specifically influenza, pneumonia, and tuberculosis, were the most common causes of death in the United States (Taylor, 1995). Thanks to advances in medical science, and especially in public health, far fewer people die of infectious diseases at the beginning of the twenty-first century (see Figure 8–3). Today, most

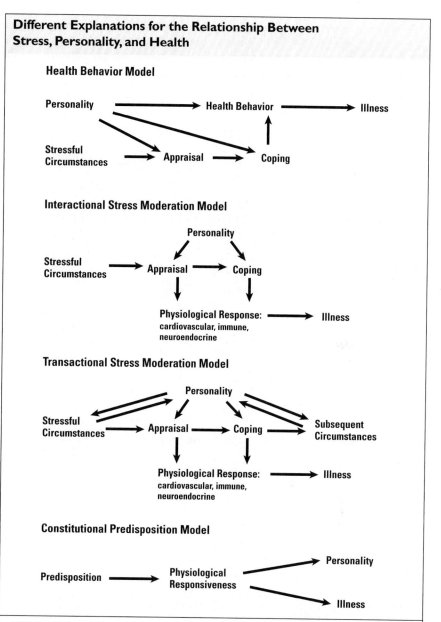

FIGURE 8–2 Models of mechanisms linking personality and health. In the *health behavior model*, personality traits influence health behavior (e.g., smoking, exercise, sleep) or changes in health behavior in response to stressful life circumstances, or events. In the *interactional stress moderation model*, personality factors influence appraisal and coping in response to stressful circumstances, which in turn influence physiological responses contributing to illness. The *transactional stress moderation model* extends the interactional model by including the bidirectional effect of personality on exposure to stressful life circumstances and the availability of stress-reducing resources. In the *constitutional predisposition model*, underlying genetic or other psychobiologic factors influence both personality characteristics and the development of illness.

Source: Figure 1, p. 229 from "Personality as Risk and Resilience in Physical Health" by T. W. Smith, *Current Directions in Psychological Science, 15* (2006). Copyright © 2007. Reprinted by permission of Blackwell Publishing Ltd.

of the leading causes of death are *lifestyle diseases* that are affected in many ways by stress and health behavior (Human Capital Initiative, 1996).

In the following sections we briefly review evidence on stress and lifestyle in the etiology, course, and treatment of cancer, HIV infection,

Table 8–4   DSM-IV-TR Diagnostic Criteria for Psychological Factors Affecting Medical Condition

A. A general medical condition (coded on Axis III) is present.

B. Psychological factors adversely affect the general medical condition in one of the following ways:

1. The factors have influenced the course of the general medical condition as shown by a close temporal association between the psychological factors and the development or exacerbation, or delayed recovery from, the general medical condition.
2. The factors interfere with the treatment of the general medical condition.
3. The factors constitute additional health risks for the individual.
4. Stress-related physiological responses precipitate or exacerbate symptoms of the general medical condition.

Source: Reprinted with permission from the *Diagnostic and Statistical Manual of Mental Disorders,* Fourth Edition, Text Revision. Copyright © 2000 by the American Psychiatric Association.

Can stress and health behavior contribute to cancer and AIDS?

chronic pain, and sleep disorders. After this, we consider in some detail the relation between stress and today's number-one killer, cardiovascular disease.

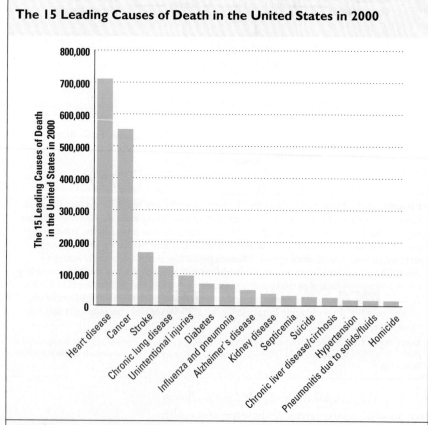

The 15 Leading Causes of Death in the United States in 2000

FIGURE 8–3 Stress and health behavior play a central role in most of the major causes of death in the United States today.

Source: A. M. Minino and B. L. Smith, 2001, "Deaths: Preliminary Data for 2000," *National Vital Statistic Report,* 49, no. 12, Hyattsville, MD: National Center for Health Studies.

Cancer

Cancer is the second leading cause of mortality in the United States today, accounting for 23 percent of all deaths. In contrast to the declining rate of death due to heart disease, moreover, cancer deaths increased until recent years (Jemal et al., 2006). At first glance, cancer seems to be a purely biological illness, but the importance of psychological factors quickly becomes apparent. For example, health behavior such as cigarette smoking contributes to exposure to various *carcinogens,* cancer-causing agents.

Psychological factors also are at least modestly associated with the course of cancer (McKenna et al., 1999). Not surprisingly, cancer patients often are anxious or depressed, and their negative emotions can lead to increases in negative health behavior such as alcohol consumption and decreases in positive health behavior such as exercise. PTSD among cancer patients also is quite common (Kangas, Henry, & Bryant, 2005). These outcomes are important, because cancer patients who are more emotionally expressive have fewer medical appointments, better quality of life, and better health status (Stanton et al., 2000). The absence of social support also can undermine compliance with unpleasant but vitally important medical treatments (Anderson, Kiecolt-Glaser, & Glaser, 1994). In facing the specter of cancer, the encouragement and physical assistance of family and friends can boost patients' resolve to bear side effects such as hair loss and intense nausea, and partners' specific reactions to breast cancer and its treatment predict relationship quality a year later (Wimberly et al., 2005). Of course, a diagnosis of cancer is a source of considerable emotional distress to loved ones, as well as to victims (Hagedoorn et al., 2008).

Stress also may directly affect the course of cancer. In animal analogue studies, rats exposed to inescapable shock are less able to reject implanted cancer tumors than rats exposed to escapable shock or no stress at all (Visintainer, Seligman, & Volpicelli, 1982). Immunity plays an important role in limiting the spread of cancerous tumors, and immunosuppression due to stress may disrupt this protective function (Anderson, Kiecolt-Glaser, & Glaser, 1994).

Can psychological treatment alter the course of cancer? One study found that 6 years after treatment, significantly fewer patients who participated in a support group died (9 percent) in comparison to patients who received no psychosocial treatment (29 percent) (Fawzy et al., 1993). Other researchers have failed to replicate these results, however. For example, a more recent investigation of 235 women with breast cancer found that support groups decreased reports of pain and psychological symptoms but did not affect survival rates (Goodwin et al., 2001). Still, the effects of support groups on quality of life, if not longevity, are important and pervasive and include reports of less social disruption, greater well-being, and more positive affect (Antoni et al., 2006).

Acquired Immune Deficiency Syndrome (AIDS)

Acquired immune deficiency syndrome (AIDS) is caused by the **human immunodeficiency virus (HIV),** which attacks the immune system and leaves the patient susceptible to infection, neurological complications, and cancers that rarely affect people with normal immune function. HIV positive patients vary widely in how rapidly they develop AIDS. Some develop AIDS within months; others remain symptom-free for 10 years or more.

HIV and AIDS have reached epidemic proportions throughout the world, with a notably high prevalence in Africa. In the United States, over 1 million cases of HIV/AIDS have been reported to the Centers for Disease Control and Prevention (CDC) (CDC, 2008). In 1981, AIDS was diagnosed for the first time; in 1996, it was the eighth leading cause of death in the United States (Peters, Kochanek, & Murphy, 1998). Fortunately, death due to AIDS has declined rapidly since the middle of the 1990s due to treatments that do not cure the illness but do promote a longer, healthier life. As a result, AIDS no longer is among the 15 leading causes of death in the United States (Minino & Smith, 2001).

Behavioral factors play a critical role in the transmission of HIV. Scientists have yet to determine precisely how HIV is transmitted, but researchers have isolated a number of high-risk behaviors. Contact with bodily fluids, particularly blood and semen, is very risky. The Center for Disease Control reports that the highest incidence of new cases of HIV are among men who have unprotected sex with men and individuals who participate in high-risk heterosexual sexual intercourse, such as unprotected anal and vaginal

intercourse (CDC, 2008). The use of condoms greatly reduces the risk of the sexual transmission of HIV. Other behaviors that increase the risk for HIV infection include behaviors associated with intravenous drug use. Additionally, a mother infected with HIV can transmit the infection to her unborn child (U.S. Department of Health and Human Services, 1993).

JULIA

"HIV was the absolute prism through which I began to see the world ..."

Watch the video "HIV: Julia" on MyPsychLab. As you watch the video, pay attention to the critical role health behavior plays in illness. Also, consider how HIV made Julia stronger, not weaker.

Scientists and policymakers have launched large-scale media campaigns to educate the public about HIV and AIDS and to change risky behavior. Are the media campaigns effective? Evidence indicates that prevention interventions do produce significant but small changes in behavior (for example, condom use). Knowledge and attitudes change more, and more rapidly, than behavior (Albarracín et al., 2006). The most effective programs focus on changing specific behaviors and attitudes; the least effective programs use fear tactics (Albarracín et al., 2005).

Stress is linked with a more rapid progression of HIV, while social support is associated with a more gradual onset of symptoms (Evans et al., 1997; Leserman et al., 1999). Support groups lower distress among treated patients, but no benefits for longevity have been found. Broader social support also is extremely important to the AIDS patient's social and psychological well-being. Unfortunately, misunderstanding and fear cause many people, including many health professionals, to distance themselves from AIDS rather than offering understanding, acceptance, and support.

◄ Basketball superstar Ervin (Magic) Johnson became a spokesman for increasing awareness of HIV and AIDS after he tested HIV positive.

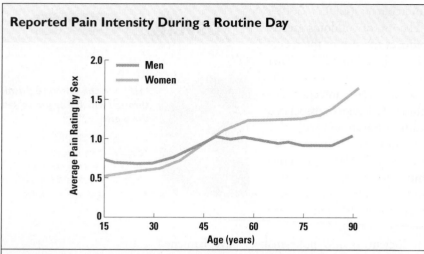

Reported Pain Intensity During a Routine Day

FIGURE 8–4 Reports of routine pain intensity increase with age but are not strongly associated with gender in this nationally representative U.S. sample. 0 = no pain.

Source: From "Assessment of Pain: A Community-Based Diary Survey in the USA" by A. B. Kreuger and A. A. Stone, *The Lancet, 371* (2008). Copyright © 2008 by The Lancet. Reprinted by permission of Elsevier.

Pain Management

Pain can be useful. Pain signals a problem and motivates people to seek treatment for acute injuries and illnesses. But pain is not always adaptive. In many cases, pain is *not* a sign of an underlying condition that can be treated. Examples of maladaptive pain include recurrent acute problems like headaches or chronic ones like lower back problems.

Pain can take a huge toll on the sufferer, family members, and financial resources. In a typical day, 28.8 percent of American men and 26.6 percent of women report feeling some pain (Krueger & Stone, 2008; see Figure 8–4). The past year prevalence of chronic neck or back pain is 19 percent of the U.S. population (Von Korff et al., 2005), while perhaps 50 million American experience some type of dysfunctional pain, costing society $70 billion in annual health care (Gatchel et al., 2007).

Pain is subjective. This makes pain difficult to evaluate, particularly when there is no identifiable injury or illness, as is common with headaches and lower back pain. Reports of greater pain are associated with depression and anxiety (Gatchel et al., 2007), and conversely, higher levels of positive affect predict lower levels of reported pain (Zautra, Johnson, & Davis, 2005). People who are anxious or depressed may be more sensitive to pain, less able to cope with it, and simply more willing to complain (Pincus & Morley, 2001).

Many experts view emotion or insight-focused psychotherapy as counterproductive and potentially damaging in treating pain (Keefe et al., 2001). More direct treatments include hypnosis, biofeedback, relaxation training, and cognitive therapy. Each approach has some research support, but pain reduction typically is modest (Patterson, 2004). Most current efforts therefore focus on the *pain management,* not pain reduction. The goal of pain management is to help people to cope with pain in a way that minimizes its impact on their lives, even if the pain cannot be eliminated or controlled entirely. Programs typically include education about pain and its consequences, pain control methods such as relaxation or exercise, attempts to change maladaptive expectations about pain, and interventions with families or support groups.

Pain management programs have been shown to help with a wide variety of problems, including headaches, lower back pain, and facial pain. Following treatment, patients report greater satisfaction with their life and relationships, improved employment status, and less reliance on medication. Once they are better able to function in their lives, patients also often say that their pain has lessened (Gatchel et al., 2007). Improved life functioning actually may reduce pain or perhaps only alter patients' awareness of discomfort. Either way, the benefits clearly justify making behavioral medicine a key part of the treatment of maladaptive pain.

Sleep Disorders

Historically, sleep disturbances were a focus of concern to mental health professionals only as a symptom of a mental disorder such as depression or anxiety. In 1994, however, DSM first included a diagnostic category for **primary sleep disorder,** a condition where the difficulty in sleeping is the principal complaint. Two types of primary sleep disorders are listed in DSM-IV-TR. *Dyssomnias* are difficulties in the amount, quality, or timing of sleep. *Parasomnias* are characterized by abnormal events that occur during sleep, for example, nightmares.

The dyssomnias include primary insomnia, primary hypersomnia, narcolepsy, breathing-related sleep disorder, and circadian rhythm sleep disorder. *Primary insomnia* involves difficulties initiating or maintaining sleep, or poor quality of sleeping (e.g., restless sleep). Primary insomnia is a common problem that is associated with lower ratings of subjective well-being even after controlling for social characteristics, mental, and physical health (Hamilton et al., 2007). Fortunately, effective treatments are available. Treatment includes stimulus control techniques (only staying in bed during sleep) and resetting circadian rhythms (going to bed and getting up at set times), as well as not napping, regardless of the length of sleep (Bastein et al., 2004; Bootzin, 2000). *Primary hypersomnia* is excessive sleepiness characterized by prolonged or daytime sleep, lasting at least a month and significantly interfering with life functioning. Primary hypersomnia is similar to *narcolepsy,* irresistible attacks of refreshing sleep that occur over the course of at least 3 months. However, narcolepsy also is characterized by the sudden loss of muscle tone for brief periods of time (usually following intense emotion) and/or intrusive periods of dreaming just before awakening. The "sleep-attacks" in narcolepsy are also less resistible than is the general desire to sleep in primary hypersomnia (APA, 2000).

Breathing-related sleep disorder involves the disruption in sleep due to breathing problems such as *sleep apnea,* the temporary obstruction of the respiratory airway. People with sleep apnea typically snore loudly due to an airway that is partially obstructed as a result of obesity or other conditions. Sleep apnea patients will stop breathing for 20 to 30 seconds when the obstruction becomes complete. This is followed by gasping, body movements, or even louder snoring. Not surprisingly, sleep apnea disrupts both the patient's sleep and the sleep of others in their vicinity. *Circadian rhythm sleep disorder* is a mismatch between the patients' 24-hour sleeping patterns and their 24-hour life demands that causes significant life distress. The disorder is found more commonly among adolescents and people who work night shifts (APA, 2000).

Parasomnias include nightmare disorder, sleep terror disorder, and sleepwalking disorder. People with *nightmare disorder* are frequently awakened by terrifying dreams. *Sleep terror disorder* also involves abrupt awakening from sleep, typically with a scream, but it differs from nightmare disorder in important respects. People with nightmare disorder recall their dreams and quickly orient to being awake; people with sleep terror disorder recall little of their dreams, show intense autonomic arousal, and are difficult to soothe. Moreover, a person with sleep terror typically returns to sleep fairly quickly and recalls little, if anything, about the episode the following morning.

▲ Nightmares and other sleep disorders are common problems, but scientists only recently have begun to study sleep disorders systematically.

Finally, *sleepwalking disorder* involves rising from the bed during sleep and walking about in a generally unresponsive state. In extreme cases, the person may use the bathroom, talk (with a minimum of meaningful dialogue), eat, or even run in a frantic attempt to escape some threat. Upon awakening, however, the person cannot remember the episode. Occasional episodes of sleepwalking are fairly common, especially among children. Like all sleep disorders, sleepwalking disorder tends to be diagnosed only if it causes significant distress or impairs the person's ability to function (APA, 2000).

CARDIOVASCULAR DISEASE

The number-one killer in the United States today is cardiovascular disease, and we focus on this disease as a more detailed example of stress research and treatment. **Cardiovascular disease (CVD)** is a group of disorders that affect the heart and circulatory system. The most important of these illnesses are **hypertension** (high blood pressure) and **coronary heart disease (CHD).** The most deadly and well-known form of coronary heart disease is **myocardial infarction (MI),** commonly called a heart attack. Hypertension increases the risk for CHD, as well as for other serious disorders, such as stroke.

Cardiovascular disorders are the leading cause of mortality not only in the United States, where they account for over one-third of all deaths (Minino & Smith, 2001), but also in most industrialized countries. About two-thirds of the deaths due to

▲ Over half of all victims of sudden death following myocardial infarction (heart attack) have no previous history of treatment for CHD.

The most notable symptom of CHD is chest pain. Typically, the pain is centralized in the middle of the chest, and it often extends through the left shoulder and down the left arm. In less severe forms of the disorder, the pain is mild, or it may be sharp but brief. The pain of myocardial infarction typically is so intense, however, that it is crippling. Two-thirds of all deaths from CHD occur within 24 hours of a coronary event (Kamarck & Jennings, 1991). In over half of these sudden deaths, the victim received no previous treatment for CHD, an indication that either there were no warning symptoms or the symptoms were mild enough to ignore. Research using portable electrocardiogram monitoring and diary recordings indicates that patients are unaware of many episodes of inadequate oxygen supply to the heart (Krantz et al., 1993; Schneiderman, Chesney, & Krantz, 1989).

cardiovascular disorders are caused by coronary heart disease. Mortality due to CHD is of particular concern because victims of the disease tend to be relatively young. About half of all Americans with CHD and about a quarter of all stroke victims are under the age of 65 (Jenkins, 1988).

An individual's risk for developing CVD, and particularly CHD, is associated with a number of health behaviors, including weight, diet, exercise, and cigarette smoking. In addition, personality styles, behavior patterns, and forms of emotional expression appear to contribute directly to the development of CVD (Rozanski, Blumenthal, & Kaplan, 1999).

Symptoms of Hypertension and CHD

Hypertension is often referred to as the "silent killer" because it produces no obvious symptoms. For this reason, high blood pressure often goes undetected, and routine blood pressure monitoring is extremely important. The measurement of blood pressure includes two readings. *Systolic* blood pressure is the highest pressure that the blood exerts against the arteries. This occurs when the heart is pumping blood. *Diastolic* blood pressure is the lowest amount of pressure that the blood creates against the arteries. This occurs between heartbeats. Generally, hypertension is defined by a systolic reading above 140 and/or a diastolic reading above 90 when measured while the patient is in a relaxed state.

Diagnosis of CVD

Myocardial infarction and angina pectoris are the two major forms of coronary heart disease. *Angina pectoris* involves intermittent chest pains that are usually brought on by some form of exertion. Attacks of angina do not damage the heart, but the chest pain can be a sign of underlying pathology that puts the patient at risk for a myocardial infarction. MI (heart attack) does involve damage to the heart, and as noted, it often causes *sudden cardiac death,* which is usually defined as death within 24 hours of a coronary episode.

Hypertension can be primary or secondary. *Secondary hypertension* results from a known problem such as a diagnosed kidney or endocrine disorder. It is called secondary hypertension because the high blood pressure is secondary to—that is, a consequence of—the principal physical disorder. Primary or **essential hypertension** is diagnosed when the high blood pressure is the principal or only disorder. There is no single, identifiable cause of essential hypertension, which accounts for approximately 85 percent of all cases of high blood pressure. Instead, multiple physical and behavioral risk factors contribute to the elevated blood pressure, which is why it is a concern in behavioral medicine and health psychology.

Frequency of CVD

Cardiovascular disease has been the leading killer in the United States since the 1920s, but the death rate due to CVD has declined by 25 percent or more in the United States, Japan, and many Western European countries. At the same time, mortality rates attributed to CVD have increased in many eastern European countries. Some but not all of these trends are attributable to changes in diet, cigarette smoking, and blood pressure (Jenkins, 1988). Another part of the explanation may be increased awareness of the negative effects of stress in the West—and the increased industrialization and increased stress in Eastern Europe.

Risk Factors for CHD Epidemiologists have identified several risk indicators for CHD. Men are twice as likely to suffer from CHD as are women, and sex differences are even greater with more severe forms of the disorder. Age is another major risk factor. For men, risk for CHD increases in a linear fashion with increasing age after 40. For women, risk for CHD accelerates more slowly until they reach menopause and increases sharply afterwards. Rates of CHD also are higher among low-income groups, a finding that likely accounts for the higher rates of CHD among black than among white Americans. Finally, a positive family history is also linked to an increased risk for CHD, due at least in part to genetic factors (Jenkins, 1988).

Behavior and CHD Several health behaviors also are linked to CHD, which is why it is called a "lifestyle disease." Hypertension increases the risk for CHD by a factor of 2 to 4. The risk for CHD also is two to three times greater among those who smoke a pack or more of cigarettes a day. Obesity, a fatty diet, elevated serum cholesterol levels, heavy alcohol consumption, and lack of exercise also increase the risk for CHD. Specific risk ratios are difficult to identify for each of these factors, however, because weight, diet, cholesterol, alcohol consumption, and exercise all are closely interrelated (Jenkins, 1988).

CHD also is associated with psychological characteristics, including depression (Frasure-Smith & Lespérance, 2005; Rozanski et al., 1999). However, researchers are still sorting out how much specific psychological factors increase risk. For example, in 1981, the National Heart, Lung, and Blood Institute officially concluded that the *Type A behavior pattern* (a competitive, driven personality) increased the risk for CHD. However, recent research has challenged this conclusion, as we discuss shortly.

Risk Factors for Hypertension About 30 percent of all U.S. adults suffer from hyperten-

◀ Heart disease is a lifestyle illness. Obesity, lack of exercise, and a fatty diet all are risk factors for CHD.

sion, and many of the same risk factors that predict CHD also predict high blood pressure, including genetic factors, a high-salt diet, health behavior, and lifestyle. Hypertension is more common in industrialized countries. In the United States, high blood pressure is more common among men, African Americans, low-income groups, and people exposed to high levels of chronic life stress. Although many of these risk factors are interrelated, they appear to have independent effects in increasing the prevalence of hypertension. For example, one study found that hypertension was twice as common among blacks as whites, but among black men who lived in high-stress neighborhoods, the risk was four times as great (Roberts & Rowland, 1981).

Causes of CVD

Biological Factors in CVD The immediate cause of CHD is the deprivation of oxygen to the heart muscle. No permanent damage is caused by the temporary oxygen deprivation (*myocardial ischemia*) that accompanies angina pectoris, but part of the heart muscle dies in cases of myocardial infarction. Oxygen deprivation can be caused by temporarily increased oxygen demands on the heart, for example, as a result of exercise. More problematic is when atherosclerosis causes the gradual deprivation of the flow of blood (and the oxygen it carries) to the heart. *Atherosclerosis* is the thickening of the coronary artery wall that occurs as a result of the accumulation of blood lipids (fats) with age, and which also may be caused by inflammation resulting from stress (Black & Garbutt, 2002). The most dangerous circumstance is when oxygen deprivation is sudden, as occurs in a *coronary occlusion*. Coronary occlusions result either from arteries that are completely blocked by fatty deposits or from blood clots that make their way to the heart muscle.

Why is coronary heart disease a "lifestyle disease"?

The immediate biological causes of hypertension are less well understood, as are the more distant biological causes of both hypertension and CHD. A positive family history is a risk factor for both hypertension and CHD, and most experts interpret this as a genetic contribution. However, research using animal models of CVD suggests a gene-environment interaction. For example, rats prone to develop hypertension do so only when exposed to salty diets or environmental stress (Schneiderman et al., 1989).

Psychological Factors in CVD The most important psychological contributions to CVD are health behaviors that (1) have a well-documented association with heart disease; (2) decrease the risk for CVD when they are modified; and (3) often are difficult to change. These health behaviors include avoiding or quitting smoking, maintaining a proper weight, following a low-cholesterol diet, exercising frequently, monitoring blood pressure regularly, and taking antihypertensive medication as prescribed.

Stress also contributes to CVD in at least two ways. First, stress immediately taxes the cardiovascular system, increasing the heart rate and blood pressure which can precipitate sudden symptoms or even MI. A dramatic example of the immediate effects of stress was observed during the Los Angeles earthquake of 1994. Cardiac deaths on the day of the earthquake rose to 24, from an average of 4.6 the preceding week (Leor, Poole, & Kloner, 1996). Second, over the long run, the heart may be damaged by constant stress. Below we consider four areas of research on long-term effects: cardiovascular reactivity, job strain, Type A behavior, and depression and anxiety (Krantz et al., 1988; Rozanski et al., 1999).

Cardiovascular Reactivity to Stress Increased blood pressure and heart rate are normal reactions to stress, but researchers have long observed that different people exhibit different *cardiovascular reactivity to stress,* greater or lesser increases in blood pressure and heart rate when exposed to stress in the laboratory. Are people who show greater cardiovascular reactivity to stress more likely to develop CVD?

Yes. In a study of patients with coronary artery disease, patients who reacted to mental stress in the laboratory with greater myocardial ischemia (oxygen deprivation to the heart) had a higher rate of fatal and nonfatal cardiac events over the next 5 years in comparison to their less reactive counterparts. In fact, mental stress was a better predictor of subsequent cardiac events than was physical stress (exercise testing) (Jiang et al., 1996).

Life Stressors and CVD: Job Strain A high-level of cardiovascular reactivity will have little effect if an individual experiences little stress. Exposure to real-life stress also must be part of the equation predicting CVD, and research shows that chronic stress does increase the risk (Krantz et al., 1988; Schneiderman et al., 2004). For example, increased rates of CHD are found among people with high-stress occupations. What appears to be most damaging is *job strain,* a situation that pairs high psychological demands with a low degree of decisional control (Karasek et al., 1982). A waitress has relatively high demands and low control, for instance, whereas a forest ranger has relatively few demands and a high degree of control. Figure 8–5

Occupational Control and Demand

FIGURE 8–5 Occupations classified according to the degree of demand and control that are associated with them. Jobs with low control and high demands cause more job strain and increased cardiovascular risk.

Source: From R. A. Karasek, 1988. Cited in D. S. Krantz, R. J. Contrada, D. R. Hill, and E. Friedler, "Environmental Stress and Biobehavioral Antecedents of Coronary Heart Disease," *Journal of Consulting and Clinical Psychology,* 56, p. 334.

portrays a number of occupations and how they vary in terms of psychological demands and decisional control.

Several studies have found a relationship between job strain and CHD (Krantz et al., 1988; Rozanski et al., 1999). For example, the risk for CHD was one and one-half times higher among women who had high job strain based on objective evaluations of their occupations in the Framingham Heart Study, a major *longitudinal study* of the development of coronary heart disease (see the Research Methods box). The risk was three times higher among women whose self-reports indicated high job strain (LaCroix & Haynes, 1987).

Work strain is not limited to employment but also includes work that is performed in other life roles. In an earlier analysis of the Framingham study, women who were employed for more than half of their adult lives were no more likely to develop CHD than were homemakers. However, employed women with children were more likely to suffer from heart disease. In fact, the risk increased with the number of children for employed women but not for homemakers (Haynes & Feinleib, 1980).

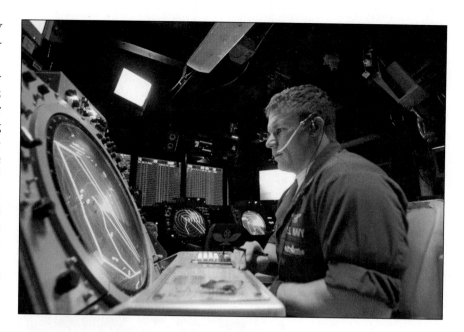

Women (and men) encounter strain not only in their occupations, but also in the competition between their various life roles.

▲ Air traffic controllers perform a job with high demands, limited control, and lives at stake, a recipe for stress.

Type A Behavior and Hostility Characteristic styles of responding to stress may also increase the risk for CVD, particularly the **Type A**

RESEARCH METHODS Longitudinal Studies: Lives Over Time

A **longitudinal study** involves studying people repeatedly over time. The approach contrasts with the **cross-sectional study** in which people are studied at only one time point. One goal of a longitudinal study can be to learn whether the effects of an experiment (such as a treatment outcome study) grow smaller, perhaps stronger, or stay the same over time. When a longitudinal study involves a correlational design, a common goal is to determine whether hypothesized causes come before their assumed effects. We know that causes must precede effects in time. The bat is swung before the ball flies over the fence. If we demonstrate that stress precedes heart disease in longitudinal research, this helps scientists rule out the alternative interpretation (reverse causality) that the illness caused the stress.

A major liability of a longitudinal study is higher cost. It is much less expensive to study stress and heart disease at one point in time than to assess stress now and CHD as it devel-

ops over the next 10 years. One way around the expense is to use a *retrospective study* (sometimes called a follow-back study). In this research design, scientists look backward in time either by asking people to recall past events or by examining records from the past. The retrospective method is less expensive, but it is of limited value because of distorted memories and limited records (see the Research Methods box in Chapter 7).

> **How can longitudinal studies distinguish causes from effects?**

The **prospective design** (sometimes called a follow-forward study) is a more effective but more expensive alternative. In prospective research, supposed causes are assessed in the present, and subjects are followed longitudinally to see if the hypothesized effects develop over time. Using the follow-up

method, scientists can assess a range of predictions more thoroughly and more objectively than in follow-back studies.

Researchers use both methods in studying health and illness (and abnormal psychology generally). When a finding is supported in prospective longitudinal research, you can have greater confidence in an investigator's causal hypothesis than in cross-sectional research. However, correlation does not mean causation, even in a longitudinal study. The supposed "cause" and the "effect" could both result from some third variable. For example, a researcher might find that Type A behavior measured at one point in time predicts CHD several years later. But chronic job stress may cause both Type A behavior and later heart disease. Scientists need many studies using many different research methods to establish causation. And you need to understand the strengths and weaknesses of research methods in order to be an informed consumer of scientific information.

▶ These stock traders illustrate the Type A behavior pattern. Type A is a personality style characterized by competitiveness, hostility, urgency, impatience, and achievement striving in response to challenge.

behavior pattern—a competitive, hostile, time urgent, impatient, and achievement-striving style of responding to challenge. As originally identified by cardiologists Meyer Friedman and Ray Rosenman (1959), the *Type A* individual is a "superachiever" who, like Bob Carter (see Case study on page 231), reminder of case study knows no obstacle to success and who may sacrifice everything for the sake of achievement (Jenkins, 1988). *Type B* individuals, in contrast, are more calm and content.

In 1981, the National Blood, Heart, and Lung Institute concluded that Type A was a risk factor for CHD, independent of other risks, for example, diet. This official sanction stimulated a great deal of additional research, but many studies conducted since 1980 have failed to support earlier findings (Rozanski et al., 1999). Why? Research methods may have contributed to the conflicting findings. Some researchers used self-report measures of Type A, but prediction is better when Type A is assessed in a structured interview (during which the interviewer provokes Type A behavior) (Miller et al., 1991). Also, *hostility* predicts future CHD better than other aspects of Type A behavior (Miller et al., 1996;

Smith & Ruiz, 2002). A Finnish investigation found that three items reliably predicted death among men who had a history of CHD or hypertension: ease with which anger was aroused, argumentativeness, and irritability (Koskenvuo et al., 1988). This aspect of Type A behavior may be more critical than the pattern as a whole.

Depression and Anxiety Depression is three times more common among patients with CHD than in the general population, and depression doubles the risk for future cardiac events (Frasure-Smith & Lespérance, 2005; Rozanski et al., 1999). Is depression a reaction to heart disease? Or does depression increase CHD, and if so, how? A study of over 2,400 depressed or isolated heart attack patients supports the first interpretation. A major randomized trial of cognitive behavior therapy, sometimes combined with antidepressant medication, alleviated depression somewhat, but the treatment group had no better coronary outcome than untreated controls (ENRICHD, 2003).

Anxiety seems to be associated with one crucial aspect of CHD: sudden cardiac death (Rozanski et al., 1999). *Heart-focused anxiety,* preoccupation with heart and chest sensations, is another important concern (Eifert, Zvolensky, & Lejuez, 2000).

Social Factors in CVD Social factors can influence the risk for CVD in many ways. Friends and family members can encourage a healthy—or an unhealthy—lifestyle (Pennix et al., 1997). Interpersonal conflict can create anger and hostility, which increase the risk for coronary heart disease. Economic resources, being married, and/or having a close confidant all are related to a more positive prognosis among patients with coronary artery disease (Williams et al., 1992). In fact, a *spouse's* confidence in coping with heart disease predicts *patients'* increased survival over 4 years (Rohrbaugh, Shoham, Coyne, et al., 2004). Finally, societal values (for example, about smoking) and cultural norms (for example, about job stress) also can affect the risk for CVD.

Recognizing the importance of interpersonal and societal influences, many efforts have been directed toward structuring the *social ecology*—the interrelations between the individual and the social world—to promote health (Stokols, 1992). As a child, you were exposed to many of these efforts, such as antismoking campaigns or the awards given in school for physical fitness. Good health is commonly promoted in the media, and more employers also are encouraging positive health behavior. Do these broad-scale efforts work? We address this question shortly.

Integration and Alternative Pathways CVD is an excellent example of the value of the systems approach. For the purpose of integration, we return to the analogy between the functioning of the cardiovascular system and an automobile. Some cars are built for high performance, some for economy. Some are defective when they leave the factory. Whatever its original condition, a car's state of repair is affected by how it is driven and how it is maintained. Similarly, CVD is caused by a combination of genetic makeup, an occasional structural defect, maintenance in the form of health behavior, and how hard the heart is driven by stress, depression, coping, and societal standards.

Much progress has been made in identifying biological, psychological, and social risk factors for CVD. An important goal for future research is to integrate knowledge across risk factors (Kop, 1999). Numerous questions need to be addressed. For example, how do we distinguish the effects of stress as an immediate, precipitating cause of CHD from its cumulative effects on health over long periods of time? To what extent are the risks associated with stress caused by poor health behavior and not by stress itself? What protects those individuals who do not become ill, even when they are exposed to multiple risk factors?

Prevention and Treatment of CVD

Several medications known as *antihypertensives* are effective treatments for reducing high blood pressure. Other drugs, called *beta blockers,* reduce the risk of myocardial infarction or sudden coronary death following a cardiac episode (Johnston, 1989). Still other biomedical interventions reduce the risk factors associated with CVD. For example, serum cholesterol can be lowered with medication. Because many of the risk factors for CVD are linked with health behavior, it also may be possible to prevent heart disease with psychological intervention.

Primary Prevention Numerous public service efforts attempt to prevent CVD by encouraging people to quit smoking, eat well, exercise, monitor

"Once upon a time, there was a frozen pizza, and inside the pizza some very bad monsters lived. Their names were refined white flour, reconstituted tomato, and processed cheese. But the worst monster of all was called pepperoni!"

their blood pressure, and otherwise improve their health behavior. Few of these familiar efforts have been evaluated systematically, although researchers have conducted a handful of careful studies. One of the most important took place in three small California communities near Stanford

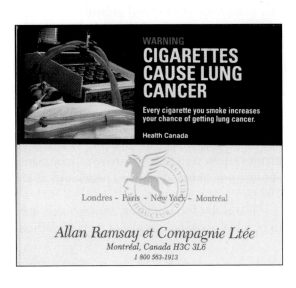

◄ A graphic health warning on a pack of cigarettes sold in Canada. In 2000, the Canadian government approved such warnings, the first country in the world to take such an aggressive anti-smoking stance.

Do public service efforts to promote good health lower the risk of CHD?

University (Farquhar et al., 1977). Media campaigns designed to improve knowledge and change behavior were offered in two towns that formed the experimental groups, whereas no intervention was given in one town that was used as a control group. The media campaigns were supplemented with face-to-face interviews in one of the two towns receiving the intervention.

Findings indicated that the media campaigns increased the public's knowledge about CHD, particularly in the community where face-to-face interviews took place. Did this increased knowledge lead to changes in behavior? The answer appears to be yes—up to a point. People in the experimental communities improved their diet and lowered their serum cholesterol, but they made only minor changes in smoking (Farquhar et al., 1977). The study could not determine whether the interventions helped reduce the incidence of heart disease. Recall, however, that the rates of CVD have declined in Western countries as health behavior has improved. Increasing public awareness can slowly improve health behavior and eventually may lower the risk of heart disease.

Secondary Prevention The treatment of essential hypertension is one of the most important attempts at the secondary prevention of CHD. Treatments of hypertension fall into two categories. One focuses on improving health behavior, and the other emphasizes **stress management,** attempts to teach more effective coping skills.

Improvements in health behavior—including weight reduction, decreased alcohol consumption, and reduced intake of dietary salt—can help lower blood pressure. For many patients these behavioral changes eliminate the need for taking antihypertensive medication (Johnston, 1989). But can experts help people make the necessary lifestyle changes? Many efforts are only minimally effective, in part because they are weak or poorly constructed. For example, a physician may simply encourage a patient to lose weight or give him educational pamphlets to read. More intensive treatments appear to be more effective (Dusseldorp et al., 1999).

The major form of stress management used to treat hypertension is behavior therapy, particularly relaxation training and biofeedback. **Biofeedback** uses laboratory equipment to monitor physiological processes that generally occur outside conscious awareness and to provide the patient with conscious feedback about these processes. Blood pressure may be displayed on a video screen, for example, so that increases or decreases are readily apparent to the patient. The patient can then experiment with various coping strategies, for example, imagining lying on a beach, to see whether the technique reduces their blood pressure.

Biofeedback produces reliable reductions in blood pressure, as does relaxation training. Unfortunately, the reductions are small, often temporary, and considerably less than those produced by antihypertensive medications (Andrews et al., 1984). Overall, stress management appears to improve quality of life but has little effect on disease (Claar & Blumenthal, 2003). Biofeedback is a particularly dubious treatment for hypertension, one that some well-respected investigators suggest should be abandoned (Johnston, 1989).

The Trials of Hypertension Prevention (TOHP) is an important study of whether stress management and health behavior interventions can lower high blood pressure (TOHP Collaborative Research Group, 1992). More than 2,000 women and men with hypertension were randomly assigned to one of seven different treatments, three lifestyle interventions—weight reduction, sodium (salt) reduction, and stress management—plus four nutritional supplement conditions. Group meetings were held over several weeks for the three lifestyle interventions. In the nutrition conditions, the patient's ordinary diet was supplemented with dietary agents hypothesized to lower blood pressure: calcium, magnesium, potassium, or fish oil. Results from Phase I of the study indicated that only the weight reduction and the salt reduction programs lowered blood pressure over a follow-up period of up to 11/2 years. Neither stress management nor any of the dietary supplements produced benefits. Findings from Phase II of the TOHP underscored the importance of weight loss. Even a modest reduction in weight produced clinically significant reductions in blood pressure (Stevens et al., 2001).

The Multiple Risk Factor Intervention Trial (MRFIT), another major investigation, included over 12,000 men at risk for CHD. Participants were assigned at random to intervention programs, including both education and social support. Treatment improved health behavior, specifically reduced smoking and lower serum cholesterol. However, the treatment groups did not have a lower incidence of heart disease than controls 7 years later (MRFIT, 1982). An encouraging interpretation of this discouraging outcome is that men in the control group also improved their health behavior. The control group had a lower disease rate than expected based on their risk indicators, and the study was conducted during a time when the public's concern with health increased dramatically.

Tertiary Prevention Tertiary prevention of CHD targets patients who have already had a cardiac event, typically a myocardial infarction. The hope is to reduce the incidence of recurrence of the illness. Exercise programs are probably the most common treatment recommended for cardiac patients, but evidence of their effectiveness is limited (Johnston, 1989). The most effective programs are both structured and individualized for each patient (Blanchard, 1992; Frasure-Smith & Prince, 1985). One patient may benefit from a smoking reduction program, a second by a stress reduction workshop, and a third by exercise classes. Handing out pamphlets or delivering stern lectures does little to alter health behavior.

Optimistic evidence on preventing the recurrence of CHD comes from efforts to alter the Type A behavior pattern (Friedman et al., 1986), a somewhat surprising circumstance given the controversies about Type A. Successful intervention is multifaceted. For example, it includes **role playing**—improvisational play acting—to teach patients how to respond to stressful interactions with reduced hostility. The cardiac patient might act out his usual response to a bothersome subordinate, for example. In subsequent role plays, the patient tries out a new, less hostile way of responding. Cognitive therapy designed to alter faulty thought patterns also is a part of these interventions (Thoresen & Powell, 1992). For example, Bob Carter believed that he must be the best at everything. Cognitive therapy helps patients like Bob to develop beliefs and goals that are more realistic—and healthy.

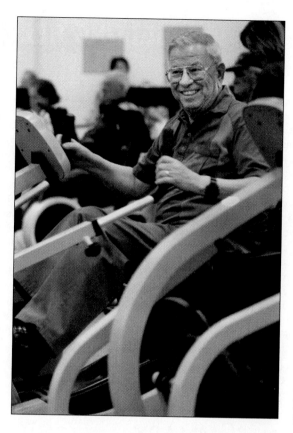

◄ Manuel Lujan, former U.S. Secretary of the Interior, works out as part of his heart rehabilitation program following his fourth heart attack.

Type A behavior can be modified, and this may reduce the subsequent risk for CHD (Nunes, Frank, & Kornfeld, 1987; Thoresen & Powell, 1992). One study of nearly 600 patients found that stress management training reduced the annual incidence of cardiac events by almost 50 percent in comparison to 300 patients who received standard medical care (Friedman et al., 1986). Importantly, subjects who showed the greatest reduction in Type A behavior were four times less likely to experience a myocardial infarction during the following 2 years.

Finally, we should note that some treatments focus on the effects of heart disease on life stress rather than the other way around. These treatments teach cardiac patients and their families to cope more effectively with the psychological consequences of having a heart attack, including depression, anxiety, and changes in sexuality, marriage, and family relationships (Johnston, 1985). Since depression is a risk factor for future cardiac illness (Carney et al., 1995), such interventions may, in turn, help improve the patient's physical health. The link between stress and physical health clearly is a reciprocal one.

GETTING HELP

Stressed out? We all are at times—when we face exams, have to deal with difficult relationships, or just have too much to do and not enough time to do it.

If there is too much stress in your life, a helpful first step is to analyze it. One great way to begin is to write about the situations that stress you out, your responses, and your attempts at coping. You could start a journal; you could write someone a letter (that you may or may not mail); or you could just jot down a few notes. Writing can help you get some things off your chest—and off your mind. Writing can also help you to sort things out. Writing takes thoughts and feelings from the inside and puts them out there, where you can look at them. Sometimes just putting your thoughts into words can help: "Whew! I don't

have to think about that anymore!" Another benefit is that you can go back and read what you wrote and correct and organize your thoughts and feelings. An engaging, research-based account of the benefits of writing is James Pennebaker's *Opening Up: The Healing Power of Expressing Emotions.*

Another way to analyze stress in your life is to complete some stress-rating forms. You can find one commonly used form in Table 8–1 (page 233), or you can complete a stress rating measure online. A quick Internet search will pull up several sites that allow you to complete stress rating measures. Some are designed specifically for college students.

What about coping with stress? If your usual strategies aren't working, a useful resource about relaxation is Herbert Benson's book *The*

Relaxation Response. Exercise is another healthy coping technique. If you have troubling physical symptoms linked with stress, you should consult your family physician. A mental health professional may be more appropriate to contact if your problems with stress are emotional.

Finally, if you are suffering from the stress of having a physical illness and want to know about the latest research, the place to start online is the homepage of the National Institutes of Health (NIH). If your illness is chronic, particularly difficult, or rare, you might find it helpful to communicate online with others who suffer from the same disease. Because there are so many resources on the Internet, most search engines contain a category specifically for "health." As you browse, remember to be skeptical and cautious in evaluating information.

■ SUMMARY

Scientists now view every physical illness as a product of the interaction between the psyche and soma, mind and body. This holistic view has influenced both psychology and medicine, as is evidenced by the rapid development of **behavioral medicine,** a multidisciplinary field that investigates psychological factors in physical illness.

Stress is a challenging event that requires physiological, cognitive, or behavioral adaptation. Stress activates the **fight or flight response,** a reaction to threat characterized by intense arousal of the sympathetic nervous system. In response, the *adrenal glands* release two key hormones, epinephrine (adrenaline), which leads to the familiar "rush of adrenaline," and **cortisol** (the "stress hormone") which helps the body make repairs similar to steroids (and which, like steroids, also can be harmful). Research on **psychoneuroimmunology (PNI)** shows that stress also impairs immune functioning.

Coping with stress may involve **problem-focused coping,** an attempt to change the stressor, or **emotion-focused coping,** an attempt to alter distress internally. Predictability and control can greatly facilitate coping, as can having outlets for frustration and **optimism.** Stress can interfere with **health behavior,** resulting in fewer positive

actions (e.g., exercise) or more negative ones (e.g., alcohol consumption). The link between stress and illness is well established, but psychologists surely have underestimated people's **resilience** in coping with stress.

Lifestyle is central to the top causes of death in the United States today. Behavior contributes to cancer through exposure to some carcinogens, health behavior, social support in coping with the illness, and perhaps through effects on immune functioning. **Acquired immune deficiency syndrome (AIDS)** is caused by the **human immunodeficiency virus (HIV),** which is transmitted through risky behaviors, such as unprotected sex and shared hypodermic needles. Psychologists also work to help people cope with chronic pain, most notably through pain management programs. More attention also is being paid to **primary sleep disorders.**

The number-one killer in the United States today is **cardiovascular disease (CVD)** disorders that affect the heart and circulatory system. Cardiovascular diseases include **essential hypertension** (high blood pressure) and **coronary heart disease (CHD),** particularly **myocardial infarction (MI),** or heart attack. Psychological factors contributing to CVD include health behavior;

cardiovascular reactivity, responses to stressors presented in a laboratory; chronic stressors in real life (e.g., job strain); the hostility that is part of the **Type A behavior pattern;** and depression and anxiety. The primary prevention of CHD includes efforts to improve health behavior. Treating hypertension by encouraging improved health behavior and **stress management** are efforts at the secondary prevention of CHD. Tertiary prevention of CHD targets patients who have already had a cardiac event, for example, attempting to modify their Type A behavior.

THE BIG PICTURE CRITICAL THINKING REVIEW

Are our evolved reactions to stress maladaptive in the face of modern stressors?

Physiologically, fight or flight heightens attention, provides energy for quick action, and prepares the body for injury. This was adaptive in the face of physical threats over the course of human evolution, but when your boss is yelling at you, the response leaves your body racing. (SEE PAGE 234)

Are resilient people completely invulnerable to stress?

Most people overcome stress, but successful coping is not the same as the absence of inner distress. One study found that among resilient young people whose parents divorced, nearly half still reported they had a harder childhood than most other kids. (SEE PAGE 238)

Can stress and health behavior contribute to cancer and AIDS?

At first glance, cancer seems to be a purely biological illness, but the importance of psychological factors quickly becomes apparent. For example, health behavior such as cigarette smoking contributes to exposure to various *carcinogens,* cancer-causing agents. (SEE PAGE 242)

Why is coronary heart disease a "lifestyle disease"?

Several health behaviors are linked to CHD, which is why it is called a "lifestyle disease." The risk for CHD is two to three times greater among smokers, and obesity, a fatty diet, elevated serum cholesterol levels, heavy alcohol consumption, and lack of exercise also increase the risk for CHD. (SEE PAGE 247)

How can longitudinal studies distinguish causes from effects?

A common goal is to determine whether hypothesized causes come before their assumed effects. Causes must precede effects in time. The bat is swung before the ball flies over the fence. (SEE PAGE 249)

■ KEY TERMS

acquired immune deficiency syndrome (AIDS) **243**
behavioral medicine **231**
biofeedback **252**
cardiovascular disease (CVD) **245**
coping **231**
coronary heart disease (CHD) **245**

cortisol **234**
cross-sectional study **249**
emotion-focused coping **237**
essential hypertension **246**
fight or flight response **234**
general adaptation syndrome (GAS) **237**

health behavior **239**
homeostasis **236**
human immunodeficiency virus (HIV) **243**
hypertension **245**
longitudinal study **249**
myocardial infarction (MI) **245**

optimism **238**
primary sleep disorder **244**
problem-focused coping **237**
prospective design **249**
psychoneuroimmunology (PNI) **236**
resilience **238**

role playing **253**
stress **230**
stress management **252**
tend and befriend **236**
Type A behavior pattern **249**

PERSONALITY DISORDERS

People are social organisms. Reproduction and survival depend on successful, cooperative interactions with other people. We form social alliances for many purposes, such as raising families, doing our jobs, and living in a community. We also compete with others, and in some cases we have to protect ourselves from others. These relationships are governed by a variety of psychological mechanisms that, taken together, constitute our personalities. **Personality** refers to enduring patterns of thinking and behavior that define the person and distinguish him or her from other people. Included in these patterns are ways of expressing emotion as well as patterns of thinking about ourselves and other people. For the most part, personality serves as the glue that anchors and facilitates interactions with other people. But it can also go awry. When enduring patterns of behavior and emotion bring the person into repeated conflict with others, and when they prevent the person from maintaining close relationships with others, an individual's personality may be considered disordered.

Of course, the dividing line between eccentricity and personality pathology is difficult to define. We all have our quirks and idiosyncrasies, and there are many different ways to manage relationships with other people. For example, it is often helpful to be skeptical of the things that other people do and say. When does a tendency to be suspicious of other people's motives cross the line into paranoia? Self-confidence is another admirable quality, but it can lead to problems if it escalates into full-blown grandiosity. In many ways, the distinctions among healthy traits, eccentricity, and personality pathology depend on the person's ability to adapt to the demands of different situations.

Variety and flexibility in interpersonal behavior are undoubtedly helpful. People with personality disorders can make their own social problems worse (often unwittingly) by persistently responding in ways that do not suit the social challenges that they face.

OVERVIEW

Personality disorders are considered separately from other forms of psychopathology in DSM-IV-TR. Most clinical disorders are listed on Axis I, whereas the personality disorders are listed on Axis II. All of the personality disorders are based on exaggerated personality traits that are frequently disturbing or annoying to other people. For example, in the first case study of this chapter, you will meet a young man whose consistently impulsive and deceitful behavior brought him into repeated conflicts with other people and with legal authorities.

In order to qualify for a personality disorder diagnosis in DSM-IV-TR, a person must fit the *general definition* of personality disorder (which applies to all 10 subtypes) and must also meet the *specific criteria* for a particular type of personality disorder. The specific criteria consist of a list of traits and behaviors that characterize the disorder. The general definition of **personality disorder** presented in DSM-IV-TR emphasizes the duration of the pattern and the social impairment associated with the traits in question. The problems must be part of "an enduring pattern of inner experience and behavior that deviates markedly from the expectations of the individual's culture" (APA, 2000). The pattern must be evident in two or more of the following domains: cognition (such as ways of thinking about the self and other people), emotional responses, interpersonal functioning, or impulse control. This pattern of maladaptive experience and behavior must also be

- Inflexible and pervasive across a broad range of personal and social situations
- The source of clinically significant distress or impairment in social, occupational, or other important areas of functioning
- Stable and of long duration, with an onset that can be traced back at least to adolescence or early adulthood

The concept of social dysfunction plays an important role in the definition of personality disorders. It provides a large part of the justification for defining these problems as mental disorders. If the personality characteristics identified in DSM-IV-TR criterion sets typically interfere with the person's ability to get along with other people and perform social roles, they become more than just a collection of eccentric traits or peculiar habits. They can then be viewed as a form of harmful dysfunction (Wakefield, 1999; see Chapter 1). In fact, most of the clusters of pathological personality traits that are described on Axis II do lead to impaired social functioning or occupational impairment (Oltmanns, Melley, & Turkheimer, 2002; Skodol et al., 2007).

What is the difference between being eccentric and having a personality disorder?

Personality disorders are among the most controversial categories in the diagnostic system for mental disorders (Kendell, 2002; Tyrer et al., 2007). They are difficult to identify reliably, their etiology is poorly understood, and there is relatively less evidence to indicate that they can be treated successfully (compared to mood and anxiety disorders, for example). For all of these reasons, you should think critically about the validity of these categories.

Although they are difficult to define and measure, personality disorders are also crucial concepts in the field of psychopathology. Several observations support this argument. First, personality disorders are associated with significant social and occupational impairment. They disrupt interpersonal relationships, including those involving friends and coworkers. Personality disorders also play an important role in many cases of marital discord and violence (Holtzworth-Munroe et al., 2000; Whisman et al., 2007). Second, the presence of pathological personality traits during adolescence is associated with an increased risk for the subsequent development of other mental disorders (Cohen et al., 2007; Krueger, 1999). Negative emotionality (high neuroticism) often predicts the later onset of major depression or an anxiety disorder. Impulsivity and antisocial personality increase the person's risk for alcoholism. Third, in some cases, personality disorders actually represent the beginning stages of the onset of a more serious form of psychopathology. Paranoid and schizoid personality disorders, for example, sometimes precede the onset of schizophrenic disorders. Finally, the presence of a comorbid personality disorder can interfere with the treatment of a disorder such as depression (Fournier et al., 2008).

The following cases illustrate several of the most important features of personality disorders. Our first case is an example of antisocial personality disorder, which is defined in terms of a pervasive and persistent disregard for, and frequent violation of, the rights of other people. This 21-year-old man was described by Hervey Cleckley (1976) in his classic treatise on this topic. The man had been referred to Cleckley by his parents and his lawyer after his most recent arrest for stealing. The parents hoped that their son might avoid a long prison sentence if Cleckley decided that he was suffering from a mental disorder.

CASE **STUDY**   A Car Thief's Antisocial Personality Disorder

Tom looks and is in robust physical health. His manner and appearance are pleasing. In his face a prospective employer would be likely to see strong indications of character as well as high incentive and ability. He is well informed, alert, and entirely at ease, exhibiting a confidence in himself that the observer is likely to consider amply justified. This does not look like the sort of man who will fail or flounder about in the tasks of life, but like someone incompatible with all such thoughts.

[In childhood, Tom] appeared to be a reliable and manly fellow but could never be counted upon to keep at any task or to give a straight account of any situation. He was frequently truant from school. No advice or persuasion [deterred] him [from] his acts, despite his excellent response in all discussions. Though he was generously provided for, he stole some of his father's chickens from time to time, selling them at stores downtown. Pieces of table silver would be missed. These were sometimes recovered from those to whom he had sold them for a pittance or swapped them for odds and ends which seemed to hold no particular interest or value for him. He resented and seemed eager to avoid punishment, but no modification in his behavior resulted from it. He did not seem wild or particularly impulsive, a victim of high temper or uncontrollable drives. There was nothing to indicate he was subject to unusually strong temptations, lured by definite plans for high adventure and exciting revolt.

He lied so plausibly and with such utter equanimity, devised such ingenious alibis, or simply denied all responsibility with such convincing appearances of candor that for many years his real career was poorly estimated.

Among typical exploits with which he is credited stand these: prankish defecation into the stringed intricacies of the school piano, the removal from his uncle's automobile of a carburetor for which he got 75 cents, and the selling of his father's overcoat to a passing buyer of scrap materials.

At 14 or 15 years of age, having learned to drive, Tom began to steal automobiles with some regularity. Often his intention seemed less that of theft than of heedless misappropriation. A neighbor or friend of the family, going to the garage or to where the car was parked outside an office building, would find it missing. Sometimes the patient would leave the stolen vehicle within a few blocks or miles of the owner, sometimes out on the road

He lied so plausibly and with such utter equanimity that for many years his real career was poorly estimated.

where the gasoline had given out. After he had tried to sell a stolen car, his father consulted advisors and, on the theory that he might have some specific craving for automobiles, bought one for him as a therapeutic measure. On one occasion while out driving, he deliberately parked his own car and, leaving it, stole an inferior model which he left slightly damaged on the outskirts of a village some miles away.

Private physicians, scoutmasters, and social workers were consulted. They talked and worked with him, but to no avail. Listing the deeds for which he became ever more notable does not give an adequate picture of the situation. He did not every day or every week bring attention to himself by major acts of mischief or destructiveness. He was usually polite, often considerate in small, appealing ways, and always seemed to have learned his lesson after detection and punishment. He was clever and learned easily. During intervals in which his attendance was regular, he impressed his teachers as outstanding in ability. Some charm and apparent modesty, as well as his very convincing way of seeming sincere and to have taken resolutions that would count, kept not only the parents but all who encountered him clinging to hope. Teachers, scoutmasters, the school principal, and others recognized that in some very important respects he differed from the ordinary bad or wayward youth. (They) made special efforts to help him and to give him new opportunities to reform or readjust.

When he drove a stolen automobile across a state line, he came in contact with federal authorities. In view of his youth and the wonderful impression he made, he was put on probation. Soon afterward he took another automobile and again left it in the adjoining state. It was a very obvious situation. The consequences could not have been entirely overlooked by a person of his excellent shrewdness. He admitted that the considerable risks of getting caught had occurred to him but felt he had a chance to avoid detection and would take it. No unusual and powerful motive or any special aim could be brought out as an explanation.

Tom was sent to a federal institution in a distant state where a well-organized program of rehabilitation and guidance was available. He soon impressed authorities at this place with his attitude and in the way he discussed his past mistakes and plans for a different future. He seemed to merit parole status precociously and this was awarded him. It was not long before he began stealing again and thereby lost his freedom. (Cleckley, 1976, pp. 64–67)

Notice that the fundamental features of Tom's problems were clearly evident by early adolescence, and they were exhibited consistently over an extended period of time. The stable, long-standing nature of personality disorders is one of their most characteristic features. In this way, they are distinguished from many other forms of abnormal behavior that are episodic in nature.

This case is an excellent example of the senseless nature of the illegal and immoral acts committed by people who meet the diagnostic criteria for antisocial personality disorder. Another puzzling feature of this disorder is the person's apparent lack of remorse and the inability to learn from experience that accompanies such a history of delinquent behavior. It is difficult to understand why someone would behave in this manner. Mental health professionals appeal to the notion of personality disorder to help them understand these irrational behaviors.

The case of Tom also illustrates some other important features of personality disorders. Most other forms of mental disorder, such as anxiety disorders and mood disorders, are ego-dystonic; that is, people with these disorders are distressed by their symptoms and uncomfortable with their situations. Personality disorders are usually *ego-syntonic*—the ideas or impulses with which they are associated are acceptable to the person. People with personality disorders frequently do not see themselves as being disturbed. We might also say that they do not have insight into the nature of their own problems. Tom did not believe that his repeated antisocial behavior represented a problem. The other people for whom he created problems were suffering, but he was not. Many forms of personality disorder are defined primarily in terms of the problems that these people create for others rather than in terms of their own subjective distress.

The ego-syntonic nature of many forms of personality disorder raises important questions about the limitations of self-report measures—interviews and questionnaires—for their assessment. Many people with personality disorders are unable to view themselves realistically and are unaware of the effect that their behavior has on others. Therefore, assessments based exclusively on self-report may have limited validity (Klein, 2003; Oltmanns & Turkheimer, 2006). They may underestimate the frequency and severity of certain aspects of personality pathology, particularly those problems associated with narcissism. The development of alternative assessment methods, such as collecting information from peers, family members, or mental health professionals, remains an important challenge for future research studies (Clark, 2007).

SYMPTOMS

The specific symptoms that are used to define personality disorders represent maladaptive variations in several of the building blocks of personality (see Chapter 2). These include motives, cognitive perspectives regarding the self and others, temperament, and personality traits. We have organized our description of typical symptoms around these issues, which run through the broad mixture of specific symptoms that define the 10 types of personality disorder included in DSM-IV-TR.

Social Motivation

The concept of a motive refers to a person's desires and goals (Emmons, 1997). Motives (either conscious or unconscious) describe the way that the person would like things to be, and they help to explain *why* people behave in a particular fashion. For example, a man might have neglected to return a telephone call because he wanted to be alone (rather than because he forgot that someone had called). Two of the most important motives in understanding human personality are *affiliation*—the desire for close relationships with other people—and *power*—the desire for impact, prestige, or dominance (Winter et al., 1998). Individual differences with regard to these motives have an important influence on a person's health and adjustment.

Many of the symptoms of personality disorders can be described in terms of maladaptive variations with regard to needs for affiliation and power. One particularly important issue is the absence of motivation for affiliation. While most people enjoy spending time with other people and want to develop intimate relationships with friends and family members, some people do not. They prefer isolation. Severely diminished or absent motivation for social relationships is one pervasive theme that serves to define certain kinds of personality disorder.

Exaggerated motivation for power (and achievement) also contributes to the picture that describes personality disorders. For example, some people are preoccupied with a need for admiration and the praise of others. They think of themselves as privileged people and insist on special treatment. In some cases, excessive devotion to work and professional accomplishment can lead a person to ignore friends and family members as well as the pursuit of leisure activities. This lack of balance can have a serious disruptive effect on the person's social adjustment.

Cognitive Perspectives Regarding Self and Others

Our social world also depends on mental processes that determine knowledge of ourselves and other people (Baumeister, 1997; Kihlstrom & Hastie, 1997). Distortions of these mechanisms are associated with personality disorders. For example, one central issue involves our image of ourselves. When you are able to maintain a realistic and stable image of yourself, you can plan, negotiate, and evaluate your relationships with other people. Knowing (and having confidence in) your own values and opinions is a necessary prerequisite for making independent decisions without the assistance or reassurance of others. Self-image is also intimately connected to mood states. If you vacillate back and forth between unrealistically positive and negative views of yourself, your mood will swing dramatically. You may also need constant reassurance from others and be too dependent on their opinions as a means of maintaining your own self-esteem. We have to be able to evaluate our own importance. Of course, it's useful to think of yourself in positive terms (and many maintain a positive "halo"), but extreme grandiosity can be disruptive. Perhaps even more damaging is a pattern in which people see themselves as socially inept or inferior to other people.

When we misperceive the intentions and motives and abilities of other people, our relationships can be severely disturbed. Paranoid beliefs are one example. Some people believe, without good reason, that other people are exploiting, deceiving, or otherwise trying to harm them. Unreasonable fears of being abandoned, criticized, or rejected are also examples of distorted perception of others' intentions. Working effectively in a group of people also requires

"You want only happiness, Douglas. I want wealth, power, fame, and happiness."

realistic appraisal of the talents and abilities of others. In order to cooperate with other people, we must be able to appreciate their competence. People with personality disorders run into problems because they misperceive other people in many different ways (as being either threatening, or uncaring, or incompetent).

Many elements of social interaction also depend on being able to evaluate the nature of our relationships with other people and then to make accurate judgments about appropriate and inappropriate behaviors. A successful relationship with a sexual partner involves knowing when intimacy is expected and when it should be avoided. Some people with personality disorders experience persistent problems in social distance (either becoming too intimate or maintaining too much distance from others). Finally, another important element of interpersonal perception is the ability to empathize with others—to anticipate and decipher their emotional reactions and use that knowledge to guide our own behavior. Deficits in the ability to understand the emotions of other people represent one of the core features of personality disorders.

Temperament and Personality Traits

If motivation helps to explain *why* people behave in certain ways, temperament and personality traits describe *how* they behave. *Temperament* refers to a person's most basic, characteristic styles of relating to the world, especially those styles that are evident during the first year of life (Caspi & Roberts, 1999; Mervielde et al., 2005). Definitions of temperament typically include dimensions such as activity level and emotional reactivity (see Chapter 2). These factors vary considerably in level or degree from one infant to the next and have important implications for later development, such as social and academic adjustment when the child eventually enters school. For example, children who demonstrate a "lack of control" when they are very young are much more likely than their peers to experience problems with hyperactivity, distractibility, and conduct disorder when they are adolescents (Caspi et al., 1995). Young children who are extremely shy are more likely to be anxious and socially inhibited in subsequent years (Eisenberg et al., 1998; see Chapter 16).

Experts disagree about the basic dimensions of temperament and personality. Some theories are relatively simple, using only three or four dimensions. Others are more complicated and consider as many as 30 or 40 traits. One point of view that has come to be widely accepted is known as the five-factor model of personality (Digman, 2002; Trull & McCrae, 2002). The basic traits (also known as domains) included in this model have already been summarized in Chapter 2. They are neuroticism, extraversion, openness to experience, agreeableness, and conscientiousness. Each of the five principal domains can be subdivided into six more specific elements or facets (see Table 9–1, on page 262). Taken as a whole, the five-factor model provides a relatively comprehensive description of any person's behavior.

Many personality disorders are defined in terms of maladaptive variations on the kinds of traits listed in Table 9–1 (Widiger & Simonsen, 2005). Problems may arise in association with extreme variations in either direction (high or low). Dramatically elevated levels of anger–hostility, impulsiveness, and excitement seeking are particularly important, as are extremely low levels of trust, compliance, and tendermindedness. Although some forms of personality disorder are associated with high levels of anxiousness and vulnerability, people with antisocial personality disorder frequently exhibit unusually low levels of anxiety and concern about danger. We return to these dimensions in the next section of this chapter.

Context and Personality

Two important qualifications must be made about the development and persistence of individual differences in temperament and personality. First, these differences may not be evident in all situations. Some important personality features may be expressed only under certain challenging circumstances that require or facilitate a particular response. For example, Tom did not always appear to be impulsive and irresponsible. He was usually polite when he was with adults, and he went through intervals in which he followed rules and attended school regularly.

The second qualification involves the consequences of exhibiting particular traits. Social circumstances frequently determine whether a specific

TABLE 9–1   Domains and Facets of the Five-Factor Model of Personality

	PEOPLE WITH HIGH SCORES ARE	PEOPLE WITH LOW SCORES ARE
NEUROTICISM		
Anxiousness	extremely nervous	lacking appropriate anxiety
Anger–Hostility	hypersensitive; easily angered	unable to express anger
Depressiveness	continually depressed	unable to appreciate losses
Self-Consciousness	very easily embarrassed	indifferent to opinions of others
Impulsiveness	extremely impulsive	restrained or restricted; dull
Vulnerability	easily overwhelmed by stress	oblivious to danger
EXTRAVERSION		
Warmth	inappropriately affectionate	unable to develop intimate relations
Gregariousness	unable to tolerate being alone	socially isolated
Assertiveness	domineering, pushy	resigned and ineffective
Activity	driven; frantic; distractible	sedentary and passive
Excitement-Seeking	reckless, careless	dull; monotonous
Positive Emotions	giddy; lose control of emotions	solemn; unable to enjoy things
OPENNESS TO EXPERIENCE		
Fantasy	preoccupied with daydreams	unimaginative
Aesthetics	obsessed with unusual interests	don't appreciate culture or art
Feelings	governed by strong emotionality	seldom have strong feelings
Actions	unpredictable	avoid change; stick to routine
Ideas	preoccupied with strange ideas	reject new ideas
Values	lack guiding belief systems	dogmatic and closed minded
AGREEABLENESS		
Trust	gullible	paranoid and suspicious
Straightforwardness	too self-disclosing	dishonest and manipulative
Altruism	often exploited or victimized	lacking regard for rights of others
Compliance	acquiescent; docile; submissive	argumentative; defiant
Modesty	meek and self-denigrating	conceited; arrogant; pompous
Tender-Mindedness	overwhelmed by others' pain	callous; coldhearted; ruthless
CONSCIENTIOUSNESS		
Competence	overly perfectionistic	lax; incapable of work
Order	preoccupied with rules, order	disorganized; sloppy
Dutifulness	places duty above morality	not dependable; unreliable
Achievement Striving	workaholic	aimless; no clear goals
Self-Discipline	single-minded pursuit of goals	hedonistic; self-indulgent
Deliberation	ruminate to excess	careless making decision

Source: Adapted from T. A. Widiger, P. T. Costa, Jr., and R. R. McCrae, 2002, "A Proposal for Axis II: Diagnosing Personality Disorders Using the Five-Factor Model," in P. T. Costa, Jr., and T. A. Widiger, Eds., *Personality Disorders and the Five-Factor Model of Personality,* 2nd ed, pp. 431–456. Washington, DC: American Psychological Association.

pattern of behavior will be assigned a positive or negative meaning by other people. Difficult temperament, for example, may serve an adaptive function when it is beneficial for an infant to be demanding and highly visible—for example, during a famine or while living in a large institution. On the other hand, in some circumstances, difficult temperament can be associated with an increased risk for certain psychiatric and learning disorders.

Consider the traits that Tom exhibited, especially impulsivity and lack of fear. These characteristics might be maladaptive under normal circumstances, but they could be useful—indeed, admirable—in certain extraordinary settings. War is one extreme example. People in combat situations have to act quickly and decisively, often at great risk to their own physical health. A disregard for personal safety might be adaptive under these circumstances. Tom's ability to lie in a calm and convincing fashion was another interesting trait. Again, this might have been a valuable adaptive skill if Tom had been an espionage agent. The meanings that are assigned to particular traits depend on the environment in which they are observed.

DIAGNOSIS

The authors of DSM-IV-TR have organized 10 specific forms of personality disorder into three clusters on the basis of broadly defined characteristics. The specific disorders in each cluster are listed in Table 9–2. In the following pages we give brief descriptions of these personality disorder subtypes. These descriptions provide an overview that will be useful when we review the epidemiology of personality disorders. Later in the chapter we describe in considerably more detail four disorders that are relatively frequent and have been studied extensively: schizotypal, borderline, antisocial, and dependent personality disorders.

Cluster A: Paranoid, Schizoid, and Schizotypal Personality Disorders

Cluster A includes three disorders: paranoid, schizoid, and schizotypal forms of personality disorder. The behavior of people who fit the subtypes in this cluster is typically odd, eccentric, or asocial. All three types share similarity with the symptoms of schizophrenia (see Chapter 13). One implicit assumption in the DSM-IV-TR system is that these types of personality disorder may represent behavioral traits or interpersonal styles that precede the onset of full-blown psychosis. Because of their close association with schizophrenia, they are sometimes called *schizophrenia spectrum disorders.*

Paranoid personality disorder is characterized by the pervasive tendency to be inappropriately suspicious of other people's motives and behaviors. People who fit the description for this disorder are constantly on guard. They expect that other people are trying to harm them, and they take extraordinary precautions to avoid being exploited or injured. Although we can all benefit from being cautious and skeptical, paranoid thinking is much more than that. The pattern is so stable and wide-ranging that it interferes with the person's social and occupational adjustment. People who are paranoid are completely inflexible in the way that they view the motives of other people, and they are unable to choose situations in which they can trust other people (see Critical Thinking Matters).

TABLE 9–2 Personality Disorders Listed in DSM-IV-TR

CLUSTER A INCLUDES PEOPLE WHO OFTEN APPEAR ODD OR ECCENTRIC

Paranoid	Distrust and suspiciousness of others.
Schizoid	Detachment from social relationships and restricted range of expression of emotions.
Schizotypal	Discomfort with close relationships; cognitive and perceptual distortions; eccentricities of behavior.

CLUSTER B INCLUDES PEOPLE WHO OFTEN APPEAR DRAMATIC, EMOTIONAL, OR ERRATIC

Antisocial	Disregard for and frequent violation of the rights of others.
Borderline	Instability of interpersonal relationships, self-image, emotions, and control over impulses.
Histrionic	Excessive emotionality and attention seeking.
Narcissistic	Grandiosity, need for admiration, and lack of empathy.

CLUSTER C INCLUDES PEOPLE WHO OFTEN APPEAR ANXIOUS OR FEARFUL

Avoidant	Social inhibition, feelings of inadequacy, and hypersensitivity to negative evaluation.
Dependent	Excessive need to be taken care of, leading to submissive and clinging behavior.
Obsessive–Compulsive	Preoccupation with orderliness and perfectionism at the expense of flexibility.

CRITICAL THINKING MATTERS

Can Personality Disorders Be Adaptive?

Andrew Grove, former chairman of the board of Intel Corporation, has written a popular book about business management entitled *Only the Paranoid Survive*. He argues that successful corporate leaders must be vigilant; they have to anticipate negative events in the business world as well as future problems with their competitors. Grove's title raises an interesting point about the nature of personality disorders. Their definition does reflect a tension between adaptive personality traits and more extreme, maladaptive ways of thinking about oneself and other people. It can be useful to be suspicious, vigilant, skeptical, or even jealous (in some circumstances), but we should not confuse these traits with paranoid thought. By promoting an informal and misleading use of the word "paranoia," Grove's title does the field of psychopathology a disservice. In order to make progress toward understanding the nature of mental disorders, we have to be precise in our use of terms.

How can we distinguish between a cautious approach to the motives of other people and pathological paranoia? The difference depends, in part, on emotional reactions—such as irritability and hostility—that are associated with chronic suspicion and vigilance (Frances, et al., 1995). Because they believe that others are causing problems for them, paranoid people are angry (Clifton, Turkheimer, & Oltmanns, 2004). Paranoid people can also become anxious and withdrawn. Their fear is based on the conviction that others intend to cause them harm, and they try to protect themselves by avoiding other people. The exaggerated negative emotions that accompany paranoid thinking are not likely to foster survival in the business world or in other social circumstances.

What is the difference between skepticism and paranoia?

Another way to distinguish between normal suspicions and paranoia involves the amount of time that the person spends thinking about threats posed by other people. While most people become suspicious from time to time, paranoid people are *preoccupied* with the notion that others are out to get them. They are unable to think otherwise (Shapiro, 1965). Paranoid people are also impaired in their ability to consider information from another person's point of view. Most of us are able to seek and consider another person's perception or interpretation of uncertain events; paranoid people cannot. For all of these reasons, paranoia will promote failure rather than survival in the business world.

One of the most important elements of critical thinking involves the careful definition of terms. Sloppy talk leads to sloppy thinking. People who suggest that "a little paranoia can be useful" or "only the paranoid survive" are engaging in a misleading use of terms. It is clearly useful to be skeptical and cautious when considering the motives of other people. But the rigid and maladaptive patterns of thought that are characteristic of paranoid personality disorder are clearly pathological. The failure to appreciate the complexity and extent of these phenomena represents a distraction from, rather than a contribution to, serious scholarship

Because paranoid people do not trust anyone, they have trouble maintaining relationships with friends and family members. They frequently overreact in response to minor or ambiguous events to which they attribute hidden meaning. When they overreact, people with paranoid personality disorder often behave aggressively or antagonistically. These actions can easily create a self-fulfilling prophesy. In other words, thinking (incorrectly) that he or she is being attacked by others, the paranoid person strikes. The other person is, naturally, surprised, annoyed, and perhaps frightened by this behavior and begins to treat the paranoid person with concern and caution. This response serves to confirm the original suspicions of the paranoid individual, who does not comprehend how his or her own behavior affects others.

Paranoid personality disorder must be distinguished from psychotic disorders, such as schizophrenia and delusional disorder. The pervasive suspicions of people with paranoid personality disorder do not reach delusional proportions. In other words, they are not sufficiently severe to be considered obviously false and clearly preposterous. In actual practice, this distinction is sometimes quite subtle and difficult to make.

Schizoid personality disorder is defined in terms of a pervasive pattern of indifference to other people, coupled with a diminished range of emotional experience and expression. These people are loners; they prefer social isolation to interactions with friends or family. Other people see them as being cold and aloof. By their own report, they do not experience strong subjective emotions, such as sadness, anger, or happiness.

Schizotypal personality disorder centers around peculiar patterns of behavior rather than on the emotional restriction and social withdrawal that are associated with schizoid personality disorder. Many of these peculiar behaviors take the form of perceptual and cognitive disturbance. People with this disorder may report bizarre fantasies and unusual perceptual experiences. Their speech may be slightly difficult to follow because they use words in an odd way or because they express themselves in a vague or disjointed manner. Their affective expressions may be constricted in range, as in schizoid personality disorder, or they may be silly and inappropriate.

In spite of their odd or unusual behaviors, people with schizotypal personality disorder are not psychotic or out of touch with reality. Their bizarre fantasies are not delusional, and their unusual perceptual experiences are not sufficiently real or compelling to be considered hallucinations.

Cluster B: Antisocial, Borderline, Histrionic, and Narcissistic Personality Disorders

Cluster B includes antisocial, borderline, histrionic, and narcissistic personality disorders. According to DSM-IV-TR, these disorders are characterized by dramatic, emotional, or erratic behavior, and all are associated with marked difficulty in sustaining interpersonal relationships. The rationale for grouping these disorders together is less compelling than that for Cluster A. In particular, antisocial personality disorder clearly involves something more than just a dramatic style or erratic behavior.

Antisocial personality disorder is defined in terms of a persistent pattern of irresponsible and antisocial behavior that begins during childhood or adolescence and continues into the adult years. The case study of Tom, with which we opened this chapter, illustrates this pattern of behavior. The DSM-IV-TR definition is based on features that, beginning in childhood, indicate a pervasive pattern of disregard for, and violation of, the rights of others. Once the person has become an adult, these difficulties include persistent failure to perform responsibilities that are associated with occupational and family roles. Conflict with others, including physical fights, is also common. These people are irritable and aggressive with their spouses and children as well as with people outside the home. They are impulsive, reckless, and irresponsible.

We have all read newspaper accounts of famous examples of antisocial personality disorder. These often include people who have committed horrendous acts of violence against other people,

◀ Ted Bundy was executed in 1989 for killing at least 22 women. He was charming, intelligent, and self-assured.

including genocidal war crimes and serial murders. You should not be misled, however, into thinking that only serious criminals meet the criteria for this disorder. Many other forms of persistently callous and exploitative behavior could lead to this diagnosis.

Borderline personality disorder is a diffuse category whose essential feature is a pervasive pattern of instability in mood and interpersonal relationships. People with this disorder find it very difficult to be alone. They form intense, unstable relationships with other people and are often seen by others as being manipulative. Their mood may shift rapidly and inexplicably from depression to anger to anxiety over a pattern of several hours. Intense anger is common and may be accompanied by temper tantrums, physical assault, or suicidal threats and gestures.

Many clinicians consider identity disturbance to be the diagnostic hallmark of borderline personality disorder. People with this disturbance presumably have great difficulty maintaining an integrated image of themselves that simultaneously incorporates their positive and negative features. Therefore, they alternate between thinking of themselves in unrealistically positive terms and then unrealistically negative terms at different moments in time. When they are focused on their own negative features, they have a deflated view of themselves and may become seriously depressed. They frequently express uncertainty about such issues as personal values, sexual preferences, and career alternatives. Chronic feelings of emptiness and boredom may also be present.

In what ways are borderline and narcissistic personality disorders similar?

BRIEF CASE **STUDY**
Borderline Personality Disorder

A single woman of 35 had worked with four (therapists) over a period of 11 years, before the last of these referred her to me. Since Beatrice had graduated from college at age 22, she had seemed to circulate in a holding pattern. She saw herself as an executive-to-be in the corporate world but in actuality had held just a few entry-level jobs, and those only briefly. Once or twice she quit in a huff because the job was "not interesting enough" or because "they weren't promoting me fast enough." She had no distinct career goals, nor had she taken any special courses to prepare herself for some particular path. The work problem did not pose a threat to her well-being, since she lived off a large trust fund that her family had set up for her.

On the relational side her situation was not much better. Beatrice had never been "serious" with anyone and had little interest in men apart from their ability to pay compliments on her appearance. Her self-image was contradictory: She alternated between seeing herself as "model pretty" or else ugly. While buying an ice cream, she would feel devastated if the counterman did not make eyes at her; if he did, she would feel "insulted."

She had no hobbies or sustaining interests and found evenings with nothing to do intolerable. On such evenings she would usually engage her mother in long phone conversations (her parents lived in a different city), demanding that her mother come and visit. If this were not possible, she would slam the phone down, only to then call her mother back half an hour later to apologize.

During the time I worked with Beatrice, her most noticeable personality traits were those of anger, argumentativeness, scornfulness, irritability, and vanity. Her intensity and demandingness made her troublesome in her family; her parents and siblings were mostly good-natured and got on well when she was not in their midst (Stone, 1993, pp. 250–251).

▶ Since 1981, this successful artist has painted more than 1,500 self-portraits. He says he will never paint anything other than his own image because it is the only subject that holds his interest. Self-absorption is one central feature of narcissistic personality disorder.

Histrionic personality disorder is characterized by a pervasive pattern of excessive emotionality and attention seeking behavior. People with this disorder thrive on being the center of attention. They want the spotlight on them at all times. They are self-centered, vain, and demanding, and they constantly seek approval from others. When interacting with other people, their behavior is often inappropriately sexually seductive or provocative. Their emotions tend to be shallow and may vacillate erratically. They frequently react to situations with inappropriate exaggeration.

The concept of histrionic personality disorder overlaps extensively with other types of personality disorder, especially borderline personality disorder. People with both disorders are intensely emotional and manipulative. Unlike people with borderline personality disorder, however, people with histrionic personality disorder have an essentially intact sense of their own identity and a better capacity for stable relationships with other people.

There may also be an etiological link between histrionic and antisocial personality disorders. Both may reflect a common, underlying tendency toward lack of inhibition. People with both types of disorder form shallow, intense relationships with others, and they can be extremely manipulative. Family history studies indicate that this predisposition to disinhibition may be expressed as histrionic personality disorder in women and as antisocial personality disorder in men (Cale & Lilienfeld, 2002; Pfohl, 1995).

The essential feature of **narcissistic personality disorder** is a pervasive pattern of grandiosity, need for admiration, and inability to empathize with other people. Narcissistic people have a greatly exaggerated sense of their own importance. They are preoccupied with their own achievements and abilities. Because they consider themselves to be very special, they cannot empathize with the feelings of other people and are often seen as being arrogant or haughty.

There is a considerable amount of overlap between narcissistic personality disorder and borderline personality disorder. Both types of people feel that other people should recognize their needs and do special favors for them. They may also react with anger if they are criticized. The distinction between these disorders hinges on the inflated sense of self-importance that is found in narcissistic personality disorder and the deflated or devalued sense of self found in borderline personality disorder (Ronningstam & Gunderson, 1991).

Cluster C: Avoidant, Dependent, and Obsessive–Compulsive Personality Disorders

Cluster C includes avoidant, dependent, and obsessive–compulsive personality disorders. The common element in all three disorders is presumably anxiety or fearfulness. This description fits most easily with the avoidant and dependent types. In contrast, obsessive–compulsive personality disorder is more accurately described in terms of preoccupation with rules and with lack of emotional warmth than in terms of anxiety.

Avoidant personality disorder is characterized by a pervasive pattern of social discomfort, fear of negative evaluation, and timidity. People with this disorder tend to be socially isolated when outside their own family circle because they are afraid of criticism. Unlike people with schizoid personality disorder, they want to be liked by others, but they are extremely shy—easily hurt by even minimal signs of disapproval from other people. Thus they avoid social and occupational activities that require significant contact with other people.

Avoidant personality disorder is often indistinguishable from generalized social phobia (see Chapter 6). In fact, some experts have argued that they are probably two different ways of defining the same condition (Frances, First, & Pincus, 1995). Others have argued that people with avoidant personality disorder have more trouble than people with social phobia in relating to other people (Millon & Martinez, 1995). People with avoidant personality disorder are presumably more socially withdrawn and have very few close relationships because they are so shy. People with social phobia may have a lot of friends, but they are afraid of performing in front of them. This distinction is relatively clear when social phobia is defined narrowly in terms of a particular kind of situation, such as public speaking. It is much more difficult to make if the social phobia becomes more generalized.

The essential feature of **dependent personality disorder** is a pervasive pattern of submissive and clinging behavior. People with this disorder are afraid of separating from other people on whom they are dependent for advice and reassurance. Often unable to make everyday decisions on their own, they feel anxious and helpless when they are alone. Like people with avoidant personality disorder, they are easily hurt by criticism, extremely sensitive to disapproval, and lacking in self-confidence. One difference between avoidant and dependent personality disorders involves the point in a relationship at which they experience the most difficulty. People who are avoidant have trouble initiating a relationship (because they are fearful). People who are dependent have trouble being alone or separating from other people with whom they already have a close relationship. For example, a person with dependent personality disorder might be extremely reluctant to leave home in order to attend college.

Obsessive–compulsive personality disorder (OCPD) is defined by a pervasive pattern of orderliness, perfectionism, and mental and interpersonal control, at the expense of flexibility, openness, and efficiency. People with this disorder set ambitious standards for their own performance that frequently are so high as to be unattainable. Many would be described as "workaholics." In other words, they are so devoted to work that they ignore friends, family members, and leisure activities. They are so preoccupied with details and rules that they lose sight of the main point of an activity or project. Intellectual endeavors are favored over feelings and emotional experience. These people

"Oh, get over yourself. We were all in the movie."

© The New Yorker Collection 2006 Donald Reilly from cartoonbank.com. All Rights Reserved.

are excessively conscientious, moralistic, and judgmental, and they tend to be intolerant of emotional behavior in other people.

The central features of this disorder may involve a marked need for control and lack of tolerance for uncertainty (Gibbs, South, & Oltmanns, 2003). At modest levels, these traits can represent an adaptive coping style, particularly in the face of the demands of our complex, technological society. Very high levels of these characteristics begin to interfere with a person's social and occupational adjustment. For example, people with OCPD find it difficult to delegate responsibilities to others, and their perfectionism makes it extremely difficult for them to finish projects within established deadlines.

Obsessive–compulsive personality disorder should not be confused with obsessive–compulsive disorder (OCD), a type of anxiety disorder (see Chapter 6). A pattern of intrusive, unwanted thoughts accompanied by ritualistic behaviors is used to define OCD. The definition of obsessive–compulsive personality disorder, in contrast, is concerned with personality traits, such as excessively high levels of conscientiousness. Traditional psychodynamic theory has maintained that obsessive–compulsive personality disorder often precedes the onset of OCD, in much the same way that schizotypal personality disorder is presumably an early manifestation of the predisposition to schizophrenia. Research evidence is ambiguous on the issue (Nestadt et al., 1991). In fact, people who meet the criteria for obsessive–compulsive personality disorder seem to be at risk for various kinds of anxiety disorders, including generalized anxiety disorder and panic disorder as well as OCD.

A Dimensional Perspective on Personality Disorders

DSM-IV-TR treats personality disorders as discrete categories, and it assumes that there are sharp boundaries between normal and abnormal personalities. In fact, there are a lot of people with serious personality problems who do not fit the official DSM-IV-TR subtypes. The categorical approach to diagnosis forces clinicians to employ an arbitrary threshold that has been set to distinguish between normal and abnormal personality types.

Another frequent complaint about the description of personality disorders is the considerable overlap among categories. Many patients meet the criteria for more than one type (Grant et al., 2005). It is cumbersome to list multiple diagnoses, especially when the clinician is already asked to list problems on both Axis I and Axis II. In fact, many clinicians are reluctant to make more than one diagnosis on Axis II; consequently, much information is frequently left out.

For these reasons, many experts favor the development of an alternative classification system for PDs, one that would be based on a dimensional view of personality pathology that is grounded in extensive research on the basic elements of personality. A dimensional system might provide a more complete description of each person, and it would be more useful with patients who fall on the boundaries between different types of personality disorder. It might also be easier to use than the DSM-IV-TR approach. One proposal is to use the five-factor model as the basic structure for a comprehensive description of personality problems (Widiger & Trull, 2007). This approach would require the clinician to consider information regarding the 30 personality facets listed in Table 9–1. This system would be economical compared to making a judgment regarding the presence of nearly 80 PD features in DSM-IV-TR (approximately 8 features for each of the 10 PD categories). An example of a description based on the five-factor dimensional approach to PDs is provided in the following brief case study.

BRIEF CASE **STUDY**
Narcissism from the Perspective of the Five-Factor Model

Patricia was a 41-year-old married woman who presented at an outpatient mental health clinic complaining of interpersonal difficulties at work and recurring bouts of depression. [She] reported a long history of banking jobs in which she had experienced interpersonal discord. Shortly before her entrance into treatment, Patricia was demoted from a supervisory capacity at her current job because of her inability to interact effectively with those she was supposed to supervise. She described herself as always feeling out of place with her coworkers and indicated that most of them failed to adequately appreciate her skill or the amount of time she put in at work. She reported that she was beginning to think that perhaps she had something to do with their apparent dislike of her. However, even during the initial treatment sessions, her descriptions of her past and current job situations quickly and inevitably reverted to defensive statements concerning others' mistreatment and lack of appreciation of her. Despite her stated goal of changing her own behavior to be better liked, it quickly became clear that her actual wish was to cause her coworkers and supervisors to realize her superiority and to treat her accordingly.

Patricia often made condescending remarks about coworkers working under her, indicating that they were inferior to her in intelligence and abilities and thus had little or nothing to offer her. Patricia pretended to have a back injury as an excuse to avoid sales work, thus forcing the other employees to do this less pleasant job while she was given more prestigious loan accounts. [She] also reported one incident in which a friend had agreed to meet her for dinner but was late because her child was ill. Patricia was highly offended and irritated by what she referred to as her friend's "lack of consideration" in being late. She felt no compassion for her friend or the child.

Patricia's tendency toward suspiciousness was exemplified by her belief that others did not like her and conspired against her to make her job harder (e.g., by "purposely" failing to get necessary paperwork to her on time). Finally, her uncooperativeness was illustrated by her tendency not to follow instructions at work and to refuse to cooperate with her husband at home. For example, although her boss had asked Patricia not to stay at the bank after hours because of security considerations, she often stayed late to work, saying that the boss's request was "stupid and restrictive."

Patricia described herself as both depressed and anxious. She also tended to become enraged when criticized or "treated badly." Although Patricia denied feelings of humiliation and insecurity, when criticized [she] would blush and either defensively make excuses for her behavior or negate the criticism ("She's just envious of me because I'm smarter than she is").

Other people seldom called or visited with her to talk about their problems; when they did, she responded with intellectual advice usually delivered in a condescending manner, such as, "When you're older, you'll understand better how things are." Her solitary nature in having few friends and keeping to herself at work may in fact have resulted in part from actual rebuffs from others in response to her antagonistic behavior.

Finally, Patricia perceived herself as accomplished, persistent, and strongly committed to the highest standards of conduct. These impressions may indicate a classic narcissistic inflation of self-image, especially given that she was, even by her own report, having considerable difficulties at work (Corbitt, 2002, pp. 294–297).

This woman's interpersonal difficulties could be succinctly described in terms of a combination of low agreeableness (trust, modesty, altruism, and compliance), low extraversion (warmth and gregariousness), high neuroticism (anger–hostility, anxiousness, and depression), and high conscientiousness (competence, dutifulness, and achievement striving). Based on DSM-IV-TR, she would meet the criteria for narcissistic personality disorder. If the categorical approach were used, however, a complete description of her personality problems would also require that the clinician note the presence of some features of paranoid PD (such as unjustified doubts about the loyalty of coworkers; reacting with rage to perceived attacks on her character or reputation) and obsessive–compulsive PD (excessive devotion to work to the exclusion of leisure activities and friendships), even though she did not exhibit enough features of these other disorders to meet their diagnostic threshold. A dimensional approach like the one illustrated in this case may eventually replace the 10 PD categories on Axis II when the next version of DSM is published.

▲ Anger and hostility are important symptoms of several forms of personality disorder, including paranoid, antisocial, borderline, and narcissistic PDs.

How are normal personality traits related to personality disorders?

FREQUENCY

Personality disorders are generally considered to be among the most common forms of psychopathology, when they are considered as a general category. Several epidemiological studies in the United States and in Europe have used semistructured diagnostic interviews to assess personality disorders in samples of people living in the community.

Prevalence in Community and Clinical Samples

How many people in the general population would meet the criteria for at least one personality disorder if they were given a diagnostic interview?

In studies that have examined community-based samples of adults, the overall lifetime prevalence for having at least one personality disorder (any type) varies between 10 and 14 percent (Coid et al., 2006; Lenzenweger et al., 2007; Torgersen, Kringlen, & Cramer, 2001). While this figure tends to be relatively consistent from one study to the next, prevalence rates for specific types of personality disorder vary quite a bit from one study to the next. The highest prevalence rates are usually found to be associated with obsessive–compulsive personality disorder, antisocial personality disorder, and avoidant personality disorder, which may affect 3 or 4 percent of adults.

The most precise information that is available regarding the prevalence of personality disorders in community samples is concerned specifically with the antisocial type (Moran, 1999). In two large-scale epidemiological studies of mental disorders, structured interviews were conducted with several thousand participants. The overall lifetime prevalence rate for antisocial personality disorder (men and women combined) was 3 percent in both studies (Kessler et al., 1994; Robins & Regier, 1991).

The prevalence rates for other specific types tend to be approximately 1 or 2 percent of the population. The most obvious exception is narcissistic personality disorder, which appears to be the least common form, affecting much less than 1 percent of the population.

Investigators identified very few cases of narcissistic personality disorder when they have interviewed people in community samples (as opposed to clinic settings). The fact that almost no one endorses narcissistic symptoms does not necessarily mean, however, that the disorder does not occur. Rather, it seems possible that people who experience these features do not recognize the nature of their own problems or are unwilling to admit them. Self-report measures, such as questionnaires and interviews, may not be effective instruments for assessing narcissistic personality disorder. More accurate information might be obtained from other people who know the person well and can report examples of grandiosity, exploitation, or lack of empathy (Oltmanns & Turkheimer, 2006).

One final issue regarding prevalence rates involves comorbidity. There is considerable overlap among categories in the personality disorders. At least 50 percent of people who meet the diagnostic criteria for one personality disorder also meet the criteria for another disorder (Coid et al., 2006). To some extent, this overlap is due to the fact that similar symptoms are used to define more than one disorder. For example, impulsive and reckless behaviors are part of the definition of both antisocial and borderline PDs. Social withdrawal is used to define schizoid, schizotypal, and avoidant PD.

There is also extensive overlap between personality disorders and disorders that are diagnosed on Axis I of DSM-IV-TR. Approximately 75 percent of people who qualify for a diagnosis on Axis II also meet criteria for a syndrome such as major depression, substance dependence, or an anxiety disorder (Dolan-Sewell, Krueger, & Shea, 2001). This overlap may also be viewed from the other direction: Many people who are treated for a mental disorder listed on Axis I, such as depression or alcoholism, would also meet the criteria for a personality disorder (Thomas et al., 1999). Borderline personality disorder appears to be the most common personality disorder among patients treated at mental health facilities (both inpatient and outpatient settings). Averaged across studies, the evidence suggests that this disorder is found among slightly more than 30 percent of all patients who are treated for psychological disorders (Lyons, 1995).

Gender Differences

The overall prevalence of personality disorders is approximately equal in men and women (Weissman, 1993). There are, however, consistent gender differences with regard to at least one specific disorder: Antisocial personality disorder is unquestionably much more common among men than among women, with rates of approximately 5 percent reported for men and 1 percent for women (Kessler et al., 1994; Robins et al., 1991). Thus antisocial personality disorder is actually an alarmingly common problem among adult males in the United States.

Epidemiological evidence regarding gender differences for the other types of personality disorder is much more ambiguous. Borderline personality disorder and dependent personality disorder may be somewhat more prevalent among women than men, but the evidence is not strong (Skodol & Bender, 2003). There has been some speculation that paranoid and obsessive–compulsive personality disorders may be somewhat more common among men than women (Coid et al., 2006).

Gender Bias and Diagnosis   One of the controversies surrounding the diagnosis of personality disorders involves the issue of gender bias

(Widiger, 1998). Critics contend that the definitions of some categories are based on sex role stereotypes and therefore are inherently sexist. The dependent type, for example, might be viewed as a reflection of certain traditionally feminine traits, such as being unassertive or putting the needs of others ahead of one's own. It has been suggested that DSM-IV-TR arbitrarily labels these traits as maladaptive. Traditionally masculine traits, such as being unable to identify and express a wide range of emotions, are presumably not mentioned in the manual. This practice arbitrarily assigns responsibility for interpersonal difficulties to the women themselves. Therefore these definitions may turn traditional sex role behaviors into "disorders" and minimize the extent to which women may simply be trying to cope with unreasonable or oppressive environmental circumstances, including discrimination and sexual abuse (Bjorklund, 2006; Caplan, 1995).

This argument leads to a number of interesting and important questions. One is concerned with the presence of bias within the criterion sets themselves. If the criteria for certain categories are based on stereotypes of feminine traits, is it relatively easy for a woman to meet the criteria for that diagnosis even if she is not experiencing significant distress or impairment in other areas of her life? The answer to that question is, tentatively, no (Funtowicz & Widiger, 1999). In other words, the threshold for assigning a diagnosis of personality disorder does not appear to be lower for those types that are based largely on traits that might be considered traditionally feminine (dependent, histrionic, borderline) than for those that are based on traits that might be considered traditionally masculine (antisocial, paranoid, compulsive).

A second question is concerned with the possibility of gender bias in the ways that clinicians assign diagnoses to their clients, regardless of whether the criteria themselves are biased. Are clinicians more likely to assign diagnoses such as dependent and borderline personality disorder to a woman than to a man, if both people exhibit the same set of symptoms? The answer to this question is, tentatively, yes. Both male and female mental health professionals may be somewhat (though not overwhelmingly) more likely to describe a person as exhibiting symptoms of borderline personality disorder if that person is female rather than male (Becker & Lamb, 1994; Crosby & Sprock, 2004).

◄ Vivien Leigh won Academy Awards for her performances as Scarlett O'Hara in *Gone with the Wind* (1940) and Blanche DuBois in *A Streetcar Named Desire* (1952). Both characters exhibit blends of histrionic and narcissistic features that fit stereotyped views of female personality traits.

Stability of Personality Disorders over Time

Temporal stability is one of the most important assumptions about personality disorders. Evidence for the assumption that personality disorders appear during adolescence and persist into adulthood has, until recently, been limited primarily to antisocial personality disorder. A classic follow-up study by Lee Robins (1966) began with a large set of records describing young children treated for adjustment problems at a clinic during the 1920s. Robins was able to locate and interview almost all of these people, who by then were adults. The best predictor of an adult diagnosis of antisocial personality was conduct disorder in childhood. The people who were most likely to be considered antisocial as adults were boys who had been referred to the clinic on the basis of serious theft or aggressive behavior; who exhibited such behaviors across a variety of situations; and whose antisocial behaviors created conflict with adults outside their own homes. More than half of the boys who exhibited these characteristics were given a diagnosis of antisocial personality disorder as adults.

Another longitudinal study has collected information regarding the prevalence and stability of personality disorders among adolescents

(Bernstein et al., 1993). This investigation is particularly important because it did not depend solely on subjects who had been referred for psychological treatment and because it was concerned with the full range of personality disorders. The rate of personality disorders was relatively high in this sample: Seventeen percent of the adolescents received a diagnosis of at least one personality disorder. Categorically defined diagnoses were not particularly stable; fewer than half of the adolescents who originally qualified for a personality disorder diagnosis met the same criteria 2 years later. Nevertheless, many of the study participants continued to exhibit similar problems over the next 8 years. Viewed from a dimensional perspective, the maladaptive traits that represent the core features of the disorders remained relatively stable between adolescence and young adulthood (Crawford, Cohen, & Brook, 2001).

Which personality disorders are least likely to change as a person gets older?

Several studies have examined the stability of personality disorders among people who have received professional treatment for their problems, especially those who have been hospitalized for schizotypal or borderline disorders. Many patients who have been treated for these problems are still significantly impaired several years later, but the disorders are not uniformly stable (Grilo et al., 2004; Paris, 2003). Recovery rates are relatively high among patients with a diagnosis of borderline personality disorder. If patients who were initially treated during their early twenties are followed up when they are in their forties and fifties, only about one person in four would still qualify for a diagnosis of borderline personality disorder. The long-term prognosis is less optimistic for schizotypal and schizoid personality disorders. People with these diagnoses are likely to remain socially isolated and occupationally impaired.

Culture and Personality

In DSM-IV-TR, personality disorders are defined in terms of behavior that "deviates markedly from the expectations of the individual's culture." In setting this guideline, the authors of DSM-IV-TR recognized that judgments regarding appropriate behavior vary considerably from one society to the next. Some cultures encourage restrained or subtle displays of emotion, whereas others promote visible, public displays of anger, grief, and other emotional responses. Behavior that seems highly dramatic or extraverted (histrionic) in the former cultures might create a very different impression in the latter cultures. Cultures also differ in the extent to which they value individualism (the pursuit of personal goals) as opposed to collectivism (sharing and self-sacrifice for the good of the group; Triandis, 1994). Someone who seems exceedingly self-centered and egotistical in a collectivist society, such as Japan, might appear to be normal in an individualistic society like the United States.

The personality disorders may be more closely tied to cultural expectations than any other kind of mental disorder (Alarcon, 2005). Some studies have compared the prevalence and symptoms of personality disorders in different countries, and the data suggest that similar problems do exist in cultures outside the United States and Western Europe (Pinto et al., 2000; Yang et al., 2000). Nevertheless, much more information is needed before we can be confident that the DSM-IV-TR system for describing personality disorders is valid in other societies. Two questions are particularly important:

1. In other cultures, what are the personality traits that lead to marked interpersonal difficulties and social or occupational impairment? Are they different from those that have been identified for our own culture?
2. Are the diagnostic criteria that are used to define personality disorder syndromes in DSM-IV-TR (and ICD-10) meaningful in other cultures?

Cross-cultural studies that are designed to address these issues must confront a number of difficult methodological problems (see Research Methods).

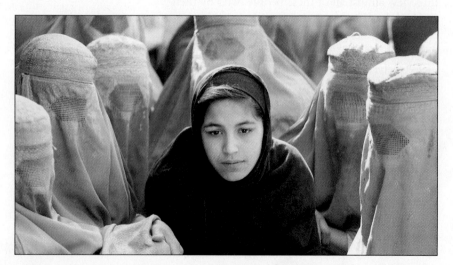

▼ Is this young Afghan woman more extraverted than the others? Is she a risk-taker? It is impossible to make these personality judgments without more knowledge of the culture in which she lives. She may be unveiled because she is younger than the other women, or because she is not married.

RESEARCH METHODS Cross-Cultural Comparisons: The Importance of Context

Over the past 30 years, psychologists have begun to adopt a broader focus in their consideration of human behavior, including mental disorders. This means paying more attention to cultural diversity in the samples used in research studies.

At the broadest level, culture is a system of meanings that determines the ways in which people think about themselves and their environments. It shapes their most basic view of reality. Consider, for example, the process of bereavement following the death of a close relative. In some Native American cultures, people learn to expect to hear the spirit of the dead person calling to them from the afterworld (Kleinman, 1988). This is a common experience for people in these cultures. It resembles auditory hallucinations (perceptual experiences in the absence of external stimulation) that are seen in people with psychotic disorders. But among some Native American peoples, hearing voices from the dead is a "normative" or common response; it is not a sign of dysfunction. Perhaps most importantly, this type of experience is not regularly associated with social or occupational impairment. It would be a mistake, therefore, to consider these experiences to be symptoms of a mental disorder.

Cross-cultural psychology is the scientific study of ways that human behavior and mental processes are influenced by social and cultural factors (Berry et al., 2002). This field includes the study of ethnic differences (among cultural groups living in close proximity within a single nation). Comparison is a fundamental element of any cross-cultural study. Cross-cultural psychologists examine ways in which human behaviors are different, as well as ways in which they are similar, from one culture to the next.

Cross-cultural comparisons are relevant to the study of psychopathology in many ways (Draguns & Tanaka-Matsumi, 2003; Kirmayer, 2006). One way involves epidemiology—comparisons of the prevalence of disorders across cultures. Investigations aimed at etiological mechanisms, including biological, psychological, and social variables, can also be extremely informative when viewed in cross-cultural perspective. For example, we know that negative patterns of thinking are correlated with depressed mood in middle-class Americans. Is the same relationship found among people living in rural China? Virtually any study of psychopathology would provide useful information if it were replicated in different cultures.

> **What are the most important challenges in collecting and interpreting cross-cultural data?**

The valuable process of making cross-cultural comparisons can actually be quite difficult (Draguns, 2006; Ratner & Hui, 2003). Several complex issues must be faced by investigators who want to study psychopathology in cross-cultural perspective:

1. *Identifying meaningful groups:* The first step in making cross-cultural comparisons is the selection of participants who are representative members of different cultures. This might be a relatively straightforward process if the comparison is to be made between two small, homogeneous groups such as two isolated rural villages in two very different countries (say, Peru and Zimbabwe). The situation becomes much more complex if the investigator's goal is to compare ethnic groups within a large, multicultural society such as the United States. Hispanic Americans, for example, include people whose cultural backgrounds can be traced to many different Spanish-speaking homelands with very different cultural traditions, such as Puerto Rico, Mexico, and Cuba. Even greater cultural diversity is found among various Native American peoples. How do we determine which people share a common culture? What is the cultural "unit," and how do we find its boundaries?

2. *Selecting equivalent measurement procedures:* Comparison between groups can be valid only if equivalent measurement procedures are used in both cultures (or in all groups). Participants in different cultures often speak different languages (or different dialects). Questionnaires and psychological tests must be cross validated to ensure that they measure the same concepts in different cultures.

3. *Considering causal explanations:* Suppose that investigators identify a reliable difference between people in two different cultures. They must now decide how to interpret this difference. Is it, in fact, due to cultural variables? Or would the differences disappear if other variables, such as poverty, education, and age, were held constant between the two groups?

4. *Avoiding culturally biased interpretations:* Investigators, who are often middle class and white, must interpret the results of cross-cultural research cautiously. In particular, scientists must not interpret differences between cultures or ethnic groups as being indicative of deficits in minority groups or non-Western cultures. Some cross-cultural psychologists have suggested that it is more important to study developmental processes within cultures or ethnic groups than to compare outcomes between groups.

Within a particular society, the experiences of people from cultural and ethnic minorities should also be considered carefully before diagnostic decisions are made. Phenomena associated with paranoid personality disorder, including strong feelings of suspicion, alienation, and distrust, illustrate this issue. People who belong to minority groups (and those who are recent immigrants from a different culture) are more likely than members of the majority or dominant culture to hold realistic concerns about potential victimization and exploitation. For example, black Americans may develop and express mild paranoid tendencies as a way of adapting to ongoing experiences of oppression (Whaley, 2001). Clinicians may erroneously diagnose these conditions as paranoid personality disorder if they do not recognize or understand the cultural

► People with schizotypal PD tend to be loners, and many have social anxiety that can be traced to distrust of other people.

experiences in which they are formed. In this particular case, it is obviously important for the clinician to consider the person's attitudes and beliefs regarding members of his or her own family or peer group, as well as the person's feelings about the community as a whole.

SCHIZOTYPAL PERSONALITY DISORDER (SPD)

Now that we have reviewed some of the important general issues for the entire set of personality disorders, we consider four specific types of disorder in more detail. We have decided to focus on schizotypal, borderline, and antisocial types because they have been the subject of extended research and debate in the scientific literature. We will also discuss dependent personality disorder to illustrate current thinking about one of the Cluster C disorders, even though this disorder has not been studied as extensively as the other three categories.

We begin each of the four sections with a brief case study. We have chosen cases that are prototypes for each disorder. In other words, these are people who exhibit most, if not all, of

the features of the disorder. You should not infer from these descriptions that everyone who meets the criteria for these disorders would represent this type of typical case. Remember, also, that many people simultaneously meet the criteria for more than one personality disorder; these cases are relatively simple examples. The following case illustrates some of the most important features of schizotypal personality disorder (SPD).

BRIEF CASE **STUDY**
Schizotypal Personality Disorder

Sandra, when she first came for treatment at the age of 27, presented with marked anxiety in social situations and in getting along with coworkers, eccentric behavior, and paranoid ideas. She had no close female friends and only one male friend, and though the latter was a sexual relationship, she revealed almost nothing to him about her past. She had many strange beliefs involving astrology, foods, and medicines.

Sandra had only one friend during her adolescence: someone who shared her faddishness about foods and her beliefs in astrology. Girls excluded her from their school clubs. She never understood why they rejected her, though it is probable that they considered her "weird" because of her inability to make small talk, and her voice pattern: a flat, high-pitched, stilted-sounding monotone that made her come across as mannered and insincere. Added to this peculiarity of speech was her tendency to skip from topic to topic abruptly, giving equal emphasis to each, such that it was difficult to distinguish the trivial from the important. From a therapeutic standpoint, this was particularly bedeviling, since it strained one's intuitive capacities to the uttermost just to figure out what was really bothering her or what was the "main theme" on any particular day.

Her empathic skills were very limited, leading her to comment at times that she found people and their motives completely puzzling: "I can't connect up with them. If they invite me to lunch with them, I can't seem to join in the conversation or else I say the wrong thing, so after a while they don't invite me anymore and I eat by myself." If a teaching supervisor wore a dour expression walking down the hall, Sandra assumed the supervisor was dissatisfied with her work, even though it might be a person who was not even assigned to her department. She tended to be surly and "superior" sounding when asking for vacation requests and the like—and often didn't get what she wanted because of having alienated the people whose favor she needed. This reinforced her notion that the world was pretty much against her.

Though considered a knowledgeable teacher, she had no charm or patience with the children and was eventually given a semi-administrative job where little interaction with others was necessary. With boyfriends, she was comfortable about having sex but made such fussy and endless-seeming preparations (such as doing her fingernails in the bathroom for half an hour) that the men lost the mood and usually ended the relationship after a few months.

More striking than her empathic difficulties was a curious inability to grasp what one might call the statistics of everyday life. Travel was a great burden, since she felt it necessary to plan for all possible contingencies. She once went to (France) on an August vacation packing her winter overcoat, because, as she reminded me, "There was a cold spell there in the '50s and it could happen again." Furthermore, she sent a packet of clothes on ahead to the hotel because, "What if my baggage got stolen?" She had great difficulty, in other words, aligning her behavior in harmony with the expectable, in contrast with the remotely possible—all thinkable events being in her mind equally probable (Stone, 1993, pp. 179–180).

The concept of schizotypal personality disorder is closely tied to the history of schizophrenia as a diagnostic entity (Gottesman, 1987). The term was originally coined as an abbreviation for *schizophrenic phenotype*. These maladaptive personality traits are presumably seen among people who possess the genotype that makes them vulnerable to schizophrenia. The symptoms of schizotypal personality disorder represent early manifestations of the predisposition to develop the full-blown disorder. It has been recognized for many years that a fairly large proportion of the family members of schizophrenic patients exhibit strange or unusual behaviors that are similar to, but milder in form than, the disturbance shown by the patient.

Symptoms

The DSM-IV-TR criteria for schizotypal personality disorder are listed in Table 9–3. These criteria represent a blend of those characteristics that have been reported among the relatives of schizophrenic patients and those symptoms that seem to characterize nonpsychotic patients with schizophrenic-like disorders (Siever, Bernstein, & Silverman, 1995). In addition to social detachment, emphasis is placed on eccentricity and cognitive or perceptual distortions.

People who meet the criteria for schizotypal personality disorder frequently meet the criteria for additional Axis II disorders. There is considerable overlap between schizotypal personality disorder and other personality disorders in Cluster A (paranoid and schizoid), as well as with avoidant personality disorder. This finding is not particularly surprising, given the conceptual origins of the schizotypal category. There is also quite a bit of overlap between schizotypal personality disorder and borderline personality disorder.

TABLE 9–3   DSM-IV-TR Criteria for Schizotypal Personality Disorder

A. A pervasive pattern of social and interpersonal deficits marked by acute discomfort with, and reduced capacity for, close relationships as well as by cognitive or perceptual distortions and eccentricities of behavior, beginning by early adulthood and present in a variety of contexts, as indicated by five (or more) of the following:

1. Ideas of reference (excluding delusions of reference).
2. Odd beliefs or magical thinking that influences behavior and is inconsistent with subcultural norms (such as superstitiousness, belief in clairvoyance, or telepathy).
3. Unusual perceptual experiences, including bodily illusions.
4. Odd thinking and speech (vague, circumstantial, metaphorical, overelaborate, or stereotyped).
5. Suspiciousness or paranoid ideation.
6. Inappropriate or constricted affect.*
7. Behavior or appearance that is odd, eccentric, or peculiar.
8. Lack of close friends or confidants other than first-degree relatives.
9. Excessive social anxiety that does not diminish with familiarity and tends to be associated with paranoid fears rather than with negative judgments about self.

B. Does not occur exclusively during the course of Schizophrenia, a Mood Disorder with Psychotic Features, another Psychotic Disorder, or a Pervasive Developmental Disorder.

---

*Inappropriate affect refers to emotional responses that appear to be inconsistent with the social context—for example, uncontrollable giggling at a wake or funeral. Constricted affect refers to the absence of emotional responsiveness, such as lack of facial expressions. See Chapter 13 for a more detailed discussion.

Source: Reprinted with permission from the *Diagnostic and Statistical Manual of Mental Disorders*, Fourth Edition, Text Revision. Copyright © 2000 by the American Psychiatric Association.

Causes

Most of the interest in the etiology of schizotypal personality disorder has focused on the importance of genetic factors. Is schizotypal personality disorder genetically related to schizophrenia? Family and adoption studies indicate that the answer is "yes"? (Appels et al., 2004; Battaglia & Torgersen, 1996). Twin studies have examined genetic contributions to schizotypal personality disorder from a dimensional perspective in which schizotypal personality traits are measured with questionnaires. This evidence also points to a significant genetic contribution (Linney et al., 2003).

The first degree relatives of schizophrenic patients are considerably more likely than people in the general population to exhibit symptoms of schizotypal personality disorder. Several studies have examined the prevalence of schizotypal personality disorder among the parents and siblings of patients being treated for schizophrenia (Kendler & Gardner, 1997; Tienari et al., 2003). The most striking and consistent finding has been an increased prevalence of schizotypal personality disorder among the relatives of the schizophrenic patients. Prevalence rates for paranoid and avoidant personality disorder also tend to be higher among the relatives of the schizophrenic patients. These types of personality disorder are not more prevalent among the relatives of people with mood disorders. Results from these studies are consistent with the conclusion that schizotypal personality disorder is genetically related to schizophrenia.

Treatment

Two important considerations complicate the treatment of people with personality disorders in general and SPD in particular and make it difficult to evaluate the effectiveness of various forms of intervention. One consideration involves the ego-syntonic nature of many personality disorders (discussed earlier). Many people with these disorders do not seek treatment for their problems because they do not see their own behavior as being the source of distress. A related difficulty involves premature termination: A relatively high proportion of personality disorder patients drop out of treatment before it is completed.

Why are personality disorders so difficult to treat?

When people with personality disorders appear at hospitals or clinics, it is often because they are also suffering from another type of mental disorder, such as depression or substance abuse. This comorbidity is the second consideration that complicates treatment. "Pure forms" of personality disorder are relatively rare. There is tremendous overlap between specific personality disorder categories and other forms of abnormal behavior, including disorders that would be listed on both Axis I and Axis II. Treatment is seldom aimed at problem behaviors that are associated with only one type of personality disorder, and the efficacy of treatment is, therefore, difficult to evaluate.

The literature regarding treatment of schizotypal personality disorder, like that dealing with its causes, mirrors efforts aimed at schizophrenia. A few studies have focused on the possible treatment value of antipsychotic drugs, which are effective with many schizophrenic patients. Some studies have found that low doses of antipsychotic medication are beneficial in alleviating cognitive problems and social anxiety in patients who have received a diagnosis of schizotypal personality disorder (Koenigsberg et al., 2003). There is also some indication that patients with schizotypal personality disorder may respond positively to antidepressant medications, including SSRIs. In general, the therapeutic effects of medication are positive, but they tend to be modest.

Clinical experience seems to suggest that these patients do not respond well to insight oriented psychotherapy, in part because they do not see themselves as having psychological problems and also because they are so uncomfortable with close personal relationships. Some clinicians have suggested that a supportive, educational approach that is focused on fostering basic social skills may be beneficial if the goals of treatment are modest (Crits-Christoph, 1998; Gabbard, 2000). Unfortunately, controlled studies of psychological forms of treatment with schizotypal personality disorder have not been reported.

BORDERLINE PERSONALITY DISORDER (BPD)

Borderline personality disorder is one of the most perplexing, most disabling, and most frequently treated forms of personality disorder. Because of the severity of their problems, people with BPD are more likely to come into clinics seeking treatment. Experts on psychiatric classification have discussed the possibility that this diagnostic category might be better placed with the Axis I disorders when the official diagnostic manual is revised (using a different name, such as "emotion dysregulation disorder," for the new diagnostic category). Of course, this possibility raises challenging conceptual and empirical issues regarding the validity of the diagnostic system (see Chapter 4). What are the most important problems faced by these patients, and what is the most useful way to think about their disorders? The following case illustrates many of the features associated with borderline personality disorder.

BRIEF CASE **STUDY**
Borderline Personality Disorder

Barbara, single woman of 24, sought treatment with me shortly after discharge from a hospital, where she had spent three weeks because of depression, panic attacks, and a suicide gesture. This had been her seventh hospitalization—all of them brief, and all for similar symptoms—since age 17. Cheerful and cooperative as a young girl, she underwent a radical change of personality at the time of her menarche. Thereafter, she became irascible, rebellious, moody, and demanding.

For a time she was anorexic; later on, bulimic (maintaining her normal weight by vomiting). Schoolwork deteriorated, and she took up with a wild crowd, abusing marijuana and other drugs and engaging in promiscuous sex. At one point she ran away from home with a boyfriend and didn't return for three months.

She quit high school with one year to go. Her life became even more chaotic; she scratched her wrists on a number of occasions, and consorted with abusive men who would use her sexually and then beat her up.

By the time I began working with Barbara, she had been abusing alcohol for about a year and had also become addicted to benzodiazepines. Her proneness to panic-level anxiety now took the form of agoraphobia, necessitating her being accompanied by a parent to her therapy sessions. Premenstrually, her irritability rose to fever pitch: she would strike her parents with her fists, sometimes necessitating help from the police. She would then threaten to kill herself.

Lacking any hobbies or interests, apart from dancing, she was bored to distraction at home, yet afraid to venture out. Nothing gave her any pleasure except glitzy clothes (which her agoraphobia rendered irrelevant).

For a few weeks Barbara dated a man from her neighborhood, and although she was able to leave the house if she were with him, she used the opportunity in a self-destructive way, going to wild nightclubs and provoking him with demands to the point where he drove her only halfway home, pushing her out of the car, so that she had to hitchhike home at 2 A.M. This precipitated a suicide attempt with a variety of medications (Stone, 1993, pp. 248–249).

The intellectual heritage of borderline personality disorder (BPD) is quite diverse, and it is more difficult to trace than that of schizotypal personality disorder. It is, in fact, rather confusing. Several traditions are important, and in some cases they represent conflicting points of view (Leichtman, 1989).

Otto Kernberg (1967, 1975), a psychiatrist at Cornell University, has developed an explanation of borderline personality that is based on psychodynamic theory. According to Kernberg, borderline personality is not a specific syndrome. Rather, it refers to a set of personality features or deficiencies that can be found in individuals with various disorders. In Kernberg's model, the common characteristic of people diagnosed with borderline personality is faulty development of ego structure. Another common feature of people with borderline disorder is *splitting*—the tendency to see people and events alternately as entirely good or entirely bad. Thus a man with borderline personality might perceive his wife as almost perfect at some times and as highly flawed at other times. The tendency toward splitting helps explain the broad mood swings and unstable relationships associated with borderline personalities.

Kernberg's emphasis on a broadly defined level of pathology, rather than on discrete clinical symptoms, resulted in a relatively expansive definition of borderline personality. Viewed from this perspective, borderline disorder can encompass a great many types of abnormal behavior, including paranoid, schizoid, and cyclothymic personality disorders, impulse control disorders (see Impulse Control Disorders), substance use disorders, and various types of mood disorder.

In an effort to foster research on borderline disorders, these psychodynamic views regarding personality organization were translated into more reliable, descriptive terms by several prominent clinicians. John Gunderson (1984, 1994), a psychiatrist at Harvard University, identified a

◀ Some people with borderline personality disorder engage in recurrent suicidal gestures of self-mutilating behavior.

IMPULSE CONTROL DISORDERS

Failure to control harmful impulses is associated with several of the disorders listed in DSM-IV-TR. People who meet the criteria for borderline personality disorder and antisocial personality disorder engage in various types of impulsive, maladaptive behaviors (most often self-mutilation in the case of BPD, and theft and aggression in the case of ASPD). People in the midst of a manic episode frequently become excessively involved in pleasurable activities that can have painful consequences, such as unrestrained buying or sexual indiscretions. These are examples of impulse control problems that appear as part of a more broadly defined syndrome or mental disorder.

DSM-IV-TR includes several additional problems under a heading called **impulse control disorders** (Hollander & Stein, 2006). They are coded on Axis I rather than Axis II. Relatively little is known about these problems. They are defined in terms of persistent, clinically significant impulsive behaviors that are not better explained by other disorders in DSM-IV-TR. They include the following:

- *Intermittent explosive disorder:* Aggressive behaviors resulting in serious assaultive acts or destruction of property (Olvera, 2002; Coccaro et al., 2005). The level of aggression is grossly out of proportion to any precipitating psychosocial stressors.
- *Kleptomania:* Stealing objects that are not needed for personal use or for their financial value. The theft is not motivated by anger or vengeance (Presta et al., 2002).
- *Pyromania:* Deliberate and purposeful setting of fires, accompanied by fascination with or attraction to fire and things that are associated with it. The behavior is not motivated by financial considerations (as in arson), social or political ideology, anger, vengeance, or delusional beliefs (Lejoyeux et al., 2006).
- *Trichotillomania:* Pulling out one's own hair, resulting in noticeable hair loss as well as significant distress or impairment in social or occupational functioning (Woods et al., 2008).
- *Pathological gambling:* Repeated maladaptive gambling that is associated with other problems, such as repeated, unsuccessful efforts to stop gambling, restlessness or irritability when trying to stop gambling, lying to family members and friends to conceal the extent of gambling, and committing crimes to finance gambling (Sharpe, 2002).

In most cases, the impulsive behavior is preceded by increasing tension and followed by a feeling of pleasure, gratification, or relief. The motivation for these impulsive behaviors is, therefore, somewhat different than the motivation for compulsive behavior (see Chapter 6). Impulsive and compulsive behaviors can be difficult to distinguish, as both are repetitious and difficult to resist. The primary difference is that the original goal for impulsive behavior is to experience pleasure, and the original goal for compulsive behavior is to avoid anxiety (Frances, et al., 1995; Grant & Potenza, 2006).

In what ways are impulse control disorders different from compulsive behaviors?

The most frequent type of impulse control disorder is pathological gambling. The lifetime prevalence of pathological gambling in the United States is approximately 2 or 3 percent of the population and seems to be increasing with the spread of legalized gambling (Stucki & Rihs-Middel, 2007). Men are more likely than women to become pathological gamblers. They tend to be intelligent, well educated, competitive people who enjoy the challenges and risks involved in betting. Substance use disorders (see Chapter 11) and antisocial personality disorder are commonly associated with pathological gambling. Evidence from twin studies suggests that impulsivity represents a common form of vulnerability to all of three types of disorder, and this predisposition is influenced by genetic factors (Slutske et al., 2000; Xian et al., 2007).

Most gambling is not associated with a mental disorder. Social gambling is a form of recreation that is accepted in most cultures. Professional gambling is an occupation pursued by people whose gambling is highly disciplined. Pathological gambling, in contrast, is out of control, takes over the person's life, and leads to horrendous financial and interpersonal consequences.

The tragic life of Art Schlichter provides a vivid illustration of the devastating impact that persistent, uncontrolled, impulsive gambling can have on a person and his family (Keteyian, 1986; Valente, 1996). Schlichter, an All-American quarterback at Ohio State University, was the first player drafted by the National Football League in 1982. He had been gambling since high school, but the problem became worse after he started playing professional football. His career was disappointing. As the pressures mounted, so did his gambling debts, which eventually reached $1 million. He was cut from several teams in the National Football League and the Canadian Football League, and was ultimately banned from the NFL for betting on professional games. He entered treatment for his compulsive gambling on several occasions, but the results were unsuccessful and his repeated promises to stop gambling went unfulfilled. Schlichter has been arrested and jailed on several occasions for charges that include forgery, theft, and bank fraud. In 2001, he was sentenced to 6 years in prison for violating the terms of his probation. Schlichter's promising football career was ruined, and his young family was torn apart by his uncontrolled gambling.

The impulse control disorders occupy an interesting and controversial niche in DSM-IV-TR. The implication of impulse control disorders is that people who repeatedly engage in dangerous, illegal, or destructive behaviors must have a mental disorder. If they do not, why do they do these things? Unfortunately, this reasoning quickly becomes circular. Why does he gamble recklessly? Because he has a mental disorder. How do you know he has a mental disorder? Because he gambles recklessly. This logical dilemma is particularly evident in the case of impulse control disorders when the problem behaviors do not appear as part of a broader syndrome in which other symptoms of disorder are also present. In other words, the problem behavior is the disorder. Until we can step outside this loop, validating the utility of the diagnostic concept by reference to other psychological or biological response systems, we are left with an unsatisfying approach to the definition of these problems.

number of descriptive characteristics that are commonly associated with Kernberg's concept of borderline personality. Gunderson and his colleagues developed a structured interview that would allow clinicians to diagnose the condition reliably and served as the basis for the current definition of BPD in DSM-IV-TR.

Symptoms

The DSM-IV-TR criteria for borderline personality disorder are presented in Table 9–4. The overriding characteristic of borderline personality disorder is a pervasive pattern of instability in self-image, in interpersonal relationships, and in mood.

> To be borderline means to lack grounding emotionally and to exist from moment to moment without any sense of continuity, predictability, or meaning. Life is experienced in fragments, more like a series of snapshots than a moving picture. It is a series of discrete points of experience that fail to flow together smoothly or to create an integrated whole.
>
> (Moskovitz, 1996, pp. 5–6)

Borderline personality disorder overlaps with several other categories on Axis II, including the histrionic, narcissistic, paranoid, dependent, and avoidant types. There is also a significant amount of overlap between borderline personality disorder and Axis I disorders, especially depression (Trull et al., 2006). Many patients with other types of impulse control problems, such as substance dependence and eating disorders, also qualify for a diagnosis of borderline personality disorder.

Follow-up studies suggest many similarities between borderline personality disorder and mood disorders. In many cases, the symptoms of BPD are evident before the onset of major depression. For example, one study focused on a group of 100 outpatients with a diagnosis of borderline personality disorder (Akiskal, 1992). During follow-up, 29 percent of the sample developed severe depression. Another longitudinal study of patients who were discharged from a private psychiatric hospital is also interesting in this regard. In a sample of patients with a pure diagnosis of borderline personality disorder (that is, those who did not receive any other diagnosis on Axis I or II), 23 percent developed major depressive episodes during the course of the 15-year follow-up (McGlashan, 1986).

Causes

Genetic factors do not seem to play a central role in the etiology of borderline personality disorder when it is viewed in terms of the syndrome that is defined in DSM-IV-TR (Torgersen, 1994). This does not mean, however, that genes are irrelevant

mypsych lab VIDEO CASE

COMPULSIVE GAMBLING
ED

"My mother was on her deathbed. Her words to me were, "You've got to stop gambling. It's ruining your life. You'll lose everything. She died the following day, and I spent the next year of my life proving her right. I did lose everything."

As you watch the interview and the day-in-the-life segments, ask yourself what purpose Ed's gambling seemed to play in his life. How was his preoccupation with gambling different from a serious commitment to a career or a hobby?

TABLE 9–4 DSM-IV-TR Criteria for Borderline Personality Disorder

A pervasive pattern of instability of interpersonal relationships, self-image, and affects, and marked impulsivity beginning by early adulthood and present in a variety of contexts, as indicated by five (or more) of the following:

1. Frantic efforts to avoid real or imagined abandonment.
2. A pattern of unstable and intense interpersonal relationships characterized by alternating between extremes of idealization and devaluation.
3. Identity disturbance: markedly and persistently unstable self-image or sense of self.
4. Impulsiveness in at least two areas that are potentially self-damaging (for example, spending, sex, substance abuse, reckless driving, binge eating).
5. Recurrent suicidal behavior, gestures, or threats, or self-mutilating behavior.
6. Affective instability due to a marked reactivity of mood (such as intense episodic dysphoria, irritability, or anxiety usually lasting a few hours and only rarely more than a few days).
7. Chronic feelings of emptiness.
8. Inappropriate, intense anger or difficulty controlling anger (for example, frequent displays of temper, constant anger, recurrent physical fights).
9. Transient, stress related paranoid ideation or severe dissociative symptoms.

Source: Reprinted with permission from the *Diagnostic and Statistical Manual of Mental Disorders*, Fourth Edition, Text Revision. Copyright © 2000 by the American Psychiatric Association.

to the development of this set of problems because the fundamental personality traits that serve to define the disorder, such as neuroticism and impulsivity, are clearly influenced by genetic factors (Livesley, 2008; Skodol et al., 2002). The most important question is how a genetic predisposition toward certain personality characteristics can interact with various types of detrimental environmental events to produce the problems in emotional regulation and attachment relationships that are seen among patients with borderline personality disorder.

Some investigators have argued that borderline patients suffer from the negative consequences of parental loss, neglect, and mistreatment during childhood (Fonagy & Bateman, 2008). This model is supported by studies of the families of borderline patients and by comparisons with the literature on social development in monkeys that examined the effects of separating infants from their mothers. Studies of patients with borderline personality disorder do point toward the influence of widespread problematic relationships with their parents. Adolescent girls with borderline personality disorder report pervasive lack of supervision, frequent witnessing of domestic violence, and being subjected to inappropriate behavior by their parents and other adults, including verbal, physical, and sexual abuse (Helgeland & Torgersen,

2004; Pally, 2002). The extent and severity of abuse vary widely across individuals. Many patients describe multiple forms of abuse by more than one person.

The association between borderline personality disorder and the patients' recollections of childhood maltreatment raises an important question about the direction of this relationship: Does childhood abuse lead to borderline personality disorder? Or are people with borderline personality disorder simply more likely to remember that they were abused by their parents, due to biased reporting?

Longitudinal data from a study of adolescents in upstate New York provide important evidence on this point (Johnson et al., 1999). Rather than relying exclusively on self-report measures, the investigators obtained data on child maltreatment from the New York State Central Registry for Child Abuse. Maltreatment included documented cases of physical abuse, sexual abuse, and childhood neglect. People with documented evidence of childhood abuse and neglect were four times more likely than those who had not been mistreated to develop symptoms of personality disorders as young adults. Strongest connections were found for Cluster B disorders (see Figure 9–1). Physical abuse was most closely associated with subsequent antisocial personality disorder; sexual abuse with borderline personality disorder; and childhood neglect with antisocial, borderline, narcissistic, and avoidant personality disorder. These data support the argument that maladaptive patterns of parenting and family relationships increase the probability that a person will develop certain types of personality disorder.

Treatment

Given that the concept of borderline personality disorder is rooted in psychodynamic theory, it should not be surprising that many clinicians have advocated the use of psychotherapy for the treatment of these conditions. In psychodynamic therapy, the *transference relationship,* defined as the way in which the patient behaves toward the therapist and which is believed to reflect early primary relationships, is used to increase patients' ability to experience themselves and other people in a more realistic and integrated way (Clarkin et al., 2001; Gabbard, 2000).

Family Environment and Risk for Personality Disorders

legend: childhood maltreatment absent; childhood maltreatment present

FIGURE 9–1   Associations between childhood maltreatment and risk for early adulthood personality disorders.

Source: J. G. Cohen., J. Brown., E. M. Smailes, and D. P. Bernstein, 1999, "Childhood Maltreatment Increases Risk for Personality Disorders during Early Adulthood," *Archives of General Psychiatry, 56,* pp. 600–606. Copyright © 1999. Reprinted by permission of American Medical Association.

As we have said, personality disorders have traditionally been considered to be hard to treat from a psychological perspective, and borderline conditions are among the most difficult. Close personal relationships form the foundation of psychological intervention, and it is specifically in the area of establishing and maintaining such relationships that borderline patients experience their greatest difficulty (see Getting Help). Their persistent alternation between overidealization and devaluation leads to frequent rage toward the therapist and can become a significant deterrent to progress in therapy. Not surprisingly, between one-half and two-thirds of all patients with borderline personality disorder discontinue treatment, against their therapists' advice, within the first several weeks of treatment (Kelly et al., 1992).

One promising approach to psychotherapy with borderline patients, called *dialectical behavior therapy* (DBT), has been developed and evaluated by Marsha Linehan (Linehan et al., 2001), a clinical psychologist at the University of Washington. This procedure combines the use of broadly based behavioral strategies with the more general principles of supportive psychotherapy. In philosophy, the term *dialectics* refers to a process of reasoning that places opposite or contradictory ideas side by side. In Linehan's approach to treatment, the term refers to strategies that are employed by the therapist in order to help the person appreciate and balance apparently contradictory needs to accept things as they are (such as intense negative emotions) and to work toward changing patterns of thinking and behavior that contribute to problems in the regulation of emotions. Emphasis is placed on learning to be more comfortable with strong emotions, such as anger, sadness, and fear, and learning to think in a more integrated way that accepts both good and bad features of the self and other people. Traditional behavioral and cognitive techniques, such as skill training, exposure, and problem solving, are also employed to help the patient improve interpersonal relationships, tolerate distress, and regulate emotional responses. Finally, considerable emphasis is placed on the therapist's acceptance of patients, including their frequently demanding, manipulative, and contradictory behaviors. This factor is important, because borderline patients are extremely sensitive to even the most subtle signs of criticism or rejection by other people.

One controlled study of dialectical behavior therapy produced encouraging results with regard to some aspects of the patients' behavior (Linehan et al., 1994, 1999). All of the patients in this study were women who met diagnostic criteria for BPD and also had a previous history of suicide attempts or deliberate self-harm. Patients were randomly assigned to receive either DBT or treatment as usual, which was essentially any form of treatment that was available within the community. The adjustment of patients in both groups was measured after 1 year of treatment and over a 1 year period following termination. One of the most important results involved the dropout rate. Almost 60 percent of the patients in the treatment as usual group terminated prematurely, whereas the rate in the DBT group was only 17 percent. The patients who received DBT also showed a significant reduction in the frequency and severity of suicide attempts, spent fewer days in psychiatric hospitals over the course of the study, and rated themselves higher on a measure of social adjustment. The groups did not differ, however, on other important measures, such as level of depression and hopelessness.

Positive results have also been reported in more recent studies in which women with BPD were randomly assigned to either dialectical behavior therapy or treatment as usual. Outcome measures indicated that women who were treated with dialectical behavior therapy experienced more improvement than women in the control groups with regard to symptoms such as depression and hopelessness (Bohus et al., 2004; Koons et al., 2001; Verheul et al., 2003).

In general, these studies suggest that DBT is a promising form of treatment for people with borderline personality disorder. It should be noted, however, that the sample sizes in these studies are quite small. Important methodological questions have been raised about the outcome results, including the possible influence of the allegiance effect (see Research Methods in Chapter 10). DBT has become one of the most popular and rapidly expanding forms of psychological treatment, and it has begun to be used in treating other problems that involve impulsive behavior, such as substance use disorders and binge eating disorders (Robins & Chapman, 2004). Enthusiasm for the therapeutic value of DBT will undoubtedly lead to more rigorous evaluations of its effectiveness in clinical settings.

Psychotropic medication is also used frequently in the treatment of borderline patients.

Unfortunately, no disorder-specific drug has been found. Psychiatrists employ the entire spectrum of psychoactive medication with borderline patients, from antipsychotics and antidepressants to lithium and anticonvulsants (Koenigsberg, Woo-Ming, & Siever, 2002; Zanarini & Frankenburg, 2001). Different types of drugs are recommended to treat individual symptoms, such as impulsive aggression, emotional instability, and transient paranoid thinking, but there is no systematic proof that a specific drug is effective for any of the borderline features.

ANTISOCIAL PERSONALITY DISORDER (ASPD)

Antisocial personality disorder (ASPD) has been studied more thoroughly and for a longer period of time than any of the other personality disorders (Blashfield, 2000; Blashfield & McElroy, 1989). One case study involving this disorder was presented at the beginning of this chapter. Tom, the man in that case, illustrated the pattern of repeated antisocial behavior that is associated with the disorder. Emotional and interpersonal problems also play an important role in the definition of antisocial personality disorder. The following case, written by Robert Hare, a clinical psychologist at the University of British Columbia, illustrates the egocentricity that is a central feature of the disorder. It also demonstrates the stunning lack of concern that such people have for the impact of their behavior on other people, especially those who are close to them.

BRIEF CASE **STUDY**
Antisocial Personality Disorder

Terry is 21, the second of three boys born into a wealthy and highly respected family. His older brother is a doctor, and his younger brother is a scholarship student in his second year of college. Terry is a first-time offender, serving 2 years for a series of robberies committed a year ago.

By all accounts, his family life was stable, his parents were warm and loving, and his opportunities for success were enormous. His brothers were honest and hardworking, whereas he simply "floated through life, taking whatever was offered." His parents' hopes and expectations were less important to him than having a good time. Still, they supported him emotionally and financially through an adolescence marked by wildness, testing the limits, and repeated brushes with the law—speeding, reckless driving, drunkenness—but no formal convictions. By age 20 he had fathered two children and was heavily involved in gambling and drugs. When he could no longer obtain money from his family, he turned to robbing banks, and he was soon caught and sent to prison. "I wouldn't be here if my parents had come across when I needed them," he said. "What kind of parents would let their son rot in a place like this?" Asked about his children, he replied, "I've never seen them. I think they were given up for adoption. How the hell should I know!" (Hare, 1993, p. 167).

The contrast between Terry's willingness to blame his problems on his parents and his apparent inability to accept responsibility for his own children is striking. It illustrates clearly the callous indifference and shallow emotional experience of the person with antisocial personality disorder.

Current views of antisocial personality disorder have been greatly influenced by two specific books. These books have inspired two different approaches to the definition of the disorder itself. The first book, *The Mask of Sanity*, was written by Hervey Cleckley (1976), a psychiatrist at the University of Georgia, and was originally published in 1941. It includes numerous case examples of impulsive, self-centered, pleasure seeking people who seemed to be completely lacking in certain primary emotions, such as anxiety, shame, and guilt. Cleckley used the term **psychopathy** to describe this disorder. According to Cleckley's definition, the psychopath is a person who is intelligent and superficially charming but is also chronically deceitful, unreliable, and incapable of learning from experience. This diagnostic approach places principal emphasis on emotional deficits and personality traits. Unfortunately, Cleckley's definition was difficult to use reliably because it contained such elusive features as "incapacity for love" and "failure to learn from experience."

The second book that influenced the concept of antisocial personality disorder was a report by Lee Robins of her follow-up study of children who had been treated many years earlier at a child guidance clinic. The book, *Deviant Children Grown Up* (1966), demonstrated that certain forms of conduct disorder that were evident during childhood, especially among boys, were reliable predictors of other forms of antisocial behavior when these same people became adults. The diagnostic approach inspired by this research study was adopted by DSM-III (APA, 1980). It places principal emphasis on observable behaviors and repeated conflict with, including failure to conform to social norms with respect to lawful behavior. This approach can be used with greater reliability than psychopathy because it is focused on concrete consequences of the disorder, which are often documented by legal records, rather than subjectively defined emotional deficits, such as lack of empathy.

Psychopathy and ASPD are two different attempts to define the same disorder. Yet they are sufficiently different that they certainly do not identify the same people, and they are no longer used interchangeably. Critics argued that DSM-III had blurred the distinction between antisocial personality and criminality. Cleckley's approach had been relatively clear on this point; all criminals are not psychopaths, and all psychopaths are not criminals. The DSM-III definition made it difficult to diagnose antisocial personality disorder in a person who did not already have a criminal record, such as an egocentric, manipulative, and callous businessperson. It also moved in the direction of including a much larger proportion of criminals within the boundaries of antisocial personality disorder (Hart & Hare, 1997). The true meaning of the concept might have been sacrificed in DSM-III for the sake of improved reliability.

Symptoms

Table 9–5 lists the DSM-IV-TR criteria for antisocial personality disorder. One prominent feature in this definition is the required presence of

◀ Andrew Fastow, former Enron chief financial officer, is now serving a 6-year prison sentence for fraud. Grandiosity, deceit, manipulativeness, and lack of remorse are traits associated with the "white collar psychopath."

symptoms of conduct disorder (see Chapter 16) prior to the age of 15, which reflects the impact of Robins's work. The definition also requires the presence of at least three out of seven signs of irresponsible and

What is the difference between antisocial personality disorder and psychopathy?

TABLE 9–5 DSM-IV-TR Criteria for Antisocial Personality Disorder

A. There is a pervasive pattern of disregard for and violation of the rights of others occurring since age 15, as indicated by three (or more) of the following:

1. Failure to conform to social norms with respect to lawful behavior as indicated by repeatedly performing acts that are grounds for arrest.
2. Deceitfulness, as indicated by repeated lying, use of aliases, or conning others for personal profit or pleasure.
3. Impulsivity or failure to plan ahead.
4. Irritability and aggressiveness, as indicated by repeated physical fights or assaults.
5. Reckless disregard for safety of self or others.
6. Consistent irresponsibility, as indicated by repeated failure to sustain consistent work behavior or honor financial obligations.
7. Lack of remorse, as indicated by being indifferent to or rationalizing having hurt, mistreated, or stolen from another.

B. The individual is at least 18 years old.

C. Evidence of Conduct Disorder with onset before age 15.

Source: Reprinted with permission from the *Diagnostic and Statistical Manual of Mental Disorders,* Fourth Edition, Text Revision. Copyright © 2000 by the American Psychiatric Association.

antisocial behavior after the age of 15. One of these criteria, "lack of remorse," did not appear in DSM-III but was one of Cleckley's original criteria. Its inclusion in DSM-IV-TR clearly signals an attempt to move the definition back toward the original concept.

Some investigators and clinicians prefer the concept of psychopathy to the DSM-IV-TR definition of antisocial personality. Robert Hare has developed a systematic approach to the assessment of psychopathy, known as the Psychopathy Checklist (PCL), that is based largely on Cleckley's original description of the disorder. The PCL includes two major factors (groups of symptoms): (1) emotional/interpersonal traits and (2) social deviance associated with an unstable or antisocial lifestyle. Key symptoms for both factors are summarized in Table 9–6. The major difference between this definition of psychopathy and the DSM-IV-TR definition of antisocial personality disorder involves the list of emotional and interpersonal traits (although DSM-IV-TR does include being deceitful and failure to experience remorse). Extensive research with the PCL indicates that, contrary to previous experience with Cleckley's criteria, the emotional and interpersonal traits can be used reliably (Hart & Hare, 1997).

The ultimate resolution of this prolonged dispute over the best definition of antisocial personality disorder will depend on systematic comparisons of the two approaches (Lilienfeld, 1994; Widiger, 2006). This situation is another classic example of studying the validity of a diagnostic concept (see Chapter 4). How different are these definitions? Which definition is most useful in predicting events such as repeated antisocial behavior following release from prison?

Antisocial Behavior over the Life Span Not everyone who engages in antisocial behavior does so consistently throughout his or her lifetime. Terrie Moffitt, a clinical psychologist at Duke University, has proposed that there are two primary forms of antisocial behavior: transient and nontransient. Moffitt (1993, 2007) considers adolescence-limited antisocial behavior to be a common form of social behavior that is often adaptive and that disappears by the time the person reaches adulthood. This type presumably accounts for most antisocial behavior, and it is unrelated to antisocial personality disorder.

A small proportion of antisocial individuals, mostly males, engage in antisocial behavior at all ages. Moffitt calls this type life-course-persistent antisocial behavior. The specific form of these problems may vary from one age level to the next:

> Biting and hitting at age 4, shoplifting and truancy at age 10, selling drugs and stealing cars at age 16, robbery and rape at age 22, and fraud and child abuse at age 30. The underlying disposition remains the same, but its expression changes form as new social opportunities arise at different points in development.
>
> (Moffitt, 1993, p. 679)

Follow-up studies suggest that in some ways psychopaths tend to "burn out" when they reach 40 or 45 years of age. These changes are most evident for the impulsive, socially deviant kinds of behavior that are represented in the second factor on Hare's Psychopathy Checklist (Harpur & Hare, 1994). Indeed, older psychopaths are less likely to exhibit a pathological "need for excitement" or to engage in impulsive, criminal behaviors. In contrast to this pattern, personality traits associated with the emotional–interpersonal factor on the PCL, such as deceitfulness, callousness, and lack of empathy, do not become less conspicuous over time. These are apparently more stable features of the disorder.

It is not clear whether the age-related decline in social deviance represents a change in personality structure (improved impulse control and diminished sensation seeking). Moffitt's theory suggests that, as psychopaths grow older, they may find new outlets for their aggression, impulsive behavior, and callous disregard for others. For example, they might resort to fraud or child abuse, for which they are less likely to get caught.

TABLE 9–6 Key Symptoms of Psychopathy	
EMOTIONAL/INTERPERSONAL TRAITS	**SOCIAL DEVIANCE (ANTISOCIAL LIFESTYLE)**
Glib and superficial	Impulsive
Egocentric and grandiose	Poor behavior controls
Lack of remorse or guilt	Need for excitement
Lack of empathy	Lack of responsibility
Deceitful and manipulative	Early behavior problems
Shallow emotions	Adult antisocial behavior

Source: R. D. Hare, 1991, *Without Conscience: The Disturbing World of the Psychopaths Among Us,* (New York: Pocket Books). Reprinted by permission of Pocket Books.

Causes

Psychologists have studied etiological factors associated with psychopathy and antisocial personality disorder more extensively than for any of the other personality disorders. Research studies on this topic fall into three general areas. One is concerned with the biological underpinnings of the disorder, especially the possible influence of genetic factors. The second focus of investigation is social factors. The relationship between familial conflict and the development of antisocial behavior in children falls under this general heading. The third group of studies has addressed the nature of the psychological factors that might explain the apparent inability of people with antisocial personality disorder to learn from experience.

Biological Factors Several investigators have used twin and adoption methods to study the contributions of genetic and environmental factors to the development of antisocial personality disorder and of criminal behavior more generally. The adoption strategy is based on the study of adoptees: people who were separated from their biological parents at an early age and raised by adoptive families (see Chapter 2). Several adoption studies have found that the development of antisocial behavior is determined by an interaction between genetic factors and adverse environmental circumstances (Waldman & Rhee, 2006). In other words, both types of influence are important. The highest rates of conduct disorder and antisocial behavior are found among the offspring of antisocial biological parents who are raised in an adverse adoptive environment.

Consider, for example, the results of one particularly informative study that was conducted by Remi Cadoret, a psychiatrist at the University of Iowa, and several colleagues (Cadoret et al., 1995; Yates, Cadoret, & Troughton, 1999). The investigators studied men and women who had been separated at birth from biological parents with antisocial personality disorder. This target group was compared to a control group of people who had been separated at birth from biological parents with no history of psychopathology. The offspring and their adoptive parents were interviewed to assess symptoms of conduct disorder, aggression, and antisocial behavior in the offspring. The adversity of the adoptive home environment was measured in terms of the total number of problems that were present, including severe marital difficulties, drug abuse, or criminal activity.

The results of the study by Cadoret and his colleagues indicated that people who were raised in more difficult adoptive homes were more likely to engage in various types of aggressive and antisocial behavior as children and as adults. Further analyses revealed that the harmful effects of an unfavorable environment were more pronounced in the target group than in the control group. In other words, offspring of antisocial parents were much more likely to exhibit symptoms of conduct disorder (truancy, school expulsion, lying, and stealing) as children and exaggerated aggressive behavior as adolescents if they were raised in an adverse adoptive home environment. Being raised in an adverse home environment did not significantly increase the probability of conduct disorder, aggression, or antisocial behavior among offspring in the control group. Thus antisocial behavior appeared to result from the interaction of genetic and environmental factors.

Social Factors Adoption studies indicate that genetic factors interact with environmental events to produce patterns of antisocial and criminal behavior. The combination of a genetic predisposition toward antisocial behavior and environmental adversity is particularly harmful. What kinds of events might be involved in this process? Obvious candidates include physical abuse and childhood neglect, as indicated by the longitudinal study of adolescents and their families (Farrington, 2006; Johnson et al., 1999).

How can the interaction between genetic factors and family processes be explained? Moffitt's explanation for the etiology of life course persistent antisocial behavior depends on the influence of multiple, interacting systems. One pathway involves the concept of children's temperament and the effect that their characteristic response styles may have on parental behavior. Children with a "difficult" temperament—that

◀ Antisocial behavior can be perpetuated when the person selects friends who share similar antisocial interests and problems.

is, those whose response style is characterized by high levels of negative emotion or excessive activity—may be especially irritating to their parents and caretakers (Bates, Wachs, & Emde, 1994). They may be clumsy, overactive, inattentive, irritable, or impulsive. Their resistance to disciplinary efforts may discourage adults from maintaining persistent strategies in this regard. This type of child may be most likely to evoke maladaptive reactions from parents who are poorly equipped to deal with the challenges presented by this kind of behavior. Parents may be driven either to use unusually harsh punishments or to abandon any attempt at discipline. This interaction between the child and the social environment fosters the development of poorly controlled behavior. Antisocial behavior is perpetuated when the person selects friends who share similar antisocial interests and problems.

After a pattern of antisocial behavior has been established during childhood, many factors lock the person into further antisocial activities. Moffitt's theory emphasizes two sources of continuity. The first is a limited range of behavioral skills. The person does not learn social skills that would allow him or her to pursue more appropriate responses than behaviors such as lying, cheating, and stealing. Once the opportunity to develop these skills is lost during childhood, they may never be learned. The second source of continuity involves the results of antisocial behavior during childhood and adolescence. The person becomes progressively ensnared by the aftermath of earlier choices. Many possible consequences of antisocial behavior, including being addicted to drugs, becoming a teenaged parent, dropping out of school, and having a criminal record, can narrow the person's options.

Psychological Factors Adoption, twin, and family studies provide clues to the types of etiological factors that may cause antisocial personality disorder. Another series of studies, beginning in the 1950s and extending to the present, has been concerned with the psychological mechanisms that may mediate this type of behavior. These investigations have attempted to explain several characteristic features of psychopathy—such as lack of anxiety, impulsivity, and failure to learn from experience—using various types of laboratory tasks (Fowles & Dindo, 2006).

Subjects in the laboratory tasks are typically asked to learn a sequence of responses in order either to receive a reward or avoid an aversive consequence, such as electric shock or loss of money. Although the overall accuracy of psychopaths' performance on these tasks is generally equivalent to that of nonpsychopathic subjects, their behavior sometimes appears to be unaffected by the anticipation of punishment.

Two primary hypotheses have been advanced to explain the poor performance of psychopaths on these tasks. One point of view is based on Cleckley's argument that psychopaths are emotionally impoverished. Their lack of anxiety and fear is particularly striking. Research support for this hypothesis is based in large part on an examination of physiological responses while subjects are performing laboratory tasks. One particularly compelling line of investigation involves the examination of the eye blink startle reflex. People blink their eyes involuntarily when they are startled by a loud, unexpected burst of noise. For most people, the magnitude of this response is increased if, at the time they are startled, they are engaged in an ongoing task that elicits fear or some other negative emotional state (such as viewing frightening or disgusting stimuli). The magnitude of the startle response is decreased if the person is engaged in a task that elicits positive emotion. Psychopaths' startle responses follow a pattern different from those observed in normal subjects (Herpertz et al., 2001; Patrick & Zempolich, 1998); they do not show the exaggerated startle response that is indicative of fear in the presence of aversive stimuli. This emotional deficit may explain why psychopaths are relatively insensitive to, or able to ignore, the effects of punishment.

The other hypothesis holds that psychopaths have difficulty shifting or reallocating their attention to consider the possible negative consequences of their behavior. Evidence for this explanation is based in large part on the observation that psychopaths respond normally to punishment in some situations, but not in others. This is especially evident in mixed-incentive situations, in which the person's behavior might be either rewarded or punished. Psychopaths are preoccupied with the potential for a successful outcome. They will continue gambling when the stakes are high, even when the odds are badly against them. And they will pursue a potential sexual encounter, even when the other person is trying to discourage their interest. They fail to inhibit inappropriate behavior because they are less able than other people to stop and consider the meaning of important signals that their behavior might lead to punishment (Hiatt & Newman, 2006; Patterson & Newman, 1993).

Critics of this line of research have noted some problems with existing psychological explanations for the psychopath's behavior. One limitation is the implicit assumption that most people conform to social regulations and ethical principles because of anxiety or fear of punishment. The heart of this criticism seems to lie in a disagreement regarding the relative importance of Cleckley's criteria for psychopathy. It might be argued that the most crucial features are not low anxiety and failure to learn from experience, but lack of shame and pathological egocentricity. According to this perspective, the psychopath is simply a person who has chosen, for whatever reason, to behave in a persistently selfish manner that ignores the feelings and rights of other people. "Rather than moral judgment being driven by anxiety, anxiety is driven by moral judgment" (Levenson, 1992).

Treatment

People with antisocial personalities seldom seek professional mental health services unless they are forced into treatment by the legal system. When they do seek treatment, the general consensus among clinicians is that it is seldom effective. This widely held impression is based, in part, on the traits that are used to define the disorder; like people with borderline personality disorder, people with antisocial personality disorder are typically unable to establish intimate, trusting relationships, which obviously form the basis for any treatment program.

The research literature regarding the treatment of antisocial personality disorder is sparse (Harris & Rice, 2006). Very few studies have identified cases using official diagnostic criteria for antisocial personality disorder. Most of the programs that have been evaluated have focused on juvenile delinquents, adults who have been imprisoned, or people otherwise referred by the criminal justice system. Outcome is often measured in terms of the frequency of repeated criminal offenses rather than in terms of changes in

behaviors more directly linked to the personality traits that define the core of antisocial personality. The high rate of alcoholism and other forms of substance dependence in this population is another problem that complicates planning and evaluating treatment programs aimed specifically at the personality disorder itself.

Although no form of intervention has proved to be effective for antisocial personality disorder, psychological interventions that are directed toward specific features of the disorder might be useful (Wallace & Newman, 2004). Examples are behavioral procedures that were originally designed for anger management and deviant sexual behaviors. Behavioral treatments can apparently produce temporary changes in behavior while the person is closely supervised, but they may not generalize to other settings.

DEPENDENT PERSONALITY DISORDER (DPD)

Dependent personality disorder (DPD) is listed in the third cluster of Axis II in DSM-IV-TR, along with avoidant and obsessive–compulsive personality disorders. Cluster C includes descriptions of various types of people who are anxious or fearful. Those who meet the criteria for DPD assume a submissive role in relationships with other people. They require an extraordinary level of reassurance and support, clinging to others who will take care of them. The following case study illustrates many of the most important features of this disorder.

BRIEF CASE **STUDY**
Dependent Personality Disorder

The patient, Mrs. S., was a 48-year-old married, Caucasian female. [She] reported numerous decision-making situations which provoke anxiety and attempts to seek reassurance. For example, buying food in the supermarket, deciding what to make for dinner, and buying furniture all provoked anxiety and led Mrs. S. to seek reassurance from her husband. Further, Mrs. S. reported feeling anxious when her husband was not there to reassure her (such as when he was away and Mrs. S. was responsible for trimming the garden bushes and lawn). Finally the patient related numerous anxiety-provoking instances in which decisions she made were initially approved of by an authority figure (such as her husband or physician) and then criticized by an important other (such as after following the instructions of her physician, she was criticized for doing so by a friend).

During school years, Mrs. S. always wanted to be part of the "group," but she felt uncomfortable because no one would assure her explicitly that she "fit in." Moreover, her high school advisor noted on Mrs. S.'s record that she "lacked initiative."

When the patient went to college, she studied nursing because "a lot of people my age went into nursing." When the time came to choose between a university-based or hospital-based program, she relied largely on her mother's advice.

The patient's first job as a nurse went rather smoothly because her supervisors were readily available. Unfortunately, her second position did not work out well. Apparently, Mrs. S. had trouble adjusting because she did not have "supportive" supervisors. She left this position after a short time.

Mrs. S. did not have much of a dating history. Her husband was her first and only lover. She was greatly attracted to him because he was "very forceful" and an "independent decision maker" (Turkat & Carlson, 1984, pp. 156–157).

Dependent personality disorder was introduced as a separate type of mental disorder in DSM-III (APA, 1980). Before then, the concept of dependency was viewed primarily as a personality trait rather than a mental disorder in its own right. It was considered to be a vulnerability factor that increased the person's risk for other types of mental disorder, particularly depression (Bornstein, 2007).

How is dependent personality disorder related to depression?

Freud proposed that dependent interpersonal relationships set the stage for later onset of depression (see Chapter 5). Contemporary investigators are still very much interested in that hypothesis. The term *sociotropy* is sometimes used to refer to dependency in that context. According to one version of this theory, people who are dependent, or sociotropic, may be particularly likely to become depressed if they experience a stressful event that is interpersonal in nature. Longitudinal studies suggest that a dependent or sociotropic interpersonal style does predict the later onset of depression (Davila, 2001; Mazure et al., 2000).

Symptoms

The DSM-IV-TR criteria for dependent personality disorder are listed in Table 9–7. These criteria reflect two underlying components: preference for affiliation and fear of criticism and rejection (Horowitz, 2004; Livesley, 1995). Preference for affiliation reflects the motivation to remain close to other people who will provide security and comfort. Fear of criticism and rejection reflects a lack of self-confidence and includes actions aimed at eliciting help and approval from others.

Dependent personality disorder overlaps with several other categories listed on Axis II of DSM-IV-TR. The greatest overlap is with bor-

---

TABLE 9–7   DSM-IV-TR Criteria for Dependent Personality Disorder

A pervasive and excessive need to be taken care of that leads to submissive and clinging behavior and fears of separation, beginning by early adulthood and present in a variety of contexts, as indicated by five (or more) of the following:

1. Has difficulty making everyday decisions without an excessive amount of advice and reassurance from others.
2. Needs others to assume responsibility for most major areas of his or her life.
3. Has difficulty expressing disagreement with others because of fear of loss of support or approval (does not include realistic fears of retribution).
4. Has difficulty initiating projects or doing things on his or her own (because of lack of self-confidence in judgment or abilities rather than a lack of motivation or energy).
5. Goes to excessive lengths to obtain nurturance and support from others, to the point of volunteering to do things that are unpleasant.
6. Feels uncomfortable or helpless when alone because of exaggerated fears of being unable to care for himself or herself.
7. Urgently seeks another relationship as a source of care and support when a close relationship ends.
8. Is unrealistically preoccupied with fears of being left to take care of himself or herself.

Source: Reprinted with permission from the *Diagnostic and Statistical Manual of Mental Disorders*, Fourth Edition, Text Revision. Copyright © 2000 by the American Psychiatric Association.

derline personality disorder (Reich, 1996). People with both types of personality disorder are fearful of being abandoned by other people. The reactions that they show are quite different, however. People with BPD become enraged and manipulative when they think they are being abandoned, whereas people with DPD respond with clinging and submissive behaviors (Hirschfeld, Shea, & Weise, 1995).

Causes

Relatively little research has been conducted on the etiology of dependent personality disorder as a separate form of mental disorder. There is, however, a substantial body of evidence concerned with the development of dependency as a personality trait. We must, therefore, use this evidence to draw inferences about pathways leading to dependent personality disorder. The available evidence points toward the importance of social and psychological factors in the development of extreme dependency. Genetic factors seem to play a relatively minor role (Nigg & Goldsmith, 1994).

Overprotective, authoritarian parents are likely to foster the development of dependency in their children (Baker, Capron, & Azorlosa, 1996; Bornstein, 1996). This conclusion is supported by the results of many different types of empirical research. It is also consistent with several different psychological theories that emphasize the importance of parent–child relationships in the formation and maintenance of dependent personality traits. For example, according to attachment theory (Ainsworth, 1989), children have a basic need to form a secure attachment to adults who will care for them (see Chapter 2). Those who are anxiously or insecurely attached as children are likely to become highly dependent during adolescence and adulthood. The process through which this pattern develops presumably involves the child's expectations about the availability of the parent. Children who have little confidence that attachment figures will be easily accessible and responsive when they need something may attempt to remain unusually close to those people, thus behaving in a clinging and dependent manner.

Treatment

There is virtually no literature on the outcome of treatment for dependent personality disorder. Therefore we cannot say whether any therapeutic procedures have been shown to be effective with this type of problem. People with this disorder may be less likely to seek treatment than people with other types of mental disorder. When they enter therapy, it is often because they also have other problems, such as depression, an anxiety disorder, or a substance use disorder. Whatever information is available on the treatment of this disorder is based on theoretical speculation and clinical experience (rather than empirical research).

Psychodynamic therapists have written most extensively about the treatment of dependent personality disorder. The primary goal in their approach is to help the person recognize the dependent pattern and the negative impact that it has on his or her relationships. Unfortunately, insight into the self-defeating nature of exceedingly dependent relationships may not be sufficient to allow the person to change his or her behavior. Behavior therapists and interpersonal therapists emphasize the need to teach skills in assertive communication (Benjamin, 2003; Perry, 2005). The client must learn to communicate feelings (both positive and negative) and desires accurately. The goal is to help the person develop interpersonal skills that will allow him or her to be more independent and self-reliant.

Cognitive therapy may also be beneficial in the treatment of dependent personality disorder. Problem-solving strategies, coupled with regular practice in making decisions, may foster independence and decrease the client's need to depend on other people for reassurance and support in routine situations. Cognitive therapy also addresses irrational or catastrophic self-statements about the potential consequences of behaving more independently or of ending a relationship (Beck, Freeman, & Davis, 2004; Crits-Christoph, 1998).

Psychopharmacology is not typically used as a specific treatment for dependent personality disorder. When medication is employed with such clients, it is usually aimed at the treatment of comorbid Axis I disorders, such as depression, agoraphobia, and panic disorder.

GETTING HELP

As we mention in this chapter, most people who would meet the diagnostic criteria for a personality disorder do not enter treatment, at least not voluntarily. Although their interpersonal problems are pervasive and deeply ingrained, they are reluctant or completely unable to see the active role that they play in maintaining their own misfortunes (regardless of their origins). The pejorative way in which personality disorders are sometimes portrayed may make some people reluctant to acknowledge that they have a personality disorder. We prefer to discuss these problems in terms of personality limitations or maladaptive response styles. No one is perfect. Being able to recognize your own weaknesses is a sign that you are open-minded and willing to change. This is the first important step toward improvement.

It also helps to have a little compassion for yourself, along with the determination to work toward a lasting change in the way you relate to the people and events of your life. *Lost in the Mirror: An Inside Look at Borderline Personality Disorder*, by Richard Moskovitz, provides an insightful and sympathetic guide to the painful emotional experiences associated with borderline personality disorder. It also illustrates ways in which these symptoms affect the lives of patients, their families, and their friends.

If you are interested in help because you have to deal with someone who you think may have a personality disorder, you probably feel confused, frustrated, and angry. You may also feel extremely guilty if you blame yourself for problems in the relationship or for the other person's unhappiness. This may be especially true if you are involved in a romantic relationship or must work closely with someone who might meet the criteria for a PD. Fortunately, it is often possible to adapt to such interactions. Several self-help guides provide advice about getting along with difficult people. One good example is *Fatal Flaws: Navigating Destructive Relationships with People with Disorders of Personality and Character* (Yudofsky, 2005). Most recommend that you begin by learning about the predictable nature of the other person's style. Recognize the presence of personality weaknesses and learn how to adapt to them. You must also accept the limits of your own ability to control the other person or to get him or her to change.

Sometimes the only solution is to end the relationship. At their most extreme, people with personality disorders cannot form reciprocal, mutually satisfying relationships with other people. This is particularly true in the case of antisocial personality disorder. Some unscrupulous people repeatedly abuse, exploit, and cheat others. We all may run across such people from time to time, and we need to learn how to protect ourselves. Robert Hare, an expert on psychopathy, concludes his book *Without Conscience* with a brief "survival guide" that may help you minimize your risk. He notes, for example, that we should be aware of the symptoms and interpersonal characteristics of psychopathy. We should be cautious in high-risk situations and know our own weaknesses. Hare's advice may be extremely helpful to someone who finds himself or herself trapped in a relationship with someone who is a psychopath. In fact, you may want to speak to a therapist or counselor to figure out why you have become involved in such an unequal, nonreciprocal relationship.

■ SUMMARY

Personality disorders are defined in terms of rigid, inflexible, maladaptive ways of perceiving and responding to oneself and one's environment that lead to social or occupational problems or subjective distress. This pattern must be pervasive across a broad range of situations, and it must be stable and of long duration. Among the hallmark features of personality disorders are major problems in interpersonal relationships. Many of the traits and symptoms that are associated with these problems are ego-syntonic. In other words, many people with personality disorders do not see themselves as being disturbed.

Personality disorders are controversial for a number of reasons, including their low diagnostic reliability and the tremendous overlap among specific personality disorder categories. They are presumably defined in terms of behaviors that deviate markedly from the expectations of the person's culture. Unfortunately, little information is currently available to indicate whether the DSM-IV-TR system for personality disorders will be useful in societies other than the United States, Canada, and Western Europe.

Many systems have been proposed to describe the fundamental dimensions of human personality. One that has become very popular is the five-factor model, which includes the basic traits of neuroticism, extraversion, openness to experience, agreeableness, and conscientiousness. Extreme variations in any of these traits—being either pathologically high or low—can be associated with personality disorders.

DSM-IV-TR lists 10 types of personality disorder, arranged in 3 clusters. There is considerable overlap among and between these types. Cluster A includes **paranoid, schizoid,** and **schizotypal personality disorders.** These categories generally refer to people who are seen as being odd or eccentric. Cluster B includes **antisocial, borderline, histrionic,** and **narcissistic personality disorders.** People who fit into this cluster are generally seen as being dramatic, unpredictable, and overly emotional. Cluster C includes **avoidant, dependent,** and **obsessive–compulsive personality disorders.** The common element in these disorders is presumably anxiety or fearfulness.

Dimensional approaches to the description of personality disorder provide an interesting alternative to this categorical system. These procedures rate a person on a number of traits, such as those included in the five-factor model. Dimensional classification systems have the advantage of being better able to account for similarities and differences among people with various combinations of personality traits. They do not require the assumption of arbitrary boundaries between normal and abnormal personality, and they are grounded in an extensive scientific literature regarding the basic elements of personality.

The overall prevalence of personality disorders among adults in the general population (i.e., the percentage of people who would qualify for a diagnosis of at least one type of personality disorder) is between 10 and 14 percent. Prevalence rates for specific types of personality disorder vary quite a bit from one study to the next. The highest prevalence rates are usually found to be associated with obsessive–compulsive, antisocial, and avoidant personality disorders, which may affect 3 or 4 percent of adults. The prevalence rates for other specific types tend to be approximately 1 or 2 percent of the population. The most obvious exception is narcissistic personality disorder, which appears to be the least common form, affecting much less than 1 percent of the population. Evidence regarding gender differences is not strong, except in the case of antisocial personality disorder where the condition is found to be at least four times more frequent in men than in women. Borderline personality disorder is the most frequently diagnosed form of personality disorder among people seeking mental health services (both inpatients and outpatients).

The disorders listed in Cluster A, especially schizoid and schizotypal personality disorders, have been viewed as possible antecedents or subclinical forms of schizophrenia. They are defined largely in terms of minor symptoms that resemble the hallucinations and delusions seen in the full blown disorder, as well as peculiar behaviors that have been observed among the first degree relatives of schizophrenic patients. Research on the etiology of schizotypal personality disorder has focused primarily on studies of its genetic relationship to schizophrenia.

The most important features of borderline personality disorder revolve around a pervasive pattern of instability in self-image, in interpersonal relationships, and in mood. Research regarding the etiology of borderline personality disorder has focused on two primary areas. One involves the impact of chaotic and abusive families. The other is concerned with the premature separation of children from their parents. Both sets of factors presumably can lead to problems in emotional regulation.

Psychopathy and antisocial personality disorder are two different attempts to define the same disorder. The DSM-IV-TR definition of ASPD places primary emphasis on social deviance in adulthood (repeated lying, physical assaults, reckless and irresponsible behavior). The concept of psychopathy places greater emphasis on emotional and interpersonal deficits, such as lack of remorse, lack of empathy, and shallow emotions. Adoption studies indicate that the etiology of antisocial behavior is determined by an interaction between genetic factors and adverse environmental circumstances. Laboratory studies of people who meet the criteria for psychopathy have focused on two hypotheses. One suggests that psychopaths are emotionally impoverished. The other is focused on cognitive deficits and holds that psychopaths have difficulty shifting their attention in order to avoid punishment.

Treatment procedures for people with personality disorders are especially difficult to design and evaluate, for three principal reasons. First, people with these disorders frequently don't have insight into the nature of their problems. Thus they are unlikely to seek treatment, and if they do, they frequently terminate treatment prematurely. Second, pure forms of personality disorder are relatively rare. Most people with a personality disorder who are in treatment also exhibit comorbid forms of personality disorder and/or comorbid Axis I disorders, such as depression or drug addiction. Third, people with a personality disorder have difficulty establishing and maintaining meaningful, stable interpersonal relationships of the sort that are required for psychotherapy.

Treatment for schizotypal and borderline personality disorders often involves the use of antipsychotic medication or antidepressant medication. A few controlled studies indicate that these drugs can be beneficial. Long-term outcome tends to be better for patients with borderline than schizotypal personality disorder. Various types of psychological intervention, including psychodynamic procedures as well as dialectical behavior therapy, have frequently been employed with borderline patients. People with antisocial personality disorder seldom seek treatment voluntarily. When they do, the general consensus among clinicians is that it is seldom effective.

THE BIG PICTURE CRITICAL THINKING REVIEW

What is the difference between being eccentric and having a personality disorder?

People who are unconventional are not necessarily disagreeable or difficult interpersonally. The concept of personality disorder, on the other hand, carries the assumption that the characteristic features by which they are defined are also associated with subjective distress or social impairment. (SEE PAGES 257–258)

In what ways are borderline and narcissistic personality disorders similar?

People in both groups can be hypersensitive and self-centered, thinking that others should be especially concerned with their needs and interests. When these expectations are not met, they may react with intense anger. (SEE PAGES 265–266)

What are the advantages of a dimensional approach that would describe personality problems as variations on normal personality traits?

This alternative perspective would minimize problems associated with comorbidity (a person meeting criteria for more than one diagnostic category) and arbitrary cut-off points between normal and abnormal personality. (SEE PAGES 268–269)

Which personality disorders are least likely to change as a person gets older?

Schizoid and schizotypal personality disorders are relatively intractable problems and are associated with enduring social isolation and occupational difficulties. (SEE PAGES 271–272)

Why are personality disorders so difficult to treat?

Many people with personality disorders are unable to recognize the nature of their problems. They may also be uncomfortable with the type of close, personal relationship that must be formed with a therapist if psychological treatment is going to be successful. (SEE PAGE 276)

What is the difference between antisocial personality disorder and psychopathy?

The DSM-IV definition of antisocial personality disorder is focused largely on repeated conflict with authorities and failure to conform to social norms, while the definition of psychopathy places greater importance on emotional deficits (lack of remorse, shallow emotions) and personality traits (impulsivity, grandiosity, lack of responsibility). (SEE PAGES 282–283)

How is dependent personality disorder related to depression?

People who are excessively dependent on other people may be more vulnerable to becoming depressed if they experience serious interpersonal difficulties. (SEE PAGE 288)

■ KEY TERMS

antisocial personality
  disorder **265**

avoidant personality
  disorder **267**

borderline personality
  disorder **265**

cross-cultural
  psychology **273**

dependent personality
  disorder **267**

histrionic personality
  disorder **265**

impulse control
  disorders **278**

narcissistic personality
  disorder **266**

obsessive–compulsive
  personality disorder **267**

paranoid personality
  disorder **263**

personality **256**

personality disorder **257**

psychopathy **282**

schizoid personality
  disorder **264**

schizotypal personality
  disorder **264**

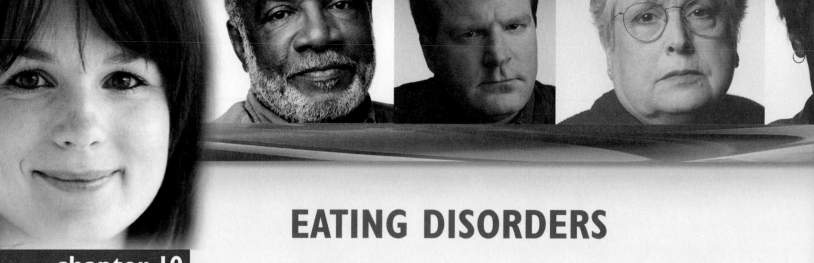

EATING DISORDERS

Popular culture in the United States is obsessed with physical appearance. We are told that "beauty is only skin deep," but the entertainment, cosmetic, fashion, and diet industries are eager to convince young people that "looks are everything." Perfect men are handsome, muscular, and successful. Perfect women are beautiful and thin—extremely thin. In fact, women's thinness is equated with beauty, fitness, success, and ultimately with happiness. Given our national obsession with appearance, diet, and weight, we should not be surprised that many people, especially young women, become obsessed to the point of developing eating disorders.

OVERVIEW

Eating disorders are severe disturbances in eating behavior that result from the sufferer's obsessive fear of gaining weight. Some experts have suggested that *dieting disorder* is a more accurate term, because dread of weight gain and obsession with weight loss are central features of eating disorders (Beumont, Garner, & Touyz, 1994). DSM-IV-TR lists two major types of eating disorders: anorexia nervosa and bulimia nervosa. The most obvious characteristic of **anorexia nervosa** is extreme emaciation, or more technically, the refusal to maintain a minimally normal body weight. The term *anorexia* literally means "loss of appetite," but this is a misnomer. People with anorexia nervosa *are* hungry, yet they starve themselves nevertheless. Some unfortunate victims literally starve themselves to death.

Bulimia nervosa is characterized by repeated episodes of binge eating, followed by inappropriate compensatory behaviors such as self-induced vomiting, misuse of laxatives, or excessive exercise. The literal meaning of the term *bulimia* is "ox appetite" ("hungry enough to eat an ox"), but people with bulimia nervosa typically have a normal appetite and maintain a normal weight. In fact, most sufferers view their binge eating as a failure of control, not as an indulgence of their hunger. People with bulimia nervosa usually are ashamed and secretive about their binge eating and purging.

Both anorexia and bulimia are about 10 times more common among females than males, and they develop most commonly among women in their teens and early twenties. The in-

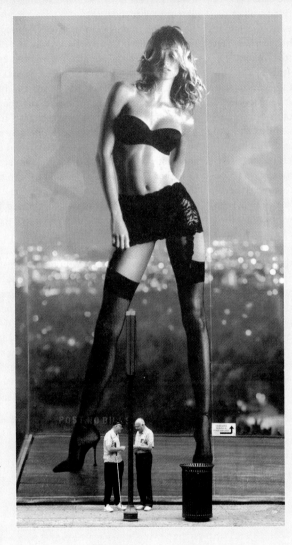

creased incidence among young people reflects both the intense focus on young women's physical appearance and the difficulties many adolescent girls have in adjusting to the rapid changes in body shape and weight that begin with puberty (Hsu, 1990). According to the National Centers for Disease Control and Prevention, at any point in time 44 percent of high school females are attempting to lose weight compared with 15 percent of males. (Many adolescent boys want to *gain* weight in order to look bigger and stronger; Serdula et al., 1993). A national survey found that almost half of American women have a negative body image, particularly concerning their waist, hips, and/or thighs (Cash & Henry, 1995; see Figure 10–1). European American and Latina women report higher rates of body dissatisfaction than African Americans (Bay-Cheng et al., 2002; Grabe & Hyde, 2006), with dissatisfaction increasing from the 1980s to the 1990s among white women (Cash et al., 2004). Fortunately, levels of body dissatisfaction declined between the 1990s and 2001 among both European American and African American women, perhaps indicating a growing resistance to the popular media's culture of thinness (Cash et al., 2004).

In this chapter, we discuss the symptoms of anorexia nervosa separately from those of bulimia nervosa, because they differ considerably. We combine the two disorders when reviewing diagnosis, frequency, and causes, however, because they share many developmental similarities. For example, many people with anorexia nervosa also binge and purge on occasion; many people with bulimia nervosa have a history of anorexia nervosa. When considering treatment, we again dis-

◄ The images of women portrayed in advertising and the popular media contribute to the development of eating disorders.

cuss the two disorders separately, reflecting the important differences in the focus and effectiveness of therapy for each disorder (Keel et al., 2000). We begin with a case study.

CASE **STUDY** Serrita's Anorexia

Serrita was an attractive, well-dressed, and polite 15-year-old high school sophomore who was living in a friendly joint-custody arrangement. She spent alternating weeks living with each of her successful, middle-class parents. Serrita was an excellent student. Her mother described as a "sweet girl who never gave me an ounce of worry—until now." When she was first seen by a clinical psychologist for the treatment of anorexia nervosa, Serrita was 5 feet 2 inches tall and weighed 81 pounds. Serrita's gaunt appearance was painfully obvious to anyone who looked at her. Despite her constant scrutiny of her own body, however, Serrita firmly denied that she was too thin. Instead, she asserted that she looked "almost right." She was still on a diet, and every day she carefully inspected her stomach, thighs, hips, arms, and face for any signs of fat. Although Serrita was generally pleased with the image she saw in her bathroom mirror, she remained deathly afraid of gaining weight. She monitored her food intake with incredible detail. She could recite every item of food she had consumed recently and discuss its caloric and fat content.

Serrita began her diet 9 months earlier after visiting her family doctor, who told her that she could stand to lose a pound or two. At the time, Serrita weighed 108 pounds, a normal weight for her age, height, and body type. Serrita claimed that the doctor's comment motivated her to begin a diet, and she also wanted to look more attractive. Serrita wanted to look like the women in her favorite magazines, but she felt that she wasn't the "cute, all-American girl"— she saw herself as too short, too dark, and her features as too sharp. Serrita secretly hoped that having a "great body" would compensate for her perceived inadequacies.

Serrita's diet began normally enough. She read extensively about food, weight, and diet and quickly lost the 6 pounds she wanted to lose. Without really planning to do so, Serrita simply continued her diet. She developed the habit of scouring her image in the mirror, and she invariably found some spot that was just a bit "too fat." As a result, she continually set a new goal to lose another couple of pounds. She weighed herself constantly and said that the bathroom scale became her "best friend." Her friends' and family's compliments soon turned into worried warnings, but privately Serrita was exhilarated. To her, the concerned remarks only proved that her diet was working.

Serrita's diet was extreme and rigid, and she adhered obsessively to a routine. Breakfast consisted of one slice of dry wheat toast and a small glass of orange juice. Lunch was either an apple or a small salad without dressing. In between meals, Serrita drank several diet colas, which helped control her constant, gnawing appetite. Dinner typically was a family meal whether Serrita was at her mom's or her dad's house. During these meals, Serrita picked at whatever she was served. Sometimes her parents would plead with her to eat more, and Serrita would eat a bit to appease them. On occasion, perhaps once a week, Serrita forced herself to vomit after dinner, because she felt that her parents made her to eat too much.

Serrita's parents eventually became so concerned about her weight loss that they made her go to see her family physician. The physician also was very concerned about Serrita's low weight, and she discovered that Serrita had not menstruated in over 6 months. The physician said that Serrita was suffering from anorexia nervosa. She immediately made a referral to a psychologist as well as to a nutritionist, who, the physician hoped, would correct Serrita's extreme views about dieting.

In talking with the psychologist, Serrita agreed that she understood why everyone was concerned about her health. She knew about anorexia nervosa, which she realized was a serious problem. Serrita even hinted that she knew that she was suffering from anorexia nervosa. Nevertheless, Serrita steadfastly denied that she needed to gain weight. Although she was happy to talk with the psychologist, she was not prepared to change her eating habits. Serrita was deathly afraid that eating even a little more would cause her to "lose control" and "turn into a blimp." Perhaps more importantly, she was *proud* of her mastery of her hunger. She was not about to give up the control she had fought so hard to obtain.

Women's Dissatisfaction with Their Appearance

Percentage of women reporting dissatisfaction

Face	Height	Hair	Upper torso	Muscle tone	Weight	Lower torso	Mid-torso
11.7	13.4	16.3	25.1	36.9	46.0	47.4	51.0

FIGURE 10–1 Percentage of females reporting that they were "very or mostly dissatisfied" with specific physical attributes in a national sample of women aged 18 to 70 interviewed in 1993.

Source: T. F. Cash and P. E. Henry, 1995, "Women's Body Images: The Results of a National Survey in the U.S.A.," *Sex Roles, 33,* pp. 19–28. Copyright © 1995. Reprinted by permission of Springer Science and Business Media.

SYMPTOMS OF ANOREXIA

Serrita showed all the classic symptoms of anorexia nervosa: extreme emaciation, a disturbed perception of her body, an intense fear of gaining weight, and, in women, the cessation of menstruation. Serrita also exhibited a number of problems that are commonly associated with anorexia nervosa but are not defining symptoms: obsessive preoccupation with food, occasional purging, and a "successful" struggle for control over persistent hunger. Finally, Serrita did not suffer from a few important problems that are sometimes associated with anorexia nervosa, particularly mood disturbance, sexual difficulties, a lack of impulse control, and medical problems secondary to the weight loss.

Refusal to Maintain a Normal Weight

The most obvious and most dangerous symptom of anorexia nervosa is a *refusal to maintain a minimally normal body weight.* Like Serrita, anorexia nervosa often begins with a diet to lose just a few pounds. A young woman weighs near her healthy body weight, and she decides to lose a little weight, perhaps to fit into some new clothes. The diet goes awry, however, and losing weight eventually becomes the key focus. Weight falls well below the normal range and often plummets to dangerously low levels.

DSM-IV-TR contains no formal cutoff as to how thin is too thin but suggests 85 percent of expected body weight as a rough guideline. The *body mass index,*[1] a calculation derived from weight and height, is another useful way to determine whether or not someone is significantly underweight. Both DSM-IV-TR and the body mass cutoffs represent weights well beyond "thin" and into the realm of "emaciated," but weight loss often is more extreme: The average victim of anorexia loses 25 to 30 percent of normal body weight (Hsu, 1990). Unlike Serrita, who was fortunate in this sense, some people with anorexia nervosa are not treated until their weight loss becomes life threatening. In fact, about 10 percent of people with anorexia nervosa are estimated to die of starvation, suicide, or medical complications stemming from their extreme weight loss (APA, 2000; Hsu, 1995).

Disturbance in Evaluating Weight or Shape

A second defining symptom of anorexia nervosa is a perceptual, cognitive, or affective disturbance in evaluating one's weight and shape. Like Serrita, many individuals steadfastly *deny problems with their weight.* Even when confronted with their own withered image in a mirror, some people with anorexia nervosa nevertheless insist that their weight is not a problem.

---

[1]You calculate the body mass index as follows: (1) Multiply weight in pounds by 700; (2) divide this number by height in inches; (3) divide this second number by height in inches. You can interpret the resulting number as follows: Under 16 = extremely underweight; 16–18 = significantly underweight; 20–25 = healthy weight; 27–30 = overweight; 30–40 = significantly overweight; over 40 = extremely overweight.

Other people with the disorder suffer from *a disturbance in the way body weight or shape is experienced.* Sometimes this may include a **distorted body image,** an inaccurate perception of body size and shape. One early study found that young women with anorexia nervosa overestimated the size of various body parts in comparison to a normal control group (Slade & Russell, 1973). The following excerpt, which we received anonymously from a student, illustrates the symptom.

> I'll try to explain how a person with an eating disorder sees a distorted image of herself. It's almost like she sees herself as bloated—of course she sees herself, she recognizes herself, but as bigger than usual. Also, the skinnier she gets, the more she notices fat deposits around the waist, under the arms, etc., because the more fat is lost, the more attention is drawn to the little bit of fat that still exists. Also, it's the point of reference in the background that may sometimes be distorted. She looks in the bathroom mirror and thinks, "Did I take up that much space against this wall yesterday?"

Not all people with anorexia nervosa suffer from a distorted body image, and many people without the disorder inaccurately estimate the size of their body (Garfinkel, Kennedy, & Kaplan, 1995; Thompson, 1996). Still, all people with the disorder are *unduly influenced by their body weight or shape in self-evaluation.* Whatever its specific form, a defining characteristic of anorexia nervosa is a disturbance in the way one's body or weight is perceived or evaluated. People with anorexia nervosa do not recognize their emaciation for what it is.

How do people with anorexia nervosa evaluate their weight and shape?

Fear of Gaining Weight

An *intense fear of becoming fat* is a third defining characteristic of anorexia. The fear of gaining weight presents particular problems for treatment. A therapist's encouragement to eat more can terrify someone who fears that

▶ Caraline, 28 years old, told a reporter, "I'm not telling you how much I weigh because I'm ashamed I don't weigh less." She later died of complications due to anorexia nervosa.

▶ Olympic-class gymnast Christy Heinrich with her boyfriend in 1993. After a 5-year struggle with anorexia nervosa, she died of multiple organ failure in 1994. She weighed less than 50 pounds at the time.

relaxing control, even just a little, will lead to a total loss of control. Ironically, the fear of gaining weight is not soothed by the tremendous weight loss. In fact, the fear may grow more intense as the individual loses more weight (APA, 2000).

Cessation of Menstruation

Amenorrhea, the absence of at least three consecutive menstrual cycles, is the final DSM-IV-TR symptom of anorexia nervosa (in females). The presence of amenorrhea has led to speculation about the role of sexuality and sexual maturation in causing anorexia nervosa. However, amenorrhea typically is a *reaction* to the loss of body fat and associated physiological changes, not a symptom that precedes anorexia (Pinheiro et al., 2007). Sexual disinterest also is a common reaction to severe weight loss (Keys et al., 1950). Many experts recommend dropping the amenorrhea criterion for this reason, and because some apparently anorectic women do menstruate, the presence or absence of menstruation does not differentiate between women who meet other diagnostic criteria. Menstrual irregularities also often are associated with bulimia (Pinheiro et al., 2007; Wilfley et al., 2008).

Medical Complications

Anorexia nervosa can cause a number of medical complications. People with anorexia commonly complain about constipation, abdominal pain, intolerance to cold, and lethargy. Some of these complaints stem from the effects of semistarvation on blood pressure and body temperature, both of which may fall below normal. In addition, the skin can become dry and cracked, and some people develop *lanugo,* a fine, downy hair, on their face or trunk of their body. Broader medical difficulties may include anemia, infertility, impaired kidney functioning, cardiovascular difficulties, dental erosion, and osteopenia (bone loss; Pomeroy, 1996). A particularly dangerous medication complication is an *electrolyte imbalance,* a disturbance in the levels of potassium, sodium, calcium, and other vital elements found in bodily fluids. Electrolyte imbalance can lead to cardiac arrest or kidney failure. Anorexia nervosa may begin with the seemingly harmless desire to be a bit thinner, but the eating disorder can lead to serious health problems, including death.

Struggle for Control

Some people with anorexia act impulsively, but clinical accounts and some research suggest that more are conforming and controlling. People with anorexia nervosa often take great pride in their self-denial, feeling like masters of control. Some theorists speculate that the disorder actually develops out of a desperate sense of having no control. Excessively compliant "good girls" may find that obsessively regulating their diet allows them to be in charge of at least one area of their lives (Bruch, 1982).

Comorbid Psychological Disorders

Anorexia nervosa is associated with other psychological problems, particularly obsessive–compulsive disorder (Kasvikis et al., 1986), obsessive–compulsive personality disorder (Gillberg, Rastam, & Gillberg, 1995), and depression (Braun, Sunday, & Halmi, 1994). In many cases, however, these comorbid psychological problems may be reactions to anorexia, not causes of it.

People with anorexia nervosa are obsessed with food and diet, and they often follow compulsive rituals in regard to eating. However, a unique study found that obsessive–compulsive behavior can result from starvation rather than cause it. In this study, 32 World War II conscientious objectors fulfilled their military obligation by voluntarily undergoing semistarvation for 24 weeks. (The researchers wanted to learn about the effects of starvation on military personnel in the field.) As the men reduced their food intake and lost more and more weight, they developed extensive obsessions about food and compulsive eating rituals. For many of the men, in fact, the obsessions and compulsions continued long after they returned to their normal weight (Keys et al., 1950). Obsessive–compulsive personality disorder may sometimes contribute to anorexia nervosa, but some obsessive–compulsive *behavior* may be a reaction to starvation.

◀ Conscientious objectors participating in a study of semistarvation duing World War II. Many starving men developed obsessions about food similar to those sometimes found in anorexia nervosa.

Most people with anorexia nervosa also show symptoms of mild depression, such as sad mood, irritability, insomnia, social withdrawal, and diminished interest in sex (Braun, Sunday, & Halmi, 1994). Like obsessive–compulsive behavior, however, depression is a common secondary reaction to starvation. Mood disturbances sometimes play a role in the development of anorexia nervosa, but depression can also be a reaction to the eating disorder (Cooper, 1995; Hsu, 1990).

Finally, anorexia often co-occurs with the symptoms of bulimia. In some cases, purging follows episodes of binge eating. In other cases, purging may be a means of further controlling eating that already is dramatically restricted. People with anorexia nervosa who do *not* binge eat or purge generally are better adjusted on measures of their mental health—for example, they have lower rates of depression (Braun, Sunday, & Halmi, 1994).

SYMPTOMS OF BULIMIA

Bulimia nervosa and anorexia nervosa, although different, share similarities. One connection is that many people with bulimia nervosa have a history of anorexia nervosa, as in the following case study.

CASE **STUDY** Michelle's Secret

Michelle was a sophomore at a state university when she first sought help for a humiliating problem. Several times a week, she fell into an episode of uncontrollable binge eating followed by self-induced vomiting. Michelle had enough control to limit her binge eating to times when her roommate was away. But when Michelle was alone and feeling bad—the episodes usually occurred on "bad days," of which Michelle had many—she would buy a half-gallon of ice cream and perhaps a bag of cookies and bring the food back to her room, where she secretly gorged herself. The binge brought her some comfort at first, but by the time she was finished, she felt physically uncomfortable, sickened by her lack of control, and terrified of gaining weight. To compensate, she would walk across the street to an empty bathroom in the psychology department. There, she forced herself to vomit by sticking her finger down her throat.

The vomiting brought relief from the physical discomfort, but it did not relieve her shame. Michelle was disgusted by her actions, but she could not stop herself. In fact, the pattern of binge eating and purging had been going on for most of the school year. Michelle decided to seek treatment only when a friend from her psychology class discovered her purging in the bathroom. The friend also had a history of bulimia nervosa, but she had gotten her eating under control. She convinced Michelle to try therapy.

Michelle's eating problems began when she was in high school. She had studied ballet since she was 8 years old, and with the stern encouragement of her instructor she had struggled to maintain her willowy figure as she became an adolescent. At first she dieted openly, but her parents constantly criticized her inadequate eating. In order to appease them, Michelle would eat a more normal meal but force herself to vomit shortly afterwards. When she was a junior in high school, Michelle's parents confronted her and took her to a psychologist, who treated her for anorexia nervosa. She was 5 feet 6 inches tall at the time, but she weighed only 95 pounds. Michelle was furious and refused to talk in any depth with the therapist. She allowed herself to gain a few pounds—to about 105—only to convince her parents that she did not need treatment.

Michelle's weight eventually stabilized between 105 and 110 pounds—enough of a gain that her parents allowed her to stop therapy. Even though she was very thin, Michelle continued to plan her diet with great care. She avoided fat with a vengeance. She counted every calorie at every meal every day. Throughout college, she starved herself all week so she could eat normally on dates during the weekend. Occasionally, she forced herself to vomit after eating too much, but she did not see this as a big problem. Until the previous summer, she had maintained her weight near her goal of 105 pounds. Over the summer, however, Michelle relaxed her diet as she "partied" with old friends. She gained about 15 pounds, a healthy weight for her height and body type. When she returned to college, however, Michelle grew disgusted with her appearance and fearful of gaining even more weight.

Michelle tried to lose weight, but she met with little success. She started to purge more frequently in a desperate attempt to "diet," but she soon found herself binge eating more frequently, too. Michelle was extremely frustrated by her "lack of self-control." Although she now recognized her past problems with anorexia nervosa, Michelle openly longed for the discipline she had once achieved over her hunger and diet.

By all outward appearances, Michelle was a bright, attractive, and successful young woman. Inwardly, she felt like a failure and a "fake." She longed to have a boyfriend but never found one despite many casual dates. She was intensely, if privately, competitive with her girlfriends. She wanted to be more beautiful and intelligent than other girls, but she inevitably felt inferior to one classmate or another. She was determined at least to be thinner than her girlfriends, but she felt that she had lost all control over this goal. Michelle also was furious with her parents. Their constant questions about her well-being caused her to feel angry and resentful instead of loved and supported. Michelle said that they asked all the right questions, but cared more about the family's image than about Michelle as a person. Michelle pretended to be happy and normal, but inside she felt as though she was going to explode. Secretly, she was miserable.

Michelle's frequent struggles with binge eating and purging, her sense of lost control during a binge, and her undue focus on her weight and figure are the core symptoms that define bulimia nervosa. Depression also is commonly associated with the disorder, as it was for Michelle.

Binge Eating

Binge eating is defined as eating an amount of food that is clearly larger than most people would eat under similar circumstances in a fixed period of time, for example, less than 2 hours. There have been some attempts to define a binge more objectively, such as eating more than 1,000 calories, or subjectively, such as based on the individual's appraisal. Variations in normal eating complicate these alternative definitions, however. Eating a very large number of calories may be normal under certain circumstances (think: Thanksgiving) and having two cookies may be considered a "binge" by other people. Thus the present DSM-IV-TR definition relies on a clinician's judgment about normal eating patterns (Garfinkel et al., 1995).

Sadly, many of the inappropriate eating behaviors border on being statistically normal—and clearly unhealthy—in our food- and weight-obsessed society. Over 35 percent of people report occasional binge eating. Distressingly large numbers of people also report that they fast (29 percent) and use self-induced vomiting (8 percent) or laxatives (over 5 percent) in an attempt to compensate for their eating (Fairburn & Beglin, 1990).

Binges may be planned in advance, or they may begin spontaneously. In either case, binges typically are secret. Most people with bulimia nervosa are ashamed and go to elaborate efforts to conceal their binge eating. During a binge, the individual typically eats very rapidly and soon feels uncomfortably full. Although the types of foods can vary widely, the person often selects ice cream, cookies, or other foods that are high in calories. Foods also may be selected for smooth texture to make vomiting easier, one reason why ice cream is a popular binge food.

Binge eating is commonly triggered by an unhappy mood, which may begin with an interpersonal conflict, self-criticism about weight or appearance, or intense hunger following a period of fasting. The binge initially is comforting and alleviates some unhappy feelings, but physical discomfort and fear of gaining weight soon override the positive aspects of binge eating (Garfinkel et al., 1995).

A key feature of binge eating is a sense of lack of control during a binge. Some individuals experience a binge as a "feeding frenzy," where they lose all control and eat compulsively and rapidly. Others describe a dissociative experience, as if they were watching themselves gorge. But the lack of control is not absolute. For example, people with bulimia can stop a binge if they are interrupted unexpectedly. In fact, as the disorder progresses, some people feel more in control during a binge but unable to stop the broader cycle of binge eating and compensatory behavior.

Inappropriate Compensatory Behavior

Almost all people with bulimia nervosa engage in **purging,** designed to eliminate consumed food from the body. The most common form of purging is self-induced vomiting; as many as 90 percent of people with bulimia nervosa engage in this behavior (APA, 2000). Other less common forms of purging include the misuse of laxatives, diuretics (which increase the frequency of urination), and, most rarely, enemas. Ironically, purging has only limited effectiveness in reducing caloric intake. Vomiting prevents the absorption of only about half the calories consumed during a binge, and laxatives, diuretics, and enemas have few lasting effects on calories or weight (Kaye et al., 1993).

Inappropriate compensatory behaviors other than purging include extreme exercise or rigid fasting following a binge. The extent to which these actions actually compensate for binge eat-

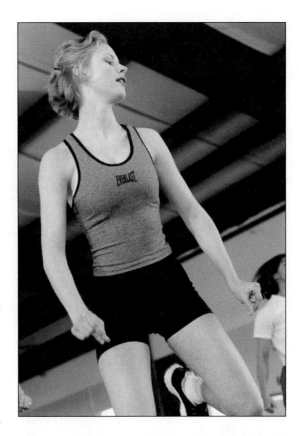

◄ Physical fitness offers many benefits, but some people exercise excessively to compensate for binge eating.

ing also is questionable, given what we know about the body's biological regulation of weight (Brownell & Fairburn, 1995).

Excessive Emphasis on Weight and Shape

People with bulimia nervosa place *excessive emphasis on body shape and weight* in evaluating themselves, a symptom shared with anorexia nervosa (see Table 10–1). Their self-esteem, and much of their daily routine, center around weight and diet. Some people with bulimia nervosa are exhilarated by positive comments or interest in their appearance, but their esteem plummets if a negative comment is made or if someone else draws more attention. Other people with the disorder constantly criticize their appearance, and the struggle with binge eating and purging only adds to their self-denigration. In either case, the individual's sense of self is linked too closely to appearance instead of personality, relationships, or achievements.

BULIMIA NERVOSA

JESSICA

"It started out with a diet for me..."

Watch the video "Bulimia: Jessica" on MyPsychLab. As you watch the video, listen for Jessica's struggles with appearance and weight and how they were magnified—sometimes very directly—by her efforts to pursue a career in the performing arts.

TABLE 10–1	Anorexia Nervosa and Bulimia Nervosa: Key Differences and Similarities	
ISSUE	**ANOREXIA NERVOSA**	**BULIMIA NERVOSA**
	DIFFERENCES	
Eating/weight	Extreme diet; below minimally normal weight	Binge eating/compensatory behavior; normal weight
View of disorder	Denial of anorexia; proud of "diet"	Aware of problem; secretive/ashamed of bulimia
Feelings of control	Comforted by rigid self-control	Distressed by lack of control
	SIMILARITIES	
Self-evaluation	Unduly influenced by body weight/shape	Unduly influenced by body weight/shape
Comorbidity of AN/BN	Some cases of AN also binge and purge	Many cases of BN have history of AN
SES, age, gender	Prevalent among high SES, young, female	Prevalent among high SES, young, female

Comorbid Psychological Disorders

Depression is common among individuals with bulimia nervosa, especially those who self-induce vomiting (APA, 2000). Some individuals become depressed prior to developing the eating disorder, and the bulimia may be a reaction to the depression in some of these cases. In many instances, however, depression begins at the same time as or follows the onset of bulimia nervosa (Braun, Sunday, & Halmi, 1994). In such circumstances, the depression is likely to be a reaction to the bulimia. In fact, depression often lifts following successful treatment of bulimia nervosa (Mitchell et al., 1990). Whether depression is an effect or cause of bulimia, eating disturbances are more severe and social impairment is greater when the two problems are comorbid (Stice & Fairburn, 2003).

Other disorders that may co-occur with bulimia nervosa include anxiety disorders, personality disorders (particularly borderline personality disorder), and substance abuse, particularly excessive use of alcohol and/or stimulants. Although each of these psychological difficulties presents special challenges in treating bulimia, the comorbidity with depression is most common and most significant (Brewerton et al., 1995).

What are some similarities and differences between anorexia and bulimia?

Medical Complications

A number of medical complications can result from bulimia nervosa. Repeated vomiting can erode dental enamel, particularly on the front teeth, and in severe cases teeth can become chipped and ragged looking. Repeated vomiting can also produce a gag reflex that is triggered too easily and perhaps unintentionally. One consequence of the sensitized gag reflex—one that is rarely reported in the scientific literature—is *rumination:* the regurgitation and rechewing of food (Parry-Jones, 1994). Another possible medical complication is the enlargement of the salivary glands, a consequence that has the ironic effect of making the sufferer's face appear puffy. As in anorexia nervosa, potentially serious medical complications can result from electrolyte imbalances. Finally, rupture of the esophagus or stomach has been reported in rare cases, sometimes leading to death (Pomeroy, 1996).

DIAGNOSIS OF EATING DISORDERS

Brief Historical Perspective

Isolated cases of eating disorders have been reported throughout history. The term *anorexia nervosa* was coined in 1874 by a British physician, Sir William

Withey Gull (1816–1890). Still, the history of professional concern with the disorders is very brief. References to eating disorders were rare in the literature prior to 1960, and the disorders have received scientific attention only in recent decades (Fairburn & Brownell, 2002; Striegel-Moore & Smolak, 2001). The term *bulimia nervosa* was used for the first time only in 1979 (Russell, 1979).

The diagnoses of anorexia nervosa and bulimia nervosa first appeared in DSM in 1980 (DSM-III). Although the diagnostic criteria have changed somewhat, the same eating behaviors remain as the central features of these disorders. The only major change was the creation of a separate diagnostic category for eating disorders. They previously had been listed as a subtype of the Disorders Usually First Diagnosed in Infancy, Childhood, or Adolescence, because many eating disorders begin during the teenage years. The new, separate grouping reflects the fact that eating disorders also can begin during adult life.

Contemporary Classification

Anorexia Nervosa DSM-IV-TR lists two types of eating disorders: anorexia nervosa and bulimia nervosa. Anorexia nervosa is defined by four symptoms described earlier (see Table 10–2). DSM-IV-TR also includes two subtypes of anorexia nervosa. The *restricting type* includes people who rarely engage in binge eating or purging. In contrast, the *binge eating/purging*

type is defined by regular binge eating and purging during the course of the disorder. The validity of the subtypes is questionable, however, as they do not differ in terms of comorbidity, recovery, relapse, or mortality (Wonderlich et al., 2007). Moreover, an 8-year longitudinal study found that 62 percent of the former restrictors met diagnostic criteria for binge eating/purging, and only 12 percent of the restrictors had never regularly engaged in binge eating and purging (Eddy et al., 2002).

▲ Actress Jessica Biel was *Esquire* magazine's "sexiest woman alive." She is athletic, shapely, and fit, but not abnormally thin.

TABLE 10–2 DSM-IV-TR Diagnostic Criteria for Anorexia Nervosa

A. Refusal to maintain body weight at or above a minimally normal weight for age and height (e.g., weight loss leading to maintenance of body weight less than 85 percent of that expected; or failure to make expected weight gain during period of growth, leading to body weight less than 85 percent of that expected).

B. Intense fear of gaining weight or becoming fat, even though underweight.

C. Disturbance in the way in which one's weight or shape is experienced, undue influence of body weight or shape on self-evaluation, or denial of the seriousness of the current low body weight.

D. In postmenarcheal females, amenorrhea, that is, the absence of at least three consecutive menstrual cycles.

SPECIFY TYPE

Restricting type: During the current episode, the person has not regularly engaged in binge eating or purging behavior.

Binge-eating/purging type: During the current episode, the person has regularly engaged in binge eating or purging behavior.

Source: Reprinted with permission from the *Diagnostic and Statistical Manual of Mental Disorders,* Fourth Edition, Text Revision. Copyright © 2000 by the American Psychiatric Association.

Bulimia Nervosa Bulimia nervosa is defined by five symptoms described earlier (see Table 10–3) and also is divided into two subtypes in DSM-IV-TR. The *purging type* regularly uses self-induced vomiting, laxatives, diuretics, or enemas. The *nonpurging type* instead attempts to compensate for binge eating only with fasting or excessive exercise. Like anorexia subtypes, however, research does not support these bulimia subtypes, and experts have recommended dropping them (Wilfley et al., 2008).

Binge Eating Disorder and Obesity There is debate about whether other eating problems should be considered to be eating disorders. **Binge eating disorder,** episodes of binge eating but without compensatory behavior, is one possible new diagnosis. In fact, provisional diagnostic criteria for binge eating disorder are included in an appendix of DSM-IV-TR for diagnostic categories requiring further study.

Binge eating is associated with a number of psychological and physical difficulties (Hudson et al., 2007). Among these problems is **obesity,** excess body fat corresponding with being 20 percent *above* expected weight. A cutoff of 40 percent above normal is a rough marker of severe overweight (Brownell, 1995). Calling obesity a "mental disorder" is controversial, especially given the high prevalence of overweight individuals in the United States and throughout the world. In fact, some professionals question our society's constant focus on dieting and our castigation of obese people. Obesity is not just a lack of "willpower," as biological factors contribute substantially to body shape and weight (Brownell & Rodin, 1994).

FREQUENCY OF EATING DISORDERS

Estimates of the epidemiology of anorexia and bulimia vary, but both disorders appear to have increased in frequency since the 1960s and 1970s (Hoek, 1995; Kendler et al., 1991; Lucas et al., 1999). Figure 10–2 illustrates the surge in new cases of anorexia nervosa based on one investigator's compilation of evidence (Hoek, 1995). According to this summary, the annual *incidence*, the number of new cases each year, of anorexia nervosa rose from 1 case per million people in 1930–1940 to over 50 cases per million people in 1980–1990. Figure 10–2 also suggests that anorexia nervosa is rare in the general population. It is far more common among certain segments of the population, however, particularly among young women. DSM-IV-TR indicates that lifetime prevalence of anorexia nervosa is 0.5 among

---

TABLE 10–3   DSM-IV-TR Diagnostic Criteria for Bulimia Nervosa

A. Recurrent episodes of binge eating. An episode of binge eating is characterized by both of the following:

  1. Eating, in a discrete period of time (e.g., within any 2-hour period), an amount of food that is definitely larger than most people would eat during a similar period of time and under similar circumstances.

  2. A sense of lack of control over eating during the episode (e.g., a feeling that one cannot stop eating or control what or how much one is eating).

B. Recurrent inappropriate compensatory behavior in order to prevent weight gain, such as self-induced vomiting; misuse of laxatives, diuretics, enemas, or other medications; fasting; or excessive exercise.

C. The binge eating and inappropriate compensatory behaviors both occur, on average, at least twice a week for 3 months.

D. Self-evaluation is unduly influenced by body shape and weight.

E. The disturbance does not occur exclusively during episodes of anorexia nervosa.

SPECIFY TYPE

Purging type: During the current episode, the person has regularly engaged in self-induced vomiting or the misuse of laxatives, diuretics, or enemas.

Nonpurging type: During the current episode, the person has used other inappropriate compensatory behaviors, such as fasting or excessive exercise, but has not regularly engaged in self-induced vomiting or the misuse of laxatives, diuretics, or enemas.

Source: Reprinted with permission from the *Diagnostic and Statistical Manual of Mental Disorders,* Fourth Edition, Text Revision. Copyright © 2000 by the American Psychiatric Association.

females, similar to a 0.9 estimate based on a recent U.S. national survey (Hudson et al., 2007). Anorexia nervosa also occurs among males, but most estimates indicate the disorder is about 10 times more common among women than men. Establishing the exact prevalence in males is difficult, because only a few cases are identified even in large national surveys (Hudson et al., 2007).

Recent decades also have witnessed a torrent of new cases of bulimia nervosa. Changes in the frequency of bulimia nervosa are difficult to document, however, because the diagnostic term was introduced only in 1979. Instead, investigators have examined cohort effects in prevalence rates. A **cohort** is a group that shares some feature in common, for example, year of birth; thus **cohort effects** are differences that distinguish one cohort from another.

Figure 10–3 portrays birth cohort effects in lifetime prevalence rates of bulimia nervosa among a large sample of American women who were born either before 1950, between 1950 and 1959, or in 1960 or after. The figure clearly indicates substantial cohort effects. The lifetime prevalence of bulimia nervosa was far greater among the cohort of women born after 1960 than it was for the cohort of women born before 1950. The risk for women born between 1950 and 1959 was intermediate between these two extremes (Kendler et al., 1991). Figure 10–3 also shows that the risk of developing bulimia declines with increasing age, at least among older cohorts. A recent study of a national U.S. sample also found this declining risk with age and replicated the cohort effects (Hudson et al., 2007). Thus the surge in bulimia nervosa—some say an epidemic—is due to dramatic increases among women born after about 1960. Not coincidentally, cultural standards of beauty changed for these and subsequent generations of women.

Bulimia nervosa has a lifetime prevalence of 1.5 percent among U.S. women and .5 percent among U.S. men. Binge eating disorder and occasional binge eating are even more common, with a respective lifetime prevalence of 3.5 percent and 4.9 percent among women and 2.0 percent and 4.0 percent among men (Hudson et al., 2007). Finally, we should note again the overlap between anorexia nervosa and bulimia nervosa. About 50 percent of all people with anorexia nervosa engage in episodes of binge eating and purging (Agras, 1987; Garfinkel et al., 1995), and many cases of bulimia nervosa have a history of anorexia nervosa (Wonderlich et al., 2007).

FIGURE 10–2 Anorexia nervosa has increased dramatically in recent decades. This figure portrays the annual incidence per 100,000 people in the general population based on data pooled from studies of hospital records and outpatient mental health care. Considerably higher rates are found among population subgroups, particularly young women.

Source: Figure, p. 209, "Incidence of Anorexia Nervosa, 1930–1980" from "The Distribution of Eating Disorders" by H. W. Hoek in EATING DISORDERS AND OBESITY: A Comprehensive Handbook ed. by K. D. Brownell and C. G. Fairbanks. Copyright © 1995. Reprinted by permission of Guilford Publications, Inc.

Standards of Beauty

Both anorexia and bulimia nervosa are approximately 10 times more common among women than among men. Many scientists believe that this huge difference is explained by gender roles and standards of beauty (Hsu, 1990; Striegel-Moore, 1995). Popular attitudes about women in the United States tell us that "looks are

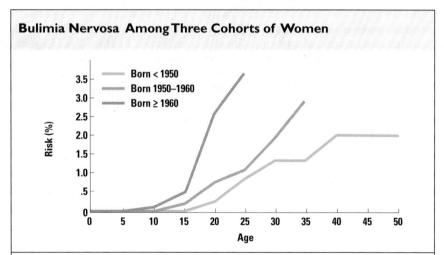

FIGURE 10–3 The lifetime cumulative risk for developing bulimia nervosa is far greater for women born after 1960 than for women born before 1950. The risk for developing the disorder decreases with age, at least among the earlier birth cohort. Later birth cohorts have not yet moved through the entire age of risk.

Source: Graph, p. 1631, "Bulimia Nervosa among Three Cohorts of Women" in "The Genetic Epidemiology of Bulimia Nervosa" by K. S. Kendler, C. MacLean, M. Neale, R. Kessler, A. Heath and L. Evans, *American Journal of Psychiatry*, (1991), 148. Copyright © 1991. Reprinted by permission of American Psychiatric Association.

everything," and thinness is essential to good looks. In contrast, young men are valued as much for their achievements as for their appearance, and the ideal body type for men is considerably larger and more muscular than for women (Hsu, 1990; Striegel-Moore, 1995; see Critical Thinking Matters). In fact, women are much more likely than men to have a negative body image, and that disparity has been growing over time (Feingold & Mazzella, 1998).

The surge in eating disorders also might be explained by changing standards of beauty. *Playboy* centerfolds and Miss America Beauty Pageant contestants—cultural icons but dubious role models for young women—provide the statistics. Between 1959 and 1988, their ratio of weight to height declined dramatically. In fact, 69 percent of *Playboy* centerfolds and 60 percent of Miss America contestants weigh at least 15 percent below expected weight for their height (Garner et al., 1980; Wiseman et al., 1992). Marilyn Monroe, the movie idol of the 1950s, is chunky according to today's "culture of thinness."

Standards of beauty are relative, not absolute. Today, eating disorders are much more common in North America, Western Europe, and Japan and other industrialized Asian countries; bulimia

CRITICAL THINKING MATTERS

The Pressure to be Thin

Critical thinking matters in the classroom—and in everyday life. Consider how young women (and men) embrace standards of beauty based on the images of women in the media, and, in turn, apply fashion model standards to themselves and others.

The images are everywhere. Super-thin models routinely grace the cover and inside of fashion magazines. The average fashion model is 5′11″ and 117 pounds; the average woman in the U.S. is 5′ 4″ and 140 pounds. Television and movie actresses are not only talented and beautiful, but also exceptionally thin. Cameron Diaz and Julia Roberts, for example, both meet the body mass index requirement for anorexia nervosa (Owen & Laurel-Seller, 2000). Advertisements in all kinds of media for all kinds of products use images of sexy, beautiful, and very thin women, images that often are altered not only to erase facial blemishes, but also to lengthen legs or otherwise distort body shape. Even girls' dolls are unrealistically thin and beautiful. The ubiquitous Barbie Doll has a shape that translates into a 39–18–33 figure in human equivalents. (In 1994, Dolly Parton claimed that she measured 40–20–36.) And real-life GI Joe would have a 55″ chest and a 27″ bicep. (At his bodybuilding peak, Arnold Schwarzenegger had a 57″ chest and 22″ biceps.)

The pressure to be thin greatly affects women who make their careers as actresses,

models, and singers. The Brazilian model Ana Carolina Reston died of complications due to anorexia in 2006. (In the same year, the Spanish government banned too-thin models from a popular fashion show.) The dubious "who's who" of women in the popular media who have *publicly admitted* to having an eating disorder (often in an attempt to encourage healthier body images among the girls and women who admire them) includes actresses Mary-Kate Olsen, Courtney Thorne-Smith, and Kate Winslet; fashion model Carre Otis; singers Ashlee Simpson, Paula Abdul, and Victoria Beckham (Posh Spice of the Spice Girls); and Oprah Winfrey.

Why are media images of women's bodies unrealistic?

Psychological studies repeatedly show that exposure to images of super-thin women increases body image dissatisfaction among girls and young women (Halliwell & Dittmar, 2004). Yet, young women face contradictory messages when parents or others tell them, "Beauty is only skin deep." For one, both extensive psychological research and everyday experience repeatedly tell us that attractiveness *does* matter, not only to romantic attraction (although men prefer a more curvaceous figure than women *think* they like), but also appearance matters in the evaluations of same-gender

peers, teachers, employers, and on and on. And even as public health advocates battle the culture of thinness, other public health officials tell young people—rightly—to be careful about what they eat, not to eat too much, and try to lose weight. In fact, obesity is a much more prevalent public health problem than eating disorders. In the United States, one out of every two adults and 20 percent of children are overweight, and obesity is associated with a great many health risks (Heinberg et al., 2001).

So where does critical thinking come in? Critical thinking is all about being reasonable and thinking for yourself. Appearance does matter, but few of us, female or male, can hope to look like models or movie stars. After all, these professionals literally are one in a million (or a billion). The stars of popular media devote much of their life to their appearance, and they *still* need the help of makeup, camera angles, creative fashions, and various electronic "corrections." Health matters too, and exercise is a great way to promote health, maintain an attractive physical appearance, and remember that your body is good for something other than being looked at. And most of us are more impressed by what someone does, by who they are, than what they look like. Remembering this is a useful reminder when we start to think critically—instead of using critical thinking—in evaluating our own weight and shape.

may be completely culture bound (Keel & Klump, 2003). In other cultures, women who are more rounded are considered to be more beautiful (Hsu, 1990; Striegel-Moore, 1995). In Third World countries, where food is scarce, wealth is positively correlated with body weight. Being larger is a symbol of beauty and success. In industrialized nations, where food is plentiful, wealth is negatively correlated with weight (Hsu, 1989). As the saying goes, "You can never be too rich or too thin."

Age of Onset

Both anorexia and bulimia nervosa typically begin in late adolescence or early adulthood (Hudson et al., 2007). A significant minority of cases of anorexia nervosa begin during early adolescence, particularly as girls approach puberty. The adolescent onset of eating disorders has provoked much speculation about their etiology, including hormonal changes (Garfinkel & Garner, 1982), autonomy struggles (Minuchin, Rosman, & Baker, 1978), and various sexual problems (Coovert, Kinder, & Thompson, 1989). A more simple explanation is the natural and normal changes in adolescent body shape and weight. Weight gain is normal during adolescence, but the addition of a few pounds can trouble a young woman focused on the numbers on her scale. Breast and hip development not only change body shape, but they affect self-image, social interaction, and the fit of familiar clothes.

Weight and dieting become less of a concern, and disordered eating declines, as adolescent girls become women. Changes are particularly sharp following marriage and parenthood (Keel et al., 2007). Men, however, become *more* concerned with weight as they age. As men's metabolism slows with increasing age, losing weight is more of a worry than gaining weight.

CAUSES OF EATING DISORDERS

The culture of thinness clearly contributes to the high rate of eating disorders today. However, other social, psychological, and biological risk factors play a role in eating disorders, because not every young woman suffers from these problems.

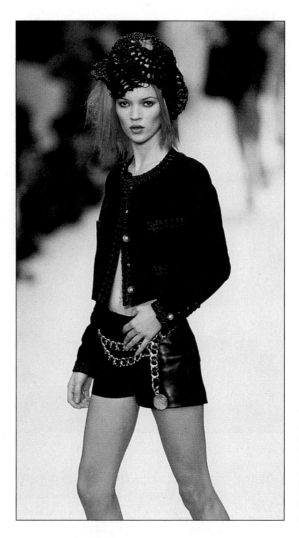

◀ Model Kate Moss. Contemporary images of women place a premium on slimness and suggest that women should be judged by their appearance. Both of these messages apparently contribute to the etiology of eating disorders.

Social Factors

Standards of beauty and the premium placed on young women's appearance contribute to causing eating disorders. This conclusion is supported by epidemiological evidence and other research documenting that

- Eating disorders are far more common among young women than young men (Hoek, 1995; Hsu, 1990). As Striegel-Moore and Bulik (2007) recently summarized, "The single best predictor of risk for developing an eating disorder is being female . . ." (p. 182).
- The prevalence of eating disorders in the United States has risen, as the image of the ideal woman has increasingly emphasized extreme thinness (Hoek, 1995; Kendler et al., 1991; Wiseman et al., 1992).
- Eating disorders are even more common among young women working in fields that emphasize weight and appearance, such as models, ballet dancers, and gymnasts (Bryne, 2002).

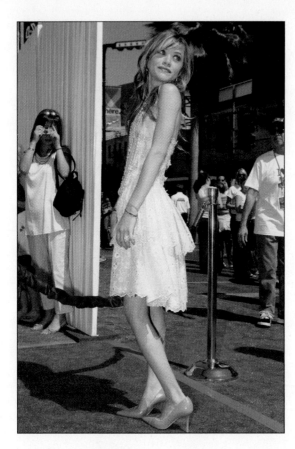

▶ Actress Mary-Kate Olsen admitted battling with anorexia nervosa. Actresses and models face strong pressures to be perfectly beautiful and perfectly thin. They can create unrealistic standards for themselves—and for their fans.

How does the culture of thinness contribute to eating disorders?

- Young women are particularly likely to develop eating disorders during adolescence and young adult life, an age during which our culture places a particular emphasis on appearance, beauty, and thinness (Hoek, 2002; Hsu, 1990).
- Eating disturbances are more common among young women who report greater exposure to popular media, endorse more gender-role stereotypes, or internalize societal standards about appearance (Heinberg, Thompson, & Stormer, 1995; Stice et al., 1994).
- Eating disorders are more common among middle- and upper-class whites, who are especially likely to equate thinness with beauty in women. Eating disorders also may be increasing among well-to-do African Americans, who increasingly hold to the thinness ideal (Roberts et al., 2006; Wildes, Emery, and Simons, 2001).
- Eating disorders are far more prevalent in industrialized societies, where thinness is the ideal, than in nonindustrialized societies, where a more rounded body type is preferred (Hsu, 1990).
- The prevalence of eating disorders is higher among Arab and Asian women living or studying in Western countries than among women living in their native country (Hoek, 2002).

These facts make it clear that adolescent girls and young women are at risk for developing eating disorders, in part because they attempt to shape themselves, quite literally, to fit the image of the ideally proportioned, thin woman (see Eating Disorders in Males box). We should note, however, that the culture of thinness plays a stronger role in the development of bulimia than anorexia. Cases of anorexia nervosa are found in the historical literature, occur in non-Western cultures, and appear to have increased less than cases of bulimia nervosa in response to cultural ideals of thinness (Keel & Klump, 2003).

Of course, not every woman in the United States develops an eating disorder, so other factors must interact with culture to produce eating disorders (Striegel-Moore & Bulik, 2007). One basic influence is the individual's *internalization* of the ideal of thinness (Cafri et al., 2005). Same-gender peers can influence internalization (Zalta & Keel, 2006), and so can popular media. For example, in one study 9th- and 10th-grade high school girls randomly received a free subscription to *Seventeen* magazine. One year later, those who received the magazine reported increased negative affect, but only if their body image was negative and they felt pressure to be thin when the study began (Stice, Spangler, & Agras, 2001). These girls apparently were more vulnerable to the media's "thin" message. For examples of this "thin" message, look at the images and articles in *any* magazine aimed a teen girls or young women.

▶ Rounded bodies once were the Western ideal of beauty for women, as illustrated in *Turkish Bath* painted by Jean Auguste Dominique Ingres in 1859–1863 (Louvre, Paris).

EATING DISORDERS IN MALES

What do psychologists know about eating disorders among males? Our culture clearly values different body types for males than it does for females. Adolescent boys often want to be bigger and stronger, not slimmer. Women rate themselves as being thin only when they are below 90 percent of their expected body weight. In contrast, men see themselves as thin even when they weigh as much as 105 percent of their expected weight (Anderson, 2002). Surveys indicate that the majority of females want to lose weight, but males are about equally divided between those who want to lose weight and those who want to gain weight.

In fact, some experts argue that pressures to be strong and muscular have created a new eating disorder among males. The problem, sometimes called "reverse anorexia" or the "Adonis complex," is characterized by excessive emphasis on extreme muscularity and often accompanied by the abuse of anabolic steroids (Anderson, 2002; Ricciardelli & McCabe, 2004). You may recall that baseball slugger Mark McGwire was taking androstenedione ("andro," an over-the-counter steroid hormone) when he broke the record for most home runs in a single season. McGwire's popularity and success apparently contributed to growing steroid use among young males in the United States, where 3 percent to 12 percent of teenage boys have tried steroids (Ricciardelli & McCabe, 2004).

> ## How are men with eating disorders different from women with eating disorders?

More realistic expectations about thinness surely contribute to the lower prevalence of anorexia and bulimia among males. However, men with these eating disorders are less likely to seek treatment than are women, perhaps because they are less likely to recognize the problem or feel more stigmatized because of it (Woodside et al., 2001). Men with anorexia or bulimia deviate far from male norms, and this can lead to rejection and stigmatization by other men, therapists, and even females with eating disorders. The stigma of being a man with an eating disorder also alters one common symptom of anorexia nervosa. Females with anorexia nervosa typically view their appearance positively, perhaps even with a degree of pride. In contrast, anorexia nervosa can negatively affect the self-esteem of men, because weight and/or eating struggles are "unmanly," that is, different from the cultural image of the ideal male (Andersen, 1995).

Anorexia and bulimia are more common among certain subgroups of males than in the general population. Male wrestlers have a particularly high prevalence of bulimia, a result of the intense pressure to "make weight"—to weigh below the weight cutoffs used to group competitors in a wrestling match. Eating disorders also are more common among gay than heterosexual men, who place more emphasis on appearance (Carlat, Camargo, & Herzog, 1997; Russell & Keel, 2002) and also endure minority stress (Kimmel & Mahalik, 2005).

Other aspects of eating disorders are similar for males and females. For both men and women, the disorders typically begin during adolescence or young adulthood. Other than the exceptions we have noted, similar factors also predict a risk for developing eating disorders in both females and males, including "reverse anorexia" (Ricciardelli & McCabe, 2004). Whether the ideal image is unrealistically thin or unrealistically muscular, cultural stereotypes about appearance can be risky for both males and females who internalize them.

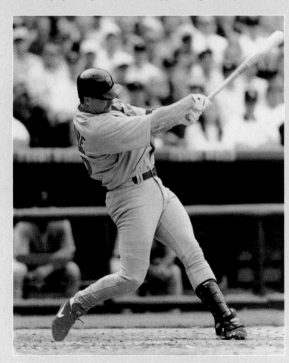

▲ Mark McGwire took androstenedione ("andro"), an over-the-counter steroid hormone, when he broke the single season home run record. Many teenage boys take steroids to build their bodies, a trend some consider to be a new eating disorder.

▲ Billy Bob Thornton dieted for a movie role, but his weight loss got out of control prompting speculation that he suffered from anorexia nervosa.

Troubled Family Relationships Troubled family relationships may also increase vulnerability to the culture of thinness (Fairburn et al., 1997). Young people with bulimia nervosa report considerable conflict and rejection in their families, difficulties that also may contribute to their depression. In contrast, young people with anorexia generally perceive their families as cohesive and nonconflictual (Fornari et al., 1999; Vandereycken, 1995).

Although the families of young people with anorexia nervosa appear to be well functioning, some theorists see them as being too close—as *enmeshed families,* families whose members are overly involved in one another's lives. According to the enmeshment hypothesis, young people with anorexia nervosa are obsessed with controlling their eating, because eating is the *only* thing they can control in their intrusive families (Minuchin et al., 1978). It is not clear, however, whether intrusive parental concern is a cause or an effect of the eating disorder. Parents of an adolescent with anorexia nervosa may become "enmeshed" as a worried reaction to their daughter's obviously emaciated appearance, not as a cause of it.

Child sexual abuse also may contribute to eating disorders. However, sexual abuse does not appear to play a *specific* developmental role. Women with eating disorders are more likely than normal controls to report a history of sexual abuse, but they are no more likely to report a history of sexual abuse than are women who suffer from other psychological problems (Palmer, 1995; Welch & Fairburn, 1996). Sexual abuse may increase the risk for a variety of psychological problems, including, but not limited to, eating disorders.

How do "control issues" differ in anorexia and bulimia?

Finally, we should note that there are many direct ways in which parents may influence children toward developing eating disorders. Many parents struggle with diet and thinness themselves, and they are models of preoccupation for their children; other parents directly encourage their children to be extra thin as a part of the general push to compete with their peers (Vandereycken, 2002).

Psychological Factors

Researchers have hypothesized about many psychological factors contributing to eating disorders. Here we highlight four of the most important: control issues, depression/dysphoria, body image dissatisfaction, and reactions to dietary restraint.

A Struggle for Perfection and Control One of the first and most prolific clinical observers of eating disorders was Hilde Bruch (1904–1984), a physician who fled her native Germany in 1933 to escape the Nazi regime and subsequently studied psychiatry in the United States. Bruch viewed a struggle for control as the central psychological issue in the development of eating disorders (Bruch, 1982). Bruch observed that girls with eating disorders seem to be exceptionally "good"— conforming and eager to please. She suggested that these girls give up too much of the normal adolescent struggle for autonomy and, instead, attempt to please others, particularly their parents. Bruch viewed their obsessive efforts to control eating and weight as a way that overly compliant "good girls" control themselves further. At the same time, she also saw their dieting as an attempt to wrest at least a little control from their parents—control over what they eat. In this *struggle for control,* young people with anorexia nervosa "succeed" and take pride in their extreme self-control. In contrast, people with bulimia nervosa continually strive— and fail—to control their eating and weight.

Perfectionism is another, endless pursuit of control. Perfectionists set unrealistically high standards, are self-critical, and demand a nearly flawless performance from themselves. Research demonstrates that young women with eating disorders endorse perfectionist goals both about eating and weight and about general expectations for themselves (Bastiani et al., 1995; Garner, Olmstead, & Polivy, 1983).

Young people with eating disorders may also try to control their own emotions excessively (Bruch, 1982). They may lack **introceptive awareness**— recognition of internal cues, including hunger and various emotional states. One large study found that lack of introceptive awareness predicted the development of eating disorders 2 years in the future (Leon et al., 1993; Leon et al., 1995). People with eating disorders appear to be more tuned in to how they look than how they feel—sad, angry, happy, or hungry (Viken et al., 2002).

Depression, Low Self-Esteem, and Dysphoria Depression is often comorbid with eating disorders, particularly bulimia nervosa. Researchers have found an increased prevalence of depression not only among people with eating disorders but also among the members of their families (Strober, 1995). Research also shows that antidepressant medications reduce some symptoms of bulimia nervosa (Mitchell, Raymond, & Specker,

1993). In some cases, bulimia therefore appears to be at least partly a reaction to depression.

In other cases, however, depression may instead be a reaction to an eating disorder (Hsu, 1990; Polivy & Herman, 2002). Depression improves markedly following successful group psychotherapy for bulimia (Mitchell et al., 1990). And a study of anorexia nervosa found considerable depression at the time of the original diagnosis but not at a 6-year follow-up (Rastam, Gillberg, & Gillberg, 1995).

Depressive *symptoms,* and not necessarily clinical depression, also may play a role in eating disorders. Low self-esteem is a particular concern (Fairburn et al., 1997). In particular, women with eating disorders may be preoccupied with their *social self,* how they present themselves in public and how other people perceive and evaluate them (Jones, 1985; Striegel-Moore, Silberstein, & Rodin, 1993). Women with bulimia nervosa or a negative body image report more public self-consciousness, social anxiety, and perceived fraudulence (Striegel-Moore et al., 1993). They also show increases in self-criticism and deterioration in mood following negative social interactions (Steiger et al., 1999). In short, people with eating disorders often depend on others for self-esteem.

Depressive symptoms also can play a role in maintaining problematic eating behaviors. *Dysphoria* or negative mood states commonly trigger episodes of binge eating (Steiger et al., 1999). The dysphoria may be brought on by social criticism or conflict, dissatisfaction with eating and diet, or an ongoing depressive episode. In summary, clinical depression can either be a cause or a reaction to eating disorders, while depressed moods, low self-esteem, and dysphoria may contribute to the onset or maintenance of symptoms.

Negative Body Image *A negative body image,* a highly critical evaluation of one's weight and shape, is widely thought to contribute to the development of eating disorders (Polivy & Herman, 2002). Psychologists have used a number of techniques to evaluate a negative body image, including self-report measures, calipers or other devices used to directly estimate the size of various body parts, and schematic figures such as the ones in Figure 10–4 (Thompson, 1996).

Early studies focused on a *distorted body image,* a perceptual inaccuracy in judging one's size, particularly in cases of anorexia nervosa. Current research focuses on *dissatisfaction* with body image, a negative evaluation of one's body that includes cognitive

FIGURE 10–4 These schematic figures are used in research to assess differences between real and ideal body image. People pick two figures, their current and their ideal shape. The discrepancy between the ratings is an index of negative body image.

Source: From p. 79 in "Assessing Body Image Disturbance: Measures, Methodology, and Implementation" by J. K. Thompson in BODY IMAGE, EATING DISORDERS, AND OBESITY ed. by J. K. Thompson. Copyright © 1996. Reprinted by permission of the author. Published by American Psychological Association.

and affective elements and not just perceptual distortions. One way to assess a negative body image is to compare people's ratings of their "current" and "ideal" size by asking them to pick from the schematics in Figure 10–4. Several longitudinal studies have found negative evaluations of weight, shape, and appearance to predict the subsequent development of disordered

How does depression contribute to eating disorders?

◄ Many women with eating disorders have a negative body image. Perceptions of weight and shape sometimes are distorted, but a more common problem is body dissatisfaction.

eating (Attie & Brooks-Gunn, 1989; Cattarin & Thompson, 1994). A negative body image may be a particular problem when combined with other risk factors, including perfectionism and low self-esteem (Vohs et al., 1999).

Dietary Restraint Some symptoms of eating disorders may be effects of *dietary restraint,* that is, direct consequences of restricted eating (Heatherton & Polivy, 1992; Herman & Polivy, 1988). This is ironic, because many of the "out-of-control" symptoms of eating disorders appear to be caused by inappropriate efforts to control eating! These symptoms include binge eating, preoccupation with food, and perhaps out-of-control feelings of hunger.

Inappropriate dieting can contribute directly to subsequent binge eating. An overly restrictive diet increases hunger, frustration, and lack of attention to internal cues, all of which make binge eating more likely. In addition, "quick-fix" diets rarely work, and dieters are likely to be left with a sense of failure, disappointment, and self-criticism. The negative affect, in turn, may make further binge eating likely and lower self-esteem (Heatherton & Polivy, 1992; Herman & Polivy, 1988).

Dietary restraint also may directly cause some of the symptoms of anorexia nervosa. The military studies of semistarvation conducted during World War II found that, during refeeding, many men felt intense, uncontrollable hunger, even after eating a considerable amount of food (Keys et al., 1950). Perhaps a similar reaction explains some of the intense fear of losing control and gaining weight found in anorexia nervosa.

While extreme restriction and quick-fix diets are unhealthy, sensible dieting is not. Normal weight women randomly assigned to a low-calorie diet both lost weight and decreased binge eating 18 weeks later in comparison to women assigned to no diet (Presnell & Stice, 2003). As with so many things, the key to healthy weight is finding a balanced middle ground.

Biological Factors

Our bodies, in fact, seek a middle ground. Physiologically, weight is maintained around **weight set points,** fixed weights or small ranges of weight. Weight regulation around set points results from the interplay between behavior (e.g., exercise, eating), peripheral physiological activity (e.g., digestion, metabolism), and central physiological activity (e.g., neurotransmitter release; Blundell, 1995). The process is very much like the way a thermostat regulates heating and cooling to maintain air temperature at a given setting. Thus, if weight declines, hunger increases and food consumption goes up (Keesey, 1995). There is a slowing of the *metabolic rate,* the rate at which the body expends energy, and movement toward *hyperlipogenesis,* the storage of abnormally large amounts of fat in fat cells throughout the body (Brownell & Fairburn, 1995). All these reactions have obvious survival value and are likely products of evolution. The body does not distinguish between intentional attempts to lose weight and potential starvation.

Genetic factors also contribute to eating disorders. An extensive twin study of bulimia nervosa found a concordance rate of 23 percent for MZ twins and 9 percent for DZ twins (Kendler et al., 1991). Higher MZ than DZ concordance rates for anorexia nervosa (Bulik et al., 2006) and for dysfunctional eating attitudes have also been reported (Klump, McGue, & Iacono, 2000).

MZ–DZ twin differences in early disorders could be explained by several different heritable mechanisms. It is unlikely that eating disorders are directly inherited, especially given the historically recent surge in prevalence rates. Rather, genetics may influence some personality characteristic that,

▶ Beyonce is a gorgeous example of a bigger but ideal body type.

in turn, increases the risk for bulimia nervosa such as anxiety (Klump & Culbert, 2007). Or a certain body type may be inherited (Bouchard, 2002), and this may account for the genetic effect. Inheriting a thin body type may increase the risk for anorexia—when combined with the culture of thinness, internalization of the standard, and perfectionism. Similarly, a more rounded body type may increase the risk for bulimia when combined with similar social and psychological risk factors. This latter scenario may create a dieting struggle to obtain a "normal" shape. Genes clearly affect weight and body type, but we cannot mindlessly conclude that eating disorders are "genetic."

Finally, several neurophysiological measures are correlated with eating disorders, including elevations in endogenous opioids, low levels of serotonin, and diminished neuroendocrine functioning (Yates, 1990). Most of these differences in brain functioning, however, appear to be effects of eating disorders and not causes of them. In extremely rare cases, eating disorders have been linked with a specific biological abnormality, such as a hormonal disturbance or a lesion in the *hypothalamus,* the area of the brain that regulates routine biological functions, including appetite.

Integration and Alternative Pathways

Social and cultural values that emphasize thinness, beauty, and appearance over agency are the starting point in understanding eating disorders, particularly among young women. Risk factors that combine with cultural attitudes to produce eating disorders include direct familial and social pressures to be thin, a negative body image, dietary restraint, and genetic influences on body weight and shape (Jacobi et al., 2004; Stice, 2001, 2002). Less obvious risk factors include preoccupation with external evaluation, lack of introceptive awareness, and excessive conformity and self-control.

The etiology of eating disorders underscores the importance of *equifinality*—there are many pathways to developing an eating disorder (Halmi, 1997). Some women are naturally thin, but their perfectionism drives them to become even thinner. Other women may have a more rounded body type determined by genetics, and they struggle, and repeatedly fail, to mold their body into something it was never meant to be. For some people, an eating disorder is an expression of depression. Others may develop an eating disorder because they focus on outward appearances instead of internal values. Finding the middle ground of a healthy weight can be very difficult, particularly when the culture of thinness sets unrealistic standards of beauty, especially for young women.

TREATMENT OF ANOREXIA NERVOSA

The treatments for anorexia nervosa and bulimia nervosa differ in approach and effectiveness; therefore, we consider them separately. The treatment of anorexia nervosa usually focuses on two goals. The first is to help the patient gain at least a minimal amount of weight. If weight loss is severe, the patient may be treated in an inpatient setting. Hospitalized patients may receive forced or intravenous feeding, or participate in strict behavior therapy programs that make rewards contingent on weight gain. Hospitalization also may be needed to prevent suicide, to address severe depression or medical complications, or to remove the patient temporarily from a dysfunctional social circumstance (Garner & Needleman, 1996).

The second goal in treating anorexia nervosa is to address the broader eating and personal difficulties. Many different treatments have been

◄ In treating anorexia nervosa, the first goal is establishing a safer, more normal body weight.

tried toward this end. Some evidence indicates that family therapy is more effective than individual treatment, at least for children and adolescents (Wilson et al., 2007). The most carefully studied family therapy is the *Maudsley method,* which involves parents initially taking complete control over the child's eating. Age-appropriate autonomy is returned to the child as eating improves (Lock et al., 2001; Loeb et al., 2007).

Many individual therapies also have been tried. Three approaches of note are (1) Bruch's (1982) modified psychodynamic therapy designed to increase introceptive awareness and correct distorted perceptions of self; (2) cognitive behavioral approaches that aim to alter the belief that "weight, shape, or thinness can serve as the sole or predominant referent for inferring personal value or self-worth" (Garner & Bemis, 1982, p. 142); and (3) *feminist therapies,* which encourage young women to pursue their own values rather than blindly adopting prescribed social roles (Fallon, Katzman, & Wooley, 1994). Unfortunately, little evidence supports the effectiveness of any individual treatment. Even worse, medication (antidepressants often are prescribed) and nutritional counseling not only offer little benefit, but patients also routinely drop out of these treatments (Vitousek,

► Brazilian model Ana Carolina Reston died in 2006 as a result of complications due to anorexia nervosa. Bans on super-thin models have been considered in order to protect both the models and their fans.

2002; Wilson, Grilo, & Vitousek, 2007). Clearly, finding effective treatments for anorexia nervosa should be a research and public health priority.

Course and Outcome of Anorexia Nervosa

Evidence on the course and outcome of anorexia nervosa further shows the limited effectiveness of contemporary treatments. At posttreatment follow-up, 50 percent to 60 percent of patients have a weight within the normal range, 10 percent to 20 percent remain significantly below their healthy body weight, and the remainder are intermediate in weight (Hsu, 1990; Steinhausen, 1996). Perhaps 10 percent of patients starve themselves to death or die of related complications, including suicide.

Although important, weight gain is not the only measure of the course of anorexia nervosa. In fact, more than half the women with a history of anorexia nervosa continue to have difficulties with eating, notwithstanding gains in weight. Menstruation returns along with weight gain for most women, but many continue to be preoccupied with diet, weight, and body shape. Moreover, people may also develop new problems with social life, depression, or bulimia, as a result of their perfectionism, reliance on external evaluation, or continued struggles with body image (Hsu, 1990). Predictors of a better prognosis include an early age of onset, conflict-free parent–child relationships, early treatment, less weight loss, and the absence of binge eating and purging (Steinhausen, 1996). The following account, written by a young woman after her long and, finally, successful struggle with anorexia nervosa, illustrates some of the continuing problems:

> I do not have a story that ends with a miraculous recovery, and I would be suspicious of anyone who claimed that they had completely gotten over an eating disorder. I continue to struggle with worries about food and my body. I exercise every day without fail. I am prone to stress fractures and will most likely encounter early osteoporosis due to the irreversible effects of starvation on my bones. I am lucky that I will be able to have children someday, though many long-term anorexics are never able to. Despite these lingering effects of the disorder, they pale in comparison to what I consider to be the most detrimental of all. When I look back on those six or so years, it sickens me to realize how much of life I missed. I allowed my obsession with my weight to take over my life.
>
> (Zorn, 1998, p. 21)

TREATMENT OF BULIMIA NERVOSA

In recent years, researchers have developed several effective approaches to treating bulimia nervosa. The most effective treatments include antidepressant medication, cognitive behavior therapy, and interpersonal psychotherapy.

Antidepressant Medications

All classes of antidepressant medications are somewhat effective in treating bulimia nervosa; however, medication alone is *not* the treatment of choice. Binge eating and compensatory behavior improve only among a minority of people treated with antidepressants, and relapse is common when medication is stopped (Walsh, 1995). Most importantly, research shows that, alone or perhaps in combination with medication, psychotherapy is an important component of treatment (Agras et al., 1992; Mitchell et al., 1990; Walsh et al., 1997; Wilson et al., 1999). One exception may be treating bulimia in a primary care setting, where most patients fail to complete self-help cognitive behavior therapy programs but are more likely to follow through with antidepressant medication (Walsh et al., 2004).

Cognitive Behavior Therapy

The most thoroughly researched psychotherapy for bulimia nervosa is cognitive behavior therapy (Wilson et al., 2007). As developed by the British psychiatrist Christopher Fairburn, the cognitive behavioral approach views bulimia as stemming from several maladaptive tendencies, including an excessive emphasis on weight and shape; perfectionism; and dichotomous "black or white" thinking (Fairburn, 1996). Fairburn's cognitive behavioral treatment includes three stages. First, the therapist uses education and behavioral strategies to normalize eating patterns. The goal is to restore more normal eating and end the cycle where extreme dietary restraint leads to binge eating and, in turn, to purging. Second, the therapist addresses the client's broader, dysfunctional beliefs about self, appearance, and dieting. Techniques include a variation of Beck's cognitive therapy to address perfectionism or depression, and individual problems such as poor impulse control or troubled relationships also may be addressed at this stage. Third, the therapist attempts to consolidate gains and prepare the client for expected relapses in the future. Key goals at this final stage of treatment are to develop realistic expectations about eating, weight concerns, and

binge eating, as well as clear strategies for coping with relapses in advance (Fairburn, 2002).

Overall, cognitive behavior therapy leads to a 70 percent to 80 percent reduction in binge eating and purging. Between one-third and one-half of all clients are able to cease the bulimic pattern completely, and the majority of individuals maintain these gains at 6-month to 1-year follow-up (Agras et al., 2000; Fairburn et al., 1993). Cognitive behavior therapy also may be effective in group therapy (Mitchell et al., 1990) and self-help formats (Carter & Fairburn, 1998), although individual therapy is more effective (Thompson-Brenner et al., 2003).

Interpersonal Psychotherapy

Interpersonal psychotherapy, which was originally developed for the treatment of depression, also can be an effective treatment for bulimia nervosa. This is surprising because interpersonal therapy does not address eating disorders directly but instead focuses on difficulties in close relationships. Interpersonal therapy for bulimia initially was studied as a *placebo* treatment in a study of cognitive behavior therapy. Fairburn and colleagues (1991, 1993) planned to evaluate whether cognitive behavior therapy had specific treatment effects above and beyond the general benefits of psychotherapy. The investigators chose interpersonal therapy as a credible placebo treatment because interpersonal problems often are associated with bulimia nervosa. However, they hypothesized that cognitive behavior therapy would outperform the interpersonal approach. The study also included a third condition, a behavior therapy alone group, which essentially was cognitive behavior therapy without the cognitive elements.

When Fairburn and colleagues (1991) evaluated outcome shortly after treatment, they found that cognitive behavior therapy was more effective than interpersonal therapy in changing dieting behavior, self-induced vomiting, and attitudes about weight and shape. Cognitive behavior therapy also was more effective than behavior therapy alone when attitude change was the outcome measure; however, the results of the two behavioral treatments were similar in other respects.

A very different picture emerged at 12-month follow-up (Fairburn et al., 1993; see Figure 10–5). The improvements brought about by behavior therapy alone deteriorated over time, and a large number of patients dropped out of this group, perhaps reflecting their dissatisfaction with the

What treatments are most effective for bulimia?

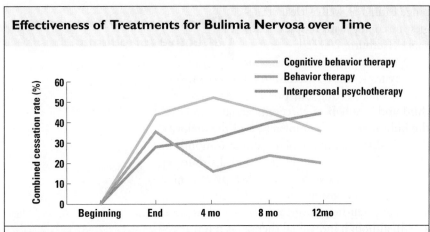

Effectiveness of Treatments for Bulimia Nervosa over Time

- Cognitive behavior therapy
- Behavior therapy
- Interpersonal psychotherapy

FIGURE 10–5　Percentage of patients who no longer purged or had episodes of bulimia according to objective or subjective reports. Note the decline for the behavior therapy group and continued improvement for the interpersonal therapy group over the 1-year follow-up interval.

Source: From "Psychotherapy and Bulimia Nervosa: Longer-Term Effects of Interpersonal Psychotherapy, Behavior Therapy, and Cognitive Behavior Therapy" by C. G. Fairburn, R. Jones, R. C. Peveler, R. A. Hope, *Archives of General Psychiatry,* (1993), 50, p. 423. Copyright © 1993. Reprinted by permission of American Medical Association.

treatment. In comparison, the improvements in the cognitive behavior therapy group remained fairly stable. Most surprising, members of the interpersonal therapy group *continued to improve* in the 12 months following the end of treatment. At 1-year follow-up, in fact, the improvements for interpersonal therapy equaled the improvements for cognitive behavior therapy and outdistanced the behavior therapy alone group.

The continued improvement for the interpersonal therapy group was surprising and impressive, for at least two reasons. First, the interpersonal treatments explicitly excluded direct discussions of eating, diet, and related topics. Second, the investigators had lower expectations for the interpersonal therapy group, and the *allegiance effect* often influences treatment outcome (see the Research Methods box). A recent, larger study replicated the results of this investigation, although cognitive behavior therapy again produced more rapid improvement (Agras et al., 2000). Cognitive behavior therapy clearly is the first-line treatment for bulimia nervosa, but interpersonal therapy and antidepressant medication may be useful supplemental or alternative treatments.

Course and Outcome of Bulimia Nervosa

Bulimia nervosa also has a persistent course, although the outcome is more positive than for anorexia nervosa, especially with treatment (Her-

zog et al., 1999; Thomson-Brenner et al., 2003). Without treatment, one-third to one-half of women with bulimia have an eating disorder 5 years later, many continuing to meet diagnostic criteria for bulimia nervosa (Fairburn et al., 2003). Following treatment, in contrast, about half of clients are free of all symptoms, about one in five continue to meet the diagnostic criteria for bulimia nervosa, and the remainder have occasional relapses or subclinical levels of binge eating and compensatory behavior (Keel et al., 2002). Most clients manage to maintain a weight that is generally in the normal range, and—in contrast to anorexia nervosa—mortality is rare (Keel & Mitchell, 1997). Comorbid psychological disorders also tend to improve with improvements in bulimia nervosa (Hsu, 1995; Keel & Mitchell, 1997). Predictors of continued binge eating include a longer duration, greater emphasis on shape and weight, childhood obesity, poorer social adjustment, and persistent compensatory behavior (Fairburn et al., 2003).

PREVENTION OF EATING DISORDERS

Can eating disorders be prevented? This question is of huge importance, especially given the pervasive body dissatisfaction and disordered eating found among women today. Until recently, the results of prevention research were discouraging. Few, if any, benefits were produced by first-generation prevention efforts, which focused on education about the adverse effects of eating disorders, or by second-generation initiatives offering education about resisting the culture of thinness. However, a third generation of more subtle prevention efforts is promising (Stice & Shaw, 2004).

More successful prevention efforts do not directly focus on body image or disordered eating. Instead, they attack the thinness ideal indirectly, or focus on promoting healthy eating rather than eliminating unhealthy habits (Stice, Burton, & Wade, 2006). An important example of the former approach is a "dissonance intervention," in which participants complete tasks inconsistent with the thinness ideal, for example, discussing how to help "younger girls" from becoming obsessed with their appearance. The latter, healthy approach emphasizes the benefits of eating well and exercising. An important, recent study randomly assigned 481 adolescent girls to one of

RESEARCH METHODS Psychotherapy Placebos

A placebo is a treatment that contains no active ingredients for the disorder being treated. A placebo control group is a group of people who receive only a placebo treatment in an outcome study. Scientists must include placebos and placebo control groups in treatment outcome research, because the mere expectation of change can produce many psychological and physical benefits. New treatments work, in part, because the client and the therapist expect them to work.

Medication placebos are easily administered. Physicians give patients a pill that looks like the real medication but contains no active chemical ingredients. Psychotherapy placebos are much more challenging. How can we create a psychological treatment that contains no active ingredients but increases the client's and the therapist's expectations for change just as much as the real treatment?

One approach psychologists use is to offer an established, alternative therapy, but one not designed to treat the disorder being studied. In their study of bulimia nervosa, Fairburn et al. (1993) thought interpersonal therapy was a reasonable placebo psychotherapy. The investigators believed that interpersonal therapy contained no "active ingredients" for treating bulimia nervosa, but thought clients' therapists would view it as legitimate.

But this does not fully resolve the problem of creating a psychotherapy placebo. Re-searchers typically "believe" in their new treatment—otherwise they would not be studying it. Evidence on the allegiance effect shows that the therapist's beliefs help make a treatment work. The allegiance effect tells us that cognitive behavior therapy should have been more successful in the Fairburn and colleagues (1993) study, because the investigators were cognitive behavior therapists. In fact, we are particularly impressed by the results for interpersonal therapy in this study, because interpersonal therapy overcame the allegiance effect in this study and in a replication (Agras et al., 2000).

> How can scientists tell if a psychological treatment is more than a placebo?

What research methods control for the influence of the experimenter's expectations on outcome? In drug research, scientists use the double-blind study, where neither the patient nor the therapist knows whether the patient is receiving an active treatment or a placebo. Unfortunately, "real" and placebo psychotherapies are transparent to therapists, making it impossible to conduct double-blind studies of psychotherapy. An alternative approach is to include a pill placebo, a method that also can facilitate comparisons between studies of the effectiveness of drugs and psychotherapy (Klein, 1996). This is a positive step, but even pill placebo effects are not always easy to interpret. For example, medications are more effective when they produce more side effects (Greenberg et al., 1994). There are at least two possible reasons for this. More side effects may increase the patient's expectations for change, because they make the drug seem powerful. Or even in a double-blind study, clinicians may be able to determine whether patients are receiving the real medication or a placebo based on the side effects.

Another way of addressing the allegiance effect in psychotherapy outcome research is to have investigators who hold opposing allegiances participate in the same study. Cognitive behavior therapy is offered by cognitive behavior therapists, interpersonal therapists deliver interpersonal therapy, and so on. This overcomes the allegiance effect but creates a new problem: Because the same therapists cannot deliver the different treatments, effects due to the individual therapists are uncontrolled.

In the absence of a perfect psychotherapy placebo, two conclusions seem clear. First, we must recognize that the expectations of clients, therapists, and experimenters can influence the findings of therapy outcome research. Second, we are particularly impressed when, contrary to expectations, a placebo psychotherapy is as effective as the "real thing."

---

these two prevention programs (each involving only three 1-hour group meetings) or to an assessment-only group (no-treatment control group) or 3 hours of writing about emotional issues (placebo control group; Stice et al., 2006). Results showed improvements due to one or both interventions in body dissatisfaction, internalization of the thin ideal, dieting, and binge eating/purging one month after intervention, and to a lesser extent, at 6- and 12-month follow-ups. Figure 10-6 shows the results for binge eating.

Psychologists and society clearly have a long way to go to help women, and men, find the right balance between eating too little and too much, being obsessed with appearance, and being lax about health. Still, the results of a new generation of prevention research are an encouraging step in the right direction.

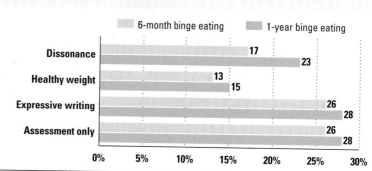

FIGURE 10–6 Binge eating 6 and 12 months after either dissonance, healthy weight, or control interventions. At both times, the healthy weight program produced significantly less binge eating than control conditions. Differences for dissonance training approached significance at 6 months.

Source: From E. Stice, H. Shaw, E. Burton, and E. Wade, 2006, "Dissonance and Healthy Weight Eating Disorder Prevention Programs: A Randomized Efficacy Trial," *Journal of Consulting and Clinical Psychology, 74*, pp. 263–275. Copyright © 2006 by American Psychological Association.

GETTING HELP

Eating disorders are very common, so it is likely that you or someone close to you may be struggling with eating issues. What can help?

One step is to get more information, but you need to be careful. Some self-help books and Web sites on eating disorders offer misleading or inaccurate information. And please beware of "pro-ana" and "pro-mia" Web sites that actually *encourage* eating disorders. One Web site that we recommend is the homepage of the National Eating Disorders Awareness Association, a nonprofit organization dedicated to increasing the awareness and prevention of eating disorders. The Web page of the National Institute of Mental Health also contains helpful information about eating disorders. An excellent self-help book is *Overcoming Binge Eating*, by Christopher Fairburn, whose treatment research is discussed in this chapter. *Living with Anorexia and Bulimia*, by James Moorey, is another good book that deals with a broader range of eating issues.

If you are seriously concerned about your own eating, weight, or body shape, you should talk with a professional. Colleges and universities often have special information and treatments for eating disorders. Call your student health service for information and referral. If no student health resources are available to you, another option is to talk with your family physician. You should have a physical exam to explore possible medical complications caused by your abnormal eating, and your physician also should know of mental health professionals who specialize in eating disorders. As indicated by the research we review in this chapter, some of the treatment options you should consider include cognitive behavior therapy, the most strongly supported treatment alternative; interpersonal therapy; family therapy; and antidepressant medication. Hospitalization may be another option, but only for very serious problems like severe weight loss.

If you are concerned about a friend's eating, you should make a plan and talk to her or him. Bring some information on local resources for treating eating disorders. And be prepared to listen as well as to talk! Your friend probably has not confided about his or her problems with many people. If your friend denies a problem, there is no point in arguing. You have done your job by raising the issue. It will be up to him or her to admit to the problem and get help. A good resource before and after talking with a friend is *Surviving an Eating Disorder: Strategies for Friends and Families*, by Michele Siegel, Judith Brisman, and Margot Weinshel.

■ SUMMARY

Eating disorders are severe disturbances in eating behavior that result from the sufferer's obsessive fear of gaining weight. DSM-IV-TR lists two major subtypes of eating disorders: anorexia nervosa and bulimia nervosa. The defining symptoms of **anorexia nervosa** include extreme emaciation, a disturbed perception of one's body, an intense fear of gaining weight, and the cessation of menstruation (in women). People with anorexia nervosa are preoccupied with food, revel in their control over eating, and may have mood disturbances, sexual difficulties, lack of impulse control, and medical problems secondary to the weight loss. The defining symptoms of **bulimia nervosa** are **binge eating** and compensatory behavior (**purging** or excessive exercise), a sense of lost control during a binge, and undue focus on weight and shape. Depression is commonly associated with bulimia nervosa; substance abuse and personality disorders are to a much lesser degree.

DSM-IV-TR includes two subtypes of anorexia nervosa. The restricting type includes people who rarely engage in binge eating or purging behavior, whereas the binge eating/purging type is characterized by regular binge eating and purging. Bulimia nervosa also is divided into two subtypes. The purging type is characterized by the regular use of self-induced vomiting or the misuse of laxatives, diuretics, or enemas. The nonpurging type compensates for binge eating with fasting or excessive exercise. There has been debate about adding to the DSM-IV-TR list of eating disorders. **Binge eating disorder** is included in a special appendix. **Obesity** has been considered for inclusion but rejected.

The prevalence of both anorexia nervosa and bulimia nervosa has increased dramatically in recent years, particularly among young women. Both anorexia and bulimia nervosa are approximately 10 times more common among women than among men, and many scientists blame our society's gender roles and standards of beauty for encouraging eating disorders. Standards of beauty and pubertal changes in body shape and weight also may account for the onset of eating disorders during adolescence and early adulthood.

Adolescent girls and young women are at risk for developing eating disorders, in part, because they attempt to shape themselves to fit the image of the ideal woman. The emphasis on appearance also lessens the value of other roles filled by girls and women. To a lesser extent, family relationships also may influence eating disorders. Four of the most prominent psychological factors in the development of eating disorders are issues of control and perfectionism, dysphoria combined with a lack of **introceptive awareness,** body image dissatisfaction, and reactions to dietary restraint. Biological contributions include the body's attempts to maintain **weight set points,** genetic influences on body weight and shape, and in rare cases a dysfunction of the hypothalamus.

Treatments for anorexia nervosa and bulimia nervosa differ in approach and effectiveness. Anorexia nervosa may require inpatient treatment with the initial goal of gaining weight, even through the use of coercive methods if necessary. Following treatment, 50 percent to 60 percent of people with anorexia nervosa have a normal weight, and 10 percent to 20 percent have weights well below normal (the remainder are in between these two groups). About 10 percent of people with the disorder die of starvation, suicide, or medical complications. Changing long-term eating patterns and attitudes in anorexia nervosa is difficult, and no clearly effective psychological treatment or medication has been identified for the disorder.

Treatments for bulimia nervosa are more promising, particularly cognitive behavior therapy, and to a lesser extent, interpersonal psychotherapy and antidepressant medication. About half the clients with bulimia nervosa are free of all symptoms following treatment, about one in five continues to meet the diagnostic criteria, and the remainder have occasional relapses or subclinical levels of binge eating and compensatory behavior. Weight is generally in the normal range, and comorbid psychological disorders appear to improve with improvements in bulimia nervosa. Finally, recent research provides hope for the prevention of disordered eating, particularly for indirect efforts focused on healthy weight or creating dissonance.

THE BIG PICTURE CRITICAL THINKING REVIEW

Why are media images of women's bodies unrealistic?

The ubiquitous Barbie Doll has a shape that translates into a 39–18–33 figure in human equivalents. (SEE PAGE 306)

How does the culture of thinness contribute to eating disorders?

Adolescent girls and young women are at risk for eating disorders, in part because they attempt to shape themselves, literally, to fit the image of the ideal woman. But not every woman develops an eating disorder, so other factors must interact with culture. (SEE PAGE 308)

How do "control issues" differ in anorexia and bulimia?

People with anorexia nervosa "succeed" and take pride in their extreme self-control; people with bulimia nervosa continually strive—and fail—to control their eating and weight. (SEE PAGE 310)

What treatments are most effective for bulimia?

The most effective treatments include antidepressant medication, cognitive behavior therapy, and interpersonal psychotherapy. (SEE PAGE 315)

How can scientists tell if a psychological treatment is more than a placebo?

One approach is to offer an established, alternative therapy, but one not designed to treat the disorder being studied. Yet, this does not fully resolve the problem. (SEE PAGE 317)

■ KEY TERMS

amenorrhea **298**
anorexia nervosa **294**
binge eating **300**

binge eating disorder **304**
bulimia nervosa **294**
cohort **305**

cohort effects **305**
distorted body image **297**
eating disorders **294**

introceptive
  awareness **310**
obesity **304**

purging **301**
weight set point **312**

SUBSTANCE USE DISORDERS

The abuse of alcohol and other drugs is one of the most serious problems facing our society today. It is likely that you or someone close to you will be affected by the substance use issues outlined in this chapter. Alcohol and drug problems receive a great deal of attention in the popular media, as illustrated by actor Robert Downey Jr.'s, repeated struggles with cocaine addiction and the drug-related suicide of Kurt Cobain, leader of the rock group Nirvana. Research efforts, treatment priorities, and national publicity have all helped transform national attitudes about the abuse of chemical substances. The picture of the drug addict as a homeless derelict whose personality defects and lack of motivation are largely responsible for the problem is being replaced by a new view in which substance abuse is seen as a chronic mental disorder that affects people from all walks of life.

OVERVIEW

The costs of substance abuse are astronomical. According to the Global Burden of Disease Study, alcohol use was the fourth leading cause of disability worldwide in 1990. Cirrhosis of the liver, which is frequently the result of chronic alcoholism, is a leading cause of death in the United States. In addition, alcohol plays a prominent role in many suicides, homicides, and motor vehicle accidents. The rate of deaths attributable to the use of tobacco is growing rapidly, particularly in developing countries, where 50 percent of adult men are regular smokers. By the year 2020, tobacco is expected to kill between 8 million and 9 million people annually worldwide, more than any single disease, including AIDS (Lopez et al., 2006).

DSM-IV-TR uses two terms to describe substance use disorders, and these terms reflect different levels of severity. **Substance dependence,** the more severe of the two forms, refers to a pattern of repeated self-administration that often results in tolerance, the need for increased amounts of the drug to achieve intoxication; withdrawal, unpleasant physical and psychological effects that the person experiences when he or she tries to stop taking the drug; and compulsive drug-taking behavior. **Substance abuse** describes a more broadly conceived, less severe pattern of drug use that is defined in terms of interference with the person's ability to fulfill major role obligations at work or at home, the recurrent use of a drug in dangerous situations, and repeated legal difficulties associated with drug use.

Addiction is another, older term that is often used to describe problems such as alcoholism. The term has been replaced in official terminology by the term substance dependence, with which it is synonymous, but it is still used informally by many lay people.

A **drug of abuse,** sometimes called a *psychoactive substance,* is a chemical substance that alters a person's mood, level of perception, or brain functioning (Schuckit, 1999a). All drugs of abuse can be used to increase a person's psychological comfort level (make one feel "high") or to alter levels of consciousness. The list of chemicals on which people can become dependent is long and seems to be growing longer. It includes drugs that are legally available, whether over the counter or by prescription only, as well as many that are illegal (see Table 11–1).

Depressants of the central nervous system (CNS) include alcohol as well as types of medication that are used to help people sleep, called *hypnotics,* and those for relieving anxiety, known as *sedatives* or *anxiolytics.* The CNS stimulants include illegal drugs like amphetamine and cocaine, as well as nicotine and caffeine. The opiates, also called *narcotic analgesics,* can be used clinically to decrease pain. The *cannabinoids,* such as marijuana, produce euphoria and an altered sense of time. At higher doses, they may produce hallucinations. People with a substance use disorder frequently abuse several types of drugs; this condition is known as **polysubstance abuse.**

One basic question we must address is whether we should view each type of addiction as a unique problem. Experts who answer "yes" to this question

TABLE 11–1 Commonly Abused Drugs		
CLASS	**EXAMPLES**	**BRAND NAMES AND STREET NAMES**
CNS Depressants	Alcohol	beer, wine, liquor
	Barbiturates	*barbs,* Amytal, Nembutal, Seconal
	Benzodiazepines	*roofies, tanks,* Xanax, Valium, Halcion
	Methaqualone	*quaalude, ludes*
CNS Stimulants	Amphetamine	*black beauties, crosses, hearts*
	Cocaine	*blow, coke, crack, flake, rocks, snow*
	Methamphetamine	*crank, crystal, glass, ice, speed*
	Nicotine	cigars, cigarettes, smokeless tobacco
	Caffeine	coffee, tea, soft drinks
Opiates	Heroin	*horse, smack, H, junk, skag*
	Opium	laudanum, paregoric, dover's powder
	Morphine	Roxanol, Duramorph
	Methadone	Amidone, Dolophine, Methadose
	Codeine	Tylenol w/Codeine, Robitussin A-C
Cannabinoids	Marijuana	*grass, herb, pot, reefer, smoke, weed*
	Hashish	*hash*
Hallucinogens	LSD	*acid, microdot*
	Mescaline	*buttons, cactus, mesc, peyote*
	Psilocybin	*magic, mushroom, purple passion*
	Phencyclidine	PCP, *angel dust, boat, hog, love boat*
	MDMA	*ecstasy, XTC,* Adam

Note: Street names for drugs appear in italics.

"Excuse me, Reverend, but what, exactly, do you have to do to get a drink around here?"

© The New Yorker Collection, 1994 Jack Ziegler from cartoonbank.com. All Rights Reserved.

point out that each class of abused substance seems to affect the body in distinct ways. For example, when taken orally, some opiates can be used for long periods of time without leading to significant organ damage (Jaffe & Jaffe, 1999). Chronic use of alcohol and tobacco, on the other hand, can have a devastating impact on a person's physical health.

Despite these differences, the various forms of substance abuse share many common elements. All forms of abuse represent an inherent conflict between immediate pleasure and longer-term harmful consequences. The psychological and biochemical effects on the user are often similar, as are the negative consequences for both social and oc-

cupational behaviors. The reasons for initial experimentation with a drug, the factors that influence the transition to dependence, and the processes that lead to relapse after initial efforts to change are all similar in many respects. For these reasons, many clinicians and researchers have adopted a view of substance abuse that emphasizes common causes, behaviors, and consequences (Hughes, 2007a; Marlatt et al., 1988). In fact, DSM-IV-TR employs a single set of diagnostic criteria that defines dependence for all types of drugs.

The variety of problems associated with substance use disorders can be illustrated using a case study of alcohol dependence. Ernest Hemingway (1899–1961), a Nobel Prize–winning writer, was severely dependent on alcohol for many years. The following paragraphs, quoted from an article by Paul Johnson (1989), describe the progression of Hemingway's drinking and the problems that it created. They illustrate many typical features of substance dependence, as well as the devastating impact that alcohol can have on various organs of the body. Johnson's description also raises a number of interesting questions about the etiology of this disorder. Most men and women consume alcoholic beverages at some point during their lives. Why do some people become dependent on alcohol while others do not? What factors influence the transition from social drinking to abuse?

CASE **STUDY** Ernest Hemingway's Alcohol Dependence

Hemingway began to drink as a teenager, the local blacksmith secretly supplying him with strong cider. His mother noted his habit and always feared he would become an alcoholic. In Italy he progressed to wine, then had his first hard liquor at the officers' club in Milan. His wound [from World War I] and an unhappy love affair provoked heavy drinking: In the hospital, his wardrobe was found to be full of empty cognac bottles, an ominous sign. In Paris in the 1920s, he bought Beaune by the gallon at a wine cooperative and would and did drink five or six bottles of red at a meal. He taught Scott Fitzgerald to drink wine direct from the bottle, which, he said, was like "a girl going swimming without her swimming suit." In New York he was "cockeyed," he said, for "several days" after signing his contract for *The Sun Also Rises*, probably his first prolonged bout.

Hemingway particularly liked to drink with women, as this seemed to him, vicariously, to signify his mother's approval. Hadley [the first of his four wives] drank a lot with him, and wrote: "I still cherish, you know, the remark you made that you almost worshipped me as a drinker." The same disastrous role was played by his pretty 1930s companion in Havana, Jane Mason, with whom he drank gin followed by champagne chasers and huge jars of iced daiquiris; it was indeed in Cuba in this decade that his drinking first got completely out of hand. One bartender there said he could "drink more martinis than any man I have ever seen." On safari, he was seen sneaking out of his tent at 5 A.M. to get a drink. His brother Leicester said that, by the end of the 1930s, at Key West, he was drinking 17 Scotch-and-sodas a day and often taking a bottle of champagne to bed with him at night.

At this period, his liver for the first time began to cause him acute pain. He was told by his doctor to give up alcohol completely, and indeed he tried to limit his consumption to three whiskeys before dinner. But that did not last. During World War II his drinking mounted

steadily and by the mid-1940s he was reportedly pouring gin into his tea at breakfast. A. E. Hotchner, interviewing him for *Cosmopolitan* in 1948, said he dispatched seven double-size Papa Doubles (the Havana drink named after him, a mixture of rum, grapefruit and maraschino), and when he left for dinner took an eighth with him for the drive. And on top of all, there was constant whiskey: His son Patrick said his father got through a quart of whiskey a day for the last 20 years of his life.

Hemingway's ability to hold his liquor was remarkable. Lillian Ross, who wrote his profile for the *New Yorker*, does not seem to have noticed he was drunk a lot of the time he talked to her. Denis Zaphior said of his last safari: "I suppose he was drunk the whole time but seldom showed it." He also demonstrated an unusual ability to cut down his drinking or even to eliminate it altogether for brief periods, and this, in addition to his strong physique, enabled him to survive.

But despite his physique, his alcoholism had a direct impact on his health, beginning with his damaged liver in the late 1930s. By 1959, following his last big drinking bout in Spain, he was experiencing both kidney and liver trouble and possibly hemochromatosis (cirrhosis, bronzed skin, diabetes), edema of the ankles, cramps, chronic insomnia, blood-clotting and high blood uremia, as well as his skin complaints. He was impotent and prematurely aged. Even so, he was still on his feet, still alive; and the thought had become unbearable to him. His father had committed suicide because of his fear of mortal illness. Hemingway feared that his illnesses were not mortal: On July 2, 1961, after various unsuccessful treatments for depression and paranoia, he got hold of his best English double-barreled shotgun, put two canisters in it, and blew away his entire cranial vault.

Why did Hemingway long for death [and why did he drink]? He felt he was failing his art. Hemingway had many grievous faults, but there was one thing he did not lack: artistic integrity. It shines like a beacon through his whole life. He set himself the task of creating a new way of writing English, and fiction, and he succeeded. It was one of the salient events in the history of our language and is now an inescapable part of it. He devoted to this task immense resources of creative skill, energy, and patience. That in itself was difficult. But far more difficult, as he discovered, was to maintain the high creative standards he had set himself. This became apparent to him in the mid-1930s and added to his habitual depression. From then on his few successful stories were aberrations in a long downward slide.

If Hemingway had been less of an artist, it might not have mattered to him as a man. He would simply have written and published inferior novels, as many writers do. But he knew when he wrote below his best, and the knowledge was intolerable to him. He sought the help of alcohol, even in working hours. He was first observed with a drink, a "Rum St. James," in front of him while writing in the 1920s. This custom, rare at first, became intermittent, then invariable. By the 1940s, he was said to wake at 4:30 A.M. [He] "usually starts drinking right away and writes standing up, with a pencil in one hand and a drink in another." The effect on his work was exactly as might be expected, disastrous. Hemingway began to produce large quantities of unpublishable material, or material he felt did not reach the minimum standard he set himself. Some was published nonetheless and was seen to be inferior, even a parody of his earlier work. There were one or two exceptions, notably *The Old Man and the Sea* (1952), which won him the Nobel Prize, though there was an element of self-parody in that, too. But the general level was low, and falling, and Hemingway's awareness of his inability to recapture his genius, let alone develop it, accelerated the spinning circle of depression and drink (Johnson, 1989, pp. 58–59).

SYMPTOMS

Substance use disorders are associated with a host of problems, many of which are illustrated in the life of Ernest Hemingway. Nevertheless, substance dependence is difficult to define. Alcoholism is one important example. George Vaillant (1995), a psychiatrist at Harvard Medical School and the author of an important longitudinal study of alcoholic men, notes that it is difficult to say that one specific problem or set of problems represents the core features of this disorder:

> Not only is there no single symptom that defines alcoholism, but often it is not who is drinking but who is watching that defines a symptom. A drinker may worry that he has an alcohol problem because of his impotence. His wife may drag him to an alcohol clinic because he slapped her during a blackout. Once he is at the clinic, the doctor calls him an alcoholic because of his abnormal liver-function tests. Later society labels him a drunk because of a second episode of driving while intoxicated. (p. 24)

The number of problems that a person encounters seems to provide the most useful distinction between people who are dependent on a substance and those who are not. These problems can be sorted loosely into two general areas: (1) patterns of pathological consumption, including psychological and physiological dependence; and (2) consequences that follow a prolonged pattern of abuse, including social and occupational impairment, legal and financial difficulties, and deteriorating medical condition.

It might seem that the actual amount of a drug of abuse that a person consumes would be the best indication of the existence of a problem. Hemingway, for example, clearly consumed enormous quantities of alcohol over a period of many years. The average person with an alcohol use disorder does drink more frequently and in larger quantities than the average person without an alcohol use disorder (Dawson, 2000). Nevertheless, the amount of a drug that a specific person consumes is not a good way to define substance use disorders, because people vary significantly in the amount of any given drug they can consume. Factors such as age, gender, activity level, and overall physical health influence a person's ability to metabolize various kinds of drugs. For example, some people can drink a lot without developing problems; others drink relatively little and have difficulties.

ALCOHOLISM

CHRIS

"The toughest thing I ever did was admitting that I had a problem."

Watch the video "Alcoholism: Chris" on MyPsychLab. How was Chris's pattern of drinking different from that of his friends?

The Concept of Substance Dependence

Many psychological features or problems are associated with dependence on chemical substances. One such feature involves *craving*. This word is frequently used to describe a forceful urge to use drugs, but the relationship between craving and drug use is actually very complex (Eliason & Amodia, 2007; Sayette et al., 2000). People who are dependent on drugs often say that they take the drug to control how they are feeling. They need it to relieve negative mood states or to avoid withdrawal symptoms from previous episodes. They may feel compelled to take the drug as a way to prepare for certain activities, such as public speaking, writing, or sex. Some clinicians refer to this condition as **psychological dependence.**

One useful index of craving is the amount of time that the person spends planning to take the drug. Is access to drugs or alcohol a constant preoccupation? If the person is invited to a party or is planning to eat at a restaurant, does he or she always inquire about the availability of alcoholic drinks? If the person is going to spend a few days at the beach in a neighboring state, will

What evidence is needed to show that a drug is addictive?

he or she worry more about whether liquor stores will be closed on weekends or holidays than about having enough food, clothes, or recreational equipment?

As the problem progresses, it is not unusual for the person who abuses drugs to try to stop. In the case of alcoholism, for example, it is possible for even heavy drinkers to abstain for at least short periods of time. Most clinicians and researchers agree that diminished control over drinking is a crucial feature of the disorder (Walters, 1999). Some experts have described this issue as "freedom of choice." When a person first experiments with the use of alcohol, his or her behavior is clearly voluntary; the person is not compelled to drink. After drinking heavily for a long period of time, most people with a drinking disorder try to stop. Unfortunately, efforts at self-control are typically short-lived and usually fail.

Tolerance and Withdrawal Two particularly important features of substance dependence are the phenomena known as tolerance and withdrawal. These symptoms are usually interpreted as evidence of *physiological dependence.* **Tolerance** refers to the process through which the nervous system becomes less sensitive to the effects of alcohol or any other drug of abuse. For example, a person who has been regularly exposed to alcohol will need to drink increased quantities to achieve the same subjective effect ("buzz," "high," or level of intoxication).

The development of drug tolerance seems to be the result of three separate mechanisms (Julien, 2001). Two are pharmacological and the third is behavioral. *Metabolic tolerance* develops when repeated exposure to a drug causes the person's liver to produce more enzymes that are used to metabolize, that is, break down, the drug. The drug, therefore, is metabolized more quickly and the person has to take increasing larger doses in order to maintain the same level in his or her body. *Pharmacodynamic tolerance* occurs when receptors in the brain (see Figure 2–2 on page 38) adapt to continued presence of the drug. The neuron may adapt by reducing the number of receptors or by reducing their sensitivity to the drug. This process is known as *down regulation.* The third process involved in drug tolerance involves *behavioral conditioning mechanisms* (Siegel, 2005). Cues that are regularly associated with the administration of a drug begin to function as conditioned stimuli and elicit a conditioned response that is opposite in direction to the natural effect of the drug. As this compensatory response increases in strength, it competes with the drug response so that larger amounts of the drug must be taken to achieve the same effect.

Some drugs are much more likely than others to produce a buildup of tolerance (APA, 2000). The most substantial tolerance effects are found among heavy users of opioids, such as heroin, and CNS stimulants, such as amphetamine and cocaine. Pronounced tolerance is also found among people who use alcohol and nicotine. The evidence is unclear regarding tolerance effects and prolonged use of marijuana and hashish. Most people who use cannabinoids are not aware of tolerance effects, but these effects have been demonstrated in animal studies. Hallucinogens (LSD) and phencyclidine (PCP) may not lead to the development of tolerance.

Withdrawal refers to the symptoms experienced when a person stops using a drug. The symptom can go on for several days. For example, alcohol is a CNS depressant, and the heavy drinker's system becomes accustomed to functioning in a chronically depressed state. When the person stops drinking, the system begins to rebound within several hours, producing many unpleasant side effects—hand tremors, sweating, nausea, anxiety, and insomnia. The most serious forms of withdrawal include convulsions and visual, tactile, or auditory hallucinations. Some people develop delirium, a sudden disturbance of consciousness that is accompanied by changes in cognitive processes such as lack of awareness of the environment or inability to sustain attention (see Chapter 14). This syndrome is called *alcohol withdrawal delirium* in DSM-IV-TR (more traditionally known as *delirium tremens,* or DTs) if it is induced by withdrawal from alcohol.

The symptoms of withdrawal vary considerably for different kinds of substances. Table 11–2 compares various drugs of abuse in terms of withdrawal and other related characteristics. Unpleasant reactions are most evident during withdrawal from alcohol, opioids, and the general class of sedatives, hypnotics, and anxiolytics (such as Valium and Xanax). Withdrawal symptoms are also associated with stimulants, such as amphetamine, cocaine, and nicotine, though they are sometimes less pronounced than those associated with alcohol and opioids.

Withdrawal symptoms are not often seen after repeated use of cannabis or hallucinogens, and they have not been demonstrated with phencyclidine. Caffeine is the most widely used psychoactive substance in the world. We all know people who crave coffee, especially in the morning. And some heavy coffee users experience severe headaches when they stop drinking caffeine (James & Keane, 2007). You may be surprised to see in Table 11–2 that, according to DSM-IV-TR, the use of caffeine is not considered to lead to dependence or withdrawal symptoms. The authors of DSM-IV-TR acknowledged these symptoms, but they decided that the symptoms did not cause clinically significant distress and impairment and, therefore, should not be included in the manual as a type of mental disorder.

All these problems serve to emphasize the fact that symptoms of substance use disorders fall along a continuum. It is convenient to consider these problems in terms of qualitative distinctions: people who can control their drinking and those who cannot; people who crave alcohol and those who do not; people who have developed a tolerance to the drug and those who have not; and so on. In fact, there are no clear dividing lines on any of these dimensions. Drug use disorders lie on a continuum of severity (Helzer et al., 2008). For this reason it is extremely difficult to define the nature of substance dependence disorders.

People can become dependent on many different kinds of drugs. Although patterns of dependence are similar in some ways for all drugs, each type of drug also has some unique features. In the next few pages we briefly review some of the most important classes of drugs. For each group, we will describe short-term effects on physiology and behavior, as well as the consequences of long-term abuse. Unless otherwise specified, these descriptions are based on information presented by William McKim (2006) in his textbook on drugs and behavior.

Alcohol

Alcohol affects virtually every organ and system in the body. After alcohol has been ingested, it is absorbed through membranes in the stomach, small intestine, and colon. The rate at which it is absorbed is influenced by many variables, including the concentration of alcohol in the beverage (for example, distilled spirits are absorbed more rapidly than beer or wine), the volume and rate of consumption, and the presence of food in the digestive system. After it is absorbed, alcohol is distributed to all the body's organ systems. Almost all the alcohol that a person consumes is eventually broken down or metabolized in the liver. The rate at which alcohol is metabolized varies from person to person, but the average person can metabolize about 1 ounce of 90-proof liquor or 12 ounces of beer per hour (Nathan, 1993). If the person's consumption rate exceeds this metabolic limit, then blood alcohol levels will rise.

TABLE 11–2 Comparison of Various Psychoactive Substances

SUBSTANCE	CAN PRODUCE DEPENDENCE	CAN PRODUCE INTOXICATION	ASSOCIATED WITHDRAWAL	CAN PRODUCE DEMENTIA
Alcohol	yes	yes	yes	yes
Amphetamines	yes	yes	yes	no
Caffeine	no	yes	no	no
Marijuana/hashish	yes	yes	no	no
Cocaine	yes	yes	yes	no
Hallucinogens	yes	yes	no	no
Inhalants	yes	yes	no	yes
Nicotine	yes	no	yes	no
Opiates	yes	yes	yes	no
Phencyclidine (PCP)	yes	yes	no	no
Sedatives, hypnotics, and anxiolytics	yes	yes	yes	yes

Source: Reprinted with permission from the *Diagnostic and Statistical Manual of Mental Disorders,* Fourth Edition, Text Revision. Copyright © 2000 by the American Psychiatric Association.

Short-Term Effects Blood alcohol levels are measured in terms of the amount of alcohol per unit of blood. A "drink" is considered to be 12 ounces of beer, 4 ounces of wine, or 1 ounce of 86-proof whiskey. The average 160-pound man who consumes 5 drinks in 1 hour will have a blood alcohol level of 100 milligrams (mg) per 100 milliliters (ml) of blood, or 100 mg percent (Kowalski, 1998). There is a strong correlation between blood alcohol levels and CNS intoxicating effects. According to DSM-IV-TR, the symptoms of alcohol intoxication include slurred speech, lack of coordination, an unsteady gait, nystagmus (involuntary to-and-fro movement of the eyeballs induced when the person looks upward or to the side), impaired attention or memory, and stupor and coma.

In most states, the legal limit of alcohol concentration for driving is 100 mg percent. Some state legislatures have lowered this limit to 80 mg percent, because slowed reaction times and interference with other driving skills may occur at lower blood alcohol levels (Mejeur, 1999). People with levels of 150 to 300 mg percent will almost always act intoxicated. Neurological and respiration complications begin to appear at higher levels. There is an extreme risk of coma leading to toxic death when blood alcohol levels go above 400 mg percent.

Long-Term Consequences The prolonged use and abuse of alcohol can have a devastating impact on many areas of a person's life. The disruption of relationships with family and friends can be especially painful. The impact of Hemingway's drinking on his writing career and his family life is clearly evident. Most critics agree that his literary accomplishments were confined primarily to the early stages of his career, before his alcoholism began to interfere with his ability to write. Drinking also took its toll on his marriages, which were characterized by frequent and occasionally furious conflict in public and by repeated episodes of verbal and physical abuse in private (Johnson, 1989). Also, the heavy use of alcohol by a pregnant woman can cause damage to her fetus (see Chapter 15).

Many people who abuse alcohol experience blackouts. In some cases, abusers may continue to function without passing out, but they will be unable to remember their behavior. An example is the person who drives home drunk from a party and in the morning finds a dent in the car bumper but can't remember how it got there. Sometimes problem drinkers will be told by a friend about how they behaved at the previous night's party, but they cannot remember what they did.

Regular heavy use of alcohol is also likely to interfere with job performance. Coworkers and supervisors may complain. Attendance at work may become sporadic. Eventually the heavy drinker may be suspended or fired. Related to job performance is the problem of financial difficulties. Losing one's job is clearly detrimental to one's financial stability, as are the costs of divorce, health care, liquor, and so on.

Many heavy drinkers encounter problems with legal authorities. These problems may include arrests for drunken driving and public intoxication, as well as charges of spouse and child abuse. Many forms of violent behavior are more likely to be committed when a person has been drinking.

On a biological level, prolonged exposure to high levels of alcohol can disrupt the functions of several important organ systems, especially the liver, pancreas, gastrointestinal system, cardiovascular system, and endocrine system. The symptoms of alcoholism include many secondary health problems, such as cirrhosis of the liver, heart problems (in part, the result of being overweight), and various forms of cancer, as well as severe and persistent forms of dementia and memory impairment or amnestic disorders, such as Korsakoff's syndrome (see Chapter 14). Alcoholism is also associated with nutritional disturbances of many types, because chronic abusers often drink instead of eating balanced meals. In fact, over an extended period of time, alcohol dependence has more negative health consequences

▼ The negative consequences of alcohol dependence typically include a devastating impact on social relationships and work performance.

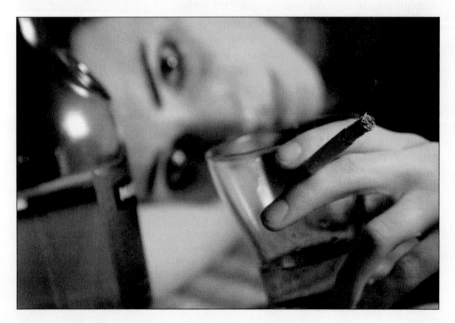

than does abuse of any other drug, with the exception of nicotine.

The misuse of alcohol leads to an enormous number of severe injuries and premature deaths in every region of the world (Cornelius et al., 2008). The specific impact of alcohol varies among geographic regions, in part because of differences in the age structure of different populations. Deaths that result from alcohol-related injuries are much more common among young men, while deaths from alcohol-related diseases are responsible for more deaths among older men (Murray & Lopez, 1997; see Figure 11–1).

Nicotine

Nicotine is the active ingredient in tobacco, which is its only natural source. Nicotine is almost never taken in its pure form because it can be toxic. Very high doses have extremely unpleasant effects. Controlled doses are easier to achieve by smoking or chewing tobacco, which provides a diluted concentration of nicotine. Another way of ingesting nicotine is to inhale snuff (powdered tobacco) into the nostrils. When tobacco smoke is inhaled, nicotine is absorbed into the blood through the mucous membranes of the lungs. This route of administration results in the highest concentrations of nicotine because it is carried directly from the lungs to the heart and from there to the brain.

Short-Term Effects The effects of nicotine on the peripheral nervous system (see Chapter 2) include increases in heart rate and blood pressure. In the central nervous system, nicotine has pervasive effects on a number of neurotransmitter systems (Houezec, 1998). It stimulates the release of norepinephrine from several sites, producing CNS arousal. Nicotine also causes the release of dopamine and norepinephrine in the mesolimbic dopamine pathway, also known as the reward system of the brain. The serotonin system, which also mediates the effects of antidepressant medication, is influenced by nicotine. In fact, some people have suggested that nicotine mimics the effects of antidepressant drugs.

Nicotine has a complex influence on subjective mood states. Many people say that they smoke because it makes them feel more relaxed. Some believe that it helps them control their subjective response to stress. This phenomenon is somewhat paradoxical in light of the fact that nicotine leads to increased arousal of the sympa-

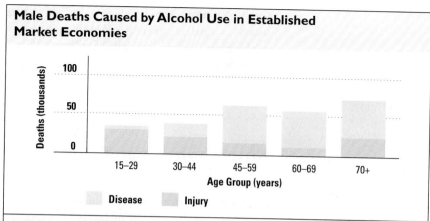

FIGURE 11–1 Young men are more likely to be killed by alcohol-related injuries, while older men often die as a result of alcohol-related disease.

Source: C. J. L. Murray and A. D. Lopez, 1997, "Global Mortality, Disability, and the Contribution of Risk Factors: Global Burden of Disease Study," *Lancet, 349,* pp. 1436–1442. Copyright © 1997. Reprinted by permission of Elsevier, Ltd.

thetic nervous system. Various explanations may account for this apparent inconsistency. One involves differences in dosage levels; low doses of nicotine may lead to increased arousal while higher doses lead to relaxation. Another alternative involves withdrawal. Regular smokers may feel relaxed when they smoke a cigarette because it relieves unpleasant symptoms of withdrawal.

Long-Term Consequences Nicotine is one of the most harmful and deadly addicting drugs. Considerable evidence points to the development of both tolerance and withdrawal symptoms among people who regularly smoke or chew tobacco. The physiological symptoms of withdrawal from nicotine include drowsiness, lightheadedness, headache, muscle tremors, and nausea. People who are attempting to quit smoking typically experience sleeping problems, weight gain, concentration difficulties, and mood swings ranging from anxiety to anger and depression (Hughes, 2007b). From a psychological point of view, withdrawal from nicotine is just as difficult as withdrawal from heroin. Many people report that these symptoms disappear after a few months, but some have serious cravings for several years after they quit.

People who smoke tobacco increase their risk of developing many fatal diseases, including heart disease, lung disease (bronchitis and emphysema), and various types of cancer (Kozlowski et al., 2001). Eighty percent of all deaths caused by lung cancer can be attributed to smoking tobacco. More than 3.5 million people in the world die prematurely each year as a result of tobacco. Large numbers of people are also killed or injured in fires caused by careless smoking. Women who smoke are also more likely to experience fertility problems. Babies born to mothers who smoked during pregnancy are also likely to weigh less than those born to mothers who do not smoke, and they may be more vulnerable to certain types of birth defects.

Amphetamine and Cocaine

Members of the class of drugs known as **psychomotor stimulants** produce their effects by simulating the actions of certain neurotransmitters, specifically epinephrine, norepinephrine, dopamine, and serotonin (as discussed later in this chapter). Cocaine is a naturally occurring stimulant drug that is extracted from the leaf of a small tree that grows at high elevations, as in the Andes Mountains. The amphetamines (such as dexedrine and methamphetamine) are produced synthetically.

The stimulants can be taken orally, injected, or inhaled. It is easier to maintain a constant blood level when the drugs are taken orally. They are absorbed more slowly through the digestive system, and their effects are less potent. More dramatic effects are achieved by injecting the drug or sniffing it. Cocaine can also be smoked, using various procedures that have been popularized in the past several years. Some people em-

▶ Lenny Bruce was an irreverent standup comedian and brilliant social critic. His abuse of various drugs, including amphetamines and heroin, disrupted his personal life and interfered with his ability to perform. He died from an overdose in 1966 at the age of 40.

ploy a particularly dangerous procedure called "freebasing," in which the drug is heated and its vapors are inhaled. Many people have been seriously burned when these highly combustible chemicals are accidentally ignited.

Short-Term Effects Cocaine and amphetamines are called stimulants because they activate the sympathetic nervous system (Constable, 2004). They increase heart rate and blood pressure and dilate the blood vessels and the air passages of the lungs. Stimulants also suppress the appetite and prevent sleep. These effects have been among the reasons for the popularity and frequent abuse of stimulants. They have been used, for example, by truck drivers who want to stay awake on long trips and by students who want to stay awake to study for exams. Unfortunately, in addition to their addicting properties, large doses of amphetamines can also lead to dizziness, confusion, and panic states, which clearly interfere with activities such as driving and studying.

Many people use (and abuse) stimulants because they induce a positive mood state. When they are injected, amphetamines and cocaine produce very similar subjective effects, but the effects of cocaine do not last as long. Low doses of amphetamines make people feel more confident, friendly, and energetic. At higher doses, the person is likely to experience a brief, intense feeling of euphoria. The rushes associated with snorting or injecting cocaine are frequently described in sexual terms. Although many people believe that cocaine enhances sexual arousal and pleasure, most of the evidence suggests that prolonged use leads to sexual dysfunction (Jaffe, 1995). Tolerance develops quickly to the euphoric effects of stimulant drugs. The feelings of exhilaration and well-being are typically followed, several hours later, by the onset of lethargy and a mildly depressed or irritable mood.

Acute overdoses of stimulant drugs can result in irregular heartbeat, convulsions, coma, and death. The highly publicized overdose deaths of several prominent athletes, such as that of All-American basketball star Len Bias in 1986, indicate that the intense cardiovascular effects of cocaine can be fatal, even among people who are otherwise strong and healthy. Individual differences in sensitivity to the subjective effects of cocaine may play a role in cocaine-related deaths. In other words, people who are resistant to cocaine-induced euphoria may consume unusually large quantities of the drug while trying to achieve the rush that others have described.

Long-Term Consequences High doses of amphetamines and cocaine can lead to the onset of psychosis. The risk of a psychotic reaction seems to increase with repeated exposure to the drug (Bolla, Cadet, & London, 1998). This syndrome can appear in people who have no prior history of mental disorder, and it usually disappears a few days after the drug has been cleared. Stimulants can also increase the severity of symptoms among people who had already developed some type of psychotic condition. The symptoms of amphetamine psychosis include auditory and visual hallucinations, as well as delusions of persecution and grandeur.

As with other forms of addiction, the most devastating effects of stimulant drugs frequently center around the disruption of occupational and social roles. The compulsion to continue taking cocaine can lead to physical exhaustion and financial ruin. People who are dependent on cocaine must spend enormous amounts of money to support their habit. They may have to sell important assets, such as their homes and cars, in order to finance extended binges. Some people become involved in a variety of criminal activities in order to raise enough money to purchase drugs.

Prolonged use of amphetamines has also been linked to an increase in violent behavior, but it is not clear whether this phenomenon is due to the drug itself or to the lifestyles with which it is frequently associated. Some violence might be related to a drug-induced increase in paranoia and hostility. Statistics concerning drugs and violent crime are very difficult to interpret. The direct effects of the drug on human behavior are confounded with various economic and social factors that are associated with buying, selling, and using an expensive, illegal drug like cocaine.

People who discontinue taking stimulant drugs do not typically experience severe withdrawal symptoms. The most common reaction is depression. Long-term exposure to high doses of amphetamine can lead to a profound state of clinical depression, which is often accompanied by ideas of suicide.

Opiates

The **opiates** (sometimes called opioids) are drugs that have properties similar to those of opium. The natural source of opium is a poppy with a white flower. The main active ingredients in opium are morphine and codeine, both of which are widely used in medicine, particularly to relieve pain. They are available legally only by prescription in the United States. In Canada, small quantities of codeine are available without a prescription in over-the-counter painkillers and cough medicines. Heroin is a synthetic opiate that is made by modifying the morphine molecule. It was originally marketed as an alternative to morphine when physicians believed, erroneously, that heroin is not addictive.

The opiates can be taken orally, injected, or inhaled. Opium is sometimes eaten or smoked. When morphine is used as a painkiller, it is taken orally so that it is absorbed slowly through the digestive system. People who use morphine for subjective effects most often inject the drug because it leads more quickly to high concentrations in brain tissue. Heroin can be injected, inhaled through the nose in the form of snuff, or smoked and inhaled through a pipe or tube.

What are the long-term consequences of abusing psychomotor stimulants?

Short-Term Effects The opiates can induce a state of dreamlike euphoria, which may be accompanied by increased sensitivity in hearing and vision. People who inject morphine or heroin also experience a rush—a brief, intense feeling of pleasure that is sometimes described as being like an orgasm in the entire body.

Laboratory studies of mood indicate that the positive, emotional effects of opiates do not last. They are soon replaced by long-term negative changes in mood and emotion. These unpleasant experiences are relieved for 30 to 60 minutes after each new injection of the drug, but they eventually color most of the rest of the person's waking experience.

◀ The positive, emotional effects of opiates do not last. They are soon replaced by long-term negative changes in mood and emotion.

The opiates can induce nausea and vomiting among novice users, constrict the pupils of the eye, and disrupt the coordination of the digestive system. Continued use of opiates decreases the level of sex hormones in both women and men, resulting in reduced sex drive and impaired fertility.

Some people mix cocaine and opiates into a mixture known as a *speedball* to enhance these subjective feelings. The following brief case describes the preparation of this combination of drugs and one heroin addict's immediate reaction to the injection of a speedball.

BRIEF CASE **STUDY**
Feelings After Injecting Heroin

He pushes the plunger on the syringe, squirting water into the heroin powder, then strikes a match and waves it just under the metal lid. The liquid bubbles and the heroin quickly dissolves with very little heat required. *That's good,* he thinks. Sometimes the dope is so good it needs hardly any fire to dissolve it. Next, he shakes in a couple of small rocks of cocaine from the foil wrapper and is impressed that they vanish immediately in the solution. He swirls the liquid around, rips open the filter from one of his Marlboros, and uses the white fibers as a strainer through which to draw the liquid speedball into the syringe. He carefully places the loaded syringe between his teeth. He rolls up his sleeve, removes his belt with one hand, and takes a seat on the edge of the toilet. He wraps the belt tight around his right arm and hopes he can get a clean hit on one of the veins he watches come up. *There, I'll go there.*

The needle point feels sharp going in, which is good; it means he's got an unused needle. When he pulls back on the plunger a little stream of blood slithers up into the syringe, discoloring the slightly yellow liquid. He loosens the belt, careful not to dislodge the needle from the vein, takes a breath, and slowly pushes the liquid into his arm. He pulls the needle out and dabs with his finger at the drop of blood left behind on his arm. As he does this he feels the freeze in his arm from the cocaine. His arm feels numb. Then it reaches his stomach and mouth. His heart races. He tastes the medicinal flavor just as the first wave of rushes is reaching his brain. His stomach heaves. His scalp tingles and he gets a little scared at first—the wave of sensation is stronger than usual. He fights the urge to vomit, the heroin kicks in and the nausea retreats as the warm, heroin heat replaces the heart-thumping freeze caused by the cocaine. His heart starts to slow down, or so it seems. A quiet, hollow siren rages in his head. The familiar beads of perspiration crowd each other on his forehead, and one drops onto his arm when he bends over to begin cleaning everything up. He puts away his paraphernalia, threads his belt into his pants, and sits down again. *Good stuff, very good,* he thinks as he nods for a second.

Back on Houston Street now, he decides to have a cup of espresso in a little coffee shop he comes upon. Sitting back at a table with a view of the street, he savors the thick hot coffee, lights a cigarette, and blows the smoke to the ceiling. *Nothing hurts,* he thinks. The lousy job that he needs to hold onto, the flak he catches from his wife, the fact that he is turning 40 and doesn't have anything to show for his life—none of it fazes him, but he still thinks about it. A spotty work history, no college, and rent that is three weeks late don't matter right now. He feels warm, loose, and sexy. Was the waitress's smile a flirt or was she smiling because she caught him nodding? Doesn't matter. He smiles back and thinks maybe he can buy his wife a gold-plated necklace instead of the real one. It will look just like the one she pointed out anyway.

And that was what he did (Fernandez, 1998, pp. 72–73).

High doses of opiates can lead to a comatose state, severely depressed breathing, and convulsions. The number of people admitted to hospital emergency rooms for treatment of heroin overdoses increased substantially during the 1990s. Between 3,000 and 4,000 people die from accidental overdoses of heroin in the United States each year (Leland, 1996).

Long-Term Consequences The effects of opiates on occupational performance and health depend in large part on the amount of drugs that the person takes. At high doses, people who are addicted to opiates become chronically lethargic and lose their motivation to remain productive. At low doses, some people who use opiates for an extended period of time can remain healthy and work productively in spite of their addiction. This functioning is, of course, dependent on the person having easy and relatively inexpensive access to opiates. One possibility is being maintained by a physician on methadone, a synthetic opiate that is sometimes used therapeutically as an alternative to heroin.

People who are addicted to opiates become preoccupied with finding and using the drug, in order to experience the rush and to avoid withdrawal symptoms. Tolerance develops rather quickly, and the person's daily dose increases regularly until it eventually levels off and remains steady. Many of the severe health consequences of opiate use are the result of the lifestyle of the addict rather than the drug itself. The enormous expenses and difficulties associated with obtaining illegal opiates almost invariably consume all the person's resources. The person typically neglects housing, nutrition, and health care in the search for another fix. Heroin addicts are much more likely than other people in the general population to die from AIDS, violence, and suicide.

Barbiturates and Benzodiazepines

The families of drugs known as barbiturates and benzodiazepines are also known informally as tranquilizers, hypnotics, and sedatives. *Tranquilizers* are used to decrease anxiety or agitation. *Hypnotics* are used to help people sleep. *Sedative* is a more general term that describes drugs that calm people or reduce excitement (other than the relief of anxiety). The **barbiturates,** such as phenobarbital (Nembutal) and amobarbital (Amytal), were used for a variety of purposes, including the treatment of chronic anxiety. The **benzodiazepines,** which include diazepam (Valium) and alprazolam (Xanax), have replaced the barbiturates in the treatment of anxiety disorders, in large part because of their lower potential for producing a lethal overdose.

Short-Term Effects Sedatives and hypnotics can lead to a state of intoxication that is identical to that associated with alcohol. It is characterized by impaired judgment, slowness of speech, lack of coordination, a narrowed range of attention, and disinhibition of sexual and aggressive impulses. Intravenous use of barbiturates can lead quickly to a pleasant, warm, drowsy feeling that is similar to the experience achieved when taking opiates. The benzodiazepines can sometimes lead to an increase in hostile and aggressive behavior. Some clinicians call this a "rage reaction" or aggressive dyscontrol.

Long-Term Consequences People who abruptly stop taking high doses of benzodiazepines may experience symptoms that are sometimes called a *discontinuance syndrome.* These symptoms can include a return—and, in some cases, a worsening—of the original anxiety symptoms, if the medication was being used to treat an anxiety disorder. The person may also develop new symptoms that are directly associated with drug withdrawal. These include irritability, paranoia, sleep disturbance, agitation, muscle tension, restlessness, and perceptual disturbances. Withdrawal symptoms are less likely to occur if the medication is discontinued gradually rather than abruptly.

Cannabis

Marijuana and hashish are derived from the hemp plant, *Cannabis sativa.* The most common active ingredient in cannabis is a compound called delta-9-tetrahydro-cannabinol (THC). Because every part of the plant contains THC, cannabis can be prepared for consumption in several ways. **Marijuana** refers to the dried leaves and flowers, which can be smoked in a cigarette or pipe. It can also be baked in brownies and ingested orally. **Hashish** refers to the dried resin from the top of the female cannabis plant. It can be smoked or eaten after being baked in cookies or brownies.

Oral administration of cannabis material leads to slow and incomplete absorption. Therefore the dose must be two or three times larger to achieve the same subjective effect as when it is smoked. Most of the drug is metabolized in the liver.

Short-Term Effects The subjective effects of marijuana are almost always pleasant. "Getting high" on marijuana refers to a pervasive sense of well-being and happiness. Laboratory research has shown that marijuana can have variable effects on a person's mood. Many people begin to feel happy, but some become anxious and paranoid. The mood of other people seems to be especially important. After smoking marijuana, a person's mood may become more easily influenced by how other people are behaving.

Cannabis intoxication is often accompanied by *temporal disintegration,* a condition in which people have trouble retaining and organizing information, even over relatively short periods of time. Conversations may become disjointed because the drug interferes with the people's ability to recall what they have said or planned to say. Lapses in attention and concentration problems are frequent.

Long-Term Consequences The issue of the addictive properties of cannabis remains controversial (Hall & Pacula, 2003; Onaivi, 2002). Some tolerance effects to THC have been observed in laboratory animals. Tolerance effects in humans remain ambiguous. Most evidence suggests that people do not develop tolerance to THC unless they are exposed to high doses over an extended period of time. Some people actually report that they become more sensitive (rather than less sensitive) to the effects of marijuana after repeated use. This phenomenon is called *reverse tolerance.* Although reverse tolerance has been reported casually by frequent users, it has not been demonstrated in a laboratory situation, where dosage levels can be carefully controlled.

Withdrawal symptoms are unlikely to develop among occasional smokers of marijuana. People who have been exposed to continuous, high doses of THC may experience withdrawal symptoms, such as irritability, restlessness, and insomnia.

Prolonged heavy use of marijuana may lead to certain types of performance deficits on neuropsychological tests, especially those involving sustained attention, learning, and decision making (Pope & Yurgelun-Todd, 1996). These effects should be interpreted cautiously. Follow-up studies of adults who used cannabis over a period of several years did not find evidence of cognitive decline associated with the drug (Lyketsos et al., 1999).

Hallucinogens and Related Drugs

Drugs that are called **hallucinogens** cause people to experience hallucinations. Although many other types of drugs can lead to hallucinations at toxic levels, hallucinogens cause hallucinations at relatively low doses. There are many different types of hallucinogens, and they have very different neurophysiological effects. The molecular structure of many hallucinogens is similar to the molecular structure of various neurotransmitters, such as serotonin and norepinephrine. The most common hallucinogen is a synthetic drug called

LSD (D-lysergic acid diethylamide), which bears a strong chemical resemblance to serotonin. It achieves its effect by interacting with certain types of serotonin receptors in the brain. *Psilocybin* is another type of hallucinogen whose chemical structure resembles that of serotonin. It is found in different types of mushrooms, which grow primarily in the southern United States and Mexico. Mescaline is a type of hallucinogen that resembles norepinephrine. It is the active ingredient in a small, spineless cactus called peyote. Mescaline and psilocybin have been used in religious ceremonies by various Native American peoples for many centuries.

MDMA (methylene-dioxy-methamphetamine, also known as ecstasy) is one of several synthetic amphetamine derivates. It could be classified as a stimulant, but most texts list it as a type of hallucinogen (Julien, 2001). MDMA is also known as a "club drug" because it is popular among people who attend "raves" and dance clubs (LSD and methamphetamine are also known as club drugs). MDMA is usually taken as a tablet, but the powder form can be inhaled or injected. Within half an hour of ingesting MDMA orally, the person begins to experience an enhanced mood state and a feeling of well-being that often lasts several hours. Although it does not produce vivid hallucinations, MDMA does lead to changes in perceptual experiences, such as distortions in the sense of time and space, as well as increased sensory awareness. It also produces changes in blood pressure and can interfere with the body's ability to regulate its temperature.

Phencyclidine (PCP) is another synthetic drug that is often classified with the hallucinogens, although its effects are very different than those associated with LSD and mescaline. It was originally developed as a painkiller. Small doses of PCP lead to relaxation, warmth, and numbness. At higher doses, PCP can induce psychotic behavior, including delusional thinking, catatonic motor behavior, manic excitement, and sudden mood changes. The drug is typically sold in a crystallized form that can be sprinkled on leaves, such as tobacco, marijuana, or parsley, and then smoked. Some people snort it or inject it after dissolving the crystals in water.

Short-Term Effects The effects of hallucinogenic drugs are difficult to study empirically because they are based primarily in subjective experience. They typically induce vivid, and occasionally spectacular, visual images. During the

▼ MDMA is known as a "club drug" because it is popular among people who attend "raves" and dance clubs. It causes changes in perceptual experiences, such as distortions in the sense of time and space, as well as increased sensory awareness.

early phase of this drug experience, the images often take the form of colorful geometric patterns. The later phase is more likely to be filled with meaningful images of people, animals, and places. The images may change rapidly, and they sometimes follow an explosive pattern of movement.

Although these hallucinatory experiences are usually pleasant, they are occasionally frightening. "Bad trips" are a decidedly unpleasant experience that can lead to panic attacks and the fear of losing one's mind. People can usually be talked through this process by constantly reminding them that the experience is drug-induced and will be over soon.

Most hallucinogens are not particularly toxic. People do not die from taking an overdose of LSD, psilocybin, or mescaline. However, PCP is much more toxic. High doses can lead to coma, convulsions, respiratory arrest, and brain hemorrhage. MDMA (Ecstasy) can damage serotonin neurons on a permanent basis, and it has been associated with some fatalities (Gold, Tabrah, & Frost-Pineda, 2001).

Long-Term Consequences The use of hallucinogens follows a different pattern than that associated with most other drugs. Hallucinogens, with the possible exception of PCP, are used sporadically and on special occasions rather than continuously. If these drugs are taken repeatedly within 2 or 3 days, their effects disappear. Most people do not increase their use of hallucinogens over time. People who stop taking hallucinogens after continued use do not experience problems; there seem to be no withdrawal symptoms associated with the hallucinogens that resemble serotonin and norepinephrine. The perceptual effects of hallucinogenic drugs almost always wear off after several hours. There are cases, however, in which these drugs have induced persistent psychotic behavior. Most experts interpret these examples as an indication that the drug experience can trigger the onset of psychosis in people who were already vulnerable to that type of disorder. As genes involved in the predisposition toward psychosis are identified, it will become possible to test this hypothesis.

Some people who have taken hallucinogens experience *flashbacks*—brief visual aftereffects that can occur at unpredictable intervals long after the drug has been cleared from the person's body. Scientists do not understand the mechanisms that are responsible for flashbacks. Flashbacks may be more likely to occur when the person is under stress or after the person has used another drug, such as marijuana.

DIAGNOSIS

The problems that we have reviewed indicate that substance dependence represents an extremely diverse set of problems. Everyone—clinicians and researchers, as well as drug abuser and their families—seems to recognize the existence of a serious psychological disorder. But does it have a core? What is the best way to define it? In the following pages we briefly review some of the ways in which alcoholism and drug abuse have been defined. We must begin with the recognition that alcoholism and other types of addiction have not always been viewed as medical conditions that require treatment (Walters, 1999).

Brief History of Legal and Illegal Substances

One of the most widely recognized facts about alcohol consumption is that drinking patterns vary tremendously from one culture to the next and, within the same culture, from one point in time to another. Public attitudes toward the consumption of alcohol have changed dramatically during the course of U.S. history. For example, heavy drinking was not generally considered to be a serious problem in colonial times (Levine, 1978). In fact, it seemed to be an integral part of daily life. The average amount of alcohol consumed per person each year was much higher in those days than it is today. A typical American in the eighteenth century drank approximately 4 gallons of alcohol a year;

▼ During the Prohibition era in the United States (1922–1933), it was illegal to manufacture, transport, or sell alcoholic beverages. Nevertheless, alcohol continued to be widely available from illegal sources, and the law was eventually changed. Similar efforts to control access to addicting drugs have failed in other countries.

the corresponding figure for our own society is about 2.5 gallons (Fingarette, 1988). Drunkenness was not considered to be either socially deviant or symptomatic of medical illness.

Public attitudes toward alcohol changed dramatically in the United States during the first half of the nineteenth century. Members of the temperance movement preached against the consumption of alcohol in any form. Temperance workers ardently believed that anyone who drank alcohol would become a drunkard. Their arguments were largely moral and religious rather than medical or scientific, and many of their publications included essays on the personality weaknesses that were associated with such morally reprehensible behaviors (Levine, 1978). The temperance movement was, in fact, able to persuade many thousands of people to abandon the consumption of alcohol.

The movement finally succeeded in banning the manufacture and sale of alcoholic beverages when Congress approved the Eighteenth Amendment to the Constitution in 1919. During the following years, known as the Prohibition era, the average consumption of alcohol fell substantially, and the incidence of associated medical illnesses, such as cirrhosis of the liver, also declined. Nevertheless, these laws were extremely difficult to enforce, and Prohibition was repealed in 1933.

DSM-IV-TR

As we noted at the beginning of this chapter, DSM-IV-TR divides addictions into two categories: substance abuse and substance dependence, with the latter being the more severe and advanced form of disorder. This distinction is based, in part, on the recognition that many people who suffer serious impairment from substance abuse do not progress to the level of dependence (Bucholz, 1999). The manual lists 11 types of drugs that can lead to problems of abuse and dependence (refer to Table 11–2). Rather than including separate definitions of dependence and abuse for each class of substance, the manual provides one generic set of criteria for substance dependence and another for substance abuse. These criterion sets can be applied to any type of drug.

The DSM-IV-TR criteria for substance dependence are presented in Table 11–3. Tolerance and withdrawal are listed along with five other problems that describe a pattern of compulsive use and loss of control. The person has to exhibit at least three of the seven criteria for a diagnosis of substance dependence to be made. Tolerance and withdrawal are not required for the person to meet this definition of dependence. Their importance is recognized with a subtype designation. If

---

TABLE 11–3   DSM-IV-TR Criteria for Substance Dependence

A maladaptive pattern of substance use, leading to clinically significant impairment or distress, as manifested by three (or more) of the following, occurring at any time in the same 12-month period:

1. Tolerance, as defined by either of the following:

   a. A need for markedly increased amounts of the substance to achieve intoxication or desired effect.
   b. Markedly diminished effect with continued use of the same amount of the substance.

2. Withdrawal, as manifested by either of the following:

   a. The characteristic withdrawal syndrome for the substance (criteria sets for withdrawal are listed separately for specific substances).
   b. The same (or a closely related) substance is taken to relieve or avoid withdrawal symptoms.

3. The substance is often taken in larger amounts or over a longer period than was intended.
4. There is a persistent desire or unsuccessful efforts to cut down or control substance use.
5. A great deal of time is spent in activities necessary to obtain the substance (for example, visiting multiple doctors or driving long distances), use the substance (for example, chain-smoking), or recover from its effects.
6. Important social, occupational, or recreational activities are given up or reduced because of substance use.
7. The substance use is continued despite knowledge of having a persistent or recurrent physical or psychological problem that is likely to have been caused or exacerbated by the substance (for example, current cocaine use despite recognition of cocaine-induced depression, or continued drinking despite recognition that an ulcer was made worse by alcohol consumption).

Source: Reprinted with permission from the *Diagnostic and Statistical Manual of Mental Disorders*, Fourth Edition, Text Revision. Copyright © 2000 by the American Psychiatric Association.

there is evidence of either tolerance or withdrawal (or both), the additional specification of *physiological dependence* is made. Symptoms of withdrawal seem to be more important than symptoms of tolerance in this regard. People with a history of physiological dependence report more severe drug-related problems, greater intensity of exposure to drugs, and more comorbid conditions such as anxiety and depression (Schuckit et al., 1998a, 1998b).

This approach to the definition of substance dependence is convenient because it points to a unified view of addiction. However, it also has some disadvantages. Perhaps most important is the fact that the use of a single definition of dependence may conceal differences between the kinds of problems that are associated with various classes of drugs (Budney, 2007; Frances, First, & Pincus, 1995). For example, dependence on opiates almost always involves physiological symptoms of tolerance and withdrawal, whereas dependence on cannabis or hallucinogens seldom does.

Substance abuse is defined in terms of harmful consequences that appear in the absence of tolerance, withdrawal, or a pattern of compulsive use (dependence). The DSM-IV-TR definition of substance abuse is presented in Table 11–4. One difficult issue in defining this condition involves the identification of a boundary between substance abuse and the recreational use of drugs. The diagnostic manual emphasizes the terms *recurrent* and *maladaptive pattern* for this purpose. The problem must be persistent before this diagnosis would be considered. Someone involved in a single drug-related incident would not meet the criteria for this disorder, regardless of how serious the incident might have been (Frances, First, & Pincus, 1995).

Important questions have been raised about the validity of the DSM-IV-TR substance abuse category, especially with regard to alcoholism (Martin, Chung, & Langanbucher, 2008). Many people who receive a diagnosis of alcohol abuse do so on the basis of a single symptom—hazardous use—which usually involves driving while intoxicated. This is certainly a grave problem with enormous negative consequences, but it is not clear whether this form of maladaptive behavior should be considered a mental disorder if it occurs in the absence of other symptoms of alcohol abuse. Perhaps the drunk driver would be better viewed as a person who has persistently chosen, for whatever reason, to engage in reckless and illegal behavior that ignores the safety of other people. One group of investigators has recommended that the alcohol abuse category be retained but with the stipulation that people cannot meet the criteria for this disorder if the diagnosis is based only on driving after drinking (Hasin et al., 1999).

> *Where is the boundary between substance abuse and recreational drug use?*

Proposed Subtypes

DSM-IV-TR does not recognize any systems for subtyping substance dependence, other than the presence or absence of physiological symptoms (tolerance or withdrawal). Nevertheless, procedures for subdividing alcoholism have been employed extensively in research studies (Hesselbrook & Hesselbrook, 2007). One influential system was proposed by Robert Cloninger, a psychiatrist at Washington University in St. Louis (Cloninger, Sigvardsson, & Bohman, 1996).

Cloninger suggested that there are two prototypical varieties of alcoholism. According to this system, Type 1 alcoholism is characterized by a somewhat later onset, prominent psychological

---

TABLE 11–4 DSM-IV-TR Criteria for Substance Abuse

A. A maladaptive pattern of substance use leading to clinically significant impairment or distress, as manifested by one (or more) of the following, occurring within a 12-month period:

1. Recurrent substance use resulting in a failure to fulfill major role obligations at work, school, or home.
2. Recurrent substance use in situations in which it is physically hazardous.
3. Recurrent substance-related legal problems.
4. Continued substance use despite having persistent or recurrent social or interpersonal problems caused or exacerbated by the effects of the substance.

B. The symptoms have never met the criteria of substance dependence for this class of substance.

Source: Reprinted with permission from the *Diagnostic and Statistical Manual of Mental Disorders*, Fourth Edition, Text Revision. Copyright © 2000 by the American Psychiatric Association.

dependence (loss-of-control drinking), and the absence of antisocial personality traits. It is found in both men and women. Type 2 alcoholism, which is found almost exclusively among men, typically has an earlier onset and is associated with the co-occurrence of persistent antisocial behaviors. This proposed distinction has been useful in many research studies. On the other hand, the difference between Type 1 and Type 2 alcoholism may be more quantitative than qualitative in nature (Vaillant, 1994).

Course and Outcome

It is impossible to specify a typical course for substance dependence, especially alcoholism. Age of onset varies widely, ranging from childhood and early adolescence throughout the life span.

Although we can roughly identify stages that intervene between initial exposure to a drug and the eventual onset of tolerance and dependence, the timing with which a person moves through these phases can vary enormously. The best available information regarding the course of substance use disorders comes from the study of alcoholism. The specific course of this problem varies considerably from one person to the next. The only thing that seems to be certain is that periods of heavy use alternate with periods of relative abstinence, however short-lived they may be (Schuckit et al., 2002).

In an effort to examine the natural history of alcoholism, George Vaillant (2003) studied the lives of 456 inner-city adolescents from Boston and 268 former undergraduate students from Harvard University. Initial information was collected in 1940, when the participants were adolescents. Follow-up information was collected every other year by questionnaire and every fifth year by physical examination. The college group has been followed until 70 years of age, and the core city group has been followed to age 60. At some point during their lives, 21 percent of the college men and 35 percent of the core city men met diagnostic criteria for alcohol abuse, which Vaillant defined as the presence of four or more problems in such areas as employer complaints, marital and family difficulties, medical complications, and legal problems.

As expected, the mortality rate was higher among men who abused alcohol than among those who did not. Heart disease and cancer were twice as common among the alcohol abusers, perhaps in part because they were also more likely to be heavy cigarette smokers.

Most of the alcoholic men went through repeated cycles of abstinence followed by relapse. The life course of alcohol abuse could be charted most clearly for 121 of the core city men who abused alcohol and remained in the study until age 60 and 46 college men who abused alcohol and remained in the study until age 70. These data are illustrated in Figure 11–2. In the graphs in Figure 11–2, abstinence is defined as less than one drink per month for more than a year. Social drinking refers to problem-free drinking for 10 years or more. Controlled drinking is more than one drink per month for at least 2 years with no reported problem. The main differences between the groups were that the core city men began abusing alcohol at an earlier age, and they were also more likely than the college men eventually to achieve stable abstinence.

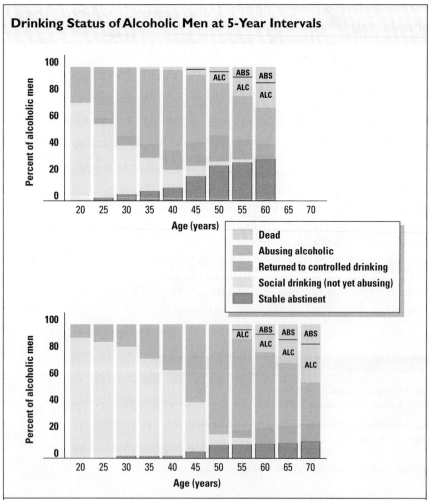

Drinking Status of Alcoholic Men at 5-Year Intervals

FIGURE 11–2 Results of a long-term follow-up study of two groups of alcoholics: 121 core city men (top) and 46 college men (bottom). The core city men began abusing alcohol at a younger age and were more likely to achieve stable abstinence by age 60.

Source: G. E. Vaillant, 1996, "A Long-term Follow-up of Male Alcohol Abuse," *Archives of General Psychiatry, 53*, pp. 243–249. Copyright © 1996. Reprinted by permission of American Medical Association.

The average age of onset of alcohol abuse was 40 years for the college men and 29 years for the core city men.

Many men spent the previous 20 years alternating between periods of controlled drinking and alcohol abuse. The proportion of men who continued to abuse alcohol went down after the age of 40. The proportion of alcoholic men in both groups who became completely abstinent went up slowly, but consistently during the follow-up period. The longer a man remained abstinent, the greater the probability that he would continue to be abstinent. Vaillant's data indicated that relapse to alcohol abuse was unlikely among men who were able to remain abstinent for at least 6 years.

Many important questions remain to be answered about the relapse process. Is there a "safe point" that separates a period of high risk for relapse from a period of more stable change? Vaillant's data suggest that the 6-year mark may be important for men who abuse alcohol. Will this suggestion be replicated in other studies? And does it generalize to other drugs? Do relapse rates stabilize over time? Is an addicted person more likely to succeed on a later attempt to quit than on an early attempt? Answers to these questions will be useful in the development of more effective treatment programs.

Other Disorders Commonly Associated with Addictions

People with substance use disorders often exhibit other forms of mental disorder as well. Most prominent among these are antisocial personality disorder (ASPD), mood disorders, and anxiety disorders. Conduct disorder (the childhood manifestation of ASPD) is strongly related to concurrent alcohol use in adolescence and the subsequent development of alcohol dependence (McGue & Iacono, 2008). ASPD and alcohol/drug dependence frequently co-occur, and there is evidence to suggest that they represent alternative manifestations of a general predisposition toward behavioral disinhibition (Kendler et al., 2003).

The complexity of the association between substance use disorders and mood/anxiety disorders makes them difficult to untangle (Grant et al., 2006). In some cases, prolonged heavy drinking or use of psychoactive drugs can result in feelings of depression and anxiety. The more the person drinks or uses drugs, the more guilty the person feels about his or her inability to control the problem. In addition, continued use of

◄ Singer Amy Winehouse has received considerable media attention for alcohol and drug dependence, depression, and eating problems. Her struggles provide a sad, public illustration of the complex relations among substance use disorders and other mental health problems.

alcohol and drugs often leads to greater conflict with family members, coworkers, and other people. Sometimes the depression and anxiety precede the onset of the substance use problem. In fact, some people seem to use alcohol and drugs initially in a futile attempt to self-medicate for these other conditions. Ultimately, the drugs make things worse.

FREQUENCY

Drug-related problems are found in most countries. There are interesting variations, however, in patterns of use for specific types of drugs. The use of specific drugs is determined, in part, by their availability. For example, opium is used most heavily in Southeast Asia and in some Middle Eastern countries, where the opium poppy is cultivated. Cocaine is used frequently in certain countries of South America where coca trees grow; it is also imported into North America, particularly the United States. Use of cannabis is widespread around the world, in part because the plants can grow in many different climates. In contrast, in Japan, where the amount of land available for cultivation is severely limited, the largest drug problem involves amphetamine, a synthetic drug.

The fact that people in some regions are frequent drug users does not necessarily imply that a particular population will have a high rate of substance dependence. Culture shapes people's choices about the use of drugs and the ways in which they are used. It influences such factors as the amount of a drug that is typically ingested, the route of administration, and the person's beliefs about drug effects (Room, 2007). These considerations, in turn, influence the probability that serious problems will develop. Consider, for example, the Indians of South America who produce coca for market. They have traditionally used the leaves as medicines and in religious ceremonies. They also roll the leaves into a ball that can be tucked in the cheek and sucked for an extended period of time. This form of use relieves cold, hunger, and thirst. It does not produce the severe dependence problems that are associated with the use of refined cocaine, a much more potent drug that can be sniffed or injected.

When we consider the epidemiology of drug addiction, we must keep in mind the distinction between use and dependence. Many people who use drugs do not become dependent on them. Nevertheless, people have to use the drug before they can become dependent, and the age at which they *begin* to use drugs is an important risk factor. For example, the prevalence rate for alcoholism among males who began drinking alcohol before the age of 14 is double that found among males who began drinking at age 18 (McGue et al., 2001). The same pattern is found among women; those who begin to use alcohol at an earlier age have a much higher risk of becoming dependent. It is not clear whether earlier initiation leads directly to increased risk of alcohol dependence or whether people who are already predisposed toward the development of drinking problems simply start using earlier.

Patterns of increased use can be alarming, particularly in adolescence. Consider, for example, evidence from the National Household Survey on Drug Abuse in the United States. In 2002, 12 percent of youths between 12 and 17 years of age used some kind of illicit drug within the 30 days prior to being interviewed. The highest rate of illicit drug use for this age group was reported in 1979 (16 percent). It went down to 5 percent in 1992 and then it went back up, particularly for heroin, marijuana, and cocaine. You can retrieve recent results of this survey from the Internet Web site of the Substance Abuse and Mental Health Services Administration. The address is www.samhsa.gov.

Increases in the frequency of illicit drug use provide reason for serious concern; however, most people who occasionally use alcohol and illicit drugs do not become addicted. Dependence almost always develops slowly after extended exposure to a drug. The average time between initial use of illicit drugs and the onset of symptoms of dependence is between 2 and 3 years (Anthony & Helzer, 1991). The distinction between people who eventually become addicted and those who use drugs without becoming addicted is an important consideration in the study of psychopathology.

Prevalence of Alcohol Abuse and Dependence

Approximately two out of every three males in Western countries drink alcohol regularly, at least on a social basis; less than 25 percent abstain from drinking completely. Among all men and women who have ever used alcohol, roughly 20 percent will develop serious problems—abuse or dependence—at some point in their lives as a consequence of prolonged alcohol consumption (Anthony, Warner, & Kessler, 1994).

The National Epidemiologic Survey on Alcohol and Related Conditions (NESARC) collected information on substance use disorders and related mental health problems in a nationally representative sample of more than 43,000 adults (Grant et al. 2006). This study provides the most recent, comprehensive evidence regarding the prevalence of alcoholism in the United States. Results from the NESARC study, summarized in Figure 11–3, indicate a lifetime prevalence rate of 30 percent for some form of alcohol

Gender Differences in Substance Use Disorders

FIGURE 11–3   Lifetime prevalence of substance use disorders in the United States.

Sources: From "Prevalence, Correlates, Disabilities, and Comorbidities of DSM-IV-TR Drug Abuse and Dependence in the United States" by W. M. Compton, et al., *Archives of General Psychiatry, 64* (2007), pp. 566–576. Copyright © 2007. Reprinted by permission of American Medical Association.

use disorder (18 percent for alcohol abuse and 12 percent for alcohol dependence). Alcohol-related disorders are clearly among the most common forms of mental disorder in the United States. These problems most often went untreated; only 24 percent of the men and women who were assigned a diagnosis of alcohol dependence had ever received treatment for these problems.

Gender Differences Approximately 60 percent of women in the United States drink alcohol at least occasionally, but, in comparison to men, fewer develop alcoholism. Among people who chronically abuse or become dependent upon alcohol, men outnumber women by a ratio of approximately 2 to 1 (see Figure 11–3). This disparity is narrower today than it was 50 years ago, especially among younger people. Although the rate of alcoholism among younger women has increased, prevalence is still higher in men, and the rates do not seem likely to converge (Grant & Weissman, 2007). Persistent differences can probably be attributed to social and biological variables. American culture traditionally has held a negative view of intoxication among women. Social disapproval probably explains why women are more likely than men to drink in the privacy of their own homes, either alone or with another person. Women, therefore, may be less likely than men to drink heavily because the range of situations in which they are expected to drink, or in which they can drink without eliciting social disapproval, is narrower.

Biologically, there are also important gender differences in alcohol metabolism. A single standard dose of alcohol, measured in proportion to total body weight, will produce a higher peak blood alcohol level in women than in men. One explanation for this difference lies in the fact that men have a higher average content of body water than women do. A standard dose of alcohol will be less diluted in women because alcohol is distributed in total body water. This may help to explain the fact that women who drink heavily for many years are more vulnerable to liver disorders than are male drinkers.

Prevalence of Drug and Nicotine Dependence

The National Epidemiologic Survey on Alcohol and Related Conditions (NESARC) also reported the frequency of problems associated with other

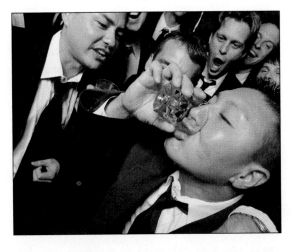

◀ When it comes to abusing alcohol, men outnumber women 2 to 1, though this proportion may be lower than it was 20 years ago.

kinds of drugs (Compton et al., 2007). The combined lifetime prevalence for abuse of or dependence on any type of controlled substance (those that are illegal or available only by prescription) was 10.3 percent. This is approximately one-third the rate for alcohol abuse and dependence. As in the case of alcohol-related disorders, drug abuse and dependence were significantly more common among men than women. Lifetime prevalence rates generated by this study for substance use disorders associated with specific types of drugs are listed in Figure 11–4.

The lifetime prevalence of nicotine dependence was reported to be 24 percent in the National Comorbidity Survey (Kessler et al., 1994). The percentage of adults in the United States who smoke tobacco has actually declined since 1964, when the

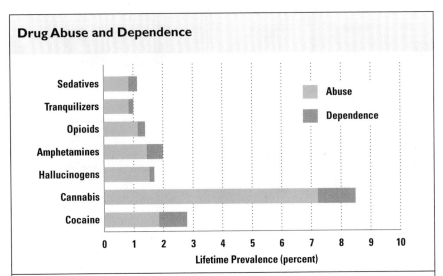

FIGURE 11–4 Lifetime prevalence of abuse and dependence associated with specific types of drugs in the United States.

Source: From "Prevalence, Correlates, Disabilities, and Comorbidities of DSM-IV-TR Drug Abuse and Dependence in the United States" by W. M. Compton, et al., *Archives of General Psychiatry, 64* (2007), pp. 566–576. Copyright © 2007. Reprinted by permission of American Medical Association.

U.S. Surgeon General's Report announced it had found a definite link between smoking and cancer and other diseases (see Critical Thinking Matters). The rate of decline has been greatest among men, who traditionally have smoked more than women. Among people between the ages of 18 and 25, however, smoking rates increased during the 1990s (Chaloupka, 2005). Furthermore, although overall tobacco consumption has declined in industrialized countries, it has increased dramatically in the developing countries, where people may be less educated about the health risks associated with smoking (McKim, 2000).

Risk for Addiction Across the Life Span

Older people do not drink as much alcohol as younger people. The proportion of people who abstain from drinking alcohol is only 22 percent for people in their thirties, goes up to 47 percent for people in their sixties, and is approximately 80 percent for people over 80 years of age. Prevalence rates for alcohol dependence are highest among young adults and lowest among the elderly (Hasin et al., 2007). Most elderly alcohol abusers are people who have had drinking problems for many years.

In what ways are drug problems different among the elderly?

The use of illegal drugs is relatively infrequent among the elderly, but there is a problem associated with their abuse of, and dependence on, prescription drugs and over-the-counter medications, especially hypnotics, sedatives, anxiolytics, and painkillers. The elderly use more legal drugs than do people in any other age group. One estimate suggested that 25 percent of all people over the age of 55 use psychoactive drugs of one kind or another (Koch & Knapp, 1987). The risk for substance dependence among the elderly is increased by frequent use of multiple psychoactive drugs combined with enhanced sensitivity to drug toxicity (caused by slowed metabolic breakdown of alcohol and other drugs).

The following case illustrates several issues that are associated with substance use disorders among the elderly, including the abuse of alcohol together with abuse of prescription medications, the presence of prominent symptoms of anxiety and depression, and the tendency to deny the extent of their use or abuse of drugs.

"Before we begin, I think you should all know that I once smoked a reefer in 1935."

BRIEF CASE **STUDY**
Ms. E's Drinking

Ms. E is an 80-year-old woman who was brought in for an evaluation by her daughters because they noticed depressive symptoms, appetite disturbance, and memory deficits. She denied all problems related to her daughters' concerns. She had a depressed affect, mild psychomotor agitation, and decrements of recent and remote memory. She was disoriented to time. She verbalized statements of guilt and self-deprecation. She denied ever drinking alcohol, which was corroborated by the daughter with whom she lived but was refuted by her other daughter, who stated that Ms. E drank one or two glasses of brandy almost every day. She had been taking various barbiturates for "nerves" for over 30 years. The dosage she ingested gradually increased over the years, and she frequently took more medications than were prescribed. Because it was unclear if her symptoms were related to her barbiturate use, she reluctantly agreed to be slowly and gradually detoxified. She refused a dementia work-up. Once detoxification was complete, her affect and appetite were improved, but her cognitive deficits were unchanged. Several months later, she and her family dropped out of treatment. She was reportedly drinking brandy, wine, and "hard liquor" every afternoon and evening, with her hired caregiver mixing the drinks (Solomon et al., 1993).

CRITICAL THINKING MATTERS

Should Tobacco Products be Illegal?

In 1996, the U.S. Food and Drug Administration (FDA) issued a regulation prohibiting the sale and distribution of tobacco products to children and adolescents. They remain legally available to adults. Previous efforts to limit smoking had focused more narrowly on restricting smoking in public places, eliminating cigarette advertisements on television, and increasing sales taxes. The new rule asserted that, as a drug, nicotine should be controlled by the government. The decisions behind this regulation raise a number of critical thinking issues with regard to substance use disorders. How does the FDA decide whether a product is a drug? Should the government control people's access to addicting drugs? If so, what is the best way to control access?

The FDA conducted an extensive investigation to examine the effects of tobacco products and to determine whether they were designed by their manufacturers to deliver nicotine to consumers. Independent research studies as well as documents from the tobacco industry's own laboratories pointed to the conclusion that *nicotine is addictive* (Dreyfuss, 1996). People who use tobacco products clearly develop symptoms of dependence, including tolerance, withdrawal, and a pattern of compul-sive use. In fact, nicotine is one of the most addicting drugs, viewed in terms of the high proportion of people who become dependent if they use the drug for some period of time.

> **What evidence supports the conclusion that nicotine is an addicting drug?**

After officially recognizing that nicotine is an addicting drug, the FDA could have banned tobacco products entirely (because they are not safe for human consumption). Another option would have been to require a complete elimination of nicotine from cigarettes. The FDA did not consider these options to be practical or politically viable. Because so many adults are already addicted to nicotine, extensive black markets would spring up immediately, similar to those involved with other illegal drugs. An outright ban on nicotine would fail, just as efforts to ban other drugs have failed (Husak, 2002; MacCoun, Reuter, & Wolf, 2001).

The FDA decided instead to approach the nicotine problem by invoking its authority to regulate medical devices (and treating ciga-rettes as a type of drug-delivery system). The tobacco regulations imposed by the FDA are *prevention* efforts designed to break the cycle of addiction to nicotine. They prohibit the sale of tobacco products to anyone under 18 years old and also severely restrict advertising (Cooper, 1994). Nicotine addiction almost always begins during adolescence. The FDA regulations are intended to reduce the rate at which young people are recruited to become new smokers and to minimize future health casualties from tobacco use.

This policy represents a moderate and thoughtful approach to the problem of nicotine dependence. It is a compromise between two extreme alternatives: allowing completely open access to a dangerous drug, or attempting to ban it completely. Preliminary evidence suggests that the FDA regulations regarding tobacco products have been modestly successful. Between 1997 and 2004, prevalence rates for current smoking among adults in the United States dropped from 25 percent to 21 percent (Schiller et al., 2005). Public policy will not be able to eliminate completely the use of harmful drugs by adults in our society. It can reduce the risk of dependence, however, by minimizing their use at an early age.

Diagnostic criteria for substance dependence and abuse are sometimes difficult to apply to the elderly, primarily because drug use has somewhat different consequences in their lives. Tolerance to many drugs is reduced among the elderly, and the symptoms of withdrawal may be more severe and prolonged. They are less likely to suffer occupational impairment because they are less frequently employed than younger people. The probability of social impairment may be reduced because elderly people are more likely to live apart from their families.

CAUSES

Our discussion of causal factors will focus primarily on alcohol dependence and abuse. We have chosen this approach because clinical scientists know more about alcohol and its abuse than about any of the other drugs. Twin studies also suggest that alcohol dependence and other forms of drug dependence share a common etiology (Kendler & Prescott, 2006). Research on alcohol abuse illustrates the factors that are also important in the etiology of other forms of substance dependence.

Most contemporary investigators approach the development of alcoholism in terms of multiple systems (Sher, Grekin, & Williams, 2005). Biological factors obviously play an important role. The addicting properties of certain drugs are crucial: People become addicted to drugs like heroin, nicotine, and alcohol, but they do not become addicted to drugs like the antidepressants or to food additives like Nutrasweet. We must, therefore, understand how addicting drugs affect the brain in order to understand the process of dependence. At the same time, we need to understand the social and cultural factors that influence

▲ The circumstances in which an adolescent is initially exposed to alcohol can influence the person's pattern of drinking. Drinking small amounts of wine with meals or during religious ceremonies may be less likely to lead to alcohol dependence than the sporadic consumption of hard liquor for the purpose of becoming intoxicated.

how and under what circumstances an individual first acquires and uses drugs. Our expectations about the effects of drugs are shaped by our parents, our peers, and the media. These are also important etiological considerations.

The etiology of alcoholism is best viewed within a developmental framework that views the problem in terms of various stages: (1) initiation and continuation, (2) escalation and transition to abuse, and (3) development of tolerance and withdrawal (Leonard et al., 2000; Tarter, Vanyukov, & Kirisci, 2008). In the following pages we review some of the social, psychological, and biological factors that explain why people begin to drink, how their drinking behaviors are reinforced, and how they develop tolerance after prolonged exposure.

Social Factors

People who don't drink obviously won't develop alcoholism, and culture can influence that decision. Some cultures prohibit or actively discourage alcohol consumption. Many Muslims, for example, believe that drinking alcohol is sinful. Other religions encourage the use of small amounts of alcohol in religious ceremonies—such as Jewish people drinking wine at Passover seders—while also showing disdain for those

What are the most important risk factors for alcoholism?

who drink to the point of intoxication (Westermeyer, 1999). This type of cultural constraint can decrease rates of substance dependence. In one large epidemiological

study, for example, Jews had significantly lower rates of alcohol abuse than Catholics and Protestants (Yeung & Greenwald, 1992).

Among those young people who choose to drink alcohol (or smoke cigarettes, or consume other addictive substances), which ones will eventually develop problems? The development of drug dependence requires continued use, and it is influenced by the manner in which the drug is consumed. In other words, with regard to alcohol, will the person's initial reaction to the drug be pleasant, or will he or she become sick and avoid alcoholic beverages in the future? If the person continues drinking, will he or she choose strong or weak drinks, with or without food, with others or alone, and so on?

Several studies have examined social factors that predict substance use among adolescents. Initial experimentation with drugs is most likely to occur among those individuals who are rebellious and extroverted and whose parents and peers model or encourage use (Chassin et al., 2003). The relative influence of parents and friends varies according to the gender and age of the adolescent as well as the drug in question.

Parents can influence their children's drinking behaviors in many ways. They can serve as models for using drugs to cope with stressful circumstances. They may also help promote attitudes and expectations regarding the benefits of drug consumption, or they may simply provide access to licit or illicit drugs (Kirisci et al. 2007). Adolescents with alcoholic parents are more likely to drink alcohol than those whose parents do not abuse alcohol. This increased risk seems to be due to several factors, including the fact that alcoholic parents monitor their children's behavior less closely, thereby providing more opportunities for illicit drinking. Parental monitoring and discipline have an important impact on adolescent substance use; higher parental monitoring is associated with reduced risk of tobacco and alcohol use (Latendresse et al., 2008).

The level of negative affect is also relatively high in the families of alcoholic parents. This unpleasant emotional climate, coupled with reduced parental monitoring, increases the probability that an adolescent will affiliate with peers who use drugs (Chassin & Handley, 2006). Peer and sibling substance use are robust predictors of adolescent alcohol and drug use, even more than parental alcohol use. The impact of friends' alcohol use is greater among adolescent girls than adolescent boys. Girls who have opposite-sex friends are more susceptible to being influenced by the amount of alcohol that their friends drink (Dick et al., 2007).

Biological Factors

Initial physiological reactions to alcohol can have a dramatic negative influence on a person's early drinking experiences. For example, millions of people are unable to tolerate even small amounts of alcohol. These people develop flushed skin, sometimes after only a single drink. They may also feel nauseated, and some experience an abnormal heartbeat. This phenomenon is most common among people of Asian ancestry and may affect 30 to 50 percent of this population. The adverse reaction is due to genetic variants in the ADH and ALDH genes, which are involved in the metabolism of alcohol, and are much more common in Asian populations than in other races (Dick & Foroud, 2003). Not coincidentally, the prevalence of alcoholism is unusually low among Asian populations. Research studies indicate a link between these two phenomena. For example, Japanese Americans who experience the fast-flushing response tend to drink less than those who do not flush (Yamashita, Koyama, & Ohmori, 1995). The basic evidence suggests that in addition to looking for factors that make some individuals especially vulnerable to the addicting effects of alcohol, it may also be important to identify protective factors that reduce the probability of substance dependence.

A person's initial use of addictive drugs is obviously one important step toward the development of substance dependence, but the fact remains that most people who drink alcohol do not develop alcoholism. What accounts for the next important phase of the disorder? Why do some people abuse the drug while others do not? In the following pages we outline several additional biological variables. We begin by examining genetic factors, and then we consider the neurochemical effects of the drugs themselves.

Genetics of Alcoholism An extensive literature attests to the fact that patterns of alcohol consumption, as well as psychological and social problems associated with alcohol abuse, tend to run in families. The lifetime prevalence of alcoholism among the parents, siblings, and children of people with alcoholism is at least three to five times higher than the rate in the general population (Bierut et al., 1998). Of course, this elevated risk among first-degree relatives could reflect the influence of either genetic or environmental factors, because families share both types of influence. Therefore we must look to the results of twin and adoption studies in an effort to disentangle these variables.

Twin Studies Several twin studies have examined twin concordance rates when the proband meets diagnostic criteria for substance dependence. Concordance rates are higher among MZ than among DZ twin pairs. For example, one study analyzed data from a large sample of twins in Australia. The investigators found concordance rates for alcohol dependence of 56 percent in male MZ twins and 33 percent in male DZ twins (Heath et al., 1997). Corresponding figures for MZ and DZ female twin pairs were 30 percent and 17 percent, respectively. Differences between MZ and DZ concordance rates were significant for both genders. The fact that concordance rates were higher for men than for women reflects the much higher prevalence rate for alcoholism among men. Heritability estimates were the same for both men and women, with approximately two-thirds of the variance in risk for alcoholism being produced by genetic factors.

Adoption Studies As discussed in Chapter 2, the strategy followed in an adoption study allows the investigator to separate relatively clearly the influence of genetic and environmental factors. The probands in this type of study are individuals who meet two criteria: (1) They had a biological parent who was alcoholic, and (2) they were adopted from their biological parents at an early age and raised by adoptive parents.

Two adoption studies were conducted in Sweden by Robert Cloninger and his colleagues (Cloninger, 1987; Sigvardsson, Bohman, & Cloninger, 1996). The results of these investigations are consistent with the data from twin studies and point toward the influence of genetic factors in the etiology of alcohol abuse and dependence. They also indicate, however, that the manner in which genetic and environmental events combine probably differs from one type of alcoholism to another. Alcohol dependence with an earlier age of onset and alcohol dependence that is comorbid with antisocial personality disorder and/or other drug dependence appear to be more heritable forms of the disorder.

What can we conclude from the adoption studies? Like the twin studies, they indicate that genetic factors play some role in the etiology of alcohol abuse and dependence. The offspring of alcoholic parents who are reared by nonalcoholic adoptive parents are more likely than people in the general population to develop drinking problems of their own. Thus the familial nature of alcoholism is at least partially determined by genes. Being reared by an alcoholic parent, in the absence of other etiological factors, does not appear to be a critical consideration in the development of the disorder.

What exactly is inherited as the predisposition toward alcohol dependence? Some of the genes that influence the risk of developing alcohol dependence are genes involved in the metabolism of alcohol, such as the ADH and ALDH genes (discussed earlier and related to the skin flushing response). Other genes that alter the risk for alco-

hol dependence may be genes involved in personality traits (Dick, 2007; Slutske et al., 2002). For example, to the extent that genes influence novelty seeking and sensation seeking, these genes may also increase the person's risk for alcohol dependence because the person is more likely to participate in dangerous patterns of consumption (such as drinking several shots of liquor in rapid succession rather than sipping beer or wine).

Neuroanatomy and Neurochemistry All of the addicting drugs produce changes in the chemical processes by which messages are transmitted in the brain, including systems that involve catecholamines (for example, dopamine, norepinephrine, and serotonin), as well as the neuropeptides. In the following sections, we will outline some of the ways in which psychoactive drugs influence neural transmission and the areas of the brain in which these effects are most pronounced.

Dopamine and Reward Pathways Scientists who study the biological basis of addiction have devoted a considerable amount of their attention to understanding the rewarding or reinforcing properties of drugs (Koob, 2006; Self & Tamminga, 2004). People may become dependent on psychoactive drugs because they stimulate areas of the brain that are known as "reward pathways" (see Figure 11–5). One primary circuit in this pathway is the medial forebrain bundle, which connects the ventral tegmental area to the nucleus accumbens. Connections from these structures to the frontal and prefrontal cortex as well as areas of the limbic system, such as the amygdala, also moderate the influence of reward. For many years, scientists have known electrical stimulation of the medial forebrain bundle can serve as a powerful source of positive reinforcement for animals as they perform an operant learning task. Natural rewards, such as food and sex, increase dopamine levels in certain crucial sections of this pathway, which is also known as the *mesolimbic dopamine pathway.*

Drugs of abuse have a dramatic effect on brain reward pathways. Some points at which different drugs influence the dopamine pathway between the ventral tegmental area and the nucleus accumbens are illustrated in Figure 11–6. For example, stimulants such as amphetamine and cocaine affect reward pathways by inhibiting the reuptake of dopamine into nerve terminals. Brain imaging studies with human participants have

Reward Pathways in the Brain

Planning, judgment
Prefrontal cortex
Frontal cortex

Reward
Nuclues accumbens
Medial forebrain bundle
Ventral tegmental area

Emotions, conditioned effects — Amygdala

FIGURE 11–5 The limbic dopamine reward pathways include connections from the ventral tegmental area to the nucleus accumbens and the frontal cortex.

Source: After D. M. Tomkins and E. M. Sellers, 2001, "Addiction and the Brain: The Role of Neurotransmitters in the Cause and Treatment of Drug Dependence," *Canadian Medical Association Journal, 164,* pp. 817–821.

found that the administration of cocaine increases dopamine concentrations in limbic areas of the brain as well as the medial prefrontal cortex (Tomkins & Sellers, 2001). Furthermore, when people who are dependent on cocaine are exposed to cues that have previously signaled drug use, their medial prefrontal cortex becomes activated, suggesting that this area of the brain is involved in feelings of drug craving.

The effects of alcohol on reward pathways in the brain are more complex and less clearly understood than the effects of many other drugs (Julien, 2001). Alcohol clearly affects several different types of neurotransmitters. It may stimulate the mesolimbic dopamine pathway directly, or it may act indirectly by decreasing the activity of GABA neurons (which normally inhibit dopamine neurons). Interesting findings from genetic studies support the latter possibility. Several genes that affect GABA reception have been identified as influencing the risk for alcohol dependence (Covault et al., 2004; Radel et al., 2005).

Endogenous Opioid Peptides One of the most interesting and important advances in neuroscience research was the discovery of the endogenous opioids known as **endorphins** and enkephalins. These relatively short chains of amino acids, or *neuropeptides,* are naturally synthesized in the brain and are closely related to morphine in their pharmacological properties. Opioid peptides possess a chemical affinity for specific receptor sites, in the same way that a key fits into a specific lock. Several types of opioid peptides are distributed widely throughout the brain. They appear to be especially important in the activities associated with systems that control pain, emotion, stress, and reward, as well as such biological functions as feeding and growth (Froehlich, 1997; Julien, 2001).

Research studies have demonstrated many interesting features of the endorphins. Laboratory animals can develop tolerance to injections of endorphins, just as they develop tolerance to addicting drugs like morphine, and they also exhibit symptoms of withdrawal if the injections are suddenly discontinued. These studies confirm the pharmacological similarity between endogenous and exogenous opioids.

Some theorists associate alcoholism with exaggerated activation of the endogenous opioid system in response to alcohol stimulation (Gianoulakis, DeWaele, & Thavundayil, 1996). Several lines of evidence support this hypothesis. One is that opioid receptor antagonists (drugs

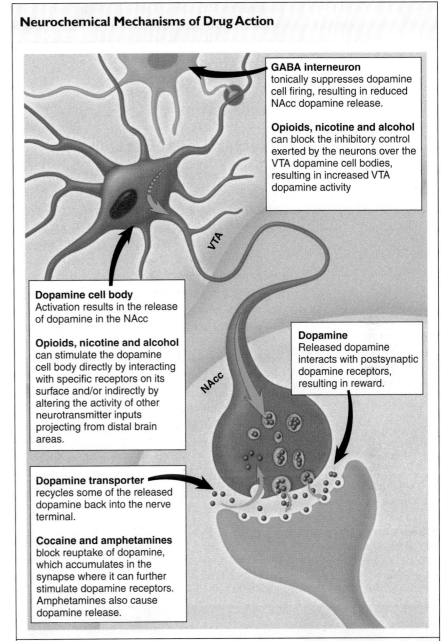

Neurochemical Mechanisms of Drug Action

GABA interneuron
tonically suppresses dopamine cell firing, resulting in reduced NAcc dopamine release.

Opioids, nicotine and alcohol
can block the inhibitory control exerted by the neurons over the VTA dopamine cell bodies, resulting in increased VTA dopamine activity

VTA

Dopamine cell body
Activation results in the release of dopamine in the NAcc

Opioids, nicotine and alcohol
can stimulate the dopamine cell body directly by interacting with specific receptors on its surface and/or indirectly by altering the activity of other neurotransmitter inputs projecting from distal brain areas.

Dopamine
Released dopamine interacts with postsynaptic dopamine receptors, resulting in reward.

NAcc

Dopamine transporter
recycles some of the released dopamine back into the nerve terminal.

Cocaine and amphetamines
block reuptake of dopamine, which accumulates in the synapse where it can further stimulate dopamine receptors. Amphetamines also cause dopamine release.

FIGURE 11–6 Effects of psychoactive drugs on dopamine activity in reward pathway from the ventral tegmental area (VTA) to the nucleus accumbens (NAcc).

Source: After D. M. Tomkins and E. M. Sellers, 2001, "Addiction and the Brain: The Role of Neurotransmitters in the Cause and Treatment of Drug Dependence, *Canadian Medical Association Journal, 164,* pp. 817–821.

that block the effects of opioid peptides) produce a decrease in alcohol self-administration in laboratory animals. Another important bit of information comes from drug trials with human participants: When alcoholic patients take naltrexone, an antagonist of endogenous opioids, they drink less alcohol and report that the subjective "high" associated with drinking is noticeably diminished (see the section on treatment with medication, later in this chapter). Finally, in both rodents and humans, a genetic predisposition toward increased consumption of alcohol is associated with high levels of opioid system response to the ingestion of alcohol (Froehlich, 1997). For all of these reasons, it seems likely that endogenous opioid peptides are somehow involved in mediating alcohol dependence.

Psychological Factors

Genetic factors and neurochemistry undoubtedly account for many of the problems associated with addictive drugs, but as the systems perspective indicates, biological explanations are not incompatible with psychological ones. In fact, extensive research over the past several decades has found that the progression of substance dependence depends on an interaction between environmental and biological events. One time-honored perspective on the development of alcoholism is the tension-reduction hypothesis. At its most general level, this viewpoint holds that people drink alcohol in an effort to reduce the impact of a stressful environment.

The tension-reduction hypothesis became the focal point for scientific investigation when Conger (1956) adapted formal learning theory to the problem and proposed that alcohol consumption is reinforced by its ability to relieve unpleasant emotional states, especially fear and anxiety. As we will see in the following pages, the relation between stress and alcohol has turned out to be more complex than this theory suggests (Sayette, 1999b). Drug effects interact with the person's beliefs and attitudes, as well as with the social context in which the drugs are taken.

Expectations About Drug Effects Placebo effects demonstrate that expectations are an important factor in any study of drug effects (see Chapter 3). During the 1970s and 1980s, several research studies sought to evaluate the influence of alcohol on various facets of behavior using the *balanced placebo design.* This procedure allows the investigator to separate the direct, biological effects of the drug from the subjects' expectations about how the drug should affect their behavior. The results indicated that expectations can account for many effects that have often been attributed to the drug itself. For example, subjects who believed that they had ingested alcohol but who had actually consumed only tonic water displayed exaggerated aggression and reported enhanced feelings of sexual arousal (Quigley & Leonard, 2006; Testa et al., 2006). Much less is known about expectancies for drugs other than alcohol, but there is good reason to believe that these cognitive factors also influence the ways in which people respond to cannabis, nicotine, stimulants, anxiolytics, and sedatives (Brandon, Wetter, & Baker, 1996).

The results of experiments using the balanced placebo design stimulated considerable thought about the role that alcohol expectancies—expectations about alcohol or drug effects—may play in the etiology of drinking problems. These studies do not manipulate expectancies directly, however. They only lead subjects to believe that they have consumed alcohol when, in fact, they have not. The investigators infer that the subjects believed that alcohol would make them aggressive.

But is that really the case? Subsequent investigations began to examine alcohol expectancies directly (Goldman, Darkes, & Del Boca, 1999; Hittner, 1997). Investigators asked people, Why do you drink? What do you expect to happen after you have consumed a few beers or a couple of glasses of wine? Subjects' answers to these questions fit into six primary categories:

1. Alcohol transforms experiences in a positive way (for example: Drinking makes the future seem brighter).
2. Alcohol enhances social and physical pleasure (for example: Having a few drinks is a nice way to celebrate special occasions).
3. Alcohol enhances sexual performance and experience (for example: After a few drinks, I am more sexually responsive).

▼ Common expectations about the effects of drinking alcohol include the notion that it enhances sexual arousal and experience.

RESEARCH METHODS Studies of People at Risk for Disorders

We have used the term *risk* informally throughout this book to refer to a hazard—the possibility of suffering harm. In scientific research, a risk is a statement about the probability that a certain outcome will occur. For example, the NCS found that the risk that a person in the United States will develop alcoholism at some point in his or her life is about 14 in 100 (see Figure 11–3). The combined risk for all types of illegal and controlled substances (such as cannabis, cocaine, heroin, and barbiturates) is about 8 in 100. The concept of risk implies only probability, not certainty. Someone who is "at risk" may or may not suffer harm, depending on many other events and circumstances. For example, men are at greater risk than women for the development of alcoholism, but that does not mean that all men will become alcoholics.

Risk factors are variables that are associated with a higher probability of developing a disorder. Notice that this use of the term risk implies association, not causality. The concept of risk simply reflects a correlation between the risk factor and the disorder. Some risk factors are demographic variables, such as gender and race. Others are biological and psychological variables. In the case of alcoholism, and many other types of psychopathology, family history of the disorder is an important risk factor. Expectancies about the effects of drugs represent another important risk factor for alcoholism.

People who expect that alcohol will reduce tension or transform experiences in a positive way are more likely to drink frequently and heavily than those who have negative expectancies about the effects of alcohol.

> How does the high-risk strategy increase efficiency of longitudinal studies?

In order to determine whether certain risk factors might play a *causal* role in the development of the disorder, it is often necessary to conduct longitudinal studies (see Research Methods in Chapter 8). The investigator collects information about each person before the onset of the disorder. He or she can therefore determine whether the risk factor is present before or only after the onset of symptoms. In other words, do people believe that alcohol reduces tension before they start to drink heavily, or do they develop this belief after they have been drinking heavily for some time? Longitudinal studies can be extremely expensive, and often they take several years to complete. They also require large numbers of participants because everyone in the study will not go on to develop the disorder in question.

Some of these shortcomings of longitudinal studies are especially relevant to research on substance abuse disorders. The risk for developing such disorders is quite low in the general population. For example, even though alcoholism is one of the most prevalent forms of mental disorder, a longitudinal study that follows the development of 100 randomly selected people from childhood to middle age will find only about 14 alcoholic adults (based on NCS data). Thus, to collect a useful amount of data, researchers need to study a large sample, which can be very expensive.

Recognition of this problem led scientists to develop special methods to increase the productivity of longitudinal research. One important technique is the **high-risk research design**. In high-risk research, subjects are selected from the general population based on a well-documented risk factor (Knop et al., 2003; Tarter & Vanyukov, 2001). A number of risk factors might be used to select subjects: positive family history for a given disorder, the presence of certain psychological characteristics, or perhaps a set of demographic variables such as age, gender, and/or race. High-risk research studies are designed to follow their participants over time, beginning before the onset of serious disorders. They hope to identify factors that increase or decrease the probability that people who are vulnerable to a disorder will eventually develop its active symptoms.

---

4. Alcohol increases power and aggression (for example: After a few drinks it is easier to pick a fight).
5. Alcohol increases social assertiveness (for example: Having a few drinks makes it easier to talk to people).
6. Alcohol reduces tension (for example: Alcohol enables me to fall asleep more easily).

These expectations may constitute one of the primary reasons for continued and increasingly heavy consumption of alcoholic beverages. In fact, expectancy patterns can help predict drinking behaviors. Longitudinal studies have found that adolescents who are just beginning to experiment with alcohol and who initially have the most positive expectations about the effects of alcohol go on to consume greater amounts of alcoholic beverages (Smith et al., 1995). This type of

demonstration is important because it indicates that, in many cases, the expectations appear before the person begins to drink heavily. Therefore, expectations may play a role in the onset of the problem rather than being consequences of heavy drinking (see Research Methods).

Where do these expectations come from, and when do they develop? In some cases they may arise from personal experiences with alcohol, but they can also be learned indirectly. Many adolescents hold strong beliefs about the effects of alcohol long before they take their first drink. These expectations are influenced by a variety of environmental factors, including parental and peer attitudes as well as the portrayal of alcohol in the mass media (Agrawal et al., 2008). Follow-up studies have demonstrated that adolescents' expectations about the effects of alcohol are useful in predicting which individuals will later develop drinking problems (Jones, Corbin, & Fromme, 2001). Positive expectancies about alcohol, which are likely to encourage people to drink, are especially influential. Negative expectancies are associated with diminished use but seem to be less powerful.

Integrated Systems

Alcoholism and other forms of addiction clearly result from an interaction among several types of systems. Various social, psychological, and biological factors influence the person's behavior at each stage in the cycle, from initial use of the drug through the eventual onset of tolerance and withdrawal. Furthermore, it appears that different influences are important at different stages of use. The process seems to progress in the following way. Initial experimentation with drugs is influenced by the environment—the person's family, peers, school, and neighborhood (Rhee et al., 2003). Other people also influence the person's attitudes and expectations about the effects of drugs. Access to drugs, in addition to the patterns in which they are originally consumed, is determined, in part, by cultural factors.

For many people, drinking alcohol leads to short-term positive effects that reinforce continued consumption. The exact psychological mechanisms that are responsible for reinforcing heavy drinking may take several different forms. They may involve diminished self-awareness, stress reduction, or improved mood. These effects of alcohol on behavior and subjective experience are determined, in part, by the person's expectations about the way in which the drug will influence his or her feelings and behavior (Baer, 2002).

Genetic factors play an important role in the etiology of alcoholism (Crabbe, 2002; Kendler & Prescott, 2006). After the person has begun to use alcohol, genetic factors become increasingly important in shaping patterns of use (Dick et al., 2007). There are most likely several different types of genetic influence, as illustrated by the results of the Swedish adoption studies. Genes interact strongly with environmental events for certain types of the disorder. A genetic predisposition to alcohol dependence probably causes the person to react to alcohol in an abnormal fashion. It is not clear whether those who are vulnerable to alcoholism are initially more or less sensitive than

other people to the reinforcing effects of alcohol. Research studies have demonstrated both patterns of response (Sher, Grekin, & Williams, 2005).

The biological mechanisms responsible for abnormal reactions to alcohol seem to involve several interrelated neurotransmitter systems (Hyman & Malenka, 2001). Dopamine activity in the brain's reward pathway is stimulated by alcohol as well as other drugs of abuse. Another important consideration may be a deficiency in serotonin activity in certain areas of the limbic system. Drinking alcohol initially corrects this problem and increases serotonin activity, but the person eventually begins to feel worse after tolerance develops.

Drinking gradually becomes heavier and more frequent. The person becomes tolerant to the effects of alcohol and must drink larger quantities to achieve the same reinforcing effects. After he or she becomes addicted to alcohol, attempts to quit drinking are accompanied by painful withdrawal symptoms. Prolonged abuse can lead to permanent neurological impairment, as well as the disruption of many other organ systems.

TREATMENT

The treatment of alcoholism and other types of substance use disorders is an especially difficult task. Many people with substance use disorders do not acknowledge their difficulties, and only a relatively small number seek professional help. When they do enter treatment, it is typically with reluctance or on the insistence of friends, family members, or legal authorities. Compliance with treatment recommendations is often low, and dropout rates are high. The high rate of comorbidity with other forms of mental disorder presents an additional challenge, complicating the formulation of a treatment plan. Treatment outcome is likely to be least successful with those people who have comorbid conditions.

The goals of treatment for substance use disorders are a matter of controversy. Some clinicians believe that the only acceptable goal is total abstinence from drinking or drug use. Others have argued that, for some people, a more reasonable goal is the moderate use of legal drugs. Important questions have also been raised about the scope of improvements that might be expected from a successful treatment program. Is the goal simply to minimize or eliminate drug use, or should we expect that treatment will also address the social, occupational, and medical problems that are typically associated with drug problems? If these associated problems are the result of the person's prolonged abuse of alcohol or other drugs, the problems may improve on their own if the person becomes abstinent. However, to the extent that family problems or interpersonal difficulties contribute to the person's use of drugs, it may be necessary to address these difficulties before the drug problem can be resolved (Lewis, Allen-Byrd, & Rouhbakhsh, 2004). Getting Help at the end of this chapter offers additional resources for those seeking help and information on recovering from substance abuse.

Detoxification

Alcoholism and related forms of drug abuse are chronic conditions. Treatment is typically accomplished in a sequence of stages, beginning with a brief period of **detoxification**—the removal of a drug on which a person has become dependent—for 3 to 6 weeks (Coombs, Howatt, & Coombs, 2005). This process is often extremely difficult, as the person experiences marked symptoms of withdrawal and gradually adjusts to the absence of the drug. For many types of CNS depressants, such as alcohol, hypnotics, and sedatives, detoxification is accomplished gradually. Stimulant drugs, in contrast, can be stopped abruptly (Schuckit, 2005). During the detoxification period, medical professionals closely monitor the patient's vital signs to prevent seizures and delirium. Although detoxification usually takes place in a hospital, some evidence indicates that it can be accomplished with close supervision on an outpatient basis.

People who are going through alcohol detoxification are often given various types of medication, including benzodiazepines and anticonvulsants, primarily as a way of minimizing withdrawal symptoms (O'Brien & McKay, 2007). This practice is controversial, in part because many people believe that it is illogical to use one form of drug, especially one that can be abused itself, to help someone recover from dependence on another drug.

Medications During Remission

Following the process of detoxification, treatment efforts are aimed at helping the person maintain a state of remission. The best outcomes are associated with stable, long-term abstinence from drinking. Several forms of medication are used to help the person achieve this goal.

Disulfiram (Antabuse) is a drug that can block the chemical breakdown of alcohol. It was introduced as a treatment for alcoholism in Europe in 1948 and is still used fairly extensively (Fuller & Gordis, 2004). If a person who is taking disulfiram consumes even a small amount of alcohol, he or she will become violently ill. The symptoms include nausea, vomiting, profuse sweating, and increased heart rate and respiration rate. People who are taking disulfiram will stop drinking alcohol in order to avoid this extremely unpleasant reaction. Unfortunately, voluntary compliance with this form of treatment is poor. Many patients discontinue taking disulfiram, usually because they want to resume drinking or because they believe that they can manage their problems without the drug. Research studies report inconsistent results regarding outcome for patients who are treated with disulfiram (Mann, 2004). It may be most useful when used in combination with one of the other more recently developed forms of medication for treating alcoholism (Hart et al., 2001).

Naltrexone (Revia) is an antagonist of endogenous opioids that has been found to be useful in the treatment of alcohol dependence following detoxification. Several research studies have demonstrated that patients who received naltrexone and psychotherapy are less likely to relapse than patients who receive psychotherapy plus a placebo (Carmen et al., 2004; Modesto-Lowe & Van Kirk, 2002). Among those who do drink some alcohol during recovery, people taking naltrexone are less likely to lose control and return to heavy drinking. Some clinical patients report that, if they drink while also taking naltrexone, they do not feel as "high" as they would without naltrexone. Naltrexone may dampen the person's craving by blocking alcohol's ability to stimulate the opioid system. In other words, it works by reducing the rewarding effects of alcohol rather than by inducing illness if the person drinks. The best effects for naltrexone are found with patients who are compliant with the medication (take it at least 80 percent of the time) and are also involved in a psychological treatment program.

Another promising medication for treating alcoholism is acamprosate (Campral). An extensive body of evidence indicates that people taking acamprosate are able to reduce their average number of drinking days by 30 percent to 50 percent (Mann, Lehert, & Morgan, 2004). It also increases the proportion of people who are able to achieve total abstinence (approximately 22 percent among people taking acamprosate and 12 percent taking placebo after 12 months of treatment). Its mechanism of action is not entirely clear, but acamprosate appears to reduce symptoms of acute alcohol withdrawal. It is particularly effective with people who drink in order to neutralize symptoms of withdrawal and to reduce anxiety. Like naltrexone, acamprosate is intended to be used in conjunction with a psychological treatment program. The dropout rate is very high without these added features (Hart et al., 2001; Malcolm, 2003).

Psychiatrists also use SSRIs, such as fluoxetine, for the long-term treatment of alcoholic patients. Outcome studies suggest that SSRIs have small and inconsistent effects in reducing drinking among those patients who are not also depressed. They do seem to be effective, however, for the treatment of people with a dual diagnosis of alcohol dependence and major depression (O'Brien & McKay, 2002). Among these patients, fluoxetine can reduce drinking levels as well as symptoms of depression.

Self-Help Groups: Alcoholics Anonymous

One of the most widely accepted forms of treatment for alcoholism is Alcoholics Anonymous (AA). Organized in 1935, this self-help program is maintained by alcohol abusers for the sole purpose of helping other people who abuse alcohol become and remain sober. Because it is established and active in virtually all communities in North America and Europe, as well as in many other parts of the world, AA is generally considered to be "the first line of attack against alcoholism" (Nathan, 1993). Surveys conducted by AA indicate that its membership increased considerably during the 1970s and 1980s. By the late 1990s, worldwide membership in AA was approximately 1.8 million people (Wallace, 1999). Many members of AA are also involved in other forms of treatment offered by various types of

How does AA differ from other approaches to treating alcoholism?

mental health professionals, but AA is not officially associated with any other form of treatment or professional organization. Similar self-help programs have been developed for people who are dependent on other drugs, such as opioids (Narcotics Anonymous) and cocaine (Cocaine Anonymous).

The viewpoint espoused by AA is fundamentally spiritual in nature (Kaskutas et al., 2003). AA is the original "12-step program." In the first step, the person must acknowledge that he or she is powerless over alcohol and unable to manage his or her drinking. The remaining steps involve spiritual and interpersonal matters such as accepting "a Power greater than ourselves" that can provide the person with direction; recognizing and accepting personal weaknesses; and making amends for previous errors, especially instances in which the person's drinking caused hardships for other people. One principal assumption is that people cannot recover on their own (Emrick, 1999).

The process of working through the 12 steps to recovery is facilitated by regular attendance at AA meetings, as often as every day of the first 90 days after the person stops drinking. Most people choose to attend less frequently if they are able to remain sober throughout this initial period. Meetings provide chronic alcohol abusers with an opportunity to meet and talk with other people who have similar problems, as well as something to do instead of having a drink. New members are encouraged to call more experienced members for help at any time if they experience an urge to drink. There is enormous variability in the format and membership of local AA meetings (Montgomery, Miller, & Tonigan, 1993).

It is difficult to evaluate the effectiveness of AA, for a number of reasons. Long-term follow-up is difficult, and it is generally impossible to employ some of the traditional methods of outcome research, such as random assignment to groups and placebo controls. Early dropout rates are relatively high: About half of all the people who initially join AA leave in less than 3 months. On the other hand, survival rates (defined in terms of continued sobriety) are much higher for those people who remain in AA. About 80 percent of AA members who have remained sober for between 2 and 5 years will remain sober in the next year (Tonigan, Connors, & Miller, 2003).

Although AA does seem to help people, it is not clear how it helps, or why. Several mechanisms are possible (Owen et al., 2003). One explanation centers on the personal growth process that is described in the 12-step program, but the active ingredients may be more social than spiritual. Membership in AA provides people with a stable social network that discourages rather than encourages the use of drugs. It also provides training in communication skills and cognitive coping strategies for stressful life events. Another possible explanation involves personality traits that are present before the person enters treatment. Those people with traits that are compatible with continued membership in a group like AA may be most likely to recover. People who exhibit antisocial traits of the type associated with Cloninger's Type 2 alcoholism, who also presumably have an earlier onset and more difficulty abstaining from drinking, may be least likely to benefit from AA.

Cognitive Behavior Therapy

Psychological approaches to substance use disorders have often focused on cognitive and behavioral responses that trigger episodes of drug abuse. In the case of alcoholism, heavy drinking has been viewed as a learned, maladaptive response that some people use to cope with difficult problems or to reduce anxiety. Cognitive behavior therapy teaches people to identify and respond more appropriately to circumstances that regularly precipitate drug abuse (Finney & Moos, 2002).

Coping Skills Training One element of cognitive behavior therapy involves training in the use of social skills, which might be used to resist pressures to drink heavily. It also includes problem-solving procedures, which can help the person both to identify situations that lead to heavy drinking and to formulate alternative courses of action. Anger management is one example. Some people drink in response to frustration. Through careful instruction and practice, people can learn to express negative emotions in constructive ways that will be understood by others. The focus in this type of treatment is on factors that initiate and maintain problem drinking rather than the act of drinking itself.

Cognitive events also play an important part in this approach to treatment. Expectations about the effects of alcohol are challenged, and more adaptive thoughts are rehearsed. Negative patterns of thinking about the self and events in the person's environment are also addressed because they are linked to unpleasant emotions that trigger problem drinking.

Relapse Prevention Most people who have been addicted to a drug will say that quitting is the easy part of treatment. The more difficult challenge is to maintain this change after it has been accomplished. Unfortunately, most people will slip up and return to drinking soon after they stop. The same thing can be said for people who stop smoking or using any other drug of abuse. These slips often lead to a full-scale return to excessive and uncontrolled use of the drug. Successful treatment, therefore, depends on making preparations for such incidents.

Alan Marlatt, a clinical psychologist at the University of Washington, and his colleagues have proposed a cognitive behavioral view of the relapse process (Marlatt, Blume, & Parks, 2001; Witkiewitz, Marlatt, & Walker, 2005). This process applies to all forms of substance dependence, ranging from alcoholism to nicotine dependence (Shiffman et al., 1996). It has also been applied to other disorders associated with impulsive behavior, such as bulimia and inappropriate sexual behaviors (see Chapters 10 and 12). It places principal emphasis on events that take place after detoxification and the initial efforts at intensive treatment.

The relapse prevention model addresses several important issues that confront the addict in

◀ Group therapy is an important part of most inpatient treatment programs. It offers an opportunity for patients to acknowledge and confront openly the severity of their problems.

trying to deal with the challenges of life without drugs. The model emphasizes increasing people's belief that they will be able to control their own behavior and events in their lives. The therapist also helps patients learn more adaptive coping responses, such as applied relaxation and social skills, that can be used in situations that formerly might have triggered drug use.

Another important feature of the relapse prevention model is concerned with the *abstinence violation effect,* which refers to the guilt and perceived loss of control that the person feels whenever he or she slips and finds himself or herself having a drink (or a cigarette or whatever drug is involved) after an extended period of abstinence. People typically blame themselves for failing to live up to their promise to quit. They also interpret the first drink or use of the drug as a signal that further efforts to control their drinking will be useless. The following brief case study describes one man's thoughts and feelings, shortly after he returned to the use of heroin. Just prior to this relapse, he had been actively involved in a treatment program and had stayed "clean" for several months.

BRIEF CASE **STUDY**
Relapse to Heroin Use

"It was like goin' home," he tells me later, "and mom's got your favorite dish on the stove, and you smell it, to the back of your tongue, way back. That's the rush of the dope. It's right there, and for like two, three minutes I'm floating. But it was just a quarter of a bag, a baby rush. So I get up and lay down in my bed, put on the (music) again. And I'm feeling dirty, man. I'm thinking, that wasn't nothing, it wasn't worth it. Two, three minutes of this hot euphoria and then I just nod off to sleep."

He slams his fist on his knee. "I can't believe how bad I (screwed) up," Mike wails through his tears. "Damn! I know what happened ain't nobody's fault but mine, and I'm eating myself up over it. I'm scared out of my mind. I mean, it's like I'm afraid of myself. I really see it now, there's so much (stuff) inside me from my past that I ain't worked out yet that I scare even me. So where do I go with that if they kick me out? How do I stay off the dope if I'm alone again?"

Mike looks up, his eyes wide, wet with tears.

"Maybe what they say is true, I'm already a junkie again. It's too late. But I did just one hit, that's all. And I can't be doing more dope, I know that. If I go on a real run of heroin this time, I won't come back, ever. I've seen it now—I *can* blow it, I *can* relapse, I can die. Damn! This is the time I need help more than ever, and this is when they're going to kick me out." (Shavelson, 2001, pp. 161 and 166)

Relapse prevention programs are aimed at exactly this type of conflict. They teach patients to expect that they may slip occasionally and to interpret these behaviors as a temporary "lapse" rather than a total "relapse."

Short-Term Motivational Therapy Many people with substance use disorders do not seek or take full advantage of treatment opportunities because they fail to recognize the severity of their problems. Motivational interviewing is a nonconfrontational procedure that can be used to help people resolve their ambivalence about using drugs and make a definite commitment to change their behavior (Miller, 1995). It is based on the notion that in order to make a meaningful change, people must begin by recognizing the inconsistency between their current behavior and their long-term goals. For example, chronic heavy drinking is not compatible with academic or occupational success.

Motivational interviewing begins with a discussion of problems—issues reported by the patient as well as concerns that have been expressed by others such as friends and family members. The person is asked to reflect on feedback that is provided in a nonthreatening way. Rather than confronting the person, arguing about the reasons for drinking, or demanding action, the therapist responds empathically in an effort to avoid or minimize defensive reactions that will interfere with attempts to change.

The primary goal of this process is to increase the person's awareness of the nature of his or her substance use problems. Central features of motivational interviewing include a comprehensive assessment of the situation and personalized feedback. Emphasis is placed on ways in which the person sees his or her problems rather than assigning diagnostic labels, such as "alcoholism." Various options for creating change are discussed. The therapist and the patient work together to select the most appropriate method to follow. This stage of the interaction is designed to encourage the person's belief in his or her own ability to accomplish positive change.

Motivational interviewing may be most helpful to people whose substance abuse problems are not yet severe or chronic. It can be used as a stand-alone intervention or in combination with other approaches to treatment. If the person is not ready to abstain completely, short-term motivational therapy can be used to help the person reduce the frequency or intensity of alcohol consumption (Roberts & Marlatt, 1999).

Outcome Results and General Conclusions

Although many studies have evaluated the effects of alcohol treatment programs, two deserve special attention because of their large sample sizes and the rigorous methods that the investigators employed. One is known as Project MATCH because it was designed to test the potential value of matching certain kinds of clients to specific forms of treatment (Babor & Del Boca, 2003). In other words, would the outcomes associated with different forms of intervention be related to certain characteristics of the patients (such as the presence or absence of antisocial personality traits)?

The study evaluated three forms of psychological treatment: cognitive behavior therapy (12 sessions focused on coping skills and relapse prevention), 12-step facilitation therapy (12 sessions designed to help patients become engaged in AA), and motivational enhancement therapy (4 sessions over 12 weeks designed to increase commitment to change). Most of the people in all three groups attended at least some AA meetings in addition to their assigned form of treatment. More than 1,700 patients were randomly assigned to one of these three conditions. Outcome measures were collected for 3 years after the end of treatment.

Results indicated that all three forms of treatment led to major improvements in amount of drinking as well as other areas of life functioning (Miller & Longabaugh, 2003). Before treatment, patients in this study averaged 25 drinking days per month. After treatment, they averaged fewer than 6 days per month (across all forms of treatment). Patients who did drink decreased their average number of drinks from 15 to 3 drinks per day. Very few differences were found between the different treatment methods. The one exception favored 12-step facilitation therapy, in which 24 percent of patients were completely abstinent one year after treatment, compared to approximately 15 percent in the other two groups. Analyses that focused on the characteristics of individual clients suggested that there is relatively little reason to try to match certain kinds of patients to specific forms of treatment.

The second study involved a naturalistic evaluation of substance abuse treatment programs administered at 15 sites by the Department of Veterans Affairs (VA) (Finney, Moos, & Humphreys, 1999; Moos et al., 1999). The VA study compared programs that emphasized three approaches to the treatment of substance use disorders: 12-step programs, cognitive behavior therapy, and "eclectic therapy" (a combination of several approaches). The study included more than 3,000 patients. Most of these people had a diagnosis of alcohol dependence, but many also abused other types of drugs. Unlike Project MATCH, they were not randomly assigned to treatments. Despite these differences in methodology, results of the VA study were very similar to those obtained in Project MATCH. Patients in all three groups made significant improvements with regard to both patterns of substance use and levels of social and occupational functioning. People who participated in more treatment sessions had better outcomes than people who received less treatment. When differences were found between different forms of treatment, they tended to favor the 12-step programs. No support was found for the assumption that certain types of patients would do better in one form of treatment than in another.

Comprehensive reviews of these studies and the rest of the research literature regarding treatment of alcoholism and drug abuse point to several general conclusions (Babor, 2008; Donavan, 1999):

What factors predict better long-term outcome for treatment of alcoholism?

- People who enter treatment for various types of substance abuse and dependence typically show improvement in terms of reduced drug use that is likely to persist for several months following the end of treatment. Unfortunately, relapse is also relatively common.
- There is little evidence to suggest that one form of treatment (inpatient or outpatient, professional or self-help, individual or group) is more effective than another. When differences have been found, they tend to favor self-help groups, such as AA, particularly in terms of success in achieving abstinence.
- There is only limited support for the assumption that certain kinds of patients do better in one kind of treatment than another (the matching hypothesis).
- Increased amount of treatment and greater frequency of attendance in self-help meetings and aftercare counseling are associated with better outcomes.
- Among those people who are able to reduce their consumption of drugs, or abstain altogether, improvements following treatment are usually not limited to drug use alone but extend to the person's health in general as well as his or her social and occupational functioning.

Long-term outcome for the treatment of alcoholism is best predicted by the person's coping resources (social skills and problem-solving abilities), the availability of social support, and the level of stress in the environment. These considerations appear to be more important than the specific type of intervention that people receive. Those individuals who are in less stressful life situations, whose families are more cohesive and less supportive of continued drinking, and who are themselves better equipped with active coping skills are most likely to sustain their improvement over several years (Finney & Moos, 2002).

GETTING HELP

If you have been looking for help in the area of substance dependence, you have probably noticed two things: (1) There are so many different sources of advice and information that the situation can quickly become quite confusing, and (2) the field is sharply divided on a number of crucial issues. Whose advice should you follow? Among all of the self-help books dealing with drugs and alcohol, one stands out on the basis of its strong link to the research literature as well as the extensive clinical experience of the author. Marc Schuckit's book *Educating Yourself About Alcohol and Drugs: A People's Primer* provides sensible answers to the questions asked by people who are wondering about their own, or someone else's, substance use problems.

Denial is a prominent feature of most substance use disorders. It is usually easier to dismiss suggestions that you have begun to use alcohol or drugs in a self-destructive pattern than it is to face the problem directly. Schuckit's book includes a perceptive chapter titled "Is there really a problem?" The bottom line is this: "If you repeatedly have returned to substance use even though that substance has caused a disruption in your life, you do have a problem." Subsequent chapters in Schuckit's book provide thoughtful and practical guidance on topics such as the symptoms of withdrawal, the process of detoxification, the relative merits of self-help groups, outpatient therapy, and hospitalization, and how to find a specific treatment program in your area.

The Internet also provides an enormous amount of information regarding substance use disorders. For information about problems associated with the use of alcohol and drugs, you might want to visit Web pages maintained by the National Institute on Alcohol Abuse and Alcoholism (www.niaaa.nih.gov) and the National Institute on Drug Abuse (www.nida.nih.gov). These Web sites are primarily concerned with information about federally funded research programs, but they also include answers to frequently asked questions, as well as treatment referral information.

Most people who enter treatment for substance use problems become involved, at least temporarily, with self-help groups such as Alcoholics Anonymous (AA) and Narcotics Anonymous (NA). Related groups, like Alanon and Alateen, are designed for the families and children of people who are dependent on alcohol. You can contact these groups through the Internet. The URL for Alcoholics Anonymous is www.alcoholics-anonymous.org. Many people believe, often passionately, that AA is the most beneficial program for helping people to recover from alcoholism. Others disagree. If you want to consider alternative points of view, visit the Web site maintained by Stanton Peele, who is one of AA's most persistent, enthusiastic, and articulate critics. The URL for his homepage is www.peele.net. Peele challenges the biological reductionism that often dominates current views of alcoholism, and he promotes approaches to treatment that do not rely exclusively on total abstinence from drinking.

Evidence regarding the long-term outcome of serious substance use disorders can be discouraging, but it is important to remember that a substantial minority of people with these problems does manage to achieve an extended, stable recovery. The research literature does not point to one form of treatment as being clearly superior to another. Therefore, you should consider several alternatives to treatment and select the one that makes most sense in terms of your own life and your own view of the world.

■ SUMMARY

DSM-IV-TR uses two terms to describe substance use disorders. **Substance dependence,** the more severe of the two forms, refers to a pattern of repeated self-administration that often results in **tolerance, withdrawal,** or compulsive drug-taking behavior. **Substance abuse** describes a more broadly conceived, less severe pattern of drug use that is defined in terms of interference with the person's ability to fulfill major role obligations at work or at home, recurrent use of a drug in dangerous situations, or repeated legal difficulties that are associated with drug use.

A **drug of abuse**—sometimes called a *psychoactive substance*—is a chemical substance that alters a person's mood, level of perception, or brain functioning. The list of chemicals on which people become dependent includes drugs that are legally available in the United States as well as many that are illegal. Although patterns of dependence are similar in some ways for all drugs, each type of drug also has some unique features.

Prolonged abuse of alcohol can have a devastating impact on social relationships and occupational functioning while disrupting the functions of several important organ systems. Alcohol dependence has more negative health consequences than does abuse of almost any drug, with the possible exception of nicotine.

Nicotine is one of the most harmful addicting drugs. Recognizing the serious long-term health consequences of exposure to nicotine, the U.S. Food and Drug Administration has prohibited the sale and distribution of tobacco products to children and adolescents. This policy attempts to prevent the development of nicotine addiction rather than trying to ban use of the drug completely.

The **psychomotor stimulants,** such as amphetamine and cocaine, activate the sympathetic nervous system and induce a positive mood state. High doses of amphetamines and cocaine can lead to the onset of psychosis. The most devastating effects of stimulant drugs center around the disruption of occupational and social roles.

Opiates have properties similar to those of opium and can induce a state of dreamlike euphoria. Tolerance develops quickly to opiates. After repeated use, their positive emotional effects are replaced by long-term negative changes in mood and emotion. Many of the severe health consequences of opiate use are the result of the lifestyle of the addict rather than the drug itself.

Barbiturates and **benzodiazepines** can be used, as prescribed by a physician, to decrease anxiety (tranquilizers) or help people sleep (hypnotics). They can also lead to a state of intoxication that is identical to that associated with alcohol. People who abruptly stop taking high doses of benzodiazepines may experience withdrawal symptoms, including a return of the original anxiety symptoms. Tolerance and withdrawal can develop after using barbiturates for several weeks.

Marijuana and **hashish** can induce a pervasive sense of well-being and happiness. People do not seem to develop tolerance to THC (the active ingredient in marijuana and hashish) unless they are exposed to high doses over an extended period of time. Withdrawal symptoms are unlikely to develop among people who smoke marijuana occasionally.

Hallucinogens induce vivid visual images that are usually pleasant but occasionally frightening. Unlike other drugs of abuse, hallucinogens are used sporadically rather than continuously. Most people do not increase their use of hallucinogens over time, and withdrawal symptoms are not observed.

It is impossible to specify a typical course for substance dependence. The specific pattern varies from one person to the next. In the case of alcoholism, the only thing that seems certain is that periods of heavy use alternate with periods of relative abstinence. Among alcoholic men in one long-term follow-up study, the proportion who became completely abstinent went up slowly but consistently over a period of many years. Relapse to alcohol abuse was unlikely among men who were able to remain abstinent for at least 6 years.

Alcohol dependence and abuse are the most common forms of mental disorder, with a lifetime prevalence of 30 percent in the NESARC study. Among people with alcohol use disorders, men outnumber women by a ratio of approximately 2 to 1. Prevalence rates for alcohol dependence are highest among young adults and lowest among the elderly. According to the NESARC study, the combined lifetime prevalence for dependence on any type of controlled substance (those that are illegal or available only by prescription) was 10 percent.

Research on the etiology of alcoholism illustrates the ways in which various systems interact to produce and maintain drug dependence. The etiology of alcoholism is probably heterogeneous in nature. There are several pathways to the disorder. Social factors are particularly influential in the early phases of substance use. Initial experimentation with drugs is most likely to occur among those adolescents whose parents and peers model or encourage drug use. The culture in which a person lives influences the types of drugs that are used, the purposes for which they are used, and the expectations that people hold for the ways in which drugs will affect their experiences and behavior.

Considerable attention has been paid to the role of biological factors in the etiology of alcoholism, particularly the influence of genetic factors and neurochemical processes. Twin studies indicate that genetic factors influence patterns of social drinking as well as the onset of alcohol dependence. Adoption studies indicate that the offspring of alcoholic parents who are raised by nonalcoholic parents are more likely than people in the general population to develop drinking problems of their own. Genetic factors may be more influential in the development of alcoholism among men than among women.

All of the psychoactive drugs cause increased dopamine activity in the reward pathways of the brain. Alcohol may stimulate the mesolimbic dopamine pathway directly, or it may act indirectly by inhibiting GABA neurons. Another focus of neurochemical research has been the role of endogenous opioids known as **endorphins.** Some theorists have argued that alcoholism is associated with excessive production of endorphins.

Psychological explanations for the etiology of substance use disorders have often focused on the ability of drugs to relieve unpleasant emotional states. Expectations about drug effects have an important influence on the ways in which people respond to alcohol and other drugs. People who believe that alcohol enhances pleasure, reduces tension, and increases social performance are more likely than other people to drink frequently and heavily.

Treatment of substance use disorders is an especially challenging and difficult task, in light of the fact that many people with these problems do not recognize or acknowledge their own difficulties. Recovery begins with a process of detoxification. Self-help programs, such as Alcoholics Anonymous, are the most widely used and probably one of the most beneficial forms of treatment.

THE BIG PICTURE CRITICAL THINKING REVIEW

What evidence is needed to show that a drug is addictive?

If repeated use of a drug is associated with the development of tolerance and withdrawal, or if it leads to a pathological pattern of use, then it is considered to be addictive. (SEE PAGE 324)

What are the long-term consequences of abusing psychomotor stimulants?

Prolonged use of amphetamines and cocaine increases the person's risk for having a psychotic episode, but the most common and devastating effects of stimulant drugs are the serious disruption of occupational and social roles. (SEE PAGE 329)

Where is the boundary between substance abuse and recreational drug use?

The transition to abuse from recreational use can be subtle and is not easily recognized, especially by the person who is using drugs. The distinction hinges on the pattern of use, which must be persistent over time and lead to maladaptive consequences before this diagnosis would be considered. (SEE PAGE 335)

In what ways are drug problems different among the elderly?

Tolerance to many drugs is reduced among the elderly, and the symptoms of withdrawal may be more severe and prolonged. (SEE PAGE 340)

What are the most important risk factors for alcoholism?

Increased risk is associated with both genetic and environmental factors. Some of the genes that influence risk of alcohol dependence have an impact on the metabolism of alcohol. Others may influence personality traits which increase the tendency to participate in dangerous patterns of consumption. (SEE PAGE 342)

How does AA differ from other approaches to treating alcoholism?

Alcoholics Anonymous is a self-help program and is not officially associated with any other form of treatment. Its viewpoint is fundamentally spiritual in nature. (SEE PAGE 350)

What factors predict better long-term outcome for treatment of alcoholism?

Long-term outcome is best predicted by the person's coping resources (social skills and problem-solving abilities), the availability of social support, and the level of stress in the environment. (SEE PAGE 353)

■ KEY TERMS

barbiturates **331**

benzodiazepines **331**

detoxification **349**

drug of abuse **321**

endorphins **345**

hallucinogens **332**

hashish **331**

high-risk research
design **347**

marijuana **331**

opiates **329**

polysubstance abuse **321**

psychological
dependence **324**

psychomotor
stimulants **328**

substance abuse **321**

substance dependence **320**

tolerance **324**

withdrawal **324**

SEXUAL AND GENDER IDENTITY DISORDERS

Sex is often a perplexing area of our lives. Sexual experience can be a source of extreme pleasure, while also providing for the development and expression of intimacy with one's partner. From an evolutionary point of view, reproduction is the key to our survival. Sexual behavior also provides fertile ground for intense feelings of fear and guilt.

When something interferes with our ability to function sexually, it can be devastating both to the person who is affected and to the person's partner. Sometimes a person's inability to enjoy sexual experiences becomes so pervasive or so personally distressing that the person seeks professional help—alone or, more often, with his or her partner. In other instances, a person may enjoy sex but his or her sexual interest may be triggered by unusual stimuli, or it may involve nonconsenting partners or the pain and suffering of themselves or others. The point at which occasional sexual difficulties become a "sexual dysfunction" is quite subjective and may say as much about sexual norms and expectations as anything else. Similarly, the definition of sexual conduct that is considered deviant has also changed over time. This chapter explores the mix of factors that influence what it means to be a man or a woman and the ways in which we engage in sexual relationships. It also offers a picture of the shifting ground that surrounds what mental health professionals consider to be normal and abnormal sexual practices.

OVERVIEW

Any discussion of sexual disorders requires some frank consideration of normal sexuality. Such openness has been encouraged and promoted by mental health professionals who specialize in the study and treatment of sexual behavior.

William Masters (1915–2001), a physician, and Virginia Johnson (1925–), a psychologist, were undoubtedly the best-known sex therapists and researchers in the United States during the second half of the twentieth century. Their first book, *Human Sexual Response,* published in 1966, was based on their studies of nearly 700 normal men and women. Observations and physiological recordings were made in a laboratory setting while these individuals engaged in sexual activities, including masturbation and intercourse. Masters and Johnson's research received widespread attention in the popular media and helped make laboratory studies of sexual behavior acceptable.

On the basis of their data, Masters and Johnson described the human sexual response cycle in terms of a sequence of overlapping phases: excitement, orgasm, and resolution. Analogous processes occur in both men and women, but the timing may differ. There are, of course, individual differences in virtually all aspects of this cycle. Variations from the most common pattern may not indicate a problem unless the person is concerned about the response.

Sexual *excitement* increases continuously from initial stimulation up to the point of orgasm. It may last anywhere from a few minutes to several hours. Among the most dramatic physiological changes during sexual excitement are those associated with *vasocongestion*—engorgement of the blood vessels of various organs, especially the genitals. The male and female genitalia become swollen, reddened, and warmed. Sexual excitement also increases muscular tension, heart rate, and respiration rate. These physiological responses are accompanied by subjective feelings of arousal, especially at more advanced stages of excitement.

The experience of *orgasm* is usually distinct from the gradual buildup of sexual excitement that precedes it. This sudden release of tension is almost always experienced as being intensely pleasurable, but the specific nature of the experience varies from one person to the next. The female orgasm occurs in three stages, beginning with a "sensation of suspension or stoppage," which is associated with strong genital sensations. The second stage involves a feeling of warmth spreading throughout the pelvic area. The third

◄ Sexual dysfunctions are best defined in terms of the couple rather than individual persons. They are frequently associated with marital distress.

stage is characterized by sensations of throbbing or pulsating, which are tied to rhythmic contractions of the vagina, the uterus, and the rectal sphincter muscle.

The male orgasm occurs in two stages, beginning with a sensation of ejaculatory inevitability. This is triggered by the movement of seminal fluid toward the urethra. In the second stage, regular contractions propel semen through the urethra, and it is expelled through the urinary opening.

During the *resolution* phase, which may last 30 minutes or longer, the person's body returns to its resting state. Men are typically unresponsive to

further sexual stimulation for a variable period of time after reaching orgasm. This is known as the refractory period. Women, on the other hand, may be able to respond to further stimulation almost immediately. They are capable of experiencing a series of distinct orgasmic responses that are not separated by a period of noticeably lowered excitement.

Sexual dysfunctions can involve a disruption of any stage of the sexual response cycle. The following case study, written by Barry McCarthy, a psychologist at American University, is concerned with a man who had difficulty controlling the rate at which he progressed from excitement to orgasm.

CASE **STUDY** Margaret and Bill's Sexual Communication

Margaret and Bill, both in their late twenties, had been married for 2 years, and they had intercourse frequently. Margaret seldom reached orgasm during these experiences, but she was orgasmic during masturbation. The central feature of their problem was the fact that Bill was unable to delay ejaculation for more than a few seconds after insertion.

Unbeknownst to Margaret, Bill had attempted a "do-it-yourself" technique to gain better control [of ejaculation]. He had bought a desensitizing cream he'd read about in a men's magazine and applied it to the glans of his penis 20 minutes before initiating sex. He also masturbated the day before the couple had sex.

During intercourse he tried to keep his leg muscles tense and think about sports as a way of keeping his arousal in check. Bill was unaware that Margaret felt emotionally shut out during the sex. Bill was becoming more sensitized to his arousal cycle and was worrying about erection. He was not achieving better ejaculatory control, and he was enjoying sex less. The sexual relationship was heading downhill, and miscommunication and frustration were growing.

Margaret had two secrets that she had never shared with Bill.

Although she found it easier to be orgasmic with manual stimulation, she had been orgasmic during intercourse with a married man she'd had an affair with a year before meeting Bill. Margaret expressed ambivalent feelings about that relationship. She felt that the man was a very sophisticated lover, and she had been highly aroused and orgasmic with him. Yet the relationship had been a manipulative one. He'd been emotionally abusive to Margaret, and the relationship had ended when he accused Margaret of giving him herpes and berated her. In fact, it was probably he who gave Margaret the herpes. Margaret was only experiencing herpes outbreaks two or three times a year, but when they did occur, she was flooded with negative feelings about herself, sexuality, and relationships. She initially saw Bill as a loving, stable man who would help rid her of negative feelings concerning sexuality. Instead, he continually disappointed her with the early ejaculation. Bill knew about the herpes but not about her sexual history and strong negative feelings.

Bill was terribly embarrassed about his secret concerning masturbation, which he engaged in on a twice-daily basis. From adolescence on, Bill had used masturbation as his primary means of stress reduction. For him, masturbation was a humiliating secret (he believed married men should not masturbate). The manner in which he masturbated undoubtedly contributed to the early ejaculation pattern. Bill focused only on his penis, using rapid strokes with the goal of ejaculating as quickly as he could. This was both to prevent himself from being discovered and from a desire to "get it over with" as soon as he could and forget about it.

When it came to his personal and sexual life, Bill was inhibited, unsure of himself, and had particularly low sexual self-esteem. As an adolescent, Bill remembered being very interested sexually, but very unsure around girls. Bill's first intercourse at 19 was perceived as a failure because he ejaculated before he could insert his penis in the woman's vagina. He then tried desperately to insert because the young woman urged him to, but he was in the refractory period (a phenomenon Bill did not understand), and so he did not get a firm erection and felt doubly humiliated (McCarthy, 1989, pp. 151–159).

The case of Bill and Margaret illustrates several important points. First, many sexual problems are best defined in terms of the couple rather than each partner individually. Second, although problems in sexual behavior clearly involve basic physiological responses and behavioral skills, each

person's thoughts about the meaning of sexual behavior are also extremely important. Sexual behavior usually takes place in the context of a close, personal relationship. Current views of the sexual response cycle have expanded beyond a simple focus on the mechanisms related to excitement and orgasm (Basson et al., 2005). They begin at a point of sexual neutrality and consider factors that influence whether the person will seek or be receptive to stimuli that might lead to arousal. They also extend beyond the experience of arousal and orgasm to consider feelings of emotional and physical satisfaction, which ultimately serve to build intimacy.

The classification of sexual disorders was revised dramatically in the United States and Western Europe during the twentieth century. This process reflects important changes in the way that our culture views various aspects of sexual behavior. Before describing the disorders that are included in DSM-IV-TR, we outline briefly some of the clinical and scientific perspectives on sexuality that laid the foundation for our current system.

Brief Historical Perspective

Early medical and scientific approaches to sexual behavior were heavily influenced by religious doctrines and prevailing cultural values. The exclusive purpose of sexual behavior was assumed to be biological reproduction; anything that varied from that narrow goal was considered a form of psychopathology and was usually subject to severe moral and legal sanctions. Medical authorities were more worried about excessive sexuality and inappropriate or unusual sexual activities than they were about a person's subjective dissatisfaction or impaired sexual performance.

The period between 1890 and 1930 saw many crucial changes in the ways in which society viewed sexual behavior (D'Emilio & Freedman, 1988). A significant number of people were beginning to think of sex as something other than a simple procreative function. If the purpose of sexual behavior was to foster marital intimacy or to provide pleasure, then interference with that goal might become a legitimate topic of psychological inquiry. Changes in prevailing social attitudes led to a change in the focus of systems for the classification of sexual problems. Over the course of the late twentieth century and into the twenty-first, there has been a trend toward greater tolerance of sexual variation among consenting adult partners and toward increased concern about impairments in sexual performance and experience.

Several leading intellectuals influenced public and professional opinions regarding sexual behavior during the first half of the twentieth century (Hogan, 1990). The work of Alfred Kinsey (1894–1956), a biologist at Indiana University, was especially significant. In keeping with his conscious adherence to scientific methods, Kinsey adopted a behavioral stance, focusing specifically on those experiences that resulted in orgasm. In their efforts to describe human sexual behavior, Kinsey and his colleagues interviewed 18,000 men and women between 1938 and 1956 (Jones, 1997). They asked each participant a standard series of questions such as, "How old were you the first time that you had intercourse with another person?" Or, "How many times a week do you masturbate?"

The incredible diversity of experiences reported by his subjects led Kinsey to reject the distinction between normal and abnormal sexual behavior (Robinson, 1976). He argued that differences among people are quantitative rather than qualitative. For example, Kinsey suggested that the distinction between heterosexual and homosexual persons was essentially arbitrary and fundamentally meaningless. This argument was later used in support of the decision to drop homosexuality from DSM-III (see Chapter 1) and to cease regarding homosexuality as a form of abnormal behavior. Kinsey's comments regarding sexual dysfunction reflected a similar view. He believed that low sexual desire was simply a reflection of individual differences in erotic capacity rather than a reflection of psychopathology (Kinsey, Pomeroy, and Martin, 1948).

SEXUAL DYSFUNCTIONS

Sexuality represents a complex behavioral process that can easily be upset. Inhibitions of sexual desire and interference with the physiological responses leading to orgasm are called **sexual dysfunctions.** Problems can arise anywhere, from the earliest stages of interest and desire through the climactic release of orgasm. Some people also experience pain during sexual intercourse.

Symptoms

How do people evaluate the quality of their sexual relationships? Subjective judgments obviously have an important impact on each person's commitment to a partnership. Dissatisfaction sometimes leads the couple to seek help from a mental health professional. It is useful,

▲ Satisfaction in a sexual relationship is influenced by feelings of intimacy and successful communication as well as by the experience of orgasm.

and Social Life Survey (NHSLS), the first large-scale follow-up to the Kinsey reports (Laumann, Paik, & Rosen, 1994). The NHSLS research team conducted detailed, face-to-face interviews with nearly 3,500 men and women between the ages of 18 and 59 throughout the United States. Their questionnaire asked about masturbation and four basic sexual techniques involving partners: vaginal intercourse, fellatio, cunnilingus, and anal intercourse. The results indicate that masturbation is relatively common among both men and women. Virtually all of the men (95 percent) and women (97 percent) had experienced vaginal intercourse at some time during their lives. The investigators concluded that the vast majority of heterosexual encounters focus on vaginal intercourse. Most of the men (75 percent) and women (65 percent) also reported that they had engaged in oral sexual activities (as both the person giving and receiving oral-genital stimulation). Relatively few men (25 percent) and women (20 percent) reported that they had ever engaged in anal intercourse. Most sexual activity occurs in the context of monogamous relationships. In the year of the survey, only 16 percent of the participants had more than one sexual partner, 73 percent had only one partner, and 11 percent had no partner.

therefore, to know something about the ways in which normal couples evaluate their own sexual activities before we consider specific symptoms of sexual dysfunction.

The most comprehensive information that is available regarding normal sexual behavior and satisfaction was collected by the National Health

One of the most interesting aspects of the NHSLS results involves the ways in which the participants described the quality of their experiences during sexual activity. Figure 12–1 illustrates the proportion of people who said that they always had an orgasm during sexual activity with their primary partner during the past year. Several aspects of these data are worth mentioning. First, there is a very large difference between men and women with regard to the experience of orgasm. Only 29 percent of women reported that they always have an orgasm with a specific partner, compared to 75 percent of men. Second, notice that 44 percent of men reported that their partners always had orgasms during sex. This figure is much higher than the rate reported by women themselves. There are several plausible explanations for this discrepancy. Because female orgasm is sometimes less clearly defined than male orgasm, men may misinterpret some events as signs that their partners have had an orgasm. It may also be the case that women sometimes mislead their partners into thinking that they have reached orgasm so that their partners will feel better about their own sexual prowess (Wiederman, 1997).

Sexual Response in Primary Partnership During Previous Year

FIGURE 12–1 This graph illustrates the frequency of orgasmic response as well as differences in perception by men and women in their partners' responses.

Source: E. O. Laumann, J. H. Gagnon, R. T. Michael, and S. Michaels, 1994, *The Social Organization of Sexuality: Sexual Practices in the United States,* Chicago: University of Chicago Press. Copyright © 1994. Reprinted by permission of The University of Chicago Press.

Figure 12–2 depicts data on participants' ratings of physical and emotional satisfaction. Here the differences between men and women are less marked. Physical and emotional satisfaction in a sexual relationship might reasonably be expected to be influenced by the experience of orgasm, but the relations among these variables are complex. A relationship may be considered intimate and satisfying simply because sexual activity occurs, regardless of whether it always results in orgasm. In fact, a large proportion of both men and women indicated that they were extremely satisfied with their partners, on both the physical and emotional dimensions. Notice in particular that, although only 29 percent of women indicated that they always have an orgasm with their partner, 41 percent of women said that they were extremely physically satisfied with their partners. This pattern suggests that the experience of orgasm is only one aspect of sexual satisfaction, especially for women. Other aspects of the relationship, including tenderness, intimacy, and affection, are also critically important (Mitchell & Graham, 2008; Tiefer, 2001).

Strong negative emotions, such as anger, fear, and resentment, are often associated with sexual dissatisfaction. In some cases, these emotional states appear before the onset of the sexual problem, and sometimes they develop later. Given the connection that many cultures make between virile sexual performance and "manhood," it is not surprising that men with erectile difficulties are often embarrassed and ashamed. Their humiliation can lead to secondary problems, such as anxiety and depression. Similar feelings frequently accompany premature ejaculation and the recognition that a partner's sexual expectations have not been fulfilled. Women who have trouble becoming aroused or reaching orgasm also frequently experience profound frustration and disappointment. The emotional consequences of sexual problems can be devastating for both partners.

Diagnosis

DSM-IV-TR subdivides sexual dysfunctions into several types (see Table 12–1 on page 364). The diagnostic criteria for these problems are much less specific than those used to define other kinds of disorders in DSM-IV-TR. Much is left to the judgment of the individual clinician. Failure to reach

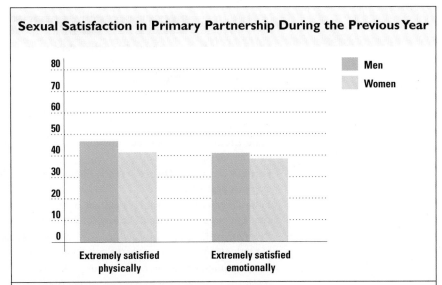

Sexual Satisfaction in Primary Partnership During the Previous Year

■ Men
■ Women

Extremely satisfied physically / Extremely satisfied emotionally

FIGURE 12–2 This graph illustrates the physical and emotional satisfaction reported by men and women in their primary partnerships.

Source: E. O. Laumann, J. H. Gagnon, R. T. Michael, and S. Michaels, 1994, *The Social Organization of Sexuality: Sexual Practices in the United States,* Chicago: University of Chicago Press. Copyright © 1994. Reprinted by permission of The University of Chicago Press.

orgasm is not considered a disorder unless it is persistent or recurrent and results in marked distress or interpersonal difficulty. The DSM-IV-TR criteria also require that the sexual dysfunction is not better explained by another Axis I disorder (such as major depression) and is not the direct result of a chemical substance (such as alcohol) or a general medical condition.

For many types of disorder, the clinician must decide whether the person has engaged in sexual activities that would normally be expected to produce sexual arousal or orgasm. Diagnostic judgments must take into consideration the person's age, as well as the circumstances in which the person is living, such as the presence of a partner, access to privacy, and so on. For all of these reasons, the reliability of diagnostic decisions for sexual dysfunctions is probably quite low (McConaghy, 2005).

One diagnostic criterion that is required for all forms of sexual dysfunction defined in DSM-IV-TR is the demonstration that the problem in question leads to marked distress or interpersonal difficulty (Segraves et al., 2007). In other words, someone who is not interested in sex or who experiences problems in sexual responsiveness would not qualify for a diagnosis of sexual dysfunction unless this circumstance is upsetting to him or her or causes interpersonal problems. Subjective distress and relationship problems will

Should sexual problems be defined primarily in terms of difficulty reaching orgasm?

TABLE 12–1 Sexual Dysfunctions Listed In DSM-IV-TR
Hypoactive Sexual Desire Disorder: Persistently or recurrently deficient (or absent) sexual fantasies and desire for sexual activity.
Sexual Aversion Disorder: Persistent or recurrent extreme aversion to, and avoidance of, all (or almost all) genital sexual contact with a sexual partner.
Female Sexual Arousal Disorder: Persistent or recurrent inability to attain, or to maintain until completion of the sexual activity, an adequate lubrication–swelling response of sexual excitement.
Male Erectile Disorder: Persistent or recurrent inability to attain or maintain until completion of the sexual activity, an adequate erection.
Female Orgasmic Disorder: Persistent or recurrent delay in, or absence of, orgasm following a normal sexual excitement phase.
Male Orgasmic Disorder: Persistent or recurrent delay in, or absence of, orgasm following a normal sexual excitement phase during sexual activity.
Premature Ejaculation: Persistent or recurrent ejaculation with minimal sexual stimulation before, on, or shortly after penetration and before the person wishes it.
Dyspareunia: Recurrent or persistent genital pain associated with sexual intercourse in either a male or a female.
Vaginismus: Recurrent or persistent involuntary spasm of the musculature of the outer third of the vagina that interferes with sexual intercourse.

Source: Reprinted with permission from the *Diagnostic and Statistical Manual of Mental Disorders,* Fourth Edition, Text Revision. Copyright © 2000 by the American Psychiatric Association.

be evident in many of the brief case studies that are included in this chapter.

We must be cautious, however, in weighing the diagnostic importance of relationship problems and the feelings of the person's partner. A panel of leading experts on women's reproductive health recommended that the only consideration in this regard should be personal distress experienced by the woman (Basson et al., 2000). The satisfaction and concerns of her partner might be an important consideration in terms of their relationship itself, but it should not be grounds for assigning to the woman a diagnosis of sexual dysfunction unless she is personally dissatisfied with her own sexual experience.

Hypoactive Sexual Desire Disorder Sexual desire sets the stage for sexual arousal and orgasm. Some clinicians refer to sexual desire as the person's willingness to approach or engage in those experiences that will lead to sexual arousal. Inhibited, or **hypoactive, sexual desire** is defined in terms of subjective experiences, such as lack of sexual fantasies and lack of interest in sexual experiences. The absence of interest in sex must be both persistent and pervasive to be considered a clinical problem.

The absolute frequency with which a person engages in sex cannot be used as a measure of inhibited sexual desire because the central issue is *interest*—actively seeking out sexual experiences—rather than participation (Warnock, 2002). For example, some people acquiesce to their partners' demands, even though they would not choose to engage in sexual activities if it were left up to them. In the absence of any specific standard, the identification of hypoactive sexual desire must depend on a clinician's subjective evaluation of the level of desire that is expected given the person's age, gender, marital status, and many other relevant considerations.

Almost everyone recognizes that sexual desire fluctuates in intensity over time, sometimes dra-

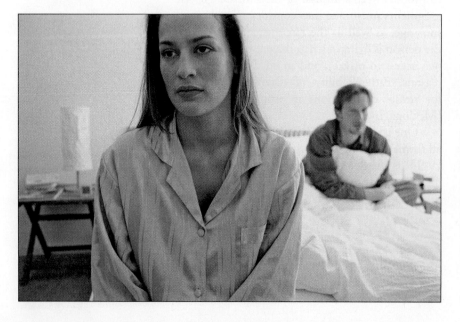

▼ Low sexual desire can reflect the impact of many factors ranging from unhappiness (including anger and worry) to poor physical health.

matically and frequently, for reasons that we do not understand. The fact that hypoactive sexual desire is listed in DSM-IV-TR as a type of disorder should not lead us to believe that it is a unitary condition with a simple explanation. It is, in fact, a collection of many different kinds of problems. People who suffer from low levels of sexual desire frequently experience other mental and medical disorders. Perhaps as many as 85 percent of males and 75 percent of females seeking treatment for hypoactive sexual desire report other forms of sexual dysfunction (Donahey & Carroll, 1993), such as problems with arousal or genital pain. Men and women with low sexual desire also have high rates of mood disorders. The mood disorder typically appears before the onset of low sexual desire. It appears likely, therefore, that many cases of low sexual desire develop after the person has experienced other forms of psychological distress.

Sexual Aversion Disorder Some people develop an active aversion to sexual stimuli and begin to avoid sexual situations altogether. Some people avoid only certain aspects of sexual behavior, such as kissing, intercourse, or oral sex. This reaction is stronger than a simple lack of interest. Fear of sexual encounters can occasionally reach intense proportions, at which point it may be better characterized as **sexual aversion disorder.** This problem might be viewed as a kind of phobia because it extends well beyond anxiety about sexual performance (Kingsberg & Janata, 2003). Consider, for example, the following case from our files. The couple sought help at a psychological clinic in the hope that they might improve their sexual relationship.

BRIEF CASE **STUDY**
Sexual Aversion Disorder

Doug and Jennifer were both 32 years old. They had been married for 5 years, but they had never had sexual intercourse. They cared for each other very much and described themselves as being like brother and sister. Their inability to have intercourse was upsetting to them both for many reasons. Most important was their mutual desire to have children. Doug also felt that their marriage would be stronger and more enjoyable if they were sexually intimate. Jennifer wasn't interested in sexual activity; she never experienced sexual fantasies or erotic thoughts. She did view sex as her duty, however, and she felt guilty about not fulfilling that part of her "marital obligation." Jennifer's primary concern about the

relationship involved a different kind of intimacy; she wished that Doug would spend more time with her talking, taking walks, and doing things together that did not involve sex.

Neither Doug nor Jennifer had been experienced sexually at the time of their marriage. Jennifer was clearly anxious in the presence of stimuli that were sexual in nature, such as movies or books with a sexual theme, but she did not avoid these situations or sexual interactions altogether. She and Doug had engaged in kissing and gentle touching early in their marriage. Jennifer masturbated Doug to orgasm several times, but she felt disgusted at the sight of semen when he ejaculated. Doug had persuaded her to engage in oral sex on a few occasions. She found it unpleasant and was unable to continue long enough for Doug to reach orgasm. They attempted intercourse once, but Jennifer was unable to become aroused and insertion had been impossible.

Doug and Jennifer gradually lost interest in sexual activities. He was extremely busy with his work and said that he no longer thought about sex very often, although he continued to masturbate. Since their failed attempt at intercourse, Doug had also begun to feel less sexually attracted to Jennifer. They eventually entered treatment in order to explore their feelings for each other and to see if they could do anything to salvage their sexual relationship, primarily in the hope that they would be able to have children.

Several weeks after entering therapy, Jennifer reluctantly confided in her therapist that she had been sexually abused by an uncle with whom she had lived for 2 years as a child. He had forced her to perform oral sex several times when she was about 9 years old. She had never told anyone about the abuse—her parents, her aunt, or Doug—for many reasons. She was ashamed of the experience and frightened of what her uncle might do to her. The memories of this experience were still vivid, especially when she attempted to have sex with her husband.

Jennifer's aversion to sexual activity was easily understandable in the context of previous abuse. The symptoms of sexual aversion disorder are often more pronounced than those that were exhibited by Jennifer. In some people, full-blown symptoms of a panic attack may be triggered by exposure to sexual stimuli.

Male Erectile Disorder Many men experience difficulties either in obtaining an erection that is sufficient to accomplish intercourse or maintaining an erection long enough to satisfy themselves and their partners during intercourse. Both problems are examples of **erectile dysfunction.** Men with this problem may report feeling subjectively aroused, but the vascular reflex mechanism fails, and sufficient blood is not pumped to the penis to make it erect (Wylie & Machin, 2007). These difficulties can appear at any time prior to orgasm. Some men have trouble achieving an erection during sexual foreplay, whereas others lose their erection around the time of insertion or during intercourse. This phenomenon used to be called *impotence,* but the term has been dropped because of its negative implications.

Erectile dysfunctions can be relatively transient, or they can be more chronic. Occasional experiences of this type are not considered unusual. When they persist and become a serious source of distress to the couple, however, erectile difficulties can lead to serious problems. Consider, for example, the feelings expressed by the man and woman in our next case study, who were treated by Bernie Zilbergeld, an expert in the treatment of sexual dysfunction.

BRIEF CASE **STUDY**
Male Erectile Disorder

Norm and Linda are both 44 and have been married 15 years, the first marriage for him, the second for her. Linda called to ask if I would be available immediately to work with her and her husband, who had low sexual desire and erection problems. Individually, they are very different. Linda is attractive, vivacious, impulsive, and very critical. Norm seemed generally timid and reluctant to express his feelings in front of his wife, spoke slowly and usually only after some time, and then said only nice things in a nice way, and he struck me as being depressed. (They) had a serviceable relationship in many ways. Neither had close friends and tended to rely on each other for support and companionship. They shared a number of common interests and held similar values about most things.

The only problem, as far as they were concerned, was sex. When they first met, Linda was far more sexually experienced than Norm. She was surprised that a man could have had so little knowledge and experience. He, on the other hand, was somewhat intimidated by her experience and knowledge. But he tried to be a good student and they enjoyed frequent lovemaking at the beginning, although not as frequent or as passionate as she would have liked.

Over the years, however, Norm gradually lost interest in sex and developed erection problems. Either he wouldn't get an erection or he would lose it before or during insertion. Norm sought help from a urologist who, although he found nothing physically wrong, gave him an injection in his penis, which produced an erection that lasted for three hours.

But neither Norm nor Linda was overjoyed by the idea of him taking injections. Norm had always been fearful of needles and almost fainted when the urologist gave him the first injection. Linda didn't like the needles either. In her mind, they weren't "natural or normal." For Norm to have to take shots to get erections meant that he didn't love her or wasn't aroused by her.

Linda appeared to be hurt and angry in my individual session with her. "I know you're sympathetic toward men with erection problems. But what about me? I feel totally defeminized. How can I feel loved or desirable when he can't get it up for me? You don't have any idea what that's like. Even with the help of modern chemistry, he can't do it for me. It's obvious he doesn't want me, doesn't desire me. Even at my age, other men look at me and want me. But not my husband. I feel (awful)."

In my session with Norm, he repeated several times that he loved Linda and wanted to stay with her. When I asked if he found her sexually attractive, he hesitated and then said yes. When I asked about the hesitation, he was silent for a few moments and then said, "No, it's nothing. I am turned on to her." Further prodding on my part yielded nothing, but I thought his arousal was not as unambivalent as he said. As we continued our discussion, I asked how he felt when he was first dating her. He began by saying how beautiful he found her and how surprised he was that a woman like her would take an interest "in a nerd like me." When I asked what else he felt at that time, he answered, "To tell the truth, I was frightened by her experience and sexual openness. It was like I was in kindergarten and she was a professor. I'm not sure I've ever gotten over that. I've always felt at least a little inadequate. And things really got bad after I started having trouble with erections." I wanted to know more about how their sex had been before the erection problem. He said that it had been good and added in a voice so low I could barely hear his words, "She was always teaching and correcting me. Somehow I wasn't able to do exactly what she wanted. I didn't touch her right, my erections were never as hard as she liked, and when we had intercourse, I wasn't passionate enough" (Zilbergeld, 1995, pp. 315–316).

Norm and Linda experienced the frustrations and anxiety that often accompany sexual arousal difficulties. Their relationship also illustrates the marital distress that can develop when people begin to have problems with self-esteem and doubts about the affection of their partner.

Female Sexual Arousal Disorder Sexual arousal can also be impaired in women, but it is somewhat more difficult to describe and identify than is erectile dysfunction in men. Put simply, a woman is said to experience **inhibited sexual arousal** if she cannot either achieve or maintain genital responses, such as lubrication and swelling, that are necessary to complete sexual intercourse. The desire is there, but the physiological responses that characterize sexual excitement are inhibited (Meston & Bradford, 2007).

The capacity for intercourse is somewhat less obvious and more difficult to measure for a woman than for a man, whose erect penis usually serves as a signal of readiness (see Research Methods box). Investigators who have studied sexual responses in normal women have reported low correlations between self-reports of subjective arousal and physiological measures, such as the amount of vaginal lubrication or vasocongestion (Leiblum, 2001; Segraves & Blindt-Segraves, 2001). Among women who experience sexual difficulties, the problem may more often be decreased subjective arousal rather than impaired physiological responses. Therefore, inhibitions in sexual arousal must be defined in terms of this self-report dimension as well as in terms of specific genital responses.

◄ Sexual arousal is somewhat more difficult to measure for women than for men. Women's subjective feelings of arousal are not always directly connected to physiological responses.

RESEARCH METHODS Hypothetical Constructs: What Is Sexual Arousal?

The term *sexual arousal* refers to the state that precedes orgasm. It is defined in terms of two factors: physiological responses, such as vascular engorgement of the genitals, and subjective feelings of pleasure and excitement. Psychologists refer to sexual arousal as a **hypothetical construct.** Many of the concepts that we have discussed in this book are hypothetical constructs: anxiety, depression, psychopathy, and schizophrenia. Hypothetical constructs are theoretical devices. In the field of psychopathology, they refer to events or states that reside within the person and are proposed to help us understand or explain a person's behavior.

Constructs cannot be observed directly, but in order to be scientifically meaningful they must be defined in terms of observable responses (Cronbach & Meehl, 1955; Kimble, 1989). These responses are all associated with the construct, but they are not perfectly related, and the construct is not exhaustively defined by them. For example, an erect penis is not always accompanied by subjective feelings of sexual excitement, and subjective feelings of arousal are not always associated with physiological responses. In other words, the construct of sexual arousal is anchored by feelings and responses that

can be measured directly, but it is more than the sum of these parts.

An **operational definition** is a procedure that is used to measure a theoretical construct. Such a definition usually includes measures of the different components of the construct. For men, one obvious component of sexual arousal is penile erection. The most widely accepted procedure for measuring male sexual arousal uses a device called a *penile plethysmograph* (Rosen et al., 2007). In this procedure, the man places a thin elastic strain gauge around his penis, underneath his clothing. The rubber loop is filled with a column of mercury that changes in its electrical conductance as the circumference of the penis changes. The wire extending from the strain gauge is connected to a plethysmograph, which amplifies the electrical signal passing through the strain gauge and produces a record reflecting changes in penile tumescence.

How is sexual arousal measured in the lab?

The *vaginal photometer*, a device shaped like a tampon and inserted into the vagina, is used to measure female sexual arousal. Like the penile

strain gauge, the photometer can be placed in position in private and worn underneath clothing during the assessment procedure. As the woman becomes sexually aroused, the walls of the vagina become congested with blood. Vasocongestion causes changes in the amount of red light that can be transmitted through the tissue. The photometer is sensitive to subtle changes in vaginal tissue and is probably most useful in measuring moderate to low levels of sexual arousal (Heiman, 1998; Janssen, 2002).

Clinical scientists must always think carefully about the meaning of their operational definitions. Although the penile strain gauge and the vaginal photometer measure physiological events that are directly related to sexual arousal, the responses that they measure are not the same thing as sexual arousal. They are reflections of the construct, which has many dimensions (Berman et al., 1999). One important goal of scientific studies is to determine more specifically how (and when) these physiological measures are related to the other observable referents of sexual arousal. This process will determine the **construct validity** of the penile strain gauge and the vaginal photometer—that is, the extent to which these specific measures produce results that are consistent with the theoretical construct.

Premature Ejaculation Many men experience problems with the control of ejaculation. They are unable to prolong the period of sexual excitement long enough to complete intercourse. This problem is known as **premature ejaculation.** Once they become intensely sexually aroused, they reach orgasm very quickly (Metz & Pryor, 2000). Almost all the literature on this topic is concerned with men, but some women are also bothered by reaching orgasm too quickly. Therefore, some clinicians have suggested that "premature orgasm" might be a more appropriate description of the problem.

There have been many attempts to establish specific, quantitative criteria for premature ejaculation (Broderick, 2006). None of the attempts has been entirely satisfactory, but certain boundaries identify conditions that can be problematic. If the man ejaculates before or immediately upon insertion, or after only three or four thrusts, almost all clinicians will identify his response as premature ejaculation. Among men suffering from lifelong premature ejaculation, 90 percent routinely ejaculate within 1 minute after insertion of the penis in the vagina (Waldinger, 2003).

Another way to think about premature ejaculation places emphasis on subjective control and the couple's satisfaction rather than on the amount of time required to reach orgasm. The DSM-IV-TR definition defines the problem in terms of recurrent ejaculation shortly after penetration and before the person wishes it. If progression to orgasm is beyond the man's voluntary control once he reaches an intense level of sexual arousal, he has a problem with premature ejaculation (Symonds et al., 2003).

Female Orgasmic Disorder Some women are unable to reach orgasm even though they apparently experience uninhibited sexual arousal. Women who experience orgasmic difficulties may have a strong desire to engage in sexual relations; they may find great pleasure in sexual foreplay and may show all the signs of sexual arousal. Nevertheless, they cannot reach the peak erotic experience of orgasm. Women whose orgasmic impairment is *generalized* have never experienced orgasm by any means. *Situational orgasmic* difficulties occur when the woman is able to reach orgasm in some situations, but not in others. That might mean that she is orgasmic during masturbation but not during intercourse, or perhaps she is orgasmic with one partner but not with another (Basson, 2002).

Orgasmic disorder in women is somewhat difficult to define in relation to inhibited sexual arousal because the various components of female sexual response are more difficult to measure than are erection and ejaculation in the male. One experienced researcher described this issue in the following way:

> In my experience, many women who have never reached orgasm present the following set of symptoms: They report that when engaging in intercourse they do not have difficulty lubricating and experience no pain. However, they report no genital sensations (hence the term *genital anesthesia*) and do not appear to know what sexual arousal is. Typically they do not masturbate and often have never masturbated. They do not experience the phenomenon that a sexually functional woman would call sexual desire. Most of these women seek therapy because they have heard from others or have read that they are missing something, rather than because they themselves feel frustrated. (Morokoff, 1989, p. 74)

Pain During Sex Some people experience persistent genital pain during or after sexual intercourse, which is known as **dyspareunia.** The problem can occur in either men or women, although it is considered to be much more common in women (Davis & Reissing, 2007; Kaneko, 2001). The severity of the discomfort can range from mild irritation following sexual activity to searing pain during insertion of the penis or intercourse. The pains may be sharp and intense, or they may take the form of a dull, aching sensation; they may be experienced as coming from a superficial area near the barrel of the vagina or as being located deep in the lower abdominal area; they may be intermittent or persistent. The experience of severe genital pain is often associated with other forms of sexual dysfunction. Not surprisingly, many women with dyspareunia develop a lack of interest in, or an aversion toward, sexual activity.

The following first-person account was written by a 40-year-old woman who had been experiencing vaginal pain for several months. She had consulted several different health professionals about the problem, and none of their treatments had relieved her discomfort. This passage describes her experience one night when she and the man with whom she had been living seemed to be on the brink of enjoying a renewed interest in their sexual relationship.

BRIEF CASE **STUDY**
Genital Pain

We went to bed. For a while it was nice—more than nice. It was novel and thrilling, as if we had just met. We hadn't approached each other in more than a month. I was surprised by how wonderful I could feel. I was used to feeling lousy most of the time. The sensations of excitement were overwhelming. I'd forgotten about that. Then he pushed himself into me and it was horrible.

First I felt as if I were being torn or sliced. As he settled into a rhythm, I felt that something was scraping me over and over in the same raw spot, until the rawness and soreness were all I could feel. He didn't notice. He was intent on what he was doing. I decided to let him get on with it, but the pain was really bothering me. I pulled away inside myself, so that the events on the bed were far from where "I" was, and the pain was far away also. That worked, but I didn't like doing it. There was something nasty about it. I had the thought, People who don't like sex must feel this way. Then I realized that now I was somebody who didn't like sex (Kaysen, 2001, pp. 60–61).

Access to the vagina is controlled by the muscles surrounding its entrance. Some women find that whenever penetration of the vagina is attempted, these muscles snap tightly shut, preventing insertion of any object. This involuntary muscular spasm, known as **vaginismus,** prevents sexual intercourse as well as other activities, such as vaginal examinations and the insertion of tampons. Women with vaginismus may be completely sexually responsive in other respects, fully capable of arousal and orgasm through manual stimulation of the clitoris. Women who seek therapy for this condition often report that they are afraid of intercourse and vaginal penetration (Reissing et al., 2004). The problem can be severe or partial in nature. Some couples report that a mild form of vaginismus occurs from time to time, making intercourse difficult and sometimes painful.

Many women experience genital pain during sexual stimulation other than intercourse. Thus one recommendation made by the Consensus Development Conference on Female Sexual Dysfunction was the addition of a new category for noncoital sexual pain (Basson et al., 2000). This suggestion was made because the DSM-IV-TR definitions of dyspareunia and vaginismus focus exclusively on problems that occur during sexual intercourse. Some experts have suggested that these problems should be viewed as genital pain disorders (similar to pain disorders, such as back pain) that interfere with intercourse rather than as forms of sexual dysfunction (Binik, 2005; Binik et al., 2002).

Sexual Addiction: A Proposal DSM-IV-TR includes unusually low sexual desire as a sexual dysfunction, but it does not mention unusually *high* sexual desire. In contrast, ICD-10 does include a category called *excessive sexual drive*. Symptoms associated with this condition presumably include such behaviors as seeking new sexual encounters out of boredom with old ones, frequent use of pornography, and legal problems resulting from sexual behaviors (Gold & Heffner, 1998). Additional features include obsessive thoughts about sexual encounters, guilt resulting from problematic sexual behavior, and rationalization for continued reckless sexual behavior. Reckless and uncontrolled sexual activity can obviously disrupt a person's life and cause significant personal distress. But should it be considered a form of abnormal behavior? Some clinicians believe that the next version of DSM should include some form of this concept (Briken et al., 2007; Vesga-Lopez et al., 2007).

One approach to the problem views uncontrolled sexual behavior as being a form of addiction, similar to substance use disorders (Gold & Heffner, 1998). Consider, for example, the definition of substance dependence presented in Table 11–3 on page 334. Replace the word *substance* with the term *sexual behavior* in this definition and you have one version of a definition of sexual addiction. The person develops a tolerance to previous sexual partners and forms of sexual experience; the person experiences symptoms of withdrawal when deprived of sexual opportunities; and the person engages in a repeated pattern of compulsive sexual behavior. Some clinicians suggest that sexual addiction can progress from victimless behaviors, such as excessive masturbation, to increasingly harmful forms of behavior, such as exhibitionism, voyeurism, and sexual assault. Unfortunately, there are no empirical data to support this idea.

Opposition to this proposal is based on several factors. One is the somewhat circular definition of the problem, which also plagues the concept of *impulse control disorders* (see page 278 in Chapter 9). Another limitation is the heterogeneous nature of excessive or uncontrolled sexual behavior. Failure to control sexual impulses can be associated with several disorders in

> *Should excessive sexual behavior be considered a disorder in its own right? Or is it a symptom of other mental disorders?*

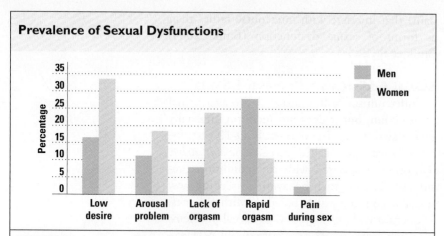

FIGURE 12–3 This graph shows the percentage of NHSLS respondents who reported having sexual difficulties at some time during the previous 12 months. Note the differences in the problems reported by men and women.

Source: E. O. Laumann, J. H. Gagnon, R. T. Michael, and S. Michaels, 1994, *The Social Organization of Sexuality: Sexual Practices in the United States.* Chicago: University of Chicago Press. p. 369. Copyright © 1994. Reprinted by permission of The University of Chicago Press.

DSM-IV-TR, including paraphilias, impulse control disorders, and bipolar mood disorder (Schneider & Irons, 1996). Many people who admit to compulsive sexual behavior also suffer from mood disorders, anxiety disorders, and substance use disorders (Black et al., 1997). The concept obviously includes a diverse set of behavioral problems that may not represent a meaningful diagnostic category. Inclusion of this diagnosis in future editions of DSM will depend on further evidence supporting the construct validity of the disorder (see Research Methods).

Frequency

Surveys conducted among the general population indicate that some forms of sexual dysfunction are relatively common (Bancroft, Loftus, & Long, 2003). We must keep in mind, however, that this impression is based on self-report questionnaires and judgments made by lay persons, which are less precise than those made by experts. Diagnoses made by experienced therapists would take into account the person's age, the context of the person's life, and whether the person had experienced stimulation that would ordinarily be expected to lead to sustained arousal and orgasm. Clinicians would also take into consideration the amount of distress and interpersonal difficulty associated with the problem before arriving at a diagnosis of sexual dysfunction. Therefore, we must be cautious in our interpretations of survey data (Hayes et al., 2008).

The most extensive set of information regarding sexual problems among people living in the community comes from the National Health and Social Life Survey (NHSLS). Each participant was asked whether during the past 12 months he or she had experienced "a period of *several months or more* when you lacked interest in having sex; had trouble achieving or maintaining an erection or (for women) had trouble lubricating; were unable to come to a climax; came to a climax too quickly; or experienced physical pain during intercourse." For each item, the person was asked for a simple yes or no response. Figure 12–3 indicates the overall percentage of men and women who indicated that they had experienced each of these specific problems. There are obviously significant gender differences in the prevalence of all types of problems. Premature ejaculation is the most frequent form of male sexual dysfunction, affecting almost one out of every three adult men. All the other forms of sexual dysfunction are reported more often by women. One-third of women said that they lacked interest in sex, and almost one-quarter indicated that they experienced a period of several months during which they were unable to reach orgasm (Laumann, Paik, & Rosen, 1999).

Sexual Behavior Across the Life Span Sexual behavior changes with age. Masters and Johnson devoted considerable attention to this topic in their original studies. Their data challenged the myth that older adults are not interested in, or capable of performing, sexual behaviors. The NHSLS data also indicate that many people remain sexually active later in life. Gender differences become marked in the late fifties, when rates of inactivity increase dramatically for women. Between ages 70 and 74, 65 percent of men are still sexually active, compared to only 30 percent of women. These differences may be, at least partly, the result of biological factors that are part of the aging process. They may also reflect the influence of a cultural prejudice against sexual activity among older women.

Differences between younger and older people are mostly a matter of degree. As men get older, they tend to achieve erections more slowly, but they can often maintain erections for longer periods of time. Older men find it more difficult to regain an erection if it is lost before orgasm. As women get older, vaginal lubrication may occur at a slower rate, but the response of the clitoris remains essentially unchanged. The intensity of the subjective experience of orgasm is decreased for older men and women. For both men and women, healthy sexual responsiveness is most likely to be maintained among those who have been sexually active as younger adults (Hillman, 2000).

The prevalence of certain types of sexual dysfunction increases among the elderly, particularly among men (DeRogatis & Burnett, 2008). In the NHSLS, for example, the proportion of men reporting erectile problems increased from 6 percent in the 18–24 age range to 20 percent in the 55–59 age range. In contrast, several types of sexual problems actually declined in frequency among older women. Women in the 55–59 age range were less likely than women between the ages of 18 and 24 to report pain during sex or inability to reach orgasm, though they did report a slight increase in trouble with lubrication during sexual activity.

The relation between sexual experience and aging is closely related to other health problems that increase with age. People who rate their health as being excellent have many fewer sexual problems than people who rate their health as being only fair or poor (Laumann et al., 1994).

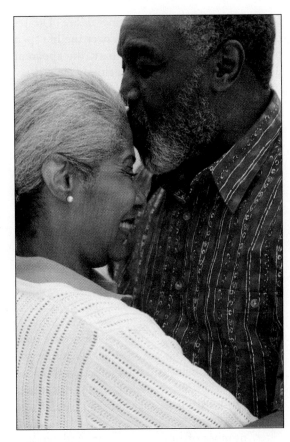

◄ Many people remain sexually active later in life. Differences in sexual responsiveness between younger and older people are mostly a matter of degree.

Cross-Cultural Comparisons Patients with sexual disorders seek treatment at clinics all over the world (Steggall, Gann, & Chinegwundoh, 2004). Therefore, these problems are not unique to any particular culture. Cultural and ethnic differences have been reported for sexual practices, beliefs about sexuality, and patterns of sexual decision making. For example, Asians are more conservative than Caucasians in many regards, such as the prevalence and frequency of masturbation (Meston, Trapnell, & Gorzalka, 1996). It is not clear whether variations in sexual behavior are accompanied by cultural differences in the frequency and form of sexual dysfunctions. Cross-cultural studies of prevalence rates for specific sexual dysfunctions have not been reported. This kind of investigation may be difficult to perform because the DSM-IV-TR definitions of sexual dysfunctions may not be well suited to describing the sexual experiences and satisfaction of people living in non-Western cultures (Ghanem & El-Sakka, 2007).

Causes

At each stage of the sexual response cycle, a person's behavior is determined by the interaction of many biological and psychological factors, ranging from vasocongestion in the genitals to complex cognitive events involving the perception of sexual stimuli and the interpretation of sexual meanings. Interference with this system at any point can result in serious problems. In the following pages we review some of the factors that contribute to the etiology of various types of sexual dysfunction.

Biological Factors The experience of sexual desire is partly controlled by biological factors. Sexual desire is influenced by sex hormones for both men and women (LeVay & Valente, 2003). Testosterone is particularly important for male sexual desire. Studies of men with inadequate levels of sex hormones show an inhibited response to sexual fantasies, but they are still able to have erections in response to viewing explicit erotic films. The influence of male sex hormones on sexual behavior is, therefore, thought to be on sexual appetite rather than on sexual performance. This process probably involves a threshold level of circulating testosterone (Schiavi & Segraves, 1995). In other words, sexual appetite is impaired if the level of testosterone falls below a particular point (close to the bottom of the laboratory normal range), but above that threshold, fluctuations in testosterone levels will not be associated with changes in sexual desire. The reduction of male sex hormones over the life span probably explains, at least in part, the apparent decline in sexual desire among elderly males.

Many cases of erectile dysfunction can be attributed to vascular, neurological, or hormonal impairment (Goldstein, 2004). Erection is the direct result of a threefold increase in blood flow to the penis. Thus it is not surprising that vascular diseases, which may affect the amount of blood reaching the penis, are likely to result in erectile difficulties. Neurological diseases, such as epilepsy and multiple sclerosis, can also produce erectile difficulties, because erection depends on spinal reflexes. Diabetes may be the most common neurologically based cause of impaired erectile responsiveness.

Various kinds of drugs can also influence a man's erectile response (Clayton & West, 2003). One interesting set of results indicates that men who smoke cigarettes are more likely to experience erectile difficulties than are men in the general population. Many other drugs, including alcohol and marijuana, may have negative effects on sexual arousal.

A number of biological factors and physiological diseases can impair a woman's ability to become sexually aroused (Clayton, 2007). Various types of neurological disorder, pelvic disease, and hormonal dysfunction can interfere with the process of vaginal swelling and lubrication. Unfortunately, relatively little research has been conducted on problems of sexual arousal in women (Andersen & Cyranowski, 1995), and thus these mechanisms are not well understood.

Inhibited orgasm, in both men and women, is sometimes caused by the abuse of alcohol and other drugs. The problem may improve if the person is able to stop drinking and maintain a stable period of sobriety (Schiavi et al., 1995). Orgasm problems can also be associated with the use of prescribed forms of medication. For example, as we discussed in Chapter 5, many people who take SSRIs such as fluoxetine (Prozac) for the treatment of depression have difficulty achieving orgasm as a side effect (Werneke et al., 2006).

Psychological Factors Although sexual desire is rooted in a strong biological foundation, psychological variables also play an important role in the determination of which stimuli a person will find arousing. Sexual desire and arousal are determined, in part, by mental

What role do mental scripts play in sexual arousal?

scripts that we learn throughout childhood and adolescence (Laumann & Gagnon, 1995; Wiegel, Scepkowski, & Barlow, 2007). These scripts provide structure or context to the otherwise confusing array of potential partners who might become the object of our desires. In other words, there are certain kinds of people to whom we may be sexually attracted, and there are certain circumstances in which sexual behavior is considered appropriate. According to this perspective, the personal meaning of an event is of paramount importance in releasing the biological process of sexual arousal. Both members of the potential couple must recognize similar cues, defining the situation as potentially sexual in nature, before anything is likely to happen.

Beliefs and attitudes toward sexuality, as well as the quality of interpersonal relationships, have an important influence on the development of low sexual desire, especially among women (Nobre & Pinto-Gouveia, 2006). Women seeking treatment for hypoactive sexual desire report negative perceptions of their parents' attitudes regarding sexual behavior and the demonstration of affection. In comparison to other women, they also indicate that they feel less close to their husbands, have fewer romantic feelings, and are less attracted to their husbands. The quality of the relationship is an important factor to consider with regard to low sexual desire (Metz & Epstein, 2002).

Culturally determined attitudes toward sexual feelings and behaviors can also have a dramatic impact on women's ability to become sexually aroused (Al-Sawaf & Al-Issa, 2000). Some societies openly encourage female sexuality; others foster a more repressive atmosphere. Within U.S. culture, there are tremendous variations with regard to women's ability to experience and express their sexuality. For example, many women feel guilty about having sexual fantasies, in spite of the fact that such fantasies are extremely common. Women who feel guilty about fantasizing while they are having intercourse are more likely to be sexually dissatisfied and to encounter sexual problems. The most important factors contributing to failure to reach orgasm involve negative attitudes, feelings of guilt, and failure to communicate effectively (Kelly, Strassberg, & Turner, 2004).

Couples that experience communication problems, power conflicts, and an absence of intimacy and trust are more likely than others to experience sexual problems. Lack of assertiveness and lack of comfort in talking about sexual activities and pleasures are associated with various types of female sexual dysfunction (Rosen & Leiblum, 1995). The following brief case study provides one example of serious relationship difficulties that were experienced by one couple in which the woman, a married, 34-year-old lawyer, was being treated for long-standing vaginismus as well as alcohol dependence.

BRIEF CASE **STUDY**
Vaginismus and Alcohol Dependence

Gina speculated that living with Paul exacerbated her sexual anxieties and she became increasingly dependent on alcohol to "loosen her up" sexually. Paul was sexually naive and did not press Gina to have intercourse, especially when she so visibly panicked at the approach of his penis. He, too, was sexually anxious and was afraid of inflicting pain on her. Sexually, they depended on drinking to disinhibit them, and they developed a sexual script that relied on manual stimulation and oral sex. Although sexual contact was relatively infrequent, both were reasonably content.

This state of affairs continued for many years. It was not without its costs, though. Gina felt inadequate and deficient as a woman and avoided gynecological examinations. Paul would occasionally become enraged at a seemingly small provocation and verbally attack Gina. Internally, he reported feeling humiliated, emasculated, and ashamed about the nonconsummation of their marriage. When his coworkers teased and joked about "getting it on" sexually, he felt alone in the private knowledge that he had never penetrated his wife despite 13 years of living and sleeping together.

Eventually, as Gina's drinking escalated, the marital conflict grew intolerable. When Gina was drunk, she would verbally berate and abuse Paul. Her attacks and complaints about his passivity and lack of assistance with housework and her disparagement of his passion for sports undermined the earlier closeness they had experienced. Although he would usually tolerate her drunken tirades silently, he began to blow up more readily (Leiblum, 1995, p. 256).

Previous harmful or traumatic experiences can also have an important effect on various aspects of sexual interests and arousal. As we have already discussed in the case of Jennifer, a previous history of sexual abuse can lead to sexual aversion, and it can interfere with a woman's ability to become sexually aroused (Najman et al., 2005). Premature ejaculation and low sexual desire in men have also been linked to various kinds of long-lasting, adverse relationships with adults during childhood (Loeb et al., 2002). For example, boys who grow up in a home in which their father is physically abusive may learn to associate sex with violence and become convinced that they do not want to function—sexually or interpersonally—as their father had.

Among the psychological factors contributing to impaired sexual arousal, Masters and Johnson (1970) gave primary emphasis to *performance anxiety*, or fear of failure. People who have experienced inhibited sexual arousal on one or two occasions may be likely to have further problems to the degree that these difficulties make them more self-conscious or apprehensive regarding their ability to become aroused in future sexual encounters. Several prominent and experienced sex therapists have assumed that anxiety and sexual arousal are incompatible emotional states. People who are anxious will presumably be less responsive to sexual stimuli. And men who have sexual arousal disorders are more likely to report feeling high levels of performance anxiety (McCabe, 2005).

Anxiety disrupts sexual performance to the extent that it alters certain cognitive processes. These mechanisms have been studied by David Barlow and his colleagues, who have examined the relation between performance concerns and interfering thoughts in men with erectile difficulties. Several of their studies have compared the responses of sexually dysfunctional men with those of control subjects in laboratory settings. Dysfunctional men experience more negative emotions in the presence of erotic stimuli, and they are also more likely to shift their attention from the arousing properties of sexual stimuli to the threatening consequences of potential failures in sexual performance (Bach, Brown, & Barlow, 1999). In comparison to men without erectile disorder, men with sexual dysfunction rate negative sexual events as being more important and then are more likely to attribute the problem to something about themselves rather than external considerations (Scepkowski et al., 2004).

Treatment

Masters and Johnson (1970) were pioneers in developing and popularizing a short-term, skills-based approach to the treatment of sexual dysfunctions. Hundreds of couples who visited their clinic in St. Louis went through a 2-week course of assessment and therapy in which they became more familiar with their bodies, learned to communicate more effectively with their partners, and received training in procedures

▲ Sensate focus exercises help people become aware of physical sensations that are associated with touching and being touched while minimizing demands for sexual performance.

designed to help them diminish their fears about sexuality. The results of this treatment program were very positive and quickly spawned a burgeoning industry of psychosocial treatment for sexual dysfunction. Getting Help at the end of this chapter discusses some of the options and resources available to anyone experiencing problems in sexual functioning or health.

Psychological Procedures Psychological treatments for sexual dysfunction address several of the causes discussed earlier, especially negative attitudes toward sexuality, failure to engage in effective sexual behaviors, and deficits in communication skills. Sex therapy centers around three primary types of activity: sensate focus and scheduling; education and cognitive restructuring; and communication training (Meston & Rellini, 2008; Wincze et al., 2008).

What are the primary targets of psychological approaches to treating sexual dysfunction?

The cornerstone of sex therapy is known as **sensate focus,** a procedure developed by Masters and Johnson. Sensate focus involves a series of simple exercises in which the couple spends time in a quiet, relaxed setting, learning to touch each other. They may start with tasks as simple as holding hands or giving each other back rubs. The rationale for sensate focus hinges on the recognition that people with sexual problems must learn to focus on erotic sensations rather than on performance demands. The goal is to help them become more comfortable with this kind of physical sharing and intimacy, to learn to relax and enjoy it, and to talk to each other about what feels good and what does not.

Another facet of psychological approaches to treating sexual dysfunction involves *scheduling.* This is, in fact, closely related to sensate focus because the technique of sensate focus requires that people schedule time for sex. Couples need a quiet, relaxed, and private environment in order to engage in pleasurable and satisfying sexual behavior.

A third aspect of sex therapy involves education and cognitive restructuring—changing the way in which people think about sex. In many cases the therapist needs to help the couple correct mistaken beliefs and attitudes about sexual behavior. Examples are the belief that intercourse is the only true form of sex, that foreplay is an adolescent interest that most adults can ignore, and that simultaneous orgasm is the ultimate goal of intercourse. Providing information about sexual behaviors in the general population can often help alleviate people's guilt and anxiety surrounding their own experiences. Some people are relieved to know that they are not the only ones who fantasize about various kinds of sexual experiences, or that the fact that they fantasize about these things does not mean that they are going to be compelled to behave in deviant ways.

The final element of psychological treatment for sexual dysfunction is communication training. This is another technique that was emphasized by Masters and Johnson in their early work with sexually dysfunctional couples. Many different studies have indicated that people with sexual dysfunction often have deficits in communication skills. They find it difficult to talk to their partners about matters involving sex, and they are especially impaired in the ability to tell their partners what kinds of things they find sexually arousing and what kinds of things turn them off. Therefore, sex therapists often employ structured training procedures aimed at improving the ways in which couples talk to each other. Of course, sex therapy techniques must be used with special care when the clients' communication problems are grounded in a cultural tradition that actively discourages discussion of sexual issues.

The outcome results of psychological treatment programs for sexual disorders have generally been considered to be positive (Dutere, Segraves, & Althof, 2007). Early reports from Masters and Johnson's clinic were especially glowing. One summary of their results reported an overall success rate of 85 percent for male patients and 78 percent for female patients. Unfortunately, more recent studies have reported less positive results. Serious questions have been raised about the adequacy of the research methods employed in several outcome studies. Interventions have not been standardized, sample sizes have been relatively small, and long-term follow-up data are often lacking. Therefore, although psychological treatments for sexual dysfunction are frequently successful, empirical support for the efficacy of these procedures is not strong (O'Donohue et al., 1999). Better studies are clearly needed.

Important questions have also been raised about the utility of these procedures for clients in other cultures. Clinics in India, Iran, Japan, Saudi Arabia, and South Africa report that men and women from many different backgrounds seek help for sexual dysfunctions (Osman & Al-Sawaf, 1995; Verma et al., 1998). Culture dictates the ways in which sexual issues may be discussed, and beliefs about sexuality and reproduction influence decisions about acceptable sexual behaviors. These beliefs vary extensively across cultures. For example, people in some Asian cultures believe that a man's health can be damaged through unnecessary loss of semen (Davis & Herdt, 1997). Such concerns may prohibit use of masturbation as a therapeutic exercise. Implicit rules governing communication patterns between partners are also determined by culture. Some societies value and encourage sharp differences in gender roles, with men being expected to make decisions about the timing and type of sexual activity (Quadagno et al., 1998). Therefore, communication training must be tailored to meet the expectations that each couple holds regarding the nature of their relationship. Mental health professionals must give careful consideration to their clients' cultural background when they conduct an assessment and design a treatment program.

Biological Treatments Biological treatments—primarily medications—are also useful in the treatment of sexual dysfunctions. This is especially true for erectile disorder, the most frequent sexual problem for which men seek professional help. Sildenafil citrate (Viagra) was approved by the FDA in 1998 for the treatment of erectile dysfunction and quickly became one of the most popular drugs on the market. Competing pharmaceutical companies soon developed and began vigorously promoting similar drugs known as tadalafil (Cialis) and vardenafil (Levitra). All three drugs are phosphodiesterase-5 (PDE-5)[1] inhibitors that facilitate

"It's a shame there isn't a pill to stimulate conversation."

erection by increasing blood flow to certain areas of the penis. They increase the man's ability to respond to stimuli that he would ordinarily find sexually arousing, but they do not influence overall sexual desire (Pryor, 2002; Rosen & McKenna, 2002).

Double-blind, placebo-controlled studies have evaluated the use of Viagra in men with erectile problems associated with various conditions, including hypertension, diabetes, and coronary artery disease. It is effective, increasing the number of erections for approximately two-thirds of men with severe erectile dysfunction (Fink et al., 2002). Men taking Viagra were also more likely than those on placebo to accomplish successful vaginal penetration during intercourse (46 percent compared to 8 percent). Unfortunately, some men experience negative side effects, such as headache, facial flushing, nasal congestion, and altered vision. Perhaps most important, Viagra can lead to sudden drops in blood pressure if taken with various forms of medication known as "nitrates," which are used in the treatment of heart disease. Some deaths were reported after Viagra was introduced because of this misuse. The research evidence indicates that Viagra and other PDE-5 inhibitors should be used in combination with psychological treatments for sexual dysfunction (see Critical Thinking Matters).

Pharmaceutical companies are also developing and evaluating medications that might be used to treat sexual dysfunction in women. One product, known as Intrinsa, is a patch that delivers testosterone through the skin and could serve to increase sexual desire, especially in postmenopausal women and those who have had their ovaries removed. The FDA decided in 2004 to delay approval for Intrinsa because it did not have enough information about its long-term safety, particularly regarding increased risk for cancer and cardiovascular disease. The use of

---

[1]PDE-5 is an enzyme that metabolizes nitric oxide, which triggers sexual arousal.

CRITICAL THINKING MATTERS

Does Medication Cure Sexual Dysfunction?

Can you remember watching a sporting event on television without seeing an advertisement for Cialis or Levitra? Attractive men and women cuddle and smile as they talk enthusiastically about the satisfaction that can be achieved with pharmacologically induced *strong, lasting erections*. It's difficult to imagine a new form of treatment for a psychological disorder that has been promoted more aggressively, or achieved a more dramatic impact on public awareness, than the PDE-5 inhibitors. In a few short years, they have generated a market that is estimated to approach $2 billion per year. They've become very popular, but do these pills offer a quick fix for all people suffering from arousal disorders?

Viagra and similar medications are clearly an important option for men with erectile problems. Countless men and their partners are grateful for their beneficial effects. Unfortunately, in many other cases, they are not a complete solution to sexual dysfunction in the absence of additional treatment. Couples that have experienced sexual problems have often struggled with a number of difficult issues for several years. Increasing the man's capacity for erection will address only one part of the problem. As one expert puts it, "Viagra can increase blood flow to the penis, but it doesn't create intimacy, love, or desire" (Morgentaler, 2003). Most experts recommend a treatment approach that combines the use of medication with cognitive behavior therapy. Therapists need to work with couples to improve intimacy and communication while also helping them to overcome frustrations and anxiety that have accumulated over years (McCarthy, 2004; Rosen, 2000).

Is an erect penis the most important consideration in a satisfying sexual relationship? What other ingredients are necessary?

A related product for women, which the media have nicknamed the *female Viagra,* may be available soon. Intrinsa, a patch that delivers testosterone through the skin, is being developed to address low desire, the most frequent sexual problem reported by women (see Figure 12–3). Small doses of testosterone can increase sexual desire in some women who have had their ovaries removed, but it seems unlikely that they will be effective with women who have lost interest in sex because of relationship difficulties or other motivational and cognitive factors. Problems with fatigue, scheduling difficulties, anxiety, and low self-esteem are all issues that don't go away simply because testosterone levels increase. Medication may facilitate some of the biological functions that are necessary prerequisites for healthy sexual behaviors, but it cannot guarantee that people will find their partners appealing or that sex will be pleasurable. Consumers and medical professionals all need to think critically about the complex factors that contribute to sexual dysfunction. We should not expect to find a magic bullet that will cure them all at once.

testosterone could also lead to other side effects, such as facial hair growth, deepening of the voice, and the development of other masculine features in women.

Another less frequently used procedure for the treatment of erectile dysfunction involves surgically inserting a penile implant (or prosthesis), which can be used to make the penis rigid during intercourse (Melman & Tiefer, 1992; Schwartz et al., 2000). Several devices have been used. One option is a semirigid silicone rod that the man can bend into position for intercourse. Another device is hydraulic and can be inflated for the purpose of sexual activity. The man squeezes a small pump, which forces fluid into the inflatable cylinder and produces an erection. The inflatable device is preferred by partners, but it is also more expensive and can lead to more frequent postsurgical complications, such as infection.

The various forms of treatment that are available for the treatment of sexual dysfunction are certainly promising. They offer several constructive options for people who are experiencing distress as a consequence of problems in sexual desire or performance. That is the good news with regard to sexual disorders. The bad news is concerned with another type of sexual disorder, which are known collectively as the paraphilias. They are less well understood, in comparison to the sexual dysfunctions, and they are also more difficult to treat. The next section of this chapter reviews the current state of our knowledge regarding these difficult problems.

PARAPHILIAS

For some people, sexual arousal is strongly associated with unusual things and situations, such as inanimate objects, sexual contact with children, exhibiting their genitals to strangers, or inflicting pain on another person. The person is preoccupied with or consumed by these interests and activities. These conditions are known as **paraphilias.** Literally translated, paraphilia means "love" (*philia*) "beyond the usual" (*para*). This term refers to conditions that were formerly called perversions or sexual deviations. According to DSM-IV-TR, the central features of all paraphilias are persistent sexual urges and fantasies that are associated with (1) nonhuman objects, (2) suffering or humiliation of oneself or one's partner, or (3) children or other nonconsenting persons. In the following pages we summarize a few of the most common types of paraphilias, and we consider some of the factors that might influence the development of unusual sexual preferences.

Symptoms

One hundred years ago, many psychiatrists considered any type of sexual behavior other than heterosexual intercourse to be pathological. Contemporary researchers and clinicians have expanded the boundaries of normal behavior to include a much broader range of sexual behavior. A large proportion of men and women engage in sexual fantasies and mutually consenting behaviors such as oral sex. These experiences enhance their relationships without causing problems (Soble, 2004).

Problems with sexual appetites arise when a pattern develops involving a long-standing, unusual erotic preoccupation that is highly arousing, coupled with a pressure to act on the erotic fantasy. DSM-IV-TR requires that the erotic preoccupation must have lasted at least 6 months before the person would meet diagnostic criteria for a paraphilia. Furthermore, the diagnosis of paraphilia is made only if the person's paraphilic urges lead to clinically significant distress or impairment. The person would be considered to be impaired if the urges have become compulsory, if they produce sexual dysfunction, if they require the participation of nonconsenting persons, if they lead to legal problems, or if they interfere with social relationships. For several specific types of paraphilias, the person would qualify for a diagnosis if he acted on the urge (Hilliard & Spitzer, 2002). These include pedophilia, exhibitionism, voyeurism, and frotteurism (see descriptions in the following pages). For sexual sadism, acting on the urge would qualify the person for a diagnosis only if the partner had not consented to the activity. Acting on the other forms of paraphilic urges (masochism, fetishism, and transvestic fetishism) would not be sufficient for a diagnosis unless the urges of fantasies lead to significant personal distress or interfere with the person's ability to function.

It is actually somewhat misleading, or imprecise, to say that paraphilias are defined solely in terms of reactions to unusual stimuli. The central problem is that sexual arousal is dependent on images that are detached from reciprocal, loving relationships with another adult (Levine, Risen, & Althof, 1990). Themes of aggression, violence, and hostility are common in paraphilic fantasies, as are impulses involving strangers or unwilling partners. Rather than focusing on whether the stimuli are common or uncommon, some experts place principal emphasis on the lack of human intimacy that is associated with many forms of paraphilias (Marshall et al., 1996; Moser, 2001).

Compulsion and lack of flexibility are also important features of paraphilic behaviors. Paraphilias may take up a lot of time and consume much of the person's energy. In that sense, they are similar to the addictions. People with paraphilic disorders are not simply aroused by unusual images or fantasies. They feel *compelled* to engage in certain acts that may be personally degrading or harmful to others, in spite of the fact that these actions are often repulsive to others and are sometimes illegal. The following case describes some of the central features of paraphilias.

> *How have changing attitudes toward sexuality influenced the definition of paraphilias?*

BRIEF CASE **STUDY**
Paraphilia

For the past 40 years, Jon has masturbated to images of barely clad women violently wrestling each other. Periodically throughout his marriage, he has tried to involve his wife in wrestling matches with her friends and, eventually, with their adolescent daughter. When Jon was drunk, he occasionally embarrassed his wife by trying to pick fights between her and other women. On summer vacations, he sometimes jokingly suggested the women wrestle. During much of his sober life, however, his daydreams of women wrestling were private experiences that preoccupied only him. He amassed a collection of magazines and videotapes depicting women wrestling, to which he would resort when driven by the need for excitement.

Jon presented for help with his inability to maintain his erection with his wife for intercourse. With the exception of procreational sex, he was not able to consummate his long marriage. He was able to (become) erect if his wife described herself wrestling other women while he stimulated his penis in front of her, but he always lost his erection when intercourse was attempted (Levine, Risen, & Althof, 1990).

TABLE 12–2 Other Types of Paraphilias	
NAME	**FOCUS OF SEXUAL URGES AND FANTASIES**
Telephone scatologia	Obscene phone calls
Necrophilia	Corpses
Partialism	One specific part of the body
Zoophilia	Animals
Coprophilia	Feces
Klismaphilia	Enemas
Urophilia	Urine
Stigmatophilia	Piercing; marking body; tattoos

This case illustrates the way in which paraphilias can interfere with a person's life, especially relationships with other people. Jon's preoccupation with fantasies of women wrestling led him to say and do things that disrupted his marriage and his friendships with other people. Many people with paraphilias experience sexual dysfunction involving desire, arousal, or orgasm during conventional sexual behavior with a partner. The wives of men with paraphilias frequently protest that their husbands are not interested in their sexual relationship. In fact, the husband may be actively engaged in frequent masturbation to paraphilic fantasies. Cases of this sort present an interesting diagnostic challenge to the clinician, who must distinguish a paraphilia from what might otherwise appear to be low sexual desire.

Diagnosis

Although they are listed as distinct disorders, it might be more useful to think of the paraphilias as one diagnostic category, with the specific

▶ Many men find women's clothing attractive or sexy, but for a man with a fetish, sexual arousal is focused *exclusively* on the object. The partner is largely irrelevant.

forms listed in DSM-IV-TR representing subtypes of this single disorder (Fedoroff, 2003). The primary types of paraphilias described in the following pages are the ones most often seen in clinics that specialize in the treatment of sexual disorders. Not surprisingly, they are also the ones that frequently lead to a person being arrested. Other types of paraphilias are listed in Table 12–2.

Fetishism Anthropologists use the word *fetish* to describe an object that is believed to have magical powers to protect or help its owner. In psychopathology, **fetishism** refers to the association of sexual arousal with nonliving objects. The range of objects that can become associated with sexual arousal is virtually unlimited, but fetishism most often involves women's underwear, shoes and boots, or products made out of rubber or leather (Junginger, 1997; Wiederman, 2003). The person may go to great lengths, including burglary, to obtain certain kinds of fetish objects.

People who fit the description of fetishism typically masturbate while holding, rubbing, or smelling the fetish object. Particular sensory qualities of the object—texture, visual appearance, and smell—can be very important in determining whether or not the person finds it arousing. In addition to holding or rubbing the object, the person may wear, or ask his sexual partner to wear, the object during sexual activity. The person may be unable to become sexually aroused in the absence of the fetish object.

Transvestic Fetishism A *transvestite* is a person who dresses in the clothing of the other gender. In DSM-IV-TR, **transvestic fetishism** is defined as cross-dressing for the purpose of sexual arousal. It has been described primarily among heterosexual men and should not be confused with the behavior of some gay men known as *drag queens* (for whom cross-dressing has a very different purpose and meaning). DSM-IV-TR restricts the definition to heterosexual men, but research evidence suggests that a small proportion of transvestites are bisexual, homosexual, or not sexually active with another person (Bullough & Bullough, 1997).

People who engage in transvestic fetishism usually keep a collection of female clothes that are used to cross-dress. Some wear only a single article of women's clothing, such as female underwear, covered by male clothing. Others dress completely as women, including makeup, jewelry, and accessories. Cross-dressing may be done in public or only in private. The person masturbates while he is cross-dressed, often imagining himself to be a male as well as the female object of his own sexual fantasy. Aside from their interest in cross-dressing, men with transvestic fetishism are unremarkably masculine in their interests, occupations, and other behaviors. Most of these men get married and have children (Schott, 1995).

For some men, transvestism may eventually lead to feelings of dissatisfaction with being male (Zucker & Blanchard, 1997). They may eventually want to live permanently as women. These men, who develop persistent discomfort with their gender role or identity, would be assigned a subtype diagnosis of *transvestic fetishism with gender dysphoria.*

Sexual Masochism People who become sexually aroused when they are subjected to pain or embarrassment are called masochists. DSM-IV-TR defines **sexual masochism** as recurrent, intense sexually arousing fantasies, urges, or impulses involving being humiliated, beaten, bound, or otherwise made to suffer. People may act on these impulses by themselves or with a partner. In some large cities, clubs cater to the sexual interests of masochistic men and women, who pay people to punish and abuse them (Ernulf & Innala, 1995).

The person may become aroused by being bound, blindfolded, spanked, pinched, whipped, verbally abused, forced to crawl and bark like a dog, or in some other way made to experience pain or feelings of shame and disgrace. One relatively common masochistic fantasy takes the form of being forced to display one's naked body to other people. Masochists desire certain types of pain (which are carefully controlled to remain within specified limits, usually unpleasant but not agonizing), but they also go to great lengths to avoid injury during their contrived, often ritualized experiences (Stoller, 1991). They do not enjoy, and are not immune to, painful experiences that lie outside these limited areas of their lives.

The following first-person account was written by Daphne Merkin (1996), an accomplished writer whose fascinating and controversial essay on masochism appeared in *The New Yorker.*

▲ Some gay men who dress in women's clothes refer to themselves as "drag queens." This is different from transvestic fetishism, which applies only to heterosexual men whose cross-dressing is associated with intense, sexually arousing fantasies or urges.

BRIEF CASE **STUDY**
Masochism

The fact is that I cannot remember a time when I didn't think about being spanked as a sexually gratifying act, didn't fantasize about being reduced to a craven object of desire by a firm male hand. Depending on my mood, these daydreams were marked by an atmosphere of greater or lesser ravishment, but all of them featured similar ingredients. Most important among them was a heightened—and deeply pleasurable—sense of exposure, brought about by the fact that enormous attention was being paid to my bottom, and by the fact that there was an aspect of helpless display attached to this particular body part. This scenario, in which my normally alert self was reduced to a condition of wordless compliance via a specific ritual of chastisement, exerted a grip that was the more strong because I felt it to be so at odds with the intellectually weighty, morally upright part of me. (p. 99)

These fantasies and urges made Merkin feel uncomfortable, and she kept them to herself for many years. Being cautious and somewhat inhibited—certainly not prone to illicit sexual adventures—she worried about the boundaries of her masochistic desires. If she ever acted on them, where would she stop? And how would her partner respond? After many years of privately harboring masochistic sexual fantasies, Merkin finally described her fascination with spanking to a man whom she had been dating for several months. She was in her late twenties at the time, and eventually married this man. The following paragraph describes what happened after her admission:

He appeared delighted at the prospect of implementing my wishes, and so it was that I found myself in the position I had been dreaming of for years: thrust over a man's knee, being soundly spanked for some

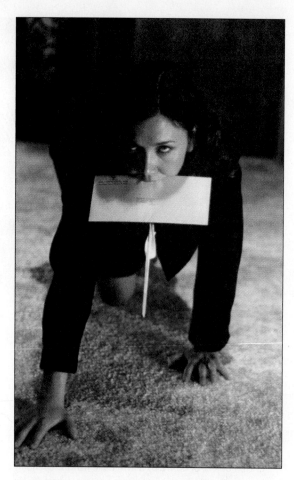

▶ In the movie *Secretary*, Maggie Gyllenhall plays a submissive young woman who develops a sadomasochistic sexual relationship with her boss.

concocted misdeed. The sheer tactile stimulation of it—the chastening sting—would have been enough to arouse me, but there was also, at last, the heady sense of emotional release: I was and was not a child; was and was not being reduced; was and was not being forced into letting go; was and was not the one in control. I had fantasized about this event for so long that in the back of my mind there had always lurked the fear that its gratification would prove disappointing. I needn't have worried; the reality of spanking, at least initially, was as good as the dream. (pp. 112–113)

Merkin tired of the spankings after she gave birth to her daughter, but the fantasies and urges returned several years later, after she had been separated from her husband. She eventually became involved in a relationship with another man that she described as "a fairly conventional romance that included some light (sadism and masochism)." After their mutual interests and consenting activities had escalated, Merkin found the relationship disturbing:

It occurred to me that underneath my own limited participation in this world I felt enormous resentment; I was following the steps in a dance I couldn't control. Spanking and its accoutrements may have helped to subdue my simmering rage toward men—as well as theirs toward me—but it also demonstrated how far I was from healthy intimacy, from the real give-and-take that makes a relationship viable. (p. 114)

This case illustrates the compelling and often contradictory nature of the fantasies that are associated with paraphilias. This successful and independent woman, who did not believe in using corporal punishment with her own daughter, found great pleasure associated with fantasies of being spanked by a man. Merkin would not have qualified for a diagnosis of sexual masochism, even after she had acted on her fantasies, unless she experienced subjective distress or social impairment as a result.

Like Daphne Merkin, many people who engage in masochistic sexual practices are highly educated and occupationally successful (Levitt, Moser, & Jamison, 1994). Masochists tend to be disproportionately represented among the privileged groups in society. This pattern leads to the suggestion that masochism may be motivated by an attempt to escape temporarily from the otherwise constant burden of maintaining personal control and pursuing self-esteem (Baumeister & Butler, 1997).

Sexual Sadism Someone who derives pleasure by inflicting physical or mental pain on other people is called a *sadist*. The term is based on the writings of the Marquis de Sade, whose novels describe the use of torture and cruelty for erotic purposes. DSM-IV-TR defines **sexual sadism** in terms of intense, sexually arousing fantasies, urges, or behaviors that involve the psychological or physical suffering of a victim. Sadistic fantasies often involve asserting dominance over the victim; the experience of power and control may be as important as inflicting pain (Hucker, 1997). Some people engage in sadistic sexual rituals with a consenting partner (who may be a sexual masochist) who willingly suffers pain or humiliation. Others act on sadistic sexual urges with nonconsenting partners. In some cases, the severity of the sadistic behaviors escalates over time.

Exhibitionism DSM-IV-TR defines **exhibitionism** in terms of the following criteria: "1. Over a period of at least 6 months, recurrent, intense sexually arousing fantasies, sexual urges, or behaviors involving exposure of one's genitals to an unsuspecting stranger. 2. The person has acted on these sexual urges, or the sexual urges or fantasies cause marked distress or interpersonal difficulty" (p. 569). This behavior is also known as *indecent exposure*. Many different patterns of behavior fit into this category. About half of these men have erections while exposing themselves, and some masturbate at the time. The others usually masturbate shortly after the experience while fantasizing about the victim's reaction. Their intent usually involves a desire to shock the observer, but sometimes they harbor fantasies that the involuntary observer will become sexually aroused. They rarely attempt to touch or otherwise molest their victims, who are usually women or children (Maletzky, 1997; Murphy, 1997).

Exhibitionism is almost exclusively a male disorder. Most exhibitionists begin to expose themselves when they are teenagers or in their early twenties. As adults, most are either married or living with a sexual partner. Exhibitionism is seldom an isolated behavior; men who engage in this type of behavior tend to do it frequently (Abel & Osborn, 1992).

Voyeurism The focus of sexual arousal in **voyeurism** is the act of observing an unsuspecting person, usually a stranger, who is naked, in the process of disrobing, or engaging in sexual activity (Metzl, 2004). Many people, especially men, are sexually aroused by the sight of people who are partially clad or naked. Voyeurs are not aroused by watching people who know that they are being observed. The process of looking ("peeping") is arousing in its own right. The person might fantasize about having a sexual relationship with the people who are being observed, but direct contact is seldom sought. In fact, the secret nature of the observation and the risk of discovery may contribute in an important way to the arousing nature of the situation. The voyeur reaches orgasm by masturbating during observation or later while remembering what he saw. Most keep their distance from the victim and are not dangerous, but there are exceptions to this rule (King, 1996).

Frotteurism In **frotteurism,** a person who is fully clothed becomes sexually aroused by touching or rubbing his genitals against other, nonconsenting people. The frotteur usually chooses crowded places, such as sidewalks and public transportation, so that he can easily escape arrest. He either rubs his genitals against the victim's thighs and buttocks or fondles her genitalia or breasts (Horley, 2001; Krueger & Kaplan, 1997).

Like exhibitionism, frotteurism is a high-frequency form of paraphilia; interviews with

"Will he know what this is in reference to?"

people being treated for frotteurism indicate that they may engage in hundreds of individual paraphilic acts (Abel et al., 1987). People who engage in frotteurism seek to escape as quickly as possible after touching or rubbing against the other person. They do not want further sexual contact.

Pedophilia People who persistently engage in sexual activities with children exhibit what is undoubtedly the most alarming and objectionable form of paraphilic behavior: pedophilia. Every year, more than 100,000 children in the United States are referred to child protective services because of suspected child abuse (see Chapter 18). The effects of child abuse on victims have been the subject of intense debate in recent years.

▼ To protect women from frotteurs, some railway companies in Japan set aside special women-only cars during peak hours and late at night. This sign in a Tokyo subway station says, "Beware of men who fondle women on crowded trains."

Some victims later engage in excessive and risky sexual activities that lead to additional problems (Browning & Laumann, 1997). One controversial review concluded that negative consequences are neither pervasive nor typically intense (Rind, Tromovitch, & Bauserman, 1998). We must be cautious, however, about accepting the null hypothesis (see Research Methods in Chapter 1). Failure to detect significant differences between victims of abuse and other people may indicate that investigators have not examined the appropriate dependent measures. Harmful consequences of sexual abuse may take many forms, including the disruption of future relationships and discomfort with sexual activity (Emery & Laumann-Billings, 1998). Other forms of mental disorder, such as PTSD and eating disorders, can also be the product of prior sexual abuse (see Chapters 7 and 10).

Pedophilia entails recurrent, intense, sexually arousing fantasies, sexual urges, or behaviors involving sexual activity with a prepubescent child (generally age 13 years or younger). In order to qualify for a diagnosis of pedophilia in DSM-IV-TR, the person must be at least 16 years of age and at least 5 years older than the child. The terms *pedophile* and *child molester* are sometimes used interchangeably, but this practice confuses legal definitions with psychopathology. A child molester is a person who has committed a sexual offense against a child victim. Therefore the term depends on legal definitions of "sexual offense" and "child victim," which can vary from one state or country to another. In many locations, a child might be anyone under the age of consent, even if that person has reached puberty. All child molesters are not pedophiles. Furthermore, some pedophiles may not have molested children, because the diagnosis can be made on the basis of recurrent fantasies in the absence of actual behavior (Barbaree & Seto, 1997).

Pedophilia includes a great variety of behaviors and sexual preferences (Cohen & Galynker, 2002; Fagan et al., 2002). Some pedophiles are attracted only to children, whereas others are sometimes attracted to adults. Most pedophiles are heterosexual, and the victims of pedophilia are more often girls than boys. Some offenders are attracted to both girls and boys. Sexual contact with children typically involves caressing and genital fondling. Vaginal, oral, and anal penetration are less common, and physical vio-

lence is relatively rare. In many cases, the child willingly and naively complies with the adult's intentions. In most cases, the child knows the person who molests him or her. More than half of all offenses occur in the home of either the child or the offender.

Incestuous relationships, in which the pedophile molests his own children, should perhaps be distinguished from those in which the offender is only casually acquainted with the victim. **Incest** refers to sexual activity between close blood relatives, such as father–daughter, mother–son, or between siblings. The definition may also be expanded to include stepchildren and their stepparents in reconstituted families. Most reported cases of incest involve fathers and stepfathers sexually abusing daughters and stepdaughters (Cole, 1992).

Many incest perpetrators would not be considered pedophiles, either because their victims are postpubescent adolescents or because they are also young themselves (such as male adolescents molesting their younger sisters). Perhaps as many as half of the men who commit incest have also engaged in sexual activity with children outside their own families (Abel & Osborn, 1992). This subgroup of pedophilic incest perpetrators may be the most harmful and the most difficult to treat. Their personality style is typically passive and dependent. They are unable to empathize with the plight of their victims, perhaps in part because they were absent or uninvolved in early child-care responsibilities (Williams & Finkelhor, 1990).

Rape and Sexual Assault The legal definition of **rape** includes "acts involving nonconsensual sexual penetration obtained by physical force, by threat of bodily harm, or when the victim is incapable of giving consent by virtue of mental illness, mental retardation, or intoxication" (Goodman, Koss, & Russo, 1993). One conservative estimate of rape prevalence based on a national survey indicated that 14 percent of adult women had been raped (National Victims Center, 1992). The actual rate is probably higher, perhaps in the vicinity of 20 percent (Watts & Zimmerman, 2002). The impact of sexual assault on the victim is described in Chapter 7.

The frequency of coercive sex was studied as part of the NHSLS (Laumann et al., 1994). The 3,500 participants were asked whether they had ever been forced to do something sexually that they did not want to do. The question was focused broadly and did not necessarily focus only on acts involving penetration or threats of violence. Slightly more than one out of every five women in the sample reported that they had been forced by a man to engage in some kind of sexual activity against their will. Among those women who had experienced forced sex, 30 percent said that they had been forced sexually by more than one person.

Some rapes are committed by strangers, but many others—known as *acquaintance rapes*—are committed by men who know their victims. Most female victims know the person who raped them (Wiehe & Richards, 1995). Consider, for example, evidence from women in the NHSLS who had been victims of forced sex. Their relationship to the people who forced them to have sex is illustrated in Figure 12–4. Most reported that the person was either someone with whom they were in love or their spouse. Only 4 percent were forced to do something sexual by a stranger.

Rapes are committed by many different kinds of people for many different reasons (Bachar & Koss, 2001). The feminist perspective on rape emphasizes male aggression and violence. The traditional clinical perspective has been concerned with sexual deviance. The authors of DSM-IV-TR considered including rape as a type of paraphilia. This proposal was rejected, primarily because it might imply that rape is *always* motivated by sexual arousal, and it is not. Nevertheless, the behavior of some rapists does include essential features of paraphilias: recurrent, intense sexually arousing fantasies and urges that involve the suffering of nonconsenting persons. Half the convicted rapists in one study reported a history of other types of paraphilia: pedophilia (24 percent), exhibitionism (19 percent), and voyeurism (17 percent; Abel & Gouleau, 1990).

Current efforts to classify sexual offenders attempt to distinguish between those for whom deviant sexual arousal contributes to the act and those whose behavior is motivated primarily by anger or violent impulses. Raymond Knight, a psychologist at Brandeis University, and his colleagues have developed a classification system for convicted rapists who were imprisoned at an institution for sexually dangerous persons (Knight & Guay, 2006). They identified four different types of rapists. Two categories include men whose motivation for sexual assault is primarily sexual in nature. *Sadistic rapists* exhibit

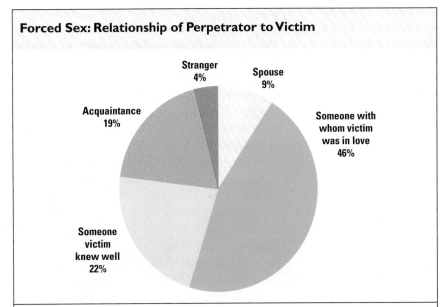

Forced Sex: Relationship of Perpetrator to Victim

- Stranger 4%
- Spouse 9%
- Acquaintance 19%
- Someone with whom victim was in love 46%
- Someone victim knew well 22%

FIGURE 12–4 As this chart shows, most NHSLS respondents who were forced into sexual activity knew the person who coerced them.

Source: E. O Laumann, J. H. Gagnon, R.T. Michael, and S. Michaels, 1994, *The Social Organization of Sexuality: Sexual Practices in the United States,* Chicago: University of Chicago Press, p. 338. Copyright © 1994. Reprinted by permission of The University of Chicago Press.

features that are close to the DSM-IV-TR definition of a paraphilia. Their behavior is determined by a combination of sexual and aggressive impulses. The *nonsadistic* category also includes men who are preoccupied with sexual fantasies, but these fantasies are not blended with images of violence and aggression. The sexual aggression of these men may result, in part, from serious deficits in the ability to process social cues, such as the intentions of women.

Does deviant sexual arousal ever play a role in sexual assaults?

The other two categories describe men whose primary motivation for rape is not sexual. *Vindictive* rapists seem intent on violence directed exclusively toward women. Their aggression is not erotically motivated, as with sadistic rapists. *Opportunistic* rapists are men with an extensive history of impulsive behavior in many kinds of settings and who might be considered psychopaths (see Chapter 9). Their sexual behavior is governed largely by immediate environmental cues. They will use whatever force is necessary to ensure compliance, but they express anger only in response to the victim's resistance. This research program helps to confirm the impression that sex offenders are, in fact, an extremely heterogeneous group (McCabe & Wauchope, 2005).

Frequency

There is very little evidence regarding the frequency of various types of unconventional sexual behavior. This is especially true for victimless or noncoercive forms of paraphilia, such as fetishism, transvestic fetishism, and sexual masochism, because most of these people seldom seek treatment or come to the attention of law enforcement officials. Furthermore, the fact that these forms of behavior are considered deviant or perverse makes it unlikely that people who engage in them will readily divulge their secret urges and fantasies.

With the exception of sexual masochism, paraphilias are almost always male behaviors. Some 95 percent of the people who seek treatment for paraphilic disorders are men (Kaplan, 1989; Levine, Risen, & Althof, 1990). Paraphilias are seldom isolated phenomena. People who exhibit one type of paraphilia often exhibit others (Marshall, 2007). Gosselin and Wilson (1980) surveyed men who belonged to private clubs that cater to fetishists, sadomasochists, and transvestites, and they found that the members of different clubs often shared the same interests. This overlap is illustrated in Figure 12–5. This pattern has been called *crossing* of paraphilic behaviors.

Another study also reported a considerable amount of crossover among paraphilias. The investigators categorized 500 sexual offenders on the basis of many different features: whether or not they touched their victims, whether their victims were relatives, whether their victims were male or female, and whether their victims were children or adults. Of the offenders who had carried out paraphilic acts against male victims, 63 percent had previously engaged in similar behaviors against female victims; 49 percent of those who had committed acts against adults had previously committed acts against children; and 64 percent of those who committed acts that did not involve touching their victims had previously committed acts that involved touching (Abel & Osborn, 1992).

Causes

The high rate of overlap among paraphilias indicates that the etiology of these behaviors might be most appropriately viewed in terms of common factors rather than in terms of distinct pathways that lead exclusively to one form of paraphilia or another. Those experiences and conditions that predispose an individual to one form of paraphilia are apparently also likely to lead to another. In the following pages we review a number of proposals regarding the etiology of paraphilias. Some of these have been associated with specific types of paraphilia. For the most part, however, they are concerned more generally with many forms of paraphilias.

The epidemiological evidence suggests another important pattern that must be explained by any theory of paraphilias: They are more prevalent among men than among women. The exception to this rule seems to be masochism, which may be equally common in both genders. We might conclude, therefore, that the development of masochism may be governed by different factors than those that account for the etiology of other types of paraphilias.

Biological Factors Most of the research regarding the role of biological factors in the etiology of paraphilias has focused on the endocrine system (see Figure 2–4 on page 44), the collection of glands that regulate sexual responses through the release of hormones (Collaer & Hines, 1995). Some studies of convicted sexually violent offenders have found evidence of elevated levels of testosterone. These reports must be viewed with some skepticism, however, for two reasons. First, the participants in these studies are invariably convicted sexual offenders. Thus, it is not clear that the findings can be generalized to

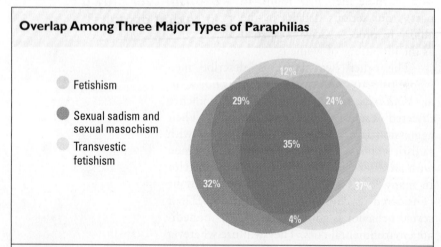

Overlap Among Three Major Types of Paraphilias

● Fetishism

● Sexual sadism and sexual masochism

● Transvestic fetishism

12%
29%   24%
35%
32%   37%
4%

FIGURE 12–5 The extent of overlap in the interests of three major types of paraphilias. Note that only 37 percent of men who practice fetishistic transvestism, 32 percent of men who practice sexual sadism and masochism, and 12 percent of those who practice fetishism exhibited those interests exclusively.

Source: G. D. Wilson, 1987, "An Ethological Approach to Sexual Deviation." In G. D. Wilson, ed., *Variant Sexuality: Research and Theory*, p. 92. London: Croom Helm. Copyright © 1987. Reprinted by permission of The Johns Hopkins University Press.

all people with paraphilias. Second, there is a high rate of alcoholism and drug abuse among men convicted of sexual crimes. For that reason, we do not know whether the biological abnormalities observed in these men are causes of their deviant sexual behavior or consequences of prolonged substance abuse (Langevin, 1992).

Neurological abnormalities may also be involved in the development of paraphilias. Structures located in the temporal lobes of the brain, especially the amygdala and the hippocampus, appear to play an important role in the control of both aggression and sexual behavior. These limbic structures, in conjunction with the hypothalamus, form a circuit that regulates biologically significant behaviors that sometimes are whimsically called the four F's—feeding, fighting, fleeing, and (sexual behavior; Valenstein, 1973). In 1937, two scientists reported that after extensive bilateral damage to their temporal lobes, rhesus monkeys showed a dramatic increase in sexual activity, as well as a number of related behavioral and perceptual abnormalities. The monkeys apparently tried to copulate with a variety of inappropriate partners, including the investigators. This pattern has subsequently been called the Kluver–Bucy syndrome, named after the scientists who made the original observation.

Inspired by the suggestion that damage to the temporal lobe can lead to unusual patterns of sexual behavior, clinical scientists have studied a number of neurological and neuropsychological factors in convicted sex offenders. Some reports indicate that men with pedophilia and exhibitionism show subtle forms of left temporal lobe dysfunction, as evidenced by abnormal patterns of electrophysiological response and impaired performance on neuropsychological tests (Bradford, 2001; Murphy, 1997).

Some men with fetishism exhibit diffuse signs of neurological impairment, but these are also focused predominantly in the left temporal lobe. Similar findings have been reported for sexually sadistic criminals (Gratzer & Bradford, 1995). Before these results are interpreted too broadly, however, it should also be noted that most people who suffer from temporal lobe epilepsy do not engage in paraphilic behaviors. In fact, the most frequent result of temporal lobe epilepsy is a reduction in sexual activity (Murphy, 1997). It seems reasonable to conclude that some cases of paraphilia are caused, at least in part, by endocrine and neurological abnormalities, but the relations among these factors are not entirely clear.

Social Factors Some types of paraphilias seem to be distortions of the normal mating process when viewed in a broad, evolutionary context. For male primates, sexual behavior involves a sequence of steps: location and appraisal of potential partners; exchange of signals in which partners communicate mutual interest; and tactile interactions that set the stage for sexual intercourse. Voyeurism, exhibitionism, and frotteurism may represent aberrant versions of these social processes. Therefore, the paraphilias have been described as "courtship disorders" (Freund & Blanchard, 1993; Freund & Seto, 1998). Something has apparently gone wrong, disrupting whatever mechanisms facilitate the identification of a sexual partner and govern behaviors used to attract a partner.

Why are paraphilias sometimes called "courtship disorders"?

If people with paraphilias have somehow failed to learn more adaptive forms of courtship behavior, what sort of childhood experiences might have produced such unexpected results? Several background factors have been observed repeatedly among people who engage in atypical sexual behaviors (Seto & Barbaree, 2000; Wincze, 1989). These include the following:

- Early crossing of normative sexual boundaries through a direct experience (for example, sexual abuse by an adult) or an indirect experience (hearing about a father's atypical sexual behavior)
- Lack of a consistent parental environment in which normative sexual behavior and values were modeled
- Lack of self-esteem
- Lack of confidence and ability in social interactions
- Ignorance and poor understanding of human sexuality

All these factors may increase the probability that a person might experiment with unusual types of sexual stimulation or employ maladaptive sexual behaviors.

Although the most notable feature of paraphilias is sexual arousal, ultimately the paraphilias are problems in social relationships. Interpersonal skills may, therefore, play as important a role as sexual arousal. William Marshall, a psychologist at Queen's University in Canada, has argued that the core feature of unusual sexual behavior is a failure to achieve intimacy in relationships with other adults (Marshall, 1989; Seidman et al.,

1994). According to this perspective, people with paraphilias are lonely, insecure, and isolated and have significant deficits in social skills. Offensive sexual behaviors, such as those observed in pedophilia, are maladaptive attempts to achieve intimacy through sex. These efforts are invariably unsuccessful and self-defeating in the sense that they serve to isolate the person further from the rest of the community. Paradoxically, the pattern may become deeply ingrained because it results in the momentary pleasure associated with orgasm and because it offers the illusory hope of eventually achieving intimacy with another person.

Psychological Factors John Money (1921–2006), a psychologist at Johns Hopkins University, described the development of paraphilias in somewhat different terms, using a geographic metaphor that he calls a *lovemap* (Money, 1984). A lovemap is a mental picture representing a person's ideal sexual relationship. It might also be viewed as the software that encodes his or her sexual fantasies and preferred sexual practices. These "programs" are written early in life, and they are quite persistent. Children learn their lovemaps during sexual play, by imitation of their parents and other adults, and through messages that they digest from the popular media. According to Money, when optimal conditions prevail, the child develops a lovemap that includes intercourse as a preferred form of sexual expression. The child learns that love—romantic attachment to another adult—and lust—erotic attraction—can be directed toward the same person.

The lovemap can be distorted, according to Money's metaphor, if the child learns that romantic attachment and sexual desire are incompatible—that these feelings cannot be directed toward the same person. The inability to integrate these aspects of the lovemap lies at the heart of Money's explanation of paraphilias. One solution to this dilemma would be to avoid or deny sexual expression altogether. That might explain the development of lack of sexual desire. Sexual impulses are powerful, however, and they are not easily denied. In some cases, they are rerouted rather than being shut off completely. Various types of paraphilias represent alternative strategies through which the person finds it possible to express sexual feelings outside an intimate, loving relationship with another adult. Exhibitionism, voyeurism, and fetishism, therefore, are partial solutions to the perceived incompatibility of love and lust.

The etiological mechanisms that we have considered thus far seem most applicable to paraphilias that are found predominantly among men, such as fetishes, voyeurism, and exhibitionism. A different story may be necessary to explain masochism, the association of sexual arousal with pain and suffering, because this condition is equally common in women and men.

One intriguing clue regarding the origins of masochism was reported by Robert Stoller (1924–1991), a psychoanalyst at UCLA who wrote extensively about unusual erotic behaviors. He spent several months conducting detailed interviews with people who were seriously involved in sadomasochistic behaviors with consenting partners. Those who were most committed to physical sadism and masochism had, as children, experienced traumatic physical disease followed by frightening forms of medical treatment. These people described to Stoller how they had "consciously forced themselves to master what at first, in infancy and childhood, was uncontrollable physical agony and terror by taking the pain and working with it in their heads, eventually via daydreams, altered states of consciousness, or genital masturbation, until it was converted into pain-that-is-pleasure" (Stoller, 1991, p. 25). In other words, a strong positive emotion like sexual arousal can be actively employed to control intolerable physical pain. The unfortunate consequence is the development of a persistent association between pain and arousal.

Treatment

The treatment of paraphilias is different from the treatment of sexual dysfunctions in several ways. Perhaps most important is the fact that most people with paraphilias do not enter treatment voluntarily. They are often referred to a therapist by the criminal justice system after they have been arrested for exposing themselves, peeping through windows, or engaging in sexual behaviors with children. Their motivation to change is, therefore, open to question. Participation in treatment may help them receive reduced sentences or avoid other legal penalties. In many cases, they are being asked to abandon highly reinforcing behaviors in which they have engaged for many years. Their families and other members of society may be much more concerned about change than they are. We mention this issue at the beginning of our discussion because the results of outcome studies in this area are typically less positive than are those concerning the treatment of sexual dysfunctions (McConaghy, 1999b; Prentky et al., 1997).

Aversion Therapy For several decades, the most commonly used form of treatment for paraphilias was aversion therapy. In this procedure, the therapist repeatedly presents the stimulus that elicits inappropriate sexual arousal—such as slides of nude children—in association with an aversive stimulus, such as repulsive smells, electric shock, or chemically induced nausea. Revolting cognitive images are sometimes used instead of tangible aversive stimuli. Whatever the exact procedure, the rationale is to create a new association with the inappropriate stimulus so that the stimulus will no longer elicit sexual arousal. Some studies suggested that aversion therapy produces positive effects (Kilmann et al., 1982). This treatment has more recently fallen into disfavor, however, because the studies that were used to evaluate it suffered from design flaws.

Cognitive Behavioral Treatment Current behavioral treatment programs for paraphilic behaviors reflect a broader view of the etiology of these conditions. There is considerable reason to believe that paraphilias are based on a variety of cognitive and social deficits. Marshall, Eccles, and Barbaree (1991) compared two approaches to the treatment of exhibitionists. One was based on aversion therapy and the other employed cognitive restructuring, social skills training, and stress management procedures. The men who received the second type of treatment were much less likely to return to their deviant forms of sexual behavior than were the men who received aversion therapy. Treatment with aversion therapy was no more effective than was treatment with a placebo. These data suggest that broad-based cognitive and social treatment procedures may ultimately be most useful in the treatment of paraphilias and sexual disorders (Marshall et al., 1996).

Unfortunately, research results regarding the effectiveness of psychological treatment for sexual offenders are discouraging. The only large-scale evaluation of such programs that has employed random assignment to treatment conditions is the California Sex Offender Treatment and Evaluation Project (SOTEP; Marques et al., 1993), which was designed for men convicted of either rape or child molestation. Men selected for this comprehensive treatment program are transferred

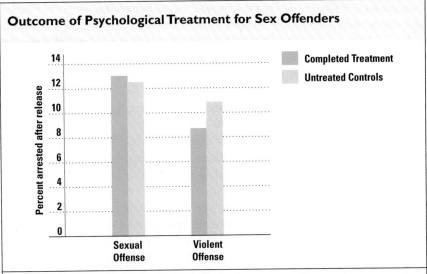

FIGURE 12–6 Repeat arrest rates among male sex offenders (4 years after treatment).

Source: From "How to Answer the Question: Does Sex Offender Treatment Work?" by J. K. Marques, *Journal of Interpersonal Violence, 14* (1999), pp. 437–451. Copyright © 1999. Reprinted by permission of Sage Publications, Inc.

to a special hospital unit, where they remain for several months. They receive education in human sexuality as well as cognitive behavior therapy, including applied relaxation and social skills training and stress and anger management. Treatment also includes a relapse prevention component that is based on procedures used in the treatment of alcoholism (see Chapter 11). Relapse prevention procedures help the men confront personal, social, and sexual difficulties that may increase their risk of relapse after they are released from prison.

The men in the treatment group are compared to those in two control groups. Outcome is measured in several ways, but the most important consideration is being arrested again for similar crimes. Figure 12–6 illustrates some of the results from this study, highlighting the comparison between 138 men who completed the treatment and 184 men who had originally volunteered to participate in the program but were assigned to a no-treatment control group (Marques, 1999). Within 4 years after their release from prison, the percentage of men who were arrested for another sexual offense was essentially identical to that of the men who had been treated and of those in the control group (13 percent). The rate of arrest for subsequent violent offenses was somewhat lower for the treatment group than for the controls, but the difference was not significant.

Results were somewhat more encouraging with men convicted of rape than with those who had molested children. Nevertheless, the data from this study are discouraging. They suggest that a broadly based behavioral program focused on education, social skills, and relapse prevention procedures does not lead to obviously better outcomes than a routine period of incarceration (Maletzky, 2002).

Hormones and Medication Another approach to the treatment of paraphilias involves the use of drugs that reduce levels of testosterone, on the assumption that male hormones control the sexual appetite (Hill et al., 2003). One study reported that treatment of paraphilic men with cyproterone acetate, a drug that blocks the effects of testosterone, produced a significant reduction in some aspects of sexual behavior, especially sexual fantasies (Bradford & Pawlak, 1993). Among men with pedophilia, the study found a greater reduction of sexual fantasies of children than of images of sex between consenting adults. Positive results have also been reported for use of triptorelin, which reduces testosterone secretion by inhibiting pituitary–gonadal function. In an uncontrolled trial, 30 male patients (25 with pedophilia) received monthly injections of triptorelin as well as supportive psychotherapy. All of the patients showed a reduction in deviant fantasies and in the number of incidents of paraphilic behaviors (Rosler & Witztum, 1998). We must remember, however, that the absence of double-blind, placebo-controlled studies leaves the efficacy of these drugs in doubt. One review of this literature concludes that treatment programs should never rely exclusively on the use of medications that reduce levels of testosterone (Prentky, 1997).

Antidepressants and antianxiety drugs have also been used to treat paraphilias. Case studies as well as some small uncontrolled outcome studies indicate that the SSRIs can have beneficial effects for some male patients (Balon,

1998). The process by which these drugs manage to alter sexual behavior is open to question. For example, medication may work directly by decreasing deviant sexual interests without affecting other forms of sexual arousal. On the other hand, SSRIs may work by reducing social anxiety, which interferes with the ability to enjoy an intimate sexual relationship with another adult (Golwyn & Sevlie, 1992). This hypothesis is consistent with the approach taken by Marshall and his colleagues, whose psychological treatment program is aimed at similar types of social deficits.

Legal Issues The U.S. Congress and all 50 states have passed laws that are intended to protect society from people who have been convicted of violent or repeated sexual offenses. These laws fall into two categories. The first includes *community notification laws* (such as "Megan's Law"), which require the distribution of information to the public regarding the presence of child molesters and sexually violent offenders when they are released from prison or placed on parole. These laws are based on two assumptions: (1) Notification will reduce the offender's opportunities to commit further crimes, and (2) citizens are better able to protect themselves and their children if they know that a dangerous person lives in their neighborhood. Critics of community notification laws argue that they violate the former offender's constitutional rights by imposing an additional, unfair penalty after his sentence has been served. These laws are popular, but their impact has not been evaluated. It is not clear that people are actually better able to protect themselves after they have been notified. Furthermore, we do not know whether relapse rates are lower among sexual offenders who live in communities where such laws are strictly enforced (Edwards & Hensley, 2001; Younglove & Vitello, 2003).

The second category includes *sexual predator laws,* which are designed to keep some criminals in custody indefinitely. For example, a Kansas law passed in 1994 and later upheld by the U.S. Supreme Court permits authorities to commit certain sex offenders to a mental hospital after their prison terms are over. Each case is evaluated in a series of steps that end with a civil trial. The person can be hospitalized involuntarily and for an indefinite period of time if the jury decides the person has a "mental abnormality" that will lead

▶ Leroy Hendricks, a pedophile, was committed to a mental hospital after serving repeated prison terms for molesting children. He challenged the Kansas sexual predator law, and the law was upheld by the Supreme Court.

him to commit further sexual offenses. Involuntary civil commitment is an infrequent outcome of this law. When it does occur, however, serious questions are raised about the need to balance public safety against the protection of the offender's constitutional rights (see the discussion of civil commitment in Chapter 18).

GENDER IDENTITY DISORDERS

Our sense of ourselves as being either male or female is known as **gender identity.** Gender identity almost always reflects the child's physical anatomy: Toddlers who possess a penis learn that they are boys, and those with a vagina learn that they are girls. Gender identity is usually fixed by the time a child reaches 2 or 3 years of age (Parker & Aldwin, 1997).

Gender identity must be distinguished from *sex roles,* which are characteristics, behaviors, and skills that are defined within a specific culture as being either masculine or feminine. For example, certain aspects of appearance and behavior are more often associated with men than with women. These are considered to be masculine. Those behaviors and appearances that are more often associated with women are considered feminine. In our own culture, masculine and feminine sex roles have changed considerably in recent years, and they overlap to a degree (Tiefer & Kring, 1995).

Symptoms

Some people are firmly convinced that their anatomy and their gender identity do not match up. In males, this means that they feel strongly that they are women trapped in a man's body. For females, the opposite pattern holds. DSM-IV-TR categorizes this sense of discomfort with one's anatomical sex as **gender identity disorder.** It has also been called *transsexualism* or *gender dysphoria.* People with gender identity disturbances do not literally believe that they are members of the other gender. Rather, they feel that, with the exception of their physical anatomy, they are more like the other gender (Bower, 2001; Lev, 2005).

Most transsexuals report that they were aware of these feelings very early in childhood.

Many report that they dressed in clothing and adopted sex-role behaviors of the other gender during childhood and adolescence. The intensity of the person's discomfort varies from one individual to the next. Invariably it becomes more intense during adolescence, when the person develops secondary sexual characteristics, such as breasts and wider hips for girls, and facial hair, voice changes, and increased muscle mass for boys. These characteristics make it more difficult for a person to pass for the other gender. Many transsexuals become preoccupied with the desire to change their anatomical sex through surgical procedures.

Gender identity disorders should be distinguished from transvestic fetishism, discussed earlier, which is a form of paraphilia in which a heterosexual man dresses in the clothing of the other gender in order to achieve sexual arousal. These are, in fact, very different conditions. Transvestic fetishists do not consider themselves to be women, and transsexuals are not sexually aroused by cross-dressing. They dress as women to feel more comfortable about themselves.

What is the difference between gender identity and sex roles?

◀ Candis Cayne is the first transgender actress to play a regular role on a television series. She was born Brendan McDaniel and made the transition from male to female in 1996.

The relation between gender identity disorder and sexual orientation has been a matter of some controversy. Some clinicians have suggested that transsexuals are homosexuals who claim to be members of the other gender as a way to avoid cultural and moral sanctions that discourage sexual relationships with members of their own sex. This proposal doesn't make sense for two reasons. First, lesbians and gay men are not uncomfortable with their own gender identity. This observation suggests that transsexuals are not simply escaping the stigma of homosexuality. Second, laboratory studies suggest that transsexual and homosexual subjects exhibit different patterns of sexual arousal in response to erotic stimuli (Bradley & Zucker, 1997).

Frequency

Gender identity disorders are rare in comparison to most of the other disorders that we have considered in this book. Male-to-female transsexuals are apparently more common than female-to-male transsexuals, at least based on the numbers of people who seek treatment at clinics. One

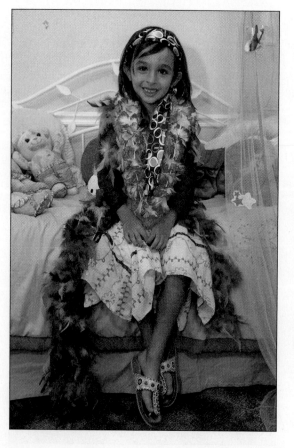

▼ Jazz was a 6-year-old male-to-female transgender child when he and his family appeared on the television news programm "20/20." When Jazz was 2 years old, if his parents praised him as a "good boy," he would correct them, saying he was a good girl.

study estimated the prevalence figures to be 1 person with gender identity disorder for every 12,000 males and 30,000 females (Olsson & Moller, 2003).

Deeply ingrained cross-gender behaviors and attitudes among children occur infrequently in the general population (Zucker, 2005). Mild forms of cross-gender behavior, such as dressing up in the clothes of the other gender or expressing a desire to be a member of the other sex, are relatively common during the preschool years. Extreme forms of these behaviors are relatively rare, however, especially among boys.

Causes

Very little is known about the origins of gender identity in normal men and women, so it is not surprising that the etiology of gender identity disorders is also poorly understood. There is some reason to believe that gender identity is strongly influenced by sex hormones, especially during the prenatal period (LeVay, 1993; Swaab & Gofman, 1995). Much of the research in this area has been done with animals, but an interesting set of data comes from studies of people with a condition that is sometimes called *pseudohermaphroditism*. Individuals with this condition are genetically male, but they are unable to produce a hormone that is responsible for shaping the penis and scrotum in the fetus. Therefore the child is born with external genitalia that are ambiguous in appearance—thus the term *pseudohermaphrodite*.[2]

Many of these children are raised as girls by their families. When they reach puberty, a sudden increase in testosterone leads to dramatic changes in the appearance of the adolescent's genitals. The organ that had previously looked more like a clitoris becomes enlarged and turns into a penis, and testicles descend into a scrotum. The child's voice becomes deeper, muscle mass increases, and the child quickly begins to consider himself to be a man (Imperato-McGinley et al., 1974). The speed and apparent ease with which people with these conditions adopt a masculine gender identity suggest that their brains had been prenatally programmed for this alternative (Hoenig, 1985).

---

[2]A hermaphrodite has both male and female reproductive organs.

Treatment

There are two obvious solutions to problems of gender identity: Change the person's identity to match his or her anatomy, or change the anatomy to match the person's gender identity. Various forms of psychotherapy have been used in an effort to alter gender identity, but the results have been fairly negative.

One alternative to psychological treatment is *sex-reassignment surgery,* in which the person's genitals are changed to match the gender identity (Sohn & Bosinski, 2007). Medical science can construct artificial male and female genitalia. The artificial penis is not capable of becoming erect in response to sexual stimulation, but structural implants can be used to obtain rigidity. These surgical procedures have been used with thousands of patients over the past 50 or 60 years. Clinics that perform these operations employ stringent selection procedures, and patients are typically required to live for several months as a member of the other gender before they can undergo the surgical procedure.

The results of sex-reassignment surgery have generally been positive (Jain & Bradbeer, 2007; Smith, van Goozen, & Cohen-Kettenis, 2001). Interviews with patients who have undergone surgery indicate that most are satisfied with the results, and the vast majority believe that they do not have trouble passing as a member of their newly assumed gender. Psychological tests obtained from patients who have completed surgery indicate reduced levels of anxiety and depression.

GENDER IDENTITY DISORDER

DENISE

"I didn't do it for the sexual purpose. It was just to be someone I always thought of myself as—to be the person I wanted to be."

Watch the video "Gender Identity Disorder: Denise" on MyPsychLab. At what age did Denise become dissatisfied with the sexual parts of her body?

GETTING HELP

Many sexual problems can be traced to the absence of information regarding the nature of sexual attitudes, feelings, preferences, and behaviors. Fortunately, access to these data, as well as public attitudes toward their discussion, has improved dramatically in recent years. The Sexuality Information and Education Council of the United States (SIECUS) collects and disseminates information and promotes education about sexuality. The council's Internet homepage (www.siecus.org) contains an extensive list of resources, including books and links to other Web sites, dealing with topics that range from reproduction, women's health, gender identity, and sexual orientation to sexually transmitted diseases and various types of sexual disorders.

If you have been troubled by problems with sexual arousal, inhibited orgasm, or premature orgasm, behavioral procedures can be helpful. Many of these problems can be treated successfully using procedures that were originally developed by Masters and Johnson. Before you seek professional therapy, you may want to try some self-help techniques that have developed from this treatment tradition. Two exceptionally well-written and practical books describe how these procedures can be used by people who want to enhance the pleasure that they experience in their sexual relationships. They are *Becoming Orgasmic: A Sexual and Personal Growth Program for Women,* by Julia Heiman and Joseph LoPiccolo, and *The New Male Sexuality,* by Bernie Zilbergeld.

If you are still experiencing problems after trying self-help procedures, you should seek treatment with a professional sex therapist. The person's professional background is less important than her or his training for treatment of these specific problems. When you contact potential therapists, ask them whether their treatment methods are similar to those developed by Masters and Johnson. Information regarding counseling, therapy, medical attention, and other sexuality resources for people with sexual problems is available from the Sexual Health Network (www.sexualhealth.com). Concise, readable descriptions of various forms of sexual dysfunction and treatments used to address them can be found at the Sexual Health Info-Center (www.sexhealth.org). These sites can help you increase your knowledge of sexuality, ways in which its expression can be inhibited, and procedures that can be used to improve sexual performance and experience.

Anyone who is interested in additional information regarding gender identity disorder will find help in a book called *True Selves: Understanding Transsexualism—for Families, Friends, Coworkers and Helping Professionals* (Brown & Rounsley, 2003). The authors use extended interviews with patients and families to provide valuable insights regarding important issues encountered by people who struggle with these conditions.

■ SUMMARY

DSM-IV-TR recognizes two major forms of sexual disorders. **Sexual dysfunctions** involve an inhibition of sexual desire or disruption of the physiological responses leading to orgasm. **Paraphilias** are defined in terms of extreme forms of unusual sexual behavior, in which sexual arousal is associated with atypical stimuli. The central problem in paraphilias is that sexual arousal has become detached from a reciprocal, loving relationship with another adult.

Sexual dysfunctions are subdivided into several types, based on the stages of the sexual response cycle. These include problems related to sexual desire, sexual arousal, and orgasm. Related difficulties include **sexual aversion disorder** and **premature ejaculation. Dyspareunia** is defined in terms of persistent genital pain during or after sexual intercourse. **Vaginismus** is an involuntary spasm of the muscles surrounding the entrance to the vagina. All forms of sexual dysfunction can lead to personal distress, including anxiety and depression, as well as interpersonal and marital difficulties.

Sexual behavior is dependent on a complex interaction among biological, psychological, and social factors. These factors include cognitive events related to the perception of sexual stimuli, social factors that influence sexual meanings or intentions, and physiological responses that cause vasocongestion of the genitals during sexual arousal.

Biological factors that contribute to sexual dysfunction include inadequate levels of sex hormones, which can contribute to diminished sexual desire, and a variety of medical disorders. Vascular and neurological diseases are important factors in many cases of erectile disorder. The effects of alcohol, illicit drugs, and some forms of medication can also contribute to **erectile dysfunction** in men and to **orgasmic disorder** in both men and women.

Several psychological factors are involved in the etiology of sexual dysfunction. Prominent among these are performance anxiety and guilt.

Communication deficits can also contribute to sexual dysfunction. Previous experiences, including sexual abuse, play an important role in some cases of sexual dysfunction.

Psychological treatments for sexual dysfunction are quite successful. They focus primarily on negative attitudes toward sexuality, failure to engage in effective sexual behaviors, and deficits in communication skills.

Common characteristics of paraphilias include lack of human intimacy and urges toward sexual behaviors that the person feels compelled to perform. Many people with paraphilias experience sexual dysfunctions during conventional sexual behavior with an adult partner. The diversity and range of paraphilic behavior are enormous. DSM-IV-TR describes a few of the most prominent forms, such as **exhibitionism, fetishism, frotteurism, pedophilia, sexual masochism, sexual sadism, transvestic fetishism,** and **voyeurism.** These are not typically isolated preferences or patterns of behavior; people who exhibit one form of paraphilia often exhibit others.

Treatment outcome is generally less successful with paraphilias than with sexual dysfunction. Currently, the most promising approaches to the treatment of paraphilias use a combination of cognitive and behavioral procedures to address a broad range of etiological factors, including deficits in social skills and stress and anger management, as well as knowledge and attitudes regarding sexuality.

Gender identity disorder is a disturbance in the person's sense of being either a man or a woman. People with this problem, which is also known as *transsexualism,* have developed a **gender identity** that is inconsistent with their physical anatomy. These disorders are extremely rare, and very little is known about their etiology. Gender identity seems to be strongly influenced by sex hormones, perhaps during the process of fetal development. Treatment of gender identity disorders may involve sex-reassignment surgery.

THE BIG PICTURE — CRITICAL THINKING REVIEW

Should sexual problems be defined primarily in terms of difficulty reaching orgasm?

It's important to most people, but it's not the only purpose of sexual activity. The person's satisfaction with intimate relationships is also an important consideration. (SEE PAGE 363)

Should excessive sexual behavior be considered a disorder in its own right? Or is it a symptom of other mental disorders?

One problem with the concept of "sexual addiction" is the heterogeneous nature of poorly regulated sexual behavior, which can be associated with many different forms of mental disorder. (SEE PAGE 369)

What role do mental scripts play in sexual arousal?

Scripts provide a perceptual structure, helping the person to recognize a situation as being potentially sexual in nature. (SEE PAGE 372)

What are the primary targets of psychological approaches to treating sexual dysfunction?

They focus on negative attitudes toward sexuality, failure to engage in effective sexual behaviors, and deficits in communication between partners. (SEE PAGE 374)

How have changing attitudes toward sexuality influenced the definition of paraphilias?

A wider range of sexual behaviors is now considered to be normal when these activities occur in the context of an adult, mutually consenting, reciprocal relationship. (SEE PAGE 377)

Does deviant sexual arousal ever play a role in sexual assaults?

Although rapes are often motivated by aggressive and violent impulses, some rapists are preoccupied by a sadistic blend of sexual and aggressive impulses that resembles qualities of other paraphilias. (SEE PAGE 383)

Why are paraphilias sometimes called "courtship disorders"?

An evolutionary perspective suggests that some forms of paraphilia, such as voyeurism and exhibitionism, may represent maladaptive distortions of normal mating behaviors. (SEE PAGE 385)

What is the difference between gender identity and sex roles?

The answer hinges on the distinction between a belief about "who you are" versus "what you do." Gender identity is the fundamental sense of being either male or female. Sex roles are characteristics and behaviors that are considered to be either masculine or feminine. (SEE PAGE 389)

■ KEY TERMS

construct validity **367**
dyspareunia **368**
erectile dysfunction **365**
exhibitionism **380**
fetishism **378**
frotteurism **381**

gender identity **389**
gender identity
  disorder **389**
hypoactive sexual
  desire **364**
hypothetical construct **367**

incest **382**
inhibited sexual arousal **366**
operational definition **367**
orgasmic disorder **368**
paraphilias **376**
pedophilia **382**

premature ejaculation **368**
rape **382**
sensate focus **374**
sexual aversion
  disorder **365**
sexual dysfunction **361**

sexual masochism **379**
sexual sadism **380**
transvestic fetishism **378**
vaginismus **369**
voyeurism **381**

SCHIZOPHRENIC DISORDERS

Schizophrenia is a severe form of abnormal behavior that encompasses what most of us have come to know as "madness." People with schizophrenia exhibit many different kinds of psychotic symptoms, indicating that the person has lost touch with reality. They may hear voices that aren't there or make comments that are difficult, if not impossible, to understand. Their behavior may be guided by absurd ideas and beliefs. For example, a person might believe that spaceships from another planet are beaming thoughts into his brain and controlling his behavior. Some people with schizophrenia recover fairly quickly, whereas others deteriorate progressively after the initial onset of symptoms. It is a disorder with "many different faces" (Andreasen, 2001). Because of the diversity of symptoms and outcomes shown by these patients, many clinicians believe that schizophrenia, or "the group of schizophrenias," may actually include several forms of disorder that have different causes. Others contend that schizophrenia is a single pathological process and that variations from one patient to the next in symptoms and course of the disorder reflect differences in the expression or severity of this process.

OVERVIEW

Many of the disorders that we have discussed in this book strike us as being familiar, at least in form if not in severity. For example, depression and anxiety are experiences with which we can easily empathize. Short-lived versions of these emotions help to shape our responses to daily events. Some clinical scientists speculate that mood and anxiety disorders may be viewed as evolved adaptations or mechanisms that can serve a useful purpose, but the symptoms of schizophrenia represent a different kind of problem. It is much harder for us to understand when someone hears voices that aren't there or speaks sentences that are meaningless. These symptoms seem to stem from a fundamental breakdown in basic cognitive functions that govern the way the person perceives and thinks about the world (Burns, 2004).

The most common symptoms of schizophrenia include changes in the way a person thinks, feels, and relates to other people and the outside environment. No single symptom or specific set of symptoms is characteristic of all schizophrenic patients. All the individual symptoms of schizophrenia can also be associated with other psychological and medical conditions. Schizophrenia is officially defined by various combinations of psychotic symptoms in the absence of other forms of disturbance, such as mood disorders (especially manic episodes), substance dependence, delirium, or dementia (see Chapter 14).

Schizophrenia is a devastating disorder for both the patients and their families. It can disrupt many aspects of the person's life, well beyond the experience of psychotic symptoms. The impact of this disorder is felt in many different ways. For people who develop schizophrenia, it often has a dramatic and lasting impact on their quality of life, both in terms of their own subjective satisfaction and their ability to complete an education, hold a job, and develop social relationships with other people. Approximately 10 percent of schizophrenic patients commit suicide (Heisel, 2008).

For family members of patients with schizophrenia, the consequences can also be cruel. They must come to grips with the fact that their son or daughter, or brother or sister, has developed a severe disorder that may change his

or her life forever. One woman whose daughter, then in her mid-thirties, had exhibited symptoms of schizophrenia for 17 years, described her feelings in the following way: "Nothing in (our daughter's) growing up years could have prepared us for the shock and devastation of seeing this normal, happy child become totally incapacitated by schizophrenia" (Smith, 1991, p. 691).

Schizophrenia also has an enormous impact on society. Among mental disorders, it is the second leading cause of disease burden (see Figure 1–2 on page 14). Most people who develop the disorder do not recover completely, and many become homeless because long-term institutional care is not available (see Chapter 18). Above and beyond the direct costs of providing treatment to patients and their families, substantial indirect costs are associated with loss of productivity and unemployment. In the United States the financial costs associated with schizophrenia were approximately $63 billion in 2002 (Wu et al., 2005).

◀ Painting by a young schizophrenic patient, illustrating his hallucinations. He saw monsters, like the one painted here, crawling on the floor. He also believed that the chairs next of to his bed had turned into devils. Patient's description of the picture: "I was very sick at the time I painted this picture. The head represents my fragmented personality and a feeling of being helpless, hopeless, and off balance and of being in a cocoon of unreality. The bright colored rain and outlines represent the level of intensity of myself. The bright colors provided insulation and protected me. The colors felt like microwaves passing through my control center."

In the following case studies we describe the experiences of two people who exhibited symptoms of schizophrenia. DSM-IV-TR divides schizophrenic disorders into several subtypes, based primarily on the type of symptoms that the patient exhibits. Our first case illustrates the paranoid subtype of schizophrenia, which is characterized by a preoccupation with one or more delusions or by frequent auditory hallucinations, most often persecutory.

CASE STUDY A New Mother's Paranoid Schizophrenia

Ann was 21 years old the first time that she was admitted to a psychiatric hospital. She had completed business college and had worked as a receptionist until she became pregnant with her son, who was born 6 months prior to her admission. She and her husband lived in a small apartment with his 5-year-old daughter from a previous marriage. This was her first psychotic episode.

The first signs of Ann's disturbance appeared during her pregnancy, when she accused her husband of having an affair with her sister. The accusation was based on a conversation that Ann had overheard on a bus. Two women (who were neighbors in Ann's apartment building) had been discussing an affair that some woman's husband was having. Ann believed that this might have been their way of telling her about her husband's infidelity. Although her husband and her sister denied any romantic interest in each other, Ann clung to her suspicions and began to monitor her husband's activities closely. She also avoided talking with her neighbors and friends.

Before this period of time, Ann had been an outgoing and energetic person. Now she seemed listless and apathetic and would often spend days without leaving their apartment. Her husband at first attributed this change in her behavior to the pregnancy, believing that she would "snap out of it" after the baby was born. Unfortunately, Ann became even more socially isolated following the birth of her son. She seldom left her bedroom and would spend hours alone, mumbling softly to herself.

Ann's behavior deteriorated markedly 2 weeks prior to her hospital admission, when she noticed that some photographs of herself and her baby were missing. She told her husband that they had been stolen and were being used to cast a voodoo spell on her. Ann became increasingly preoccupied with this belief in subsequent days. She called her mother repeatedly, insisting that something would have to be done to recover the missing photographs. Her friends and family tried to reassure Ann that the photographs had probably been misplaced or accidentally discarded, but she was totally unwilling to consider alternative explanations.

Ann finally announced to everyone who would listen that someone was trying to kill her and the children.

Believing that all the food in the house had been poisoned, she refused to eat and would not feed the children.

She became increasingly suspicious, hostile, and combative. Her husband and parents found it impossible to reason with her. She was no longer able to care for herself or the children. The family sought advice from their family physician, who recommended that they contact a psychiatrist. After meeting with Ann briefly, the psychiatrist recommended that she be hospitalized for a short period of time.

After admission, Ann argued heatedly with the hospital staff, denying that she was mentally disturbed and insisting that she must be released so that she could protect her children from the conspiracy. She had no insight into the nature of her problems.

The onset of schizophrenia typically occurs during adolescence or early adulthood. The period of risk for the development of a first episode is considered to be between the ages of 15 and 35. The number of new cases drops off slowly after that, with very few people experiencing an initial episode after the age of 55 (Thompson et al., 2004).

The problems of most patients can be divided into three phases of variable and unpredictable duration: prodromal, active, and residual. Symptoms such as hallucinations, delusions, and disorganized speech are characteristic of the active phase of the disorder. The **prodromal phase** precedes the active phase and is marked by an obvious deterioration in role functioning as a student, employee, or homemaker. The person's friends and relatives often view the beginning of the prodromal phase as a change in his or her personality. Prodromal signs and symptoms are similar to those associated with schizotypal personality disorder (see Chapter 9). They include peculiar behaviors (such as talking to one's self in public), unusual perceptual experiences, outbursts of anger, increased tension, and restlessness. Social withdrawal, indecisiveness, and lack of willpower are often seen during the prodromal phase (Lencz et al., 2003).

The **residual phase** follows the active phase of the disorder and is defined by signs and symptoms that are similar in many respects to those seen during the prodromal phase. At this point, the most dramatic symptoms of psychosis have improved, but the person continues to be impaired in various ways. Negative symptoms, such as impoverished expression of emotions, may remain pronounced during the residual phase (McGlashan, 1998).

After the onset of schizophrenia, many people do not return to expected levels of social and occupational adjustment. Some prefer social isolation and avoid contact with other people. The man in our second case illustrates this pattern.

He is also an example of the disorganized type of schizophrenia. Patients who fit criteria for this category say things that are difficult to understand, behave in a disorganized way, and fail to express expected emotions.

CASE STUDY   Edward's Disorganized Schizophrenia

Edward was 39 years old and had lived at home with his parents since dropping out of school after the tenth grade. Edward worked on and off as a helper in his father's roofing business prior to his first psychotic episode at the age of 26. After that time, he was socially isolated and unable to hold any kind of job. He was hospitalized in psychiatric facilities 10 times in the next 14 years. When he was not in the hospital, most of his time at home was spent watching television or sitting alone in his room.

The tenth episode of psychosis became evident when Edward told his mother that he had seen people arguing violently on the sidewalk in front of their house. He believed that this incident was the beginning of World War II. His mother tried to persuade him that he had witnessed an ordinary, though perhaps heated, disagreement between two neighbors, but Edward could not be convinced. He continued to mumble about the fight and became increasingly agitated over the next few days. When he wasn't pacing back and forth from his bedroom to the living room, he could usually be found staring out

the front window. Several days after witnessing the argument, he took curtains from several windows in the house and burned them in the street at 2 A.M. A neighbor happened to see what Edward was doing and called the police. When they arrived, they found Edward wandering in a snow-covered vacant lot, talking incoherently to himself. Recognizing that Edward was psychotic, the police took him to the psychiatric hospital.

Although his appearance was somewhat disheveled, Edward was alert and cooperative. He knew the current date and recognized that he was in a psychiatric hospital. Some of his speech was incoherent, and his answers to questions posed by the hospital staff were frequently irrelevant. For example, the following exchange occurred during a structured diagnostic interview. The psychologist asked Edward whether he had any special powers or abilities that other people do not have. He responded by saying that he didn't know because he didn't date women. Puzzled by this tangential response, the psychologist asked him to explain what he meant. Edward responded by asking his own question, "If you had a

star in the middle of your head, would you swallow marbles?"

Edward's expressive gestures were severely restricted, and he sat in a relatively motionless position. Although he said that he was frightened by the recent events that he reported to his mother, his face did not betray any signs of emotion. He mumbled slowly in a monotonous tone of voice that was difficult to understand. He said that he could hear God's voice telling him that his father was "the Master of the universe" and he claimed that he had "seen the shadow of the Master."

Other voices seemed to argue with one another about Edward's special calling and whether he was worthy of this divine power.

The voices told him to prepare for God's return to earth. At times Edward said that he was a Nazi soldier and that he was born in Germany in 1886. He also spoke incoherently about corpses frozen in Greenland and maintained that he was "only half a person."

SYMPTOMS

In this section we describe in greater detail various types of symptoms that are commonly observed among schizophrenic patients and that are currently emphasized by official diagnostic systems, such as DSM-IV-TR. All of these symptoms can fluctuate in severity over time. Some patients exhibit persistent psychotic symptoms. Others experience symptoms during acute episodes and are better adjusted between episodes.

The symptoms of schizophrenia can be divided into three dimensions: positive symptoms, negative symptoms, and disorganization (Andreasen et al., 1995; Lenzenweger, 1999). **Positive symptoms,** also called *psychotic symptoms,* include hallucinations and delusions. In contrast, **negative symptoms** include character-

istics such as lack of initiative, social withdrawal, and deficits in emotional responding. Some additional symptoms of schizophrenia, such as incoherent or disorganized speech, do not fit easily into either the positive or negative types. Verbal communication problems and bizarre behavior represent this third dimension, which is sometimes called disorganization. Note that these symptom dimensions overlap and combine in various ways within individual patients.

Positive Symptoms

The term *positive symptoms* of schizophrenia does not imply that these symptoms are beneficial or adaptive. Rather, it suggests that they are characterized by the presence of an aberrant response (such as hearing a voice that is not really there). Negative symptoms, on the other hand, are characterized by the absence of a particular response (such as emotion, speech, or willpower).

Hallucinations Our senses provide us with basic information that is vital to our notions of who we are, what we are doing, and what others think of us. Many people with schizophrenia experience perplexing and often frightening changes in perception. The most obvious perceptual symptoms are **hallucinations,** or sensory experiences that are not caused by actual external stimuli. Although hallucinations can occur in any of the senses, those experienced by schizophrenic patients are most often auditory. Many patients hear voices that comment on their behavior or give them instructions. Others hear voices that seem to argue with one another. Edward heard the voice of God talking to him. Like Edward, most patients find such voices to be frightening. In some cases, however, hallucinations can be comforting or pleasing to the patient.

What is the difference between a delusion and most other false beliefs?

Hallucinations should be distinguished from the transient mistaken perceptions that most people experience from time to time (Brébion et al., 2008). Have you ever turned around after thinking you heard someone call your name, to find that no one was there? You probably dismissed the experience as "just your imagination." Hallucinations, in contrast, strike the person as being real, in spite of the fact that they have no

basis in reality. They are also persistent over time. Patients who experience auditory hallucinations often hear the voice (or voices) speaking to them throughout the day and for many days at a time.

Delusional Beliefs Many schizophrenic patients express **delusions,** or idiosyncratic beliefs that are rigidly held in spite of their preposterous nature (Maher, 2001). Delusions have sometimes been defined as false beliefs based on incorrect inferences about reality. This definition has a number of problems, including the difficulty of establishing the ultimate truth of many situations. Ann's accusation that her husband was having an affair, for example, could easily become a choice between her word and his. This suspicion would not, on its own, be considered a delusion. The judgment that her beliefs were delusional depended to a large extent on their expansion to more absurd concerns about stolen photographs, voodoo spells, and alleged plots to kill her children.

Several additional characteristics are important in identifying delusions (Lincoln et al., 2007). In the most obvious cases, delusional patients express and defend their beliefs with utmost conviction, even when presented with contradictory evidence. For example, Ann's belief that the stolen photographs were being used to cast a spell on her was totally fixed and resistant to contradiction or reconsideration. Preoccupation is another defining characteristic of delusional beliefs. During periods of acute psychosis, many patients like Ann find it difficult, if not impossible, to avoid thinking or talking about these beliefs. Finally, delusional patients typically are unable to consider the perspective that other people hold with regard to their beliefs. Ann, for example, was unable to appreciate the fact that other people considered her paranoid beliefs to be ridiculous.

Although delusional beliefs can take many forms, they are typically personal. They are not shared by other members of the person's family or cultural group. Common delusions include the belief that thoughts are being inserted into the patient's head, that other people are reading the patient's thoughts, or that the patient is being controlled by mysterious, external forces (Gutierrez-Lobos et al., 2001). Many delusions focus on grandiose or paranoid content. For example, Edward expressed the grandiose belief that his father was the Master of the universe. Ann clung persistently to the paranoid belief that someone was trying to kill her and her children.

▼ Many of the symptoms of schizophrenia, including hallucinations and delusions, can be extremely distressing.

In actual clinical practice, delusions are complex and difficult to define (Lesser & O'Donohue, 1999; Oltmanns, 1988). Their content is sometimes bizarre and confusing, as in the case of Edward's insistence that he had witnessed the beginning of World War II. Delusions are often fragmented, especially among severely disturbed patients. In other words, delusions are not always coherent belief systems that are consistently expressed by the patient. At various times, for example, Edward talked about being a Nazi soldier and half a person. Connections among these fragmented ideas are difficult to understand.

The subjective experiences of people who struggle with schizophrenia are an important source of knowledge about this disorder, particularly delusional beliefs. Some of the most fundamental elements of psychosis involve private events that cannot be observed directly by others. Fortunately, many articulate patients have provided compelling accounts of their own internal struggles. The following paragraphs were written by a patient who was being treated for schizophrenia. She describes experiences that are part of an elaborate delusional belief system.

FIRST-PERSON ACCOUNT OF DELUSIONAL BELIEFS

At the beginning of my last year at (the university), 'feelings' began to descend on me. I felt distinctly different from my usual self. I would sit for hours on end staring at nothing, and I became fascinated with drawing weird, disconnected monsters. I carefully hid my drawings, because I was certain I was being watched. Eventually I became aware of a magical force outside myself that was compelling me in certain directions. The force gained power as time went on, and soon it made me take long walks at 2 or 3 o'clock in the morning down dark alleys in my high-crime neighborhood. I had no power to disobey the force. During my walks I felt as though I was in a different, magical, four-dimensional universe. I understood that the force wanted me to take those walks so that I might be killed.

I do not clearly understand the relationship between the force and the Alien Beings (alas, such a name!), but my universe soon became populated with them. The Alien Beings were from outer space, and of all the people in the world, only I was aware of them. The Alien Beings soon took over my body and removed me from it. They took me to a faraway place of beaches and sunlight and placed an Alien in my body to act like me. At this point I had the distinct impression that I did not really exist, because I could not make contact with my kidnapped self. I also saw that the Aliens were starting to take over other people as well, removing them from their bodies and putting Aliens in their place. Of course, the other people were unaware of what was happening; I was the only person in the world who had the power to know it. At this point I determined that the Aliens were involved in a huge conspiracy against the world.

The Alien Beings were gaining strength and had given me a complex set of rules. The rules were very specific and governed every aspect of my behavior. One of the rules was that I could not tell anyone else about the Aliens or the rules, or else the Aliens would kill me. Another of the rules was that I had to become utterly, completely mad. So now I was living in a world of great fear.

I had a number of other symptoms as well. I felt as though I had been pushed deep within myself, and I had little or no reaction to events or emotions around me. Almost daily the world became unreal to me. Everything outside of me seemed to fade into the distance; everything was miles away from me. I came to feel that I had the power to influence the behavior of animals; that I could, for instance, make dogs bark simply by hooking up rays of thought from my mind to theirs. Conversely, I felt that certain people had the capacity to read my mind. I became very frightened of those people and tried my best to avoid them. Whenever I saw a group of two or three people, I was sure they were talking about me. Paranoia is a very painful emotion! But when I saw crowds of people (as in a shopping mall), I felt an acute longing to wander among them, singing hymns and nursery rhymes (Payne, 1992, pp. 726–727).

Negative Symptoms

Negative symptoms of schizophrenia are defined in terms of responses or functions that appear to be missing from the person's behavior. In that sense, they may initially be more subtle or difficult to recognize than the positive symptoms of this disorder. Negative symptoms tend to be more stable over time than positive symptoms, which fluctuate in severity as the person moves in and out of active phases of psychosis (Buchanan, 2007; Stahl & Buckley, 2007).

Affective and Emotional Disturbances One of the most common symptoms of schizophrenia involves a flattening or restriction of the person's nonverbal display of emotional responses. This symptom, called **blunted affect,** or *affective* *flattening,* was clearly present in Edward's case. Blunted patients fail to exhibit signs of emotion or feeling. They are neither happy nor sad, and they appear to be completely indifferent to their surroundings. The faces of blunted patients are apathetic and expressionless. Their voices lack the typical fluctuations in volume and pitch that other people use to signal changes in their mood. Events in their environment hold little consequence for them. They may demonstrate a complete lack of concern for themselves and for others (Blanchard et al., 2007).

Another type of emotional deficit is called **anhedonia,** which refers to the inability to experience pleasure. Whereas blunted affect refers to the lack of outward expression, anhedonia is a lack of positive subjective feelings. People who experience anhedonia typically lose interest in recreational activities and social relationships, which they do not find enjoyable. They may also be unable to experience pleasure from physical sensations, such as taste and touch.

Longitudinal studies indicate that anhedonia associated with both social and physical experiences is an enduring feature of the disorder for many people with schizophrenia (Herbener & Harrow, 2002). For some people, it may also be an early marker, signaling the onset of the prodromal phase of the disorder (Kwapil, 1998). Like other symptoms of schizophrenia, anhedonia is not unique to this disorder; it is also found among people who are severely depressed.

What is the rationale for the distinction between the broad dimensions of positive and negative symptoms?

Apathy, Avolition, and Alogia One of the most important and seriously debilitating aspects of schizophrenia is a malfunction of interpersonal relationships (Meehl, 1993). Many people with schizophrenia become socially withdrawn. In many cases, social isolation develops before the onset of symptoms, such as hallucinations and delusions. It can be one of the earliest signs that something is wrong. This was certainly true in Ann's case. She became socially isolated from her family and friends many weeks before she started to talk openly about the stolen pictures and the plot to kill her children. Social withdrawal appears to be both a symptom of the disorder and a strategy that is actively employed by some patients to deal with their other symptoms. They may, for example, attempt to minimize interactions with other people in order to reduce levels of stimulation that can exacerbate perceptual and cognitive disorganization (Walker, Davis, & Baum, 1993).

The withdrawal seen among many schizophrenic patients is accompanied by indecisiveness, ambivalence, and a loss of willpower. This symptom is known as **avolition** (lack of volition or will). A person who suffers from avolition becomes apathetic and ceases to work toward personal goals or to function independently. He or she might sit listlessly in a chair all day, not washing or combing his or her hair for weeks.

Another negative symptom involves a form of speech disturbance called **alogia,** which refers to impoverished thinking. Literally translated, it means "speechlessness." In one form of alogia, known as *poverty of speech,* patients show remarkable reductions in the amount of speech. They simply don't have anything to say. In another form, referred to as thought blocking, the patient's train of speech is interrupted before a thought or idea has been completed.

Disorganization

Some symptoms of schizophrenia do not fit easily into either the positive or negative type. Thinking disturbances and bizarre behavior represent a third symptom dimension, which is sometimes called disorganization (Reitkerk et al., 2008).

Thinking Disturbances One important set of schizophrenic symptoms, known as **disorganized speech,** involves the tendency of some patients to say things that don't make sense. Signs of disorganized speech include making irrelevant responses to questions, expressing disconnected ideas, and using words in peculiar ways (Berenbaum & Barch, 1995). This symptom is also called *thought disorder,* because clinicians have assumed that the failure to communicate successfully reflects a disturbance in the thought patterns that govern verbal discourse. The woman described in the following case exhibited signs of disorganized speech.

CASE **STUDY** Marsha's Disorganized Speech and Bizarre Behavior

Marsha was a 32-year-old graduate student in political science. She had never been treated for psychological problems.

Marsha called Dr. Higgins, a clinical psychologist who taught at the university, to ask if she could speak with him about her twin sister's experience with schizophrenia.

When she arrived at his office, she was neatly dressed and had a Bible tucked tightly under her arm. The next 3 hours were filled with a rambling discussion of Marsha's experiences during the past 10 years. She talked about her education, her experience as a high school teacher before returning to graduate school, her relationships with her parents, and most of all her concern for her identical twin sister, Alice, who had spent 6 of the last 10 years in psychiatric hospitals.

Marsha's emotional expression vacillated dramatically throughout the course of this conversation, which was punctuated by silly giggles and heavy sighs. Her voice would be loud and emphatic one moment as she talked about her stimulating ideas and special talents. At other moments, she would whisper in a barely audible voice or sob quietly as she described the desperation, fear, and frustration that she had experienced watching the

progression of her sister's disorder. She said that she had been feeling very uptight in recent months, afraid that she might be "going crazy" like her sister. She had been scared to death to go home because her parents might sense that something was wrong with her. Her behavior was frequently inconsistent with the content of her speech. As she described her intense fears, for example, Marsha occasionally giggled uncontrollably.

Dr. Higgins also found Marsha's train of thought difficult to follow. Her speech rambled illogically from one topic to the next, and her answers to his questions were frequently tangential. For example, when Dr. Higgins asked what she meant by her repeated use of the phrase "the ideal can become real," Marsha replied, "Well, after serving the Word of Christ in California for 3 years, making a public spectacle of myself, someone apparently called my parents and said I had a problem. I said I can't take this anymore and went home. I perceived that Mom was just unbelievably nice to me. I began to think that my face was changing. Something about my forehead resembled the pain of Christ. I served Christ, but my power was not lasting."

At the end of this 3-hour interview, Dr. Higgins was convinced that Marsha should be referred to the mental health center for outpatient treatment. He explained his con-

cerns to Marsha, but she refused to follow his advice, insisting that she did not want to receive the medication with which her sister had been treated. She agreed to return to Dr. Higgins's office in 3 days for another interview, but she did not keep that appointment.

Two weeks later, Marsha called Dr. Higgins to ask if he would talk with her immediately. It was very difficult to understand what she was saying, but she seemed to be repeating in a shrill voice "I'm losing my mind." The door to his office was closed when she arrived, but he could hear her shuffling awkwardly down the hallway, breathing heavily. He opened his door and found Marsha standing in a rigid posture, arms stiffly at her sides. Her eyes were opened wide, and she was staring vacantly at the nameplate on his door. In contrast to her prim and neat appearance at their first meeting, Marsha's hair and clothes were now in disarray. She walked stiffly into the office without bending her knees and sat, with some difficulty, in the chair next to Dr. Higgins's desk. Her facial expression was rigidly fixed. Although her eyes were open and she appeared to hear his voice, Marsha did not respond to any of Dr. Higgins's questions. Recognizing that Marsha was experiencing an acute psychotic episode, Dr. Higgins and one of the secretaries took her to the emergency room at the local hospital.

Marsha's speech provides one typical example of disorganized speech. She was not entirely incoherent, but parts of her speech were difficult to follow. Connections between sentences were sometimes arbitrary, and her answers to the interviewer's questions were occasionally irrelevant.

The following excerpt from an interview with another patient illustrates a more extreme form of disorganized speech.

> **INTERVIEWER:** Have you been nervous or tense lately?
> **PATIENT:** No, I got a head of lettuce.
> **INTERVIEWER:** You got a head of lettuce? I don't understand.
> **PATIENT:** Well, it's just a head of lettuce.
> **INTERVIEWER:** Tell me about lettuce. What do you mean?
> **PATIENT:** Well, . . . lettuce is a transformation of a dead cougar that suffered a relapse on the lion's toe. And he swallowed the lion and something happened. The . . . see, the . . .

Gloria and Tommy, they're two heads and they're not whales. But they escaped with herds of vomit, and things like that.
> (Neale & Oltmanns, 1980, p. 102)

When speech becomes this disrupted, it is considered incoherent. Notice that this patient did not string words together in a random fashion. His speech followed grammatical rules. He was placing nouns and verbs together in an appropriate order, but they didn't make any sense. His speech conveyed little, if any, meaning, and that is the hallmark of disorganized speech.

Several types of verbal communication disruption contribute to clinical judgments about disorganized speech (Docherty, DeRosa, & Andreasen, 1996; Kerns & Berenbaum, 2002). Common features of disorganized speech in schizophrenia include shifting topics too abruptly, called *loose associations* or *derailment;* replying to a question with an irrelevant response, called *tangentiality;* or persistently repeating the same word or phrase over and over again, called *perseveration.* We all say things from time to time that fit these descriptions. It is not the occasional presence of a single feature but, rather, the accumulation of a large number of such features that defines the presence of disorganized speech.

Bizarre Behavior Schizophrenic patients may exhibit various forms of unusual motor behavior, such as the rigidity displayed by Marsha when she appeared for her second interview with Dr. Higgins. *Catatonia* most often refers to immobility and marked muscular rigidity, but it can also refer to excitement and overactivity. For example, some patients engage in apparently purposeless pacing or repetitive movements, such as rubbing their hands together in a special pattern for hours at a time. Many catatonic patients exhibit reduced or awkward spontaneous movements. In more extreme forms, patients may assume unusual postures or remain in rigid standing or sitting positions for long periods of time. For example, some patients will lie flat on their backs in a stiff position with their heads raised slightly off the floor as though they were resting on a pillow. Catatonic patients typically resist attempts to alter their position, even though maintaining their awkward postures would normally be extremely uncomfortable or painful.

Catatonic posturing is often associated with a *stuporous state,* or generally reduced responsiveness. The person seems to be unaware of his or her surroundings. For example, during her acute psychotic episode, Marsha refused to answer questions or to make eye contact with others. Unlike

people with other stuporous conditions, however, catatonic patients seem to maintain a clear state of consciousness, and it is likely that Marsha could hear and understand everything that Dr. Higgins said to her. Many patients report after the end of a catatonic episode that they were perfectly aware of events that were taking place around them, in spite of their failure to respond appropriately.

Another kind of bizarre behavior involves affective responses that are obviously inconsistent with the person's situation. This symptom is particularly difficult to describe in words. The most remarkable features of **inappropriate affect** are incongruity and lack of adaptability in emotional expression. For example, when Marsha described the private terror that she felt in the presence of her family, she giggled in a silly fashion. The content of Marsha's speech was inconsistent with her facial expression, her gestures, and her voice quality.

DIAGNOSIS

The broad array of symptoms outlined in the previous section have all been described as being part of schizophrenic disorders. The specific organization of symptoms has been a matter of some controversy for many years. Schizophrenic disorders have been defined in many different ways. In the following pages we briefly review some of the more prominent trends that led to the DSM-IV-TR description of these disorders.

Brief Historical Perspective

Descriptions of schizophrenic symptoms can be traced far back in history, but they were not considered to be symptoms of a single disorder until late in the nineteenth century (Gottesman, 1991). At that time, Emil Kraepelin, a German psychiatrist, suggested that several types of problems that previously had been classified as distinct forms of disorder should be grouped together under a single diagnostic category called *dementia praecox.* This term referred to psychoses that ended in severe intellectual deterioration (dementia) and that had an early or premature (praecox) onset, usually during adolescence. Kraepelin argued that these patients could be distinguished from those suffering from other disorders (most notably manic–depressive psychosis) largely on the basis of changes that occurred as the disorder progressed over time, primarily those changes involving the integrity of mental functions.

▼ These dementia praecox patients, treated by Emil Kraeplin in the late nineteenth century, display "waxy flexibility," a feature of catatonic motor behavior. "They were put without difficulty in the peculiar positions and kept them, some with a sly laugh, others with rigid seriousness."

In 1911, Eugen Bleuler (1857–1939), a Swiss psychiatrist and a contemporary of Kraepelin, published an influential monograph in which he agreed with most of Kraepelin's suggestions about this disorder. He did not believe, however, that the disorder always ended in profound deterioration or that it always began in late adolescence. Kraepelin's term *dementia praecox* was, therefore, unacceptable to him. Bleuler suggested a new name for the disorder—*schizophrenia*. This term referred to the *splitting of mental associations,* which Bleuler believed to be the fundamental disturbance in schizophrenia. One unfortunate consequence of this choice of terms has been the confusion among laypeople of schizophrenia with dissociative identity disorder (also known as multiple personality), a severe form of dissociative disorder (see Chapter 7). The two disorders actually have very little in common.

Many other suggestions have been made in subsequent years regarding the description and diagnosis of schizophrenia (Gottesman, 1991; Neale & Oltmanns, 1980). Some clinicians have favored a broader definition, whereas others have argued for a more narrow approach.

DSM-IV-TR

The current U.S. approach to the diagnosis of schizophrenic disorders gives primary consideration to three types of symptoms: positive (psy-chotic) symptoms, negative symptoms, and disorganized speech and behavior. The DSM-IV-TR definition includes a more restricted range of symptoms than Bleuler's description of the disorder, which placed less emphasis on the presence of persistent psychotic symptoms such as hallucinations and delusions. The inclusion of negative symptoms does represent, however, a remnant of Bleuler's influence.

DSM-IV-TR lists several specific criteria for schizophrenia (see Table 13–1). The first requirement (Criterion A) is that the patient must exhibit two (or more) active symptoms for at least 1 month. Notice that only one of the characteristic symptoms is required if that symptom is a bizarre delusion or hallucination that fits Schneider's description of first-rank symptoms. Negative symptoms, such as blunted affect, avolition, and social withdrawal, play a relatively prominent role in the DSM-IV-TR definition of schizophrenia, although some concern has been expressed about the reliability with which they are measured. The work group that developed DSM-IV-TR considered negative symptoms vital both to determining the causes of the disorder and to treating it successfully (Carpenter, 2006).

The DSM-IV-TR definition also takes into account social and occupational functioning as well as the duration of the disorder (Criteria B and C). These criteria reflect the influence of Kraepelin, who argued that the disorder is accompanied

---

TABLE 13–1 DSM-IV-TR Diagnostic Criteria for Schizophrenia

A. Characteristic Symptoms: Two (or more) of the following, each present for a significant portion of time during a 1-month period (or less if successfully treated):

1. Delusions
2. Hallucinations
3. Disorganized speech (such as frequent derailment or incoherence)
4. Grossly disorganized or catatonic behavior
5. Negative symptoms, such as affective flattening, alogia, or avolition

(*Note:* Only one A symptom is required if delusions are bizarre or hallucinations consist of a voice keeping up a running commentary on the person's behavior or thoughts, or two or more voices conversing with each other.)

B. Social/Occupational Dysfunction: For a significant portion of the time since the onset of the disturbance, one or more major areas of functioning such as work, interpersonal relations, or self-care is markedly below the level achieved prior to the onset.

C. Duration: Continuous signs of the disturbance persist for at least 6 months. This 6-month period must include at least 1 month of symptoms that meet Criterion A (active phase symptoms), and may include periods of prodromal or residual symptoms. During these prodromal or residual periods, the signs of the disturbance may be manifested by only negative symptoms or two or more symptoms listed in Criterion A present in an attenuated form (such as odd beliefs, unusual perceptual experiences).

Source: Reprinted with permission from the *Diagnostic and Statistical Manual of Mental Disorders,* Fourth Edition, Text Revision. Copyright © 2000 by the American Psychiatric Association.

by marked impairment in functioning as well as a chronic, deteriorating course. The DSM-IV-TR definition requires evidence of a decline in the person's social or occupational functioning as well as the presence of disturbed behavior over a continuous period of at least 6 months. Active phase symptoms do not need to be present for this entire period. The total duration of disturbance is determined by adding together continuous time during which the person has exhibited prodromal, active, and residual symptoms of schizophrenia. If the person displays psychotic symptoms for at least 1 month but less than 6 months, the diagnosis would be schizophreniform disorder. The diagnosis would be changed to schizophrenic disorder if the person's problems persisted beyond the 6-month limit.

The final consideration in arriving at a diagnosis of schizophrenia involves the exclusion of related conditions, especially mood disorders. According to DSM-IV-TR, active phase symptoms of schizophrenia must appear in the absence of a major depressive or manic episode. If symptoms of depression or mania are present, their duration must be brief relative to the duration of the active and residual symptoms of schizophrenia.

Subtypes

Schizophrenia is a heterogeneous disorder with many different clinical manifestations and levels of severity. The title of Bleuler's classic text referred to "the group of schizophrenias" in an effort to draw attention to the varied presentations of the disorder. It is not clear, however, how best to think about the different forms of schizophrenia. Many clinicians and investigators believe that schizophrenia is a general term for a group of disorders, each of which may be caused by a completely different set of factors. Other clinicians believe that the numerous symptoms of schizophrenia are most likely varying manifestations of the same underlying condition (Gottesman, 1991). Given the current state of evidence, it is not possible to choose between these conceptual options. Nevertheless, most investigators agree that we should at least consider the possibility that there are distinct forms.

DSM-IV-TR recognizes five subtypes of schizophrenia. The subtypes are used to describe the clinical state of the patient during the most recent examination. Only one subtype can be assigned at any point in time. The five subtypes are arranged in a hierarchy so that patients who

exhibit symptoms of different subtypes can be diagnosed. The catatonic type is at the top of the hierarchy. Patients who fit this description are diagnosed as catatonic even if they show additional symptoms that are characteristic of other subtypes. The remaining subtypes, in descending order, are the disorganized subtype, the paranoid subtype, the undifferentiated subtype, and the residual subtype (see Critical Thinking Matters, on the next page).

The **catatonic type** is characterized by symptoms of motor immobility (including rigidity and posturing) or excessive and purposeless motor activity. In some cases, the person may be resistant to all instructions or refuse to speak, for no apparent reason. Catatonic patients may also show a decreased awareness of their environment and a lack of movement and activity. If her disorder lasted more than 6 months, Marsha would probably have received a diagnosis of schizophrenic disorder, catatonic type, on the basis of her prominent motor symptoms and stuporous behavior.

The **disorganized type** of schizophrenia is characterized by disorganized speech, disorganized behavior, and flat or inappropriate affect. All three features must be present to make this diagnosis. Social impairment is usually quite marked in these patients. The patient's speech is frequently incoherent, and if delusions or hallucinations are present, their content is usually not well organized. Consider, for example, the delusions expressed by Edward. At various times, he talked about Nazi soldiers and World War II, frozen corpses in Greenland, being "half a person," and having special powers because he was the son of God. These fragmented and bizarre ideas were clearly delusional, but they were not woven into a coherent framework.

The most prominent symptoms in the **paranoid type** are systematic delusions with persecutory or grandiose content. Preoccupation with frequent auditory hallucinations can also be associated with the paranoid type. Ann would have received a diagnosis of schizophrenic disorder, paranoid type, because of her preoccupation with the systematic delusion about the photographs that had been stolen and the attempt to harm her children. Patients who exhibit disorganized speech, disorganized behavior, flat or inappropriate affect, or catatonic behavior are excluded from a diagnosis of paranoid schizophrenia and would fall into one of the other subtypes.

Two additional subtypes are described in DSM-IV-TR, presumably to cover those patients who do not fit one of the traditional types. The

CRITICAL THINKING MATTERS

Are Symptom-Based Subtypes of Schizophrenia Useful?

The validity of the traditional subtypes has been debated for many years. The evidence on which they are based is quite weak. Clinicians who favor continued use of subtype diagnoses claim that these categories are *moderately* stable over time (Fenton, 2000). There is also some evidence indicating that patients who fit descriptions of the catatonic and paranoid subtypes have a somewhat better prognosis, whereas those in the disorganized subtype may have—on average—a worse prognosis (McGlashan & Fenton, 1991). If we think critically, this is *not* strong support for the inclusion of these subtypes in the official diagnostic manual.

Critics point to a number of serious problems. Traditional subtypes do not strongly predict either the course of the disorder or response to treatment. The subtypes also have relatively poor diagnostic reliability and are frequently unstable over time. Patients who fit a traditional subcategory during one psychotic episode frequently qualify for a different subtype diagnosis during a subsequent episode. Based on this evidence, it seems reasonable to ask: "How does it help the clinician or the patient to assign a subtype diagnosis such as disorganized type or undifferentiated type?"

Perhaps the most important consideration with regard to the validity of subtypes involves the genetic evidence. Studies of extended families suggest that the subtypes are not etiologically distinct syndromes (Cardno et al., 1998; Kendler et al., 1994). If several members of a family—or two members of a monozygotic twin pair—have developed symptoms of schizophrenia, they will not necessarily exhibit symptoms of the same subtype. That fact argues strongly against the notion that the subtypes are qualitatively different disorders.

Why do clinical scientists say that schizophrenia is a "heterogeneous" disorder?

Manfred Bleuler, a Swiss psychiatrist and the son of Eugen Bleuler, treated and observed more than 200 schizophrenic patients over a period of many years. His experience led him to believe that distinctions among subtypes become blurred over time. His data and much of the other research evidence support the hypothesis that the traditional subtypes based on obvious symptoms are a reflection of varying stages of a single disorder

or varying levels of severity of the disorder (Gottesman, 1991).

This is perhaps the greatest irony in research on schizophrenia. For more than 100 years, clinicians and investigators have agreed that the disorder is extremely heterogenous. The diagnostic category that we now recognize as schizophrenia may well be composed of many different kinds of mental disorder. This common opinion stands in contrast to the harsh fact that no one has been able to identify truly meaningful subtypes. Don't take the official system too literally. Be skeptical. At best, the diagnostic subtypes for schizophrenia are placeholders, serving primarily to remind us that the disorder is heterogeneous in nature. We desperately need more knowledge in this area. We need better research that will help us find more meaningful subtypes based on sophisticated measurement procedures that may involve genetic factors, cognitive performance, treatment response, or some other facet of the disorder that has not yet been studied. One thing that does seem to be clear is that it has not been particularly useful to focus on symptoms as the basis for reducing the heterogeneity of the complex disorder.

---

undifferentiated type of schizophrenia includes schizophrenic patients who display prominent psychotic symptoms and either meet the criteria for several subtypes or otherwise do not meet the criteria for the catatonic, disorganized, or paranoid types. They often exhibit some disorganized symptoms together with hallucinations and/or delusions.

The **residual type** includes patients who no longer meet the criteria for active phase symptoms but nevertheless demonstrate continued signs of negative symptoms or attenuated forms of delusions, hallucinations, or disorganized speech. They are in "partial remission."

Related Psychotic Disorders

The U.S. concept of schizophrenia is relatively narrow. The boundaries of the disorder have been refined by excluding patients with certain

▲ People with paranoid delusions are constantly alert to evidence suggesting that they are being victimized. This constant search often leads them to misinterpret others' comments and behaviors.

PEARSON
mypsych lab VIDEO CASE

SCHIZOAFFECTIVE DISORDER

JOSH

"When I was first in the hospital, I thought I was in the middle of a massacre ..."

Watch the video "Schizoaffective Disorders; Josh" on MyPsychLab. In addition to describing bizarre delusional beliefs, Josh has also experienced several symptoms of bipolar mood disorder, such as racing thoughts and grandiosity.

types of psychotic symptoms from a diagnosis of schizophrenic disorder. Immediately after its description of schizophrenia, DSM-IV-TR lists three additional disorders that are characterized by prominent psychotic symptoms.

Schizoaffective disorder is an ambiguous and somewhat controversial category (Averill et al., 2004; Lake & Hurwitz, 2007). It

describes the symptoms of patients who fall on the boundary between schizophrenia and mood disorder with psychotic features. This diagnosis applies only to the description of a particular episode of disturbance; it does not describe the overall lifetime course of the person's disorder. Schizoaffective disorder is defined by an episode in which the symptoms of schizophrenia partially overlap with a major depressive episode or a manic episode. The key to making this diagnosis is the presence of delusions or hallucinations for at least 2 weeks in the absence of prominent mood symptoms. If the delusions and hallucinations are present only during a depressive episode, for example, the diagnosis would be major depressive episode with psychotic features.

People with **delusional disorder** do not meet the full symptomatic criteria for schizophrenia, but they are preoccupied for at least 1 month with delusions that are not bizarre. These are beliefs about situations that could occur in real life, such as being followed or poisoned. Ann's delusion, for example, might have fit this description. She believed that someone was trying to kill her and her children and that someone was trying to cast a voodoo spell on them. Ann would not be assigned a diagnosis of delusional disorder, however, because she also displayed negative symptoms, such as avolition. The presence of hallucinations, disorganized speech, catatonic behavior, or negative symptoms rules out a diagnosis of delusional disorder. The definition of delusional disorder also holds that the person's behavior is not bizarre and that social and occupational functioning are not impaired except for those areas that are directly affected by the delusional belief.

Brief psychotic disorder is a category that includes those people who exhibit psychotic symptoms—delusions, hallucinations, disorganized speech, or grossly disorganized or catatonic behavior—for at least 1 day but no more than 1 month. An episode of this sort is typically accompanied by confusion and emotional turmoil, often (but not necessarily) following a markedly stressful event. After the symptoms are resolved, the person returns to the same level of functioning that had been achieved prior to the psychotic episode. The long-term outcome is good for most patients who experience a brief episode of psychosis (Susser et al., 1998). This diagnosis is not assigned if the symptoms are better explained by a mood disorder, schizophrenia, or substance

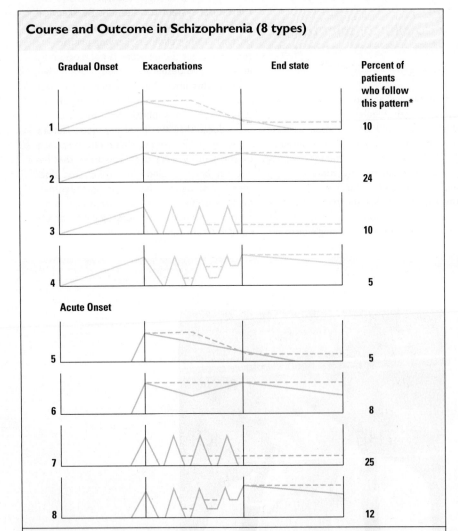

Course and Outcome in Schizophrenia (8 types)

| Gradual Onset | Exacerbations | End state | Percent of patients who follow this pattern* |

FIGURE 13–1 Patterns identified in long-term follow-up studies. The horizontal axis represents time and the vertical axis represents severity of disturbance. Dotted lines represent slight variations on the overall pattern.

*Data from Ciompi, 1980.

Source: From "Course Types in Schizophrenia: An Analysis of European and American Studies" by C. M. Harding, *Schizophrenia Bulletin*, (1988), 14, p. 635. Copyright © 1988. Reprinted by permission of Oxford University Press.

abuse. This category is used infrequently, and very little research has been conducted with people who have this disorder.

Course and Outcome

Schizophrenia is a severe, progressive disorder that most often begins in adolescence and typically has a poor outcome. In fact, Kraepelin considered the deteriorating course to be one of the principal defining features of the disorder. Current evidence suggests that this view may be unnecessarily pessimistic (Hafner et al., 2003; Perkins et al., 2006). Many patients experience a good outcome. For example, Manfred Bleuler (1978) studied a sample of 208 schizophrenic patients who had been admitted to his hospital in Switzerland during 1942 and 1943. After a follow-up period of 23 years, 53 percent of the patients were either recovered or significantly improved.

In order to describe more completely the various patterns that patients followed over time, Bleuler identified two types of onset (sudden or gradual), two types of course (undulating or simple), and two types of outcome (recovered/mild impairment or moderate/severe impairment). When combined, these elements form eight basic patterns for the onset and course of schizophrenic disorders, as illustrated in Figure 13–1.

A long-term follow-up study of schizophrenia, reported by the Swiss psychiatrist Luc Ciompi (1980), provided useful information about the proportion of patients whose disorder fits into the types of onset, course, and outcome that Bleuler proposed. Ciompi found that approximately half of the 228 patients in his study suffered an acute onset of symptoms during their initial episode. Again, during the intermediate stages of the disorder, half of the patients followed an undulating course,

whereas the others exhibited relatively stable symptoms. By the time the patients had reached the end state of their disorder, half had recovered (or showed only mild residual symptoms), whereas the other half continued to experience moderate or severe impairment. The proportions of patients in Ciompi's study who fit different combinations of onset, course, and outcome are indicated in Figure 13–1.

Follow-up studies of schizophrenic patients have found that the description of outcome can be a complicated process. Many factors must be taken into consideration other than whether the person is still in the hospital. Is the person still exhibiting symptoms of the disorder? Does he or she have any other problems, such as depression or anxiety? Is the person employed? Does she have any friends? How does he get along with other people? The evidence indicates that different dimensions of outcome, such as social adjustment, occupational functioning, and symptom severity, are only loosely correlated. As in most situations where psychologists attempt to predict future behavior, the outcome data regarding schizophrenia suggest that the best predictor of future social adjustment is previous social adjustment. Similarly, the best predictor of symptom severity at follow-up is severity of psychotic symptoms at initial assessment (Bromet et al., 2005; Carpenter & Strauss, 1991).

The long-term emotional impact of this disorder on parents and families has been described by a woman whose daughter, then in her mid-thirties, had exhibited symptoms of schizophrenia for 17 years. Her statement also indicates that even the most severely disturbed patients may eventually show signs of improvement (see First-Person Account: A Mother's Observations).

How should long-term outcome be measured in schizophrenia?

FIRST-PERSON ACCOUNT: A MOTHER'S OBSERVATIONS

The saddest thing of all is to realize that the stories of family life and previous achievements that were a part of the past lives of each of these people are no longer important to them. Nothing in (our daughter's) growing up years could have prepared us for the shock and devastation of seeing this normal, happy child become totally incapacitated by schizophrenia. Coming to grips with the

thought of your child living in a mental hospital, possibly for many years, leaves you with a gnawing sense of helplessness that never really dissipates.

In the past year, a new Cindy has emerged. Where once there was a rather unfriendly, often unpleasant girl, there is now an amiable, more responsive person. Cindy smiles more these days, something a person with schizo-

phrenia doesn't do very often. For years her face was a solemn mask, and she could neither give nor receive affection. She knew something terrible had happened to her and could not understand why no one would rescue her from the hell in her head. In the past few months she has become quite loving, and the smiles that now light her face light mine as well (Smith, 1991, pp. 690–691).

FREQUENCY

One of the most informative ways of examining the frequency of schizophrenia is to consider the lifetime prevalence—that is, the proportion of a specific population that will be affected by the disorder at some time during their lives. Most studies in Europe and the United States have reported lifetime prevalence figures of approximately 1.0 percent if they include people who meet diagnostic criteria for schizophrenia as well as related psychotic disorders (Kessler et al., 2005; Saha et al., 2008). In other words, approximately 1 out of every 100 people will experience or display symptoms of schizophrenia at some time during their lives. Of course, prevalence rates depend on the diagnostic criteria that are used to define schizophrenia in any particular study, as well as the methods that are used to identify cases in the general population. Investigators who have employed more narrow or restrictive criteria for the disorder report lower prevalence rates (Messias et al., 2007).

Gender Differences

Although experts have believed for many years that men and women are equally likely to develop schizophrenia, this conclusion has been challenged by several recent studies. Current evidence suggests that men are 30 to 40 percent more likely to develop schizophrenia than women (Seeman, 2008).

There are some interesting and widely recognized differences between male and female patients with regard to patterns of onset, symptoms, and course of the disorder. For example, the average age at which schizophrenic males begin to exhibit overt symptoms is younger by about 4 or 5 years than the average age at which schizophrenic women first experience problems. A summary of reported gender differences in schizophrenia is presented in Table 13–2. Male patients are more likely than female patients to exhibit negative symptoms, and they are also more likely to follow a chronic, deteriorating course (Atalay & Atalay, 2006; Moriarty et al., 2001).

Gender differences in the age of onset and symptomatic expression of schizophrenia can be interpreted in several ways. The alternatives fall into two types of hypotheses. One approach assumes that schizophrenia is a single disorder and that its expression varies in men and women. A common, genetically determined vulnerability to schizophrenia might be expressed differently in men than in women. Mediating factors that might account for this difference could be biological differences between men and women—perhaps involving certain hormones—or different environmental demands, such as the timing and form of stresses associated with typical male and female sex roles. An alternative approach suggests that there are two qualitatively distinct subtypes of schizophrenia: one with an early onset that affects men more often than women, and another with a later onset that affects women more often than men. Both approaches assume a combination of genetically determined predisposition to disorder with the onset of symptoms being triggered by environmental events. The available evidence does not allow us to favor one of these explanations over the other (Haefner et al., 1998; Taylor & Langdon, 2006).

Cross-Cultural Comparisons Schizophrenia has been observed in virtually every culture that has been subjected to careful scrutiny. Although it is a universal disorder, the frequency of schizophrenia is not constant around the world. The annual incidence of schizophrenia—that is, the number of *new* cases appearing in any given year—varies from one country to the next.

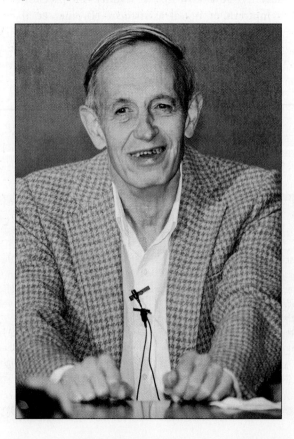

▶ The life of John Forbes Nash, a mathematician, was portrayed in the film *A Beautiful Mind*. Nash won the Nobel Prize for Economics in 1994. His thesis, written at the age of 21, revolutionized the field of game theory. He has recovered from paranoid schizophrenia, after experiencing psychotic symptoms for more than 20 years.

TABLE 13–2	Typical Gender Differences in Schizophrenia	
VARIABLE	**MEN**	**WOMEN**
Age of onset	Earlier (18–25)	Later (25–35)
Premorbid functioning; adjustment	Poor social functioning; more schizotypal traits	Good social functioning; fewer schizotypal traits
Typical symptoms	More negative symptoms; more withdrawn and passive	More hallucinations and paranoia; more emotional and impulsive
Course	More often chronic; poorer response to treatment	Less often chronic; better response to treatment

Source: Based on J. M. Goldstein, 1995, "The Impact of Gender on Understanding the Epidemiology of Schizophrenia," in M.V. Seeman, Ed., *Gender and Psychopathology,* pp. 159–199. Washington, DC: American Psychiatric Press.

Reported estimates range from 8 to 43 cases per 100,000 people (McGrath, 2005). Urban populations have higher rates than rural areas, but incidence is not related to a country's economic status (Saha et al., 2006). As epidemiologists attempt to unravel these differences and explain them, we will learn more about the causes of the disorder.

Substantial cross-cultural differences have also been found with regard to the course of schizophrenia. Two large-scale epidemiological studies, conducted by teams of scientists working for the World Health Organization (WHO), have drawn considerable attention to differences in short- and long-term outcome for schizophrenia in the third world and industrialized countries (Sartorius, 2007). The International Pilot Study of Schizophrenia (IPSS) began in the 1960s and was conducted in nine countries in Europe, North America, South America, Africa, and Asia. It included 1,200 patients who were followed for 15 to 25 years after their initial hospitalization. The Collaborative Study on the Determinants of Outcome of Severe Mental Disorders (DOS) was begun a few years later in six of the same countries that participated in the IPSS, plus four others. The DOS study included more than 1,500 patients. Both the IPSS and DOS projects examined rural and urban areas in both Western and non-Western countries. For purposes of cultural comparison, the countries were divided into those that were "developing" and those that were already "developed" on the basis of prevailing socioeconomic conditions. All the interviewers were trained in the use of a single, standardized interview schedule, and all employed the same sets of diagnostic criteria.

The IPSS results indicated that patients who exhibited characteristic signs and symptoms of schizophrenia were found in all of the study sites. Comparisons of patients across research centers revealed more similarities than differences in clinical symptoms at the time of entry into the study, which was always an active phase of disorder that required psychiatric treatment. The IPSS investigators found that clinical and social outcomes were significantly better for schizophrenic patients in developing countries than in developed countries, such as the United States, England, and Russia. The DOS study confirmed those results (Craig et al., 1997; Hopper et al., 2007).

The WHO studies provide compelling support for the conclusion that, although the frequency of schizophrenia varies around the world,

In what way does the long-term course of schizophrenia differ between developing and developed countries? Why?

▼ Schizophrenia affects people in all cultures. This Chinese man, whose symptoms include delusions and disorganized speech, lives with his adoptive parents and does not receive adequate treatment. One consequence of economic reforms in China has been reduced access to quality care for patients with chronic mental disorders.

it is expressed in terms of similar symptoms in different cultures. Most experts believe that the more favorable clinical outcome that was observed in India and Nigeria is a product of the greater tolerance and acceptance extended to people with psychotic symptoms in developing countries. This conclusion is consistent with evidence regarding the relationship between frequency of relapse and patterns of family communication, which we consider later in this chapter in the section on expressed emotion. These cross-cultural data certainly testify to the important influence of culture in shaping the experience and expression of psychotic symptoms (Thakker & Ward, 1998).

CAUSES

Having considered the defining characteristics of schizophrenia, ways in which it has been classified, and some basic information regarding its distribution within the general population, we now review the evidence regarding factors that might contribute to the development of the disorder, as well as its course and outcome.

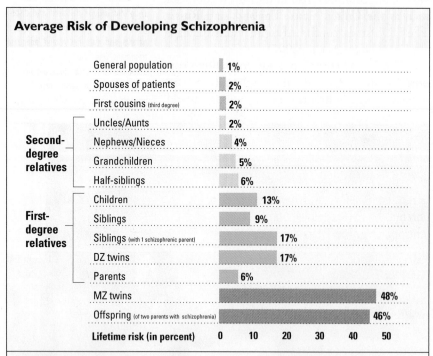

FIGURE 13–2 Average risk of schizophrenia among biological relatives of a schizophrenic proband.

Source: I. I. Gottesman, 1991, *Schizophrenia Genesis: The Origins of Madness*, p. 96. New York: Freeman. Copyright © 1991 by Irving I. Gottesman. Reprinted by permission of W. H. Freeman and Company.

Biological Factors

Many of the early investigators who defined schizophrenia at the beginning of the twentieth century believed that the disorder was the product of a biological dysfunction. At that time very little was known about human genetics or the biochemistry of the brain. Research in the areas of molecular genetics and the neurosciences has progressed at an explosive rate in the past decade. Much of what we know today about the biological substrates of schizophrenia has emerged from advances that have taken place in other sciences.

Genetics The role of genetic factors has been studied more extensively with regard to schizophrenia than with any other type of mental disorder. The existing data are based on sophisticated methods that have been refined over many years. The cumulative weight of this evidence points clearly toward some type of genetic influence in the transmission of this disorder (Pogue-Geile & Gottesman, 2007).

Family Studies Figure 13–2 illustrates the lifetime risk for schizophrenia for various types of relatives of a person with schizophrenia. Irving Gottesman, a psychologist at the University of Minnesota, created this figure by pooling data from 40 European studies that were published between 1920 and 1987 (Gottesman, 1991). All of the studies employed conservative diagnostic criteria for the disorder.

Consider the data for first-degree relatives and second-degree relatives. On average, *siblings* and children share 50 percent of their genes with the schizophrenic proband; nieces, nephews, and cousins share only 25 percent. The lifetime morbid risk for schizophrenia is much greater among first-degree relatives than it is among second-degree relatives. The risk in the second-degree relatives is greater than the 1 percent figure that is typically reported for people in the general population. As the degree of genetic similarity increases between an individual and a schizophrenic patient, the risk to that person increases. The family history data are consistent with the hypothesis that the transmission of schizophrenia is influenced by genetic factors. They do not prove the point, however, because family studies do not separate genetic and environmental events (see Chapter 2).

Twin Studies Several twin studies have examined concordance rates for schizophrenia. The results of these studies are also summarized in Figure 13–2. The average concordance rate for MZ twins is 48 percent, whereas the comparable figure for DZ twins is 17 percent. One study from Finland, published after Gottesman computed average rates for his figure, found a concordance rate of 46 percent among MZ twins and only 9 percent among DZ twins (Cannon et al., 1998). Although the specific rates vary somewhat from study to study, all of the published reports have found that MZ twins are significantly more likely than DZ twins to be concordant for schizophrenia. This pattern suggests strongly that genetic factors play an important role in the development of the disorder.

It should also be pointed out, however, that none of the twin studies of schizophrenia has found a concordance rate that even approaches 100 percent, which would be expected if genetic factors were entirely responsible for schizophrenia. Thus the twin studies also provide compelling evidence for the importance of environmental events. Some people, like Marsha in the case presented earlier, apparently inherit a predisposition to the development of schizophrenia. Among that select group of vulnerable individuals, certain environmental events must determine whether a given person will eventually exhibit the full-blown symptoms of the disorder.

Adoption Studies Studies of children who were adopted away from their biological parents and reared by foster families provide further evidence regarding the impact of genetic and environmental factors. The first adoption study of schizophrenia was reported by Leonard Heston (1966), a psychiatrist at the University of Washington. He began by identifying records for a group of 49 children who were born between 1915 and 1945 while their mothers were hospitalized for schizophrenia. All the children were apparently normal at birth and were separated from their mothers within 3 days of birth. To rule out possible exposure to the environment associated with the mother's psychosis, any child who had been in contact with maternal relatives was excluded from the study. A control group of children was selected using the admission records of foundling homes where many of the target children had originally been placed. These children were matched to the patients' children on a number of variables, including age, sex, type of eventual placement, and amount of time spent in institutions.

Heston was able to locate and interview most of the offspring, the majority of whom were then in their mid-thirties. Five of the adult offspring of schizophrenic mothers received a diagnosis of schizophrenia. Correcting for the fact that most of the participants were still within the period of risk for the disorder, this resulted in a lifetime morbidity risk for schizophrenia of 16.6 percent in the target group, which is almost exactly the rate observed among children of schizophrenic parents who were raised by their biological parents (see Figure 13–2). In contrast, none of the adult offspring in the control group received a diagnosis of schizophrenia. Because the only difference between the two groups was the genetic relationship between the target offspring and their schizophrenic biological mothers, Heston's data indicate that genetic factors play a role in the development of the disorder. Several other adoption studies have been concerned with schizophrenia, and all reach the same conclusion as Heston's original report (Kendler & Diehl, 1993).

The Spectrum of Schizophrenic Disorders Results from adoption and twin studies also provide interesting clues regarding the boundaries of the concept of schizophrenia. Several types of psychotic disorders and personality disorders resemble schizophrenia in one way or another, including schizoaffective disorder, delusional disorder, and schizotypal personality disorder (discussed in Chapter 9). Are these conditions a reflection of the same genetically determined predisposition as schizophrenia, or are they distinct disorders caused by different forces? If they are genetically related, then investigators should find that the biological relatives of schizophrenic adoptees are more likely to exhibit these conditions as well as schizophrenia. The overall pattern of results does suggest that vulnerability to schizophrenia is sometimes expressed as schizophrenia-like personality traits and other types of psychosis that are not specifically included in the DSM-IV-TR definition of schizophrenia (Kendler & Gardner, 1997).

> Why are some personality disorders considered to be schizophrenia spectrum disorders?

Linkage Studies The combined results from twin and adoption studies indicate that genetic factors are involved in the transmission of schizophrenia. This conclusion does not imply, however, that the manner in which schizophrenia develops is well understood. We know little beyond the fact

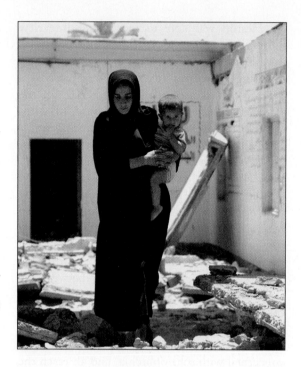

▶ The devastating consequences of war include nutritional deficiencies experienced by mothers and their children. The offspring of women who are pregnant during serious famines may be more likely to develop schizophrenia as they reach adulthood.

search for a particular gene that causes schizophrenia will simply take more time (DeLisi & Fleischhaker, 2007).

One specific gene that has attracted considerable research attention in recent years is associated with the production of catechol-O-methyltransferase (COMT), which is an enzyme that is involved in breaking down the neurotransmitter dopamine. The COMT gene is located on chromosome 22, a region that has been linked to schizophrenia. People who possess a specific form of the COMT gene (called the Val allele) seem to have a small but consistently increased risk for schizophrenia (Glatt, Faraone, & Tsuang, 2003). Scientists believe that this gene may increase risk for schizophrenia by affecting dopamine transmission in the prefrontal cortex of the brain, with the net effect being impaired cognitive ability (van Haren, Bakker, & Kahn, 2008) (see later section on working memory and vulnerability to schizophrenia).

that genetic factors are involved in some way. The mode of transmission has not been identified. Most clinical scientists believe that schizophrenia is a polygenic characteristic, which means that it is the product of a reasonably large number of genes rather than a single gene (see Chapter 2).

One of the most exciting areas of research on genetics and schizophrenia focuses on the search for genetic linkage (see Research Methods in Chapter 14 for an explanation of this process). Studies of this type are designed to identify the location of specific genes that are responsible for the disorder (or some important components of the disorder).

Linkage analysis has not been able to identify a *specific gene* for schizophrenia, but it has implicated *regions* on a small number of chromosomes that may contribute to the etiology of the disorder. For example, reports of positive linkage on regions of chromosomes 6, 8, 13, and 22 have been verified by more than one laboratory (Craddock, O'Donovan, & Owen, 2006; Waddington et al., 2007). These findings clearly narrow the search. We must remember, however, that the identification of chromosome regions is only one step in the direction of finding specific genes. The region that has been implicated on the short arm of chromosome 6 probably contains between 2,000 and 4,000 genes. Supporters of linkage analysis contend that the absence of more definitive discoveries is not surprising when we consider the complexity of this process and the magnitude of the search. They feel that the

Pregnancy and Birth Complications People with schizophrenia are more likely than the general population to have been exposed to various problems during their mother's pregnancy and to have suffered birth injuries. Problems during pregnancy include the mother's contracting various types of diseases and infections. Birth complications include extended labor, breech delivery, forceps delivery, and the umbilical cord wrapped around the baby's neck. These events may be harmful, in part, because they impair circulation or otherwise reduce the availability of oxygen to developing brain regions. Birth records indicate that the mothers of people who later develop schizophrenia experienced more complications at the time of labor and delivery (Cannon, Jones, & Murray, 2002; McNeil & Cantor-Graae, 1999).

It is not clear whether the effects of pregnancy and birth complications interact with genetic factors. They may produce neurodevelopmental abnormalities that result in schizophrenia regardless of family history for the disorder. Conversely, a fetus that is genetically predisposed to schizophrenia may be more susceptible to brain injury following certain kinds of obstetric difficulties (Walker et al., 2004).

Dietary factors may also play a role in the etiology of the disorder. Severe maternal malnutrition in the early months of pregnancy leads to an increased risk of schizophrenia among the offspring. This conclusion is based on a study of medical and psychiatric records of people who were born in the western part of the Netherlands between 1944 and 1946 (Susser et al., 1996). The German blockade of ports and other supply routes in this area led to a severe famine at the end of World War II. People who were conceived during the worst months of the famine were twice as likely to develop schizophrenia than were people whose mothers became pregnant at other times, including the early months of the famine. These results suggest that prenatal nutritional deficiencies may disrupt normal development of the fetal nervous system (Hulshoff et al., 2000).

Viral Infections Some speculation has focused on the potential role that viral infections may play in the etiology of schizophrenia (Brown, 2006). One indirect line of support for this hypothesis comes from studies indicating that people who develop schizophrenia are somewhat more likely than other people to have been born during the winter months (McGrath & Welham, 1999). Some clinicians interpret this pattern to mean that, during their pregnancies, the mothers were more likely to develop viral infections, which are more prevalent during the winter. Exposure to infection presumably interferes with brain development in the fetus. This possibility has received considerable attention in the research literature and remains an important topic of debate (Preti & Miotto, 2005).

Neuropathology One important step toward understanding the etiology of schizophrenia would be to identify its neurological underpinnings. If people with schizophrenia suffer from a form of neurological dysfunction, shouldn't it be possible to observe differences between the structure of their brains and those of other people? This is a challenging task. Scientists have invented methods to create images of the living human brain (see Chapter 4). Some of these procedures provide static pictures of various brain structures at rest, just as an X ray provides a photographic image of a bone or some other organ of the body. More recently, sophisticated methods have enabled us to create functional images of the brain while a person is performing different tasks. Studies using these techniques have produced evidence indicating that a number of brain areas are involved in schizophrenia (Davidson & Heinrichs, 2003). You may want to review the description of brain structures in Chapter 2 (Figure 2–3) before reading the next sections of this chapter.

Structural Brain Imaging Many investigations of brain structure in people with schizo-phrenia have employed magnetic resonance imaging (MRI; see Chapter 4 for an explanation of this process). The disorder is not associated with abnormalities in one specific brain region or in one particular type of nerve cell. Rather, it seems to affect many different regions of the brain and the ways in which they connect or communicate with each other (Niznikiewicz, Kubicki, & Shenton, 2003). Most MRI studies have reported a decrease in total volume of brain tissue among schizophrenic patients. Another consistent finding is that some people with schizophrenia have mildly to moderately enlarged lateral ventricles, the cavities on each side of the brain that are filled with cerebrospinal fluid.

These differences seem to reflect a natural part of the disorder rather than a side effect of treatment with antipsychotic medication. In fact, some studies have found enlarged ventricles in young schizophrenic patients before they have been exposed to any form of treatment (Steen et al., 2006). Some studies have also found enlarged ventricles prior to the onset of symptoms. Significantly, these differences do not appear to become more marked as time goes on. The structural changes seem to occur early in the development of the disorder and therefore may play a role in the onset of symptoms (DeLisi, 2008; Weinberger & McClure, 2002).

The temporal lobes have also been studied extensively using MRI scans. Several studies have reported decreased size of the hippocampus, the parahippocampus, the amygdala, and the thalamus, all of which are parts of the limbic system (Price et al., 2006). These areas of the brain (see Figure 13–3 on page 414) play a crucial role in the regulation of emotion as well as the integration of cognition and emotion. Decreased size of these structures in the limbic area of the temporal lobes may be especially noticeable on the left side of the brain, which plays an important role in the control of language. Schizophrenic patients who exhibit the greatest degree of disorganized speech may be most likely to show a decrease in the size of left temporal lobe structures (Shenton, 1996).

Many questions remain to be answered regarding the relation between structural brain abnormalities and schizophrenia. Does the pattern reflect a generalized deterioration of the brain, or is it the result of a defect in specific brain sites? We don't know. Is the presence of enlarged ventricles and cortical atrophy consistently found in some subset of schizophrenic patients? Some investigators have reported an association between

Structures of the Brain Implicated in Schizophrenia

FIGURE 13–3 Structural imaging procedures indicate reduced size of temporal lobe structures, such as the hippocampus and amygdalae, among some patients with schizophrenia.

▲ MRI scans from 4 identical twin pairs discordant for schizophrenia showing varying degrees of increased ventricular size in the twin with the disorder compared to the twin who is well.

this type of neuropathology and other factors, such as negative symptoms, poor response to medication, and absence of family history of the disorder. These are all interesting possibilities, but none has been firmly established.

Functional Brain Imaging In addition to static pictures of brain structures, clinical scientists use techniques that provide dynamic images of brain functions. One dynamic brain imaging technique, known as positron emission tomography (PET), can reflect changes in brain activity as the person responds to various task demands. Visual stimulation will produce increased cerebral blood flow in the visual cortex; people performing a simple motor task exhibit increased flow in the motor cortex. Functional MRI is another tool that can be used to observe brain activity. The results of studies using these techniques suggest dysfunction in various neural circuits, including some regions of the prefrontal cortex (see Figure 13–4) and several regions in the temporal lobes (Bonner-Jackson et al., 2005; Harrison, 1999). The problems seem to involve activities within, as well as integration between, a variety of functional circuits rather than a localized abnormality in one region of the brain.

The role of neurological abnormalities in schizophrenia has been highlighted by a study of identical twins conducted by investigators at the National Institute of Mental Health (NIMH). Participants included 27 pairs of twins discordant for schizophrenia and 13 pairs that were concordant for the disorder. Changes in brain structure, measured by MRI, and changes in brain function, measured by cerebral blood flow, were prominent in the twins who had developed schizophrenia. Their well co-twins also exhibited more neurological impairment than a group of normal control participants, but these abnormalities were less marked than those found in the probands. Among discordant monozygotic pairs, the schizophrenic twin typically had the smaller hippocampus and smaller amygdala. The schizophrenic twins always showed reduced frontal lobe activity compared with their unaffected co-twins. Results for enlarged ventricles were less consistent. In general, neurological dysfunction seemed to be associated with the overall severity of the disorder rather than being indicative of an etiologically distinct subgroup of patients (Bridle et al., 2002; Torrey et al., 1994).

General Conclusions The primary conclusion that can be drawn from existing brain imaging studies is that schizophrenia is associated with diffuse patterns of neuropathology. The most consistent findings point toward structural as well as functional irregularities in the frontal cortex and limbic areas of the temporal lobes, which play an important role in cognitive and emotional processes. The neural network connecting limbic areas with the frontal cortex may be fundamentally disordered in schizophrenia.

Speculation regarding disruptions in neural circuitry must also be tempered with caution. Evidence of neuropathology does not seem to be unique to schizophrenic patients. Many patients with other psychiatric and neurological disorders show similar changes in brain structure and function. Furthermore, a specific brain lesion has not been identified, and it is unlikely that one will be found. It is unlikely that a disorder as complex as schizophrenia will be traced to a single site in the brain (Meehl, 1990). The various symptoms and cognitive deficits that have been observed in schizophrenic patients may be linked to a host of subtle disruptions in neurological functions (Green, 2001).

It should also be emphasized that brain imaging procedures are not diagnostically meaningful tests for mental disorders. For example, an MRI showing enlarged ventricles does not prove that a patient has schizophrenia. Brain imaging procedures have identified interesting group differences, but they do not predict the presence of schizophrenia for individuals. The group differences that have been observed are very subtle in comparison to the levels of neuropathology found in disorders such as Alzheimer's disease and Huntington's disease (see Chapter 14). Some schizophrenic patients do not show abnormalities in brain structure or function.

A dramatic example of this point was found in the NIMH study of discordant MZ twins. In one pair, the well twin was a successful businessman who had never had any problems with mental disorder. His twin brother had been severely impaired with schizophrenia for 20 years. The well twin had ventricles that were five times larger than those of the schizophrenic twin. Thus we should approach all these hypotheses with caution and skepticism.

Neurochemistry   The neurological underpinnings of schizophrenia may not take the form of changes in the size or organization of brain structures. They may be even more subtle, involving alterations in the chemical communications among neurons within particular brain circuits.

Areas of Brain Function Implicated in Schizophrenia

Dorsolateral Prefrontal Cortex

FIGURE 13–4   Neural circuits in the dorsolateral prefrontal cortex may function improperly in schizophrenia.

The Dopamine Hypothesis   Scientists have proposed various neurochemical theories to account for the etiology of schizophrenia. The most influential theory, known as the *dopamine hypothesis,* focuses on the function of specific dopamine pathways in the limbic area of the brain. The original version of the dopamine hypothesis proposed that the symptoms of schizophrenia are the product of excessive levels of dopaminergic activity. This hypothesis grew out of attempts to understand how antipsychotic drugs improve the adjustment of many schizophrenic patients. Animals who receive doses of antipsychotic drugs show a marked increase in the production of dopamine. In 1963, Arvid Carlsson, a Swedish pharmacologist, suggested that antipsychotic drugs block postsynaptic dopamine receptors. The presynaptic neuron recognizes the presence of this blockade and increases its release of dopamine in a futile attempt to override it (Carlsson & Lindqvist, 1963).

Why can't we use brain imaging to diagnose schizophrenia?

If the dopamine system is dysfunctional in schizophrenic patients, what is the specific form of this problem? One possibility is that certain neural pathways have an elevated sensitivity to dopamine because of increased numbers of post-synaptic dopamine receptors. The potency of various types of antipsychotic drugs is specifically related to their ability to block one type of dopamine receptor, known as receptors. Autopsy studies of schizophrenic patients' brains have found that some patients have an excessive number of receptors in the striatum (Torrey et al., 2005). It is not clear whether this finding indicates that an elevated number of dopamine receptors plays a causal role in the original onset of the disorder because it also might be the results of prolonged treatment with antipsychotic drugs, which produce an increase in the number of receptors.

Interactions of Multiple Neurotransmitters A dysregulation and exaggerated response of certain dopamine pathways is certainly involved in schizophrenia, at least for some patients. On the other hand, experts now agree that several other neurotransmitters also play an important role. A neurochemical model focused narrowly on dopamine fails to explain many different aspects of the disorder, including the following: Some patients do not respond positively to drugs that block dopamine receptors; the effects of antipsychotic drugs require several days to become effective, but dopamine blockage begins immediately; research studies that examined the by-products of dopamine in cerebrospinal fluid were inconclusive at best.

Current neurochemical hypotheses regarding schizophrenia focus on a broad array of neurotransmitters (Carlsson et al., 2001). Special interest has been focused on serotonin pathways since the introduction of a new class of antipsychotic drugs such as clozapine (Clozaril) that are useful in treating patients who were resistant to standard antipsychotic drugs. (See the section on treatment.) These "atypical" antipsychotics produce a strong blockade of serotonin receptors and only a weak blockade of D_2 receptors. This pattern leads to speculation that the neurochemical substrates of schizophrenia may involve a complex interaction between serotonin and dopamine pathways in the brain (Downar & Kapur, 2008).

Brain imaging studies that point to problems in the prefrontal cortex have also drawn attention to glutamate and GABA (gamma-aminobutyric acid), the two principal neurotransmitters in the cerebral cortex (Wassef, Baker, & Kochan, 2003; Weinberger, 1997). Glutamate is an excitatory neurotransmitter, and GABA is an inhibitory neurotransmitter. As in the case of serotonin, hypotheses regarding the role of glutamate and GABA focus on their interactions with dopamine pathways, especially those connecting temporal lobe structures with the prefrontal and limbic cortexes.

Social Factors

There is little question that biological factors play an important role in the etiology of schizophrenia, but twin studies also provide compelling evidence for the importance of environmental events. The disorder is expressed in its full-blown form only when vulnerable individuals experience some type of environmental event, which might include anything from nutritional variables to stressful life events (Howes et al., 2004; Walker et al., 2004). What sorts of nongenetic events interact with genetic factors and other biological factors to produce schizophrenia? Specific answers are not available at the present time. We can, however, review some of the hypotheses that have been proposed and studied.

Social Class One general indicator of a person's status within a community's hierarchy of prestige and influence is social class. People from different social classes are presumably exposed to different levels of environmental stress, with those people in the lowest class being subjected to the most hardships. More than 50 years ago, social scientists working in Chicago found that the highest prevalence of schizophrenia was found in neighborhoods of the lowest socioeconomic status (Faris & Dunham, 1939). Many research studies have subsequently confirmed this finding in several other geographic areas (Boydell & Murray, 2003). The evidence supporting an inverse relationship between social class and schizophrenia is substantial.

There are two ways to interpret the relationship between social class and schizophrenia. One holds that harmful events associated with membership in the lowest social classes, which might include many factors ranging from stress and social isolation to poor nutrition, play a causal role in the development of the disorder. This is often called the *social causation* hypothesis. It is also possible, however, that low social class is an outcome rather than a cause of schizophrenia. Those people who develop schizophrenia may be less able than others to complete a higher level education or to hold a well-paying job. Their cognitive and social impairments may cause downward social mobility. In other words, regardless of the social class of their family of origin, many schizophrenic patients may gradually drift into the lowest social classes. This view is sometimes called the *social selection hypothesis.*

Research studies have found evidence supporting both views. The social selection hypothesis is supported by studies that have compared the occupational roles of male schizophrenic patients with those of their fathers. The patients are frequently less successful than their fathers, whereas the opposite pattern is typical of men who do not have schizophrenia (Jones et al., 1993).

It is also true, however, that a disproportionately high percentage of the fathers of schizophrenic patients were from the lowest social class (Harrison et al., 2001). This finding is consistent with the social causation hypothesis. Additional support for the social causation hypothesis has been found using different research strategies. For example, a unique study considered the relation between economic conditions (employment rates) and rates of psychiatric hospitalization in the state of New York between 1852 and 1967 (Brenner, 1973). Throughout this extended period of time, increases in the rate of unemployment were followed closely, usually within a year, by sharp increases in the number of patients admitted to mental hospitals. The strongest relationship was found for schizophrenia and bipolar mood disorders.

Migrant Studies Higher rates of schizophrenia have also been found repeatedly among people who have migrated to a new country (Cantor-Graae & Selton, 2005). Several influential studies of this sort focused on African-Caribbean people who moved to the United Kingdom from Jamaica, Barbados, and Trinidad. Risk for schizophrenia in these migrant groups was found to be several times higher than the risk observed in the native-born U.K. population. It was also much higher than the risk observed among people living in the migrants' countries of origin. Subsequent studies demonstrated that the effect is not unique to the United Kingdom. Larger effects are reported for migrants from developing rather than developed countries, and they are also larger for migrants from countries where the majority population is black. One possible explanation for this phenomenon is that social adversity increases risk for schizophrenia. Migrants tend to settle in urban areas where they may be exposed to discrimination and other forms of disadvantage (Fearon & Morgan, 2006).

In general, the evidence regarding socioeconomic status and schizophrenia indicates that the disorder is, to a certain extent, influenced by social factors. Adverse social and economic circumstances may increase the probability that persons who are genetically predisposed to the disorder will develop its clinical symptoms (van Os & McGuffin, 2003; Schiffman et al., 2001).

Psychological Factors

Most of the attention devoted to psychological factors and schizophrenia has focused on patterns of behavior and communication within families. Research evidence indicates that family interactions and communication problems are not primarily responsible for the initial appearance of symptoms. They may help to trigger the onset of the disorder among those who were already genetically predisposed to its development, and they also influence the course of the disorder after the symptoms have appeared.

In order to place current thinking about these issues in historical perspective, consider the sort of causal pathways that were imagined by therapists in the 1960s. One influential hypothesis was concerned with the relationship between thought disorder in schizophrenic patients and communication problems exhibited by their parents (Wynne & Singer, 1963). According to this theory, the parents of schizophrenic patients are often unable to communicate clearly. This deficiency results in disrupted conversations and confusion on the part of their children. The child is caught between parents who are locked in conflict and subsequently fails to develop either a secure identity or conventional forms of thinking and speaking. Over an extended period of time, these problems presumably lead to the onset of schizophrenic symptoms. Hypotheses of this kind were tested extensively during the 1960s and 1970s, and the results were negative (Goldstein, 1988; Miklowitz, 1995; Neale & Oltmanns, 1980). Disturbed patterns of communication among family members do not cause people to develop schizophrenia. This knowledge is important to parents of schizophrenic patients. They experience enough emotional anguish without also being made to feel that something they did or said was the primary cause of their child's problems.

Expressed Emotion The family environment does have a significant impact on the course (as opposed to the etiology) of schizophrenia. Studies

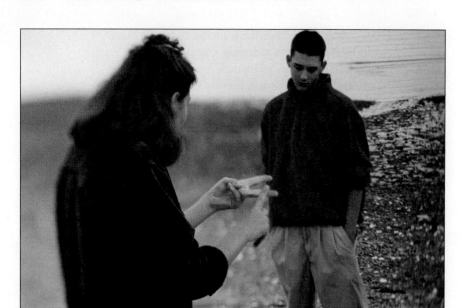

▲ Criticism and hostility can increase the risk of relapse for some patients with schizophrenia. Conversely, warmth and family support can serve as a protective factor.

that point to this conclusion do not address the original onset of symptoms. Instead, they are concerned with the adjustment of patients who have already been treated for schizophrenic symptoms.

This effect was discovered by people who were interested in the adjustment of patients who were discharged after being treated in a psychiatric hospital. Men with schizophrenia were much more likely to return to the hospital within the next 9 months if they went to live with their wives or parents than if they went to live in other lodgings or with their siblings. The patients who relapsed seemed to react negatively to some feature of their close relationship with their wives or mothers.

Subsequent research confirmed this initial impression (Brown, Birley, & Wing, 1972; Vaughn & Leff, 1976). Relatives of schizophrenic patients were interviewed prior to the patients' discharge from the hospital, and many of the relatives made statements that reflected negative or intrusive attitudes toward the patient. These statements were used to create a measure of **expressed emotion (EE)**. For example, many of the relatives expressed hostility toward the patient or repeatedly criticized the patient's behavior. The following comments, made by the stepfather of a young man with schizophrenia, illustrate generalized, hostile criticisms of the patient's behavior. These comments would be considered to be high in expressed emotion.

> INTERVIEWER: What seemed different about Stephen's behavior?
> STEPFATHER: Everything and anything. In other words, he's the type of person, you don't tell him, he tells you.

> INTERVIEWER: You say that he spent time in a juvenile facility?
> STEPFATHER: Yeah. This kid is a genuine con artist, believe me. I spent time in the service and I've been around con artists. This kid is a first-class, genuine con artist, bar none.
>
> (Leff & Vaughn, 1985, p. 42)

Other family members appeared to be overprotective or too closely identified with the patient. These phenomena are also rated as being high in expressed emotion. Of course, a certain amount of worrying and concern should be expected from a parent whose child has developed a severe disorder such as schizophrenia. In the assessment of expressed emotion, relatives were considered to be emotionally overinvolved if they reported responses such as extreme anxiety or exaggerated forms of self-sacrifice. For example, the following exchange illustrates emotional overinvolvement (high EE) by the mother of a 24-year-old male patient who had his first onset of the disorder when he was 22:

> MOTHER: He talked to me a lot—because I was his therapist—the person he shared with more than anybody else. He involves me, ruminates with me, because I allow him to do it.
> INTERVIEWER: How frequently?
> MOTHER: He would do it constantly. He would do it as much as I would be there with him.
> INTERVIEWER: Once or twice a week?
> MOTHER: No, it happened daily. All the time I was with him, particularly in the last four or five months. He would talk to me for hours at a time, worrying and sharing how bad he felt, reporting to me every change in mood or feeling from 5-minute to 5-minute period.
>
> (Leff & Vaughn, 1985, p. 51).

Patients who returned to live in a home with at least one member who was high in EE were more likely than patients from low EE families to relapse in the first 9 months after discharge.

This result has been replicated many times (Marom et al., 2005). Approximately half of schizophrenic patients live in families that would be rated as being high in EE. Average relapse rates—defined primarily in terms of the proportion of patients who show a definite return of positive symptoms in the first year following hospital discharge—are 52 percent for patients in high EE families and 22 percent for patients in low EE families. Among the various types of comments that can contribute to a high EE rating, criticism is usually most strongly related to patients' relapse (Hooley & Gotlib, 2000).

Close contact with relatives increases the risk of relapse for schizophrenic patients living with a high EE relative. The opposite pattern is seen in low EE families, where increased contact with relatives seems to have a protective influence. The relationship between family contact and patients' relapse rates is illustrated in Figure 13–5. This figure is based on a reanalysis of data from 25 studies, with a combined sample of more than 800 patients (Bebbington & Kuipers, 1994). Patients who spent more than 35 hours per week in face-to-face contact with a high EE relative were placed in the "high-contact" category; less than 35 hours per week was considered "low contact." These data indicate that the effect of close contact with relatives depends on the emotional climate of the family.

High EE seems to be related, at least in part, to relatives' knowledge and beliefs about their family member's problems. Relatives find it easier to accept the most obvious positive symptoms as being the product of a mental disorder (Brewin et al., 1991). They show less tolerance toward negative symptoms, such as avolition and social withdrawal, perhaps because the patient may appear to be simply lazy or unmotivated.

Understanding Family Attitudes The influence of expressed emotion is not unique to schizophrenia. Patients with mood disorders, eating disorders, panic disorder with agoraphobia, and obsessive–compulsive disorder are also more likely to relapse following discharge if they are living with a high EE relative (Miklowitz, 2004). In fact, EE is an even better predictor of outcome for mood disorders and eating disorders than it is for schizophrenia (Butzlaff & Hooley, 1998). The extension of this phenomenon to other disorders should not be taken to mean that it is unimportant or that the social context of the family is irrelevant to our understanding of the maintenance of schizophrenia (see Research Methods). It may indicate, however, that this aspect of the causal model is shared with other forms of psychopathology. The specific nature of the person's symptoms may hinge on the genetic predisposition.

Expressed Emotion, Interpersonal Contact, and Relapse Rates

Percent of patients relapsed

High contact (>35 hr/wk)
Low contact (<35 hr/wk)

High EE   Low EE

FIGURE 13–5 Close contact increases the risk of relapse for schizophrenic patients living with a high-EE relative. In low-EE families, increased contact has a protective effect.

Source: P. Beggington and L. Kuipers, 1994, "The Predictive Utility of Expressed Emotion in Schizophrenia: An Aggregate Analysis," *Psychological Medicine, 24,* pp. 707–718. Copyright © 1994. Reprinted by permission of Cambridge University Press.

Cross-cultural evidence suggests that high EE may be more common in Western or developed countries than in non-Western or developing countries (Kymalainen & Weissman, 2008). This observation might help explain why the long-term course of schizophrenia is typically less severe in developing countries. Some speculation has focused on family members' attitudes and beliefs: People in developing countries may be more tolerant of eccentric behavior among their extended family members. These attitudes may create environments similar to those found in low EE homes in the West. An alternative view places greater emphasis on the culturally determined relationships between patients and other members of their families (Jenkins, 1993). Studies of Mexican American families suggest that prosocial aspects of interactions between patients and their families can enhance family cohesion and decrease the stigma associated with serious mental disorders. In some cultures, family warmth serves as a protective factor and reduces the probability of patients' relapse (López et al., 2004).

We must be cautious to avoid a narrow view of this phenomenon. The concept of expressed emotion raises extremely sensitive issues for family members, who have too frequently been blamed for the problems of people with schizophrenia. Expressed emotion is not the only factor that can influence the course of a schizophrenic disorder. Some patients relapse in spite of an understanding, tolerant family environment. Furthermore, research studies have shown that the relationship between patients' behavior and relatives' expressed emotion is a transactional or reciprocal process. In other

RESEARCH METHODS Comparison Groups: What Is Normal?

Research studies in the field of psychopathology typically involve comparisons among two or more groups of participants. One group, sometimes called "cases," includes people who already meet the diagnostic criteria for a particular mental disorder, such as schizophrenia. Comparison groups are composed of people who do not have the disorder in question. This approach is sometimes called the case control design because it depends on a contrast between cases and control participants. If the investigators find a significant difference between groups, they have demonstrated that the dependent variable is correlated with the disorder (see Research Methods in Chapter 2). They hope to conclude that they have identified a variable that is relevant to understanding the etiology of this condition. Causal inferences are risky, however, in correlational research. Our willingness to accept these conclusions hinges in large part on whether the investigators selected an appropriate comparison group.

People conducting correlational research, then, must make every effort to identify and test a group of people who are just like the cases except that they do not have the disorder in question (Gehlbach, 1988). This typically means that the people in both groups should be similar with regard to such obvious factors as age, gender, and socioeconomic background. If the investigators find differences between people who have the disorder and those who do not, they want to attribute those differences to the disorder itself. Two main types of comparison groups are used in

psychopathology research: people with no history of mental disorder, sometimes called "normal participants," and people who have some other form of mental disorder, sometimes called "patient controls."

Selecting normal comparison groups is not as simple as it might seem. In fact, researchers must make several basic decisions (Kendler, 1990). Does "normal" mean that the person has never had the disorder in question, or does it mean a complete absence of any type of psychopathology? Should people be included as normal control participants if they have a family history of the disorder, even though they do not have the disorder themselves?

> **Should we expect to find unique causes for each type of mental disorder?**

A second research strategy involves comparing patients with one type of disorder to those who have another form of psychopathology. Investigators usually employ this strategy to determine whether the variable in question is specifically related to the disorder that they are studying. Are enlarged lateral ventricles or family communication problems unique to people with schizophrenia? Lack of specificity may raise questions about whether this variable is related to the cause of the disorder. It might suggest that this particular variable is, instead, a general consequence of factors such as hospitalization, which the patient control group has also experienced.

Many of the etiological variables that we have discussed in this chapter are not unique to schizophrenia. Expressed emotion predicts relapse among patients with mood disorders as well as among those with schizophrenia. Should this result be taken to mean that EE does not play an important role in the etiology of schizophrenia? Not necessarily. The answer to this question depends on the specific causal model that is being considered (Garber & Hollon, 1991). All forms of psychopathology depend on the interaction of multiple factors spanning biological, social, and psychological systems. Some of these may be specific to the disorder being studied, and others may be general. The development of schizophrenia may depend on a specific genetically determined predisposition. The environmental events that are responsible for eventually causing vulnerable people to express this disorder might be nonspecific. The course of schizophrenia is clearly influenced by the social context in which the patient lives. The fact that similar factors influence people with mood disorders should not be taken to mean that EE is not an important factor in the complex chain of events that explain the etiology and maintenance of schizophrenia.

For all these reasons, the selection of meaningful comparison groups can be a complex and difficult process. There are no perfect solutions to these issues. The research strategy chosen in any particular study will depend on the specific questions that the investigators are trying to answer.

words, patients influence their relatives' attitudes at the same time that relatives' attitudes influence patients' adjustment. Persistent negative attitudes on the part of relatives appear to be perpetuated by a negative cycle of interactions in which patients play an active role (Goldstein et al., 1997).

Interaction of Biological and Environmental

A useful etiological model for schizophrenia must include the interaction of genetic factors and environmental events. The heterogeneous nature of

the disorder, in terms of symptoms as well as course, also suggests that schizophrenia should be explained in terms of multiple pathways (Tandon et al., 2008). Some forms of the disorder may be the product of a strong genetic predisposition acting in combination with relatively common psychosocial experiences, such as stressful life events or disrupted communication patterns. For other people, relatively unusual circumstances, such as severe malnutrition during pregnancy, may be responsible for neurodevelopmental abnormalities that eventually lead to the onset of psychotic symptoms in the absence of genetic vulnerability.

Various kinds of environmental events have been linked to the etiology of schizophrenia. Some may operate in interaction with the genotype for schizophrenia; others may be sufficient to produce the disorder on their own. Considerable speculation has focused recently on biological factors, such as viral infections and nutritional deficiencies. Psychosocial factors, such as adverse economic circumstances, may also be involved. These events may be particularly harmful to people who are genetically predisposed to the disorder.

The Search for Markers of Vulnerability

Some people apparently inherit a predisposition to schizophrenia. Obviously, it would be useful to be able to identify those people. Genetic linkage studies will be part of that answer, if several genes are found to be responsible for the disorder. The search for more precise information about the development of the disorder may also hinge on our ability to identify vulnerability markers, which have also been called *endophenotypes* (Gottesman & Gould, 2003). An endophenotype is a component or trait that lies somewhere on the pathway between the genotype, which lays the foundation for the disorder, and full-blown symptoms of the disorder. It can be measured with precise laboratory procedures of many kinds, but it cannot be seen by the unaided eye.

If we are looking for signs of vulnerability— or endophenotypes—that can be detected among individuals who are genetically predisposed to schizophrenia, where should we look? What form will these signs take? Is it possible to detect signs of vulnerability among individuals who approach the threshold for developing schizophrenia spectrum disorders but have not exhibited any kind of overt symptoms? This issue has attracted considerable attention, but we don't have firm answers to these questions.

People who are vulnerable to schizophrenia might be identified by developing measures that could detect the underlying biological dysfunction or by developing sensitive measures of their subtle eccentricities of behavior. The range of possible markers is, therefore, quite large.

Assume that we have selected a specific measure, such as a biochemical assay or a psychological test, and we are interested in knowing whether it might be useful in identifying people who are vulnerable to schizophrenia. What criteria should a **vulnerability marker** fulfill? First, the proposed marker must distinguish between people who already have schizophrenia and those who do not. Second, it should be a stable characteristic over time. Third, the proposed measure of vulnerability should identify more people among the biological relatives of schizophrenic patients than among people in the general population. For example, it should be found among the discordant MZ twins of schizophrenic patients, even if they don't exhibit any symptoms of schizophrenia. Finally, the proposed measure of vulnerability should be able to predict the future development of schizophrenia among those who have not yet experienced a psychotic episode (Braff, Schork, & Gottesman, 2007; Snitz, MacDonald, & Carter, 2006).

What characteristics would define a useful marker of vulnerability to schizophrenia?

Although reliable measures of vulnerability have not been identified, they are being actively pursued by many investigators with a wide variety of measurement procedures. In the following pages we will outline some of the psychological procedures that have been shown to be among the most promising.

Working Memory Impairment Many investigators have pursued the search for signs of vulnerability by looking at measures of cognitive performance in which schizophrenic patients differ from other people. Some of these studies have focused on cognitive tasks that evaluate information processing, working memory, and attention/vigilance (Green et al., 2004; Hoff & Kremen, 2002).

Considerable emphasis has been focused on one aspect of cognitive functioning known as *working memory,* or the ability to maintain and manipulate information for a short period of time. Working memory can be broken down into several more specific processes. Some of these involve memory buffers that provide short-term storage for visual and verbal information. The most important processes in working memory involve a *central executive component* that is responsible for the manipulation and transformation of data that are held in the storage buffers. Many studies have reported that people with schizophrenia are impaired in their ability to perform laboratory tasks that depend on this central executive component of working memory (Barch, 2005).

One important set of results regarding working memory impairment is based on use of the

NBack task. In this task, the participant is presented with a series of items (such as numbers or symbols). He or she is asked to remember the sequence of items as they are being presented. Whenever the participant notices that the current item is the same as the item that was presented "N" trials previously (with N being a number from 0 to 3), he or she is supposed to press a button. The NBack task is one of the most frequently used measures of working memory, especially in studies that use functional neuroimaging in schizophrenia.

The identification of deficits in working memory is particularly interesting with regard to schizophrenia because it links to other evidence regarding brain functions and this disorder. Processes that are associated with central executive processing are associated with brain activity located in the dorsolateral area of the prefrontal cortex (see Figure 13–4) which seems to be dysfunctional in schizophrenia. Neurochemical hypotheses regarding schizophrenia are also relevant in this regard because the dopamine neurotransmitter system plays a crucial role in supporting activities involved in working memory (Goldman-Rakic, Muly, & Williams, 2000).

Working memory problems seem to be a stable characteristic of patients with schizophrenia; they do not fluctuate over time (Cannon et al., 2002). Furthermore, these cognitive deficits are found with increased prevalence among the unaffected first-degree relatives of schizophrenic persons, including discordant MZ twins (Sitskoom et al., 2004). Finally, children who later receive a diagnosis of schizophrenia are more likely to have been impaired on tests of verbal working memory than are their siblings who do not develop the disorder. Therefore, measures of working memory fulfill several of the criteria for an index of vulnerability. The research indicates that problems in working memory may be useful signs of vulnerability to schizophrenia (Barch, 2005).

Eye-Tracking Dysfunction Another promising line of work involves impairments in eye movements—specifically, difficulty in tracking the motion of a pendulum or a similarly oscillating stimulus while the person's head is held motionless. When people with schizophrenia are asked to track a moving target, like an oscillating pendulum, with their eyes, a substantial number of them show dysfunctions in smooth-pursuit eye movement (Holzman, 2000; Levy & Holzman, 1997). Instead of reproducing the motion of the pendulum in a series of smooth waves, their tracking records show frequent interruptions of smooth-pursuit movements by numerous rapid movements. Examples of normal tracking records and those of schizophrenic patients are presented in Figure 13–6. Only about 8 percent of normal people exhibit the eye-tracking dysfunctions illustrated in part (C) of Figure 13–6, although some studies have reported higher figures.

Approximately 50 percent of the first-degree relatives of schizophrenic persons show similar smooth-pursuit impairments (Curtis, Calkins, & Iacono, 2001; Hong et al., 2008). The overall pattern of results seen in people with schizophrenia and their families suggests that poor tracking performance may be associated with the predisposition to schizophrenia. That conclusion becomes even more interesting in light of evidence from additional studies suggesting that tracking ability is stable over time, influenced by genetic factors, and found among people who exhibit features associated with schizotypal personality disorder (Gooding, Miller, & Kwapil, 2000; Lenzenweger & O'Driscoll, 2006).

It is not yet possible to identify people who are specifically predisposed to the development of schizophrenia, but research studies have identified potential vulnerability markers. The real test, of course, will center around predictive validity. Can any of these measures, such as working memory deficits or smooth-pursuit eye-tracking impairment, predict the later appearance of schizophrenia in people whose scores indicate possible vulnerability? High-risk studies will be useful in providing this type of evidence.

Eye-Tracking Patterns

FIGURE 13–6 This illustration contrasts smooth-pursuit eye-tracking patterns of normal subjects with those of schizophrenic patients. Part (A) shows the actual target. Part (B) illustrates the pattern for people without schizophrenia, and part (C) shows the pattern for people with schizophrenia.

Source: From D. L. Levy, et al., Eye-tracking dysfunction and schizophrenia: A critical perspective. *Schizophrenia Bulletin,* (1993), 19, 462.

TREATMENT

Schizophrenia is a complex disorder that often must be treated over an extended period of time. Clinicians must be concerned about the treatment of acute psychotic episodes as well as the prevention of future episodes. A multifaceted approach to treatment is typically required. Antipsychotic medication is the primary mode of treatment for this disorder. Because many patients remain impaired between episodes, long-term care must often involve the provision of housing and social support. People with impaired social and occupational skills need special types of training. The treatment of schizophrenia requires attention on all of these fronts and is necessarily concerned with the cooperative efforts of many types of professionals (Lehman et al., 2004). Schizophrenia also takes its toll on families. The Getting Help section at the end of this chapter discusses some of the resources available for patients and families.

Antipsychotic Medication

The many different forms of medication that are used to treat patients with schizophrenia can be divided into two broad categories. The first generation of drugs began to be introduced in the 1950s, and a second generation swept into practice in the 1990s. Both kinds of medication are in standard use today, and both waves of discovery introduced improvements in care for patients with schizophrenia.

The first generation of antipsychotic drugs—also called classical or traditional antipsychotics—was discovered accidentally in the early 1950s by a French neurosurgeon who used them as a supplement to anesthesia. They were not effective for the purpose he intended, but they did have a calming effect on the patients. This experience prompted psychiatrists to use the same drugs with their patients. Early reports of success in treating chronic psychotic patients quickly led to the widespread use of these drugs, such as chlorpromazine (Thorazine), in psychiatric hospitals throughout Europe and the United States (Shen, 1999). The discovery of these drugs quickly changed the way in which schizophrenia was treated. Large numbers of patients who had previously been institutionalized could be discharged to community care (but see Chapter 18 on the effects of deinstitutionalization).

Several related types of drugs were developed in subsequent years. They are called **antipsychotic drugs** because they have a relatively specific effect—to reduce the severity of psychotic symptoms. Some beneficial effects on problems such as agitation and hostility may be noticed within a week after the patient begins taking antipsychotic medication, but it usually takes two or three weeks before improvement is seen with regard to psychotic symptoms (Kutscher, 2008). Positive symptoms, such as hallucinations, respond better to antipsychotic medication than negative symptoms, such as alogia and blunted affect. Viewed from the patient's perspective, medication allows them to be less bothered or preoccupied by troublesome thoughts and perceptual experiences (Mizrahi et al, 2005). In other words, they are able to distance themselves from their positive symptoms, even though the medication seldom eliminates hallucinations and delusional beliefs.

Double-blind, placebo-controlled studies have confirmed the effectiveness of antipsychotic medication in the treatment of patients who are acutely disturbed. Literally thousands of studies have addressed this issue over a period of more than 40 years (Adams et al., 2001; Sharif et al., 2007). These studies provide substantial support for the effectiveness of antipsychotic medication. Most studies find that about half of the patients who receive medication are rated as being much improved after 4 to 6 weeks of treatment. Further improvements may continue beyond that point for some patients. In contrast, patients treated with placebos exhibit much smaller rates of improvement, and many of them actually deteriorate.

Unfortunately, a substantial minority of schizophrenic patients, perhaps 25 percent, do not improve on classical antipsychotic drugs (Conley & Kelly, 2001). Another 30 to 40 percent might be considered partial responders: Their condition improves, but they do not show a full remission of symptoms. Investigators have not been able to identify reliable differences between patients who improve on medication and those who do not. Some experts have suggested that treatment-resistant patients may have more prominent negative symptoms, greater disorganization, and more evidence of neurological abnormalities (Elkis, 2007).

Maintenance Medication After patients recover from acute psychotic episodes, there is a high probability that they will have another episode. The relapse rate may be as high as 65 to 70 percent in the first year after hospital discharge if patients discontinue medication. Continued treatment with antipsychotic drugs can reduce this rate to approximately 40 percent (Davis & Chen, 2003). Therefore the great majority of schizophrenic patients continue to take medication after they recover from psychotic episodes, although usually at lower dosages. The need for maintenance medication is less clearly defined among patients who have had only one episode of schizophrenia. The relapse rate for these patients is lower than among those who have had multiple episodes.

Figure 13–7 illustrates general relapse rates for schizophrenic outpatients. The estimated rates presented in this figure were generated by analyzing data from several outcome studies (Weiden & Olfson, 1995). They apply to outpatients who have experienced more than one episode, have responded positively to classical antipsychotic drugs, and are not receiving active psychosocial treatments (discussed later in the chapter). The best-case scenario represents expected relapse rates for patients who are receiving an optimal dose of medication and who continue taking the medication on a regular basis. Under these circumstances, slightly more than half of schizophrenic outpatients will relapse and require rehospitalization within 2 years of discharge. The real-world scenario in Figure 13–7 indicates that

actual relapse rates are even higher because many patients stop taking medication, often to avoid unpleasant side effects (Falkai, 2008).

Motor Side Effects Antipsychotic drugs produce several unpleasant side effects. They come in varying degrees and affect different patients in different ways. The most obvious and troublesome are called *extrapyramidal symptoms* (EPS) because they are mediated by the extrapyramidal neural pathways that connect the brain to the motor neurons in the spinal cord. These symptoms include an assortment of neurological disturbances, such as muscular rigidity, tremors, restless agitation, peculiar involuntary postures, and motor inertia. EPS may diminish spontaneously after 3 or 4 months of continuous treatment. Additional drugs, such as benztropine (Cogentin), can be used to minimize the severity of EPS during the first few months of treatment. Unfortunately, some patients exhibit persistent signs of EPS in spite of these efforts (Kane, 2001a).

Prolonged treatment with antipsychotic drugs can lead to the development of *tardive dyskinesia* (TD). This syndrome consists of abnormal involuntary movements of the mouth and face, such as tongue protrusion, chewing, and lip puckering, as well as spasmodic movements of the limbs and trunk of the body. The latter include writhing movements of the fingers and toes and jiggling of the legs, as well as jerking movements of the head and pelvis. Taken as a whole, this problem is distressing to patients and their families. The TD syndrome is induced by antipsychotic treatment, and it is irreversible in some patients, even after the medication has been discontinued. In fact, in some patients, TD becomes worse if antipsychotic medication is withdrawn (Eberhard et al., 2006; Lauterbach et al., 2001).

Second-Generation Antipsychotics Several new forms of antipsychotic medication began to be introduced in the 1990s. Although some clinicians hailed their development as a "second revolution" in the care of patients with schizophrenia, many experts now recognize that this claim has been overstated (Gray & Roth, 2007; Lieberman, 2006). These drugs are frequently called *atypical antipsychotics* because they are less likely than the classical antipsychotics to produce unpleasant motor side effects. The best known of the atypical drugs, clozapine (Clozaril), has been used extensively throughout Europe since the 1970s. The second generation of antipsychotic medications

Relapse Rates for Schizophrenic Patients Taking Maintenance Medication

FIGURE 13–7 Estimated relapse rates for patients receiving optimal doses of standard neuroleptic medication while not receiving active psychosocial treatments. Real world: Assumes some noncompliance with medication. Best case: Assumes complete compliance with medication.

Source: From "Cost of Relapse in Schizophrenia" by P. J. Weiden and M. Olfson, *Schizophrenia Bulletin,* (1995), 421, p. 425. Copyright © 1995. Reprinted by permission of Oxford University Press.

TABLE 13–3 Examples of Medications Used to Treat Schizophrenic Disorders

		MODES OF ACTION			
		SELECTED SIDE EFFECTS		(SELECTED RECEPTORS)	
DRUG CLASS	GENERIC NAME (TRADE NAME)	EPS	WEIGHT GAIN	D₂	5HT₂ₐ
First-generation	chlorpromazine (Thorazine)	++	+	++	+
antipsychotics	haloperidol (Haldol)	++++	+	++++	+
Second-generation	clozapine (Clozaril)	+/−	++++	++	++++
antipsychotics	risperidone (Risperdal)	++	++	+++	+++++
	olanzapine (Zyprexa)	+	++++	+++	++++
	quetiapine (Seroqul)	+/−	++	++	+++
	amisulpride (Solian)*	+	++	++++	−

D₂ = dopamine receptors; 5HT₂ₐ = serotonin receptors.
*Amisulpride is not available in the United States, but it has been used for more than 15 years in France (Leucht et al., 2002).

Source: S. Kapur and G. Remington, 2001, "Atypical Antipsychotics: New Directions and New Challenges in the Treatment of Schizophrenia," *Annual Review of Medicine*, 52, pp. 503–517.

also includes risperidone (Risperdal), olanzapine (Zyprexa), quetiapine (Seroquel), and several other drugs that have recently become available or are waiting for approval by the FDA. Some of these drugs are listed in Table 13–3.

The good news about second-generation antipsychotics is that they are at least as effective as traditional drugs for the treatment of positive symptoms of schizophrenia (Lieberman et al., 2005). They are also less likely to produce tardive dyskinesia. One review of several outcome studies reported that 13 percent of patients taking second-generation antipsychotics developed tardive dyskinesia, compared to 32 percent patients taking first-generation antipsychotics (Correll & Shenk, 2008). The combination of beneficial effects on positive symptoms and reduced motor side effects makes these forms of medication a likely first choice in the treatment of schizophrenia.

The bad news is that, contrary to initial expectations, second-generation antipsychotics are not significantly more effective for treating negative symptoms (Buckley & Stahl, 2007; Murphy et al., 2006). They also produce additional side effects, and some of them are serious. For example, many of the atypical antipsychotics lead to weight gain and obesity. These problems increase the person's risk for additional medical problems, such as diabetes, hypertension, and coronary artery disease. These adverse reactions lead many patients to discontinue their medication, thus increasing risk of relapse. One influential study compared one first-generation antipsychotic with four types of second-generation drugs. The investigators reported that 74 percent of patients stopped taking their prescribed medication before the end of the 18-month treatment period (Lieberman et al., 2005). Poor compliance was found for all of the different drugs. The bottom line is that various kinds of antipsychotic medication are beneficial for patients with schizophrenia, but they all have weaknesses, and none are without adverse side effects.

All antipsychotic medications—both first and second-generation forms—act by blocking dopamine receptors in the cortical and limbic areas of the brain (Factor, 2002). They also affect a number of other neurotransmitters, including serotonin, norepinephrine, and acetylcholine. Table 13–3 includes a comparison of two first-generation and five second-generation antipsychotic drugs in terms of their ability to block specific types of dopamine and serotonin receptors. Most second-generation antipsychotics produce a broader range of neurochemical actions in the brain than do the traditional drugs, which act primarily on dopamine receptors. Clozapine and olanzapine, for example, produce a relatively strong blockade of serotonin receptors and a relatively weaker blockade of dopamine receptors (Richelson, 1999). This increased affinity of some atypical drugs for serotonin receptors might explain why they can have a beneficial effect on symptoms of schizophrenia while producing fewer motor side effects (EPS). This hypothesis is contradicted, however, by the modes of action associated with a newer form of atypical drug, amisulpride, which does not affect serotonin receptors (Leucht et al., 2002). Neurochemical differences between different forms of antipsychotic drugs are not completely understood and are currently the topic of interesting debate (Richtand et al., 2007; Seeman, 2002).

Further progress in the pharmacological treatment of schizophrenia will undoubtedly produce new drugs that have varying mechanisms of neurochemical action. The rate of progress in this field is very rapid. You can obtain regularly updated reviews of evidence regarding the treatment of schizophrenia from the Cochrane Library at its Web site: www.cochrane.org.

Psychosocial Treatment

Several forms of psychological treatment have proved to be effective for schizophrenic patients. These procedures address a wide range of problems that are associated with the disorder. Psychological treatments have usually concentrated on long-term

▼ Patients and families respond in many creative ways to the presence of mental disorder. Brandon Staglin (left) has struggled with schizophrenia for several years. His parents founded an annual Music Festival for Mental Health, which has raised millions of dollars for mental health charities and research.

strategies rather than the resolution of acute psychotic episodes (Kopelowicz, Liberman, & Zarate, 2002). More recently, several investigators have begun to explore the use of psychosocial interventions in combination with antipsychotic medication for first-episode patients (Grawe et al., 2006; Penn et al., 2005).

Family-Oriented Aftercare Studies of expressed emotion have inspired the development of innovative family-based treatment programs. Family treatment programs attempt to improve the coping skills of family members, recognizing the burdens that people often endure while caring for a family member with a chronic mental disorder. Patients are maintained on antipsychotic medication on an outpatient basis throughout this process. There are several different approaches to this type of family intervention. Most include an educational component that is designed to help family members understand and accept the nature of the disorder (see Getting Help). One goal of this procedure is to eliminate unrealistic expectations for the patient, which may lead to harsh criticism. Behavioral family management also places considerable emphasis on the improvement of communication and problem-solving skills, which may enhance the family members' ability to work together and thereby minimize conflict.

Several empirical studies have evaluated the effects of family interventions. Most have found reductions in relapse rates for people receiving family treatment. In the first year of treatment, relapse rates for patients who receive family treatment plus medication are typically below 20 percent, compared with 40 or 50 percent for those receiving medication alone (Barrowclough & Lobban, 2008; Pilling et al., 2002a). Relapse rates increase in the next year for both groups. Family-based treatment programs can delay relapse, but they do not necessarily prevent relapse in the long run. In the case of a disorder such as schizophrenia, which is often chronic, difficult decisions have to be made about priorities and the availability of services. Family-based programs can have a positive effect, but we need to find more efficient and more effective ways to integrate this aspect of treatment into an overall treatment program.

Social Skills Training Many patients who avoid relapse and are able to remain in the community continue to be impaired in terms of residual symptoms. They also experience problems in social and occupational functioning. For these patients, drug therapy must be supplemented by psychosocial programs that address residual aspects of the disorder. The need to address these problems directly is supported by evidence that shows that deficits in social skills are relatively stable in schizophrenic patients and relatively independent of other aspects of the disorder, including both positive and negative symptoms.

Social skills training (SST) is a structured, educational approach to these problems that involves modeling, role playing, and the provision of social reinforcement for appropriate behaviors (Heinssen, Liberman, & Kopelwicz, 2000). A general description of this type of approach to treatment is provided in Chapter 3. Controlled-outcome studies indicate that, in combination with neuroleptic medication, SST leads to improved performance on measures of social adjustment. It is not clear, however, that SST has any beneficial effects on relapse rates (Pilling et al., 2002b). That result may not be surprising in light of evidence regarding the course of this disorder, which suggests that various aspects of outcome, including symptom severity and social adjustment, tend to be relatively independent.

Cognitive Therapy One area of treatment that has received much greater emphasis in recent years is the use of various forms of cognitive therapy for schizophrenia (Rathod & Turkington, 2005; Temple & Ho, 2005). In some cases, these interventions have focused on the use of standard cognitive therapy procedures that are designed to help patients evaluate, test, and correct distorted ways of thinking about themselves and their social environments. Other forms of cognitive treatment have become more specialized and are aimed specifically at cognitive deficits that are particularly evident in schizophrenia.

One example of a specialized treatment program is cognitive enhancement therapy (CET) for schizophrenia (Hogarty et al., 2004). This is a comprehensive, integrated program aimed at the improvement of cognitive abilities, including those that are concerned with performance on laboratory tasks (such as attention, working memory, and problem solving) as well as social cognition (such as recognizing the perspectives of other people and appraising social contexts). It is

▲ Many people have made remarkable achievements in spite of suffering from schizophrenia. Tom Harrell has been named jazz trumpeter of the year three times by *Downbeat Magazine*. He hears disturbing auditory hallucinations, but they disappear when he is playing music.

designed for use with people who are also taking antipsychotic medication and have already recovered from active symptoms of psychosis but nevertheless continue to exhibit signs of cognitive disability. Patients spend many hours practicing computerized cognitive exercises. Several weeks after beginning cognitive training exercises, they also participate in an extended series of small group exercises (interpreting verbal messages, recognizing others' emotions, maintaining conversations, and so on). One large-scale 2-year outcome study compared patients who received cognitive enhancement therapy with patients in a control group who received enhanced supportive therapy. Those who received CET showed more improvement with regard to performance on measures of cognitive performance, social cognition, and overall social adjustment. Thus, in the context of ongoing treatment with antipsychotic medication, cognitive therapy can be beneficial for patients with schizophrenia.

What aspects of schizophrenia are addressed most directly by psychosocial treatments?

Assertive Community Treatment The treatment of a chronic disorder such as schizophrenia clearly requires an extensive range of comprehensive services that should be fully integrated and continuously available. *Assertive community treatment* (ACT) is a psychosocial intervention that is delivered by an interdisciplinary team of clinicians (DeLuca, Moser, & Bond, 2008; Stein & Santos, 1998). They provide a combination of psychological treatments—including education, support, skills training, and rehabilitation—as well as medication. Services are provided on a regular basis throughout the week and during crisis periods (any time of day and any day of the week). The program represents an intensive effort to maintain seriously disordered patients in the community and to minimize the need for hospitalization. It differs from more traditional outpatient services in its assertive approach to the provision of services: Members of an ACT team go to the consumer rather than expecting the consumer to come to them.

Outcome studies indicate that ACT programs can effectively reduce the number of days that patients spend in psychiatric hospitals, while improving their level of functioning (Phillips et al., 2001; Thornicroft & Susser, 2001). One study found that only 18 percent of the people in the ACT group were hospitalized during the first year of treatment compared to 89 percent of the people in the control group. ACT is an intensive form of treatment that requires a well-organized and extensive network of professional services. In spite of the expense that is required to maintain this kind of program, empirical studies indicate that it is more cost-effective than traditional services provided by community mental health centers (Lehman et al., 1999). Reduction in costs of inpatient care offsets the expense of the ACT program.

Institutional Programs Although schizophrenic persons can be treated with medication on an outpatient basis, various types of institutional care continue to be important. Most patients experience recurrent phases of active psychosis. Brief periods of hospitalization (usually 2 or 3 weeks) are often beneficial during these times.

Some patients are chronically disturbed and require long-term institutional treatment. Social learning programs, sometimes called *token economies,* can be useful for these patients (Dickerson, Tenhula, & Green-Paden, 2005). In these programs specific behavioral contingencies are put into place for all of the patients on a hospital ward. The goal is to increase the frequency of desired behaviors, such as appropriate grooming and participation in social activities, and to decrease the frequency of undesirable behaviors, such as violence or incoherent speech. Staff members monitor patients' behavior throughout the day. Each occurrence of a desired behavior is praised and reinforced by the presentation of a token, which can be exchanged for food or privileges, such as time to watch television. Inappropriate behaviors are typically ignored, but occasional punishment, such as loss of privileges, is used if necessary.

Gordon Paul, a clinical psychologist at the University of Houston, and his colleagues conducted an extensive evaluation of behavioral treatment with chronic schizophrenic patients (Paul & Lentz, 1977). They compared two inpatient programs in the treatment of severely disturbed patients who had been continuously hospitalized for many years. One program followed a carefully designed and closely supervised social learning model, and the other followed a more traditional approach. These experimental treatments were compared to a group of similar patients who continued to reside in their original hospital wards. The patients' adjustment was evaluated at 6-month intervals over a period of approximately 6 years.

Both groups of patients who received treatment showed significant improvement, especially during the first 6 months of the study. This finding highlights the possibility for improvement, even among chronically disturbed patients. Patients in the social learning program showed even more improvement than those in the traditional group, especially with regard to social functioning and self-care. These benefits were maintained throughout the duration of the treatment program. Perhaps most impressive was the fact that by the end of the first 4 years of active treatment, 11 percent of the patients in the social learning program were discharged to independent living in the community without being readmitted to the hospital. In contrast, none of the patients in the standard hospital comparison group was released to independent living. This study indicates that carefully structured inpatient programs, especially those that follow behavioral principles, can have important positive effects for chronic schizophrenic patients.

GETTING HELP

Schizophrenia can be a devastating condition for patients and their families. Fortunately, the past 2 decades have seen many important advances in treatment for this disorder. Perhaps no other disorder requires such an extensive array of services, ranging from medication and short-term inpatient care to long-term residential facilities and psychosocial help for family members. An extremely useful book, *Coping with Schizophrenia: A Guide for Families,* written by Kim Mueser and Susan Gingrich, offers sound advice on a variety of crucial topics. For example, the authors discuss various forms of antipsychotic drugs, their side effects, their use in preventing relapse, and ways to respond to a patient's reluctance to continue taking necessary medication. They outline available community resources that help patients and their families deal with acute episodes, as well as the long-term challenges of residual symptoms, occupational difficulties, and housing needs.

Another excellent resource is *The Family Face of Schizophrenia,* by Patricia Backlar, who is a mental health ethicist and also the mother of a son who suffers from schizophrenia. This book includes a series of seven stories about people who have struggled with this disorder and the often confusing and sometimes inadequate array of mental health services that are available in many communities. Each story is followed by a commentary that includes advice for patients and their families (e.g., how to obtain insurance benefits for treatment, how to find a missing mentally ill family member, how to cope with suicidal risks, and how to navigate legal issues that can arise in caring for someone with a serious mental disorder). Anyone who must cope with a psychotic disorder will benefit from reading these books carefully.

The National Alliance for the Mentally Ill (NAMI) is an extremely influential grassroots support and advocacy organization that has worked tirelessly to improve the quality of life for patients and their families. It has more than 1,000 state and local affiliates throughout the 50 states. Among various items on its public policy agenda, NAMI is committed to increasing access to community-based services such as housing and rehabilitation for people with severe mental disorders. The address for its Web site is www.nami.org. It is a comprehensive source of information regarding all aspects of severe mental disorders (especially schizophrenia and mood disorders), including referral to various types of support groups and professional service providers. The NAMI Web page includes "Helpline Online," which can provide direct answers to questions about severe mental disorders, as well as NAMI's own *Consumer and Family Guide to Schizophrenia Treatment.*

■ SUMMARY

People who meet the diagnostic criteria for **schizophrenia** exhibit many types of symptoms that represent impairments across a broad array of cognitive, perceptual, and interpersonal functions. These symptoms can be roughly divided into three types. **Positive symptoms** include **hallucinations** and **delusions. Negative symptoms** include **blunted affect, alogia, avolition,** and social withdrawal. Symptoms of disorganization include verbal communication problems and bizarre behavior.

The onset of schizophrenia is typically during adolescence or early adulthood. The disorder can follow different patterns over time. Some people recover fairly quickly from schizophrenia, whereas others deteriorate progressively after the initial onset of symptoms.

The disorder was originally defined by Emil Kraepelin, who emphasized the progressive course of the disorder in distinguishing it from manic—depressive psychosis. Eugen Bleuler coined the term *schizophrenia,* proposing that disturbances in speech and emotion are the fundamental symptoms of the disorder. Many clinicians believe that

schizophrenia actually includes several types of disorder with different causes. Others believe that it is a single pathological process with variations in symptomatic expression and course.

The negative symptoms of schizophrenia have been given increased emphasis in DSM-IV-TR. The manual requires evidence of a decline in the person's social or occupational functioning, as well as the presence of disturbed behavior over a continuous period of at least 6 months. DSM-IV-TR recognizes several subtypes of schizophrenia, such as **paranoid, catatonic,** and **disorganized types,** that are based on prominent symptoms. These subtypes have relatively poor diagnostic reliability and are frequently unstable over time.

The lifetime prevalence of schizophrenia is approximately 1 percent in the United States and Europe. Incidence rates vary somewhat in different countries around the world. Men are 30 to 40 percent more likely than women to be affected by the disorder, and its onset tends to occur at an earlier age in males. Male patients are more likely than female patients to exhibit negative symptoms, and they are also more likely to follow a chronic, deteriorating course. Two large cross-cultural studies found more similarities than differences in clinical symptoms of the disorder. Long-term outcome tends to be more favorable for patients living in developing countries than in developed countries.

Genetic factors clearly play a role in the development of schizophrenia. Risk for developing the disorder is between 10 percent and 15 percent among first-degree relatives of schizophrenic patients. Concordance rates are approximately 48 percent in MZ twins compared to only 17 percent in DZ pairs. Adoption studies have found that approximately 15 percent of the offspring of a schizophrenic parent will eventually develop the disorder themselves, even if they are separated from their biological parent at an early age and are raised by adoptive families. Twin and adoption studies also indicate that the disorder has variable expressions, sometimes called the schizophrenia spectrum. Related disorders include schizotypal personality disorder and **schizoaffective disorder.** Linkage studies point to several possible genes that may be involved in causing the disorder.

Advances in brain imaging technology have allowed extensive study of structural and functional brain abnormalities in schizophrenia. A specific brain lesion has not been identified, and it is unlikely that a disorder as complex as schizophrenia will be traced to a single site in the brain. Structural images of schizophrenic patients' brains reveal enlarged ventricles as well as decreased size of parts of the limbic system. Studies of brain metabolism and blood flow have identified functional changes in the frontal lobes, temporal lobes, and basal ganglia in many persons with schizophrenia. Current evidence points toward a subtle and diffuse type of neuropathology in schizophrenia.

The discovery of antipsychotic medication stimulated interest in the role of neurochemical factors in the etiology of schizophrenia. The dopamine hypothesis provided the major unifying theme in this area for many years, but it is now considered too simple to account for the existing evidence. Current neurochemical hypotheses regarding schizophrenia focus on a broad array of neurotransmitters, with special emphasis on serotonin.

The importance of environmental events in the etiology of schizophrenia is evident in the results of twin studies, which show that concordance rates in MZ twins do not approach 100 percent. Several social and psychological factors have been shown to be related to the disorder. Social class is inversely related to the prevalence of schizophrenia. In some cases, low levels of socioeconomic achievement represent a consequence of the disorder. Several kinds of investigation have also found, however, that social factors appear to make a causal contribution to the disorder. People who have migrated to a new country are at greater risk for schizophrenia, suggesting the possible influence of social adversity and discrimination.

Disturbed patterns of family communication have been presumed to be related to the etiology of schizophrenia for many years. There is no evidence to indicate that the behavior of family members contributes to the original onset of schizophrenic symptoms. Recent efforts on this topic have examined the relation between the social context of the family and the long-term course of the disorder. Patients from families that are high in **expressed emotion** are more likely to relapse than those from low EE families. Expressed emotion is the product of an ongoing interaction between patients and their families, with patterns of influence flowing in both directions.

The evidence regarding etiology supports a diathesis-stress model. It should be possible to develop **vulnerability markers** that can identify individuals who possess the genetic predisposition to the disorder. Promising research in this area is concerned with a broad range of possibilities, including laboratory measures of working memory and smooth-pursuit eye-tracking movements.

The central aspect of treatment for schizophrenia is antipsychotic medication. These drugs help to resolve acute psychotic episodes. They can also delay relapse and improve the level of patients' functioning between episodes. Unfortunately, they often produce troublesome side effects, and a substantial minority of schizophrenic patients are resistant to antipsychotic medication. The second-generation antipsychotics are able to help some patients who do not respond to other drugs, and they are less likely to produce unpleasant motor side effects. None of the currently available medications are particularly effective at treating negative symptoms of the disorder. Many patients stop taking antipsychotic drugs because of their unpleasant side effects.

Various types of psychosocial treatment also provide important benefits to schizophrenic patients and their families. Prominent among these are family-based treatment for patients who have been stabilized on medication following discharge from the hospital. Social skills training can also be useful in improving the level of patients' role functioning.

THE BIG PICTURE CRITICAL THINKING REVIEW

What is the difference between a delusion and most other false beliefs?

Delusional beliefs are more than simply mistaken ideas. They are idiosyncratic, personal in nature, patently absurd, and rigidly held in the face of contradictory evidence. (SEE PAGE 398)

What is the rationale for the distinction between the broad dimensions of positive and negative symptoms?

Positive symptoms represent distortions of normal functions, such as auditory perception and belief formation. Negative symptoms reflect the absence of an expected function, such as emotion. (SEE PAGE 400)

Why do clinical scientists say that schizophrenia is a "heterogeneous" disorder?

Schizophrenia is a disorder of many faces. It is defined by an extremely diverse set of symptoms that involve distortions of cognition, perception, and emotion. Finally, it can follow many different patterns over time. (SEE PAGE 405)

How should long-term outcome be measured in schizophrenia?

It must be viewed from a broad spectrum. Important dimensions include the presence and severity of symptoms, the ability to function socially and occupationally, the need for housing and other social services, and the impact on other family members. (SEE PAGE 407)

In what way does the long-term course of schizophrenia differ between developing and developed countries? Why?

Patients in developing countries often have a more favorable outcome than patients in developed countries. This difference may be influenced by more tolerant attitudes toward eccentric behaviors among family members. (SEE PAGE 409)

Why are some personality disorders considered to be schizophrenia spectrum disorders?

Some of the symptoms of Cluster A personality disorders represent less severe forms of psychotic symptoms. And the first-degree relatives of patients with schizophrenia are more likely than other people to qualify for a diagnosis of certain types of personality disorder. (SEE PAGE 411)

Why can't we use brain imaging to diagnose schizophrenia?

They are useful research tools, but they have not identified any aspects of brain structure or function that are unique to people with this disorder. (SEE PAGE 415)

What characteristics would define a useful marker of vulnerability to schizophrenia?

It should be found more frequently among schizophrenic patients and their first-degree relatives, it should be stable over time, and it should be present prior to the onset of psychotic symptoms. (SEE PAGE 421)

What aspects of schizophrenia are addressed most directly by psychosocial treatments?

Problems with social cognition (ways of thinking about oneself and others) and interpersonal relationships are often the targets of psychological interventions, which are designed to be used in conjunction with antipsychotic medication. (SEE PAGE 427)

■ KEY TERMS

alogia **400**	brief psychotic disorder **406**	disorganized type **404**	paranoid type **404**	schizoaffective disorder **406**
anhedonia **400**	catatonic type **404**	expressed emotion (EE) **418**	positive symptoms **397**	schizophrenia **394**
antipsychotic drugs **423**	delusion **398**	hallucinations **398**	prodromal phase **396**	undifferentiated type **405**
avolition **400**	delusional disorder **406**	inappropriate affect **402**	residual phase **396**	vulnerability marker **421**
blunted affect **399**	disorganized speech **400**	negative symptoms **397**	residual type **405**	

DEMENTIA, DELIRIUM, AND AMNESTIC DISORDERS

Most of us are absent minded from time to time. We may forget to make a phone call, run an errand, or complete an assignment. Occasional lapses of this sort are part of normal experience. Unfortunately, some people develop severe and persistent memory problems that disrupt their everyday activities and their interactions with other people. Imagine that you have lived in the same house for many years. You go for a short walk, and then you can't remember how to get home. Suppose you are shown a photograph of your parents, and you don't recognize them. These are some of the fundamental cognitive problems discussed in this chapter.

OVERVIEW

Dementia and delirium are the most frequent disorders found among elderly psychiatric patients. Both conditions involve memory impairments, but they are quite different in other ways. **Dementia** is a gradual worsening loss of memory and related cognitive functions, including the use of language, as well as reasoning and decision making. It is a clinical syndrome that involves progressive impairment of many cognitive abilities (Morris, 2003). **Delirium** is a confusional state that develops over a short period of time and is often associated with agitation and hyperactivity. The most important symptoms of delirium are disorganized thinking and a reduced ability to maintain and shift attention (Gupta et al., 2008). Delirium and dementia are produced by very different processes. Dementia is a chronic, deteriorating condition that reflects the gradual loss of neurons in the brain. Delirium is usually the result of medical problems, such as infection, or of the side effects of medication. If diagnosed and properly treated, delirium is typically short-lived. It can, however, result in serious medical complications, permanent cognitive impairment, or death if the causes go untreated.

People with **amnestic disorders** experience memory impairments that are more limited than those seen in dementia or delirium. The person loses the ability to learn new information or becomes unable to recall previously learned information, but other higher level cognitive abilities—including the use of language—are unaffected.

Dementia, delirium, and amnestic disorders are listed as Cognitive Disorders in DSM-IV-TR. Cognitive processes, including perception and attention, are related to many types of mental disorders that we have already discussed, such as depression, anxiety, and schizophrenia. In most forms of psychopathology, however, the cognitive problems are relatively subtle—mediating factors that help us understand the process by which clinical symptoms are produced. In the case of depression, for example, self-defeating biases may contribute to the onset of a depressed mood. These cognitive schemas are not used, however, as part of the diagnostic criteria for major depression in DSM-IV-TR. They are not considered to be the central, defining features of the disorder. Problems in sustained attention may represent vulnerability markers for schizophrenia, but again, they are not considered symptoms of the disorder. In dementia, memory and other cognitive functions are the most obvious manifestations of the problem. They are its defining features. As dementia progresses, the person's attention span, concentration, judgment, planning, and decision making become severely disturbed.

Dementia and amnestic disorders are often associated with specific identifiable changes in brain tissue (Volicer, McKee, & Hewitt, 2001). Many times these changes can be observed only at autopsy, after the patient's death. For example, in Alzheimer's disease, which is one form of dementia, microscopic examination of the brain reveals the presence of an unusual amount of debris left from dead neurons, called *plaque,* and neurofibrillary tangles indicating that the connections between nerve cells had become disorganized. We describe the neuropathology of Alzheimer's disease later in this chapter.

Because of the close link between cognitive disorders and brain disease, patients with these problems are often diagnosed and treated by **neurologists,** physicians who deal primarily with diseases of the brain and the nervous system. Multidisciplinary clinical teams study and provide care for people with dementia and amnestic disorders. Direct care to patients and their families is usually provided by nurses and social

What is the difference between cognitive problems in anxiety and those seen in dementia?

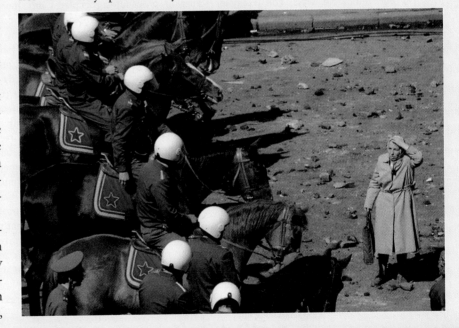

▼ Confusion and disorientation are common symptoms of dementia. This elderly woman may not have been aware that she was walking in front of a line of riot police sent to control demonstrators in Moscow.

workers. **Neuropsychologists** have particular expertise in the assessment of specific types of cognitive impairment. This is true for clinical assessments as well as for more detailed laboratory studies for research purposes.

The following two case studies illustrate the variety of symptoms and problems that are included in the general category of dementia. The first case describes the early stages of dementia.

CASE STUDY A Physician's Developing Dementia

Jonathan was a 61-year-old physician who had been practicing family medicine for the past 30 years. His wife, Alice, worked as his office manager. A registered nurse, Kathryn, had worked with them for several years. Four months earlier, Alice and Kathryn both noticed that Jonathan was beginning to make obvious errors at work. On one occasion, Kathryn observed that Jonathan had prescribed the wrong medication for a patient's condition. At about the same time, Alice became concerned when she asked Jonathan about a patient whom he had seen the day before. Much to her surprise, he did not remember having seen the patient, in spite of the fact that he spent almost half an hour with her, and she was a patient whom he had treated for several years.

Jonathan's personality also seemed to change in small but noticeable ways. For example, Jonathan had always been a gentle and easygoing man. He had a special fondness and tolerance for small children. One day, one of his patients was accompanied to the office by her 2-year-old son. As Jonathan was talking with the mother, the little boy accidentally pushed some bottles of pills off a counter. No harm was done, but Jonathan screamed loudly at the boy, chastising him for being so clumsy and careless. The mother was quite embarrassed. So were Kathryn and Alice, who witnessed Jonathan's sudden and uncharacteristic display of temper.

Although Alice tried to convince herself that these were isolated incidents, she finally decided to discuss them with Kathryn. Kathryn agreed that Jonathan's memory was failing. He had trouble recognizing patients whom he had known for many years, and he had unusual difficulty making treatment decisions. These problems had not appeared suddenly. Over the past year or two, both

women had been doing more things for Jonathan than they had ever done in the past. They needed to remind him about things that were routine parts of his practice. As they pieced together various incidents, the pattern of gradual cognitive decline became obvious.

Alice talked seriously with Jonathan about the problems that she and Kathryn had observed. He said that he felt fine, but he reluctantly allowed her to make an appointment for him to be examined by a neurologist, who also happened to be a friend. Jonathan admitted to the neurologist that he had been having difficulty remembering things. He believed that he had been able to avoid most problems, however, by writing notes to himself—directions, procedures, and so on. The results of psychological testing and brain imaging procedures, coupled with Jonathan's own description of his experiences and Alice's account of his impaired performance at work, led the neurologist to conclude that Jonathan was exhibiting early signs of dementia, perhaps Alzheimer's disease. He spoke directly with Jonathan regarding his diagnosis and recommended firmly that Jonathan retire immediately. A malpractice suit would be devastating to his medical practice. Jonathan agreed to retire.

Although Jonathan was no longer able to cope with his demanding work environment, his adjustment at home was not severely impaired. The changes in his behavior remained relatively subtle for many months. In short conversations, his cognitive problems were not apparent to his friends, who still did not know the real reason for his retirement. His speech was fluent, and his memory for recent events was largely intact, but his comprehension was diminished. Alice noticed that Jonathan's emotional responses were

occasionally flat or restricted. At other times, he would laugh at inappropriate times when they watched television programs together. If Alice asked him about his reaction, it was sometimes apparent that Jonathan did not understand the plot of even the simplest television programs.

Alice found that she had to sew labels into Jonathan's collars to distinguish for him the clothes that he wore to work in the yard from those that he wore if they were going shopping or out to eat.

Jonathan had become increasingly literal minded. If Alice asked him to do something for her, she had to spell out every last detail. For example, he began to have trouble selecting his clothes, which had been a source of pride before the onset of his cognitive problems. Alice found that she had to sew labels into Jonathan's collars to distinguish for him the clothes that he wore to work in the yard from those that he wore if they were going shopping or out to eat. His judgment about what was appropriate to wear in different situations had disappeared altogether.

It had also become difficult for Jonathan to do things that required a regular sequence of actions or decisions, even if they were quite simple and familiar. Routine tasks took longer than before, usually because he got stuck part of the way through an activity. He had, for example, always enjoyed making breakfast for Alice on weekends. After his retirement, Alice once found him standing in the kitchen with a blank expression on his face. He had made a pot of coffee and some toast for both of them, but he ran into trouble when he couldn't find coffee cups. That disrupted his plan, and he was stymied.

Jonathan's case illustrates many of the early symptoms of dementia, as well as the ways in which the beginnings of memory problems can severely disrupt a person's life. The onset of the disorder is often difficult to identify precisely because forgetfulness increases gradually. Problems are most evident in challenging situations, as in Jonathan's medical practice, and least noticeable in familiar surroundings.

Changes in emotional responsiveness and personality typically accompany the onset of memory impairment in dementia. In some cases, personality changes may be evident before the development of full-blown cognitive symptoms (Duchek et al., 2007). These personality changes may be consequences of cognitive impairment. Jonathan's irritability might easily have been aggravated by his own frustration with himself for being forgetful and indecisive. His emotional responses may have seemed unusual sometimes because he failed to comprehend aspects of the environment that were obvious to his wife and other people.

Our next case illustrates more advanced stages of dementia, in which the person can become extremely disorganized. Memory impairment progresses to the point where the person no longer recognizes his or her family and closest friends. People in this condition are unable to care for themselves, and they become so disoriented that the burden on others is frequently overwhelming. This case also provides an example of delirium superimposed on dementia. Up to 50 percent of dementia patients who are admitted to a hospital are also delirious. It is important for the neurologist to recognize the distinction between these conditions because the cause of the delirium (which might be an infection or a change in the patient's medications) must be treated promptly (Young et al., 2008).

CASE **STUDY** Dementia and Delirium—A Niece's Terrible Discoveries

Mary was an 84-year-old retired schoolteacher who had grown up in the same small rural community in which she still lived. Never married, she lived with her parents most of her life, except for the years when she was in college. Her parents had died when Mary was in her early sixties. After her retirement at age 65, Mary continued living in her parents' farmhouse. She felt comfortable there, in spite of its relative isolation, and liked the fact that it had plenty of space for animals, including her dog, which she called "my baby," several cats, and a few cows that were kept in the pasture behind the house. Mary's niece, Nancy, who was 45 years old and lived an hour's drive away, stopped to visit her once every 2 or 3 months.

Over the past year, Nancy had noticed that Mary was becoming forgetful, as well as more insistent that her routines remain unchanged. Bills went unpaid—in fact, the telephone had been disconnected for lack of payment—and the mail wasn't brought in from the roadside box. Nancy had suggested to Mary that she might be better off in a nursing home, but Mary was opposed to that idea.

At her most recent visit, Nancy was shocked to find that conditions at Mary's home had become intolerable. Most distressing was the fact that some of her animals had died because Mary forgot to feed them. The dog's decomposed body was tied to its house, where it had starved. Conditions inside the house were disgusting. Almost 30 cats lived inside the house, and the smell was unbearable. Mary's own appearance was quite disheveled. She hadn't bathed or changed her clothes for weeks. Nancy contacted people at a social service agency, who arranged for Mary's admission to a nursing home. Mary became furious, refusing to go and denying that there was anything wrong with her own home. Nancy was soon declared her legal guardian because Mary was clearly not competent to make decisions for herself.

Mary grew progressively more agitated and belligerent during the few weeks that she lived at the nursing home. She was occasionally disoriented, not knowing where she was or what day it was. She shouted and sometimes struck people with her cane. She had trouble walking, a problem that was compounded by visual and spatial judgment difficulties. After she fell and broke her hip, Mary was transferred to a general hospital.

Bills went unpaid—in fact, the telephone had been disconnected for lack of payment—and the mail wasn't brought in from the roadside box.

Mary became delirious in the hospital, apparently as a result of medication she was given for her injury. She appeared to be having visual hallucinations and often said things that did not make sense. These periods of incoherence fluctuated in severity throughout the course of the day. During her worse moments, Mary did not respond to her name being spoken, and her speech was reduced primarily to groans and nonsense words. This clouding of consciousness cleared up a few days after her medication was changed. She became less distractible and was once again able to carry on brief conversations. Unfortunately, her disorientation became more severe while she was immobilized in the hospital. When her hip eventually healed, she was moved to a psychiatric hospital and admitted to the geriatric ward.

Although Mary was no longer aware of the date or even the season of the year, she insisted that she did not have any problems with her mind. For the first 6 weeks at the psychiatric hospital, she would be surprised that she was not in her own home when she woke up each morning. After that time, she acknowledged that she was in a hospital, but she did not know why she was there, and she did not understand that the other patients on the unit were also demented. She didn't recognize hospital staff members from one day to the next. She was completely unable to remember anything that had happened recently. Nevertheless, her memory for events that had happened many years earlier was quite good. Mary repeated stories about her childhood over and over again.

Nurses on the unit were bombarded continuously with her complaints about being removed from her home. Every 20 minutes or so, Mary would approach the nurses' station, waving her cane and shouting, "Nurse, I need to go home. I have to get out of here. I have to go home and take care of my dog." The hospital staff would explain to her that she would have to stay at the hospital, at least for a while longer, and that her dog had died several months earlier. This news would usually provoke sadness, but she seemed unable to remember it long enough to complete the grieving process. Several minutes later, the whole scene would be repeated. Mary also became paranoid, claiming to anyone who would listen that people were trying to steal her things. The most common focus of her concern was her purse. If it was out of her sight, she would announce loudly that someone had stolen it.

In the midst of these obvious problems, Mary retained many other intellectual abilities. She was a well-educated and intelligent woman. Her attention span was reduced, but she was still able to do crossword puzzles and enjoyed reading short stories. Poetry had always been one of her special interests, and she was still able to recite many of her favorite poems beautifully from memory. In a quiet room, it was often possible to talk with her and pursue a meaningful conversation. Unfortunately, these lucid periods were interspersed with times of restless pacing and shouting. Her agitation would escalate rapidly unless staff members distracted her, taking her to a quiet room, talking to her, and getting her to read or recite something out loud.

SYMPTOMS

The symptoms of cognitive disorders are often overlooked in elderly patients. It can be difficult to distinguish the onset of dementia from patterns of modest memory decline that are an expected part of the aging process. Different forms of cognitive disorder can also be confused with one another. Recognition of these disorders and the distinctions among them carries important treatment implications for patients and their families.

In what ways is delirium different from dementia?

Delirium

The DSM-IV-TR criteria for delirium are listed in Table 14–1. The primary symptom of delirium is clouding of consciousness in association with a reduced ability to maintain and shift attention. The disturbance in consciousness might also be described as a reduction in the clarity of a person's awareness of his or her surroundings. Memory deficits may occur in association with impaired consciousness and may be the direct result of attention problems. The person's thinking appears disorganized, and he or she may speak in a rambling, incoherent fashion. Fleeting perceptual disturbances, including visual hallucinations, are also common in delirious patients (Cole et al., 2002).

The symptoms of delirium follow a rapid onset—from a few hours to several days—and typically fluctuate throughout the day. The person may alternate between extreme confusion and periods in which he or she is more rational and clearheaded. Symptoms are usually worse at night. The sleep/wake cycle is often disturbed. Daytime drowsiness and lapses in concentration are often followed by agitation and hyperactivity at night. If the condition is allowed to progress, the person's senses may become dulled, and he or she may eventually lapse into a coma. The delirious person is also likely to be disoriented with relation to time ("What day, month, or season is it?") or place ("Where are we? What is the name of this place?"). However, identity confusion ("What is your name?") is rare.

It isn't always easy to recognize the difference between dementia and delirium, especially when they appear simultaneously in the same patient. Table 14–2 summarizes several considerations that are useful in making this diagnostic distinction (Insel & Badger, 2002). One important consideration involves the period of time over which the symptoms appear. Delirium has a rapid onset, whereas dementia develops in a slow, progressive manner. In dementia, the person usually remains alert and responsive to the environment. Speech is most often coherent in demented patients, at least until the end stages of the disorder, but it is typically confused in delirious patients. Finally, delirium can be resolved, whereas dementia cannot.

Dementia

The cases at the beginning of this chapter illustrate the changing patterns that emerge as dementia unfolds. Jonathan's cognitive symptoms were recognized at a relatively early stage of development, in part because of his occupational situation and because of his close relationships with other people. Mary's situation was much different, because she lived in a relatively isolated setting without close neighbors or friends. By the time Nancy recognized the full severity of Mary's problems, the cognitive impairment had progressed so far that Mary was no longer able

---

TABLE 14–1 DSM-IV-TR Criteria for Delirium

A. Disturbance of consciousness (i.e., reduced clarity of awareness of the environment) with reduced ability to focus, sustain, or shift attention.

B. A change in cognition (such as memory deficit, disorientation, language disturbance) or the development of a perceptual disturbance that is not better accounted for by a preexisting, established, or evolving dementia.

C. The disturbance develops over a short period of time (usually hours to days) and tends to fluctuate during the course of the day.

Source: Reprinted with permission from the *Diagnostic and Statistical Manual of Mental Disorders*, Fourth Edition, Text Revision. Copyright © 2000 by the American Psychiatric Association.

TABLE 14–2	Distinguishing Features of Dementia and Delirium	
CHARACTERISTIC	**DELIRIUM**	**DEMENTIA**
Onset	Sudden (hours to days)	Slow (months to years)
Duration	Brief	Long/lifetime
Course	Fluctuating	Stable, with downward trajectory over time
Hallucinations	Visual/tactile/vivid	Rare
Insight	Lucid intervals	Consistently poor
Sleep	Disturbed	Less disturbed

Source: From "Deciphering the 4 Ds: Cognitive Decline, Delirium, Depression, and Dementia—A Review" by K. C. Insel and T. A. Badger, *Journal of Advanced Nursing*, 38 (2002), pp. 360–368. Copyright © 2002. Reprinted by permission of Blackwell Publishing Ltd.

to appreciate the nature of her own difficulties. In the following pages we describe in more detail the types of symptoms that are associated with dementia.

Cognitive Symptoms Dementia appears in people whose intellectual abilities have previously been unimpaired. Both of the people in our case studies were bright, well educated, and occupationally successful before the onset of their symptoms. The earliest signs of dementia are often quite vague. They include difficulty remembering recent events and the names of people and familiar objects. These are all problems that are associated with normal aging, but they differ from that process in order of magnitude (see "Memory Changes in Normal Aging" on page 438). The distinguishing features of dementia include cognitive problems in a number of areas, ranging from impaired memory and learning to deficits in language and abstract thinking. By the final stages of dementia, intellectual and motor functions may disappear almost completely (Rosenstein, 1998).

Memory and Learning The diagnostic hallmark of dementia is memory loss. In order to describe the various facets of memory impairment, it is useful to distinguish between old memories and the ability to learn new things. **Retrograde amnesia** refers to the loss of memory for events prior to the onset of an illness or the experience of a traumatic event. **Anterograde amnesia** refers to the inability to learn or remember new material after a particular point in time.

Anterograde amnesia is usually the most obvious problem during the beginning stages of dementia. Consider, for example, the case of Jonathan. Alice eventually noticed that he sometimes could not remember things that he had done the previous day. Mary, the more severely impaired person, could not remember for more than a few minutes that her dog had died. Long-term memories are usually not affected until much later in the course of the disorder. Even in advanced stages of dementia, a person may retain some recollections of the past. Mary was able to remember, and frequently described, stories from her childhood.

Verbal Communication Language functions can also be affected in dementia. **Aphasia** is a term that describes various types of loss or impairment in language that are caused by brain damage (Mesulam, 2007; Saffran, 2000). Language disturbance in dementia is sometimes relatively subtle, but it can include many different kinds of problems. Patients often remain verbally fluent, at least until the disorder is relatively advanced. They retain their vocabulary skills and are able to construct grammatical sentences. They may have trouble finding words, naming objects, and comprehending instructions.

In addition to problems in understanding and forming meaningful sentences, the demented person may also have difficulty performing purposeful movements in response to verbal commands, a problem known as **apraxia.** The person possesses the normal strength and coordination to carry out the action and is able to understand the other person's speech but is nevertheless unable to translate the various components into a meaningful action (Koski, Iacoboni, & Mazziotta, 2002).

Some aspects of the communication problems associated with dementia are captured in the following passage from a novel by J. Bernlef entitled *Out of Mind.* This account provides an insightful and poignant description of the subjective experiences of a man from Holland,

MEMORY CHANGES IN NORMAL AGING

Changes in cognitive abilities are part of the normal aging process. Most elderly adults complain more frequently about memory problems than younger adults do, and they typically perform slower and less efficiently than younger adults on laboratory tests of memory. There are, of course, individual differences in the age at which cognitive abilities begin to decline, as well as in the rate at which these losses take place. Nevertheless, some types of memory impairment are an inevitable consequence of aging (Nilsson, 2003).

In order to understand more clearly the cognitive changes associated with aging, it is useful to distinguish between two general aspects of mental functioning: fluid intelligence and wisdom (Baltes, 1993; Salthouse, 1999). The computer can be used as a metaphor to explain this distinction. Fluid intelligence refers to "the hardware of the mind." These functions are concerned with the speed and accuracy of such basic processes as perception, attention, and working memory. The proficiency of fluid intelligence depends on neurophysiological processes and on the structural integrity of the person's brain.

Wisdom, on the other hand, represents the "culture-based software of the mind." Reading and writing skills, as well as knowledge about the self and ways of coping with environmental challenges, are examples of cognitive abilities that might be included under the general heading of wisdom. These aspects of intelligence represent information about the world that is acquired continually throughout the person's lifetime (Baltes & Smith, 2008).

Fluid intelligence and wisdom follow different trajectories over the normal human life span (Kunzmann & Baltes, 2003). Fluid intelligence develops continuously during childhood and adolescence, reaching a point of optimal efficiency during young adulthood. After that point, it follows a gradual pattern of decline

(Bugg et al., 2006). Wisdom also increases throughout adolescence and young adulthood, but it does not become increasingly impaired as the person ages. In fact, it often expands. The erosion of fluid intelligence over time is presumably due to subtle atrophy of brain regions, such as the hippocampus, that take place during normal aging (Head et al., 2008).

> *Does a decline in working memory capacity and speed of information processing always signal the onset of dementia?*

Various measurement procedures have been used to explore the relationship between aging and wisdom. In one procedure, subjects are presented with a life dilemma, such as "A 15-year-old girl wants to get married right away. What should she consider and do?" The subjects' task is to think aloud about each dilemma. Responses are scored in terms of the amount of knowledge that the person displays with regard to facts, values, and procedures that must be considered in each circumstance. In contrast to the results of research on working memory and fluid intelligence, studies of wisdom have found no change in performance between the ages of 30 and 70. Elderly people are just as likely as younger adults to produce the best scores on this type of task.

The aging mind apparently depends on the coordination of gains and losses. The elderly person strikes a balance through a process that involves selection, optimization, and compensation (Freund & Baltes, 2002). Arthur Rubinstein, the brilliant pianist who performed concerts well into his eighties, provides an example of this process. Rubinstein described three strategies that he employed in his old

age: (1) He was selective, performing fewer pieces; (2) he optimized his performance by practicing each piece more frequently; and (3) he compensated for a loss of motor speed by utilizing pieces that emphasized contrast between fast and slow segments so that his playing seemed faster than it really was. Successful aging is based on this dynamic process. The person compensates for losses in fluid intelligence by taking advantage of increased knowledge and information.

The fact that an older person begins to experience a reduction in memory capacity and speed of information processing does not necessarily indicate that he or she is becoming demented. Where can we find the line between normal aging and dementia? Is this distinction simply a matter of degree, or is there a qualitative difference between the expected decline in cognitive mechanics and the onset of cognitive pathology? These issues present an important challenge for future research.

▲ Nelson Mandela won the Nobel Peace Prize at age 75. His wisdom and courage provide a remarkable example of successful aging.

---

named Maarten, who is becoming demented. In this passage, Maarten is listening to his wife, Vera, as she discusses his situation with their physician.

"Sometimes he's like a stranger to me. I can't reach him. It's a terrible, helpless feeling. He hears me but at such times I don't think he understands me. He behaves as if he were on his own."

I know exactly what she means. Like it was just then, when it all went wrong. All of a sudden I had to translate everything into English first, before I could say it. Only the forms of sentences came out, fragments, the contents had completely slipped away.

Furiously I glare into the front room. I seem to lose words like another person loses blood. And then suddenly I feel terribly frightened again. The presence of everything! Every object seems to be heavier and more solid than it should be (perhaps because for a fraction of a second I no longer know its name). I quickly lie down on the settee and close my eyes. A kind of seasickness in my mind, it seems. Under this life stirs another life in which all times, names and places whirl about topsy-turvy and in which I no longer exist as a person.

"Curious," I say to Vera as she enters the room. "Sometimes I just have to lie down for a moment. I never used to."

"It doesn't matter. Have some time to yourself." She sits down, picks up a book.

"Have some time to yourself." I repeat the phrase because it appears strange to me.

She turns the pages but she isn't reading. I can tell from the look in her eyes that she doesn't understand me.

"It should be: have some time in yourself. That describes the situation better."

"Is that how you feel?"

"Less and less so."

"What do you mean?"

"Like a ship," I say, "A ship, a sailing vessel that is becalmed. And then suddenly there is a breeze, I am sailing again. Then the world has a hold on me again and I can move along with it."

(Bernlef, 1988, pp. 54–55)

Some of the things that Maarten says in this passage reflect subtle problems in verbal communication. His description of the sailing ship, however, is a remarkable analogy that captures the intermittent quality of the cognitive impairment.

Perception Some patients with dementia have problems identifying stimuli in their environments. The technical term for this phenomenon is **agnosia,** which means "perception without meaning." The person's sensory functions are unimpaired, but he or she is unable to recognize the source of stimulation (Bauer & Demery, 2003). Agnosia can be associated with visual, auditory, or tactile sensations, and it can be relatively specific or more generalized. For example, visual agnosia is the inability to recognize certain objects or faces. Some people with visual agnosia can identify inanimate stimuli but are unable to recognize human faces.

It is sometimes difficult to distinguish between aphasia and agnosia. Imagine, for example, that a clinician shows a patient a toothbrush and asks, "What is this object?" The patient may look at the object and be unable to name it. Does that mean that the person cannot think of the word "toothbrush"? Or does it mean that the person cannot rec-

ognize the object at all? In this case, the distinction could be made by saying to the person, "Show me what you do with this object." A person suffering from aphasia would take the toothbrush in his hand and make brushing movements in front of his mouth, thereby demonstrating that he recognizes the object but cannot remember its name. A person with agnosia would be unable to indicate how the toothbrush is used.

Abstract Thinking Another manifestation of cognitive impairment in dementia is loss of the ability to think in abstract ways. The person may be bound to concrete interpretations of things that other people say. It may also be difficult for the person to interpret words that have more than one meaning (for example, "pen") or to explain why two objects are alike ("Why are a basketball and a football helmet alike?" Because they are both types of sporting equipment.)

In our opening case, Jonathan became increasingly literal minded in his conversations with other people. After he retired, he had much more time to become involved in routine tasks around the home. Alice found that she had to give him very explicit instructions if she wanted him to do anything. For example, if she asked him to mow

ALVIN

"That's one of the real difficulties. There's no sign that goes off and says, Yes, he's understanding, or No, he's not understanding it."

As you watch the interview and the day-in-the-life segment, try to identify the various signs of Alvin's cognitive impairment.

How could a clinician distinguish between aphasia and apraxia?

▼ John O'Connor, who suffers from Alzheimer's disease, no longer remembers that he has been married to Sandra Day O'Connor, the first woman to serve on the U.S. Supreme court, since 1952. He struck up a romance with a fellow patient after moving into an assisted living center. Justice O'Connor has said that she is not jealous and is simply pleased that he is comfortable.

TABLE 14–3 Mini-Mental State Examination

1. What is the (year, season, date, day, month)?
2. Where are we (state, city, hospital)?
3. Name three objects (pen, sky, dog), then ask patient to repeat them.
4. Spell "world" backwards.
5. Ask for names of three objects given in question 3.
6. Point to a pencil and a watch. Ask the patient to name each as you point.
7. Ask the patient to repeat, "No ifs, ands, or buts."
8. Three-stage command: "Take this paper in your right hand. Fold the paper in half. Put the paper on the floor."
9. Ask the patient to read and obey the following (write on card in large letters): "CLOSE YOUR EYES."
10. Have the patient write a sentence of his or her choice.
11. Have the patient copy two intersecting pentagons.

Source: M. F. Folstein, S. E. Folstein, and P. R. McHugh, 1975, "Mini-Mental State: A Practical Method for Grading the Cognitive State of Patients for the Clinician," *Journal of Psychiatric Research, 2,* pp. 189–198. Copyright © 1975. Reprinted by permission of Elsevier, Ltd.

the grass, he would do exactly that—nothing more. This was unusual for Jonathan, because he had always enjoyed taking care of their lawn and took great pride in their bushes and flower gardens. Previously, "mowing the grass" would have been taken to include trimming, pulling weeds, raking leaves from under bushes, and all sorts of related details. Now Jonathan interpreted this instruction in concrete terms.

Judgment and Social Behavior Related to deficits in abstract reasoning is the failure of social judgment and problem-solving skills. In the course of everyday life, we must acquire information from the environment, organize and process it, and then formulate and perform appropriate responses by considering these new data in the light of past experiences. The disruption of short-term memory, perceptual skills, and higher level cognitive abilities obviously causes disruptions of judgment. Examples from Jonathan's case include problems deciding which clothes to wear for working around his home as opposed to going out in public, as well as his inability to understand the humor in some television programs. Impulsive and careless behaviors are often the product of the demented person's poor judgment. Activities such as shopping, driving, and using tools can create serious problems.

Assessment of Cognitive Impairment There are many ways to measure a person's level of cognitive impairment. One is the Mini-Mental State Examination, which is outlined in Table 14–3. We include it here to give you an idea of the types of questions that a clinician might ask in order to elicit the cognitive problems of dementia. Some are directed at the person's orientation to time and place. Others are concerned with anterograde amnesia, such as the ability to remember the names of objects for a short period of time (items 3 and 5). Agnosia, aphasia, and apraxia are addressed by items 6, 7, and 8, respectively. Perceptual difficulties are tapped by the last item (11).

Neuropsychological assessment can be used as a more precise index of cognitive impairment. This process involves the evaluation of performance on psychological tests to indicate whether a person has a brain disorder (Welsh-Bohmer & Attix, 2004). Neuropsychological tests can sometimes be used to infer the location of a brain lesion. The best-known neuropsychological assessment procedure is the Halstead-Reitan Neuropsychological Test Battery, which includes an extensive series of tests that tap sensorimotor, perceptual, and speech functions. For example, in the tactile performance test, the person is blindfolded and then required to fit differently shaped blocks into spaces in a form board. The time needed to perform this test reflects one specific aspect of the person's motor skills. Complete neuropsychological test batteries are rarely used for the diagnosis of dementia because they are too long and time-consuming. It is more common to use specific tasks that focus on abilities that are impaired in patients with dementia.

Some neuropsychological tasks require the person to copy simple objects or drawings. The drawings illustrated in Figure 14–1 demonstrate this

Neuropsychological Test Performance

(1) (2) (3)

FIGURE 14–1 These drawings represent part of the neuropsychological test performance of a 59-year-old woman with a diagnosis of Alzheimer's disease. The figure at the left (1) was drawn by the psychologist, who then handed the piece of paper to the patient and asked her to make an exact copy of the figure next to the original. After the patient had completed her replica (2), the piece of paper was turned over and she was asked to draw the figure again, this time from memory. The figure that she drew based on memory is presented at the right (3).

process and the type of impairment typically seen in a patient during the relatively early stages of Alzheimer's disease. The patient was asked to reproduce a drawing. This was done initially while the original figure was still in sight and then repeated after it had been covered up. The performance of the patient indicates two problems associated with the disorder. First, inconsistencies between drawings 1 and 2 reflect perceptual difficulties. Second, the drastic deterioration from drawing 2 to drawing 3 indicates that the patient had a great deal of difficulty remembering the shape of the figure for even a few brief moments.

Personality and Emotion Personality changes, emotional difficulties, and motivational problems are frequently associated with dementia. These problems may not contribute to the diagnosis of the disorder, but they do have an impact on the person's adjustment. They can also create additional burdens for people who care for demented patients.

Hallucinations and delusions are seen in at least 20 percent of dementia cases and are more common during the later stages of the disorder (Fischer et al., 2004). The delusional beliefs are typically understandable consequences of the person's disorientation or anterograde amnesia. They are most often simple in nature and are relatively short-lived. Mary's frequent insistence that someone had stolen her purse is a typical example. Other common themes are phantom houseguests and personal persecution (Harvey, 1996).

The emotional consequences of dementia are quite varied. Some demented patients appear to be apathetic or emotionally flat. Their faces are less expressive, and they appear to be indifferent to their surroundings. Alice noticed, for example, that something seemed a bit vacant in Jonathan's eyes. At other times, emotional reactions may become exaggerated and less predictable. The person may become fearful or angry in situations that would not have aroused strong emotion in the past. Jonathan's sudden rage at the boy who pushed bottles off the counter in his office is one example. Changes like this often lead others to believe that the person's personality has changed.

Depression is another problem that is frequently found in association with dementia (Stroud et al., 2008). In many ways, feelings of depression are understandable. The realization that your most crucial cognitive abilities are

beginning to fail, that you can no longer perform simple tasks or care for yourself, would obviously lead to sadness and depression. Mary's case illustrates one way in which cognitive impairment can complicate depression: Her inability to remember from one day to the next that her dog had died seemed to interfere with her ability to grieve for the loss of her pet. Each time that she was reminded of his death was like the first time that she had heard the news.

Motor Behaviors Demented persons may become agitated, pacing restlessly or wandering away from familiar surroundings. In the later stages of the disorder, patients may develop problems in the control of the muscles by the central nervous system. Some patients develop muscular rigidity, which can be accompanied by painful cramping. Others experience epileptic seizures, which consist of involuntary, rapidly alternating movements of the arms and legs.

Some specific types of dementia are associated with involuntary movements, or **dyskinesia**—tics, tremors, and jerky movements of the face and limbs called chorea. These motor symptoms help to distinguish among different types of dementia. We return to this area later in the chapter when we discuss the classification of differentiated and undifferentiated dementias.

Amnestic Disorder

Some cognitive disorders involve more circumscribed forms of memory impairment than those seen in dementia. In amnestic disorders, a person exhibits a severe impairment of memory while other higher level cognitive abilities are unaffected. The memory disturbance interferes with social and occupational functioning and represents a significant decline from a previous level of adjustment. Subtypes of amnestic disorder are diagnosed on the basis of evidence, acquired from the patient's history, from a physical examination, or from laboratory tests, regarding medical conditions or substance use that is considered to be related to the onset of the memory impairment.

The following case, written by Oliver Sacks (1985), illustrates a form of amnestic disorder, involving severe anterograde amnesia, that developed after the patient had been dependent on alcohol for several years.

CASE **STUDY** Alcohol-Induced Persisting Amnestic Disorder—19 Going on 45

Jimmie G. was admitted to our Home for the Aged near New York City early in 1975, with a cryptic transfer note saying, "Helpless, demented, confused and disoriented." Jimmie was a fine-looking man, with a curly bush of grey hair, a healthy and handsome 49-year-old. He was cheerful, friendly, and warm.

"Hiya, Doc!" he said. "Nice morning! Do I take this chair here?" He was a genial soul, very ready to talk and to answer any questions I asked him. He told me his name and birth date, and the name of the little town in Connecticut where he was born. He described it in affectionate detail, even drew me a map. He spoke of the houses where his family had lived—he remembered their phone numbers still. He spoke of school and school days, the friends he'd had, and his special fondness for mathematics and science. He talked with enthusiasm of his days in the navy—he was 17, had just graduated from high school when he was drafted in 1943. With his good engineering mind he was a "natural" for radio and electronics, and after a crash course in Texas found himself assistant radio operator on a submarine. He remembered the names of various submarines on which he had served, their missions, where they were stationed, the names of his shipmates. He remembered Morse code and was still fluent in Morse tapping and touch-typing.

A full and interesting early life, remembered vividly, in detail, with affection. But there, for some reason, his reminiscences stopped. He recalled, and almost relived, his war days and service, the end of the war, and his thoughts for the future. He had come to love the navy, thought he might stay in it. But with the GI Bill, and support, he felt he might do best to go to college.

With recalling, reliving, Jimmie was full of animation; he did not seem to be speaking of the past but of the present, and I was very struck by the change of tense in his recollections as he passed from his school days to his days in the navy. He had been using the past tense, but now used the present and (it seemed to me) not just the formal or fictitious present tense of recall, but the actual present tense of immediate experience.

A sudden, improbable suspicion seized me. "What year is this, Mr. G.?" I asked, concealing my perplexity under a casual manner.

"Forty-five, man. What do you mean?" He went on, "We've won the war, FDR's dead, Truman's at the helm. There are great times ahead."

"And you, Jimmie, how old would you be?"

Oddly, uncertainly, he hesitated a moment, as if engaged in calculation. "Why, I guess I'm 19, Doc. I'll be 20 next birthday."

Looking at the grey-haired man before me, I had an impulse for which I have never forgiven myself—it was, or would have been, the height of cruelty had there been any possibility of Jimmie's remembering it.

"Here," I said, and thrust a mirror toward him. "Look in the mirror and tell me what you see. Is that a 19-year-old looking out from the mirror?"

He suddenly turned ashen and gripped the sides of the chair. "Jesus Christ," he whispered. "Christ, what's going on? What's happened to me? Is this a nightmare? Am I crazy? Is this a joke?" and he became frantic, panicked.

"It's okay, Jimmie," I said soothingly. "It's just a mistake. Nothing to worry about. Hey!" I took him to the window. "Isn't this a lovely spring day. See the kids there playing baseball?" He regained his color and started to smile, and I stole away, taking the hateful mirror with me.

"Am I a patient? Am I sick and don't know it, Doc? It's crazy, it's scary . . . Is it some sort of joke?"

Two minutes later I re-entered the room. Jimmie was still standing by the window, gazing with pleasure at the kids playing baseball below. He wheeled around as I opened the door, and his face assumed a cheery expression.

"Hiya, Doc!" he said. "Nice morning! You want to talk to me—do I take this chair here?" There was no sign of recognition on his frank, open face.

"Haven't we met before, Mr. G.?" I asked casually.

"No, I can't say we have. Quite a beard you got there. I wouldn't forget you, Doc!"

"Why do you call me 'Doc'?"

"Well, you are a doc, ain't you?"

"Yes, but if you haven't met me, how do you know what I am?"

"You talk like a doc. I can see you're a doc."

"Well, you're right, I am. I'm the neurologist here."

"Neurologist? Hey, there's something wrong with my nerves? And 'here'—where's 'here'? What is this place anyhow?"

"I was just going to ask you—where do you think you are?"

"I see these beds, and these patients everywhere. Looks like a sort of hospital to me. But hell, what would I be doing in a hospital and with all these old people, years older than me. I feel good, I'm strong as a bull. Maybe I work here. Do I work? What's my job? . . . No, you're shaking your head, I see in your eyes I don't work here. If I don't work here, I've been put here. Am I a patient, am I sick and don't know it, Doc? It's crazy, it's scary . . . Is it some sort of joke?" (Sacks, 1985, pp. 22–25)

The preceding case illustrates the most common type of amnestic disorder, alcohol-induced persisting amnestic disorder, also known as Korsakoff's syndrome. In this disorder, which is caused by chronic alcoholism, memory is impaired but other cognitive functions are not. More detailed examinations of the patient's cognitive abilities, using neuropsychological tests, have found evidence of more widespread cognitive deficits, especially those related to visuoperceptual skills and abstract thinking (Brand, 2007).

One widely accepted theory regarding this condition holds that lack of vitamin B_1 (thiamine) leads to atrophy of the medial thalamus, a subcortical structure of the brain, and mammillary bodies (MB). Support for one aspect of this theory comes from studies that used magnetic resonance imaging to compare brain structures in alcoholic patients with amnesia, alcoholic patients without amnesia, and normal controls. Deficits in MB volume occur in both types of alcoholics, and greater volume deficits are found in alcoholic patients with amnesia (Sullivan et al., 1999). Other data suggest, however, that these problems cannot be traced exclusively to thiamine deficiency (Homewood & Bond, 1999). In fact, prolonged exposure to alcohol may have direct toxic effects on cortical and subcortical tissue that are independent of vitamin deficiencies. Alcohol apparently can cause brain damage regardless of the person's nutritional habits (Crews et al., 2004).

Diagnosis

Cognitive disorders have been classified by a somewhat different process than most other forms of psychopathology because of their close link to specific types of neuropathology. Description of specific cognitive and behavioral symptoms has not always been the primary consideration. In the following pages we describe the ways in which these disorders have been defined and some of the considerations that influence the way in which they are classified.

Brief Historical Perspective

Alois Alzheimer (1864–1915), a German psychiatrist, worked closely in Munich with Emil Kraepelin, who is often considered responsible for modern psychiatric classification (see Chapters 4, 5, and 13). Alzheimer's most famous case involved a 51-year-old woman who had become delusional and also experienced a severe form of recent memory impairment, accompanied by apraxia and agnosia. This woman died 4 years after the onset of her dementia. Following her death, Alzheimer conducted a microscopic examination of her brain and made a startling discovery: bundles of neurofibrillary tangles and amyloid plaques. Alzheimer presented the case at a meeting of psychiatrists in 1906 and published a three-page paper in 1907. Emil Kraepelin began to refer to this condition as Alzheimer's disease in the eighth edition of his famous textbook on psychiatry, published in 1910. He distinguished between this form of dementia, which is characterized by early onset, and senile dementia, which presumably has an onset after the age of 65 (Fox, Kelly, & Tobin, 1999).

For many years, there was an argument about the distinction between senile and presenile dementia. As more and more evidence accumulated regarding these conditions, questions were raised about the value of the distinction. For example, several cases were reported in which two siblings developed dementia, but one had the presenile form and the other had the senile form. Clinical symptoms and brain pathology in the siblings were often the same. Katzman (1976) proposed that both types are forms of Alzheimer's disease,

◄ Alois Alzheimer (left) on a pleasure cruise with his friend Emil Kraepelin. The form of dementia that Alzheimer described in his famous case was named after him in part because of the influence of Kraepelin's textbook.

which may have either an early or a late onset, and that they are distinctly different from normal aging. Age of onset may be a reflection of the severity of the disorder. Most clinicians and researchers still believe that Alzheimer's disease is a heterogeneous category, and the genetic literature supports that contention.

Until recently, the diagnostic manual classified the various forms of dementia as Organic Mental Disorders because of their association with known brain diseases. That concept has fallen into disfavor because it is founded on an artificial dichotomy between biological and psychological processes. If we call dementia an organic mental disorder, does that imply that other types of psychopathology are not organically based (Spitzer et al., 1992)? Obviously not. Therefore, in order to be consistent with the rest of the diagnostic manual, and so as to avoid falling into the trap of simplistic mind–body dualism, dementia and related clinical phenomena are now classified as Cognitive Disorders in DSM-IV-TR. These disorders are divided into three major headings: deliria, dementias, and amnestic disorders (see Table 14–4 on page 444).

Specific Disorders Associated with Dementia

Many specific disorders are associated with dementia. They are distinguished primarily on the basis of known neuropathology—specific brain

TABLE 14–4	Cognitive Disorders Listed in DSM-IV-TR
Delirium	Delirium due to a general medical condition
	Substance-induced delirium
	Delirium due to multiple etiologies
Dementia	Dementia of the Alzheimer's type
	Vascular dementia
	Dementia due to other general medical conditions
	HIV disease
	Head trauma
	Parkinson's disease
	Huntington's disease
	Pick's disease
	Creutzfeldt-Jakob disease
	Substance-induced persisting dementia
	Dementia due to multiple etiologies
Amnestic disorders	Amnestic disorder due to a general medical condition
	Substance-induced persisting amnestic disorder

Source: Reprinted with permission from the *Diagnostic and Statistical Manual of Mental Disorders,* Fourth Edition, Text Revision. Copyright © 2000 by the American Psychiatric Association.

lesions that have been discovered throughout the twentieth century. DSM-IV-TR lists several categories of dementia. The criteria for cognitive deficits of dementia are the same for each type, and they are listed in Table 14–5 as they relate to Dementia of the Alzheimer's Type (see Critical Thinking Matters). The only part of this definition that changes from one type of dementia to the next is the description listed under "C" (gradual onset and continuing cognitive decline). In order to qualify for a diagnosis of dementia, the person must exhibit memory impairment (either anterograde or retrograde amnesia) and at least one other type of cognitive disturbance, such as aphasia, apraxia, agnosia, or problems in abstract thinking. There must also be evidence that the person's cognitive impairment interferes with his or her social or occupational functioning. Finally, for all forms of dementia, DSM-IV-TR notes that the cognitive problems must be above and beyond anything that could be attributed solely to delirium.

Dementia of the Alzheimer's Type The speed of onset serves as the main feature to distinguish **Alzheimer's disease** from the other types of dementia listed in DSM-IV-TR. In this disor-

TABLE 14–5	DSM-IV-TR Criteria for Dementia of the Alzheimer's Type

A. The development of multiple cognitive deficits manifested by both:

  1. Memory impairment (impaired ability to learn new information or to recall previously learned information)

  2. One (or more) of the following cognitive disturbances:

    a. Aphasia (language disturbance)
    b. Apraxia (impaired ability to carry out motor activities despite intact motor function)
    c. Agnosia (failure to recognize or identify objects despite intact sensory function)
    d. Disturbance in executive functioning (that is, planning, organizing, sequencing, abstracting)

B. The cognitive deficits each cause significant impairment in social or occupational functioning and represent a significant decline from a previous level of functioning.

C. The course is characterized by gradual onset and continuing cognitive decline.

Source: Reprinted with permission from the *Diagnostic and Statistical Manual of Mental Disorders,* Fourth Edition, Text Revision. Copyright © 2000 by the American Psychiatric Association.

CRITICAL THINKING MATTERS

How Can Clinicians Establish an *Early* Diagnosis of Alzheimer's Disease?

The DSM-IV-TR diagnostic criteria for Dementia of the Alzheimer's Type (DAT) represent an interesting example of a point that we have tried to make throughout this book. In the field of psychopathology, diagnostic criteria usually represent a "work in progress." Do not take any of these definitions as being the final word with regard to the identification of a disorder. Prevailing views about the best way to identify mental disorders will continue to evolve as more evidence is collected and evaluated.

One of the most important problems with regard to the diagnosis of DAT involves the initial identification of the disorder. Symptoms associated with advanced stages of the disorder are obvious. But what are the *earliest* reliable indications that a person has developed the disorder? Are these early signs the same as (though perhaps more subtle than) the symptoms that are present when the disorder has progressed for several years? If the disorder could be identified in its beginning stage, it might be possible to develop treatment procedures that can prevent it from progressing further.

Is memory impairment the only indication that a person is developing dementia?

Do people in the early stages of DAT show changes specifically in memory performance, or does the disorder have a more generalized impact on many different aspects of cognition, such as reasoning and planning, attention, perception, and use of language? In an effort to answer this question, research studies have been conducted to investigate "mild cognitive impairment" in elderly persons (Kawas, 2003). Investigators have tested people who meet various definitions for this condition. The participants are later followed up and retested, in an effort to determine whether specific kinds of problems do, in fact, indicate that the person will go on to develop a more disabling form of dementia.

The most useful definition of mild cognitive impairment seems to be one that includes evidence of a decline in any area of cognitive performance, not simply memory (Storandt et al., 2006). For example, people who show a decline in *executive functioning* (reasoning and planning) are just as likely to develop DAT three or four years after initial testing. These data suggest that Alzheimer's disease does not always begin as a memory problem.

The definition of DAT that is presented in Table 14–5 may be revised when the next edition of the manual is published. Studies of the progression of mild cognitive impairment suggest that, in the earliest stages of the disorder, memory impairment may not be its only symptom. Increased emphasis may be placed on evidence regarding a decline in executive functioning (Storandt, 2008). Longitudinal studies also indicate that more obvious symptoms, such as aphasia, apraxia, and agnosia, are primarily evident during the advanced stages of the disorder. Critical thinking about this kind of evidence will lead to better refined and more useful diagnostic criteria.

---

der, the cognitive impairment appears gradually, and the person's cognitive deterioration is progressive (Cummings & Cole, 2002). If the person meets these criteria, the diagnosis is then made on the basis of excluding other conditions, such as vascular disease, Huntington's disease, Parkinson's disease, or chronic substance abuse.

A definite diagnosis of Alzheimer's disease can only be determined by autopsy because it requires the observation of two specific types of brain lesions: neurofibrillary tangles and amyloid plaques (see Figure 14–2 on page 446). The brain is composed of millions of neurons. The internal structure of branches that extend from each neuron includes microtubules, which provide structural support for the cell and help transport chemicals used in the production of neurotransmitters (Caselli et al., 2006). These microtubules are reinforced by tau proteins, which are organized symmetrically. Tau proteins are proteins associated with the assembly and stability of microtubules. In patients with Alzheimer's disease, enzymes loosen tau from their connections

to the microtubule, and they break apart. The microtubules disintegrate in the absence of tau proteins, and the whole neuron shrivels and dies. The disorganized tangles of tau that are left at the end of this process are known as **neurofibrillary tangles.** They are found in both the cerebral cortex and the hippocampus. Neurofibrillary tangles have also been found in adults with Down syndrome and patients with Parkinson's disease.

The other type of lesion in Alzheimer's disease is known as **amyloid plaques,** which consist of a central core of homogeneous protein material known as **beta-amyloid** surrounded by clumps of debris left over from destroyed neurons. These plaques are located primarily in the cerebral cortex. They are found in large numbers in the brains of patients with Alzheimer's disease, but they are not unique to that condition. The brains of normal elderly people, especially after the age of 75, often contain some neurofibrillary tangles and amyloid plaques. A few widely scattered cells of this type do not appear to interfere with normal cognitive functioning.

Forms of Brain Tissue Damage Associated with Alzheimer's Disease

Plaques

1) All plaques possess round, spherically shaped structures. These structures lie outside nerve cells and are embedded in the brain the way pieces of fruit might be embedded in gelatin.

2) The second component of plaque consists of many irregularly shaped neural structures surrounding the sphere. These appear to be patches of degenerating axon terminals and dendrite branches of local neurons.

Tangles

Tangles without nerve cell (cell destroyed).

Tangles inside an intact nerve cell.

Distribution of Amyloid Plaques

LEFT HEMISPHERE, LATERAL VIEW

LEFT HEMISPHERE, MEDIAL VIEW

Abundance of Amyloid Plaques

Least | Most

Distribution of Neurofibrillary Tangles

LEFT HEMISPHERE, LATERAL VIEW

LEFT HEMISPHERE, MEDIAL VIEW

Abundance of Neurofibrillary Tangles

Least | Most

FIGURE 14–2 The top panel illustrates the appearance of amyloid plaques and neurofibrillary tangles. The bottom panel illustrates the areas of the brain in which each type of lesion is most likely to appear.

Source: J. Medina, 1999, *What You Need to Know About Alzheimer's,* New Harbinger Publications. Copyright © 1999. Reprinted by permission of J. Medina, and J. L. Cummings, 2002, "Alzheimer's Disease," *Journal of the American Medical Association, 287,* pp. 2335–2338. Copyright © 2002. Reprinted by permission of American Medical Association.

Frontotemporal Dementia (Pick's Disease)

A rare form of dementia associated with circumscribed atrophy of the frontal and temporal lobes of the brain is known as *frontotemporal dementia (FTD)*. This syndrome is very similar to Alzheimer's disease in terms of both behavioral symptoms and cognitive impairment. Patients with both disorders display problems in memory and language. Early personality changes that precede the onset of cognitive impairment are more common among FTD patients. Impaired reasoning and judgment are more prominent than anterograde amnesia in FTD. In comparison to Alzheimer patients, patients with FTD are also more likely to engage in impulsive sexual actions, roaming and aimless exploration, and other types of disinhibited behavior (Mendez, Lauterbach, & Sampson, 2008).

Another, more traditional diagnostic term that has been used to describe many patients who exhibit the behavioral syndrome of FTD is *Pick's disease* (Rossor, 2001). This term refers to a unique form of neural pathology that is found among some, but not all, patients with FTD. Detailed examination of brain tissue from patients with FTD often reveals the presence of unusual protein deposits, called *Pick's bodies,* within nerve cells (Hardin & Schooley, 2002). The loss and degeneration of neurons are usually concentrated in structures associated with the limbic system, such as the hippocampus and amygdala. The neurofibrillary tangles and amyloid plaques found in Alzheimer's disease are no more common in patients with Pick's disease than in normal people of the same age (Dickson, 2001). The more recent diagnostic term, FTD, is preferred by many neurologists because it describes a behavioral syndrome (deterioration of personality, antisocial behavior, abnormal sense of humor, and memory disorder) rather than a specific form of neural pathology that is not found in all FTD patients.

Huntington's Disease Unusual involuntary muscle movements known as **chorea** (from the Greek word meaning "dance") represent the most distinctive feature of **Huntington's disease.** These movements are relatively subtle at first, with the person appearing to be merely restless or fidgety. As the disorder progresses, sustained muscle contractions become difficult. Movements of the face, trunk, and limbs eventually become uncontrolled, leaving the person to writhe and grimace. A large proportion of Huntington's patients also exhibit a variety of personality

Areas of the Brain Implicated in Huntington's Disease

FIGURE 14–3 Huntington's disease involves deterioration of the basal ganglia (also known as the cerebral nuclei). The primary units of this system are the caudate nucleus, putamen, globus pallidus, and the claustrum.

Source: Adapted from R. Martini and M. Timmons, 1995, *Human Anatomy,* p. 378, Upper Saddle River, NJ: Prentice Hall.

changes and symptoms of mental disorders, primarily depression and anxiety. Between 5 and 10 percent develop psychotic symptoms. The symptoms of mental disorder may be evident before the appearance of motor or cognitive impairment (Naarding & Janzing, 2003).

The movement disorder and the cognitive deficits are produced by progressive neuronal degeneration in the basal ganglia (Chesselet & Delfs, 1996). This is a group of nuclei, including the caudate nucleus, the putamen, and the globus pallidus, that form a collaborative system of connections between the cerebral cortex and the thalamus (see Figure 14–3).

Dementia appears in all Huntington's disease patients, although the extent of the cognitive impairment and the rate of its progression vary widely. Impairments in recent memory and learning are the most obvious cognitive problems. Patients have trouble encoding new information. Higher-level cognitive functions are typically well preserved, and insight is usually intact. Unlike the pattern of dementia seen in Alzheimer's disease, patients with Huntington's do not develop aphasia, apraxia, or agnosia (Morris, 1995).

The diagnosis of Huntington's disease depends on the presence of a positive family history for the disorder. It is one of the few disorders that are transmitted in an autosomal dominant pattern with complete penetrance. In other words, the person must only inherit one gene—from either parent—to be vulnerable, and an individual who inherits the problematic gene will always develop the disorder (see Research Methods on page 454).

▲ Boxing legend Muhammed Ali and actor Michael J. Fox joke around before testifying at a government hearing on Parkinson's disease. Both men have the disorder, and they encouraged the committee to increase funds for research.

Parkinson's Disease A disorder of the motor system, known as *Parkinson's disease,* is caused by a degeneration of a specific area of the brain stem known as the substantia nigra and loss of the neurotransmitter dopamine, which is produced by cells in this area. Typical symptoms include tremors, rigidity, postural abnormalities, and reduction in voluntary movements (Kontakos & Stokes, 1999). Unlike people with Huntington's disease, most patients with Parkinson's disease do not become demented. Follow-up studies suggest that approximately 20 percent of elderly patients with Parkinson's disease will develop symptoms of dementia. Their risk is approximately double the risk of dementia found among people of similar age who do not have Parkinson's disease (Marder et al., 1995).

Vascular Dementia Many conditions other than those that attack brain tissue directly can also produce symptoms of dementia. The central

▶ Electron micrograph of a section through a Lewy body in a nerve cell in the brain. Lewy bodies are largely made up of filaments of a specific brain protein (shown here in blue), and these filaments are presumably responsible for degeneration of nerve cells.

agent in these problems can be either medical conditions or other types of mental disorder. Diseases that affect the heart and lungs, for example, can interfere with the circulation of oxygen to the brain. Substance abuse can also interfere with brain functions.

One cause of dementia is vascular or blood vessel disease, which affects the arteries responsible for bringing oxygen and sugar to the brain (Roman, 2002). A *stroke,* the severe interruption of blood flow to the brain, can produce various types of brain damage, depending on the size of the affected blood vessel and the area of the brain that it supplies. The area of dead tissue produced by the stroke is known as an *infarct.* The behavioral effects of a stroke are usually obvious and can be distinguished from dementia on several grounds: (1) They appear suddenly rather than gradually; (2) they affect voluntary movements of the limbs and gross speech patterns, as well as more subtle intellectual abilities; and (3) they often result in unilateral rather than bilateral impairment, such as paralysis of only one side of the body.

There are instances, however, in which the stroke affects only a very small artery and may not have any observable effect on the person's behavior. If several of these small strokes occur over a period of time, and if their sites are scattered in different areas of the brain, they may gradually produce cognitive impairment. DSM-IV-TR refers to this condition as **vascular dementia.** The cognitive symptoms of vascular dementia that are listed in the diagnostic manual are the same as those for Alzheimer's disease, but DSM-IV-TR does not require a gradual onset for vascular dementia, as it does for dementia of the Alzheimer's type. In addition, the diagnosis of vascular dementia depends on the presence of either focal neurological signs and symptoms associated with the experience of stroke, such as gait abnormalities or weakness in the extremities, or laboratory evidence of blood vessel disease (Paul, Garrett, & Cohen, 2003).

Dementia with Lewy Bodies *Lewy bodies* (also called *intracytoplasmic inclusions*) are rounded deposits found in nerve cells. Named after F. H. Lewy, who first described them in 1912, Lewy bodies are often found in the brain-stem nuclei of patients with Parkinson's disease. Neurologists later discovered occasional cases of progressive dementia in which autopsies revealed Lewy bodies widespread throughout the brain. The development of more sensitive staining techniques that can identify cortical Lewy bodies led to greatly increased interest in this phenomenon during the 1990s.

Clinicians have defined a syndrome known as **dementia with Lewy bodies (DLB),** but the boundaries of DLB are not entirely clear. It overlaps, both in terms of clinical symptoms and brain pathology, with other forms of dementia such as Alzheimer's disease and Parkinson's disease. An international workshop established consensus criteria for the diagnosis of DLB in 1995. Many experts now agree that DLB may be the second most common form of dementia, after Alzheimer's disease. Among patients who meet diagnostic criteria for Alzheimer's disease, 30 percent also have evidence of diffuse Lewy bodies in cortical neurons (McKeith, 2002; Simard et al., 2000).

Symptoms of DLB typically begin with memory deficits followed by a progressive decline to dementia. Patients' cognitive impairment includes problems in attention, executive functions, problem solving, and visuospatial performance. Unlike patients with Alzheimer's disease, patients with DLB often show a fluctuation in cognitive performance, alertness, and level of consciousness. Their episodic confusional states sometimes resemble delirium. These changes may be evident over a period of hours or several days.

The symptom that is most likely to distinguish DLB from Alzheimer's disease and vascular dementia is the presence of recurrent and detailed visual hallucinations. The patient usually recognizes that the hallucinations are not real. Many patients with DLB also develop Parkinsonian features, such as muscular rigidity, which appear early in the development of the disorder (Ballard et al., 2001).

The course of dementia appears to be different between patients with Alzheimer's disease and DLB. Patients with DLB show a more rapid progression of cognitive impairment, and the time from onset of symptoms to death is also shorter. They are also likely to develop adverse reactions to neuroleptic medication, which is sometimes used to treat their psychotic symptoms, such as hallucinations (Rojas-Fernandez & MacKnight, 1999).

Dementia Versus Depression Another condition that can be associated with symptoms of dementia, especially among the elderly, is depression. There are, indeed, many areas of overlap between these disorders, but the nature of the relationship is not yet clear. Approximately 25 percent of patients with a diagnosis of dementia also exhibit symptoms of major depressive disorder (Steffens &

Potter, 2008). The symptoms of depression include a lack of interest in, and withdrawal of attention from, the environment. People who are depressed often have trouble concentrating, they appear preoccupied, and their thinking is labored. These cognitive problems closely resemble some symptoms of dementia. Some depressed patients exhibit poverty of speech and restricted or unchanging facial expression. A disheveled appearance, due to self-neglect and loss of weight, in an elderly patient may contribute to the impression that the person is suffering from dementia.

Despite the many similarities, there are important differences between depression and dementia. These are summarized in Table 14–6. Experienced clinicians can usually distinguish between depression and dementia by considering the pattern of onset and associated features (Insel & Badger, 2002). In those cases where the distinction cannot be made on the basis of these characteristics, response to treatment may be the only way to establish a differential diagnosis. If the person's condition, including cognitive impairments, improves following treatment with antidepressant medication or electroconvulsive therapy, it seems reasonable to conclude that the person was depressed.

The relationship between depression and dementia has been the topic of considerable debate. Is depression a consequence of dementia, or are the symptoms of dementia a consequence of depression? Some clinicians have used the term *pseudodementia* to describe the condition of patients with symptoms of dementia whose cognitive impairment is actually produced by a major depressive disorder. There is no doubt that cases of this sort exist (Raskind, 1998). In fact, depression

Why is depression in an elderly person sometimes confused with dementia?

TABLE 14–6 Signs and Symptoms Distinguishing Depression from Dementia

DEPRESSION	DEMENTIA
Uneven progression over weeks	Even progression over months or years
Complains of memory loss	Attempts to hide memory loss
Often worse in morning, better as day goes on	Worse later in day or when fatigued
Aware of, exaggerates disability	Unaware or minimizes disability
May abuse alcohol or other drugs	Rarely abuses drugs

Source: Adapted from I. I. Heston and J. A. White, 1991, *The Vanishing Mind: A Practical Guide to Alzheimer's Disease and Other Dementias*, New York: Freeman.

and dementia are not necessarily mutually exclusive disorders. We know that these conditions co-exist more often than would be expected by chance, but we do not know why (Jorm, 2001).

FREQUENCY OF DELIRIUM AND DEMENTIA

Cognitive disorders represent one of the most pressing health problems in our society. Detailed evidence regarding the prevalence of delirium is not available, but it does seem to be one of the most frequent symptoms of disease among elderly people. At least 15 percent of elderly hospitalized medical patients exhibit symptoms of delirium (Fann, 2000). The rate is much higher among nursing home patients, where delirium is often combined with dementia (as in the case study at the beginning of this chapter).

Dementia is an especially important problem among elderly people. Although it can appear in people as young as 40 to 45, the average age of onset is much later. The incidence of dementia will be much greater in the near future, because the average age of the population is increasing steadily (see Chapter 17). People over the age of 80 represent one of the fastest growing segments of our population. By the year 2030, more than 9 million people in the United States will be affected by Alzheimer's disease (Kukull & Bowen, 2002). The personal and economic impact of dementia on patients, their families, and our society clearly warrants serious attention from health care professionals, policymakers concerned with health care reform, and clinical scientists seeking more effective forms of treatment.

Epidemiological studies must be interpreted with caution, of course, because of the problems associated with establishing a diagnosis of dementia. Mild cases are difficult to identify reliably. At the earliest stages of the disorder, symptoms are difficult to distinguish from forgetfulness, which can increase in normal aging. Definitive diagnoses depend on information collected over an extended period of time so that the progressive nature of the cognitive impairment, and deterioration from an earlier, higher level of functioning, can be documented. Unfortunately, this kind of information is often not available in a large-scale epidemiological study.

Also bear in mind the fact that the diagnosis of specific subtypes of dementia, such as dementia of the Alzheimer's type and dementia due to Pick's disease, requires microscopic examination of brain tissue after the person's death. Again, these data are not typically available to epidemiologists. With these limitations in mind, we now consider what is known about the frequency of dementia in the general population.

Prevalence of Dementia

The incidence and prevalence of dementia increase dramatically with age. Studies of community samples in North America and Europe indicate that the prevalence of dementia in people between the ages of 65 and 69 is approximately 1 percent. For people between the ages of 75 and 79, the prevalence rate is approximately 6 percent, and it increases dramatically in older age groups. Almost 40 percent of people over 90 years of age exhibit symptoms of moderate or severe dementia (Fitzpatrick et al., 2004; Hendrie, 1998).

Survival rates are reduced among demented patients. In Alzheimer's disease, for example, the average time between onset of the disorder and the person's death is less than 6 years. Higher mortality rates are found for men and for patients who also have symptoms involving involuntary muscle movements (Stern et al., 1997). There is considerable variability in these figures. Some patients have survived more than 20 years after the first appearance of obvious symptoms.

There are no obvious differences between men and women with regard to the overall prevalence of dementia, broadly defined. It seems, however, that dementia in men is more likely to be associated with vascular disease or to be secondary to other medical conditions or to alcohol abuse. The incidence of Alzheimer's disease is the same in men and women up to age 90; after that, the number of new cases continues to increase for women while it apparently

▶ Prevalence rates for Alzheimer's may be lower in developing countries than in developed countries. For example, Alzheimer's disease is more prevalent among African Americans than among sub-Saharan Africans.

declines for men (Lerner, 1999; Ruitenberg et al., 2001). Figure 14–4 illustrates gender differences in the number of new cases of Alzheimer's disease and vascular dementia that appear in different age groups. The incidence of vascular dementia is generally lower in women than in men at all age groups.

Prevalence by Subtypes of Dementia

The studies we have already reviewed refer to cross-sectional examinations of populations, which do not allow diagnosis of specific subtypes of dementia. Some clinical studies, based on hospital populations, have allowed investigators to look at the frequency of specific subtypes of dementia. Alzheimer's disease appears to be the most common form of dementia (Breteler, Ott, & Hofman, 1998; Kaye, 1995), accounting for perhaps half of all cases (depending on the diagnostic criteria employed and the geographic location of the study). Dementia with Lewy bodies may be the second leading cause of dementia; studies report prevalence rates between 12 and 27 percent for DLB among patients with primary dementia (Kalra, Bergeron, & Lang, 1996). Prevalence rates for vascular dementia are similar to those for DLB (Leys, Pasquier, & Parnetti, 1998). Pick's disease is much less common than Alzheimer's disease, vascular dementia, or DLB. Huntington's disease is rare by comparison. It affects only 1 person in every 20,000 (Shoulson, 1990).

Cross-Cultural Comparisons

Several issues make it difficult to collect cross-cultural data regarding the prevalence of dementia. Tests that are used to measure cognitive impairment must be developed carefully to be sure that they are not culturally or racially biased (see Chapter 4 on the validity of assessment procedures). Elderly people in developing countries who have little formal education pose a special challenge, since most cognitive tasks have been developed for use with a different population. Those who follow more traditional ways of life, such as the Australian aboriginal people, may have very different views of old age and its problems. For all these reasons, we must interpret preliminary results on this topic with great caution (Prince et al., 2003).

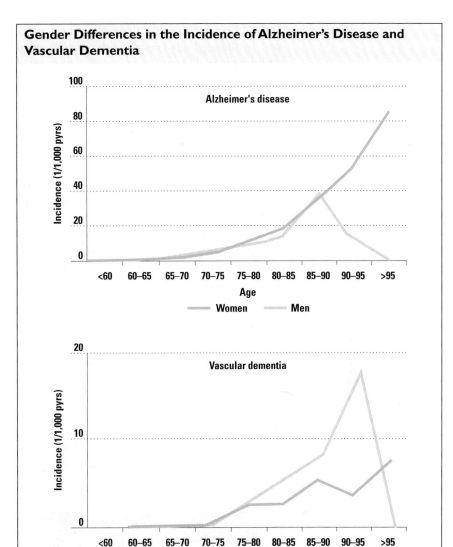

Gender Differences in the Incidence of Alzheimer's Disease and Vascular Dementia

FIGURE 14–4   This figure shows the number of new cases of dementia that appeared among people in specific age groups. The participants included 7,000 people, 55 years and older, in the Netherlands.

Source: A. Ruitenberg et al., 2001, "Incidence of Dementia: Does Gender Make a Difference?" *Neurobiology of Aging,* 22, pp. 575–580. Copyright © 2001. Reprinted by permission of Elsevier, Ltd.

Some studies have reported that prevalence rates for dementia vary geographically. Alzheimer's disease may be more common in North America and Europe, whereas vascular dementia may be more common in Japan and China (Chiu et al., 1998). There are also some tentative indications that prevalence rates for dementia may be significantly lower in developing countries than in developed countries. For example, Alzheimer's disease is more prevalent among African Americans than among sub-Saharan Africans (Hendrie et al., 1995).

What underlying factors might be responsible for cross-cultural differences in the incidence of dementia?

These differences may be influenced by many factors, including both genetic and environmental considerations. Dietary practices and educational opportunities are examples of environmental risk factors that may account for these patterns.

CAUSES

Delirium and dementia are clearly associated with brain pathology. Damage to various brain structures and neurotransmitter pathways can be the product of various biological and environmental events. In the following pages, we review some of the considerations that guide current thinking about the causes of these disorders.

Delirium

The underlying mechanisms responsible for the onset of delirium undoubtedly involve neuropathology and neurochemistry (Goldstein, 2003). The incidence of delirium increases among elderly people, presumably because the physiological effects of aging make elderly people more vulnerable to medication side effects and cognitive complications of medical illnesses

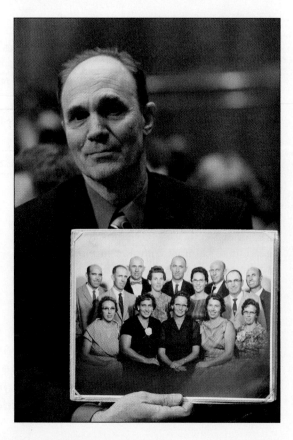

▶ Chuck Jackson was diagnosed at the age of 50 with a rare, early-onset form of Alzheimer's disease. Speaking at a Congressional hearing on the disease, Jackson showed a family photo because he is the fifth generation of his family to have Alzheimer's.

(Jacobson, 1997). Delirium can be caused by many different kinds of medication, including the following:

• Psychiatric drugs (especially antidepressants, antipsychotics, and benzodiazepines)
• Drugs used to treat heart conditions
• Painkillers
• Stimulants (including caffeine)

Delirium also develops in conjunction with a number of metabolic diseases, including pulmonary and cardiovascular disorders (which can interfere with the supply of oxygen to the brain), as well as endocrine diseases (especially thyroid disease and diabetes mellitus). Various kinds of infection can lead to the onset of delirium. Perhaps the most common among elderly people is urinary tract infection, which can result from the use of an indwelling urinary catheter (sometimes necessary with incontinent nursing home patients).

Dementia

In discussing the classification of dementia, we have touched on many of the factors that contribute to the etiology of these problems. Most of the other disorders listed in DSM-IV-TR are classified on the basis of symptoms alone. The classification of dementia is sometimes determined by specific knowledge of etiological factors, even though these may be determined only after the patient's death, as in Alzheimer's disease. In the following discussion we consider in greater detail a few of the specific pathways that are known to lead to dementia.

Genetic Factors Neurologists who treat demented patients have recognized for many years that the disorder often runs in families. Until recently, twin studies have not been used extensively to evaluate the influence of genetic factors in dementia because of the comparatively late age of onset of these disorders. By the time a proband develops symptoms of dementia, his or her co-twin may be deceased. A few studies have capitalized on national samples to find an adequate number of twin pairs. They confirm the impression, based on family studies, that genetic factors play an important role in the development of dementia. One Swedish study, for example, found that the concordance rate in monozygotic twins was over 50 percent, more than double the dizygotic rate (Pedersen et al., 2004). A U.S. study, based on a registry of aging twin veterans of World War II and the Korean War, found an MZ concordance rate of 35 percent in 24 male pairs. None of the 16 DZ pairs was concordant at the time of the report (Breitner et al., 1993).

Most of the research concerned with genetic factors and Alzheimer's disease has focused on gene identification strategies (see Research Methods on page 454). The astounding advances that have been made in molecular genetics since 1980 have been applied to Alzheimer's disease with fruitful results. Experts now agree that Alzheimer's disease is genetically heterogeneous. In other words, there are several forms of the disorder, and each seems to be associated with a different gene or set of genes. Three genes (located on chromosomes 21, 14, and 1) have been identified that, when mutated, cause early-onset forms of Alzheimer's disease. A fourth gene,

located on chromosome 19, serves as a risk factor for late-onset forms of the disorder (Holmes, 2002; McQueen & Blacker, 2008). The locations of these genes are illustrated in Figure 14–5, along with graphs that indicate the average age of onset for dementia associated with the different genes.

It has been known for many years that amyloid plaques and neurofibrillary tangles are found in the brains of all people who have Down syndrome (see Chapter 15), as well as in people with Alzheimer's disease. This similarity led investigators to search for a link between the gene for Alzheimer's disease and known markers on chromosome 21, because people with Down syndrome possess three copies of chromosome 21 in every cell instead of the normal two. In fact, the gene responsible for producing proteins (amyloid precursor protein, or APP) that serve as precursors

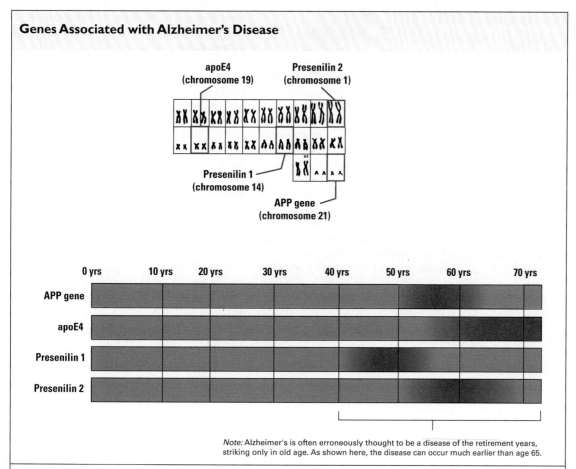

FIGURE 14–5 Four different genes are associated with the creation of plaques found in Alzheimer's disease (AD). The top panel, which illustrates the 23 pairs of human chromosomes, identifies which chromosome carries which AD-related gene. The bottom panel indicates that average age of onset of the disorder depends, in part, on the gene that is involved. The age of first diagnosis is illustrated in red.

Source: J. Medina, 1999, *What You Need to Know About Alzheimer's,* New Harbinger Publications, pp. 94–95. Copyright © 1999. Reprinted by permission of J. Medina.

RESEARCH METHODS   Finding Genes that Cause Behavioral Problems

Behavior genetic studies have demonstrated that most clinical disorders are under some degree of genetic influence. However, it is one thing to say that genetic factors "are involved" in the development of a disorder, and quite another to identify the specific genes involved. Discovery of the genes that are involved in a disorder would be an exciting step toward explaining the etiology of the disorder. It would also have important implications for developing targeted prevention and intervention programs for those people at greatest risk. Rapid advances in the field of molecular genetics are making it possible for scientists to identify specific genes involved in many disorders.

Finding genes involved in complex behavioral disorders has been difficult because there is no straightforward pattern of inheritance. Many genes are thought to be involved, and each of these genes on its own only increases or decreases risk a small amount. In addition, the environment is known to play an important role in the development of most clinical disorders. Whether or not an individual develops a disorder is a product of the combination of genetic and environmental risk and protective factors that the individual experiences. This has complicated efforts to identify genes involved in psychiatric disorders because the original methods developed for gene identification were based on simple, Mendelian disorders which are caused by a single defective gene. The application of these methods to complex psychiatric disorders led to many early failures and disappointments. Fortunately, new methods have been developed to take into account the complexities introduced when studying psychiatric phenotypes.

Most cells in the human body have 46 chromosomes grouped in 23 pairs. These chromosomes are transferred from the parents to the child during fertilization, with each parent providing 23 chromosomes. These chromosomes contain a chemical sequence called deoxyribonucleic acid (DNA). The characteristics of an individual that are inherited from one generation to the next are controlled by segments of DNA called genes. Any two human beings are about 99.9 percent identical genetically, but this 0.1 percent difference translates to about 3 million differences in our DNA. Some of these differences in DNA sequence contribute to individual differences in many human characteristics, ranging from eye color to personality. Most of these DNA differences are "silent" and don't appear to have any effect. These locations where the DNA comes in different forms can be used as genetic "markers," and they provide a useful way to find genes.

> **What do linkage and association studies tell us that twin studies cannot?**

One method to find genes is a strategy called *linkage analysis*. **Genetic linkage** studies focus on families that have multiple members affected with the disorder. Investigators systematically search the entire genome by testing for linkage between genetic markers, evenly spaced across all chromosomes, and the expression of a particular disease or behavior. They are looking for stretches of DNA that are more likely to be shared among the affected individuals, and less likely to be found in the unaffected individuals, suggesting that there is a gene in that region that contributes to the disorder. One strength of the linkage analysis approach is that it allows susceptibility genes to be identified when we have no, or limited, knowledge about what causes the disorder. This strategy led to the identification of the gene causing Huntington disease, which is a single gene, Mendelian disorder (Gusella et al., 1983).

Another strategy that is used to identify genes is case-control *association analysis*. This involves identifying two groups of individuals: One group consists of people affected with the disorder (cases) and the other group consists of people who do not have the disorder (controls). The two groups should be matched on factors such as gender, ethnicity, and age, so they only differ on disease status. The frequency with which particular versions of a gene occur in the two groups is then compared. If a gene is involved in the disorder, the "risk variant" should be more frequent among the affected individuals. This approach is often used to test genes that have been targeted as good candidates for involvement in the disorder for biological reasons (for example, genes involved in serotonin reception are considered good candidates for involvement in depression because antidepressants work by altering serotonin levels) or because they lie within a region of linkage identified in family studies, as described above.

It is currently a very exciting time in gene identification efforts for complex disorders. Genes involved in the predisposition to schizophrenia (O'Donovan, Williams, & Owen, 2003), alcoholism (Dick et al., 2006), and ADHD (Faraone, 2003), among others, have all been recently reported, with replications across multiple studies. Another exciting advance is the incorporation of gene-environment interaction into the study of genetic effects. A recent study found that a particular version of the serotonin transporter gene contributes to the development of depression, *but only when the individual also experiences stressful life events* (Caspi et al., 2003). Identifying the specific genes involved in clinical disorders, and how these genes interact with environmental risk factors, promises to enhance dramatically our understanding of the etiology of these disorders.

to beta-amyloid, found in the core of amyloid plaques, is located on chromosome 21. Several research groups have independently confirmed this association. Therefore, within some families, the gene for Alzheimer's disease is located on chromosome 21.

Mutations on chromosome 14 (presenilin 1, or PS1) and chromosome 1 (presenilin 2, or PS2) have also been found to be associated with early-onset forms of Alzheimer's disease (Plassman & Breitner, 1997). Like the APP gene, both of the presenilin genes are inherited in an autosomal dominant mode of transmission and cause over-production of beta-amyloid. Mutations in the PS1 gene are probably responsible for 50 percent of early-onset cases of the disorder (which represent less than 10 percent of all patients with Alzheimer's disease).

A fourth gene produces vulnerability to late-onset Alzheimer's disease without having a direct or necessary effect on the development of dementia. In other words, people who carry this gene have an increased risk for Alzheimer's disease, but many people without the gene develop the disorder, and some people who do have the gene do not develop the disorder. The apolipoprotein E (APOE) gene is located on chromosome 19. There are three common alleles (forms) of APOE, called e-2, e-3, and e-4. The APOE-2 allele is correlated with a decreased risk for Alzheimer's disease. People who have the APOE-4 allele at this locus have an increased probability of developing the disorder (Farrer et al., 1997). Although the effect may be weaker in some groups of people (such as Hispanics and African Americans), the finding has been replicated in more than 100 different laboratories. The risk for Alzheimer's disease is between 25 and 40 percent among people who have at least one APOE-4 allele (Mayeux & Ottman, 1998). Because most cases of Alzheimer's disease have a late onset, the APOE gene is probably involved in more cases of the disorder than the genes on chromosomes 21, 14, and 1.

Research findings with regard to specific genes and Alzheimer's disease are obviously exciting, but a word of caution is also in order. Although some important genes have been identified, most people who develop the disorder do *not* posses one of these specific genes. In other words, these genes do increase the risk for the disorder, but most cases of the disorder do not follow this pattern. Many questions remain to be answered about the ways in which specific genes interact with other causal factors.

Neurotransmitters In patients suffering from dementia, the process of chemical transmission of messages within the brain is probably disrupted, but the specific mechanisms that are involved have not been identified. We know that Parkinson's disease, which is sometimes associated with dementia, is caused by a degeneration of the dopamine pathways in the brain stem. This dysfunction is responsible for the motor symptoms seen in patients with that disorder. It is not entirely clear, however, that the intellectual problems experienced by patients with Parkinson's disease are directly related to dopamine deficiencies.

Other types of dementia have also been linked to problems with specific neurotransmitters. Huntington's disease may be associated with deficiencies in gamma-aminobutyric acid (GABA). A marked decrease in the availability of acetylcholine (ACh), another type of neurotransmitter, has been implicated in Alzheimer's disease. Reductions in ACh levels, especially in the temporal lobes, are correlated with the severity of dementia symptoms (Kihara & Shimohama, 2004; Raskind & Peskind, 1997).

Viral Infections Some forms of primary dementia are known to be the products of "slow" viruses—infections that develop over a much more extended period of time than do most viral infections. Creutzfeldt-Jakob disease is one

▼ Cary Henderson, a patient with Alzheimer's disease, celebrates his 62nd birthday. The drawing and note from his granddaughter illustrate the impact this disorder has on families. Henderson described his experiences as the disorder progressed in *Partial View: An Alzheimer's Journal.*

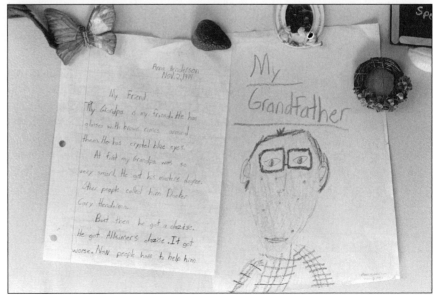

example. Susceptibility to infection by a specific virus can be influenced by genetic factors. The demonstration that a condition is transmitted in a familial fashion does not rule out the involvement of viral infection. In fact, familial transmission has been demonstrated for the forms of dementia that are known to be associated with a specific virus.

Immune System Dysfunction The immune system is the body's first line of defense against infection. It employs antibodies to break down foreign materials, such as bacteria and viruses, that enter the body. The regulation of this system allows it to distinguish between foreign bodies that should be destroyed and normal body tissues that should be preserved. The production of these antibodies may be dysfunctional in some forms of dementia, such as Alzheimer's disease. In other words, the destruction of brain tissue may be caused by a breakdown in the system that regulates the immune system.

The presence of beta-amyloid at the core of amyloid plaques is one important clue to the possible involvement of immune system dysfunction. This protein is the breakdown product of a structural component of brain cells. It is made and eliminated constantly as part of normal brain functioning. For some reason, which probably involves genetic factors, some people develop problems with the elimination of beta-amyloid. Clumps of beta-amyloid accumulate. Some clinical scientists believe that immune cells in the brain attempt to destroy these amyloid plaques and inadvertently harm neighboring, healthy brain cells. Some research evidence supports this hypothesis (McGeer & McGeer, 1996; Richardson, 1996).

How could education help to reduce a person's risk for dementia?

Environmental Factors Epidemiological investigations have discovered several interesting patterns that suggest that some types of dementia, especially Alzheimer's disease, may be related to environmental factors. One example is head injury, which can cause a sudden increase of amyloid plaque. Elderly people who have been knocked unconscious as adults have an increased risk of developing Alzheimer's disease, compared to people with no history of head injury (Holsinger et al., 2002; O'Meara et al., 1997).

Some studies have reported significant relationships between Alzheimer's disease and variables that seem to protect the person from developing dementia. People who have achieved high levels of education are less likely to develop Alzheimer's disease than are people with less education (Johnson et al., 1997; Stern et al., 1994). For example, one fascinating study has reported that among elderly Catholic nuns those who graduated from college were much less likely to be cognitively impaired than were those who had less than a college education (Butler, Ashford, & Snowdon, 1996). This finding may be interpreted to mean that increased "brain work" leads to a facilitation of neuronal activation, increased cerebral blood flow, and higher levels of glucose and oxygen consumption in the brain. All of this may increase the density of synaptic connections in the person's cortex and reduce risk for later neuronal deterioration. The discovery of environmental experiences (e.g., going to school) that serve a protective function points to the important role that cultural factors may play in moderating risk for dementia.

TREATMENT AND MANAGEMENT

The most obvious consideration with regard to treatment of the cognitive disorders is accurate diagnosis (Cummings & Cole, 2002). The distinction between delirium and dementia is important because many conditions that cause delirium can be treated. Delirium must be recognized as early as possible so that the source of the problem, such as an infection or some other medical condition, can be treated (Bourne et al., 2008). Some types of secondary dementia can also be treated successfully. For example, if the patient's cognitive symptoms are the products of depression, there is a relatively good chance that he or she will respond positively to antidepressant medication or electroconvulsive therapy.

When the person clearly suffers from a primary type of dementia, such as dementia of the Alzheimer's type, a return to previous levels of functioning is extremely unlikely. No form of treatment is presently capable of producing sustained and clinically significant improvement in cognitive functioning for patients with Alzheimer's disease (Tune, 2007). Realistic goals include helping the person to maintain his or her level of functioning for as long as possible in spite of cognitive impairment and minimizing the level of distress experienced by the person and the person's family. Several treatment options are typically used in conjunction, including medication, management of the patient's environment, behavioral strategies, and providing support to caregivers.

Medication

Some drugs are designed to relieve cognitive symptoms of dementia by boosting the action of acetylcholine (ACh), a neurotransmitter that is involved in memory and whose level is reduced in patients with Alzheimer's disease. One drug that has been approved for use with Alzheimer's patients—donepezil (Aricept)—increases ACh activity by inhibiting acetylcholinesterase, the enzyme that breaks down ACh in the synapse. Research studies have demonstrated that donepezil can provide temporary symptomatic improvement for some patients (Kumagai et al., 2008; Rojas-Fernandez et al., 2001). Unfortunately, it usually works for only 6 to 9 months and is not able to reverse the relentless progression of the disease. Furthermore, its use has been seriously questioned because of the relatively small effects on memory that it is able to produce (Pryse-Phillips, 1999). A statistically significant change in scores on a cognitive task does not necessarily imply a clinically significant improvement in overall clinical condition (see Research Methods in Chapter 6).

New drug treatments are being pursued that are aimed more directly at the processes by which neurons are destroyed (Sabbagh, Richardson, & Relkin, 2008). One possibility involves the use of synthetic peptides and natural proteins that inhibit the formation of amyloid plaques. Others focus on blocking the construction of neurofibrillary tangles by keeping tau protein anchored to microtubules. These alternatives are being developed and tested at a rapid pace. Recent evidence regarding these new treatment options can be obtained on the Web from the Cochrane Library.

Although the cognitive deficits associated with primary dementia cannot be completely reversed with medication, neuroleptic medication can be used to treat some patients who develop psychotic symptoms (Martinez & Kunik, 2006). These are the same drugs that are used to treat schizophrenia. Low doses are preferable because demented patients are especially vulnerable to the side effects of neuroleptics. Care must be taken to avoid use of these drugs with patients suffering from dementia with Lewy bodies because they may experience a severe negative reaction.

Environmental and Behavioral Management

Patients with dementia experience fewer emotional problems and are less likely to become agitated if they follow a structured and predictable daily schedule (Stewart, 1995). Activities such as eating meals, exercising, and going to bed are easier and less anxiety-provoking if they occur at regular times. The use of signs and notes may be helpful reminders for patients who are in the earlier stages of the disorder. As the patient's cognitive impairment becomes more severe, even simple activities, such as getting dressed or eating a meal, must be broken down into smaller and more manageable steps. Directions have to be adjusted so that they are appropriate to the patient's level of functioning. Patients with apraxia, for example, may not be able to perform tasks in response to verbal instructions. Caregivers need to adjust their

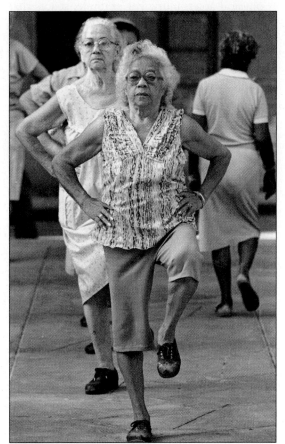

◀ These elderly residents of Havana, Cuba, are participating in an exercise program that is designed to keep the aging population fit and healthy.

WIFE OF PATIENT WITH ALZHEIMER'S DISEASE

SARAH

"You kinda have hope whenever you have cancer, (but with) Alzheimer's you die just a little each day . . ."

Watch the video "Alzheimer's Disease: The case of Wilburn Johnson" on MyPsychLab. What are the special challenges faced by family members and those who care for people suffering from Alzheimer's disease?

expectations and assume increased responsibilities as their patients' intellectual abilities deteriorate.

Severely impaired patients often reside in nursing homes and hospitals. The most effective residential treatment programs combine the use of medication and behavioral interventions with an environment that is specifically designed to maximize the level of functioning and minimize the emotional distress of patients who are cognitively impaired. Several goals guide the design of such an environment (Kettl, 1993; Lawton, 1989). These include considerations that enhance the following aspects of the patient's life.

- *Knowledge of the environment:* For example, rooms and hallways must be clearly labeled, because patients frequently cannot remember directions.
- *Negotiability:* In the case of dementia, psychological accessibility is at least as important as physical accessibility. For example, spaces that the person would use (a commons area or the dining room) should be visible from the patient's room if they cannot be remembered.
- *Safety and health:* For example, access to the setting must be secured so that patients who would otherwise wander away can remain as active as possible.

One important issue related to patient management involves the level of activity expected of the patient. It is useful to help the person remain active and interested in everyday events. Patients who are physically active are less likely to have problems with agitation, and they may sleep better. Engaging in a home-based exercise program can reduce functional dependence and delay institutionalization among patients with dementia (Rockwood & Middleton, 2007). Nevertheless, expectations regarding the patient's activity level may have to be reduced in proportion to the progression of cognitive impairment. Efforts should be made to preserve familiar routines and surroundings in light of the inevitable difficulties that are associated with learning new information and recalling past events. Helping the person to cope with these issues may minimize the emotion-

al turmoil associated with the increasing loss of cognitive abilities.

Social interactions are often troublesome for patients with dementia. An example of this type of problem was described in the case of Mary at the beginning of this chapter. After Mary had been admitted to the hospital, she frequently approached the nurses, insisting that she had to go home to take care of her dog which had, in fact, died. Creative problem-solving strategies that accommodate the patient's distorted view of reality are sometimes useful in this type of situation. Imagine, for example, a patient who continually insists that he must go to his former place of employment. It might be more effective to inform him each morning that his office called to say that he was not needed until the next day, rather than engaging in futile and upsetting arguments about whether he had, in fact, retired for medical reasons—a fact that he is incapable of remembering (Zarit, Zarit, & Rosenberg-Thompson, 1990).

Support for Caregivers

A final area of concern is the provision of support to people who serve as caregivers for demented patients. In the United States, spouses and other family members provide primary care for more than 80 percent of people who have dementia of the Alzheimer's type (Ballard, 2007). Their burdens are often overwhelming, both physically and emotionally. Consider, for example, the situation described by Bernlef in *Out of Mind.* In the following passage, Maarten describes the experience of listening to his wife, Vera, describe to a young woman (whom Vera has hired to help care for Maarten) how she has felt while attempting to cope with his progressive cognitive deterioration:

I hear Vera. "More than 40 years I have been married to him. And then suddenly this. Usually these things happen more slowly, gradually. But with him it came all at once. I feel it has been sprung on me. It's cruel and unfair. Sometimes I get so angry and rebellious when I see him looking at me as if from another world. And then again I feel only sad and I would so much like to understand him. Or I just talk along with him and then I feel ashamed afterwards. I'm glad you're here because it really gets on top of me at times, when I just can't bear watching it any more. At least now I'll be able to get out occasionally."

There is a moment of silence. I feel the tears running under my eyelids and down my cheeks.

"And sometimes, sometimes his face radiates perfect peace. As if he's happy. Like a child can be. Those moments are so brief I sometimes think I imagine them. But I know only too well what I see at such moments: someone who looks exactly like my husband of long ago. At your age it's difficult to understand that. But people like us live by their memories. If they no longer have those there's nothing left. I am afraid he is in the process of forgetting his whole life. And to live alone with those memories while he sits there beside me . . . empty."

(Bernlef, 1988, pp. 80–81)

In addition to the profound loneliness and sadness that caregivers endure, they must also learn to cope with more tangible stressors, such as the patient's incontinence, functional deficits, and disruptive behavior. Relationships among other family members and the psychological adjustment of the principal caregiver are more disturbed by caring for a demented person than by caring for someone who is physically disabled. Guilt, frustration, and depression are common reactions among the family members of patients (Kneebone & Martin, 2003).

Some treatment programs provide support groups, as well as informal counseling and ad hoc consultation services, for spouses caring for patients with Alzheimer's disease. The New York University Aging and Dementia Research Center has evaluated the effects of this approach, which attempts to help the caregiver survive the spouse's illness and to postpone the need to place the patient in a nursing home (Mittelman et al., 1997). Compared to caregivers in a control group, those who participated in the special support program were able to delay for a longer time placing the Alzheimer's patient in a nursing home. They were also less likely to become depressed and more likely to express satisfaction with the social support that they received from their families.

Some treatment programs arrange for direct assistance in addition to social support. Respite programs provide caregivers with temporary periods of relief away from the patient. One model program was designed and evaluated by M. Powell Lawton and his colleagues at the Philadelphia Geriatric Center (Brody, Saperstein, & Lawton, 1989). They either would send someone to the patient's home to relieve the caregiver or, in more severe cases, would temporarily institutionalize the patient if the caregiver needed to be away from home for an extended period. In some cases, these services were planned in advance so that the caregiver could take a short vacation, attend special events, or make his or her own medical appointments. Respite care was also available in response to unexpected circumstances, such as the illness of the caregiver. This type of flexible, comprehensive program is clearly needed to relieve the enormous burden that is faced by people who care for demented patients (Grasel, 1997).

What are the most difficult problems faced by people caring for a person with dementia?

GETTING HELP

Many resources are available to help people cope with problems associated with dementia. One particularly useful book, *What You Need to Know About Alzheimer's*, by John Medina, describes the symptoms of the disorder and their progression. It also explains current knowledge of the ways in which brain cells are destroyed by this disease.

When a person learns that he or she has Alzheimer's disease or some other form of dementia, a number of important challenges must be faced. Family members must be informed so that they can help make plans for the future. Decisions must be made about eventual changes in living arrangements and work (if the person is still employed). Perhaps most important, the person must prepare to cope with changes in daily life, as things that were once easy—such as communicating with other people and getting around in the community—become more difficult. The Alzheimer's Association (www.alz.org) maintains a comprehensive Web page that includes advice on all of these topics.

Family members and friends who provide care for patients with dementia face a very challenging situation. The Alzheimer's Association Web page provides information regarding strategies that can help caregivers prepare for these responsibilities. These include ways to adapt to inevitable changes in the caregivers' relationship with the patient, as well as advice about how to respond to challenging or unexpected behaviors on the part of the patient. The person with Alzheimer's disease will eventually become unable to perform daily tasks, and the caregiver will inevitably be faced with additional responsibility. As the burden mounts, he or she must locate additional sources of support and find ways to take care of his or her own health while also caring for the patient. Support groups and social services are often available locally.

■ SUMMARY

Dementia, delirium, and amnestic disorders are listed as Cognitive Disorders in DSM-IV-TR. Disruptions of memory and other cognitive functions are the most obvious symptoms of these disorders. Dementia and amnestic disorders are often associated with specific forms of neuropathology. These changes in brain tissue can often be observed only at autopsy, after the person's death. Until recently, the DSM referred to the Cognitive Disorders as Organic Mental Disorders because of their association with known brain diseases. That expression has been abandoned because it implies an artificial dichotomy between biological and psychological processes.

Dementia is defined as a gradually worsening loss of memory and related cognitive functions, including the use of language as well as reasoning and decision making. **Aphasia** and **apraxia** are among the most obvious problems in verbal communication. Perceptual difficulties, such as **agnosia,** are also common.

In amnestic disorder, the memory impairment is more circumscribed. The person may experience severe **anterograde amnesia,** but other higher-level cognitive abilities remain unimpaired. **Delirium** is a confusional state that develops over a short period of time and is often associated with agitation and hyperactivity.

Dementia can be associated with many different kinds of neuropathology. The most common form of dementia is associated with **Alzheimer's disease,** which accounts for approximately half of all diagnosed cases of dementia. **Dementia with Lewy bodies** and vascular dementia each account for 15 to 20 percent of cases. Less common forms of dementia include frontotemporal dementia (sometimes called Pick's disease), as well as dementia associated with **Huntington's disease,** and Parkinson's disease.

A definitive diagnosis of Alzheimer's disease can be made only after the patient's death. It requires the observation of two specific types of brain lesions: **neurofibrillary tangles** and **amyloid plaques,** which are found throughout the cerebral cortex. Neurofibrillary tangles are also found in the hippocampus, an area of the brain that is crucial for memory.

The incidence and prevalence of dementia increase dramatically with age. The annual incidence of dementia is 1.4 percent in people over the age of 65 and 3.4 percent for people over the age of 75. Almost 40 percent of people over 90 years of age exhibit symptoms of moderate or severe dementia. Men are more likely than women to develop vascular dementia. Men and women are equally vulnerable to Alzheimer's disease up to the age of 90, when the rate for women increases.

The etiology of dementia depends on many different factors. Some types of dementia are produced by viral infections and dysfunction of the immune system. Environmental toxins also may contribute to the onset of cognitive impairment.

Genetic factors clearly play a role in the etiology of some forms of dementia. Considerable research efforts have been devoted to the study of **genetic linkage** in Alzheimer's disease. Chromosome 21 has been examined closely because people with Down syndrome, who possess three copies of chromosome 21 in every cell, also have amyloid plaques and neurofibrillary tangles like those found in the brains of Alzheimer's patients. Within some families, the gene for Alzheimer's disease is located on chromosome 21. This pattern of linkage is not found for all families, however. Experts now assume that there are several forms of Alzheimer's disease, and each may be associated with a different gene or set of genes.

Delirium can often be resolved successfully by treating the medical condition. In some types of secondary dementia, the person can be restored to his or her original level of cognitive functioning. The intellectual deficits in primary forms of dementia are progressive and irreversible. The treatment goals in these disorders are more limited. They include maintaining the person's level of functioning for as long as possible while minimizing the level of distress experienced by the patient and the family, especially caregivers. Medication can produce modest cognitive benefits for some patients with dementia, but not all patients respond to such treatment, and the clinical significance of these changes is extremely limited. Drugs can be used to control motor dysfunctions associated with primary differentiated forms of dementia, such as Huntington's disease and Parkinson's disease.

Behavioral and environmental management are important aspects of any treatment program for demented patients. They allow patients to reside in the least restrictive and safest possible settings. Respite programs provide much-needed support to caregivers, usually spouses and other family members, who can easily be overwhelmed by the demands of caring for a person with dementia.

THE BIG PICTURE CRITICAL THINKING REVIEW

What is the difference between cognitive problems in anxiety and those seen in dementia?

In anxiety disorders and depression, subtle cognitive factors might play a role in causing the disorder. In dementia, the cognitive problems are the defining features of the disorder. (SEE PAGE 433)

In what ways is delirium different from dementia?

The two conditions differ both in terms of their characteristic symptoms and the pattern that the symptoms follow over time. (SEE PAGES 436–437)

How could a clinician distinguish between aphasia and agnosia?

A person suffering from aphasia might be unable to remember the name of an object but still be able to indicate how it is used. In agnosia, the person would be unable to recognize what it is or how it is used. (SEE PAGE 439)

Is memory impairment the only indication that a person is developing dementia?

No, decline in executive functioning is also closely linked to subsequent development of Alzheimer's disease. (SEE PAGE 445)

Why is depression in an elderly person sometimes confused with dementia?

Depressed people can exhibit cognitive symptoms that resemble some aspects of dementia, including lack of interest, trouble concentrating, and poverty of speech. (SEE PAGE 449)

What underlying factors might be responsible for cross-cultural differences in the incidence of dementia

Dietary practices and educational opportunities clearly vary from one culture to the next, and they may be responsible for variations in the frequency of new cases. (SEE PAGE 452)

How could education help to reduce a person's risk for dementia?

Higher levels of challenging cognitive activity may increase the density of synaptic connections in the person's cortex and make it less vulnerable to the impact of neuronal degeneration. (SEE PAGE 456)

What are the most difficult problems faced by people caring for a person with dementia?

Caregivers face prolonged emotional challenges, including loneliness, frustration, and guilt, as well as the overwhelming financial and physical demands of being responsible for a person who becomes increasingly unable to care for himself or herself. (SEE PAGE 459)

■ KEY TERMS

agnosia **439**
Alzheimer's disease **444**
amnestic disorder **432**
amyloid plaques **445**
anterograde amnesia **437**

aphasia **437**
apraxia **437**
beta-amyloid **445**
chorea **447**
delirium **432**

dementia **432**
dementia with Lewy bodies (DLB) **449**
dyskinesia **441**
genetic linkage **454**

Huntington's disease **447**
neurofibrillary tangles **445**
neurologists **433**
neuropsychological assessment **440**

neuropsychologists **433**
retrograde amnesia **437**
vascular dementia **448**

MENTAL RETARDATION AND PERVASIVE DEVELOPMENTAL DISORDERS

In many ways, mental retardation and the pervasive developmental disorders (PDD), the two categories of problems we discuss in this chapter, are very different from one another. Mental retardation is a familiar disability that impairs academic aptitude. *Autistic spectrum disorders* (a better name for the pervasive developmental disorders) are viewed as puzzling mental problems that impair relationships, behavior, and communication. Yet the two disorders also share important similarities. Both are either present at birth or begin early in life. Both affect many areas of intellectual, social, and life functioning. Both include a wide range of impairment. And initially at least, both disorders are a shock to parents who must learn to accept their child's developmental disability, embrace their child's positive qualities, and learn how best to raise a child who is undoubtedly different.

OVERVIEW

Autism is the most familiar PDD, which is why professionals increasingly use the term *autistic spectrum disorders*. Dustin Hoffman played a man with autism in the popular movie *Rain Man,* a largely accurate portrayal—and a reminder that children with autism grow up and often continue to have the same problems. Autistic spectrum disorders are distinguished by dramatic, severe, and unusual symptoms. Socially, the child lives in a world apart. At best, other people may be of little interest; at worst, they are a terrifying source of confusion. Many children with PDD cannot communicate. Others speak oddly, for example, echoing some phrase repeatedly. In addition, people with PDD are preoccupied with unusual repetitive behavior. In severe cases, they endlessly perform the same action, for example, flapping their hands for hours on end. Even the highest functioning people with PDD struggle to understand emotions and abstractions.

In this chapter, we discuss mental retardation before the pervasive developmental disorders for a simple and important reason: Contrary to some views, most people with PDD also have mental retardation. In order to appreciate both the wide-range of intellectual disabilities—and the autistic spectrum disorders—you need to understand what mental retardation really is.

MENTAL RETARDATION

Too often, people with mental retardation are defined in terms of what they cannot do. Today, the emphasis is on what the person with mental retardation *can* do. People with mental retardation are people first. We emphasize this with the convention of putting the "person first" in our writing. We refer to the "person with mental retardation," not to the "mentally retarded person."

A real-life triumph of ability over disability is Chris Burke, a television and recording star who also has Down syndrome, one of the most common causes of mental retardation. Burke's parents were told to institutionalize him when he was born, but they raised him at home and encouraged his interests and talents. Burke loved performing, and he eventually won starring television roles as Corky Thatcher in *Life Goes On* and Taylor in *Touched by an Angel*. He currently plays in a

◀ Christopher Burke, who has Down syndrome, has starred in two television series, *Life Goes On* and *Touched by an Angel*.

folk band—with two of his former music counselors. Despite his Down syndrome, many people would not consider someone like Chris Burke to have mental retardation—apparently including Chris Burke. He wrote this:

My name is Chris Burke and I live an exciting and happy life. That's because I am living my dreams. I love entertaining people and being an actor, and I like to help my fellow handi-capables. Many people recognize me from my role as Corky Thatcher on *Life Goes On*, an ABC-TV series for many years. Corky has Down syndrome and so do I. Only I call it Up syndrome, because having Down syndrome has never made me feel down. I'm always up. One reason it is uplifting is because of the tremendous support I have received from my family and all the people in my life. My teachers, my friends, and the people I have worked with are very important to me, just like I am important to them.

(Burke, 1995, p. ix)

Much of the focus of intervention with mental retardation is on intellectual disability. The following case illustrates both the emotional and life challenges that can accompany the disorder.

CASE **STUDY** Should This Mother Raise Her Children?

Karen Cross was a 41-year-old woman with three children when child protective services referred her and her husband, Mark, for a family evaluation. Two months earlier, the Crosses' 16-year-old daughter, Lucy, had called the police following a family fight. Lucy and her mother were arguing about Lucy's excessive use of the telephone. Mr. Cross entered the dispute, and he cuffed Lucy across her mouth in anger. Lucy was not seriously hurt, and the social workers who visited with the Cross family found no history of physical abuse. They were concerned about the adequacy of the Crosses' parenting, however, and the agency strongly recommended an evaluation for the family.

At the time of the referral, Mr. Cross was employed as a custodian at an elementary school where he had been working for 15 years. Testing indicated that he had an IQ of 88, and no serious psychopathology based on a diagnostic interview. Both Mr. Cross and his wife admitted that he had frequent, angry outbursts, but they both denied any history of violence toward the children or Mrs. Cross.

Mrs. Cross was a homemaker who cared for Lucy and a 12-year-old daughter, Sue. The Crosses' 19-year-old son was serving in the Army.

Mrs. Cross had a tested IQ of 67. She reported attending special education classes throughout her schooling. She married at the age of 19 and lived a normal life with her husband and children, but their low income barely kept the family out of poverty. Although Mrs. Cross demonstrated many adaptive skills in caring for her family, her coping currently was impaired by a severe depression. Mrs. Cross's speech and body movements were slowed, and she reported feeling constantly tired. She felt unhappy and unable to cope with her children. She was not sure what had caused her troubles, but Mr. Cross traced her problems to her mother's death a year earlier.

Mrs. Cross cried when recalling the loss of her mother. She described her mother as her best friend. They had lived in the same trailer park, and mother and daughter spent most of their days together. Her mother supported Mrs. Cross in many ways, especially in raising the children. Now the children ignored their mother's directions, and Mr. Cross was of little help. Mrs. Cross felt that her husband was too harsh, and she often contradicted him when he tried to punish the girls.

A family interview confirmed the impressions offered by the parents. Lucy looked distracted and bored throughout the interview. Sue frequently looked toward and imitated her older sister. The girls paid more attention briefly when their father got angry, but this ended when Mr. and Mrs. Cross started arguing over his tone of voice.

School records indicated that the girls had mostly C grades. Standardized test scores showed that the girls' academic abilities were in the normal range, but below average. Telephone calls to each of their homeroom teachers indicated that Sue was not much of a behavior problem in school, but Lucy had lately become very disruptive.

Based on the data obtained from multiple sources, the psychologists made several recommendations. They suggested antidepressant medication for Mrs. Cross, a referral to the school counselor for Lucy, and family therapy to help the parents agree on a set of rules and enforce discipline with a clear system of rewards and punishments. Therapy also would be an opportunity to monitor Mr. Cross's anger and Mrs. Cross's depression. Finally, they made a referral to a community service agency that could offer Mrs. Cross some parenting support.

The case of Karen Cross raises several issues to note. A basic one is whether she suffers from mental retardation. Her IQ is below the cutoff we discuss shortly, but she functioned well in her family life with her mother's support. Because of her adaptive skills, many professionals—and people in her community—would not consider her to have mental retardation. Others might argue, however, that she does have mental retardation, because she now needs additional supports because of her low IQ, her depression, or both. Karen Cross's depression also is important to note, because emotional difficulties often are overlooked among people with mental retardation.

The most important issues raised by the case, however, concern her children. How can we support families like Karen's to function better? When and why should children be removed from troubled family environments? You may have seen the movie *I Am Sam,* starring Sean Penn, which raised similar concerns. Penn played a loving father with mental retardation who fought to get his daughter back after social workers judged him to be an unfit parent. Like Karen Cross's real life experience, *I Am Sam* portrayed the tensions between supporting parents with disabilities versus protecting children from seriously troubled families. We consider these difficult issues in this chapter (and in Chapter 18 on mental illness and the law), but first we more closely examine the definition of mental retardation.

Symptoms of Mental Retardation

In addition to DSM-IV-TR, the American Association on Intellectual and Developmental Disabilities (AAIDD), the leading organization for professionals concerned with mental retardation, develops influential definitions of mental retardation. The two systems differ somewhat, including about what to call this problem— AAIDD prefers "intellectual disability" to "mental retardation," and recently changed its name accordingly. However, groups agree on the three major criteria for **mental retardation** (see Table 15–1):

- *Significant limitations in intellectual functioning.* This criterion refers to an IQ of approximately 70 or below, as measured by an individually administered intelligence test. A score of 70 is two standard deviations below the average IQ score, and it is best viewed as an approximate cutoff. Even the best measures of intelligence are subject to minor errors, and the difference between an IQ of 71 and 69 is trivial.
- *Significant limitations in adaptive functioning.* This criterion refers to deficits in life skills. People who have an IQ below 70 but who function well in life are not considered to have mental retardation.
- *Onset before age 18 years.* This criterion excludes people whose deficits begin during adult life. When factors such as injury or degenerative brain disease produce significantly subaverage IQ after the age of 18, dementia, and not mental retardation, may be the appropriate diagnosis.

Significantly Subaverage IQ The AAIDD and DSM-IV-TR both define subaverage intellectual functioning in terms of a score on an individualized *intelligence test,* a standardized measure for assessing intellectual ability. Commonly used intelligence tests include the Wechsler Intelligence Scale for Children, Third Edition (WISC-III), and the Wechsler Adult Intelligence Scale, Third Edition (WAIS-III). Intelligence tests yield a score called the **intelligence quotient**, or IQ, the test's rating of an individual's intellectual ability. However, defining *intelligence* can be controversial, and definitions and measures of intellectual ability have changed over the years.

Measuring Intelligence

Early intelligence tests derived an IQ by dividing the individual's "mental age" by his or her chronological age. Mental age was determined by comparing an individual's test results with the average obtained for various age groups. For example, someone who answered the same number of items correctly as the average 10-year-old would be given a mental age of 10. After mental age was divided by chronological age, the ratio was multiplied by 100 to yield an IQ score. According to this system, an 8-year-old with a mental age of 10 would have an IQ of 125, calculated as $10/8 \times 100$.

Contemporary intelligence tests abandoned the concept of mental age and instead calculate a "deviation IQ." According to this system, intellectual ability follows the **normal distribution**, the familiar bell-shaped frequency distribution illustrated in Figure 15–1. The deviation IQ "grades on the curve." Most people score near the average in intelligence; a few people are

TABLE 15–1 DSM-IV-TR Diagnostic Criteria for Mental Retardation

A. Significantly subaverage intellectual functioning: an IQ of approximately 70 or below on an individually administered IQ test (for infants, a clinical judgment of significantly subaverage intellectual functioning).

B. Concurrent deficits or impairments in present adaptive functioning (i.e., the person's effectiveness in meeting the standards expected for his or her age by his or her cultural group) in at least two of the following areas: communication, self-care, home living, social/interpersonal skills, use of community resources, self-direction, functional academic skills, work, leisure, health and safety.

C. Onset is before age 18 years.

Source: Reprinted with permission from the *Diagnostic and Statistical Manual of Mental Disorders,* Fourth Edition, Text Revision. Copyright © 2000 by the American Psychiatric Association.

RESEARCH METHODS

Central Tendency and Variability: What Do IQ Scores Mean?

We can explain the nature and meaning of IQ scores more fully by describing a few basic statistics. A *frequency distribution* simply is a way of arranging data according to the frequencies of different scores. For example, we might obtain the following frequency distribution of ages in a group of 10 college students:

AGE	FREQUENCY
17	1
18	4
19	1
20	2
21	2

The **mean** is the arithmetic average of a distribution of scores, as defined by the formula

$$M = \frac{\text{sum of scores}}{N}$$

where *M* is the mean and *N* is the number of scores. Thus, the mean of the frequency distribution of ages listed above is

$$M = \frac{17 + 18 + 18 + 18 + 18 + 19 + 20 + 20 + 21 + 21}{10} = 19$$

The mean is the most commonly used of various *measures of central tendency,* which are single scores that summarize and describe a frequency distribution.

Other important and commonly used measures of central tendency are the median and the mode. The **median** is the midpoint of a frequency distribution—that is, the score that half of all scores fall above and half of all scores fall below. In the above example, 19 is the median age. Finally, the **mode** is the most frequent score in a distribution. In our example, the mode is 18.

Measures of variability also provide useful summary information about a frequency distribution. The *range* is a simple measure of variability that includes the lowest and highest scores in a frequency distribution. In our example, the range of ages is 17 to 21. As a more complex measure of variability, we may wish to compute the average distance of each individual score from the overall mean (21−19, 17−19, etc.). However, when we subtract each score in a frequency distribution from the mean of the distribution, the positive and negative numbers always add up to zero. (Try this in our example.) As a way of compensating for this inevitability, statisticians created a statistic called the **variance** in which the differences from the mean are squared (to eliminate negative numbers) before they are added together and divided by their total number. The variance is a very useful measure of variability that is defined by the following formula:

$$V = \frac{\text{sum of (scores} - M)^2}{N}$$

where *V* is the variance, *M* is the mean, and *N* is the number of scores. The variance in our example is 1.8. Calculate this statistic yourself to aid your understanding.

How are IQ scores computed?

The variance is an extremely useful measure, but the variance is expressed as a different unit of measurement from the mean because the scores have been squared. This problem is easily solved by taking the square root of the variance, which results in a statistic called the **standard deviation** or the *standard deviation from the mean.* The standard deviation is defined by the formula:

$$SD = \sqrt{V}$$

where *SD* is the standard deviation and *V* is the variance. In our example, the standard deviation is 1.34, or the square root of 1.8 (the variance).

Standard scores are created by subtracting each score in a frequency distribution from the mean and dividing the difference by the standard deviation. Standard scores, or z-scores, as they are often called, are computed according to the following formula:

$$z = \frac{\text{score} - M}{SD}$$

where *z* is the standard score, *M* is the mean, and *SD* is the standard deviation. Because of the nature of the statistic, z-scores always have a mean of zero and a standard deviation of 1. This is a very useful feature of standard scores, because it allows us to readily compare or combine scores from different frequency distributions.

This brings us back to the deviation IQ, which is a standard score. Standard scores for IQ can be—and are—computed *within* different age groups. Yet the scores can be combined and compared across age groups because they all have the same mean (0) and the same standard deviation (1). IQ scores have a mean of 100 and a standard deviation of 15, simply because the z-scores are first multiplied by 15 and then a constant of 100 is added to the product. For example, a standard score of 1 translates into a deviation IQ score of 115 ([1×15]+100) or a standard score of −2 translates into a deviation IQ score of 70 ([−2 ×15]+100).

The mean and the standard deviation are basic statistics for creating deviation IQ scores. The statistics also are central to understanding numerous other psychological concepts. For example, you should now be better able to understand the discussion of standard deviation units in relation to meta-analysis (see Chapter 3). We recommend that you reread this discussion and calculate the statistics yourself if you are confused about these statistical concepts.

How is the deviation IQ like "grading on the curve"?

exceptionally low or exceptionally high. An individual's IQ is determined based on comparisons with his or her age group. Narrow age ranges are used for children, because cognitive abilities and knowledge acquisition change rapidly with age. In contrast, all adults are treated as a part of the same age group.

Intelligence tests are scored to have a *mean* IQ score of 100 and a *standard deviation* of 15 (see Research Methods). About two-thirds of the population has an IQ within one standard deviation of the mean—between 85 and 115. The cutoff score for mental retardation is approximately two standard deviations below the average. About 2 percent of the population falls below this cutoff in the normal distribution (see Figure 15–1).

One potential problem with the deviation IQ is that IQ scores are *rising* across generations, a phenomenon known as the *Flynn effect* (named for James Flynn, who first noted the trend). The Flynn effect can have substantial implications for people near the two standard deviation cutoff, because IQ averages are constantly updated. This means that, even if their intellectual abilities remain unchanged in an *absolute* sense, older people's IQ scores fall *relative* to the rising mean.[1] One calculation puts the drop at over 5 IQ points, a difference that could influence the identification of mental retardation for those close to the 70 cutoff (Kanaya, Scullin, & Ceci, 2003).

IQ tests are widely used, and they predict performance in school quite well. Measures of intelligence for very young children are unstable, but IQ scores of children 4 years old and older are good predictors of IQ scores many years later. For those with mental retardation, IQ scores are stable even when accurately assessed among infants and toddlers (Baroff & Olley, 1999; Mash & Wolfe, 2005). An infant with a significantly subaverage IQ is likely to remain below the cutoff point for mental retardation.

Controversies about Intelligence Tests

Despite their value, IQ tests can be controversial. One key question is whether intelligence tests are "culture-fair." **Culture-fair tests** contain material that is equally familiar to people who differ in their ethnicity, native language, or immigrant status. Tests that are *culturally biased* contain language, examples, or other assumptions that favor one ethnic group, the majority, over another.

In the United States, the average IQ scores of African Americans and of Latinos are lower than those of Caucasians and Asians. More members of these groups also are classified as having mental retardation (Robinson, Zigler, & Gallagher, 2000). Some of these differences have been

The Normal Distribution of IQ Scores and the IQ Cutoff Score for Mental Retardation

2.3% of the population below the IQ cutoff for mental retardation

13.6%   34.1%   34.1%   13.6%   2.3%

70   85   100   115   130

FIGURE 15–1   Contemporary IQ tests have a mean of 100 and a standard deviation of 15. The IQ cutoff for mental retardation (70) is two standard deviations below the mean.

attributed to culture bias—some test items seem geared toward the language and the experience of majority groups. However, ethnic differences may have a simpler explanation. Lower IQ is associated with poverty, and a disproportionate number of blacks and Latinos in the United States are poor. Whatever the explanation, the disparity between ethnic groups appears to be shrinking (Mash & Wolfe, 2005).

Another controversy is how well intelligence is measured among people with mental retardation. Many people with mental retardation have sensory or physical disabilities that impede their performance on standard IQ tests; thus they must take tests that are not influenced by their particular disability. Despite the difficulties, evidence indicates that, if anything, the IQ test scores of people with mental retardation are *more* reliable and valid than IQ scores in the normal range (Baroff & Olley, 1999).

The most basic concern about intelligence tests is the most important one: What is intelligence? Intelligence tests measure precisely what their original developer, Alfred Binet, intended them to measure: potential for school achievement. They correlate 0.4 to 0.7 with grades and other achievement measures (Baroff & Olley, 1999). However, performance in school is not the same as "intelligence." Common sense, social sensitivity, and "street smarts" are also part of what most of us would consider intelligence, and they are not measured by IQ tests.

Limitations in Adaptive Skills   Both the AAIDD and DSM recognize that intelligence is more than an IQ score; thus they include adaptive behavior as a part of their definitions of mental retardation. The AAIDD (2002) suggests that adaptive behavior includes conceptual, social, and practical skills, while the DSM-IV-TR lists 10 specific adaptive skills (see Table 15–1). Fortunately,

---

[1]A similar effect occurs when you move from high school to college. You are just as smart as always, but your performance in college is judged against peers who are likely to score higher, on average, than your high school classmates.

▲ This girl with Down syndrome shows that children with mental retardation can join in many normal childhood activities.

the AAIDD suggests how the two definitions can be combined. *Conceptual skills* focus largely on community self-sufficiency and incorporate communication, functional academics, self-direction, and health and safety from DSM-IV-TR. *Social skills* focus on understanding how to conduct oneself in social situations and include social skills and leisure from the DSM-IV-TR list. Finally, *practical skills* focus on the tasks of daily living and include self-care, home living, community use, health and safety, and work from the DSM-IV-TR.

Adaptive skills are difficult to quantify. How would *you* define and measure "social intelligence"? The Vineland Adaptive Behavior Scales

are one commonly used instrument (see Table 15–2). As with IQ, adaptive skills are judged by age. Among preschoolers, they include the acquisition of motor abilities, language, and self-control. Key skills during the school-age years include developing social relationships with peers. In adult life, adaptive skills include the ability to manage oneself, live independently, and assume adult interpersonal roles.

Some experts argue that mental retardation should be defined solely based on intelligence tests, because measures of adaptive skills are imprecise (Detterman & Gabriel, 2007). Moreover, the intellectual limitations imply that adaptive skills are likely to be limited (Zigler & Hodapp, 1986). Since 1959, however, deficits in adaptive behavior have been an essential part of the AAIDD's definition of mental retardation (Heber, 1959). Deficits in adaptive behavior are less stable than IQ, especially as life demands change from school to the more diverse world of work. Thus mental retardation can be "cured" in the sense that adaptive skills can be taught or environmental demands can be shaped to match an individual's unique abilities and experiences.

Onset Before Age 18 Years   The third criterion for defining mental retardation is onset before 18 years of age. This excludes people whose deficits in intellect and adaptive skills begin later in life as a result of brain injury or disease. Besides differences in cause, the most important aspect of the age criterion is the experience of normal development. People with mental retardation have not lost skills they once had mastered, nor have they experienced a notable change in their condition. Unfortunately, this means that their retardation may be perceived as "who they are" and not as something that has "happened to them." This is why we put the "person first" in writing about mental retardation, as a small but constant reminder of person behind the disorder.

Diagnosis of Mental Retardation

Many people seen as having mild mental retardation today would not have been viewed as having notable problems in the past. Academic aptitude was less necessary to successful living in earlier, agrarian societies than it is in our modern, technological world. Even today, mental retardation is defined differently in more industrialized

TABLE 15–2 Sample Items from the Vineland Adaptive Behavior Scales	
Daily Living Skills	
Age 1:	Drinks from a cup.
Age 5:	Bathes or showers without assistance.
Age 10:	Uses a stove for cooking.
Age 15:	Looks after own health.
Socialization	
Age 1:	Imitates simple adult movements like clapping.
Age 5:	Has a group of friends.
Age 10:	Watches television about particular interests.
Age 15:	Responds to hints or indirect cues in conversation.

Source: Items 6, 44, 66, and 75 from the Daily Living Skills Subtest and Items 14, 33, 48, and 56 from the Socialization Domain Subtest in VINELAND ADAPTIVE BEHAVIOR SCALES: Interview Edition Survey Form by Sara Sparrow, David Balla, and Domenic Cicchetti. Copyright © 1984 by NCS Pearson Inc. Reproduced with permission. All rights reserved. "Vineland" is a trademark, in the US and/or other countries, of Pearson Education, Inc. or its affiliate(s).

countries than in less industrialized ones because of the educational and technological requirements for work in the industrialized countries (Scheerenberger, 1982).

Early Diagnostic Efforts The beginnings of contemporary classifications of mental retardation date to the second half of the nineteenth century. In 1866, the British physician Langdon Down first described a group of children with mental retardation who had a characteristic appearance. Their faces reminded Down of the appearance of Mongolians, who he viewed as inferior, and he used the term *mongolism* to describe them. Despite this offensive terminology, Down's classification turned out to be a valid one. Scientists eventually discovered a specific cause of what we now know as Down syndrome.

The creation of IQ tests helped to improve the classification of mental retardation. The French psychologists Alfred Binet (1856–1911) and Theophile Simon (1873–1961) developed the first successful intelligence test in 1905 in response to a French government effort to identify children in need of special educational services. The Binet scale was refined by the American psychologist Lewis Terman of Stanford University, and these efforts resulted in the Stanford–Binet intelligence tests. The first Wechsler intelligence test was developed by David Wechsler in 1939. Revisions of Wechsler's individualized intelligence tests continue to dominate contemporary intellectual assessment.

There has always been some controversy about what IQ score cutoff should define mental retardation. Debates reached a climax in 1959 when the AAIDD greatly expanded the definition of retardation. In an attempt to help more people in need of services, the IQ cutoff was shifted from two standard deviations below the mean to one standard deviation below the mean. An IQ score of 85 or lower qualified for the diagnosis, a criterion that included almost 15 percent of the U.S. population. This well-intentioned change included far too many well-functioning individuals and distracted attention from those most in need of help. Thus, in 1973, the AAIDD returned to the cutoff of 70 (Grossman, 1983).

Contemporary Diagnosis Today, mental retardation can be classified according to two different systems. One system is based on IQ scores; the other is according to known or presumed etiology. Both approaches are reliable, and each is valid for different purposes.

DSM-IV-TR divides mental retardation into four levels based on IQ scores: mild, moderate, severe, and profound (see Table 15–3). AAIDD abandoned this approach and instead assesses "intensity of needed support" across nine different areas of functioning. However, critics say this new system is cumbersome and unreliable (Detterman & Gabriel, 2007). In contrast, considerable research supports the classification of mental retardation into levels (Detterman & Gabriel, 2007).

Mild mental retardation is the designation for those with IQ scores between 50–55 and 70. This category accounts for about 85 percent of people with mental retardation. People with mild mental retardation typically have few, if any, physical impairments, generally reach the sixth-grade level in academic functioning, acquire vocational skills, and typically live in the community with or without special supports.

People with *moderate mental retardation* have IQs between 35–40 and 50–55; they make up about 10 percent of those with mental retardation. They may have obvious physical abnormalities such as the features of Down syndrome. Academic achievement generally reaches second-grade level,

TABLE 15–3	DSM-IV-TR Levels of Mental Retardation		
LEVEL	**APPROXIMATE IQ RANGE**	**ADULT MENTAL AGE OF AN AVERAGE**	**PERCENT OF PEOPLE WITH MENTAL RETARDATION**
Mild	50–55 to 70	9 to 12 year old	85
Moderate	35–40 to 50–55	6 to 9 year old	10
Severe	20–25 to 35–40	3 to 6 year old	3–4
Profound	Below 20–25	3 year old or younger	1–2

Source: Reprinted with permission from the *Diagnostic and Statistical Manual of Mental Disorders*, Fourth Edition, Text Revision. Copyright © 2000 by the American Psychiatric Association.

work activities require close training and supervision, and special supervision in families or group homes is needed for living in the community.

Severe mental retardation is defined by IQ scores between 20–25 and 35–40. This category accounts for 3 to 4 percent of people with mental retardation. At this severity level, motor development typically is abnormal, communicative speech is sharply limited, and close supervision is needed for community living.

About 1 to 2 percent of people with mental retardation have *profound mental retardation.* This severity level is characterized by an IQ below 20–25. Motor skills, communication, and self-care are severely limited, and constant supervision is required in the community or in institutions.

Axis II and Comorbid Psychological Problems Because of the focus on intellectual difficulties, professionals can overlook emotional problems that actually are *more* common among people with mental retardation than the general population (Volkmar & Dykens, 2002). In order to protect against this, mental retardation is coded along with personality disorders on Axis II in DSM-IV-TR in order to call attention to possible Axis I mental disorders. The Axis II placement also reflects the fact that significantly subaverage IQ is enduring.

Accurate Diagnosis: Life and Death Diagnostic controversies are not purely academic. They can matter a great deal in the "real world." In fact, the diagnosis of mental retardation can literally mean a difference between life and death. Why? As we discuss in Chapter 18, the United States Supreme Court recently ruled that the death penalty is "cruel and unusual punishment" for someone with mental retardation and therefore is prohibited. In close cases throughout the country, lawyers are now arguing about the precise definition of mental retardation—and psychological evaluations of mental retardation can mean life or death (Greenspan & Switzy, 2007).

What is the two-curve model of mental retardation?

Frequency of Mental Retardation

Theoretically, IQ is distributed according to the normal curve, so 2.3 percent of the population should have IQs of 70 or below. In reality, however, more than 2.3 percent of people have IQs below 70. Very low IQ scores, in particular, are found more often than expected, a result of the various biological conditions that produce mental retardation (Volkmar & Dykens, 2002). We, therefore, can think of there being two IQ distributions. One is the normal distribution of IQ scores. The other is the distribution of IQs of people with biological disorders that cause mental retardation (Zigler, 1967). These two theoretical distributions are portrayed in Figure 15–2.

Even though *more* than 2.3 percent of people have IQs below the 70 cutoff, the best estimate is that only 1 percent of the population has mental retardation (Volkmar & Dykens, 2002). The prevalence of mental retardation is lower than the prevalence of IQs below 70 because (1) IQs cannot be adequately assessed among very young children, who therefore are omitted from prevalence figures; (2) many adults with low IQs are not considered to have mental retardation because they have adaptive skills; and (3) many people with mental retardation die at a younger age. As an indication of these facts, studies show that twice as many school-age children as preschoolers have mental retardation, but the prevalence rates drop again among adults (Grossman, 1983).

Mental retardation in the United States is more common among the poor and, as a result, among certain ethnic groups. However, the increased prevalence is not found for all subtypes of retardation. Mental retardation with a specific, known organic cause (for example, Down syndrome) generally has an equal prevalence among all social classes, whereas retardation of nonspecific etiology is more common among families living in poverty (Patton, Beirne-Smith, & Payne, 1990).

The Two-Curve Model of Mental Retardation

Familial

Biological abnormality

IQ   0   35   70   100   150   200

FIGURE 15–2 The two-curve model of mental retardation distinguishes between people who score below 70 in the normal distribution of IQ scores (familial retardation) and the IQ scores for people below 70 with known biological causes of mental retardation.

Source: Adapted from E. Zigler, 1967, "Familial Mental Retardation: A Continuing Dilemma," *Science, 155,* pp. 292–298. Copyright 1967 by the American Association for the Advancement of Science.

Causes of Mental Retardation

The causes of mental retardation can be grouped into two broad categories: Cases caused by known biological abnormalities and cases resulting from normal variations in IQ (see Figure 15–2). We review known biological causes before considering cases at the low end of the normal IQ distribution.

Biological Factors About one-half of all cases of mental retardation are caused by known biological abnormalities (Volkmar & Dykens, 2002). Known biological causes often lead to retardation of moderate to profound severity and are associated with physical handicaps. Of the over 250 known biological causes (AAIDD, 2002), we focus only on a few major ones here.

Chromosomal Disorders The most common known biological cause of mental retardation is the chromosomal disorder **Down syndrome.** People with Down syndrome have a distinctive physical appearance. They have slanting eyes with an extra fold of skin in the inner corner, a small head and short stature, a protruding tongue, and a variety of organ, muscle, and skeletal abnormalities. They also have physical handicaps and limited speech (Thapar et al., 1994).

The cause of Down syndrome is an extra chromosome, resulting from the failure of chromosomes to separate during cell division, a *nondisjunction*. Children with Down syndrome have 47 chromosomes instead of the normal 46. The extra chromosome is attached to the 21st pair; thus the disorder often is referred to as *trisomy 21*.

The incidence of Down syndrome is related to maternal age. For women under the age of 30, about 1 in 1,000 births are Down syndrome infants. The incidence rises to 1 in 750 births for mothers between ages 30 and 34, 1 in 300 between 35 and 39, and over 1 in 100 after age 40. Down syndrome can be detected by testing during pregnancy.

In general, children and adults with Down syndrome function within the moderate to severe range of mental retardation. They exhibit substantial variation in their intellectual level, however, and research suggests that intensive intervention can lead to higher achievement and greater independence. Institutionalization once was commonly recommended, but home or community care is now the rule. In fact, many experts report that people with Down syndrome are especially socia-

ble, although research on distinctive personality traits is not conclusive (Cicchetti & Beegly, 1990).

By their thirties, the majority of adults with Down syndrome develop brain pathology similar to that found in Alzheimer's disease. About one-third also exhibit the symptoms of dementia (Thase, 1988). Death in mid-adult life is common, although some adults with Down syndrome live into their fifties and sixties.

Fragile-X syndrome is the most common known *genetic* cause of mental retardation (Taylor, Richards, & Brady, 2005). (Down syndrome is not inherited.) Fragile-X syndrome originally was diagnosed by a weakening or break on one arm of the X sex chromosome, which is why we discuss it in this section (see accompanying photo). The disorder is now known to be transmitted genetically by the FMR1 gene (Fragile-X Mental Retardation), which was discovered in 1991.

Not all children who inherit the FMR1 gene have mental retardation. The gene affects the production of a protein, and this can lead to mental retardation, but the effect is milder in many "premutation" cases. About 1 in 4,000 male births have fragile-X mental retardation, as do about 1 in 6,000 female births. Girls with the FMR1 gene are considerably less likely to have mental retardation than are boys, because they have two X chromosomes, one of which may function normally. About 1 in 800 men and about 1 and 250 women are carriers of the FMR1 gene. Male carriers never pass the gene to their sons but always affect their daughters. Female carries with only one affected chromosome have a 50/50 chance of passing the disorder on their sons or daughters.

▲ Many adults with mental retardation learn useful skills that are both personally and financially rewarding.

▶ Top: Fragile-X syndrome is now known to be transmitted genetically. Originally, it was identified by a gap or break in the long arm of the X chromosome, as pictured.
Bottom: This adolescent boy suffers from fragile-X syndrome. His elongated face prominent forehead, and large ears are typical characteristics of the disorder.

Among FMR1 carriers with normal intelligence, learning disabilities are common. Most of those with mental retardation have a characteristic facial appearance that includes an elongated face, high forehead, large jaw, and large, underdeveloped ears (Bregman et al., 1987). Children with fragile-X tend to be socially anxious, avoid eye contact, and have stereotypic hand movements. Approximately 15 percent display the symptoms of autism (Rogers, Wehner, & Hagerman, 2001).

Several other chromosomal abnormalities have been linked to mental retardation, particularly in the sex chromosomes. *Klinefelter syndrome,* found in about 1 in 1,000 live male births, is characterized by the presence of one or more extra X chromosomes. The most common configuration is XXY. With Klinefelter syndrome, IQ functioning typically is in the low normal to mild range of mental retardation. Another chromosomal abnormality, *XYY syndrome,* once was thought to increase criminality but is now recognized to be linked with only minor social deviance and a mean IQ about 10 points lower than average. The syndrome occurs in 1 to 2 out of 2,000 male births. *Turner syndrome,* the XO configuration in females, is characterized by a missing X chromosome. Girls with Turner syndrome are small, fail to develop sexually, and generally have intelligence near or within the normal range. The disorder occurs in about 1 in every 2,200 live female births (Thapar et al., 1994).

Genetic Disorders Few cases of mental retardation result from dominant genetic inheritance, because such a mutation is unlikely to remain in the gene pool. However, mental retardation is known to be caused by several recessive gene pairings. **Phenylketonuria,** or **PKU,** is one of these. Geneticists estimate that about 1 in every 54 normal people carries a recessive gene for PKU, but the two genes are paired only in 1 of every 15,000 live births (NIH, 2000).

PKU is caused by abnormally high levels of the amino acid *phenylalanine,* usually due to the absence of or an extreme deficiency in *phenylalanine hydroxylase,* an enzyme that metabolizes phenylalanine. Children with PKU have normal intelligence at birth. However, as they eat foods containing phenylalanine, the amino acid builds up in their system. This *phenylketonuria* produces brain damage that eventually results in mental retardation. Retardation typically progresses to the severe to profound range.

Fortunately, PKU can be detected by blood testing in the first several days after birth. (The musty odor of the infant's urine is a much less exact but notable clinical indicator of PKU.) Early detection is very important, because intellectual and behavioral impairments are diminished dramatically if the child maintains a diet low in phenylalanine. In such cases the child is likely to have normal to mildly impaired intelligence. (All states have laws that require routine screening of newborns for PKU). In order to maximize the benefits of the diet, the child should be maintained on it for as long as possible—certainly until age 10 and preferably throughout his or her life (*Lancet,* 1991; NIH, 2000). It also is very important for adult women with PKU to regulate their diet shortly before and during pregnancy in order to avoid damage to the fetus. Otherwise, high levels of phenylalanine in the mother's bloodstream can damage the developing brain of the fetus and cause mental retardation (NIH, 2000). Maintaining a diet low in phenylalanine is very difficult because phenylalanine is found in most foods and many food additives. Take a look at the labels of some of the foods you have at home (such as diet sodas). You will notice a warning about phenylalanine on many of the labels.

Other relatively rare recessive-gene disorders can also cause mental retardation. *Tay-Sachs disease* is a particularly severe disorder that eventually results in death during the infant or preschool years. The recessive gene that causes Tay-Sachs is particularly common among Jews of Eastern European heritage. *Hurler syndrome,* or *gargoylism,* results in gross physical abnormalities, including dwarfism, humpback, bulging head, and clawlike hands. Children with this disorder usually do not live past the age of 10. *Lesch-Nyhan syndrome* is most notable for the self-mutilation that accompanies the mental retardation. Children with this disorder bite their lips and fingers, often causing tissue loss. As with Down syndrome and fragile-X syndrome, many of these genetic abnormalities can be detected during pregnancy.

Infectious Diseases Mental retardation can also be caused by various infectious diseases. Damaging infections may be contracted during pregnancy, at birth, or in infancy to early childhood. Among the diseases passed from mother to fetus during pregnancy are *cytomegalovirus,* the most common fetal infection (and one that is usually harmless), and *toxoplasmosis,* a protozoan infection contracted from ingestion of infected raw meats or from contact with infected cat feces. Toxoplasmosis is rare, which makes routine screening impractical.

Rubella (German measles) is a viral infection that may produce few symptoms in the mother but can cause severe mental retardation and even death in the developing fetus, especially if it is contracted in the first 3 months of pregnancy. Fortunately, rubella can be prevented by vaccination of prospective mothers before pregnancy, which is now a part of routine health care.

The *human immunodeficiency virus* (*HIV*) can be transmitted from an infected mother to a developing fetus. Fortunately, only about one-third of children who contact HIV prenatally develop *acquired immune deficiency syndrome* (*AIDS*), but those who do develop AIDS rapidly. The effects on the child are profound, including mental retardation, visual and language impairments, and eventual death (Baroff & Olley, 1999).

Syphilis is a bacterial disease that is transmitted through sexual contact. Infected mothers can pass the disease to the fetus. If untreated, syphilis produces a number of physical and sensory handicaps in the fetus, including mental retardation. The adverse consequences are avoided by testing the mother and administering antibiotics when an infection has been detected. Because penicillin crosses the placental barrier, treating the mother will also cure the disease in the fetus.

Another sexually transmitted disease, *genital herpes,* can be transmitted to an infant particularly during birth. Herpes is a viral infection that produces small lesions on the genitals immediately following the initial infection and intermittently thereafter. The disease is most likely to be transmitted when the lesions are present. If a pregnant woman has an outbreak of genital lesions near or at the time of delivery, a cesarean section can be performed. If there is no outbreak, the risk of infecting the infant is exceedingly small and a vaginal delivery is recommended. Infected infants can develop very serious problems, including mental retardation, blindness, and possible death.

Two infectious diseases that occur after birth, primarily during infancy, can cause mental retardation. *Encephalitis* is an infection of the brain that produces inflammation and permanent damage in about 20 percent of all cases. *Meningitis* is an infection of the *meninges,* the three membranes that line the brain. The inflammation creates intracranial pressure that can irreversibly damage brain tissues. Encephalitis and meningitis can be caused by a variety of infectious diseases. Cases resulting from bacterial infections can usually be treated successfully with antibiotics. In other cases, the outcome of both encephalitis and meningitis is unpredictable. Neuromuscular problems, sensory impairments, and mental retardation are possible.

Toxins Like infectious diseases, toxic chemicals can produce mental retardation when exposure occurs either before or after birth, but exposure during

▲ Both of these girls suffer from fetal alcohol syndrome, a preventable form of mental retardation caused by excessive maternal alcohol consumption during pregnancy.

▶ A newborn of a mother who used crack cocaine. "Crack babies" often are premature and have low birth weights, and they are typically irritable and difficult to soothe.

pregnancy creates the greatest risk. Both legal and illegal drugs pose a risk to the developing fetus. Because of its frequent use, alcohol presents the greatest threat. About 1 to 2 of every 1,000 births is a baby with **fetal alcohol syndrome.** This disorder is characterized by retarded physical development, a small head, narrow eyes, cardiac defects, and cognitive impairment. Intellectual functioning ranges from mild mental retardation to normal intelligence accompanied by learning disabilities.

Women who drink heavily during pregnancy (an average of 5 ounces of alcohol per day) are twice as likely to have a child with the syndrome as are women who average 1 ounce of alcohol per day or less (Baroff & Olley, 1999). Controversy continues about the risk for difficulties associated with drinking in the intermediate range. The Surgeon General of the United States recommends that pregnant women abstain from alcohol altogether.

Although heroin and methadone addiction have not been directly linked with mental retardation, they do result in the serious problems of low birth weight and drug addiction for the newborn. Particular concern has been raised about the use of crack cocaine by pregnant women. "Crack babies" are more likely to be born prematurely, to have a lower than normal birth weight, and to have a smaller than normal head circumference. Although greatly distressed at birth, the majority of these infants "catch up" with expected physical growth, while a third show a variety of behavioral and learning problems that may be attributable to cocaine exposure (Baroff & Olley, 1999).

Toxins also present a potential hazard to intellectual development after birth. *Mercury poisoning* is known to produce severe physical, emotional, and intellectual impairments, but it does not present a major public health problem because few children are exposed to mercury. The mercury compound, *thimerosal,* formerly was used as a vaccine preservative, and as discussed in Chapter 2, it is *not* linked to autism despite sometime hysterical claims otherwise. Current concerns about mercury exposure focus on game fish like tuna and swordfish, which contain elevated mercury levels (Hubbs-Tait et al., 2005).

Much more threatening to public health is **lead poisoning.** Until banned by federal legislation, the lead commonly used in paint and produced by automobile emissions exposed hundreds of thousands of children to a potentially serious risk. Although controversy continues about the effects of exposure to low levels of lead, at toxic levels lead poisoning can produce a number of adverse behavioral and cognitive impairments, including mental retardation. Despite federal bans on lead-based paints and leaded gasoline, which greatly reduced children's exposure, lead poisoning continues to pose a risk to children reared in dilapidated housing who may eat peeling, lead-based paint chips (Hubbs-Tait et al., 2005).

Other Biological Abnormalities Pregnancy and birth complications also can cause mental retardation. One major complication is *Rh incompatibility.* The Rh factor is a protein found on the surface of red blood cells, and it is a dominant hereditary trait. People who possess this protein are Rh-positive; people who don't are Rh-negative. Rh incompatibility can occur when the mother is Rh-negative and the father is Rh-positive. In such cases the mother can develop antibodies that attack the blood cells of her Rh-positive fetus. The antibodies destroy oxygen-carrying red blood cells in the developing fetus, with a number of adverse consequences, including possible mental retardation.

Rh-negative women develop antibodies only after exposure to their infant's Rh-positive blood. If this exposure occurs at all, it usually does not happen until delivery. Thus the risk of Rh incompatibility in first births is minimal; the greatest risk is for subsequent pregnancies. This risk can be largely prevented, however, by the administration of the antibiotic RhoGAM to the mother within 72 hours after the birth of the first child. RhoGAM prevents the mother's body from developing internal antibodies against the Rh-positive factors, thus eliminating most of the risk for a future pregnancy. In the event that an Rh-negative mother develops antibodies against Rh-positive factors during pregnancy, a fetal blood transfusion must be carried out to replace the destroyed red blood cells.

Another pregnancy and birth complication that can cause intellectual deficits is *premature birth.* Premature birth is defined either as birth before 38 weeks of gestation or a birth weight of less than 5 pounds. There are many potential causes of prematurity: poor maternal nutrition, maternal age of less than 18 years or more than 35 years, maternal hypertension or diabetes, and damage to the placenta. The effects of prematurity on the infant vary, ranging from few or no deficits to sensory impairments, poor physical development, and mental retardation. More serious consequences occur at lower birth weights, and infant mortality is common at very low weights.

Other pregnancy and birth complications that can cause mental retardation include extreme difficulties in delivery, particularly *anoxia,* or oxygen deprivation; severe *malnutrition* (which is rare in the United States but a major problem in less developed countries); and the seizure disorder *epilepsy.* The intellectual difficulties associated with each of these causes vary but are potentially significant.

Normal Genetic Variation

Cases of mental retardation of unknown etiology—often referred to as **cultural-familial retardation**—are generally assumed to be varia-

TABLE 15–4 Correlations Between the IQ Scores of Pairs of Relatives Reared Together or Apart

	REARED TOGETHER		REARED APART	
TYPE OF RELATIVE	CORRELATION	(N)	CORRELATION	(N)
Monozygotic twins	.86	(4,672)	.72	(65)
Dizygotic twins	.60	(5,546)	—	
Biological siblings	.47	(26,473)	.24	(203)
Adoptive siblings	.34	(369)	—	
Parent–child	.42	(8,633)	.22	(814)
Adoptive parent–child	.19	(1,397)	—	

Source: Figure 3 (adapted) from "Familial Studies of Intelligence: A Review" by T. J. Bouchard, Jr. and M. McGue, *Science, 212* (1981) pp. 1055-1059. Copyright © 1981 by the American Association for the Advancement of Science. Reprinted by permission of the publisher.

tions in the normal distribution IQ (see Figures 15–1 and 15–2). Cultural-familial retardation runs in families and is linked with poverty. A controversial issue is whether this typically mild form of mental retardation is caused primarily by genes or by psychosocial disadvantage.

Normal genetic variation clearly contributes to individual differences in intelligence (Thapar et al., 1994). As summarized in Table 15–4, numerous family, twin, and adoption studies point to a substantial genetic contribution to intelligence. For example, the IQs of adopted children are more highly correlated to the IQs of their biological parents than to those of their adoptive ones (Horn, Loehlin, & Willerman, 1979; Plomin & Daniels, 1987).

How much of intelligence is inherited? Behavior geneticists calculate an index to measure the extent of genetic contribution to a characteristic, called the *heritability ratio.* Estimates generally indicate that up to 75 percent of the normal range of intelligence is attributable to genetics, but no research specifically identifies the extent of genetic contributions to cultural-familial retardation (Thapar et al., 1994). Moreover, heritability ratios can be misleading, because genes and the environment work together, not separately (Dickens & Flynn, 2001; see Research Methods in Chapter 17).

The concept of **reaction range** better conveys how genes and environment interact to determine IQ (Gottesman, 1963). The reaction range concept proposes that heredity determines the upper and lower limits of IQ, and experience determines the extent to

How can genes and the environment both influence IQ?

Theoretical Reaction Ranges of IQ Scores

I – Impoverished environment

U – Usual environment

E – Enriched environment

Superior intelligence

Average intelligence

Cultural-familial retardation

Down syndrome

IQ 10 25 40 55 70 85 100 115 130 145

FIGURE 15–3 According to the reaction range concept, genes set the limit on IQ and environment determines variation within the limits. Note that the usual environmental contributions to IQ differ for the four groups.

Source: Figure, p. 151, "Theoretical reaction ranges of IQ Scores for Groups with Differing Genetic Predispositions" from MENTAL RETARDATION: Nature, Cause and Management by G. S. Barloff. Copyright © 1986. Reproduced by permission of Routledge/Taylor & Francis Group, LLC.

which people fulfill their genetic potential. Figure 15–3 portrays some theoretical reaction ranges for children with Down syndrome, cultural-familial retardation, normal intelligence, and superior intelligence.

Psychological Factors The genetic contributions to intelligence do *not* mean that environment matters little or not at all. Environment does matter, not only to the normal range of intelligence but also as a potential cause of mental retardation (Dickens & Flynn, 2001). Grossly abnormal environments can produce gross abnormalities in intelligence.

An example is Koluchova's (1972) case study of the effects of the abuse and deprivation experienced by two identical twin boys. Until they were discovered at the age of 6, the twins were confined to a closet in almost total isolation, and they were beaten regularly throughout their early life. When discovered, the twins could barely walk, had extremely limited speech, and showed no understanding of abstractions, like photographs. Several years of therapy raised their measured intelligence from moderate mental retardation when first discovered to the normal range by the age of 11.

Fortunately, cases of such torturous abuse are rare. They illustrate the theoretical contribution of experience to intelligence more than the actual contribution. Most children growing up in the United States live in decent environments, if far from perfect ones. As a social ideal, Americans

hope to provide all citizens with an equally advantaged environment. In working toward this laudable goal, we can overlook the fact that the influence of genes *increases* as environmental variation *decreases*. In fact, *all* individual differences in IQ would be caused by genes if everyone had exactly the same environmental advantages. Ironically, as we succeed in creating a more nurturing and stimulating world for every child, we run the risk of concluding that "environment doesn't matter" unless we remember our successes—and how truly wretched environments can devastate children's development (see Eugenics: Our History of Shame).

Social Factors Today, the range of environments in the United States still includes many undesirable circumstances for children. Millions of children are reared in psychosocial disadvantage in our cities and in the equally unstimulating environments found among the rural poor. In fact, children are the most impoverished age group in this country (America's Children, 1999).

Cultural-familial retardation is found far more frequently among the poor. Part of this is explained by the fact that lower intelligence causes lower social status. People with a below-average IQ generally make less money. However, poverty and psychosocial disadvantage also lower IQ scores.

Impoverished environments lack the *stimulation* and *responsiveness* required to promote children's intellectual and social skills throughout their development (Floyd, Costigan, & Phillippe, 1997). A stimulating environment challenges children's developing intellectual skills. For example, toys and other playthings make the toddler's environment interesting to explore. A responsive environment offers encouragement for their pursuits. For example, parents or siblings mimic the infant's first sounds and words. Mothers of children with borderline IQ, unfortunately, are less sensitive and positive than other mothers (Fenning et al., 2007).

Studies of adopted children demonstrate the positive effects of stimulating and responsive environments (Turkheimer, 1991). Skodak and Skeels (1949) first demonstrated that children who were adopted away from unfortunate circumstances early in life achieved IQ scores at least 12 points higher than those of their biological mothers. More recent studies find similarly dramatic increases (Capron & Duyme, 1989; Schiff et al., 1982). Many children with cultural-familial retardation

EUGENICS: OUR HISTORY OF SHAME

Our shameful history of embracing principles of eugenics is one reason why many people argue vehemently against evidence showing substantial genetic contributions to behavior, especially intelligence. **Eugenics** is a movement dedicated to the "genetic improvement" of the human stock. British aristocrat Francis Galton coined the term in 1883 while advocating for "good breeding" among humans. Galton promoted "positive eugenics" by encouraging the elite to intermarry and bear many children. Others took up the mission of "negative eugenics" by putting up barriers to childbearing, as well as undertaking more gruesome efforts to eliminate "undesirables" from the human gene pool (Lombardo, 2001).

You surely are aware that Adolf Hitler embraced eugenic principles while committing genocide in Nazi Germany. You may *not* be aware that the principles of eugenics were embraced widely and officially in the United States prior to World War II. Eugenic policies in the United States included laws limiting immigration from southern and eastern Europe, prohibiting interracial marriage, and permitting the forced sterilization of so-called "defectives": the insane, the diseased, the deformed, the blind, the delinquent, the alcoholic, and primarily the feebleminded (people with mental retardation) (Lombardo, 2001). About *60,000 people* in the United States were sterilized involuntarily beginning in the 1920s, mostly people with mental retardation. Despite the

> **What is eugenics?**

decline in the eugenics movement after World War II, forced sterilization continued in some states until the late 1970s (*Los Angeles Times,* May 13, 2002).

The Commonwealth of Virginia was a dubious "leader" in the eugenics movement, and second only to California in the number of sterilizations performed. Shockingly, in 1927 the U.S. Supreme Court upheld Virginia's forced sterilization law in the infamous case of *Buck v. Bell.* Carrie Buck was a young woman from Charlottesville, Virginia, who had been institutionalized in the Virginia Colony for Epileptics and Feebleminded. To justify her planned sterilization, Buck was portrayed as "morally delinquent" and "feebleminded," although it is doubtful that she was either (Lombardo, 2001). Expert witnesses relied on family "pedigrees," family trees indicating intellectual and personality defects across generations, to "prove" that Buck's problems were hereditary (see Figure 15–4).

The U.S. Supreme Court upheld the Virginia law by a vote of 8 to 1, and Buck was sterilized. In a stunning statement, Supreme Court Justice Oliver Wendell Holmes wrote in his opinion on the case: "It is better for all the world, if instead of waiting to execute degenerate offspring for crime, or to let them starve for their imbecility, society can prevent those who are manifestly unfit from continuing their kind . . . Three generations of imbeciles are enough" (*Buck v. Bell,* 274 U.S. 200, 1927). Seventy-five years later, on May 2, 2002, the governor of Virginia apologized for the state's role in embracing eugenics and sterilizing some 8,000 people in Virginia from 1927 through 1979 (*Washington Post,* May 3, 2002).

The philosopher George Santayana said, "Those who cannot remember the past are condemned to repeat it." We believe that we must acknowledge and learn from our shameful history of eugenics. We also believe that society can benefit from research on the many genetic contributions to behavior if that evidence is debated vigorously, considered cautiously, and used wisely. Finally, we strongly believe that it is essential to respect the humanity—and the human rights—of people with mental retardation.

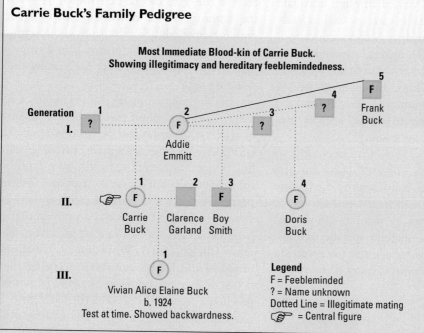

Carrie Buck's Family Pedigree

Most Immediate Blood-kin of Carrie Buck.
Showing illegitimacy and hereditary feeblemindedness.

Legend
F = Feebleminded
? = Name unknown
Dotted Line = Illegitimate mating
☞ = Central figure

FIGURE 15–4   The actual family history used in the Supreme Court Trial, *Buck v. Bell,* which, in 1927, upheld Virginia's mandatory sterilization law.

Source: P.A. Lombardo, 2001, "Carrie Buck's Pedigree," *Journal of Laboratory and Clinical Medicine, 138,* pp. 279–293 Copyright © 2001. Reprinted by permission of Elsevier, Ltd.

▶ Raymond Hudlow was involuntarily sterilized at the Virginia Colony for Epileptics and feebleminded in 1942. He was released in 1943 and drafted into the army shortly afterward. Fighting for his country in World War II, Hudlow won the Bronze Star for valor, the Purple Heart, and the Prisoner of War Medal.

could function normally if stimulating and responsive environments helped them to function near the upper end of their potential.

Treatment: Prevention and Normalization

Three major categories of intervention are essential in the treatment of mental retardation. First, many cases can be prevented through adequate maternal and child health care, as well as early psychoeducational programs. Second, educational, psychological, and biomedical treatments can help people with mental retardation to raise their achievement levels. Third, the lives of people with mental retardation can be normalized through mainstreaming in public schools and promoting care in the community.

Primary Prevention The availability and use of good maternal and child health care is one major step toward the primary prevention of many biological causes of mental retardation. Health care measures include specific actions, such as vaccinations for rubella and the detection and treatment of infectious diseases like syphilis.

▶ During amniocentesis, amniotic fluid is extracted from the sac protecting the fetus. Tests of the amniotic fluid can detect some genetic and chromosomal defects that cause mental retardation.

In addition, an adequate diet and abstinence from alcohol, cigarettes, and other drugs are essential to the health of pregnant women and the welfare of the developing fetus.

Planning for childbearing can also help prevent mental retardation. Pregnancy and birth complications are notably more common among mothers younger than 18 and older than 35. Although most babies born to women outside this age range are healthy and normal, many women are aware of the statistical risks and attempt to time their pregnancies accordingly. Children of teenage mothers also face a much greater threat of a life of poverty—a pressing issue, given that close to 10 percent of all children in the United States are born to adolescent mothers (America's Children, 1999).

A more controversial means of preventing retardation is through diagnostic testing and selective abortion. One diagnostic procedure is **amniocentesis,** in which fluid is extracted from the amniotic sac that protects the fetus during pregnancy. Some chromosomal and genetic defects in the fetus can be determined from testing the amniotic fluid, potentially leaving parents with extremely difficult decisions about terminating a pregnancy. In the future, *gene therapy* may instead offer the opportunity for treating the developing fetus.

Many parents opt for amniocentesis despite the emotional turmoil created by the possibility of selective abortion. Older women are particularly likely to consider amniocentesis, given the link between maternal age and Down syndrome. Amniocentesis can cause miscarriage, however. Fortunately, it is now possible to screen for Down syndrome using *ultrasound,* a procedure that uses harmless sound waves to create an image of the fetus (Cuckle, 2001). While not as definitive, ultrasound also has the advantage of being able to detect Down syndrome in the first trimester of pregnancy versus the second trimester with amniocentesis. In fact, the American College of Obstetricians and Gynecologists (2007) now recommends routine ultrasound screening for all interested expecting mothers, not just for women 35 years of age or older.

Secondary Prevention Early social and educational interventions can lead to the secondary prevention of cultural-familial retardation. The most important current effort is Head Start, a federal intervention program begun in 1964. The goals of Head Start include providing preschool children living in poverty with early educational experiences, nutrition, and health care monitoring. Evidence indicates that Head Start produces short-term increases in IQ (5 to 10 points) and achievement. The academic advantages diminish or disappear within a few years after intervention ends, but data indicate that children who participate in Head Start are less likely to repeat a grade or to be placed in special education classes. They also are more likely to graduate from high school (McKey et al., 1985; Zigler & Styfco, 1993). Head Start undoubtedly reduces the prevalence of cultural-familial retardation through its influence on adaptive behavior if not on IQ itself.

More specific evidence on preventing mental retardation through early intervention comes from two research programs—the Carolina Abcedarian Project (Ramey & Bryant, 1982) and the Milwaukee Project (Garber, 1988). Both interventions offered a variety of services to children of mothers with below-average IQs, and both used control groups to assess the effectiveness of intervention. Gains of 20 or more points in IQ were reported in the Milwaukee Project, but questions about the methods of this study suggest that they be interpreted with caution (Baroff & Olley, 1999). More modest gains of 5 to 10 IQ points come from the Abcedarian Project. These projects, together with adoption studies and findings from Head Start, indicate that cases of familial retardation can be prevented by increasing environmental stimulation and responsiveness.

Tertiary Prevention Careful assessment early in life is critical to tertiary prevention. Medical screening is essential for detecting conditions like PKU. Unfortunately, many cases of mental retardation are not detected early, as the doubling in prevalence during the school years indicates. Public screening of children's academic potential typically is not conducted until school age, and intelligence tests for infants and preschoolers are less reliable and valid.

Accurate detection is important, because early interventions can help. Intervention with infants typically takes place in the home and focuses on stimulating the infant, educating parents, and promoting good parent–infant relationships (Shearer & Shearer, 1976). During the preschool years, special instruction may take place in child development centers, which also offer respite care for the parents who need relief from the added demands of rearing a child with mental retardation.

◄ A mother with her son who has Down syndrome. The two-year-old was receiving speech, physical, and occupational therapy as a part of tertiary prevention efforts.

Treatment of the social and emotional needs of people with mental retardation may include teaching basic self-care skills, such as feeding, toileting, and dressing, during the younger ages and various "life-survival" skills at later ages. Children with mental retardation may also be treated for unusual behaviors, such as self-stimulation or aggressiveness. In general, research indicates that operant behavior therapy is the most effective treatment approach (Bernard, 2002). Still, problem behavior may remain despite some improvements (Scotti et al., 1991).

Medical care for physical and sensory handicaps also is critical in the treatment of certain types of mental retardation. In addition, medications are helpful in treating disorders such as epilepsy that may co-occur with mental retardation.

> How can mental retardation be prevented?

Medication is not especially helpful in treating the intellectual or socioemotional problems of people with mental retardation. Nevertheless, 30 to 50 percent of institutionalized people with mental retardation are prescribed medication, often inappropriately, to control their behavior problems (Singh, Guernsey, & Ellis, 1992). Neuroleptics are used commonly to treat aggressiveness and other uncontrolled behavior in institutions (Grossman, 1983). In some institutional settings, these drugs have been used primarily to sedate patients, and public exposés have raised broad questions about their misuse (Scheerenberger, 1982).

Normalization Normalization means that people with mental retardation are entitled to live as much as possible like other members of society. The major goals of normalization include mainstreaming children with mental retardation into public schools and promoting a role in the community for adults with mental retardation.

Prior to 1975, only about half of all children with mental retardation received an education at public expense. That year Congress passed the

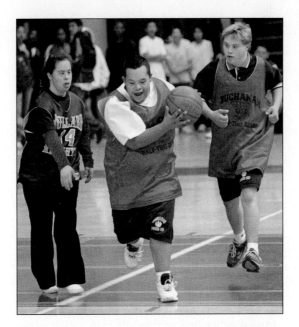

▶ The Special Olympics offers 1.7 million people with mental retardation a chance to exercise and excel in sports competitions.

Education for All Handicapped Children Act,[2] which affirmed that all handicapped children have a right to a free and appropriate education in the "least restrictive environment." Within the limits set by the handicapping condition, services must be provided in a setting that restricts personal liberty as little as possible.

For many children with mental retardation, the least restrictive environment means **mainstreaming** them into regular classrooms. Rather than being taught in special classes, children with mental retardation receive as much of their education as possible in normal classrooms. Unfortunately, the extent of mainstreaming and the quality of support services vary widely across school districts and across states (Robinson et al., 2000). This is a matter of concern, because children with mental retardation who are mainstreamed into regular classrooms may learn as much as or more than they do in special classes (Taylor et al., 2005).

The *deinstitutionalization* movement that began in mental hospitals in the 1960s also has helped to normalize the lives of many people with mental retardation. Deinstitutionalization has been particularly rapid for those with milder forms of mental retardation. Of those now living in institutions, 7.1 percent have mild, 13.0 percent have moderate, 24.4 percent have severe, and 55.5 percent have profound levels of retardation (Baroff & Olley, 1999). People with mental retardation who move from institutions to the

community receive better care and function at a higher level. These people also contribute to communities through their work and their relationships with all of us.

Changing attitudes is ultimately the most effective way to normalize the lives of people with mental retardation and their families. One of our students, whose sister has profound mental retardation, offered the following impassioned comments on attitudes:

> In my favorite picture of my family, my parents and I are all looking at the camera, but my sister is smiling expectantly up at me, waiting for me to sing the alphabet. Every time I look at this picture I smile. What makes me angry is that other people don't see why. Other people see a vegetable who will need to be cared for for the rest of her life . . . My sister has been described to me as "damaged," a "tragedy," and a "loss," all by well-meaning psychologists. I've been told that secretly when I look at my sister, I feel disgusted, which is the farthest thing from the truth . . . I will not lie, when I was in middle school I was disappointed that I didn't have a "normal" sibling who could talk with me or give me advice, but I have now reached the point where I am more upset at the world for not treating her properly and not seeing her the way that I do. This is why I have worked in a summer camp for children with severe and profound disabilities since I was in middle school—this is the only environment I have found where "my kids," as I call them, are embraced, doted over, seen as sweet, cute, and not ever as "tragedies."
>
> (Anonymous, 2003)

AUTISM AND THE PERVASIVE DEVELOPMENTAL DISORDERS

Pervasive developmental disorders (PDDs) begin early in life and involve severe impairments in relationships, communication, and behaviors. These difficulties are pronounced in *autism,* the most thoroughly researched PDD, which increasingly are called as *autistic spectrum disorders* (Lord & Bailey, 2002).

The dictionary definition of autism, "absorption in one's own mental activity," grossly understates the disorder's profound social disturbances. **Autistic disorder (autism)** is characterized by profound indifference to social relationships, odd, stereotypical behaviors, and severely

---

[2]The act, which is reauthorized periodically, was renamed Individuals with Disabilities Education Act (IDEA) in 1990.

impaired or nonexistent communication skills. The disorder typically has a chronic, unremitting course. Even those adults who achieve exceptionally good outcomes continue to show severely disturbed social emotions and social understanding. Consider the remarkable case of Temple Grandin, a woman who achieved what may be the most successful outcome of autism on record.

CASE STUDY Temple Grandin—An Anthropologist on Mars

Temple Grandin, a woman now in her sixties, suffered from the classic symptoms of autism as a child. She had not developed language by the age of 3, and she threw wild tantrums in response to social initiations, even gentle attempts to give her a hug. Grandin spent hours staring into space, playing with objects, or simply rocking or spinning herself. She also engaged in other unusual behaviors, such as repeatedly smearing her own feces. With the extensive help of her parents and teachers, and her own determination, however, Grandin learned strategies to compensate for, and cope with, her severe psychological impairments. Remarkably, she even earned a Ph.D. in animal science and has developed widely used techniques for managing cattle. In stark contrast to Grandin, the majority of people with autism spend most of their adult life in institutions.

One of Grandin's coping strategies is "computing" how other people feel. Like the characters of Data or Mr. Spock from the *Star Trek* series, with whom she identifies, Grandin does not experience normal human emotions. Rather, she describes herself as "an anthropologist on Mars." Like an anthropologist in a strange culture, she has had to learn how to relate to the human species through careful observation of "their" behavior. The following is from a book by neurologist Oliver Sacks, who wrote a detailed case study about Grandin.

"I can tell if a human being is angry," she told me, "or if he's smiling." At the level of the sensorimotor, the concrete, the unmediated, the animal, Temple has no difficulty. But what about children, I asked her. Were they not intermediate between animals and adults? On the contrary, Temple said, she had great difficulties with children—trying to talk with them, to join in their games (she could not even play peekaboo with a baby, she said, because she would get the timing all wrong)—as she had had such difficulties herself as a child. Children, she feels, are already far advanced, by the age of three or four, along a path that she, as an autistic person, has never advanced far on. Little children, she feels, already "understand" other human beings in a way she can never hope to.

(Sacks, 1985, p. 270)

Grandin finds human touch—hugging—overwhelming, but also comforting. To solve this dilemma, Grandin developed a "squeeze machine," a device that gives her a soothing, mechanical hug. In one of her two autobiographies, *Thinking in Pictures*, Grandin describes her development of her squeeze machine:

From as far back as I can remember, I always hated to be hugged. I wanted to experience the good feeling of being hugged, but it was just too overwhelming. It was like a great all-engulfing tidal wave of stimulation, and I reacted like a wild animal . . . After visiting my aunt's ranch in Arizona I watched cattle being put in the squeeze chute for their vaccinations, I noticed some of them relaxed. I asked Aunt Ann to press the squeeze sides against me and to close the head restraint bars around my neck. I hoped it would calm my anxiety. At first there were a few moments of sheer panic as I stiffened up and tried to pull away from the pressure . . . Five seconds later I felt a wave of relaxation . . . I copied the design and built the first human squeeze machine out of plywood panels when I returned to school.

(Grandin, 1995, pp. 62–63)

We know a good deal about the often bizarre behavior of children and adults with autistic disorder. But we know little the inner world of autism. The sufferer typically is too disturbed to understand or communicate about their experience. Temple Grandin is a compelling exception to this rule. While discussing how the symptoms of autism appear to the outsider, we return to Grandin's words in an effort to better understand the inner world of autism.

Symptoms of PDD

Judging from physical appearance alone, you would not expect children with autistic disorder to have a severe psychological impairment. Some children adopt unusual actions or postures (Wing, 1988), motor milestones may be reached late, and movement may appear awkward or rather uncoordinated (Prior & Ozonoff, 2007). Still, most are normal in physical appearance, there typically are no gross abnormalities, and physical growth is generally normal.

Early Onset The normal physical appearance is one reason why autism, which begins early in life, may go unrecognized. In retrospect, many parents recall abnormalities that seem to date to birth. In 20 percent to 40 percent of cases, children develop normally for a time but either stop learning new skills or lose the skills they have acquired (Volkmar, Chawarska, & Kim, 2005).

PEARSON mypsychlab VIDEO CASE

ASPERGER'S DISORDER

DAVID

"It's grueling to think about what to say, what not to say."

Watch the video "Asperger's Disorder: David." As you watch the video, observe David's odd behaviors and social problems, but ask yourself if this is a disorder on the same spectrum with autism or something different.

The National Institute of Mental Health hopes to decrease the frequency of autism through early identification and intervention (Volmar et al., 2005). And researchers are working to identify early warning signs. One clever study made use of videotapes of one-year-olds' birthday parties. The investigators compared normal children versus those later diagnosed with autism or mental retardation. The videos revealed that the infants with autism looked at others less often, and they oriented to their names less often compared to those with mental retardation. Both groups used fewer gestures, looked less at objects held by others, and engaged in more repetitive motor movements compared to normally developing babies (Osterling, Dawson, & Munson, 2002). Such findings cannot yet be used for early identification, but scientists hope to identify more definitive markers.

Impaired Communication Communication problems in PDD range from few difficulties in Asperger's disorder to profound impairments in many cases of autism. Some children with autism fail to speak at all between the ages of 1 and 2, the time when normal children typically learn their first words. Others learn a few rudimentary words such as "Mama" and then suddenly lose their language abilities. According to field studies conducted for DSM-IV, 54 percent of patients with autism remain mute, as do 35 percent of patients with other PDDs (Volkmar et al., 1994).

Other children learn to speak but not at the normal rate of language acquisition (Schreibman, 1988). Children who do acquire language, including those with Asperger's disorder, typically have oddities in their speech. A common problem is *dysprosody*, where the subtleties of speech production are unusual—disturbed in rate, rhythm, and intonation. The disturbed child or adult sounds unusual to the normal listener, even when the speech content is normal.

Another problem is *echolalia*, uttering phrases back, perhaps repeatedly. When the mother of a 1 1/2-year-old points to herself and says, "Who is this?" normal toddlers respond with "Mama." A 10-year-old child with autism and echolalia responds to the same question by repeating "Who is this?"

Another common language problem is *pronoun reversal,* which involves confusing the pronoun "you" with the pronoun "I." A child might say "You want a cookie" when he means "I want a cookie." One early interpretation suggested that pronoun reversal indicates that children with autism have failed to *individuate,* that is, to become a separate person (Bettelheim, 1967). A simpler, contemporary explanation is that pronoun reversal demonstrates a lack of understanding of the meaning of pronouns.

The speech difficulties are not the products of auditory or other sensory problems, nor are they simply disturbances in the mechanics of speech. Rather, the difficulties stem from basic disturbances in the ability to communicate and, even more basically, in the ability to imitate or reciprocate interactions. Unlike infants and toddlers who are deaf or mute, children with autism do not easily use gestures as substitutes for speech. In fact, some children do not engage in the social imitation that is essential for learning basic skills (Prior & Ozonoff, 2007).

Even high-functioning people with PDD have trouble communicating or understanding abstractions. They may fail to generate unique or imaginative speech, or have difficulty comprehending concepts like metaphors. Here is how Temple Grandin describes her struggles with language and abstraction:

I can remember the frustration of not being able to talk at age three. This caused me to throw many a tantrum. I could understand what people said to me, but I could not get my words out. It was like a big stutter, and starting words was difficult. My first few words were very difficult to produce and generally had only one syllable, such as "bah" for "ball."(1996, p. 45)

Autistics have problems learning things that cannot be thought about in pictures. The easiest words for an autistic child to learn are nouns, because they are directly related to pictures . . . Spatial words such as "over" and "under" had no meaning for me until I had a visual image to fix them in my memory. Even now, when I hear the word "under" by itself, I automatically picture myself getting under the cafeteria tables at school during an air-raid drill, a common occurrence on the East Coast during the early fifties. When I read, I translate written words into color movies or I simply store a photo of the written page to be read later. When I retrieve material, I see a photocopy of the page in my imagination. I can then read it like a TelePrompTer . . . When I am unable to convert text to pictures, it is usually because the text has no concrete meaning. Some philosophy books and articles about the cattle futures market are simply incomprehensible. (pp. 29–31)

Impaired Social Interaction The inability to relate to others is another central feature of autistic disorder. Social impairments range from relatively mild oddities, such as a lack of social or emotional reciprocity, to extreme difficulties. Some children and adults with PDD treat other people as if they were confusing and foreign objects rather than as sources of protection, comfort, and reciprocal stimulation.

People with autism often lack a **theory of mind**—they fail to appreciate that other people have a point of reference that differs from their own (Baron-Cohen, Tager-Flusberg, & Cohen, 1993). The concept of theory of mind is best illustrated by the "Sally–Ann task" (see Figure 15–5). In the Sally–Ann task, the child is shown two dolls, Sally, who has a basket, and Ann, who has a box. Sally puts a marble in her basket and then leaves. While Sally is gone, Ann takes the marble out of Sally's basket and puts it into her own box. When Sally returns, the question is: Where will she look for her marble?

Sally should look for the marble in her basket, where she left it, because she did not see Ann hide it. However, children with autism often fail to appreciate Sally's perspective—they lack a theory of mind. In one early study, 80 percent of children with autism said Sally would search in Ann's box, whereas only 14 percent of children with Down syndrome made the same error (Baron-Cohen, Leslie, & Frith, 1985).

The theory of mind construct generated considerable research, but we now know that it is not the "core" deficit of autism despite what some have claimed. Many higher functioning children with autism or Asperger's do *not* have a theory of mind deficit, while many with mental retardation do (Prior & Ozonoff, 2007; Tager-Flusberg, 2007). Furthermore, the social deficits in autism are emotional not just cognitive (Losh & Capps, 2006). In fact, some children with PDD appear to be missing the basic motivation to form attachments. As infants, they do not seek out attachment figures in times of distress, nor are they comforted by physical contact. As children, they show little interest in their peers, failing to engage in social play or to develop friendships. Throughout life, they avoid others in small but significant ways, for example, through *gaze aversion,* actively avoiding eye contact.

The Sally–Ann Task

FIGURE 15–5 Where will Sally (on left) look for the marble? Many children with autism answer "in the box," evidence that they may lack a "theory of mind."

Source: U. Frith, 1989, *Autism: Explaining the Enigma,* Oxford: Basil Blackwell, p. 41. Copyright © 1989. Reprinted by permission of Blackwell Publishing Ltd.

Stereotyped Behavior, Interests, and Activities The third defining symptom of autism is restricted, repetitive, and stereotyped patterns of behavior, interests, and activities. Many children with autistic disorder literally spend hours spinning a top or flapping a string in front of their eyes. Others might become uncontrollably agitated if the arrangement of furniture in a room is changed even slightly. Compulsively rigid adherence to daily routines is yet another example of restricted activities and interests.

Not surprisingly, these odd preoccupations and rituals create social complications. People unfamiliar with the disorder find such behavior bizarre and perhaps frightening. The ritualistic behavior

▲ Children with autistic spectrum disorders are normal in physical appearance. Their social, communication, and behavioral symptoms are obvious, however, and they may need to be taught to play even simple games like "patty-cake."

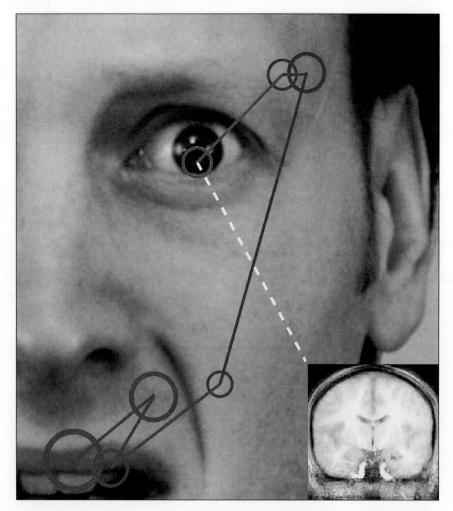

▲ A demonstration of gaze aversion in children with autism using eye tracking technology. The circles show where the subjects gazed. Larger circles indicate longer gaze time, and the straight lines indicate eye movement. The dot in the brain slice shows activation of the subjects' amygdala cluster, indicating emotional arousal due to potential eye contact

also causes problems for those who are trying to manage and educate children with autism. How do you educate a child who is totally preoccupied with flapping a string in front of his face for hours?

What purpose does such stereotyped behavior serve for the disturbed individual? Rituals such as flapping a string or spinning a top seem to serve no other function than providing sensory feedback or *self-stimulation.* A common interpretation is that the child receives too little sensory input, and ritual self-stimulation increases sensation to a more desirable level. We prefer an alternative interpretation. Self-stimulation reduces sensory input by making the stimulation monotonously predictable. In fact, all of the stereotyped behavior in PDD may help to make a terrifying world more constant and predictable. Temple Grandin's observations seem consistent with our interpretation:

When left alone, I would often space out and become hypnotized. I could sit for hours on the beach watching sand dribbling through my fingers. I'd study each individual grain of sand as it flowed between my fingers. Each grain was different, and I was like a scientist studying the grains under a microscope. As I scrutinized their shapes and contours, I went into a trance which cut me off from the sights and sounds around me.

Rocking and spinning were other ways to shut out the world when I became overloaded with too much noise. Rocking made me feel calm. It was like taking an addictive drug. The more I did it, the more I wanted to do it. My mother and my teachers would stop me so I would get back in touch with the rest of the world.

(1996, pp. 44–45)

Apparent Sensory Deficits Although not a part of the diagnosis, many people with PDD respond to auditory, tactile, or visual sensations in a highly unusual and idiosyncratic manner. For example, a patient may respond as if they were deaf, even though their hearing is intact, an *apparent sensory deficit* (Lovaas et al., 1971). The sensory deficit is "apparent," because the sense organ is not impaired even though the response suggests otherwise. Even more puzzling, the "deaf" patient may scream in pain in reaction to a much quieter sound like the scratch of chalk on a blackboard. This inconsistency suggests that the problem lies at some higher level of perception. The sensory apparatus is intact, but these unusual reactions result from some unknown, subcortical brain abnormality involved in integrating sensory input (Prior &

Ozonoff, 2007). Temple Grandin, who called this "sensory jumbling," believes that this symptom is an understudied aspect of autism:

> When I was little, loud noises were also a problem, often feeling like a dentist's drill hitting a nerve. They actually caused pain. I was scared to death of balloons popping, because the sound was like an explosion in my ear. Minor noises that most people can tune out drove me to distraction. When I was in college, my roommate's hair dryer sounded like a jet plane taking off. (p. 67)

Self-Injury *Self-injurious behavior* is one of the most bizarre and dangerous difficulties that can accompany PDD. The most common forms of self-injury are repeated head banging and biting the fingers and wrists (Rutter, Greenfield, & Lockyer, 1967). The resulting injuries may involve only minor bruises, or they can be severe enough to cause broken bones, brain damage, and even death. Self-injury should not be misinterpreted as suicidal behavior. The child with autism does not have enough self-awareness to be truly suicidal. Instead, self-injury seems to have several possible causes, the most widely accepted of which is self-stimulation (Carr, 1977). Fortunately, self-injury can be treated effectively with behavior modification techniques, as we discuss later.

Savant Performance A fascinating ability sometimes associated with PDD is the rare child who shows **savant performance**—an exceptional ability in a highly specialized area of functioning. Savant performance typically involves artistic, musical, or mathematical skills. The image on this page portrays the savant artistic abilities of Nadia, a girl with autism who drew this sophisticated picture when she was just 5 years old (Selfe, 1977).

No one has an adequate theory, let alone an explanation, for savant performance. Unfortunately, one thing does seem clear: The existence of savant performance does not indicate that, as many have hoped, children with autistic disorder really are normal or even superior in intelligence. Most people with autism do not show savant performance, and most autistics also have mental retardation (Fombonne, 2007). Past research showed that about a quarter of children with autism have IQs below 55, about half have IQs between 55 and 70, and only one-fourth have IQs over 70 (Volkmar et al., 1994; see Table 15-5). Average IQs are higher in more recent samples—perhaps 50 percent fall below 70. The change is largely because the disorder is defined

◀ Nadia, a girl with autistic disorder, drew this picture when she was about 5 years old. Like Nadia, some children with autistic disorder demonstrate savant performance, typically in drawing ability, musical performance, mathematical calculations, or feats of memory.

more broadly and perhaps because some cases are being diagnosed sooner and treated more successfully (Chakrabarti & Fombonne, 2001; Volkmar & Lord, 2007). For the most, part IQ scores are stable over time (Prior & Ozonoff, 2007).

Diagnosis of Autism and PDD

Brief Historical Perspective "Early infantile autism" was first described in 1943 by the psychiatrist Leo Kanner (1894–1981) of Johns Hopkins University. Kanner (1943) noted the inability to form relationships, delayed or noncommunicative

TABLE 15–5	IQ Scores for Patients with Autism and Other Pervasive Developmental Disorders			
	AUTISM		**OTHER PERVASIVE DEVELOPMENTAL DISORDERS**	
IQ SCORE	N	PERCENT	N	PERCENT
>70	118	26.0	122	50.8
55–69	197	43.4	61	25.4
<20–54	114	25.1	53	22.1
Unspecified	25	5.5	4	1.7

Source: From "Field Trial for Autistic Disorder in DSM-IV" by F. R. Volkmar, *American Journal of Psychiatry, 151* (1994) pp. 1361–1367. Copyright © 1994. Reprinted by permission of American Psychiatric Association.

Data from the DSM-IV field trials confirmed that most people with autism also have mental retardation.

speech, a demand for sameness in the environment, stereotyped play activities, and lack of imagination. To Kanner's credit, contemporary diagnostic criteria remain quite similar to the symptoms he described.

Viennese psychiatrist Hans Asperger (1906–1980) identified a very similar condition at virtually the same time as Kanner. However, Asperger's patients had higher intellectual functioning and better communication skills. Asperger's work received little attention in English-speaking countries until 1994 when **Asperger's disorder** was listed as a PDD in DSM-IV. As defined in DSM-IV-TR, it is identical to autism, except it involves no clinically significant delay in language.

For several decades, the term *childhood schizophrenia* was used as a synonym for autism and other severe forms of childhood psychosis (Bender, 1947). However, the symptoms of autism and schizophrenia differ dramatically (Rutter, Greenfield, & Lockyer, 1967). Fortunately, the misleading term *childhood schizophrenia* has been appropriately abandoned.

Contemporary Classification The diagnostic criteria for autistic disorder have evolved somewhat in DSM (Volkmar, 1996), but the basic diagnostic criteria for the disorder have remained the same (see Table 15–6). However, DSM-IV introduced some important changes for other pervasive developmental disorders that are retained in DSM-IV-TR.

The new diagnosis for *Asperger's disorder* refers to people who show the symptoms of autism but do not have major problems in communication and generally function higher in other areas as well. Experts differ about whether Asperger's disorder really is a separate disorder or merely a label for high-functioning individuals with autistic disorder (Volkmar & Lord, 2007). In support of the latter view, a study of 157 children with pervasive developmental disorder found *no* cases of Asperger's disorder, because all children had at least some communication problems (Mayes, Calhoun, & Crites, 2001).

Unfortunately, some contemporary practitioners seem to use the diagnosis of Asperger's disorder whenever a child shows any social oddities. This overuse of the "diagnosis" is helping to create an "epidemic" of autistic spectrum disorders, an epidemic that reflects diagnostic fads—and parents' fears—not new threats to children's mental health. Establishing new, well-accepted

---

TABLE 15–6 DSM-IV-TR Diagnostic Criteria for Autistic Disorder

A. A total of six (or more) items from (1), (2), and (3), with at least two from (1) and one each from (2) and (3):

1. Qualitative impairment in social interaction, as manifested by at least two of the following:

    a. marked impairment in the use of multiple nonverbal behaviors such as eye-to-eye gaze, facial expression, body postures, and gestures to regulate social interaction
    b. failure to develop peer relationships appropriate to developmental level
    c. a lack of spontaneous seeking to share enjoyment, interests, or achievements with other people
    d. lack of social or emotional reciprocity

2. Qualitative impairments in communication as manifested by at least one of the following:

    a. delay in, or total lack of, the development of spoken language (not accompanied by an attempt to compensate through alternative modes of communication such as gesture or mime)
    b. in individuals with adequate speech, marked impairment in the ability to initiate or sustain a conversation with others
    c. stereotyped and repetitive use of language or idiosyncratic language
    d. lack of varied, spontaneous make-believe play or social imitative play appropriate to developmental level

3. Restricted repetitive and stereotyped patterns of behavior, interests, and activities, as manifested by at least one of the following:

    a. encompassing preoccupation with one or more stereotyped and restricted patterns of interest that is abnormal either in intensity or focus
    b. apparently inflexible adherence to specific, nonfunctional routines or rituals
    c. stereotyped and repetitive motor mannerisms
    d. persistent preoccupation with parts of objects

B. Delays or abnormal functioning in at least one of the following areas, with onset prior to age 3 years: (1) social interaction, (2) language as used in social communication, or (3) symbolic or imaginative play

Source: Reprinted with permission from the *Diagnostic and Statistical Manual of Mental Disorders,* Fourth Edition, Text Revision. Copyright © 2000 by the American Psychiatric Association.

diagnostic criteria of Asperger's disorder is an important goal both for research and for practice.

Childhood disintegrative disorder is a very rare condition characterized by severe problems in social interaction and communication, in addition to stereotyped behavior. It is distinctive, because the onset occurs after at least 2 years of normal development. Previously acquired skills are lost and the course generally involves severe impairment (Volkmar & Lord, 2007).

Finally, *Rett's disorder* is characterized by at least 5 months of normal development followed by (1) a deceleration in head growth, (2) loss of purposeful hand movements, (3) loss of social engagement, (4) poor coordination, and (5) a marked delay in language. Rett's disorder was included as a PDD in DSM-IV, because the condition often was confused with autism. Scientists have since identified the genetic mutation that causes Rett's, and many experts believe the condition is better classified as a form of mental retardation. The gene is located on the X sex chromosome, and the disorder is found almost exclusively among females. Male fetuses with the mutation rarely survive to term (Dotti et al., 2002; Spector & Volkmar, 2006).

Inexperienced clinicians are not especially reliable in distinguishing among various pervasive developmental disorders, and, in fact, may misdiagnose them as cases of mental retardation. However, experienced clinicians make very reliable diagnoses for different subtypes of PDD (Volkmar et al., 1994).

Frequency of Autism and PDD

For decades autism was viewed as a very rare disorder, occurring in perhaps 4 of 10,000 children (Lotter, 1966). The diagnosis of autism exploded in the 1990s, however, and upper-level estimates now suggest that as many as 60 in 10,000 children suffer from the disorder (Fombonne, 2007; Rutter, 2005; Wing & Potter, 2002). This startling 15-fold increase has created an uproar. Many parents and some professionals believe that environmental factors, such as pollution or vaccines, caused an "epidemic of autism." The dramatic increase in the number of cases has been carefully and repeatedly documented (Barbaresi et al., 2005; Fombonne, 2007; Newschaffer, Falb, & Gurney, 2005), and it has three plausible explanations: (1) Some new environmental agent is causing more autism; (2) professionals are using broadened criteria in diagnosing the disor-

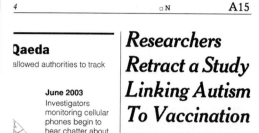

The New York Times

Researchers Retract a Study Linking Autism To Vaccination

By ANAHAD O'CONNOR

Ten of the 13 scientists who produced a 1998 study linking a childhood vaccine to several cases of autism retracted their conclusion yesterday.

In a statement to be published in the March 6 issue of The Lancet, a British medical journal, the researchers conceded that they did not have enough evidence at the time to tie the measles, mumps and rubella vaccine, known as MMR, to the autism cases. The study has been blamed for a sharp drop in the number of British children being vaccinated and for outbreaks of measles.

"We wish to make it clear that in this paper no causal link was established between MMR vaccine and autism as the data were insufficient," the researchers said in the retraction. "However, the possibility of such a link was raised and consequent events have had major implications."

◄ Most co-authors retracted their published speculation about a possible link between autism and the measles/mumps/rubella vaccine. The suggestion, based on only a few case studies, created much public concern about the vaccine. Worries continue to this day, even though no risk has been identified in studies of hundreds of thousands of children.

Copyright © 2007 by the New York Times Co. Reprinted with permission.

der (like those that apply to Asperger's disorder); and/or (3) more children are being identified because of increased awareness and more thorough assessments.

The measles/mumps/rubella (MMR) vaccination, which used to contain *thimerosal,* a mercury-based organic compound, has been the leading environmental suspect in the upsurge in autism cases. Despite the fear, even hysteria, about MMR raised in the popular media and on the Internet, no scientific evidence links MMR to autism (see Chapter 2). Other suspected environmental agents similarly have *not* proven to be linked to autism in systematic research (Rutter, 2005; Wing & Potter, 2002). While experts now view the true prevalence of autism to be far greater than previously suspected—between 30 and 60 cases per 10,000 children (Charman, 2002; Rutter, 2005)—the "epidemic of autism" may be more of a reason for celebration than paranoia. Leading experts agree that, while some undetected environmental cause cannot be completely ruled out, the increased prevalence estimates are most likely due to increased awareness and broadened diagnostic criteria (Barbaresi et al., 2005; Charman, 2002; Newschaffer et al., 2005; Rutter, 2005; Wing & Potter, 2002).

Parents of children with autism were once thought to be especially intelligent, a finding that

Is there really an "epidemic of autism"?

contributed to the mistaken view that children with autism had normal or even superior intelligence. Researchers did repeatedly find that the parents of children treated for autism were unusually well educated. However, referral bias created a false correlation (Gillberg & Schaumann, 1982). Better educated parents are more vigorous in seeking specialized treatment than parents with fewer resources. In the general population, autism is unrelated to parental education (Schopler, Andrews, & Strupp, 1979).

Two legitimate findings about the prevalence of autism have inspired research on its possible causes. Three to four times as many boys as girls suffer from autism, suggesting a gender-linked etiology, as in fragile-X syndrome. Autism also is much more common among siblings of a child with autism (Smalley, Asarnow, & Spence, 1988; Smalley & Collins, 1996), suggesting possible genetic causes.

Causes of Autism

Before discussing evidence on biological contributions to autism, we first briefly consider—and reject—environmental explanations.

Psychological and Social Factors For many years, parents were blamed for causing autism in their children. Psychoanalytic speculations said that autism results from the infant's defense against maternal hostility (Bettelheim, 1967). Behaviorists viewed the disorder as caused by inappropriate parental reinforcement (Ferster, 1961). Both views blamed parents as cold, distant, and subtly rejecting of their children. In fact, in 1960, *Time* magazine published an account of these "refrigerator parents." The article stated that the parents of children with autism "just happened to defrost long enough to produce a child" (Schreibman, 1988).

Such harmful assertions are simply wrong. Researchers have found no differences in the child-rearing styles of the parents of children with autism when compared with those of the parents of normal children (Cantwell, Baker, & Rutter, 1979). And even if differences existed, common sense would force us to challenge the "refrigerator parent" interpretation. How could a parent's emotional distance create such an extreme disturbance so early in life? Even the heinous abuse does not cause symptoms that approach the form or severity of the problems found in autism. Moreover, if parents are emotionally distant from their autistic child, could this be a reaction to the child's disturbance? If an infant shows no

Why are psychological theories of the cause of autism wrong?

normal interest in cuddling or mimicking, is it surprising if a parent grows a bit distant?

Speculation about poor parenting–or vaccines—can never be completely disproved. However, logic, null results in empirical studies, and mounting research on biological causes together make it unfathomable to think that autism has a psychological cause. And as we hope you have come to understand, the rules of science require scientists to prove their hypotheses; until a hypothesis is proven true, the community of scientists assumes it is false. Claims about "refrigerator parents" offer sad testament to the wisdom of this scientific principle.

Biological Factors Despite the severity of the disorder and its unique symptoms, autism does not appear to be one disorder. Instead, current thinking is that, like mental retardation, autism and autistic spectrum disorders include several problems that look similar but actually have different biological causes. Known causes of different "autisms" (note the plural) include fragile-X syndrome and Rett's disorder. Other suspected causes include genetics and various brain abnormalities.

Genetics Genetic factors are widely thought to play an important role in autism. The prevalence of autism is as much as 100 times among siblings of a child with autism, and several studies have found higher concordance among MZ than DZ twins (Smalley et al., 1988; Smalley & Collins, 1996; Steffenburg et al., 1989). In the largest study to date, concordance rates were 60 percent for MZ twins and 0 percent for DZ twins (Bailey et al., 1995). For a broader spectrum of disturbances, the rates were 92 percent for MZ and 10 percent for DZ twins in the same study.

These results suggest that autism is strongly genetic, but there is a puzzle. The DZ rates are *too* low. Recall that, in dominant genetic transmission, rates are 100 percent MZ and 50 percent DZ. The anomaly might be explained if autism is caused by a combination of different genes or perhaps by a spontaneous genetic mutation (Gottesman & Hanson, 2004). At present, the specific genes involved have not been identified (Szatmari & Jones, 2007), although recent research identified a "hot spot" on chromosome 16 that is linked with perhaps 1 percent of cases of autism (Weiss et al., 2008).

Neuroscience of Autism Different "autisms" might lead to similar abnormalities in brain development, structure, or function, thus accounting for similarities in symptoms. Some evidence indicates that the brains of children with autism are larger than average. The problem seems to be developmental. Brain growth appears to be unusually rapid in children with autism until the age of 2 or 3 and then is arrested, so that cerebral and cerebellar brain volume are smaller than normal at later ages (Courchesne et al., 2001).

Still, no obvious brain abnormalities have been identified in autism. Early theorizing about potential brain damage focused on the left cerebral hemisphere, where language is controlled. However, the communication deficits in autism are more basic, and current thinking focuses more on subcortical brain structures involved in emotion, perception, and social interaction (Waterhouse, Fein, & Modahl, 1996; Wing, 1988). Two likely sites of brain abnormalities are the limbic system, the area of the brain that regulates emotions, and the cerebellum, where sensorimotor input is integrated (Bauman, 1996; Courchesne et al., 2001; Schreibman, 1988; Waterhouse et al., 1996). The frontal lobe, the site of executive functioning, also may be involved (Moldin, 2003).

Recent theorizing also points to the functioning of *mirror neurons,* neurons that fire both when an individual performs an action and when the individual observes another performing the same action. Mirror neurons were first identified in the 1990s and are known to be involved in many normal abilities that are impaired in autism including imitation, understanding others' intentions, empathy, and language learning. Research on autism and the mirror neuron system is in its infancy, but it is exciting because of its seeming relevance to several key symptoms (Oberman & Ramachandran, 2007).

The most promising research on neurotransmitters and autism focuses on endorphins and neuropeptides (Polleux & Lauder, 2004). *Endorphins* are internally produced opioids that have effects similar to externally administered opiate drugs like morphine. One theory suggested that autism is caused by excess endorphins. According to this speculation, people with autism are like addicts high on heroin. They lack interest in others, because their excessive internal rewards reduce the value of the external rewards offered by relationships (Panksepp & Sahley, 1987). More recent theorizing has expanded to include various *neuropeptides,* substances that affect the action of neurotransmitters. Oxytocin and vasopression, which affect attachment and social affiliation in animals, are two neuropetides that are the subject of active investigation (Waterhouse,

▲ Scientists are using all kinds of imaging techniques in the search to locate brain abnormalities in autism.

et al., 1996). Autism is widely viewed as a brain disorder, but to date, it has defied explanation in terms of specific abnormalities.

Treatment of PDD

Controversy exists about the degree to which treatment can help children with autistic disorder. Some researchers are optimistic about new treatments, whereas others are skeptical, especially because a large number of dubious treatments have been promoted (see Critical Thinking Matters). Everyone acknowledges, however, that there is no cure for autism. Thus the effectiveness of treatment must be compared against the unhappy course and outcome of the disorder.

Course and Outcome Unfortunately, autism is a lifelong disorder. A recent review of 16 follow-up studies concluded that only about 20 percent achieve a "good" outcome, defined as living a somewhat normal and independent life. The outcome is "poor" for 50 percent who require substantial supervision and support. A major change in more recent years is that more children and adults with autism are cared for in their homes or communities instead of institutions (Howlin, 2007; see Figure 15–6). More recent studies find somewhat better outcomes, but this may be a result of including higher functioning individuals in more recent studies, not necessarily because of improved care (Howlin, 2007; see Figure 15–6). Asperger's disorder is generally thought to have a much more optimistic prognosis (Gillberg, 1991), but this has not yet been shown empirically (Howlin, 2007).

CRITICAL THINKING MATTERS

The Bogus Treatment Called Facilitated Communication

Facilitated communication is a technique that created excited optimism—and deep skepticism—as a treatment for autism. In facilitated communication, a "facilitator" supports the hand and arm of a disabled individual, thus allowing the child to type on a keyboard. Douglas Biklen (1992) has claimed that the technique allows people with autism to communicate, show insight, awareness, and literary talent, and even reveal traumatic experiences that purportedly caused their autism.

In the early 1990s, facilitated communication was touted as a cure for autism throughout the popular media. Eager for a cure, many relatives of people with autism embraced the technique. Unfortunately, but not surprisingly, systematic studies found that facilitated communication offered no benefits (Jacobson, Mulick, & Schwartz, 1995). One study was completed by Eberlin and coworkers (1993), who investigated facilitated communication in 21 adolescents diagnosed

with autism and 10 adult facilitators who were enthusiastic about the technique.

The research involved four steps. First, in the baseline condition the adolescents with autism were asked questions and allowed to type or otherwise communicate their answers to the best of their abilities. A special alphabetically configured keyboard was used for typing in this and all other conditions. Second, in the pretest, the adolescents responded to the same questions, but they were encouraged to type their answers with the aid of the facilitator, who was screened from hearing or seeing the questions being asked. Third, in the free response condition the adolescents responded to questions with the aid of the facilitator after the facilitator had received 20 hours of training in the technique. In this condition, the facilitator could see and hear the questions being asked. Finally, in the posttest, the adolescents responded to the identical questions as in the first and second condi-

tions with the aid of the facilitator. The facilitators were screened in this last condition.

Results for a few people during the free response condition contrasted dramatically with the pretest findings. For example, before facilitated communication, one autistic was able to communicate only by using two manual signs. When asked to define emotion during free response, however, with the aid of a facilitator, this same person typed "EMOTION ZOMETHIN* FEEL EXPREZ."

Such dramatic improvements surely would be more impressive if we did not know the results of the posttest. When the facilitators were again screened, the autistics performed significantly *worse* than they had at baseline. Apparently, some facilitators experienced the Ouija board effect. Their own thoughts subtly influenced the "response" they "facilitated."

How is facilitated communication like a Ouija board?

The Science Working Group on Facilitated Communication of the American Psychological Association officially concluded that facilitated communication is ineffective (Jacobson, Mulik, & Schwartz, 1995). Yet, a subsequent study found that 18 percent of service providers still used facilitated communication as a treatment (Myers, Miltenberger, & Suda, 1998). And the documentary, *Autism Is a World,* which purports to show that facilitated communication works—and was coproduced by Bilken—was nominated for an Academy Award in 2005.

In considering these unhappy circumstances, we once again urge you to be a healthy skeptic. When a real miracle treatment is discovered, it will be easy to demonstrate its effectiveness scientifically. Until then, without critical thinking, you—and desperate mentally ill people and their relatives—are susceptible to false hope and phony treatments.

▲ A teacher attempting facilitated communication with a student with autistic disorder. Evidence indicates that the technique does not allow us to communicate with people with autistic disorder.

A more positive prognosis for autism is predicted by language skills at the age of 5 or 6 Yirmiya & Sigman 1991) and higher IQ (Schreibman, 1988). Recent research also shows that *joint attention,* coordinating attention with another person through gestures, social respond-

ing, or social initiation, predicts language development from preschool age to age 9 (Anderson et al., 2007). Importantly, a quarter or more of young people with autism develop seizure disorders as teenagers (Wing, 1988). In adult life, affective disorders are common (Howlin, 2007).

Statistics offer a sobering view of autistic spectrum disorders. Can treatment help children and adults with PDD to lead more normal lives?

Medication A huge variety of medications have been tried for autism, ranging from antipsychotics to opiate agonists. Unfortunately, no medication is effective, although temporary claims of success have fueled false hope more than once.

A cautionary tale about medication can be told about secretin, a "breakthrough" medication in the late 1990s. Secretin is a hormone involved in digestion. It is sometimes used to test for gastrointestinal problems, which are common in autism. Widespread interest in the drug was sparked by three case studies of children with autism who reportedly showed remarkable improvement in language and social behavior while taking secretin for a routine gastrointestinal workup (Hovarth et al., 1998). Rumors spread on the Internet, and thousands of desperate parents across the country sought out secretin for their autistic children.

Scientists quickly responded to the intense interest in secretin. Unfortunately, the news was not good. A double-blind study using random assignment found no improvement over placebo in 58 autistic children treated with a single dose of secretin (Sandler et al., 1999). Several subsequent studies also show no benefit (Erickson et al., 2007). As with other "miracle" medications for autism, the effects of secretin are not miraculous.

Some medications may help alleviate different symptoms of autism. Certain antipsychotics, particularly the atypical *risperidone,* help in behavior management. Medications used in treating obsessive–compulsive disorder (the SSRIs) may also help with some stereotyped behavior in autistic disorder (Lewis, 1996). However, no medication can be considered to be an effective treatment (Erickson et al., 2007 Lord & Bailey, 2002).

Applied Behavior Analysis Intensive behavior modification using operant conditioning techniques called *Applied Behavior Analysis (ABA)* is the most promising approach to treating autism. ABA therapists focus on treating the specific symptoms of autism, including communication deficits, lack of self-care skills, and self-stimulatory or self-destructive behavior. Even within these different symptom areas, behavior modification emphasizes very specific and small goals. In attempting to teach language, for example, the therapist might spend hours, days, or weeks teaching the pronunciation of a specific syllable. Months of intensive effort may be needed to teach a small number of words and

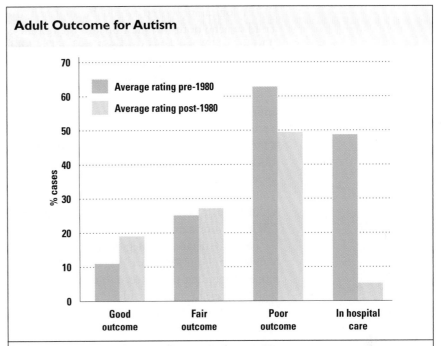

FIGURE 15–6 Adult outcomes for children diagnosed with autism. Outcomes are somewhat better in more recent studies, but good outcomes are infrequent and poor outcomes remain most common. One major change is that, in recent studies, far fewer adults with autism were cared for in institutions, reflecting increased family and community care.

Source: Figure 9.1, p. 282 from "The Outcome in Adult Life for People with ASK" by P. Howlin in AUTISM AND PERVASIVE DEVELOPMENTAL DISORDERS 2nd edition ed. by F. Volkmar. Copyright © 2007. Reprinted by permission of Cambridge University Press.

phrases. The lack of imitation among many children with autism is one reason why so much effort goes into achieving such modest goals.

If the first goal of ABA is to identify very specific target behaviors, the second is to gain control over these behaviors through the use of reinforcement and punishment. Unlike normal children, who are reinforced by social interest and approval, children with autism often do not respond to ordinary praise, or they may find all social interaction unpleasant. For these reasons, the child's successful efforts must be rewarded repeatedly with primary reinforcers such as a favorite food, at least in the beginning phases of treatment.

An example helps to illustrate the level of detail of ABA programs. A common goal in treating echolalia is to teach the child to respond by answering questions rather than repeating them. As an early step in treatment, a target behavior might be to teach the child to respond to the question "What is your name?" with the correct answer "Joshua."

In order to bring this specific response under the control of the therapist, initially it may be necessary to reward the child for simply echoing. Therapist: "What is your name?" Child: "What is your name?" Reward. This first step may have to be repeated hundreds of times over the course of several days.

A logical next step would be to teach the child to echo both the question and the response. Therapist: "What is your name? Joshua." Child: "What is your name? Joshua." Reward. Again, hundreds of repetitions may be necessary.

Gradually, the ABA therapist sets slightly more difficult goals, rewarding only increasingly accurate approximations of the correct response. One such intermediate step might be to echo the question "What is your name?" in a whisper and repeat the response "Joshua" in a normal tone of voice. Over a period of days, even weeks, the child learns to respond "Joshua" to the question "What is your name?"

Similar detailed strategies are used to teach children with autism other language skills. In the hope of speeding the process, some tried teaching sign language to children with autism (Carr, 1982).

Unfortunately, this was not a breakthrough. The communication deficits in autism are more basic than receptive or expressive problems with spoken language. Children with autism sometimes use *instrumental* gestures to get what they want, but not *expressive* gestures to show how they feel (Frith, 2003). ABA remains a painfully slow process that differs greatly from the way in which children normally learn to speak. The intensity and detail of ABA remind us that normal children come into the world remarkably well equipped to acquire language.

In addition to teaching communication skills, behavior therapists who work with children with PDD concentrate on reducing the excesses of self-stimulation, self-injurious behavior, and general disruptiveness, as well as teaching new skills to eliminate deficits in self-care and social behavior (Schreibman, 1988). ABA programs have successfully eliminated some behavioral excesses, particularly self-injury, but the treatments are controversial because they typically rely on punishment. A slap or a mild electric shock can reduce or eliminate such potentially dangerous behaviors as head banging, but are such aversive treatments justified? This question confronts therapists, parents, and others concerned with the treatment and protection of children with autism.

What is the most effective treatment for autism?

Behavior therapists have been fairly successful in teaching self-care skills and less successful in teaching social responsiveness. The struggle with social skills is unfortunate, because treatment outcomes for children with autism are especially positive when social responsiveness improves (Koegel, Koegel, & McNerney, 2001). As Schreibman (1988) noted, "It is perhaps prophetic that the be-havior characteristic which most uniquely defines autism is also the one that has proven the most difficult to understand and treat" (p. 118).

Although ABA focuses on specific target behaviors, ultimately the important question is: To what extent does treatment improve the entire syndrome of autism? Research shows that children with autism can learn specific target behaviors, but do intensive training efforts bring about improvements that are clinically significant?

An optimistic answer to this question has been provided by O. Ivar Lovaas, a psychologist at UCLA who is an acknowledged leader in ABA for autism. In a comprehensive report on the efforts of his research team, Lovaas (1987) compared the outcomes of three groups of children with autism: 19 children who received intensive ABA; 19 children who were referred to the program but who received less intensive treatment due to the unavailability of therapists; and 21 children who were treated elsewhere. Children with extremely low IQ scores were excluded, and treatment began before the children were 4 years of age. The children in the treatment group received the types of interventions described above, including both reinforcement and punishment procedures. In fact, they were treated 40 hours a week for more than 2 years.

No differences among the three groups of children were found before treatment began. Assessments following treatment were conducted between the ages of 6 and 7 at the time when the children ordinarily would have finished the first grade of school. In the intensive behavior modification group, 9 children (47 percent) completed first grade in a normal school. Eight more children (42 percent) passed first grade in a special class for children who cannot speak. In comparison, only one child (2 percent) in the two control groups completed first grade in a normal classroom, and 18 children (45 percent) completed first-grade classes for aphasic children. Table 15–7 summarizes these outcomes, and also the strong relation between IQ and classroom placement. Note the low mean IQ levels of all the children, despite the investigators' attempts to screen out the most severely impaired children.

These data are reason for considerable optimism. And a follow-up study indicated that many gains continued into late childhood and adolescence (McEachlin, Smith, & Lovaas, 1993). Other research shows significant, but notably smaller, gains with very intensive ABA approaches (Smith, Groen, & Wynn, 2000). Still, recent research with preschoolers indicates that activities designed to encourage joint attention and social coordination improve language learning in ABA treatments (Kasari et al., 2008), at least when children show prior evidence of joint attention (Yoder & Stone, 2006).

We applaud the efforts of Lovaas and others who have used ABA to teach skills to children with autism. Despite the fact that autism apparently is caused by neurological abnormalities, the most effective treatment for the disorder is highly structured and intensive ABA (Rutter, 1996). Still, we must raise cautions: Are the children who passed first grade functioning normally in other respects? Because pretreatment IQ predicted outcome (Lovaas, 1987), does ABA work only with children who are high functioning? But perhaps the most important question about ABA is its cost. Remember that the children in the intensive ABA group were treated for 40 hours per week for more than 2 years. At the same time, children in the "limited treatment" control group received almost 10 hours of weekly treatment, yet they showed few improvements. The expenses associated with early but effective treatment clearly are far less

TABLE 15–7	Educational Placement and IQ of Children with Autistic Disorder Following ABA			
GROUP	**CLASSROOM**	**N**	**(%)**	**MEAN IQ**
Intensive Behavior Modification	Normal	9	(47)	107
	Aphasic	8	(42)	74
	Retarded	2	(11)	30
Limited Treatment	Normal	0	(0)	—
	Aphasic	8	(42)	74
	Retarded	11	(58)	36
No Treatment	Normal	1	(5)	99
	Aphasic	10	(48)	67
	Retarded	10	(48)	44

Source: From "Behavioral Treatment and Normal Educational and Intellectual Functioning in Young Autistic Children" by O. I. Lovaas, *Journal of Consulting & Clinical Psychology, 55* (1987), pp. 3–9. American Psychological Association.

than those involved in a lifetime of care (Lovaas, 1987). Still, we wonder: How do we justify devoting so many resources to autism when, in comparison, we neglect intervention with children with mental retardation?

GETTING HELP

There are several reasons why you may want to learn more about getting help for mental retardation or pervasive developmental disorders. You may have a family member with a disorder. When the time comes, you may want to know more about preventing mental retardation in your own children. Or you may be thinking of a career in special education or related disciplines.

If you have a family member with one of these disorders, you may find it helpful to get some more information. The National Research Council published an authoritative book called *Educating Children with Autism*. The book not only reviews the best approaches to education, but it also suggests ways of supporting educators and family members, as well as making effective treatments more widely available. As a way of getting inside this mysterious disorder, you should find it fascinating to read one of Temple Grandin's accounts of her life with autism, *Thinking in Pictures* or *Emergence: Labeled Autistic*. A helpful guide for families is Robert and Martha Perske's *Hope for the Families: New Directions for Parents of Persons with Retardation and Other Disabilities*.

Depending on your age and relationship status, you may not yet be interested in learning how to prevent mental retardation, but you will be highly motivated when the time comes to have a baby. We hope that even if having a child seems a distant event, you will pay special attention to our discussion of what you can do to avoid prenatal risk factors such as substance abuse and environmental hazards, for personal as well as academic reasons.

If you are interested in a career in special education, we urge you to follow your interests. Working with children with special needs is a challenging and undervalued career, but it also is enormously important and personally rewarding. Even as a nonprofessional you can help people with mental retardation or PDD. In this chapter we use language that puts the person first by referring to "person with mental retardation" rather than "mentally retarded person." You can put the person first, too, not only in your language, but more importantly through your actions. How? Watch your language—and watch the language of others around you, particularly those all too familiar pejorative comments that may seem innocent

but are demeaning and dehumanizing. You can put the person first in your actions by being friendly, helpful, and inclusive when you meet people with mental retardation in your school, work, and community. You can put the person first by doing volunteer work with children or adults with mental retardation or autistic disorder. Volunteers are needed in schools and group homes, as well as in work and recreational settings.

You also can put the person first by supporting and advocating fair policies for people with mental retardation and PDD in schooling, employment, housing, and access to recreational activities. You will find many specific advocacy suggestions at the Web site of the American Association on Intellectual and Developmental Disabilities. Or if you need more motivation to become an advocate, pick up a copy of *Christmas in Purgatory*, by Burton Blatt and Fred Kaplan, a photographic essay on the horrid conditions under which people with mental retardation live in institutions. After wincing at the pictures in this book, you will find it difficult not to want to do something to help.

■ SUMMARY

Mental retardation is defined by (1) significantly subaverage intellectual functioning, (2) deficits in adaptive skills, and (3) an onset before age 18. Intellectual functioning is determined by an individualized IQ test. IQ tests are reliable and valid (if imperfect) predictors of academic performance, and also the target of important cautions. People who have significantly subaverage IQs but function adequately in the world are not considered to have mental retardation because of their adaptive behavior.

DSM-IV-TR divides mental retardation into four levels based on **IQ** scores. People with mild mental retardation, about 85 percent of those with mental retardation, complete their education at the sixth-grade level and live in the community with little or no support. People with moderate mental retardation reach a second-grade level of academic performance and require careful supervision in independent living. Severe mental retardation is characterized by major limitations in development and communication and necessitates close supervision. Finally, profound mental retardation often is accompanied by many physical handicaps and sharply restricted development that demand constant supervision in the community or in institutions.

The causes of mental retardation can be grouped into (1) known biological abnormalities and (2) normal variations in IQ. **Down syndrome,** which is caused by an extra chromosome on the 21st pair, is the most common of the known biological causes of mental retardation. **Fragile-X syndrome,** the second leading biological cause, is a genetic disorder indicated by a weakening of the X sex chromosome. Other known biological causes include **phenylketonuria (PKU),** an inherited metabolic deficiency; infectious diseases transmitted to the fetus during pregnancy or birth, such as rubella, syphilis, and genital herpes; excessive maternal alcohol consumption or drug use during pregnancy; Rh incompatibility; and malnutrition, premature birth, and low birth weight.

So-called **cultural-familial retardation** comprises most cases of mental retardation. Retardation typically is mild, and there is no known specific etiology. An important debate is the relative importance of normal genetic variation versus deprived psychosocial environments in its development. Our shameful history of **eugenics** is one reason why people worry about emphasizing genetic contributions to intelligence.

Many cases of mental retardation can be prevented by adequate health care before and during pregnancy. Testing for chromosomal or genetic abnormalities in the fetus and considering selective abortion are more controversial means of preventing retardation. Early psychoeducational programs also may prevent some cases of mental retardation by improving adaptive behavior and perhaps by increasing IQ scores. Finally, a major policy goal is **normalization** of the lives of people with mental retardation through **mainstreaming** in public schools and promoting care in the community.

The **pervasive developmental disorders (PDD),** or autistic spectrum disorders, involve profound disturbances in relationships, stereotyped activities, and communication difficulties. **Autistic disorder** is the most widely researched pervasive developmental disorder. Social impairments in autism may be relatively mild oddities, but they also may include extreme difficulties in which there is little awareness of the existence of others. One perspective on the social deficits suggests that children with autism lack a **theory of mind.** About half of all children with autism fail to develop communicative speech, and the remainder have either highly restricted language abilities or striking oddities in speech. Finally, many people with autism spend hours engaging in self-stimulation or compulsively adhere to rigid daily routines.

Other difficulties associated with autism and PDD include apparent sensory deficits and self-injurious behavior. **Savant performance** is an exceptional ability at performing mental feats such as rapid mathematical calculations. Despite such unusual abilities, most people with PDD do not have exceptional intelligence; rather, they have mental retardation. One exception is **Asperger's disorder,** characterized by the same difficulties that are found in autism except that language acquisition is not impaired. The definition of Asperger's disorder, which seems to be overdiagnosed, is controversial.

Estimates of the prevalence of PDD increased dramatically over the last decade, a trend likely due to increased awareness and broader diagnosis and not to some new toxin causing more PDD. The disorders almost certainly are caused by biological abnormalities. Several known causes of mental retardation may also cause PDD (for example, fragile-X syndrome), and genetics plays an important role. There is no easy, effective treatment for these conditions. Applied behavior analysis is a promising treatment, but the expense and effort involved are considerable. Without intensive treatment over a prolonged period of time, the prognosis for the PDD is gloomy. The majority of people with these conditions require intensive, lifelong care.

THE BIG PICTURE CRITICAL THINKING REVIEW

How is the deviation IQ like "grading on the curve"?

IQ scores follow the normal distribution, the familiar bell-shaped frequency distribution. (SEE PAGE 466)

What is the two-curve model of mental retardation?

We can think of there being two IQ distributions. One is the normal distribution of IQ scores. The other is the distribution of IQs of people with biological disorders that cause mental retardation. (SEE PAGE 470)

How can mental retardation be prevented?

The availability and use of good maternal and child health care is one major step toward the primary prevention of many biological causes of mental retardation. (SEE PAGE 479)

Is there really an "epidemic of autism"?

While experts now view the true prevalence of autism to be far greater than previously suspected, the "epidemic of autism" may be more of a reason for celebration than paranoia. (SEE PAGE 487)

Why are psychological theories of the cause of autism wrong?

Speculation about poor parenting can never be completely disproved, however, logic, null results in empirical studies, and mounting research on biological causes together make it unfathomable to think that autism has a psychological cause. (SEE PAGE 488)

What is eugenics?

Eugenics is a movement dedicated to the "genetic improvement" of the human stock. (SEE PAGE 477)

■ KEY TERMS

amniocentesis **478**	Down syndrome **471**	lead poisoning **474**	normal distribution **465**	savant performance **485**
Asperger's disorder **486**	eugenics **477**	mainstreaming **480**	normalization **479**	standard deviation **466**
autistic disorder (autism) **480**	fetal alcohol syndrome **474**	mean **466**	pervasive developmental disorders (PDDs) **480**	standard scores **466**
cultural-familial retardation **475**	fragile-X syndrome **471**	median **466**	phenylketonuria (PKU) **472**	theory of mind **483**
culture-fair tests **467**	intelligence quotient (IQ) **465**	mental retardation **465**	reaction range **475**	variance **466**
		mode **466**		

PSYCHOLOGICAL DISORDERS OF CHILDHOOD

chapter 16

OUTLINE

- Externalizing Disorders
- Internalizing and Other Disorders

Have you ever fallen to the floor, kicking, screaming, and crying because you did not get your way? Almost certainly. Temper tantrums like this are normal for frustrated 2-year-old children—but not for 20-year-old college students. Similarly, it is developmentally normal for 4-year-old children to be terrified of monsters, but not for 14-year-old adolescents. As these examples illustrate, the first question we must ask in evaluating a child's behavior is, How old is the child?

OVERVIEW

Viewing abnormal behavior within the context of normal development is important to understanding *all* abnormal behavior. However, a **developmental psychopathology** approach is absolutely essential to disorders of childhood, because children change rapidly during the first 20 years of life. Psychologists become concerned only when a child's behavior deviates substantially from **developmental norms,** behavior that is typical for children of a given age.

Children and adolescents may suffer from most of the disorders we have covered in earlier chapters. For example, children sometimes develop mood disorders, anxiety disorders, or (rarely) schizophrenia. With the exception of mental retardation and pervasive developmental disorders, however, all the problems we have discussed in earlier chapters are more prevalent among adults than children.

Psychological problems that commonly begin during childhood are listed in the DSM-IV-TR category Disorders Usually First Diagnosed in Infancy, Childhood, or Adolescence. Other than mental retardation and pervasive developmental disorders (see Chapter 15), the most important disorders in this category are the various externalizing disorders. **Externalizing disorders** create difficulties for the child's external world. They are characterized by children's failure to control their behavior according to the expectations of parents, peers, teachers, and/or legal authorities—for example, as a result of hyperactive behavior or conduct problems. Externalizing disorders are the most commonly diagnosed childhood disorders and account for about half of all children in treatment (Kazdin, 1995). For these reasons, we focus much of this chapter on them.

Internalizing disorders are psychological problems that primarily affect the child's internal world—for example, excessive anxiety or sadness. DSM-IV-TR does not list internalizing disorders as separate psychological disorders of childhood; rather, the manual notes that children may qualify for many "adult" diagnoses, such as anxiety or mood disorders. However, we think it is essential to take a developmental psychopathology approach and highlight children's unique experience of anxiety and depression. Children do not interpret events or express emotions in the same manner as adults; emotional experience changes rapidly with age, and the family, peer, and school contexts typically affect children more dramatically than they affect adults. In our view, children's mood and anxiety disorders are not simply miniature versions of adult diagnoses.

In this chapter, we also introduce many of the 26 *additional* childhood diagnoses included in DSM-IV-TR. Our coverage of these other childhood disorders is necessarily limited, not

◄ Temper tantrums are a normal, if trying, part of child development during the "terrible twos" (and beyond). Awareness of such developmental norms is essential to evaluating abnormal behavior in children.

only by their sheer number, but also by questions we have about the appropriateness of some diagnostic categories (Taylor & Rutter, 2002).

EXTERNALIZING DISORDERS

Few children or adolescents identify themselves as having an externalizing disorder. Instead, some adult, often a parent or teacher, decides that a child has a behavior problem. Some children are unable to recognize or admit to their difficult behavior. In other cases, however, the problem may be as much the adult's as the child's (Yeh & Weisz, 2001). For example, a stressed parent may have trouble coping with normal misbehavior. This makes the assessment of externalizing disorders challenging, as illustrated in the following case study.

CASE **STUDY** Bad Boy, Troubled Boy, or All Boy?

Jeremy W. was 8 years old when his mother brought him to a clinical psychologist on the recommendations of his second-grade teacher and a school counselor. Mrs. W. came to the psychologist reluctantly, because she was not sure if she agreed with the suggestions of the school personnel. In fact, Mrs. W. wasn't sure if she agreed with her husband about what was going on with Jeremy.

According to Mrs. W., Jeremy was constantly in trouble at school. His teacher reprimanded Jeremy daily for disrupting the class, not paying attention, and failing to finish his work. The teacher felt that her attempts at discipline had little effect. Sometimes Jeremy would listen for a while, but soon he was pestering another child, talking out of turn, or simply staring off into space. Lately, Jeremy had begun to talk back, and his teacher sent him to the principal's office several times.

The psychologist contacted the school to confirm this information. The teacher said that Mrs. W.'s reports were accurate and also noted that Jeremy had no close friends. Other kids thought of him as a "pain." The teacher also shared test information obtained from an earlier referral to the school psychologist. Jeremy had an IQ of 108. However, he was almost a year behind his current grade. The school psychologist suspected that Jeremy had a learning disorder but thought that his behavior problems also were interfering with his learning. She wanted Jeremy to remain in his regular classroom for the present. After he got some treatment, she would reevaluate him for possible placement in a "resource room," a special class for students with learning problems.

Mrs. W. was frightened by the suggestion that Jeremy might be "emotionally disturbed" or "learning disordered." According to his mother, Jeremy could be difficult to manage at home, but she had never considered the possibility that he needed psychological help. Jeremy had always been a handful, but in her view, he had never been a bad child. Instead, Mrs. W. thought that Jeremy expressed himself better through actions than words. In this respect, he was the opposite of his 11-year-old sister, who was an A and B student. Mrs. W. was not convinced that Jeremy's teacher was the best person to work with him, but she did agree that he was having problems in school. In her mind, Jeremy was developing low self-esteem, and many of his actions were attempts to get attention.

According to Mrs. W., Jeremy's father spent very little time with him. Mr. W. worked long hours on his construction job, and he often was off with his friends on weekends. Mrs. W. said that her husband was of little help even when he was home. He would tell his wife that it was her job to take care of the kids—he needed his rest. With tears in her eyes, Mrs. W. said that she needed a rest, too.

In any case, Mrs. W. said her husband was not concerned about Jeremy's behavior or his schoolwork. Instead, he thought that Jeremy was just "all boy" and not much of a student—just as Mr. W. had been as a child. He refused to take time off from work to see the psychologist.

In confidence, Mrs. W. said that she, too, saw a lot of his father in Jeremy—too much of him, in fact. She got no support from her husband in disciplining Jeremy or in encouraging him in his schoolwork.

She blamed her husband for Jeremy's problems, and she was secretly furious with him.

She knew that Jeremy had to do well in school in order to live a better life, and she felt like a failure as a mother. She was willing to try anything to help Jeremy, but she doubted that there was anything she could do without her husband's support.

Is Jeremy a disobedient child, as his teacher thinks? A learning-disordered child, as suggested by the school psychologist? Suffering from low self-esteem, as his mother fears? Or is he simply "all boy," as his father claims? What about Jeremy? How does he feel about himself, his family, his schoolwork, and his friendships at school?

Mental health professionals who treat children are constantly vexed by such difficult questions. Treatment often begins with an attempt to achieve consensus about the nature of a child's problem (Hawley & Weisz, 2003). Psychologists want an accurate diagnosis, but another goal is to get adults working together. In Jeremy's case, Mr. and Mrs. W. may need to present a united front to Jeremy. In order to do so, they may need to resolve issues in their marriage. Because of such conflicts, many psychologists prefer to see children in *family therapy* rather than treat children alone. Many psychologists also work to establish better communication and cooperation between parents and teachers.

Of course, Jeremy is at least part of the problem. If we can trust his teacher's report—and experienced child clinical psychologists do trust teachers—Jeremy clearly has some type of externalizing problem. Perhaps Jeremy's behavior is a reaction to his parents' conflicts; he might get better if they work out their differences. Or perhaps Jeremy is a troubled child who is causing some of his parents' conflicts, not just reacting to them. Mr. and Mrs. W. both felt that Jeremy and his father were a lot alike. Could Jeremy have learned or inherited some of his father's characteristics?

Symptoms of Externalizing Disorders

Children with externalizing disorders often break rules, are angry and aggressive, impulsive, overactive, and inattentive. These troublesome actions tend to occur together; however, different clusters of problems have different implications for the cause, treatment, and course of children's externalizing disorders.

Rule Violations Many externalizing symptoms involve violations of age-appropriate social rules, including disobeying parents or teachers, violating social or peer group norms (e.g., annoying others), and perhaps violating the law. All children break at least some social rules, of course, and we often admire an innocent and clever rule breaker. For example, we see Calvin of the Calvin and Hobbes cartoons as devilish, but he is not really "bad," and we certainly do not view him as "sick."

Serious Rule Breaking Some misconduct is normal, perhaps even healthy, for children. However, the rule violations in externalizing disorders are not trivial and are far from "cute." Many schoolteachers lament that they spend far too much time disciplining children, a circumstance that also is unfair to the well-behaved youngsters in the classroom. Even more serious, the Federal Bureau of Investigation reported that 30.9 percent of arrests for index offenses—major crimes including murder, forcible rape, and robbery—were of young people under the age of 21 in 2003 (FBI, 2004). Other evidence indicates that the worst 5 percent of juvenile offenders account for about half of all juvenile arrests (Farrington, Ohlin, & Wilson, 1986). With all our fears about youth violence, you should know, however, that the rate of violent crime among juveniles is falling (Snyder, 2002; see Figure 16–1).

Several factors influence how we evaluate the seriousness of children's rule violations. Externalizing behavior is a far greater concern when it is frequent, intense, lasting, and pervasive. That is, externalizing behavior is more problematic when it is part of a *syndrome,* or cluster of problems, than when it is a *symptom* that occurs in isolation. The existence of an externalizing syndrome has been demonstrated consistently by statistical analysis of checklists on which parents or teachers rate children's psychological symptoms. Moreover, agreement among adult raters typically is fairly high for the externalizing dimension (Duhig et al., 2000).

Children's Age and Rule Violations Children of different ages are likely to violate very different rules (Lahey et al., 2000). A preschooler with an externalizing problem may be disobedient to his

CALVIN AND HOBBES, "What Are We Going to Do, Hobbes?" (April 14, 1980) © 1980 by Watterson. Distributed by UNIVERSAL PRESS SYNDICATE, and reprinted with their permission. All rights reserved.

parents and aggressive with other children. During the school years, he is more likely to be disruptive in the classroom, uncooperative on the playground, or defiant at home. By adolescence, the problem teenager may be failing in school, ignoring all discipline at home, hanging out with delinquent peers, and violating the law.

Children's age is important to consider in relation to the timing as well as the nature of rule violations. All children break rules, but children with externalizing problems violate rules at a younger age than is developmentally normal (Loeber, 1988). For example, most young people experiment with smoking, alcohol, or sexuality, but children with externalizing disorders do so at a notably younger age.

> **Is all misbehavior an externalizing problem?**

Adolescent Limited or Life Course Persistent? Teenagers often violate the rules laid down by parents, teachers, and society as a means of asserting their independence and perhaps of conforming to

Arrests of Juveniles for Violent Crimes in the United States, 1980–2002

Arrests per 100,000 juveniles ages 10–17

Violent Crime Index

FIGURE 16–1 Despite widespread fears, youth violence in the United States has fallen for close to a decade.

Source: H. N. Snyder, September, 2002, "Juvenile arrests 2002," *Juvenile Justice Bulletin,* pp. 1–12.

the rules of their peer group. Because of this, psychologists distinguish between externalizing behavior that is *adolescent-limited*—that ends along with the teen years—and *life-course-persistent* antisocial behavior that continues into adult life (Moffitt, 1993). In fact, externalizing problems that begin *before* adolescence are more likely to persist over the individual's life course than are problems that begin *during* adolescence. Psychologists can predict adult antisocial behavior more accurately from information obtained longer ago, during childhood, than from information obtained more recently, during adolescence (Moffitt, 1993).

Can adolescent-limited and life-course-persistent antisocial behavior be distinguished in other ways? Many investigators are searching for symptoms that predict adult antisocial behavior, particularly *antisocial personality disorder* (Lynam et al., 2007). Callousness and lack of emotional response may be early indicators of this lifelong pattern of rule violations (Frick, Bodin, & Barry, 2000). For example, young people with antisocial tendencies do not readily recognize sadness and fear in other people's facial expressions (Blair et al., 2001).

Negativity, Anger, and Aggression Children with externalizing problems often are negative, angry, and aggressive. Younger children may be stubborn and uncooperative, while adolescents may be hostile and physically injure others. In addition to the actions themselves, motivation is important. We chuckle at the innocent adventures of a Calvin, but we judge children harshly if their *intent* is selfish and they show little *remorse*.

▼ Boys arguing on a school playground. Some anger is normative, but persistent hostility and aggression often are symptoms of externalizing disorders.

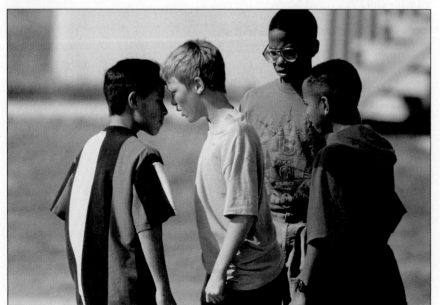

You might wonder about Jeremy W.'s private motivations and judge him differently based on whether he is an angry child who cares little about being "bad" or an impulsive child who wants to but just cannot consistently be "good."

Impulsivity Impulsive children act before they think. They fail to wait for their turn, blurt out answers in class, and annoy and disrupt others. Impulsivity in infancy predicts subsequent impulsivity, inattention, and overactivity (Olson, Schilling, & Bates, 1999), but many impulsive children are *trying* to behave. They struggle with *executive functioning*, the internal direction of behavior. Impulsive children seem unable to control their behavior according to the demands of many situations.

Hyperactivity **Hyperactivity** involves squirming, fidgeting, and restless behavior. Hyperactive children are in constant motion. They often have trouble sitting still, even during leisure activities like watching television. Hyperactivity is found across situations, even during sleep, but it is more obvious in structured settings than in unstructured ones (Barkley, 2006). Hyperactive behavior is particularly noticeable in the classroom. Because of this, reports from teachers are critical in identifying hyperactive behavior.

Attention Deficits **Attention deficits** are characterized by distractibility, frequent shifts from one uncompleted activity to another, careless mistakes, poor organization or effort, and general "spaciness" (for example, not listening well). As with impulsivity, inattention usually is not intentional or oppositional; rather, it reflects an inability to maintain a focus despite an apparent desire to do so. A particular attention problem is "staying on task," or what is called *sustained attention* (Barkley, 2006). The *continuous performance* test is a commonly used laboratory measure of sustained attention. The task requires children to monitor and respond to numbers or letters presented on a computer screen (Epstein et al., 2003).

Diagnosis of Externalizing Disorders

The DSM-IV-TR divides externalizing disorders into three major types. Attention-deficit/hyperactivity disorder (ADHD) is the problem that you may have heard called "hyperactivity" or perhaps "ADD." Oppositional defiant disorder

(ODD) includes a wide range of problem behavior generally found among school-aged children. Conduct disorder (CD) is a lot like what you may think of as juvenile delinquency, because CD involves rule violations that also are violations of the law.

Brief Historical Perspective About 100 years ago British physician George Still (1902) speculated that the overactivity of some children he treated might be due to biological "defects." Since then, professionals have debated whether the misbehavior of school-aged children should be divided into two types. Children with what we now call ADHD are assumed to have a biological problem best treated with medication. Children with what we now call ODD are seen as having a psychological problem requiring psychological treatment (Schachar & Tannock, 2002).

Interest in what DSM-IV-TR calls conduct disorder also is about 100 years old but has a very different origin. At the end of the nineteenth century, juvenile crime was distinguished from adult criminal behavior for the first time in American law. The law adopted a compassionate view, seeing juvenile delinquency as a product of a troubled upbringing. As a result, the state adopted a parental role in trying to help wayward youth, not just punish them. Thus, the criminal behavior of juveniles came to be seen as a psychological problem, not just a legal one.

Attention-Deficit/Hyperactivity Disorder **Attention-deficit/hyperactivity disorder (ADHD)** is characterized by hyperactivity, attention deficit, and impulsivity. According to DSM-IV-TR, at least some symptoms must begin before the age of 7, they must persist for at least 6 months, and there must be evidence of consistency in symptoms across situations. The manual takes a quantitative "checklist" approach to counting symptoms, implying that the underlying problem is dimensional even though the diagnosis is categorical (see Table 16–1 on the next page).

The symptoms of hyperactivity and attention deficit each have been viewed as being the core characteristics of ADHD. In fact, DSM-II called the disorder *hyperkinesis,* a synonym for "hyperactivity," whereas DSM-III referred to it as *attention-deficit disorder,* or *ADD.* Now, much theorizing focuses on impulsivity as the core characteristic (Barkley, 2006; Nigg, 2001; Olson et al., 1999). We are not concerned whether "attention deficit" or "hyperactivity"—or "impulsivity"—gets top

billing as the label for a problem with ever-changing names. Rather, we are concerned about two facts: First, contrary to what has been asserted by some professionals, hyperactivity is not merely a consequence of inattention, or vice versa (Barkley, 2006). Each is an independent symptom. Second, some children have problems primarily with only one of the two symptoms, as is evident in the subtypes of ADHD listed in DSM-IV-TR (see Table 16–1).

Oppositional Defiant Disorder **Oppositional defiant disorder (ODD)** is defined by a pattern of negative, hostile, and defiant behavior. The symptoms must last for at least 6 months, and, as with other diagnoses, they must cause clinically significant impairment in life functioning. As you can see from Table 16–2 on page 503, the rule violations in ODD typically involve minor transgressions, such as refusing to obey adult requests, arguing, and acting angry. Such misbehavior is a cause for concern among school-aged children, and it often foreshadows the development of much more serious antisocial behavior during adolescence and adult life. However, these types of rule violations fall within developmental norms for adolescents, who are typically somewhat rebellious. Thus, a problem with the DSM-IV-TR diagnostic criteria for ODD—and for virtually every childhood disorder—is that the diagnostic criteria need to reflect developmental norms more fully.

One or Two Disorders? Professionals have long debated whether ADHD and ODD are the same or separate disorders. Some argue that the two conditions are distinct in symptomatology, cause, and best treatment. Others say the distinction between ADHD and ODD is false—and used to justify treating troubled children with medication. In fact, a differential diagnosis between ADHD and ODD cannot be made with a high level of reliability, making it difficult to test such opposing viewpoints (Hinshaw, 1994).

Comorbidity Still, debate has subsided considerably in recent years with a new consensus: The two disorders are separate but frequently comorbid

PEARSON mypsychlab   **VIDEO CASE**

ADHD

JIMMY

"I think without it (medicine) I would be dreaming the whole entire day."

Watch the video "Jimmy—ADHD" on MyPsychLab. As you watch the video, remember that Jimmy did *not* take his psychostimulant before the interview and note his rapid speech as well as his "fidgetiness."

TABLE 16–1 **DSM-IV-TR Diagnostic Criteria for Attention-Deficit/Hyperactivity Disorder**

A. Either (I) or (II):

(I) **Inattention:** Six (or more) of the following symptoms of inattention have persisted for at least 6 months to a degree that is maladaptive and inconsistent with developmental level:

1. Often fails to give close attention to details or makes careless mistakes in schoolwork, work, or other activities.
2. Often has difficulty sustaining attention in tasks or play activities.
3. Often does not seem to listen when spoken to directly.
4. Often does not follow through on instructions and fails to finish schoolwork, chores, or duties in the workplace.
5. Often has difficulty organizing tasks and activities.
6. Often avoids, dislikes, or is reluctant to engage in tasks that require sustained mental effort.
7. Often loses things necessary for tasks or activities.
8. Is often easily distracted by extraneous stimuli.
9. Is often forgetful of daily activities.

(II) **Hyperactivity and Impulsivity:** Six (or more) of the following symptoms of hyperactivity-impulsivity have persisted for at least 6 months to a degree that is maladaptive and inconsistent with developmental level:

Hyperactivity

1. Often fidgets with hands or feet or squirms in seat.
2. Often leaves seat in classroom or in other situations in which remaining seated is expected.
3. Often runs about or climbs excessively in situations in which it is inappropriate.
4. Often has difficulty playing or engaging in leisure activities quietly.
5. Is often "on the go" or often acts as if "driven by a motor."
6. Often talks excessively.

Impulsivity

1. Often blurts out answers before questions have been completed.
2. Often has difficulty awaiting turn.
3. Often interrupts or intrudes on others.

B. Some hyperactive-impulsive or inattentive symptoms that caused impairment were present before age 7 years.

C. Some impairment from the symptoms is present in two or more settings.

D. There must be clear evidence of clinically significant impairment in social, academic, or occupational functioning.

Code **Based on Type**
Combined Type: Criteria for I and II are met for past 6 months.
Predominantly Inattentive Type: Criteria for I are met but Criteria for II are not met for past 6 months.
Predominantly Hyperactive-Impulsive Type: Criteria for II are met but Criteria for I are not met for past 6 months.

Source: Reprinted with permission from the *Diagnostic and Statistical Manual of Mental Disorders,* Fourth Edition, Text Revision. Copyright © 2000 by the American Psychiatric Association.

(Waschbusch, 2002; see Figure 16–2). Approximately half of all children with one disorder also have the other problem (Schachar & Tannock, 2002). This new view raises questions about interpreting older research. For example, are the long-term problems in school or with substance abuse among externalizing children due to ADHD, ODD, or the overlap between the two conditions? Emerging research suggests that future antisocial behavior among children with externalizing prob-

lems is attributable more to comorbid conduct disorders than ADHD. For example, ODD/CD but not ADHD predicts adult antisocial personality disorder (Lahey et al., 2005).

Not only are ADHD and ODD highly comorbid, but, as illustrated in Figure 16–2, about 25 percent of children with each problem also have a learning disorder (LD). ADHD also can be comorbid with internalizing disorders, particularly among girls (Rucklidge & Tannock, 2001;

TABLE 16–2   DSM-IV-TR Diagnostic Criteria for Oppositional Defiant Disorder

A. A pattern of negativistic, hostile, and defiant behavior lasting at least 6 months, during which four (or more) of the following are present:

  1. Often loses temper.
  2. Often argues with adults.
  3. Often actively defies or refuses to comply with adults' requests or rules.
  4. Often deliberately annoys people.
  5. Often blames others for his or her mistakes or misbehavior.
  6. Is often touchy or easily annoyed by others.
  7. Is often angry and resentful.
  8. Is often spiteful and vindictive.

B. The disturbance in behavior causes clinically significant impairment in social, academic, or occupational functioning.

Note: Consider a criterion only if the behavior occurs more frequently than is typically observed in individuals of comparable age and developmental level.

Source: Reprinted with permission from the *Diagnostic and Statistical Manual of Mental Disorders,* Fourth Edition, Text Revision. Copyright © 2000 by the American Psychiatric Association.

Schachar & Tannock, 2002). The overlap with internalizing disorders is not nearly as substantial as with ODD and LD, however.

Subtypes of ADHD The subtyping of ADHD into the predominantly inattentive, predominantly hyperactive-impulsive, or combined types is another sometimes controversial distinction. The predominantly inattentive subtype generally is accepted as valid. Predominantly inattentive children have difficulty with inattention and information processing, but show little or no hyperactivity (Milich, Balentine, & Lynam, 2001). They often are described as "spacey" rather than "distractible," and they struggle with learning far more than behavior control. Some people use the DSM-III term *ADD* for the predominantly inattentive type of ADHD. The term is technically inaccurate but correctly places the focus on inattention.

Most experts now view the predominantly hyperactive-impulsive subtype and the combined subtype as being the same problem. Confusion was created, because the different symptoms often emerge at different ages. Hyperactivity and impulsivity are most evident during the preschool years, but attention deficits begin (or are first noticed) during the early school years (Hart et al., 1995).

Conduct Disorder **Conduct disorder (CD)** is defined by a persistent and repetitive pattern of serious rule violations, most of which are illegal

as well as antisocial—for example, assault or robbery (see Table 16–3). CD often is developmentally related to ODD. Oppositional defiant disorder is diagnosed primarily among school-aged children and often develops into a more serious conduct disorder during preadolescence or adolescence (Loeber, Lahey, & Thomas, 1991). DSM-IV-TR distinguishes the age of onset in defining conduct disorders—a distinction between adolescent-limited versus life-course patterns of antisocial behavior.

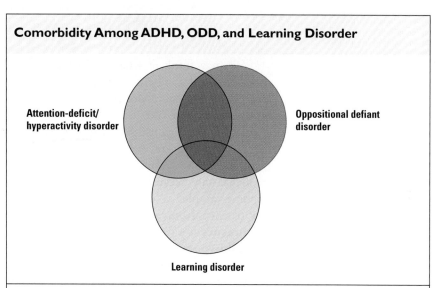

Comorbidity Among ADHD, ODD, and Learning Disorder

Attention-deficit/hyperactivity disorder

Oppositional defiant disorder

Learning disorder

FIGURE 16–2   ADHD and ODD are distinct, but overlapping conditions. As many as half of all children with one disorder also suffer from the other problem. To a lesser extent, ADHD and ODD also overlap with learning disorders.

TABLE 16–3   DSM-IV-TR Diagnostic Criteria for Conduct Disorder

A. A repetitive and persistent pattern of behavior in which the basic rights of others or major age-appropriate societal norms or rules are violated, as manifested by the presence of three (or more) of the following criteria in the past 12 months, with at least one criterion present in the past 6 months:

Aggression to people and animals

1. Often bullies, threatens, or intimidates others.
2. Often initiates physical fights.
3. Has used a weapon that can cause serious physical harm to others.
4. Has been physically cruel to people.
5. Has been physically cruel to animals.
6. Has stolen while confronting a victim.
7. Has forced someone into sexual activity.

Destruction of Property

8. Has deliberately engaged in fire setting with the intention of causing serious damage.
9. Has deliberately destroyed others' property.

Deceitfulness or Theft

10. Has broken into someone else's house, building, or car.
11. Often lies to obtain goods or favors to avoid obligations.
12. Has stolen items of nontrivial value without confronting a victim.

Serious Violations of Rules

13. Often stays out at night despite parental prohibitions, beginning before age 13 years.
14. Has run away from home overnight at least twice while living in parental or parental surrogate home.
15. Is often truant from school, beginning before age 13 years.

B. The disturbance in behavior causes clinically significant impairment in social, academic, or occupational functioning.

Code Type Based on Age at Onset
Conduct Disorder Childhood-Onset Type: Onset of at least one criterion characteristic of Conduct Disorder prior to age 10 years.
Conduct Disorder Adolescent-Onset Type: Absence of any criteria characteristic of Conduct Disorder prior to age 10 years.

Source: Reprinted with permission from the *Diagnostic and Statistical Manual of Mental Disorders,* Fourth Edition, Text Revision. Copyright © 2000 by the American Psychiatric Association.

You may think of what DSM-IV-TR calls conduct disorder as being roughly equivalent to juvenile delinquency. Most of the symptoms of conduct disorder do indeed involve *index offenses*—crimes against people or property that are illegal at any age. A few diagnostic criteria are comparable to **status offenses**—acts that are illegal only because of the youth's status as a minor. Examples are running away from home and truancy from school. However, **juvenile delinquency** is a *legal* classification, not a mental health term. Adolescents who repeatedly break the law have conduct disorders whether or not they are arrested and convicted. Technically, however, youths are not delinquent until a judge finds them guilty. In the United States, juvenile court judges may base a finding of delinquency on either criminal or status offenses, although adjudication for status offenses is increasingly rare.

Frequency of Externalizing Disorders

Between 3 and 5 percent of children in the United States are estimated to have ADHD at any point in time. Estimates in Europe are generally much lower, about 1 to 2 percent of children, but this is due to more conservative diagnostic practices in Europe, not to differences in children's behavior (Schachar & Tannock, 2002). Anywhere from 5 to 15 percent of youth in the United States may have ODD and/or CD (see Research Methods).

RESEARCH METHODS   Samples: How to Select the People We Study

Psychologists typically do not use a **representative sample**—a sample that accurately represents some larger group of people. Instead, we often use *convenience samples*—groups of people who are easily recruited and studied. For many purposes, convenience samples work just fine. For example, we do not need a representative sample to study the effectiveness of alternative treatments for ADHD.

For some purposes, however, obtaining representative samples is essential. For example, many children with externalizing problems in clinical settings come from single-parent families, and some studies of clinical samples have concluded that single parenting causes behavior problems. But we need to be cautious in *generalizing* from convenience or clinical samples. These groups are unrepresentative of the population of children and families. Consider this: Pediatricians surely would greatly overestimate the prevalence of ear infections if they generalized from *their* clinical samples! In fact, when we study representative samples of children from single-parent families, we find that most children do *not* have psychological problems. Most children, and most single parent families, are *resilient;* They cope successfully with the stressors of single parenting (Emery, 1999).

> **Why is it dangerous to generalize from clinical or convenience samples?**

How do scientists select representative samples so they can generalize accurately to a larger population? First, the researcher must identify the *population* of interest, the entire group of people to whom the researcher wants to generalize—for example, children under the age of 18 living in the United States. Second, the researcher must *randomly select* participants from the population and obtain a large enough sample to ensure that the results are statistically reliable. This allows researchers to make generalizations that sometimes seem remarkable, such as accurately predicting the outcome of a political election from polls of a relatively small number of voters.

Errors can occur in identifying the population of interest or in random selection. One of the most famous errors occurred in 1948, when newspaper headlines heralded Thomas E. Dewey's election over Harry S Truman in the U.S. presidential election. Actually, Truman won handily. Where did the pollsters go wrong? They made a mistake in identifying the population of voters. The researchers sampled randomly from the U.S. population, but more Democrats went to the polls to vote for Truman than Republicans did for Dewey. (This is one reason why election pollsters now do exit surveys.) The polls also were conducted a week or more before the election, and late voter sentiment swung from Dewey to Truman.

Political scientists have become much more sophisticated in their sampling strategies since 1948. A fortunate trend in psychology is a new collaboration with sociologists in studying normal and abnormal behavior. Many large-scale surveys now follow representative samples of children or families over time and include measures of psychological well-being. Psychological scientists increasingly are using these samples to make sure that the same pattern of findings obtained in intensive studies of small convenience samples are found in representative samples of the population.

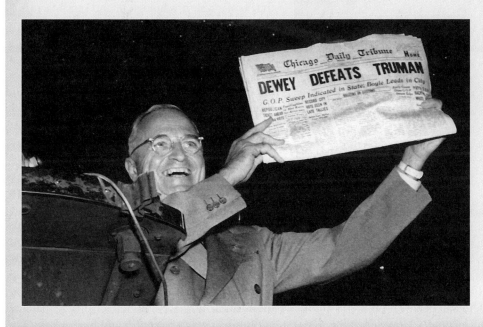

After the first few years of life, from 2 to 10 times as many boys as girls have an externalizing disorder (Keenan & Shaw, 1997; National Academy of Sciences, 1989). Except for the normative increase during adolescence, the prevalence of externalizing behavior generally declines with age, although it declines at much earlier ages for girls than for boys (Keenan & Shaw, 1997). In fact, the prevalence of life-course persistent antisocial behavior is far lower among girls than boys, even more so than for other externalizing problems (Earls & Mezzacappa, 2002).

Family Risk Factors Externalizing disorders are associated with various indicators of family adversity, a fact highlighted by British psychiatrist Michael Rutter, an international authority on the epidemiology of child psychopathology. Rutter's (1989) Family Adversity Index includes

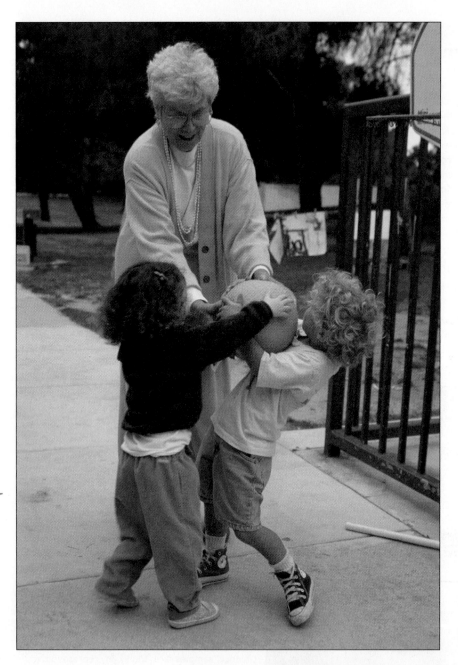

▲ Preschoolers need to learn to share, cooperate, and generally "be nice." Human nature includes selfish and aggressive motivations (as well as altruistic ones). Inborn variation and the availability and success of socialization both contribute to the development of externalizing disorders.

six family predictors of behavior problems among children: (1) low income, (2) overcrowding in the home, (3) maternal depression, (4) paternal antisocial behavior, (5) conflict between the parents, and (6) removal of the child from the home. Rutter found that the risk for externalizing problems did not increase substantially when only one family risk factor was present. However, the risk increased fourfold when two family adversity factors were present. The risk for children's antisocial behavior increased even further with three or more sources of family adversity.

Other epidemiological findings underscore the relationship between children's externalizing problems and social disadvantage (Earls & Mez-

zacappa, 2002). For example, externalizing disorders are found in more than 20 percent of children living in inner-city neighborhoods (National Academy of Sciences, 1989) and are associated with divorce and single parenting.

Causes of Externalizing Disorders

All children require some external limits in order to learn to control their behavior. If you doubt this, we suggest that you visit a preschool where children frequently need to be reminded to share, to cooperate, and not to hit, push, scratch, or bite. The natural behavior we observe in children also can be wonderful—preschoolers freely make friends, exchange favors, and show empathy when others are hurt. Still, all children need some discipline (together with a lot of love). Of course, different children need—or receive—more or less guidance, thus biological, psychological, and social factors all can contribute to causing externalizing problems.

Biological Factors Biological factors involved in externalizing disorders include a difficult temperament, neuropsychological abnormalities, and genetics. Biological risk factors can be a "double whammy," because they affect behavior problems directly and, in turn, strain relationships with parents, teachers, and peers.

Temperament Children differ in their **temperament,** inborn behavioral characteristics including activity level, emotionality, and sociability (Buss, 1991). Temperament can be classified in various ways, but Thomas and Chess's (1977) grouping into easy, difficult, and slow-to-warm-up is a useful summary. *Easy* children are friendly and obey most rules; *difficult* children challenge parental authority; *slow-to-warm-up* children are shy and withdrawn. Longitudinal research on infants and toddlers indicates that a difficult temperament is a risk factor for later externalizing disorders (Shaw, Keenan, & Vondra, 1994; Shaw et al., 1997).

Neuropsychological Abnormalities Neuropsychological research suggests other biological contributions to externalizing disorders, particularly to ADHD. Brain damage can produce overactivity and inattention, but *hard signs* of brain damage, such as an abnormal CT scan, are found in less than 5 percent of cases of ADHD (Rutter, 1983). Neurological *soft signs,* such as delays in fine motor coordination (as may be evident in poor penmanship), also are more frequent among children with ADHD. However, many children with ADHD do not show soft signs, while many normal children do (Barkley, 2006). Thus their implications are unclear.

Minor anomalies in physical appearance, delays in reaching developmental milestones, maternal smoking and alcohol consumption, and pregnancy and birth complications also are more common among children with ADHD. Still, researchers have yet to discover a specific marker of biological vulnerability. One candidate is impairment in the prefrontal cortical-striatal network, an area of the brain that may control executive functions including attention, inhibition, and emotion regulation (Barkley, 2006). Some neuropsychological evidence also indicates impaired executive functioning in ADHD children and their relatives, but only for a subset of cases in this heterogeneous disorder (Nigg et al., 2004).

Genetics and ADHD

Several studies show that genetic factors strongly contribute to ADHD. For example, a study of almost 4,000 Australian twins found concordance rates among MZ twins of roughly 80 percent, whereas DZ twins had concordance rates of approximately 40 percent (Levy et al., 1997). These rates are close to what one would expect for a *purely* genetic disorder (where the concordances would be 100 percent for MZ and 50 percent for DZ twins). In fact, genetic factors explain 90 percent of the variance in ADHD symptoms, a much higher proportion than for most behavior disorders (Plomin et al., 2001). Such evidence has spurred a search for specific genes that may cause ADHD. For example, recent evidence has linked ADHD with both dopamine receptor (DRD4) and transporter (DAT1) genes (Barkley, 2006).

Single genes may be identified as causing some cases of ADHD. However, most cases of ADHD appear to be polygenic. As we hope you know by now, this means that that ADHD is *not* an "either you have it or you don't" disorder, that is, a problem qualitatively different from normal (see Chapter 2). In fact, the best evidence indicates that variation in attention and activity level is quantitative not qualitative (Barkley, 2006; Levy et al., 1997). You cannot be "a little bit pregnant," but you *can* be "a little bit ADHD."

Why is this important? Because people tend to think of "genetic" as meaning you have a "gene for" a given condition. But like most mental disorders, most cases of ADHD appear to involve many genes. This leaves us with the very important question of deciding where to draw the line dividing "normal" activity or attention struggles from "abnormal" ADHD. The dividing line question is particularly important to consider (as we do shortly) in relation to the categorical decision of whether or not to medicate a child— and whether medications for ADHD are overused in the United States today.

Can you be "a little bit ADHD"?

Gene–Environment Interactions and Conduct Problems

Genes contribute less to ODD and especially CD than to ADHD (Burt et al., 2001; Rutter et al., 1999). Genetic influences are stronger for early- than late-onset antisocial behavior (Taylor, Iacono, & McGue, 2000). Presumably, genes play a similar role in both early-onset ODD and adult antisocial behavior, while the many environmental contributions to adolescent antisocial behavior obscure genetic effects (Gottesman & Goldsmith, 1994).

If genes contribute to ODD or CD, an essential question is: What is the inherited mechanism? Hyperactivity or inattention may be directly inherited, but rule violations surely are not (Earls & Mezzacappa, 2002). No one has suggested that there is a "crime gene," let alone an "argue with your teacher gene"!

Part of what is inherited may be a tendency to react more negatively to adverse environments. Researchers recently found that the effect of childhood maltreatment on adolescent conduct problems differs depending on the gene producing monoamine oxidase activity (MAOA). (The MAOA gene encodes an enzyme that metabolizes neurotransmitters and renders them inactive.) In a large sample of males followed from birth into adulthood, child maltreatment predicted significantly more adolescent conduct problems if the boys were genetically predisposed to low rather than high MAOA activity (Caspi et al., 2002; see Figure 16–3). Other recent research also shows that genes can contribute to externalizing problems by increasing susceptibility to family dysfunction (Button et al., 2005), and that physical maltreatment increases the risk for externalizing disorders even when controlling for genetic influences (Jaffee et al., 2005). Genes can alter susceptibility to adversity, but difficult experiences *are* critical to causing externalizing disorders.

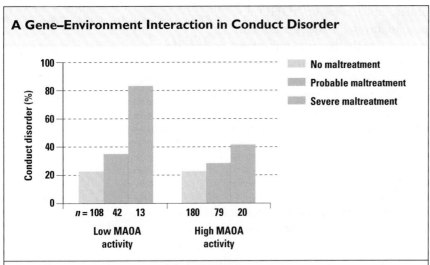

A Gene–Environment Interaction in Conduct Disorder

FIGURE 16–3 Child maltreatment increases the risk for conduct disorder, but the effect depends on an interaction with MAOA gene activity (which encodes an enzyme that metabolizes neurotransmitters and renders them inactive).

Source: Figure 2, part A from "Role of Genotype in the Cycle of Violence in Maltreated Children" by A. Caspi, et al., Science, (2002), 297, pp. 851–854. Copyright © 2002 by American Association for the Advancement of Science. Reprinted by permission of the publisher.

Social Factors Socialization is the process of shaping children's behavior and attitudes to conform to the expectations of parents, teachers, and society as a whole. Many psychologists believe that parental explanation, example, and appropriate discipline are most important in socializing children, but other influences cannot be ignored. Peer groups exert strong if sometimes subtle conformity pressures that increase as children grow older. School and television also are powerful socialization agents.

How does parental love affect parental discipline?

Parenting Styles Parental discipline is sometimes mistakenly viewed as the opposite of loving chil-

dren, but warm parent–child relationships make discipline both less necessary and more effective (Shaw & Bell, 1993). In fact, **authoritative parenting,** parenting that is both loving and firm, is most effective in rearing well-adjusted children. Warmth and control are so important that developmental psychologists classify parenting into four styles based on these dimensions (see Figure 16–4). In contrast to authoritative parents, *authoritarian* parents lack warmth, and their strict discipline is often harsh and autocratic. Children of authoritarian parents generally are compliant, but they also may be anxious. *Indulgent* parents are the opposite of authoritarian parents: affectionate but lax in discipline. Their children tend to be impulsive and noncompliant, but not extremely antisocial. Finally, *neglectful* parents are unconcerned either with their children's emotional needs or with their needs for discipline. Children with serious conduct problems often have neglectful parents (Hoeve et al., 2008; Maccoby & Martin, 1983).

Coercion More specific problems in parenting also contribute to children's externalizing problems. One of the most important is psychologist Gerald Patterson's (1982) concept of **coercion,** which occurs when parents *positively* reinforce a child's misbehavior by giving in to the child's demands. The child, in turn, *negatively* reinforces the parents by ending his or her obnoxious behavior as soon as the parents capitulate. Thus coercion describes a system of interaction in which parents and children reciprocally reinforce child misbehavior and parent capitulation. The concept is illustrated in the following brief case study.

BRIEF CASE **STUDY**
I Want Candy!

Ms. B. finally admitted that she had lost all control of her 4-year-old son Billy. Ms. B. was a single parent who was exhausted by her routine of working from 8 to 5:30 every day and managing Billy and the household in the evenings and on weekends. She had no parenting or financial support from Billy's father or anyone else, and Ms. B. was worn down. When it came time to discipline Billy, she usually gave in—either because this was the easiest thing to do or because she felt too guilty to say no.

Ms. B. described many difficult interactions with Billy. One example stood out in the mind of the psychologist she consulted. Ms. B. often stopped at the grocery store with Billy after work, and he inevitably gave her trouble. Dealing with the candy aisle was a particular problem. Billy would

A Classification of Parenting Styles

	Accepting, Responsive, Child-centered	Rejecting, Unresponsive, Parent-centered
Demanding, controlling	Authoritative	Authoritarian
Undemanding, low in control attempts	Indulgent	Neglectful

FIGURE 16–4 Four styles of parenting, based on dimensions of parental warmth and discipline efforts.

Source: E. E. Maccoby and J. A. Martin, 1983, "Socialization in the Context of the Family: Parent–child Interaction," in E. M. Hetherington (Ed.), *Socialization, Personality, and Social Development*, Vol. 4, *Handbook of Child Psychology*, pp. 1–101. New York: Wiley.

ask for some candy when they first approached the aisle. Ms. B. told him no, but in an increasingly loud voice Billy protested, "I WANT CANDY!" Ms. B. would attempt to stick to her guns, but soon she was embarrassed by the disapproving looks on the faces of other mothers. Feeling both resentful and resigned, she would grab a bag of M&Ms and give it to Billy. This gave her a few minutes of peace and quiet while she completed her shopping.

Clearly, Ms. B. rewarded Billy for his misbehavior. Billy also (negatively) reinforced his mother by quieting down when she gave in to his demands. Because both parties were reinforced, the coercive interaction should continue over time (Patterson, 1982).

The coercion concept has direct, practical implications. Parents need to break the pattern of interaction by ignoring the misbehavior (extinction), punishing it, or rewarding more positive actions (Herbert, 2002). In Billy's case, the psychologist recommended the use of **time-out,** the technique of briefly isolating a child following misbehavior. The next time Billy acted up in the grocery store, Ms. B. left her shopping cart, and she and Billy sat in the car until he quieted down. She then completed her shopping. Several trips to the car were needed the first day, but Billy's behavior improved as a result. He quickly was earning rewards for being good—not for being bad—while shopping.

Love and Discipline Children's noncompliance may not always stem from a lack of discipline. Sometimes children misbehave as a way of getting attention rather than as a way of getting what they want. Consider the concept of *negative attention,* the idea that attempts at punishment sometimes accidentally reinforce children's misbehavior. Imagine, for example, the teacher who scolds the "class clown" for misbehaving. In some circumstances, the scolding increases rather than decreases the child's misbehavior; that is, the attempt at punishment actually serves as a reinforcement. Rather than trying to find a truly effective punishment, we think it is essential to understand *why* negative attention is reinforcing. Many children are reinforced by negative attention because they are not getting enough positive attention—enough love. If so, increasing parental affection should be a better way of treating their externalizing behavior than increasing parental discipline (Emery, 1992).

Inconsistency Inconsistency also is linked with children's externalizing problems (Patterson, De-Baryshe, & Ramsey, 1989). Inconsistency can involve frequent changes in the style and standards of one parent, or two parents may be inconsistent in their rules and expectations. Inconsistency often becomes a problem when parents have conflicts in their own relationship—when they are unhappily married or are divorced (Emery, 1982; Repetti, Taylor, & Seeman, 2002). Some angry parents even deliberately undermine each other.

Yet another problem occurs when parents' actions are inconsistent with their words. For example, consider the contradiction inherent in angry and harsh physical punishment (Gershoff, 2002). On one hand, such discipline tells children to follow the rules. On the other hand, harsh physical punishment teaches children that anger and aggression are acceptable means of solving problems. Parents socialize children by modeling appropriate behavior as well as by disciplining them. Children often do what their parents do, not what they say.

Peers, Neighborhoods, Television, and Society

Peer groups also can encourage delinquent and antisocial behavior (Dishion, McCord, & Poulin, 1999), and among adolescents, peer influences may be stronger than parental ones (Walden et al., 2004). In fact, socialized delinquency, in which criminal acts occur in the company of others, may be an important subtype of externalizing disorders (Kazdin, 1995).

Neighborhood and society also contribute to externalizing problems. Television violence is rampant, as is violence in computer games, and

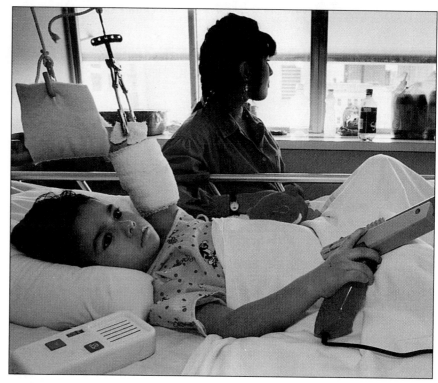

▼ Societal influences on children's behavior are pervasive. This 3-year-old boy suffered a gunshot wound during a drive-by shooting. Still, the boy plays with a toy pistol while recuperating in his hospital bed.

research shows that aggressive children both prefer and become more aggressive in response to video violence (Anderson et al., 2003). Youth who witness violence in their communities also are more likely to be violent themselves (Shahinfar, Kupersmidt, & Matza, 2001), and in general, children who grow up in unstable, poor, inner-city neighborhoods are more likely to have externalizing problems (Dupere et al., 2007; Stouthamer-Loeber et al., 2002).

Cross-cultural evidence points to other influences on externalizing behavior. Robbery, sexual offenses, assault, and burglary are far more common in the United States than in Canada, Europe, or Japan, and juveniles account for many of these crimes. Some politicians argue that this is because the United States is "soft on crime," but far *more* people are imprisoned in the United States than in Canada, Europe, or Japan (see Figure 16–5). Other aspects of U.S. culture, such as higher poverty rates and lack of gun control, apparently explain our high rates of youth violence (Costello et al., 2003; Jones & Krisberg, 1994).

Social Factors in ADHD There are no theories of how social factors play a unique role in the development of ADHD (Hinshaw, 1994). Mothers of children with ADHD are more critical, demanding, and controlling compared to the mothers of normal children (Mash & Johnston, 1982). However, research shows that problems primarily are a *reaction* to the children's troubles, not a

cause of them. In a clever study design, children are randomly given either a medication that improves ADHD symptoms or a placebo. Research shows that children with ADHD become more attentive and compliant while medicated, and their mothers' behavior "improves" as well—mothers become less negative and less controlling (Danforth, Barkley, & Stokes, 1991). Because no one knows who got the medication or the placebo, the differences must be due to the medicine's effects on the children—and the children's effects on their mothers. Children with ADHD make social interactions more difficult.

This does not mean that good parenting is unimportant. Ineffective parenting surely intensifies ADHD symptoms (Hinshaw et al., 2000), and maternal warmth and understanding may help to prevent ADHD (Tully et al., 2004). Family and social adversity also contribute to ODD and its comorbidity with ADHD (Burt et al., 2001).

Psychological Factors *Self-control,* the internal regulation of behavior, is the ultimate goal of socialization. Not surprisingly, several investigators have found problems with self-control among children with externalizing disorders. *Low self-esteem,* feelings of low worth, also is sometimes blamed as a cause of externalizing problems, but research shows, perhaps surprisingly, that children with ADHD *overestimate* rather than undervalue their competence (Hoza et al., 2004).

One area of research on self-control focuses on *delay of gratification*—the adaptive ability to defer smaller but immediate rewards for larger, long-term benefits. An example of delay of gratification is studying for an exam rather than going out with friends. In general, children with externalizing problems are less able to delay gratification and are more oriented to the present than are other children. They opt for immediate rewards rather than for long-term goals, a maladaptive characteristic for achieving educational and career goals (Nigg, 2001).

Children with externalizing problems also may fail to exert self-control because they misinterpret the intentions of others, particularly in ambiguous social situations. Studies by psychologist Ken Dodge and his colleagues indicate that aggressive children overinterpret the aggressive intentions of their peers (Dodge et al., 2003). That is, children with externalizing problems view other children as threatening to

Child Poverty, Crime, and Prison Use in the United States, Japan, Europe, and Canada

FIGURE 16–5 Prison use indicates that the United States is not "soft on crime" in comparison to other countries. Other factors, such as the higher rate of poverty, may explain the high crime rate in the United States.

Source: United Nations Interregional Crime and Justice Research Institute.

Note: Figure included here was reprinted in M. A. Jones and B. Krisberg, 1994, *Images and Reality: Juvenile Crime, Youth Violence, and Public Policy,* San Francisco: National Council on Crime and Delinquency.

them. As a result, some of their aggression may be an attempt to "get you before you get me." Psychologist Seth Pollak and his colleagues show one way that such biases may develop. Physically abused children attend to angry facial cues longer than normal children (Pollak & Tolley-Schell, 2003), a reaction that may be adaptive in a threatening family but maladaptive in other relationships.

A related psychological issue concerns the "conscience" of children with externalizing problems. Psychologist Lawrence Kohlberg (1985) created a hierarchy of moral reasoning showing that children use increasingly abstract and sophisticated moral principles as they grow older. For example, a young boy may say that the reason he behaves well is because "Mommy will get mad." An older boy may explain that the reason he behaves well is because "You need to follow the rules." A teenager might explain that he behaves well because "It is the right thing to do."

According to Kohlberg, higher moral principles are based on values regarding appropriate conduct rather than on the immediate consequences of misbehavior. He hypothesized that these more sophisticated guidelines, in turn, lead to more prosocial behavior. In support of his theorizing, some evidence indicates that aggressive children follow the hedonic principles commonly used by children at younger ages (Kohlberg, 1985).

Integration and Alternative Pathways How can we integrate evidence on the diverse contributions to the development of externalizing? Two conclusions seem clear. First, externalizing disorders have many causes, not one. Second, biological, psychological, and social factors clearly interact in causing externalizing disorders. Temperament theorists note, for example, that the *goodness of fit* between a child's temperament and the family environment may be of greatest importance to healthy psychological development (Shaw & Bell, 1993). The combination of a difficult temperament and family adversity may result in ODD and eventually conduct disorder, while a temperamentally "easy" child might turn out well-behaved despite growing up in difficult family circumstances (Kasen et al., 1996). In fact, impulsive youth have unusually high rates of juvenile offending when they grow up in poor versus better-off neighborhoods. However, whether the neighborhood is poor or better off has no effect on offending for nonimpulsive youth (Lynam et al., 2000).

▲ In contrast to boys' physical aggression, girls are more likely to engage in "relational aggression." Relational aggression includes put downs, gossip, and social exclusion, as was illustrated in the popular movie *Mean Girls*.

Treatment of Externalizing Disorders

Numerous treatments have been developed for children's externalizing disorders, but unfortunately the problems can be difficult to change (Kazdin, 1997). The most promising treatments include psychostimulants for ADHD, behavioral family therapy for ODD, and intensive programs for treating conduct disorders and delinquent youth.

Psychostimulants and ADHD Psychostimulants are medications that increase central nervous system activity; and in appropriate dosages, the medications increase alertness, arousal, and attention. Psychostimulants produce immediate and noticeable improvements in the behavior of about 75 percent of children with ADHD. Before considering their effects further, we first must consider a long-held, and mistaken, view about psychostimulants and ADHD.

The "Paradoxical Effect" Paradox Psychostimulants heighten energy and alertness, and they lead to restless, even frenetic, behavior when abused. These effects are accurately conveyed by a street name for the drugs, "speed." The U.S. psychiatrist Charles Bradley (1937) was one of the first to observe that these medications seem to have a "paradoxical effect" on overactive children: The drug slows them down. For many years, professionals believed that this was proof of abnormal brain functioning in ADHD. The real irony, however, is that the idea of a paradoxical effect was wrong.

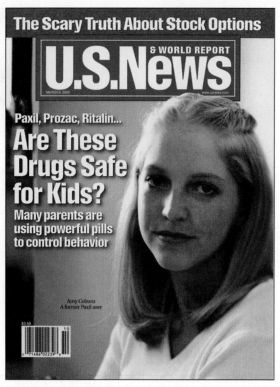

▶ Psychostimulants are effective treatments of ADHD, but concern is rising that medication may be given too quickly to too many children.

One reason for the enduring "paradoxical effect" paradox is that it was deemed unethical to experiment with psychostimulants on normal children, even though the medication was given regularly to millions of "abnormal" children. A group of researchers at the National Institute of Mental Health eventually found a clever way to address the ethical problem. They obtained permission from colleagues in the medical and mental health communities to study the effects of psychostimulants on *their* children. The researchers found that the psychostimulants affected the normal children in the same way as overactive children. The medication improved attention and decreased motor activity (Rapoport et al., 1978). In fact, psychostimulants have the same effects on *adults* when taken in comparably small dosages. There is *no* paradoxical effect of psychostimulants on children with ADHD.

Usage and Effects   The most commonly prescribed psychostimulants are known by the trade names of Ritalin (the most commonly used psychostimulant), Dexedrine, Cylert, and Adderall. Each has the effect of increasing alertness and arousal. Psychostimulants usually are prescribed by pediatricians, who typically are consulted following a child's difficulties in the early years of school. The fact that behavior problems in school are the main concern about children with ADHD is demonstrated in how

psychostimulants are prescribed. A pill is taken in the morning before school, and because the effects of many psychostimulants last only 3 or 4 hours, another pill is taken at the lunch hour.[1] A third pill may or may not be taken after school, but the medication typically is not taken on weekends or during school vacations because of concerns about side effects.

Children take psychostimulants for years, not days or weeks. Traditionally, medication was discontinued in early adolescence, because it was believed that the problem was "outgrown" by that age. However, research shows that, while hyperactivity usually improves during the teen years, problems with inattention and impulsivity often continue (Schachar & Tannock, 2002). Thus psychostimulants now are taken through the teen years, and perhaps into adulthood, as interest has grown in "adult ADHD," inattention, impulsivity, and to a lesser extent, overactivity in adults (Barkley, 2006).

Numerous double-blind, placebo-controlled studies show that psychostimulants indisputably improve children's attentiveness and decrease their hyperactivity (Barkley, 2006; Pelham et al., 1993). In the largest treatment study to date, the Multimodal Treatment of Study of Children with ADHD (MTA), 579 children with ADHD were randomly assigned to one of four treatments: (1) controlled medication management, (2) intensive behavior therapy, (3) the two treatments combined, or (4) uncontrolled community care (which typically included medication). A 14-month follow-up assessment showed that the controlled medication and combined treatments produced significantly more improvements in ADHD symptoms than the alternatives. Intensive behavior therapy (part of the combined treatment) added only a slight improvement over medication for ADHD symptoms (see Figure 16–6) but may have modestly helped comorbid aggressive behavior (MTA, 1999; Swanson et al., 2001), parenting (Wells et al., 2006), and minority children and families (Arnold et al., 2003).

More aggressive behavior therapies, including summer treatment programs, may produce more notable benefits (Pelham et al., 2002). Still, this evidence establishes psychostimulant medication as the first-line treatment for the behavioral symptoms of ADHD. However, the findings also

---

[1]Release delivery versions of psychostimulants (trade names Concerta, Adderall XR) are available that release medication in a manner similar to taking three separate pills throughout the day.

indicate that improvements are needed in standard community medication management, which was much less effective than carefully controlled medication use. Unfortunately, standard community practice often involves little ongoing monitoring of ADHD children.

Psychostimulants improve hyperactivity and impulsivity, but their effects on attention and learning are less certain. Children on medication complete more reading, spelling, and arithmetic assignments with somewhat improved accuracy (Pelham et al., 1985), but their grades and achievement test scores improve little if at all (Henker & Whalen, 1989). This pattern of improvement in behavior but not in learning also was observed in the MTA (1999).

An even more troubling and puzzling fact is that psychostimulants have not been found to lead to *long-term* improvements in behavior, learning, or any other areas of functioning (Barkley, 2006; Schachar & Tannock, 2002; see Table 16–4). For example, a three-year follow-up of the MTA Cooperative Study showed no benefits of psychostimulants on ADHD or other symptoms (Jensen et al., 2007). Is this null result due to failure to take medication consistently over the course of several years, a shortcoming of medication as a treatment for ADHD, or some other issue? No one knows, yet clearly the difference in short- versus long-term results is a puzzle that needs solving.

The important issue of the effectiveness of psychostimulants in treating ADHD preschoolers is currently being investigated in another large-scale clinical trial, the Preschoolers with ADHD Treatment Study (PATS). Randomization and other critical aspects of the design were necessarily compromised because of ethical concerns in treating this young age group. At present, two results seem evident: (1) Preschoolers who remain on the medication improve over 10-month follow-up (although there is no control group) and (2) about one-third of preschoolers discontinue medication (Vitiello et al., 2007).

Side Effects The side effects of psychostimulants can be troubling. Common side effects include decreased appetite, increased heart rate, and sleeping difficulties. These are minor problems for children's health, but can bother parents who want their children to eat right and go to bed! Other side effects are more serious, such as an increase in motor tics in a small percentage of cases.

Evidence that psychostimulants can slow physical growth also is a very important con-

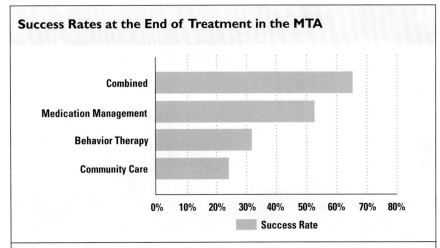

Success Rates at the End of Treatment in the MTA

FIGURE 16–6 Carefully monitored use of psychostimulants produces notable benefits for ADHD. Adding behavior therapy to medication produces a small but significant increase in success rates. Behavior therapy alone and community care—typically involving medication prescribed with little follow-up—produce much lower rates of improvement.

Source: From "Clinical Relevance of the Pirmary Findings of the MTA: Success Rates Based on Severity of ADHD and ODD Symptoms at the End of Treatment" by J. M. Swanson, et al., *Journal of the American Academy of Child and Adolescent Psychiatry,* (2001), 40, pp. 168–179. Copyright © 2001. Reprinted by permission of Lippincott, Williams & Wilkins.

cern. Past research found that children maintained on psychostimulants fell somewhat behind expected gains in height and weight, but the growth effect was interpreted as minor and rebounds in growth occur during medication-free periods (Barkley, 1998). The growth rebound is a major reason why the medication may be discontinued when children are not in school. However, concerns about effects on height and weight are likely to be renewed by emerging results from the MTA and PATS studies, both of which document significant decelerations in expected height and weight gain (Swanson et al., 2006; Swanson et al., 2007). Is the slowed growth minor? In the MTA, newly medicated children gained 6 pounds less and grew .8 inches less than never medicated children over the course of 3 years (Swanson et al., 2007). Whether this is minor or not may be a matter of interpretation, but in the eyes of school-aged boys, being smaller is *not* a minor matter.

TABLE 16–4 Short-Term and Long-Term Effects of Psychostimulants on ADHD Symptoms

	HYPERACTIVITY/IMPULSIVITY	INATTENTION/LEARNING
Short-term	Dramatic improvements; less active and more focused; fewer social problems	More work completed, but no change in grades or standardized test scores
Long-term	No demonstrated benefit	No demonstrated benefit

▲ Ritalin clearly helps the symptoms of ADHD. However, the line dividing normal from abnormal inattention and hyperactivity is debatable, and some question whether we medicate too many schoolchildren. In the United States, 3% of school-aged children are medicated, far more than elsewhere in the world.

Are Psychostimulants Overused? Despite evidence on the effectiveness of psychostimulants, parents and professionals face a basic question: Should we use medication to correct children's misbehavior? Every year 1.5 million children in the United States—almost 3 percent of the school-age population—are treated with psychostimulants for ADHD (Safer, Zito, & Fine, 1996). This startling number generates considerable controversy, as do these facts: (1) Between 1987 and 1996 stimulant use for youth under age 18 increased *300 percent to 700 percent* (Zito et al., 2003); (2) the use of psychostimulants *tripled* among preschoolers during the 1990s (Zito et al., 2000); (3) psychostimulants are used 3 to 10 times more often in the United States than in Europe, Canada, and Australia (Heyman & Santosh, 2002; Schachar & Tannock, 2002); and (4) the United States consumes 90 percent of the psychostimulants produced in the world (LeFever et al., 2003).

Are psychostimulants overused?

Are psychostimulants for ADHD overused in the United States? As we have noted, ADHD is a dimensional, not a categorical, problem. Should mental health professionals in the United States raise the threshold for making the diagnosis? Pills also can be overused as a "quick fix" not only for troubled children, but also for troubled schools. Many public schools are underfunded, overcrowded, and inadequately staffed. Moreover, competitive parents sometimes demand psychostimulants for their basically well-functioning children so they can "get an edge." Do we need to look at the bigger picture of children's lives instead of looking to a pill for a quick fix?

Psychostimulants are an inexpensive and effective treatment for ADHD, especially in comparison with the alternatives (see Critical Thinking Matters). Still, the benefits of medica-

tion are limited, various side effects are a concern, and, most importantly, there is no bright line between normal and abnormal behavior in diagnosing ADHD. Thus, it is reasonable to ask whether we are overdiagnosing ADHD and overmedicating schoolchildren.

Other Medications for ADHD Over the last decade, many children with ADHD have taken antidepressants. Although depression and ADHD often co-occur, this is not the rationale for the treatment. Rather, antidepressants may affect ADHD symptoms directly for unknown reasons. However, antidepressants clearly are a second-line treatment for ADHD. Their use is justified only following the failure of psychostimulants (DeVane & Sallee, 1996; Spencer, Biederman, & Wilens, 1998).

Strattera, a norepinephrine reuptake inhibitor, is the only nonstimulant medication approved by the U.S. Food and Drug Administration (FDA) for the treatment of ADHD. Strattera has the advantage of having less potential for abuse than psychostimulants and is often prescribed to adults with ADHD for that reason. However, strattera is less effective than psychostimulants, and it can have serious side effects, including increasing suicidal thinking (Bangs et al., 2008; Newcorn et al., 2008). Another medication, *clonidine,* is used in combination with psychostimulants in 20 percent or more of cases. Despite this frequent practice, the use of clonidine is controversial. The medication's primary use is for high blood pressure in adults, and only limited research supports its effectiveness for ADHD. Most controversial, there are isolated reports of sudden death among treated children (Hazell & Stuart, 2003).

Behavioral Family Therapy for ODD **Behavioral family therapy (BFT)** is a treatment that teaches parents to be very clear and specific about their expectations for children's behavior, to monitor children's actions closely, and to systematically reward positive behavior while ignoring or mildly punishing misbehavior. BFT is sometimes used as an adjunct or alternative to medication in treating ADHD, although it offers limited benefits for ADHD symptoms (MTA Cooperative Study, 1999). However, BFT is more promising as a treatment of ODD (Brestan & Eyberg, 1998).

BFT typically begins with *parent training.* Parents are taught to identify specific problematic behaviors such as fighting with siblings, list preferred alternative behaviors like speaking nicely,

CRITICAL THINKING MATTERS

ADHD's False Causes and Cures

No one is more desperate for answers than a parent of a child with a psychological problem. "We don't know what causes this" and "There is no cure" are *not* the kind of answers concerned parents want to hear. Unfortunately, these sorts of answers often are the most honest and scientifically accurate ones. However, the absence of scientific information does not prevent many self-appointed experts from answering parents' questions with partial truths, dubious theories, or pure fantasy. Myths abound for every mental disorder, but if we were to give a prize for the disorder with the most (and most audacious) misleading information and outright quackery, ADHD might just win.

Self-proclaimed "experts" have blamed the cause of ADHD on everything from fluorescent lights (the lights were installed in schools during a time of increasing rates of ADHD) to sugar (a favorite among teachers and parents—after all, children get "hyper" around Halloween) to a failure to learn to crawl properly before learning to walk (somehow out-of-sequence locomotion is supposed to disrupt developing brain circuitry, a theory we never understood, nor do we wish to try). We hope we do not need to say this, but just in case: There is no evidence to support any of these theories, or treatments based on them. We know, for example, that sugar can cause cavities, but increasing dietary sugar does not produce hyperactivity nor does decreasing sugar cure it (Milich et al., 1986). Today, a number of "experts" (but no scientific studies) blame the MMR vaccine for causing ADHD along with autism, learning disorders, and who knows what else (see Critical Thinking Matters in Chapter 2). Some critics claim that drug companies and the National Institute of Mental Health are conspiring to cover up evidence about this linkage. We give these worries the same credibility as theories that the government is covering up evidence of extraterrestrials visiting Earth.

Why is there so much misinformation about ADHD?

It might be instructive to consider a theory popular in the 1970s—that food additives cause ADHD, in particular *salicylates,* which are commonly found in processed foods. Physician Benjamin Feingold (1975) offered this theory in his immodestly titled book, *Why Your Child Is Hyperactive,* and recommended a natural-foods diet (the Feingold diet) as a cure. Hundreds of thousands of parents embraced the Feingold diet, and the theory became so popular that Congress considered banning salicylates. (Do a Web search, and you will still find advocates for the Feingold diet.) In fact, many parents of children with ADHD reported that their chil-

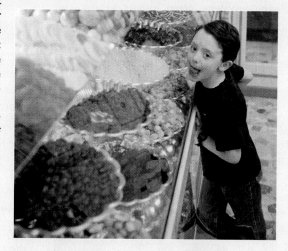

dren's symptoms improved as a result of the Feingold diet. But the "benefits" were nothing more than a placebo effect. The parents *believed* the diet would work, so it did in their minds. Unfortunately, research showed that their children's behavior did not change (Conners, 1980).

Among the other treatments that do *not* work for ADHD are food supplements (amino acids and megavitamins are two often recommended "treatments"); play therapy (the therapist plays with the child and interprets the play analogous to the way an analyst interprets free association); eye movement desensitization and reprocessing (see Chapter 7); neurofeedback (where patients watch EEG readings and try to alter their brain waves); sensorimotor integration therapy (which may include exercises like watching a pencil as you touch your nose with it); acupuncture (the ancient Chinese procedure); or various homeopathic remedies, including *pycnogenol* (an organically based substance which advocates claim is as effective as Ritalin—and also helps to cure tennis elbow!). Again, *none of these treatments work* (Waschbusch & Hill, 2004). Fortunately, there are treatments for ADHD that do work, although not as well as we (and parents) might hope.

Critical thinking is one thing that will work for you, if you learn to use it. Sure: Watch science fiction movies and suspend belief for a couple of hours. But when it comes to real life problems, critical thinking *matters*—and you have many opportunities to use critical thinking in considering various purported causes and cures of ADHD.

and set consequences for appropriate and inappropriate behavior. Parents may also make a "star chart" for recording children's progress and perhaps develop a "daily report card" that the child will carry home from school as a way of coordinating discipline in both settings (Scott, 2002).

Parent training also may include teaching parents about punishment strategies, such as the time-out technique. Conventional wisdom holds that punishment should be firm but not angry, and that rewards should far outweigh punishments as a strategy of discipline. Some experts believe that parent training should directly emphasize increasing warmth as well as discipline in parent–child relationships (Cavell, 2001). From this perspective, the goal of parent training is to teach parents to be authoritative.

Research supports the short-term effectiveness of BFT (Patterson, 1982), and parent training can be effectively delivered in groups

▲ Research shows that treatments that involve parents are most effective for children with oppositional defiant disorders.

▼ Boot camps have been advocated widely as treatments for juvenile delinquency. But like other temporarily fashionable treatments, boot camps unfortunately do not reduce recidivism.

(Webster-Stratton, 1994), to parents of toddlers (Gardner et al., 2007), or even through the popular media (Sanders, Montgomery, & Brechman-Toussaint, 2000). However, evidence on long-term effectiveness is less certain, and benefits generally are limited to children under the age of 12 (Kazdin, 1997). In considering the challenges for BFT, recall that the parents of children with externalizing problems often live in adverse circumstances that make it difficult to alter their parenting (Emery, Fincham, & Cummings, 1992). Parents can be effective in changing children's behavior, but psychologists need to develop more ways to help parents who live in difficult circumstances (Scott, 2002). In fact, BFT is less effective when parents are unhappily married, depressed, substance abusers, or harsh and critical with their children (Beauchaine, Webster-Stratton, & Reid,

2005). BFT is more effective when treatment includes efforts to help parents cope with *their* stress (Kazdin & Whitley, 2003).

Some behavioral therapies also include direct training of children as well as parents. *Problem-solving skills training (PSST)* is one commonly used technique in which children are taught to slow down, evaluate a problem, and consider alternative solutions before acting. Some evidence indicates that the combination of PSST and parent training leads to more improvement than either therapy alone in the treatment of the problems found in ODD (Kazdin, Siegel, & Bass, 1992). As with behavioral family therapy, however, PSST offers only minimal help to children with ADHD.

Treatment of Conduct Disorders and Juvenile Delinquency Numerous programs have been developed to treat conduct disorders and juvenile delinquency. In fact, exciting claims about the effectiveness of new programs for difficult youth are commonly reported in the popular media. You should be cautious about these new approaches. Research indicates that conduct disorders among adolescents are even more resistant to treatment than are externalizing problems among younger children (Kazdin, 1995, 1997).

Some BFT approaches have shown promise in treating young people with family or legal problems (Alexander & Parsons, 1982). These treatments are based on principles similar to those in programs for younger children, except that *negotiation*—actively involving young people in setting rules—is central to BFT with adolescents. An obvious reason for the negotiation strategy is that parents have less direct control over adolescents than over younger children. Because of diminishing parental control, many mental health professionals also advocate treating externalizing problems prior to adolescence.

Multisystemic Therapy *Multisystemic therapy (MST)* is another intervention with conduct disorders that has received considerable attention (Henggeler & Borduin, 1990). MST combines family treatment with coordinated interventions in other important contexts of the troubled child's life, including peer groups, schools, and neighborhoods. Several studies now document that MST therapy improves family relationships, and to a lesser extent, delinquent behavior and troubled peer relationships (Curtis, Ronan, & Borduin, 2004). A 13-year follow-up study found significantly lower **recidivism,** or repeat offending, among seriously troubled youth treated with

MST versus individual therapy, but recidivism remained high for both groups: 50 percent following MST versus 81 percent for individual therapy (Schaeffer & Borduin, 2005). The data point to the importance of coordinating efforts to help troubled youth in the various contexts of their lives—and to the frequent failure to prevent recidivism even following such extensive efforts.

Residential Programs and Juvenile Courts
Many adolescents with serious conduct problems or especially troubled families are treated in residential programs outside the home. One of the most actively researched residential programs is *Achievement Place,* a group home that operates according to highly structured behavior therapy principles. Achievement Place homes, like many similar residential programs, are very effective in improving aggression and noncompliance while the adolescent is living in the treatment setting. For this reason, professionals working in residential or inpatient settings are wise to adopt similar behavioral strategies. Unfortunately, the programs do not prevent recidivism once the adolescent leaves the residential placement (Bailey, 2002; Kazdin, 1995). Delinquent adolescents typically return to family, peer, and school environments that do not consistently reward prosocial behavior or monitor and punish antisocial behavior.

Many delinquent youths are treated in the juvenile justice system, where *rehabilitation* is supposed to be the goal. The philosophy of the juvenile justice system in the United States is based on the principle of *parens patriae*—the state as parent. In theory, juvenile courts are supposed to help troubled youth, not punish them. This lofty goal is belied by research indicating that *diversion*—keeping problem youths out of the juvenile justice system—is an effective "treatment" (Davidson et al., 1987).

Such struggles have led some to treat juvenile offenders more like criminals than troubled youth. Statistics indicate that punishment rather than rehabilitation is becoming more common in the United States (Bailey, 2002). More minors are being transferred out of the juvenile justice system and tried as adults, and more youth are placed into custody (see Figure 16–7).

Realism, Not Pessimism We see the difficulties in treating problem youth as a challenge, not a defeat. Therapists need to work to establish good relationships with troubled (and often difficult) youth, an important predictor of treatment outcome for externalizing problems (Shirk & Karver, 2003). More

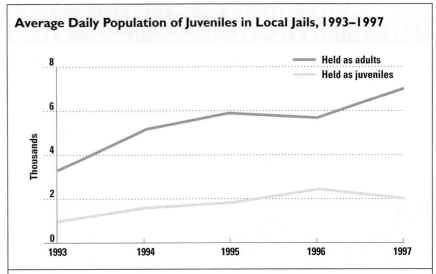

Average Daily Population of Juveniles in Local Jails, 1993–1997

FIGURE 16–7   More juveniles are being held together with adults in local jails. An increasing number of these youth are being held as adults—and awaiting trial as adults.
Source: Based on D. K. Gillard, 1999, "Prison and Jail Inmates at Midyear 1998," Washington, DC: U.S. Department of Justice.

effort also must be made to coordinate intervention across the different contexts of youths' lives (Schaeffer & Borduin, 2005). Another key is preventing externalizing disorders by easing the family adversity that creates them (Earls & Mezzacappa, 2002), or teaching new ways of coping with adversities that cannot be readily changed (Lochman & Wells, 2004). We need to be realistic about the limited effectiveness of treatment, but if we do not want troubled youth to give up on themselves, we cannot give up on them.

Course and Outcome Do children "outgrow" externalizing disorders? For ADHD, hyperactivity generally declines during adolescence, while attention deficits and impulsivity are more likely to continue. One index of these continuing difficulties is an increase in motor vehicle accidents (Barkley, 2006). The continuity of symptoms into adult life for about half of the children with ADHD is evident in the growing interest in adult ADHD (Mannuzza et al., 1998). Importantly, aspects of the prognosis of ADHD depend on whether there is comorbid ODD or CD. If so, youth are more likely to develop problems with substance abuse, criminality, and other forms of antisocial behavior (Hinshaw, 1994). In fact, roughly half of all children with ODD or CD continue to have problems with antisocial behavior into adulthood (Hinshaw, 1994; Kazdin, 1995). As we have noted, however, adolescent-onset antisocial behavior is less likely to continue than childhood-onset antisocial behavior (Moffit, 1993).

INTERNALIZING AND OTHER DISORDERS

Teachers cannot ignore disruptive children in the classroom, but they may overlook anxious or depressed children who sit quietly and un- happily alone. The negative effect of externaliz- ing disorders is an important reason why we have focused on these problems, but like schoolteachers, we do not want to overlook children whose troubles are *not* disruptive. We begin with a case study.

CASE **STUDY** Turning the Tables on Tormentors

Mark was 12 years old when his mother brought him to see a new psychologist. Both Mark and his mother agreed that he had been depressed for well over a year, and 9 months of "play therapy" resulted in little im- provement. Mark felt sad most of the time, cried often, and felt helpless and hopeless about the fu- ture. He had withdrawn from his usual activities, and his straight As had fallen to Bs, Cs, and even a few Ds—despite an IQ of 145. Teasing was a par- ticular problem, one that brought Mark to tears during the first appointment. A group of boys at his school constantly tormented Mark, calling him the "little professor." As in the office, their teasing frequently brought Mark to the point of tears.

Mark's family was well functioning, and there was no family history of depression. Mark's mother was a homemaker, and his father was a police officer. His parents were happily married, and his two younger brothers were doing well. Mark's mother attributed many of his problems to his unusual intelligence and to the fact that Mark had played with few children during the first years of his life. The family had lived in an apartment in an unsafe neighborhood before the birth of his brothers.

The new treatment followed a cognitive be- havior therapy approach but began with a care- ful period of building rapport. Establishing a good therapeutic relationship was very impor- tant to Mark who was socially isolated and un- happy with his previous therapy. Treatment eventually focused on skills training and behav- ioral activation. Mark was encouraged to rejoin various activities and to initiate relationships with his peers. His parents were told to treat Mark normally. In particular, they were encour- aged to hold the same high (but not demanding) expectations for Mark's schoolwork as they did for their other sons.

A special emphasis of treatment was how Mark could deal with his tormentors. As a step, the therapist began to tease Mark playfully at times and to encourage teasing back in return. This was viewed both as a way of teaching Mark some skills and of desensitizing him to teasing, which is normative if often vicious among 12- year-old boys. Given the strong therapeutic rela- tionship that had developed, Mark quickly learned not only to accept this game but to rel- ish it. With his high IQ,

he soon became devastatingly clever in his banter.

The benefits clearly generalized outside of the therapy session. Mark no longer cried when he was teased; instead, he learned retorts that set his tormentors on their heels. In fact, Mark did not limit his self-defense to words. He punched one particularly mean boy in the nose one day— a response that was *not* encouraged in therapy but one that did not upset his father, the police officer (or, privately, the therapist).

Over the course of about 3 months of ther- apy, Mark's mood improved considerably. He started getting As again, and re-engaged in vari- ous activities. The teasing was no longer an issue. He remained himself—a quiet, intelligent, and in- trospective boy—but he had learned to have more rational expectations for himself, the im- portance of staying involved, and how to handle his tormentors.

The case of Mark shows that children do suf- fer from "adult" disorders such as depression. Yet the diagnosis is not always so clear. Imagine, for example, if Mark were 6 years old. Although he might act and look sad, he certainly would be less able to express or reflect on his feelings or feel hopeless about the future. Moreover, his parents would have difficulty interpreting his cry- ing, withdrawal, and grades without a good awareness of how Mark himself felt. Even if 6- year-old Mark could tell them that he was sad, the meaning of his words would be difficult to in- terpret. At young ages, children do not have the same ability to experience and express their thoughts and emotions as adults.

Symptoms of Internalizing Disorders

Children's internalizing symptoms include sad- ness, fears, and somatic complaints, as well as other indicators of mood and anxiety disor- ders—for example, feeling worthless or tense. DSMIV-TR does not have a separate category for children's internalizing disorders, but the manual does identify some unique ways in which children experience the symptoms. When diagnosing major depressive episodes among children and adolescents, for example, the clinician is allowed to substitute "irritable mood" for "depressed mood." Children some- times act angry when they are feeling sad, and they may try to hide their true emotions, espe- cially when talking to adults.

The diagnosis of phobia is another example. In contrast to adults, children are not required to recognize that their fears are excessive or unrea- sonable, because children often have limited in- sight into their problems. In fact, children may lack the cognitive capacity to experience some of the symptoms found among adults with the same disorder. Self-awareness emerges across the course of development, and it is not until adolescence that children fully develop the cognitive abilities necessary for "adult" insight.

Children's capacity to experience and recognize emotions also emerges over the course of development, as does their ability to express—and to mask—their own feelings. Unfortunately, the course of children's normal emotional development is not well charted. It is much more difficult for adults to evaluate children's inner experiences than it is to observe their externalizing behavior.

Depressive Symptoms The assessment of depression in children can be particularly difficult. For example, in one study of children hospitalized for depression, clinicians found a correlation of *zero* between children's and parents' ratings on identical measures of the children's depression (Kazdin, French, & Unis, 1983). How the adults rated the children was completely unrelated to how the children rated themselves. In another study, children's ratings of depression were associated with their hopelessness, low self-esteem, and internal attributions for negative events. Their *parents'* ratings of the children's depression, in contrast, were associated with the parents' ratings of externalizing behavior, not with children's internal distress (Kazdin, 1989). Finally, and perhaps of greatest concern, parents systematically underestimate the extent of depression reported by their children and adolescents (Kazdin & Petti, 1982; Rutter, 1989).

Given parents' and children's widely differing perceptions, psychologists are rightly concerned about a child's depression if *either* a parent *or* a child notes problems. In assessing children's internalizing problems, mental health professionals must obtain information from *multiple informants*—parents, teachers, and the children themselves (Harrington, 2002).

When assessing children directly, child clinical psychologists are sensitive to different signs that may be indicative of depression at different ages: unresponsiveness to caregivers under the age of 2; sad expressions and social withdrawal in preschoolers; somatic complaints in young school-aged children; more direct admission of sad feelings or marked irritability in older school-aged children or early adolescents; and full-blown depression, including suicide risk, among adolescents.

Depression in children and adolescents often is comorbid both with externalizing problems and with anxiety. Depression in children also may differ from depression in adolescents, not only in how it is expressed but also in its lower

prevalence, equal frequency among boys and girls, stronger relation with family dysfunction, and less persistent course (Harrington, 2002).

Children's Fears and Anxiety *Anxiety* is a general and diffuse emotional reaction that often is linked with anticipation of future and unrealistic threats. In contrast, *fear* is a reaction to real and immediate danger. As with depression, children often have trouble identifying their anxiety, but they are more aware of their fears, which are immediate and have a clear environmental referent. Adults can observe much of children's fearful behavior for the same reasons. Thus research on the development of children's fears is more advanced than it is for their anxiety.

Three findings from fear research are important to note. First, children develop different fears for the first time at different ages, and the onset of new fears may be sudden and have no apparent cause in the child's environment. For example, infants typically develop a fear of strangers in the months just before their first birthday; preschoolers develop fears of monsters and the dark between the ages of 2 and 4; and children between ages 5 and 8 often develop fears related to school. (If you

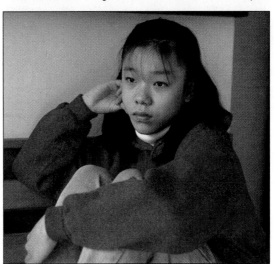

Calvin and Hobbes by Bill Watterson

◄ Depression becomes much more common during adolescence, especially among teenage girls.

Do children's fears change with age?

ever dreamed of going to school in your underwear, you are not alone. Such dreams are surprisingly common among school-aged children.) In short, many fears are developmentally normal, a conclusion that can be reassuring to parents and perhaps to children. A second finding is that some fears, particularly fears of uncontrollable events such as disasters, are both common and relatively stable across different ages. Third, many other fears, especially specific ones like fears of monsters or normal worries about death, become less frequent as children grow older (King et al., 1989). Apparently, children "outgrow" many of their fears, probably by gradually confronting them in everyday life.

Separation Anxiety Disorder and School Refusal The special case of separation anxiety illustrates the importance of development. **Separation anxiety** is distress expressed following separation from an attachment figure, typically a parent or caregiver. This normal fear develops strongly around a baby's eighth month of life. An infant who easily tolerated separations in the past may suddenly start to cling, cry, and scream whenever a parent tries to leave, even for a brief separation. Separation anxiety peaks around 15 months and lessens over time. Toddlers and preschoolers typically continue to experience dis-

tress upon separation, however, particularly when left in an unfamiliar circumstance.

Although normal at younger ages, separation anxiety can become a serious problem if children fail to "outgrow" it (Silverman & Dick-Niederhauser, 2004). DSM-IV-TR contains a diagnosis for **separation anxiety disorder,** which is defined by symptoms such as persistent and excessive worry for the safety of an attachment figure, fears of getting lost or being kidnapped, nightmares with separation themes, and refusal to be alone. For a child to be diagnosed with this disorder, he or she must exhibit three or more of these symptoms for at least 4 weeks.

Separation anxiety disorder is especially problematic when it interferes with school attendance. **School refusal,** also known as *school phobia,* is characterized by an extreme reluctance to go to school and is accompanied by various symptoms of anxiety, such as stomachaches and headaches. Some children are literally school phobic—they are afraid of school or specific aspects of attending school. But in many cases, school refusal can be traced to separation anxiety (Last & Strauss, 1990). In such cases, the parent, as well as the child, may have difficulty separating. Whatever its origins, school refusal is a serious problem that has been reported to account for more than two-thirds of referrals to an anxiety disorders clinic for children.

▶ Separation anxiety is a normal fear that typically develops just before a baby's first birthday. Toddlers and preschoolers continue to show a degree of distress even during routine separations from their attachment figures.

Troubled Peer Relationships The peer sociometric method often is used to assess children's relationships, and to identify peer difficulties that differ for children with internalizing or externalizing problems. *Peer sociometrics* evaluate children's relationships by obtaining information on who is "liked most" and who is "liked least" from a large group of children who know one another (for example, children in a classroom). Statistical procedures are then used to group children into one of five categories based on the ratings of their peers (Coie & Kupersmidt, 1983; Newcomb, Bukowski, & Pattee, 1993):

- *Popular* children receive many "liked most" and few "liked least" ratings.
- *Average* children also receive few "liked least" ratings, but they receive fewer "liked most" ratings than popular children.
- *Neglected* children receive few of either type of rating.
- *Rejected* children receive many "liked least" ratings and few "liked most" nominations.
- *Controversial* children receive many positive and many negative ratings from their peers.

Rejected children are considerably more likely to have externalizing problems in comparison to the other four peer status groups (Patterson, Kupersmidt, & Griesler, 1990), and peer rejection predicts the development of increased aggression (Dodge et al., 2003). Children with ADHD may be rejected because their symptoms impede social relationships (Greene et al., 2001; Hoza et al., 2005), whereas rejected children with ODD and CD are likely to have a few close friends—friends who, unfortunately, also engage in antisocial behavior (Olweus, 1984).

Neglected children also have more troubles than popular, average, and controversial children. Not surprisingly, neglected children are likely to have internalizing symptoms such as loneliness (Asher & Wheeler, 1985). An optimistic finding is the neglected status is not particularly stable over time and across situations (Coie & Kupersmidt, 1983; Newcomb et al., 1993). Apparently, children who are left out of one social group often succeed in finding friends as they grow older or move to a new school or participate in new activities.

Specific Developmental Deviations A number of troubling symptoms of children's psychological disorders are best understood as **developmental deviations,** significant departures from age-appropriate norms in some specific area of functioning. In fact, some developmental deviations are considered disorders in their own right. Specific deviations in reading (*dyslexia*), writing (*dysgraphia*), or arithmetic (*dyscalulia*) are considered to be learning disorders if the deviation is substantial (see What Are Learning Disorders?). Similarly, once a child is

WHAT ARE LEARNING DISORDERS?

The DSM-IV-TR category of **learning disorders** (LD)—educators use the term *learning disabilities*—includes a collection of diverse problems where students perform substantially below academic ability in a specific area of learning. Learning disorders are defined in many different ways, but all definitions have problems with reliability and validity (Swanson, Harris, & Graham, 2003). The most common approach is the "discrepancy definition," comparing scores on intelligence tests with scores on academic achievement tests. A learning disorder may be defined as a difference of one or two standard deviations between aptitude and achievement in a specific area of learning—reading, writing, or mathematics. Thus, a diagnosis of reading disorder (*dyslexia*) would follow if a child scored a standard deviation above the mean on the verbal portion of an intelligence test (an IQ of 115) but a standard deviation below the mean in reading.

School professionals almost always are on the "front line" in identifying children with learning disorders. Mental health professionals may work with children with learning disorders only when the problems co-occur with other psychological disorders. There is substantial comorbidity between learning disabilities and both ADHD and ODD (Barkley, 2006), but many wonder why learning disorders are listed in the DSM (a listing of *mental* disorders) when the problems are so clearly academic in nature.

Learning disorders appear to involve disruptions in a number of aspects of information processing, including perception, attention, language processing, and executive function. Typically, their cause is viewed as biological. Neuroimaging research on reading disorders identifies activity differences particularly in the temporal-parietal region of the left hemisphere of the brain (Miller, Sanchez, & Hynd, 2003; Shaywitz et al., 2006). (Recall that language abilities are lateralized in the left hemisphere.) Behavior genetic research shows that learning disorders, like normal reading abilities, are moderately heritable, and genetic linkage analysis suggests possible loci on chromosomes 1, 2, 6, 15, and 18 (Kovas & Plomin, 2007; Thomson & Raskind, 2003). However, no research has identified a specific psychological, neurological, or genetic cause of any learning disorder (Mash & Wolfe, 2005; Snowling, 2002; Swanson et al., 2003).

How do experts identify learning disorders?

Tremendous efforts have gone into attempts to remediate learning disorders. In 1975, the U.S. Congress passed the Education for All Handicapped Children Act (now called the Individuals with Disabilities Education Act, or IDEA), a law mandating that local school systems provide special resources for educating handicapped children, including children with learning disorders. The federal legislation dramatically increased the number of children identified as having a learning disorder rising from less than 2 percent in 1976–1977 to over 4 percent in 2002–2003 (Office of Special Education Programs, 2003). However, some commentators wonder whether this reflects overly broad definitions of learning disorders (Lyon, 1996). And it is not clear that the identification of more students has led to more effective education. Intervention attempts include intensive tutoring, individually or in small groups (including teacher-based direct instruction and student-based cooperative learning); behavior therapy programs in which academic success is systematically rewarded; psychostimulant medication; counseling for related problems (for example, low self-esteem); and various special efforts such as training in visual–motor skills. Unfortunately, no treatment has demonstrated consistent success (Lyon, 1996; Swanson et al., 2003).

Perhaps 5 percent of all schoolchildren in the United States do not achieve at a level consistent with their abilities (Lyon, 1996). Learning disorders are "real" in the sense that these children seem to have the ability and motivation to perform better in school, yet they do not. Nevertheless, the identification of a discrepancy between ability and performance has not solved the puzzle of learning disorders. Uncertainty remains about their definition, cause, and treatment.

| TABLE 16–5 | **DSM-IV-TR Disorders Usually First Diagnosed in Infancy, Childhood, or Adolescence** |

Attention-Deficit and Disruptive Behavior Disorders

Attention-deficit/hyperactivity disorder
  Combined type
  Predominantly inattentive type
  Predominantly hyperactive-impulsive type
Conduct disorder
Oppositional defiant disorder

Learning Disorders

Reading disorder
Mathematics disorder
Disorder of written expression

Motor Skills Disorder

Developmental coordination disorder

Communication Disorders

Expressive language disorder
Mixed receptive-expressive language disorder
Phonological disorder
Stuttering

Feeding and Eating Disorders of Infancy or Early Childhood

Pica
Rumination disorder
Feeding disorder of infancy or early childhood

Tic Disorders

Tourette's disorder
Chronic motor or vocal tic disorder
Transient tic disorder

Elimination Disorders

Encopresis
  With constipation and overflow incontinence
  Without constipation and overflow incontinence
Enuresis

Other Disorders of Infancy, Childhood, and Adolescence

Separation anxiety disorder
Selective mutism
Reactive attachment disorder of infancy or early childhood
Stereotypic movement disorder

Note: This listing does not include mental retardation or pervasive developmental disorders, which we discussed in Chapter 15. It also does not include "Not Otherwise Specified" (NOS) subtypes of the diagnoses.

Source: Reprinted with permission from the *Diagnostic and Statistical Manual of Mental Disorders,* Fourth Edition, Text Revision. Copyright © 2000 by the American Psychiatric Association.

Diagnosis of Internalizing and Other Disorders

Brief Historical Perspective In 1896, the psychologist Lightner Witmer (1867–1956) of the University of Pennsylvania established the first psychological clinic for children in the United States. Despite the early origins of child clinical psychology, children were largely ignored in early classifications of mental disorders (Garber, 1984). DSM-I (1952) contained only two separate diagnoses for children, and DSM-II (1968) listed only seven childhood disorders. DSM-III (1980) recognized a much wider range of childhood disorders, and in fact, contained a proliferation of diagnostic categories, 40 in all. Although laudable, the new effort was overly ambitious. Many of the new diagnoses were severely criticized and subsequently were dropped.

Contemporary Classification Table 16–5 summarizes the childhood disorders contained in DSM-IV-TR. Many of these diagnoses may be unfamiliar to you, in part because some of them are rare and unusual problems. We can consider most of these disorders only briefly.

Pica and Rumination Disorder Pica is the persistent eating of nonnutritive substances, such as paint or dirt. Many infants and toddlers put nonnutritive substances in their mouths, but the feeding disorder pica is rarely diagnosed, except among children with mental retardation. *Rumination disorder,* the repeated regurgitation and rechewing of food, is another infrequent feeding disorder. It is found primarily among infants, and it can be a serious problem that causes very low weight gain and can even lead to death.

Tourette's Disorder and Stereotypic Movement Disorder *Tourette's disorder* is a rare problem (4 to 5 cases per 10,000 people) that is characterized by repeated motor and verbal tics. The tics can be voluntarily suppressed only for brief periods of time and interfere substantially with life functioning. *Stereotypic movement disorder* is self-stimulation or self-injurious behavior that is serious enough to require treatment, as may occur in mental retardation or pervasive developmental disorder.

Selective Mutism and Reactive Attachment Disorder *Selective mutism* involves the consistent failure to speak in certain social situations (for example, in school) while speech is unrestricted in other situations (for example, at home). Selective mutism is found among less than 1 percent of the children treated for mental health disorders. *Reactive attach-*

past the age when most children toilet appropriately, delays in developing bladder or bowel control are considered to be abnormal. Of course, we can only determine if a child is delayed if we have good development norms.

ment disorder is characterized by severely disturbed and developmentally inappropriate social relationships. Children may resist comfort and cuddling, for example, or they may "freeze" and watch others from a safe distance. Reactive attachment disorder is caused by parenting that is so grossly neglectful that the infant or preschooler fails to develop a selective attachment relationship. In Chapter 18, we discuss child abuse and neglect, social problems that, unfortunately, are not rare.

Enuresis and Encopresis **Encopresis** and **enuresis** refer, respectively, to inappropriately controlled defecation and urination. According to DSM-IV-TR, enuresis may be considered abnormal beginning at age 5, as most children have developed bladder control by this age. Bedwetting is found among approximately 5 percent of 5-year-olds, 2 to 3 percent of 10-year-olds, and 1 percent of 18-year-olds. Encopresis, a much less common problem, may be diagnosed beginning at age 4. Encopresis is found among approximately 1 percent of all 5-year-olds and fewer older children.

Encopresis and enuresis typically are causes of, not reactions to, psychological distress. The symptoms that sometimes accompany enuresis or encopresis—for example, shyness or social anxiety—generally disappear once children learn to control their bowels and bladders. Encopresis and especially enuresis can be effectively treated with various biofeedback devices. The best-known is the *bell and pad,* a device that awakens children by setting off an alarm as they begin to wet the bed during the night. Research indicates that the bell and pad is about 75 percent effective in treating bedwetting among young school-aged children (Houts, 1991).

An Overinclusive List Beginning with DSM-III, too many "disorders" that are not in fact mental disorders were listed in the DSM (Garmezy, 1978). Many "disorders" have been dropped, but as you might suspect from Table 16–5, the list still is overinclusive. "Developmental coordination disorder" is perhaps the most obvious example. The manual defines this problem as, "Performance in daily activities that require motor coordination is substantially below that expected given the person's chronological age and measured intelligence" (p. 58). In poking fun at such diagnostic overzealousness, two pediatricians proposed a new diagnostic category they called "sports deficit disorder." The major diagnostic criterion is always being the last one chosen for a sports team (Burke & McGee, 1990).

The "learning disorders" and "communication disorders" are more examples of possible overinclusion in DSM-IV-TR. Educators call these childhood problems *learning disabilities* and *speech and hearing problems,* respectively. Learning disabilities and speech and hearing problems are common and serious difficulties experienced by children, but we question their status as mental disorders. We view both problems as primarily educational concerns.

Contextual Classifications? As a final note, we remind you that children's behavior is intimately linked with the family, school, and peer contexts. Because of this, some experts have suggested that diagnosing individual children is misleading and misguided. Instead, children's psychological problems could be classified within the context of key relationships, particularly the family (Group for the Advancement of Psychiatry, 1995). As you saw in the case of Jeremy, parents, teachers, and peers often are part of a child's "individual" problem. In fact, DSM-V study groups are examining the possibility of including "relational disorders" in the next edition of the manual, a topic we consider further in Chapter 17.

> *Does DSM-IV-TR include too many childhood "disorders"?*

Frequency of Internalizing Disorders

The prevalence of externalizing disorders decreases as children grow older, but the opposite is true for internalizing disorders. Depression increases dramatically during adolescence, especially among girls (Garber, Keiley, & Martin, 2002; see Figure 16–8). According to one startling estimate, 35 percent of young women and 19 percent of young men experience at least one major depressive episode by the age of 19 (Lewinsohn, Rhode, & Seeley, 1998). Some have claimed that such statistics point to an "epidemic" of teen depression. However, objective evidence suggests that the only thing that has increased is awareness of the problem (Costello et al., 2006).

Anxiety disorders may occur among as many as 5 to 10 percent of all young people (Klein & Pine, 2002). One national study estimated that 3.7 percent of boys and 6.3 percent of girls suffered from PTSD during the past 6 months (Kilpatrick et al., 2003). Precise estimates of the prevalence of both anxiety and depression are controversial, however, because of uncertainties about the best methods for diagnosing children and

Estimates of the Prevalence of Depression Among Young People

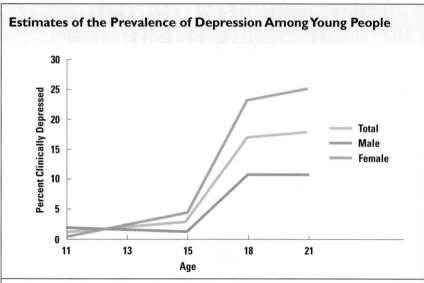

FIGURE 16–8 The prevalence of depression increases rapidly during adolescence, particularly among girls.

Source: Adapted from B. L. Hankin et al., 1998, "Development of Depression from Preadolescence to Young Adulthood: Emerging Gender Differences in a 10-Year Longitudinal Study," *Journal of Abnormal Psychology, 107,* pp. 128–140.

adolescents (Harrington, 2002). Much lower rates of clinically significant anxiety and depression are suggested by the relatively small numbers of young people in treatment for internalizing problems.

The fact that younger boys have more externalizing disorders while older girls have more internalizing problems leads to a distinctive pattern in child treatment referrals. Parents, teachers, and

U.S. Suicide Rates in the Twentieth Century: Total Population and Males Ages 15–24

FIGURE 16–9 Teen suicide rates tripled during the 1960s and 1970s but have fallen in recent years.

Source: H. Hendin, 1995, *Suicide in America,* p. 53, New York: Norton. Copyright © 1995, 1989 by Herbert Hendin, M.D. Used by permission of W. W. Norton & Company, Inc. and Georges Borchardt, Inc., on behalf of the author.

other adults seek treatment for children with externalizing problems, especially school-aged boys. The increase in depression among girls—and self-initiated treatment—begins to balance the gender ratio during the teenage years (Lewinsohn et al., 1994). By early adult life, notably more females than males are treated for psychological problems.

Suicide As we have noted, adults need to be sensitive to children's internal distress, as evidence on the epidemiology of suicide underscores in a dramatic fashion. Suicide is the third leading cause of death among teenagers, trailing only automobile accidents and natural causes. Suicide is extremely rare among children under the age of 10 (Shaffer & Gutstein, 2002). However, adolescent suicide rates tripled in recent decades (see Figure 16–9). Teen suicide declined 28.5 percent from 1990 to 2003, but increased 8 percent from 2003 to 2004 (CDC, 2007). The increase coincides with a drop in prescribing antidepressants to adolescents based on FDA "black box" warnings. As we discuss later, experts are debating whether antidepressants reduce or increase suicidality.

In comparison to adults, suicide attempts among adolescents are more impulsive, are more likely to follow a family conflict, and are more often motivated by anger than depression (Shaffer & Gutstein, 2002). *Cluster suicides* also can occur among teenagers. When one teenager commits suicide, his or her peers are at an increased risk. The risk sometimes stems from suicide pacts; the death also may make suicide more acceptable to despondent teenagers who may or may not know the victim.

Causes of Internalizing Disorders Most research on the causes of mood and anxiety disorders among children is based on the same theories of etiology we have discussed in relation to adults. Evidence simply is lacking or inadequate on the development of many other psychological problems of childhood. Thus, our discussion of causal factors is limited.

Biological Factors Except for some research documenting genetic influences on childhood onset obsessive–compulsive disorder (March, Leonard, & Swedo, 1995), few behavior genetic studies have been conducted on children's internalizing disorders. Moreover, existing research once again calls attention to the problems in classifying and assessing anxiety and depression among children. In the few studies completed to date, widely different estimates of genetic contributions are obtained based on children's versus parents' reports (Rutter et al., 1998).

Jerome Kagan and colleagues (Kagan & Snidman, 1991) have conducted important, basic research that suggests a more general, biological predisposition to anxiousness. These psychologists have identified a temperamental style that they call *inhibited to the unfamiliar.* Infants with this temperamental style cry easily and often in response to novel toys, people, or circumstances. Their psychophysiological responses (e.g., heart rate acceleration) also indicates fearfulness. About 10 percent of babies consistently show this pattern during the first 2 years of life (Kagan & Snidman, 1991), and these children are more likely to develop anxiety disorders as they grow older (Schwartz, Snidman, & Kagan, 1999; Klein & Pine, 2002). A recent prevention study found that the rate of anxiety disorders can be significantly reduced by parent education that discourages overprotectiveness, a common reaction to temperamentally inhibited children, and encourages gradually exposing children to the sources of their fear (Rapee et al., 2005).

Social Factors: A Focus on Attachments
Together with John Bowlby (1969, 1973, 1980), Canadian American psychologist Mary Ainsworth (1913–1999) developed *attachment theory,* a set of proposals about the normal development of attachments and the adverse consequences of troubled attachment relationships. Troubled attachments may include the failure to develop a selective attachment early in life; the development of an insecure attachment; or multiple, prolonged separations from (or the permanent loss of) an attachment figure.

Reactive Attachment Disorder Extreme parental neglect deprives infants of the opportunity to form a selective attachment. Such neglect can cause *reactive attachment disorder,* or what attachment researchers sometimes call *anaclitic depression*—the lack of social responsiveness found among infants who do not have a consistent attachment figure (Sroufe & Fleeson, 1986). Research on the consequences of extreme neglect for children is strongly buttressed by evidence from animal analogue research. Nonhuman primates who are raised in isolation without a parent or a substitute attachment figure have dramatically troubled social relationships (Suomi & Harlow, 1972).

Insecure Attachments Attachment theory also predicts that variations in the quality of early attachments are associated with children's psychological adjustment. Attachment quality can be broadly di-

◄ Mourners at the wake of three teenagers who committed suicide together.

vided into secure (healthy) and anxious attachments. Infants with *secure attachments* separate easily and explore away from their attachment figures, but they readily seek comfort from their attachment figures when they are threatened or distressed. Infants with **anxious attachments** are fearful about exploration and are not easily comforted by their attachment figures, who respond inadequately or inconsistently to the child's needs (Carlson & Sroufe, 1995). Anxious attachments are further subcategorized into (1) *anxious avoidant attachments,* where the infant is generally unwary of strange situations and shows little preference for the attachment figure over others as a source of comfort; (2) *anxious resistant attachments,* where the infant is wary of exploration, not easily soothed by the attachment figure, and angry or ambivalent about contact; and (3) *disorganized attachments,* where the infant responds inconsistently because of conflicting feelings toward an inconsistent caregiver who is the potential source of either reassurance or fear (Carlson & Sroufe, 1995).

A number of longitudinal studies have demonstrated that anxious attachments during infancy foreshadow difficulties in children's social and emotional adjustment throughout childhood. However, an insecure attachment does not seem to result in the development of any particular emotional disorder. Rather, insecure attachments predict a number of internalizing and social difficulties, including lower self-esteem, less competence in peer interaction, and increased dependency on others (Carlson & Sroufe, 1995; Cassidy, 1988; Sroufe & Fleeson, 1986). Stable, anxious attachments during infancy also predict externalizing behavior at 3 years of age (Shaw & Vondra, 1995). Thus, anxious attachments appear to be a general rather than a specific risk factor for children's psychological problems.

Separation and Loss Separation or loss is another threat to attachment, one that clearly causes distress among children. In the short run, children move through a four-stage process akin to grief when they are separated from or lose an attachment figure. The process includes (1) numbed responsiveness, (2) yearning and protest, (3) disorganization and despair, and ultimately (4), reorganization and detachment or loss of interest in the former attachment figure (Bowlby, 1979). However, there is considerable controversy about the long-term consequences of separation, loss, and detachment. Bowlby (1973) asserted that detachment causes dependence, which, in turn, increases the risk for depression as the child's needs go unfulfilled in subsequent relationships. Critics suggest, however, that what Bowlby called detachment is really an indication of children's adjustment to the new circumstances (Rutter, 1981). This interpretation highlights children's **resilience**—their ability to "bounce back" from adversity (Masten, 2001). The resilience interpretation of children's coping with loss is consistent with research that fails to find a relationship between childhood loss and depression during adult life (Harrington & Harrison, 1999).

Psychological Factors As with children's conduct, the regulation of children's emotions also progresses from external to internal control across the course of development. For example, attachment relationships offer security and soothe anxiety for infants and toddlers. As they grow older, however, children develop *internal working models* or expectations about relationships as extensions of their early attachment experiences (Carlson & Sroufe, 1995). **Emotion regulation** is a more general process as children learn to identify, evaluate, and control their feelings based on the reactions, attitudes, and advice of their parents and others in their social world. Anxious mothers, for example, are more anxious, less warm, more controlling, and perhaps more critical with their children, a style of interaction that can both create and fail to soothe children's fears and worries (Moore, Whaley, & Sigman, 2004).

Some research links troubles with emotion regulation to children's internalizing disorders. One area of investigation focuses on the interactions of children and their depressed mothers (Goodman & Gotlib, 1999). *Role reversal,* where children care for the parent rather than vice versa, may be a particular problem in these interactions. Children may attempt, and inevitably fail, to improve a parent's mood, leaving them feeling excessively guilty and responsible. Researchers have found excessive guilt among 5- to 6-year-old children of depressed mothers, as well as defensiveness against guilt among 7- to 9-year-olds (Zahn-Waxler et al., 1990). Other research shows increased depression among adolescent girls who respond to parental depression either by trying to be helpful or by becoming depressed themselves (Davis et al., 2000) and increased distress in response to detailed and frequent maternal disclosures (Koerner et al., 2004).

Treatment of Internalizing Disorders

Like the DSM diagnostic criteria, treatments for children's internalizing too often have viewed children as little adults. Few treatments address developmental issues, and "adult" treatments often are used without evidence that they work for children. For example, antidepressant medications are second only to psychostimulants as the most commonly prescribed psychotropic drugs for children and adolescents (Zito et al., 2000). Yet, a major review found that only fluoxetine (Prozac) has proven effectiveness. Importantly, *unpublished* data show fewer benefits than published studies of antidepressants, indicating a bias toward publishing positive results (Whittington et al., 2004).

Fortunately, new research is focusing on children. An outstanding example is the Treatment for Adolescents with Depression Study (TADS), a multisite clinical trial of 439 depressed adolescents randomly assigned to receive either (1) fluoxetine alone, (2) cognitive behavior therapy (CBT), (3) combined medication and CBT, or (4) placebo (TADS, 2004). After 12 weeks of treatment, 71 percent of patients receiving combined therapy improved, which was statically superior to medication alone, CBT alone, or placebo. Medication alone also was statistically superior to CBT or placebo at 12 weeks (see Figure 16–10; TADS, 2004). Importantly, the results at 36 weeks showed no differences between treatments (see Figure 16-10). Medication accelerated treatment response but was no more effective in the long term. (This result must be qualified, however, because random assignment was broken after 12 weeks.) Of critical importance, 14.7 percent of patients in the medication only group attempted, planned, or thought seriously about suicide at 36 weeks, significantly more that in the combined group (8.4 percent) or with CBT alone (6.3 percent) (TADS, 2007). Together with the accelerated response, this outcome strongly supports combining medication with CBT.

Evidence that antidepressants increase suicidality in TADS and other studies (Hammand, Laughren, & Racoosin, 2006) led the FDA to require manufacturers to place a "black box" warning on the medications in 2004. Prescriptions to children and adolescents declined significantly as a result (Olfson et al., 2008), but as we noted earlier, adolescent suicide *increased* during this time (CDC, 2007). To add to the confusion, a decline in antidepressant prescriptions did *not* lead to increased teen suicide in the United Kingdom (Wheeler et al., 2008).

What is the wise course given this conflicting information? Some experts argue that, while antidepressants increase suicidality for *some* teens, the medications reduce suicidality for *more* adolescents. From this perspective, the benefits of antidepressants outweigh their risks (Friedman & Leon, 2007). We generally agree. Our view is that antidepressants should be considered to be a valuable treatment option for adolescent depression. But suicide potential needs to be carefully assessed, and if there is any hint of suicide risk, medication should not be used or should be combined with CBT.

Turning to the treatment of children's anxiety, there are no large-scale clinical trials comparable to the TADS. Fortunately, however, the number of developmentally sensitive, smaller-scale studies of individual and family treatments is increasing (Barrett, Dadds, & Rapee, 1996; Beidel, Turner, & Morris, 2000; Kendall, et al., 2008; Silverman et al., 1999). CBT is an effective treatment, with benefits evident even 6 to 7 years after treatment (Barrett et al., 2001; Kendall et al., 2004). Family and individual CBT generally are equally effective (Kendall et al., 2008). Medication also may help. Imipramine in combination with CBT may be more effective in treating school refusal than therapy alone (Bernstein et al., 2000), and Luvox helps mixed anxiety in children (RUPP Anxiety Group, 2001). Both clomipramine and SSRIs also are effective in treating children with obsessive-compulsive disorders (Rapoport & Swedo, 2002), although exposure and response prevention, perhaps in combination with medication, still is the treatment of choice for children with OCD, as it is for adults (March et al., 2004).

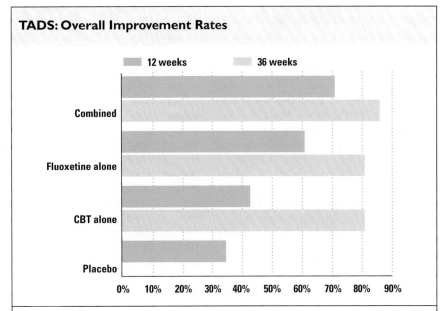

TADS: Overall Improvement Rates

Legend: ■ 12 weeks ■ 36 weeks

- Combined
- Fluoxetine alone
- CBT alone
- Placebo

(x-axis: 0% 10% 20% 30% 40% 50% 60% 70% 80% 90%)

FIGURE 16–10 The Treatment of Adolescents with Depression Study (TADS) found that combined fluoxetine and CBT significantly accelerated treatment response (at 12 weeks) compared to all other treatments. Fluoxetine alone worked significantly faster than CBT alone or placebo. No differences were found at 36 weeks. Moreover CBT, alone or combined with medication, reduced suicidality (not shown) compared to medication alone.

Sources: TADS (2004, 2007)

Course and Outcome Until recently, psychologists believed that children "outgrew" internalizing problems. Prospective research demonstrates, however, that some internalizing disorders persist over time. Specific fears tend to be relatively short-lived, but more complex disorders, such as depression (Harrington et al., 1990; Kovacs et al., 1984) and obsessive–compulsive disorder (March, Leonard, & Swedo, 1995), are likely to continue from childhood into adolescence and adult life. Childhood depression also predicts a sixfold increase in the risk for suicide in young adults (Harrington, 2002). Thus the prognosis is not optimistic for a child who has a full-blown mood or anxiety disorder, and the need to develop more effective treatments is pressing.

Do antidepressants lower or raise adolescents' suicidal risk?

Suicidality and Antidepressant Drugs

Antidepressants increased the risk compared to placebo of suicidal thinking and behavior (suicidality) in children, adolescents, and young adults in short-term studies of major depressive disorder (MDD) and other psychiatric disorders. Anyone considering the use of [Insert established name] or any other antidepressant in a child, adolescent, or young adult must balance this risk with the clinical need. Short-term studies did not show an increase in the risk of suicidality with antidepressants compared to placebo in adults beyond age 24; there was a reduction in risk with antidepressants compared to placebo in adults aged 65 and older. Depression and certain other psychiatric disorders are themselves associated with increases in the risk of suicide. Patients of all ages who are started on antidepressant therapy should be monitored appropriately and observed closely for clinical worsening, suicidality, or unusual changes in behavior. Families and caregivers should be advised of the need for close observation and communication with the prescriber. [Insert Drug Name] is not approved for use in pediatric patients. [The previous sentence would be replaced with the sentence, below, for the following drugs: Prozac: Prozac is approved for use in pediatric patients with MDD and obsessive compulsive disorder (OCD). Zoloft: Zoloft is not approved for use in pediatric patients except for patients with obsessive compulsive disorder (OCD). Fluvoxamine: Fluvoxamine is not approved for use in pediatric patients except for patients with obsessive compulsive disorder (OCD).] (See Warnings: Clinical Worsening and Suicide Risk, Precautions: Information for Patients, and Precautions: Pediatric Use)

◀ On October 15, 2004, the U.S. Food and Drug Administration (FDA) ordered drug companies to place a "black box" warning on their labels raising concerns about antidepressants increasing suicidality among adolescents. The warning caused a decline in prescriptions, but whether that is a good or bad outcome is uncertain, as there is conflicting information on the relation between antidepressants and suicidal behavior.

GETTING HELP

After reading this chapter, you might be wondering about your own mental health during your childhood. If so, your first reaction, as always, should be to caution yourself about the "medical student's syndrome": the tendency to diagnose yourself with every new disorder as you learn about it. Most psychological disorders are on a continuum with normal behavior, and most of us struggle at some time or other with a short attention span, restlessness, difficulty in learning, or moodiness. Still, we urge you to consider getting help if you are deeply concerned that you may have ADHD, a learning disorder, or long-hidden depression. Or perhaps you are struggling to come to grips with a very difficult childhood experience, anything from your parents' divorce to abuse. A first step could be to contact your college's mental health or counseling center. Or you may want to begin by talking with an advisor, professor, or dean at your school. Many schools also have evaluation centers that offer testing for learning disabilities or other academic-related problems.

Instead of wondering about yourself, you may be concerned about a younger brother or sister, or perhaps a child you are working with as a volunteer. If so, you may want to begin your search for information and help at the Web site of the National Institute of Child Health and Human Development. An excellent book for parents or teachers or student volunteers working with children with attention-deficit/hyperactivity disorder is Russell Barkley's *Taking Charge of ADHD*. For dealing with children who have ODD or other behavior problems, or simply for help with managing children, Rex Forehand and Nicholas Long's book *Parenting the Strong-Willed Child* offers a lot of sound, practical advice. Martin Seligman's engaging book *The Optimistic Child* focuses on the prevention of depression in children. Katharine Manassis' *Keys to Parenting Your Anxious Child* offers helpful advice about dealing with children who are anxious but not necessarily suffering from an anxiety disorder.

Playing a game with children is something else you can do to help them (and you) to understand their feelings. The Feelings Company sells therapeutic games online; simply looking through the games may give you some creative ideas. For example, on your own or together with your young friend, you could make up cards with different feeling words (sad, mad, scared), facial expressions, or leading questions (When was the last time you felt really, really sad?).

What if you know a child or an adolescent who you think might need professional help? If the young person has confided in you, that's a great start. You can do a lot by being a caring friend or sibling and a good role model. But you also want to encourage a child with an internalizing problem to confide in a parent—if not about the details of the problems, at least about the child's interest in getting help. Or you may know a parent who is looking to find help for a child with an externalizing disorder. In either case, asking for names from a teacher or school counselor is a good place to start. In fact, the child's school may be able to—or required to—provide free services for a troubled student. Another option is the child's pediatrician, who can prescribe medication if appropriate, or make a referral to a mental health professional.

■ SUMMARY

Psychological problems that arise more commonly among children than adults are listed in the DSM-IV-TR category "Disorders Usually First Diagnosed in Infancy, Childhood, or Adolescence." **Externalizing disorders** create difficulties for the child's external world, where children fail to control their behavior according to the expectations of others. **Attention-deficit/hyperactivity disorder (ADHD)** is particularly noticeable in school and is characterized by inattention, overactivity, and impulsivity. **Oppositional defiant disorder (ODD)** is characterized by negative, hostile, and defiant behavior and is also common among school-aged children. **Conduct disorder (CD)** is similar to ODD, except the rule violations are much more serious and it is more common among adolescents than younger children.

Internalizing disorders primarily affect the child's internal world, for example, excessive anxiety or sadness. DSM-IV-TR does not include a list of internalizing disorders but instead notes that children may qualify for many "adult" diagnoses, such as anxiety or mood disorders. DSM-IV-TR does include 26 additional childhood disorders, such as **learning disorder** and **separation anxiety disorder.** Some of these disorders are relatively rare; other categories are questionable in terms of their status as "mental disorders."

At least 12 percent of the 63 million children living in the United States suffer from a mental disorder. Boys are more likely to have externalizing problems during childhood, but girls have more internalizing in adolescence and early adult life. Family adversity is an important risk factor for externalizing problems. Teen suicide rates surged until recently but have declined over the last few years.

Parents are most effective when they are **authoritative:** loving and firm in disciplining their children. **Coercion** is a parenting problem that occurs when parents reinforce children's misbehavior by giving in to their demands. Conflict and inconsistent discipline are other parenting problems that may arise when parents are unhappily married or divorced. Other social factors that contribute to externalizing problems include television violence, deviant peer groups, poverty, and societal attitudes. The etiology of internalizing disorders in children has been studied inadequately but may involve problems with attachments.

Biological factors in ADHD include **temperament,** neuropsychological abnormalities, and especially genetics. Genetics also contribute to ODD and CD and may also affect children's reactions to difficult life experiences. Lack of self-control, a tendency to overattribute aggressive intentions to others, and less developed moral reasoning are some of the psychological characteristics related to externalizing disorders. Insecure working models of attachment or problems with emotion regulation may foreshadow the development of internalizing problems.

The most promising treatments for externalizing disorders include **psychostimulants** for attention-deficit/hyperactivity disorder, **behavioral family therapy** for oppositional defiant disorder, and multisystemic family therapy for conduct disorders and **juvenile delinquency.** Few treatments for anxiety or mood disorders (including widely used antidepressants) have been developed or tested specifically for children, but recent research shows that cognitive behavior therapy and perhaps some medications can help children's anxiety disorders. The continuity of both externalizing and internalizing disorders from childhood to adult life is one reason psychologists need to develop more effective treatments for troubled children.

THE BIG PICTURE CRITICAL THINKING REVIEW

Can you be "a little bit ADHD?"

You cannot be "a little bit pregnant," but you *can* be "a little bit ADHD." Why is this important? People tend to think of "genetic" as meaning you have a "gene for" a given condition, but like most mental disorders, most cases of ADHD appear to involve many genes. (SEE PAGE 507)

How does parental love affect parental discipline?

Parental discipline is sometimes mistakenly viewed as the opposite of loving children, but warm parent–child relationships make discipline both less necessary and more effective. (SEE PAGE 508)

Are psychostimulants overused?

Psychostimulants are an inexpensive and effective treatment, but there is no bright line between normal and abnormal behavior in diagnosing ADHD. Thus, it is reasonable to ask whether we are overdiagnosing ADHD and overmedicating schoolchildren. (SEE PAGE 514)

Does DSM-IV-TR include too many childhood "disorders?"

Beginning with DSM-III, too many "disorders" that are not in fact mental disorders were listed in the DSM. (SEE PAGE 523)

Do antidepressants lower or raise adolescents' suicidal risk?

Evidence that antidepressants increase suicidality led the FDA to place a "black box" warning on the medications. Prescriptions declined significantly as a result, but adolescent suicide *increased* during this time. (SEE PAGE 527)

■ KEY TERMS

anxious attachment **525**
attention deficit **500**
attention-deficit/hyper-
  activity disorder
  (ADHD) **501**
authoritative parenting **508**
behavioral family therapy
  (BFT) **514**

coercion **508**
conduct disorder
  (CD) **503**
developmental
  deviation **521**
developmental norms **496**
developmental
  psychopathology **496**

emotion regulation **526**
encopresis **523**
enuresis **523**
externalizing
  disorders **497**
hyperactivity **500**
internalizing disorders **497**
juvenile delinquency **504**

learning disorders
  (LDs) **521**
oppositional defiant
  disorder (ODD) **501**
psychostimulants **511**
recidivism **516**
representative sample **505**
resilience **526**

school refusal **520**
separation anxiety **520**
separation anxiety
  disorder **520**
socialization **508**
status offense **504**
temperament **506**
time-out **509**

ADJUSTMENT DISORDERS AND LIFE-CYCLE TRANSITIONS

This chapter focuses on adjustment disorders and problems in living that frequently cause people to seek guidance from a mental health professional. The topics we consider are *not* mental disorders, although individual psychological problems, for example, depression, may result from—or cause—problems in living. Young adults frequently want a therapist's perspective on struggles associated with becoming an adult, for example, sorting out values and goals, family issues, or relationship concerns. In midlife, many people seek help for conflicts that arise from an unhappy marriage, a divorce, or lifestyle choices. Older adults sometimes consult therapists about adjusting to later life, including dealing with retirement, loneliness, and bereavement.

OVERVIEW

In fact, one out of every four people in psychotherapy does *not* have a mental disorder (Kessler et al., 1994). Many otherwise well-functioning people seek treatment due to their *psychological pain,* upsetting but normal emotions that can result from difficult life events, for example, hurt feelings, sadness, anger, or longing (Laumann-Billings & Emery, 2000; MacDonald & Leary, 2005; Panksepp, 2005).

How can we conceptualize the diverse issues that bring people into therapy but are not mental disorders? DSM-IV-TR uses two approaches. First is the diagnosis, *adjustment disorder,* the development of clinically significant symptoms in response to stress that are *not* severe enough to warrant classification as a mental disorder. Second is a list of *other conditions that may be a focus of clinical attention,* such as a "partner relational problem," "bereavement," and "phase of life problem."

Unfortunately, DSM only very briefly describes adjustment disorders and other conditions that may be the focus of treatment. There are some good reasons for this shortcoming. People face an array of life problems. Trying to list every possible problem in living can seem like an impossible task. And psychologists do not agree about classification systems. In fact, few mental health experts have attempted to classify problems in living or normal reactions to life stress. Certainly this enterprise is far behind our (imperfect) efforts to classify mental disorders.

Still, we have learned much about *adult development,* the fairly predictable challenges in relationships, work, life goals, and personal identity that occur during adult life. Several theorists divide adult development into three periods—early, middle, and later life. Consistent with this division, in this chapter we highlight three major **life-cycle transitions,** struggles in moving from one stage of adult development into a new one. The *transition to adult life* is a time for grappling with the major issues related to identity, career, and relationships. *Family transitions* in the middle years may include very happy events, like the birth of the first child, or very unhappy ones, like a difficult divorce. The *transition to later life* may involve major changes in life roles (e.g., retirement), grief over the death of loved ones, and more abstract issues that accompany the inevitability of aging and mortality. As an introduction, consider the following case study.

▼ Development continues throughout the adult life cycle. Stages of adult development often are marked by key transitions in family relationships and academic or work roles.

CASE STUDY Left for Another Man

Chuck M. was 51 years old when his wife told him she wanted a divorce. Chuck had been married for 27 years, and he was totally unprepared for her announcement. He knew that his marriage was not perfect, but he had thought of his wife's complaints as normal "nagging." Chuck was content in his lifestyle, and he could not fathom what his wife was thinking. After serving in the navy for 20 years, Chuck was collecting a pension and working as a technician for an electronics company. His two children were grown, the family was financially secure, and Chuck was planning to retire to Florida in another 10 or 15 years. His life was on the course he had set long ago.

At first, Chuck simply did not believe what was happening. His wife said that she had been unhappy for years, but she only recently got the courage to leave him. This account clashed with Chuck's view of their marriage. He openly wondered if the real problem was his wife's menopause, or what he called "her change of life."

Reality began to hit Chuck when his wife moved out of their house and into an apartment. Chuck's wife said that she wanted a friendly divorce, and she telephoned him a few times a week just to talk. Chuck did not want a divorce, but he worked hard to avoid conflict. He said that he wanted to avoid hard feelings. Although he saw no need for it, Chuck consulted a clinical psychologist at his wife's suggestion. She had been seeing a counselor and found their discussions helpful.

Chuck remained stoic during the first several therapy sessions. He freely discussed the events of his life and admitted that he now realized that he had taken his wife for granted.

He grudgingly acknowledged that he was a "little upset" and "pretty angry"

but he could not or would not describe his emotions with intensity or detail. Mostly, he wanted the therapist to help him to figure out what was wrong with his wife.

A few weeks later, Chuck's feelings came flooding out when his wife told him that she was in love with another man. Chuck raged to the therapist about how he felt used and cheated. He was stunned, but he was not going to let his wife get away with this. He immediately contacted a lawyer. He wanted to make sure that his wife "didn't get a dime" out of the divorce settlement. Chuck also called his children and told them all of the details about what had happened. He seemed bent on revenge. Chuck admitted that, in addition to anger, he felt intense hurt and pain: real, physical pain, as though someone had just punched him in the chest. When the therapist asked if any of these emotions were familiar to him, Chuck recalled his feelings when he was 17 years old. His father died suddenly that year, and Chuck remembered feeling intense grief over the loss. He had controlled his feelings at the time, so he was surprised by the strong emotions he now felt in recalling the unfortunate event over 30 years later. His current feelings about his marital separation reminded him a lot of his sadness at his father's death, but his present grief was more volatile and he was much more angry than before.

Chuck talked more about his intense loneliness and sadness as therapy continued over the next few months and it became clear that his marriage really was ending. He kept up his daily routine at home and at work, but he said that it seemed as if he were living in a dream. In the midst of his grief, he sometimes wondered if his entire marriage, his entire life, had been a sham. How could he have been so blind? Who was this woman he had been married to? What was he supposed to do with himself now?

Symptoms

Are Chuck's reactions typical "symptoms" of adjustment to divorce?[1] Life-cycle transitions differ greatly, and different people respond to the same event in different ways. Chuck's feelings may have little in common with other people's reactions to divorce, let alone with people who are experiencing other major life changes.

Still, there are some similarities across diverse life-cycle transitions. The psychologist Erik Erikson (1902–1994) highlighted *conflict* as a common theme. Erikson organized each of his eight stages of psychosocial development around a central conflict, or what he termed a *crisis of the healthy personality* (Erikson, 1959, 1980). According to Erikson, the conflict inherent in change creates both intrapsychic and interpersonal tension, as the comfortable but predictable known is pitted against the fearsome but exciting unknown.

We also view conflict as a commonality across different life-cycle transitions. By definition, transitions involve change, and conflict is a frequent consequence of change. Conflict is not necessarily bad; in fact, conflict may be necessary in order for change to occur. Nevertheless, conflict often is distressing and painful. During life-cycle transitions, interpersonal conflicts commonly occur in close relationships. Emotional conflicts include uncertain and difficult feelings. Cognitive conflicts often involve broad doubts about what Erikson (1968) called *identity*, our global sense of self.

Diagnosis

DSM-IV-TR includes two ways of classifying life issues that are not considered to be mental disorders but bring people to the attention of mental health professionals. **Adjustment disorders** involve

---

[1]We discuss normal reactions to life-cycle transitions in this chapter but use the terms *symptoms* and *diagnosis* for the sake of consistency.

TABLE 17–1 DSM-IV-TR Diagnostic Criteria for Adjustment Disorder
A. The development of emotional or behavioral symptoms in response to an identifiable stressor(s) occurring within 3 months of the onset of the stressor(s).
B. These symptoms or behaviors are clinically significant as evidenced by either of the following:
1. Marked distress that is in excess of what would be expected from exposure to the stressor
2. Significant impairment in social or occupational (academic) functioning
C. The stress-related disturbance does not meet the criteria for another specific Axis I disorder and is not merely an exacerbation of a preexisting Axis I or Axis II disorder.
D. The symptoms do not represent bereavement.
E. Once the stressor (or its consequences) has terminated, the symptoms do not persist for more than an additional 6 months.

Source: Reprinted with permission from the *Diagnostic and Statistical Manual of Mental Disorders,* Fourth Edition, Text Revision. Copyright © 2000 by the American Psychiatric Association.

clinically significant symptoms in response to stress, but the symptoms are not severe enough to warrant classification as a mental disorder (see Table 17–1). Adjustment disorders are similar to acute stress disorders and posttraumatic disorders, because stress causes all three conditions. However, an adjustment disorder can be a reaction to a stressor of *any* severity, not just traumatic stress.

DSM-IV-TR also contains a list of *other conditions that may be a focus of clinical attention,* sometimes referred to as "V codes"[2] (see Table 17–2). This manual offers only very brief descriptions of each problem. For example, here is the manual's entire coverage of *partner relational problem:* "This category should be used when the focus of clinical attention is a pattern of interaction between spouses or partners characterized by negative communication (e.g., criticisms), distorted communication (e.g., unrealistic expectations), or noncommunications (e.g., withdrawal) that is associated with clinically significant impairment in individual or family functioning or the development of symptoms in one or both partners" (p. 737). (And you thought relationships were complicated!) Because of such limited coverage, we focus on other approaches to life-cycle transitions.

Brief Historical Perspective

Erik Erikson (1959, 1980) highlighted that development does not end with childhood but continues throughout adult life. His theory of psychosocial development (see Table 2–5) in-

cludes four stages of adult development: (1) identity versus role confusion, (2) intimacy versus self-absorption, (3) generativity versus stagnation, and (4) integrity versus despair.

Erikson viewed *identity versus role confusion* as the major challenge of adolescence and young adulthood. The young person's goal is to integrate various role identities into a global sense of

TABLE 17–2 DSM-IV-TR Listing of Other Conditions That May Be a Focus of Clinical Attention*
Relational Problems
Relational problem related to a mental disorder or general medical condition
Parent–child relational problem
Partner relational problem
Sibling relational problem
Additional Conditions That May Be a Focus of Clinical Attention
Noncompliance with treatment
Malingering
Adult antisocial behavior
Child or adolescent antisocial behavior
Borderline intellectual functioning
Age-related cognitive decline
Bereavement
Academic problem
Occupational problem
Identity problem
Religious or spiritual problem
Acculturation problem
Phase of life problem

*The category also includes the subgroups of *psychological factors affecting medical conditions* (see Chapter 8), *medication-induced movement disorders* (see Chapter 13), and *problems related to abuse or neglect* (see Chapter 18).

Source: Reprinted with permission from the *Diagnostic and Statistical Manual of Mental Disorders,* Fourth Edition, Text Revision. Copyright © 2000 by the American Psychiatric Association.

[2]The term *V code* has no special meaning. It refers to the letter of an appendix in the International Classification of Disease where the codes were once located.

self. The resolution of the **identity crisis,** this period of basic uncertainty about self, provides the first complete answer to the question "Who am I?" In Erikson's view, the resolution of the identity crisis allows young adults to embark on a journey toward achieving long-term life goals.

According to Erikson, one life goal is to form an intimate relationship early in adulthood. *Intimacy versus self-absorption* centers on the conflict between closeness and independence. Self-absorbed people either become dependent in intimate relationships or remain aloof from others. True intimacy is a balance between closeness and independence.

Erikson's third crisis of adult life is *generativity versus stagnation.* Generativity is defined by accomplishments in middle adult life, including career and family achievements. People who stagnate may have both a family and a job, but they live their life without a sense of purpose or direction.

Erikson's last stage of psychosocial development involves the conflict between *integrity and despair.* People can look back on their lives either with a sense of accomplishment or despair and anger. Integrity comes from "the acceptance of one's one and only life cycle as something that had

to be and that, by necessity, permitted of no substitutions" (Erikson, 1963, p. 260). Despair comes from the impossible desire to change the past and from yearning for a second chance at life.

Contemporary Classification

Erikson focused on the psychological side of psychosocial development, whereas many contemporary approaches emphasize social relationships. Psychologist Daniel Levinson (1986) emphasizes three major (and many minor) transitions between broad "eras" or "seasons" in adult life. The *early adult transition* involves moving away from family and assuming adult roles. The *midlife transition*—often called a "midlife crisis"—is a time for becoming less driven and developing more compassion. The *late adult transition* is characterized by the changing roles and relationships of later life (see Figure 17–1).

All models of adult development must be considered with some caution. History, ethnicity, gender, culture, and personal values all influence what tasks are "normal" during the course of adult development. For example, Erikson assumed that normal adult development included forming an intimate heterosexual relationship and remaining in a lifelong partnership, ideas that may seem old fashioned given the diverse lifestyles and demographics of our times.

Another caution is that transitions may not be so predictable. Not everyone experiences an identity crisis during the transition to adult life, nor do all people have a midlife crisis when they turn 40. Women also confront different issues than men in physical aging, relationships, and values (Stewart & Ostrove, 1998). Still, the outlines offered by Erikson and Levinson capture broad commonalities in the experiences of a great many people. Most of us create **social clocks**—age-related goals for ourselves—and we evaluate our achievements to the extent that we are "on time" or "off time."

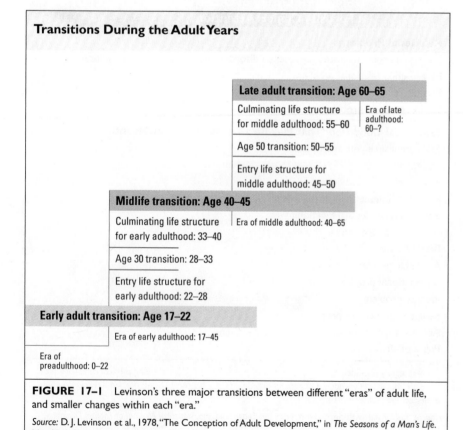

Transitions During the Adult Years

Late adult transition: Age 60–65

| Culminating life structure for middle adulthood: 55–60 | Era of late adulthood: 60–? |

| Age 50 transition: 50–55 |

| Entry life structure for middle adulthood: 45–50 |

Midlife transition: Age 40–45

| Culminating life structure for early adulthood: 33–40 | Era of middle adulthood: 40–65 |

| Age 30 transition: 28–33 |

| Entry life structure for early adulthood: 22–28 |

Early adult transition: Age 17–22

| Era of early adulthood: 17–45 |

Era of preadulthood: 0–22

FIGURE 17–1 Levinson's three major transitions between different "eras" of adult life, and smaller changes within each "era."

Source: D. J. Levinson et al., 1978, "The Conception of Adult Development," in *The Seasons of a Man's Life.* New York: Knopf.

THE TRANSITION TO ADULTHOOD

In the United States, the transition to adult life typically begins in the late teen years, and it may continue into the middle twenties or even later (Furstenberg, 2000). This is the time young adults assume increasing independence, and many leave their family home. By the end of the transition, most young adults have begun life roles in the central areas of adult development: love and work.

Symptoms of the Adult Transition

Erikson (1959/1980) argued that, in order to assume successful and lasting adult roles, young people need a **moratorium,** a time of uncertainty about themselves and their goals. In his words:

> The period can be viewed as a *psychosocial moratorium* during which the individual through free role experimentation may find a niche in some section of his society, a niche which is firmly defined and yet seems to be uniquely made for him. In finding it the young adult gains an assured sense of inner continuity and social sameness which will bridge what he was as a child and what he is about to become, and will reconcile his conception of himself and his community's recognition of him. (pp. 119–120, italics in original)

Identity Crisis Erikson focused on the *identity crisis* as the central psychological conflict during the transition to adult life. Identity conflicts are epitomized by the searching question "Who am I?" Erikson's view of identity has broad, popular appeal. In fact, a search for identity is a frequent theme in coming of age novels like Khaled Hosseini's *The Kite Runner* and movies such as *Almost Famous.* At this time of change, many of us feel unable to decide on a career, and our choices can be tentative and volatile. We question our values about religion, sex, and morality. We often doubt our ability to succeed in work or in relationships. Significantly, we also lack perspective on our experience. We feel as though we are confronting fundamental questions about who we are, not merely passing through a "stage."

During our twenties, we construct a "life story," an informal autobiography that gives our time of questioning and searching a consistent theme. By telling our life story, we make our new identity concrete and public (Pasupathi, 2001), and perhaps oversimplify the answer to the question "Who am I?" to make our narrative clear, concise, and compelling.

Changes in Roles and Relationships Other things also change during the transition to adult-

▲ Young people often explore new roles, relationships, and activities as they search for identity during the transition to young adult life.

hood. Young adults must make decisions about whether and where to go to college and what career paths to pursue. Such major decisions can permanently alter the course of life. Conflicts in parent–child relationships increase during adolescence, as young people interpret parental control as an infringement on their independence (Smetana, 1989). Young adults and their parents must negotiate new boundaries for their relationship, finding the right balance between autonomy and relatedness (Allen et al., 2002). Successfully finding this balance not only is a goal for beginning the transition to adult life, but it also predicts healthy individual and family adjustment in adult life (Bell & Bell, 2005).

The theories of the ego psychologist Karen Horney (1939) are helpful to understanding the conflicted relationships between parents and young adults, as well as other relationship difficulties throughout the adult life cycle. Horney theorized that people have competing needs to move toward, to move away from, and to move against others. *Moving toward* others fulfills needs for love and acceptance. *Moving away* from others is a way of establishing independence and efficacy. *Moving against* others meets the individual's need for power and dominance. According to Horney, relationship difficulties come from conflicts among these three basic needs. Young adults want their parents' support; they also want their own independence; and at the same time, they may also want to outdo their parents.

How is identity conflict a part of becoming an adult?

Conflicts often increase in relationships with peers as well as with parents during the transition to adult life. Young adults become less certain about their friends as they become less certain about themselves. In fact, a sense of certainty about personal identity is associated with both greater intimacy and less conflict in peer relationships, including loving relationships (Fitch & Adams, 1983). Another important change is that intimate relationships take on new meanings during the transition to adult life. Young adults seriously consider the possibility of making a lifelong commitment, a prospect that puts new pressures on love relationships.

The number of changing roles and relationships suggests that the search for self during the transition to adulthood may be less of an attempt to define a single "me" and more of a struggle to integrate new role identities with old ones. Given all the real and practical changes during the transition to adult life, it is not surprising that many of us ask: "Who am I?"

Emotional Turmoil Emotional conflicts also mark the transition to adult life (Paikoff & Brooks-Gunn, 1991). Research shows young people experience more intense and volatile emotions than adults do. In a clever series of studies, psychologists used "beepers" to signal adolescents and

"O.K., here I am in the fourth grade, but is that really what I want to be doing with my life?"

adults at various times during the day and night in order to assess their activities and emotional states. In comparison to adults, young people between the ages of 13 and 18 reported emotions that were more intense, shorter lived, and more subject to change (Csikszentmihalyi & Larson, 1984; Larson, Csikszentmihalyi, & Graef, 1980).

Anxiety and depression often increase somewhat during the transition to adult life, but in our view, many emotional conflicts stem from uncertainty about relationships. In particular, Horney's conflicting needs to move toward, away from, and against others may be experienced as emotional conflicts. That is, young people often experience the conflicting feelings of love (moving toward), sadness (moving away from), and anger (moving against; Sbarra & Emery, 2005). Their emotional struggles may stem from both conflicts among these competing feelings and the intensity with which young people feel each of these emotions.

Diagnosis of Identity Conflicts

DSM-III-R listed "identity disorder" as a mental disorder (!), but DSM-IV-TR wisely moved identity problems to the section on "other conditions that may be a focus of clinical attention." The manual includes a one sentence description: "This category can be used when the focus of clinical attention is uncertainty about multiple issues relating to identity such as long-term goals, career choice, friendship patterns, sexual orientation and behavior, moral values, and group loyalties" (DSM-IV-TR, 2000).

More detailed classifications are based on Erikson's concepts. For example, Marcia (1966) proposed several categories of identity conflict.

- **Identity diffusion:** Young people who have questioned their childhood identities but who are not actively searching for new adult roles.
- **Identity foreclosure:** Young adults who never question themselves or their goals but who instead proceed along the predetermined course of their childhood commitments.
- **Identity moratorium:** People who are in the middle of an identity crisis and who are actively searching for adult roles.
- **Identity achievement:** Young people who have questioned their identities and who have successfully decided on their own long-term goals.

Some research supports the validity of these categories (Marcia, 1994). For example, the percentage of students classified as identity achievers increases between the first and last years of college (Waterman, Geary, & Waterman, 1974), and the percentage continues to increase in the years after college graduation (Waterman & Goldman, 1976). Consistent with Erikson's theory, identity achievers also are less conforming and more confident in social interaction than others are (Adams et al., 1985; Adams, Abraham, & Markstrom, 1987). Still, the expected developmental progression from identity diffusion to identity achievement may not accurately describe many people's growth. Instead, the different identity statuses can reflect differences in personality and cultural expectations (Bosma & Kunnen, 2001).

Frequency of Identity Conflicts

You probably already know that everyone eventually becomes an adult. However, you may not know that takes *more* time to become an adult in the United States today, even in comparison to a few decades ago. The delay in the adult transition is indicated by average increases in the years young people spend in school, later age at first marriage, and lower rates of fertility (Furstenberg, 2000).

How many people experience significant distress during the transition to adult life? How many people never fully assume the responsibility of adult roles? To what extent are identity conflicts influenced by cultural expectations? Unfortunately, psychologists have few empirical answers to these crucial questions. Perhaps the most solid evidence pertains to cultural influences on identity formation. For example, research conducted during the 1960s, a time of social and political strife, particularly for college students, suggested that a new identity status was common during this historical period: *alienated identity achievement.* Young people with this status assumed an adult identity (they were identity achievers), but their definition of self was alienated; it conflicted with many values held by the larger society (Marcia, 1994). These people chose new adult roles that differed from traditional ones.

College students may be less alienated today than they were in the 1960s, but demographic data suggest more reasons for alienation among a different group of young adults. Today's alienated youth may be the "forgotten half"—young people who do not attend college and who often assume marginal roles in U.S. society. According to the William T. Grant Foundation's Commission on Work, Family, and Citizenship:

> . . . as young Americans navigate the passage from youth to adulthood, far too many flounder and ultimately fail in their efforts . . . . This is especially true of the 20 million non–college-bound young people we have termed the Forgotten Half. Opportunities for today's young workers who begin their careers with only a high school diploma or less are far more constrained than were those of their peers of 15 years ago. Typically, they cope with bleak job prospects by delaying marriage and the formation of their families. Many stop looking for work altogether. Disappointed in their ambitions and frustrated in their efforts to find a satisfying place in their communities, an unacceptably high number of young Americans give little in return to their families, their schools, and their work. (p. 1, 1988)

Young adults cannot form an enduring identity in their occupations if there are few attractive job opportunities. Identity diffusion may be a consequence of unresolved psychological conflicts, but delays in making commitments to work and family can also result from the limited opportunities available to some members of society.

Causes of Identity Conflicts

Psychological research suggests that the most successful young adults have parents who strike a balance between continuing to provide support

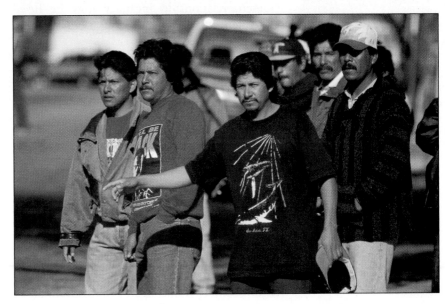

▼ Men on a street corner in Austin, Texas, hunting for day work paying $5–$10 per hour. Job prospects are limited for the "forgotten half," people who seek employment with only a high school education or less.

and supervision of their children and allowing them increasing independence (Hill & Holmbeck, 1986; Sartor & Youniss, 2002). Identity achievers often grow up in such families, whereas identity diffusers may have rejecting and distant families, and identity foreclosers may have overprotective families (Adams & Adams, 1989; Marcia, 1994). Young people from troubled families are more successful when they develop a close and supportive relationship with some other adult (Werner & Smith, 1982).

Is the absence of an identity crisis a problem that foreshadows identity conflicts later in life? Cross-cultural considerations suggest that in fact, the "storm and stress" of the transition to adult life is a consequence of the affluence, education, and independence available to young people in Western, industrialized societies (Arnett, 1999). In other cultures, people's life course may be determined by parental authority or economic necessity, neither of which allows for an identity crisis. In the not too distant past, people also assumed adult roles at much younger ages in the United States.

Does everyone have to have an "identity crisis"?

Gender roles also may influence identity formation. Erikson's theories have been criticized for focusing on men and work, while women often form identities based more on relationships than career (Gilligan, 1982). Men may form an identity *before* entering into lasting relationships with others. Women in traditional roles, however, may define themselves in terms of their significant relationships with other people; that is, their identity develops out of their relationships, not vice versa. For these women, relationship intimacy may be fused with identity rather than being a consequence of it (Dyk & Adams, 1990).

Treatment During the Transition to Adult Life

No research has been conducted on alternative treatments for people experiencing distress during the transition to adult life. Evidence indicates that many young adults seek therapy at this time, however, an observation bolstered by the frequent utilization of college counseling services. Treatment goals often include validating the young person's distress and helping him or her to understand and clarify difficult life choices. In addition, it may be helpful to "normalize"

the experience of identity conflict, that is, to conceptualize the individual's struggle as a part of the difficult but normal confusion resulting from the search for self. Finally, many clinicians suggest that supportive, nondirective therapy is a particularly appropriate treatment, because seeking autonomy is a recurring theme of the transition to adulthood. The following brief case illustrates the approach.

Brief Case **Study**
Samantha's Birth Mother

Samantha was stunned when she first came to see a clinical psychologist. She was a 21-year-old senior in college, and her birth mother had recently contacted her for the first time in Samantha's life. Samantha had not yet met her biological mother, and she was pretty certain that she did not want to. Samantha had always known that she was adopted, and she deeply loved her parents—parents, not adoptive parents, she insisted. Samantha had never yearned to meet her biological parents, and she did not welcome this unexpected intrusion in her life. She also did not want to do anything that would seem slightly disloyal to her parents, who also were surprised and distraught about the sudden appearance of Samantha's birth mother.

Apart from this recent shock, Samantha was a happy, well-adjusted, and successful young woman. She reported no history of emotional problems, talked at length about her close friends and boyfriend, seemed thoroughly attached to her parents, and was a successful psychology major who maintained a 3.4 GPA. Yet, she was understandably confused and upset about the appearance of her birth mother. She cried at length, but her overall affect was angry, not sad. She half shouted questions at her therapist like, "What right does this stranger have to intrude in my life?"

The therapist encouraged Samantha to explore and give voice to her many feelings. Samantha was uncomfortable being angry; instead, she felt guilty, frustrated, and confused. She also was afraid to meet her biological mother, in large part because she felt like she might be meeting part of herself. What if this woman were mean? Ugly? Unpleasant? What if Samantha didn't like her? What if she did? Who would her mother be then? Who would Samantha be?

With the psychologist's support and guidance, Samantha explored her feelings and her options in therapy and on her own. She read about the experiences of other adopted young people who had met their birth parents, and even chatted with some on the Internet. The sharing of their trying experiences "normalized" Samantha's feelings in a much more direct way than the psychologist's reassuring comments.

Eventually, Samantha decided that she did want to meet her birth mother after all. Despite her initial apprehension, Samantha was exuberant after the meeting. Samantha *liked* her birth mother, who was apologetic, sad, eager to get to know Samantha, but understanding of Samantha's ambivalent feelings and not at all pushy. Moreover, Samantha's mother, like Samantha herself, was relieved when the known proved to be far less frightening than the unknown. Samantha ended therapy before she had figured out who she was—now. Still, she was confident that she was going to be able to answer that question.

FAMILY TRANSITIONS

Family transitions typically involve the addition or loss of members of a family household, and include transitions to marriage, parenting, and the *empty nest*—the adjustment that occurs when adult children leave the family home. Divorce and remarriage also are common family transitions in the United States today, an observation that underscores the fact that families extend beyond the boundaries of one household.

Social scientists often conceptualize family change in terms of the **family life cycle**—the developmental course of family relationships throughout life. Table 17–3 outlines one view of the family life cycle. This outline, like most, focuses on major changes in children's developmental status. Shifts in children's development create marked changes not only for children but also for families. Of course, the developmental tasks are not the same for all families. Childless families, single-parent families, divorced families, remarried families, gay and lesbian families, and extended family groups all face unique obstacles and opportunities, as do families of different ethnic backgrounds.

Symptoms of Family Transitions

All family transitions are characterized by change—changes in time demands, changing expectations, and changes in love and power in family relationships. Early in marriage, newlyweds negotiate expectations about time together, emotional closeness, and who will assume authority and responsibility for performing different tasks inside and outside the household. The roles that couples assume early in their marriage often set a pattern that lasts a lifetime. Still, marital roles must be renegotiated when children are born. Children place numerous demands on each partner's time, energy, and patience. And although it is a joyous event, the birth of the first

TABLE 17–3	The Family Life Cycle
STAGE	**FAMILY DEVELOPMENTAL TASKS**
1. Married Couple	Establishing a mutually satisfying marriage; adjusting to pregnancy and the promise of parenthood; fitting into kin network
2. Childbearing	Having, adjusting to, and encouraging the development of infants; establishing a satisfying home for both parents and infants
3. Preschool Age	Adapting to the critical needs and interests of preschool children in stimulating, growth-promoting ways; coping with energy depletion and lack of privacy as parents
4. School Age	Fitting into the community of school-aged families in constructive ways; encouraging children's educational achievement
5. Teenage	Balancing freedom with responsibility as teenagers mature and emancipate themselves; establishing postparental interests and careers
6. Launching Center	Releasing young adults into work, military service, college, marriage, and so forth with appropriate rituals and assistance; maintaining a supportive home base
7. Middle-Aged Parents	Rebuilding the marriage relationship; maintaining kin ties with older and younger generations
8. Aging Family Members	Coping with bereavement and living alone; closing the family home or adapting to aging; adjusting to retirement

Source: E. M. Duvall and B. C. Miller, 1985, *Marriage and Family Development*, p. 62, New York: Harper & Row. Copyright © 1985 by Pearson Education. Reprinted by permission of Allyn and Bacon, Boston, MA.

child also challenges the marital relationship. A spouse's needs may become second priority to the demands of parenting, and the birth of children also confronts young adults with the substantial dilemma of choosing between priorities in work and family (Cowan & Cowan, 1992).

As children grow older, parents must gradually allow their relationships with their children to change in order to meet the children's developmental needs. Maintaining warmth while loosening the reins of control is the overriding theme. When children leave the family home, adults must discover or rediscover interests inside their marriage and outside the home. These patterns are again altered by the birth of grandchildren, retirement, and other family transitions of later life.

Family Conflict Increased family conflict is a common consequence of changing family relationships. The increase in conflict is illustrated by

"Do you want to tell him he's taking all the fun out our marriage or shall I?"

research on the relationship between children's age and parents' marital satisfaction. On average, marital satisfaction declines following the birth of the first child and does not rise again until the family nest begins to empty (Rutter & Rutter, 1993).

Family members may fight about hundreds of different issues. However, psychologists generally have been more concerned with the process than with the content of family conflicts. One analysis suggests that all disputes during family transitions ultimately involve either power struggles or intimacy struggles. *Power struggles* are attempts to change dominance relations, whereas *intimacy struggles* are attempts to alter the degree of closeness in a relationship (Emery, 1992).

Increased conflict may be a normal part of family transitions, but conflict creates great difficulties for some families. One of the most consistent findings in the study of family interactions concerns the **reciprocity,** or social exchange, of cooperation and conflict (Bradbury, Fincham, & Beach, 2000; Gottman & Notarious, 2000). Family members who have happy relationships reciprocate each other's positive actions, but they overlook negative behavior. A grouchy remark is dismissed as part of a "bad day," whereas a compliment is readily returned. In contrast, families with troubled relationships are caught in negative cycles of interaction. They ignore positive initiations but reciprocate negative ones. An unhappily married wife might ask her husband to stop reading the paper during dinner, and instead of putting the paper down, he puts her down. In far too many families, such conflict can escalate into family violence (Cordova et al., 1993).

A particular problem in marital conflict is the *demand* and *withdrawal* pattern, where the wife (more commonly) becomes increasingly demanding and the husband withdraws further and further. Conflicts go unresolved, and the couple's relationship grows increasingly distant. Evidence indicates that demand and withdrawal interactions predict future marital dissatisfaction, especially among women (Heavey, Christensen, & Malamuth, 1995). Other evidence indicates that conflicts in troubled families are more likely to continue over time and to spill over into other family relationships (Margolin, Christensen, & John, 1996). For example, marital conflicts may lead to fights between parents and children, as the children become another focus of an ongoing marital dispute.

Emotional Distress Whether family conflict is expressed through explosive outbursts, constant bickering, or the "silent treatment," fighting often causes emotional distress for all family members. Venting a little anger can be a relief, but ongoing conflict and anger can become all consuming. Moreover, anger often is an "emotional cover-up" for the angry individual, masking deeper hurts including loneliness, pain, longing, and grief (Emery, 2004; MacDonald & Leary, 2005).

Anger also affects other people, including the person the anger is directed toward—and bystanders too. Of course, some conflict is natural, even constructive during family transitions. We solve problems by working through our differences. Interestingly, happily married couples tend to blame their marital disputes on difficult but temporary circumstances. They "get over it." Unhappily married couples blame their partner's personality, however, a recipe for *not* solving problems (Bradbury & Fincham, 1990). In fact, the use of the pronoun "you" in couples' interaction predicts marital unhappiness, while the use of the pronoun "I" predicts greater satisfaction (Simmons et al., 2005).

Unresolved conflicts can lead to emotional problems (Whisman, Sheldon, & Goering, 2000). Ongoing family conflict, particularly marital conflict, is closely linked with depression, especially among women (Beach, Sandeen, & O'Leary, 1990). Parental conflict also predicts increased psychological problems among children (Emery, 1999). Emotional turmoil also is a painful part of separation and divorce, as we saw in the case of Chuck M. Emotional pain also is perhaps the most significant, ongoing consequence of divorce for children, a problem that even resilient young people report even many years after their parents' divorce (Laumann-Billings & Emery, 2000).

Cognitive Conflicts Family transitions also can set off new identity conflicts. Our identities often are closely linked with our family roles, and changes in those roles can cause us to doubt ourselves in significant ways. Our quest for a new sense of self can center on the question, "Who am I—now?" A divorce, for example, may challenge a woman's identity as wife and mother or a man's identity as a husband and father. A recently divorced adult no longer is a husband or a wife. They also may feel like a failure as a father or mother, and may question their success, or goals, for other life roles. In short, a crisis of identity is not limited to the adult transition, to turning 40, or for that matter, to divorce. Getting married, becoming a parent, infertility, or the empty nest also may trigger doubts that lead to a new search for a new sense of self.

Family transitions also confront us with an unavoidable, fundamental conflict between *acceptance and change* (Christensen et al., 2006). Our ability to mold our children, parents, partners, or ourselves is not limitless. If we want to maintain harmony and happiness in our families (and in ourselves), we must learn to accept those things we cannot change in our loved ones.

Diagnosis of Troubled Family Relationships

Some theorists have argued that we need to classify troubled relationships not just individuals (Beach et al., 2006). In fact, one major consideration for DSM-V has been whether to include diagnoses for "relational disorders," for example, "marital conflict disorder without violence" or "parent–child abuse disorder" (Heyman & Slep,

▲ Interpersonal conflict and emotional distress often accompany difficult family transitions.

2006). Reflecting the broad importance of family relationships, other possible relational disorders might replace individual diagnoses. For example, some individual psychological disorders of childhood, such as the externalizing disorders, might be replaced with relational diagnoses, since ineffective parenting is a critical component of these child behavior problems (see Chapter 16). According to this reasoning, psychological problems do not reside within the individual but, rather, in the individual's relationship with his or her social world.

Family transitions can be classified according to the major issue the family is facing, as the DSM-V study committee proposed. However, this approach provides little information on particular patterns of problematic interaction. An example of a dysfunctional interaction pattern is *scapegoating,* where one family member is blamed for all of a family's troubles. Figure 17–2 portrays one boy's view of his role as a family scapegoat. The concept of scapegoating and its function are akin to the idea of having a "common enemy." In international relations, common enemies can create alliances between former enemies, as occurred in World War II when the United States and the Soviet Union joined forces in opposing Nazi Germany. Similarly, scapegoating in families might unite unhappily married parents in blaming their difficulties on a troubled child.

A few theorists have developed listings of patterns like scapegoating or other *interpersonal diagnoses,* classifications of troubled close relationships (Group for the Advancement of Psychiatry, 1995;

Miguel's "Sculpture" of His Family

FIGURE 17–2 Miguel arranged family members in this way when asked to make a "sculpture" of his family during a family therapy session. Miguel put himself behind the table and apart from his siblings and parents, a clue to his status as the family scapegoat.

Source: Illustration by Gaston Weisz, p. 76, "Miguel's Sculpture of His Family" from HANDBOOK OF STRUCTURED TECHNIQUES IN MARRIAGE AND FAMILY by R. Sherman and N. Fredman. Copyright © 1986. Courtesy of Dr. Gaston Weisz, NYS Licensed Psychologist, Adelphi University, University of Phoenix Online.

McLemore & Benjamin, 1979). Conceptually, we find this approach appealing. However, efforts to classify troubled relationships are only in very early stages of development, and need much more refinement before we can expect them to be included in the DSM.

Annual U.S. Divorce Rates per 1,000 Population 1867–2000

FIGURE 17–3 U.S. divorce rates have risen for over 100 years. The steep rise since the 1960s has reached a plateau, but the apparent recent decline is really due to increases in cohabitation and nonmarital childbearing.

Source: R. E. Emery, 1999, *Marriage, Divorce, and Children's Adjustment*, 2nd ed., p. 13. Thousand Oaks, CA: Sage. Copyright © 1999. Reprinted by permission of Sage Publications, Inc.

Frequency of Family Transitions

Some family transitions are so important that the U.S. Census Bureau and other federal agencies regularly collect information on their frequency. For example, surveys with nationally representative samples clearly indicate that over 90 percent adults in the United States get married during their adult lives. Age at first marriage has increased by about five years, however, rising from the early to the later 20s over the last several decades. And about half of all couples today cohabit before marriage (Cherlin, 1992). About five out of every six married women in the United States bear a child, but childbirth increasingly is taking place outside marriage. In 2005, 36.9 percent of births were to unmarried mothers, including 69.9 percent of births to African American mothers, 48.0 percent for Hispanic mothers, and 25.3 percent for white mothers. Contrary to popular perception, nonmarital births to teenagers are declining. Births to teens comprised 31 percent of nonmarital births in 1995, but fell to 23 percent in 2005 (Martin et al., 2007).

Although "happily ever after" may be the stuff of fairy tales, at any point in time most people report their marriage as happy. One national survey found that 69 percent of parents of school-aged children reported their marriage to be "very happy," 28 percent said it was "fairly happy," and only 3 percent admitted it was "not too happy" (Zill, 1978). "Fairly happy" may not be good enough, however. A recent national study found significant marital discord among 31 percent of couples (Whisman, Beach, & Snyder, 2008). The number of couples who are unhappy with their marriage at some point in time is surely much larger as martial satisfaction fluctuates through the family life cycle.

Divorce rates increased dramatically in the United States from the late 1960s to the early 1980s but stabilized and fell somewhat since then (see Figure 17–3). Some are heartened by the decline in divorce, but most of the drop is due to increases in nonmarital childbearing and cohabitation. Those people who are most prone to divorce are less likely to marry today. And estimates indicate that about 40 percent of all existing marriages will still end in divorce. Divorce is likely to be followed by remarriage, especially among whites. About three out of four whites and one out of two blacks remarry following a divorce. Many divorced adults, including divorced parents, cohabit before marriage or instead of remarrying (Emery, 1999).

Causes of Difficulty in Family Transitions

Most theories of the causes of difficulties in family transitions emphasize psychological and social factors. This is not surprising, since family life is an environment. However, it is also true that individuals make their own environments; thus environments are partially *heritable* (see Research Methods on page 544). Thus, we also must consider biological contributions to family transitions.

Psychological Factors Researchers often blame family difficulties on problems with *communication*. Family members must be able to discuss their feelings and conflicts in everyday life and especially during times of transition. Good communication includes both direct conversation and nonverbal behaviors that can convey subtle or even contradictory meaning. For example, think of the different meanings you can attach to a simple statement like "You look great today." Depending on your tone of voice, emphasis, and nonverbal gestures, the same statement might be an honest compliment, a sarcastic insult, a sexual invitation, or a disinterested platitude. Verbal and nonverbal communication difficulties clearly distinguish distressed from nondistressed family relationships (Gottman, 1994).

Communication Problems Based on his extensive studies of marital interaction, John Gottman (1994), a clinical psychologist and noted marital interaction researcher, has identified four basic communication troubles. He observed these patterns in studies of married couples, but these communication problems also occur between other intimate partners, parents and children, and even divorced parents:

- **Criticism** involves attacking someone's personality rather than his or her actions, for example, "You're boring!" instead of "Can we do something different?"
- **Contempt** is an insult that may be motivated by anger and is intended to hurt the other person, for example, "I never loved you!"

- **Defensiveness** is a form of self-justification, such as, "I was only trying to help, but I guess my feelings don't matter!"
- **Stonewalling** is a pattern of isolation and withdrawal, for example, verbally or nonverbally saying, "I don't want to talk about this any more!"

Family Roles Broader family roles also can contribute to distressed family relationships. Many people believe, for example, that pressures to fulfill traditional marital roles—the wife as homemaker and the husband as breadwinner—cause difficulties for some marriages. One study found that *androgynous* couples—husbands and wives who both scored high on measures of masculinity *and* femininity—had marriages that were happier and less distressed than more traditional unions (Baucom et al., 1990). Although nontraditional gender roles may lead to better long-term outcomes, androgyny may create more conflict early on. Androgynous couples must negotiate the terms of their unique relationship instead of assuming traditional roles, and doing so takes time, effort, and conflict resolution skills.

Social Factors Numerous other social and cultural influences in addition to gender roles also contribute to the development of marital and family distress (Karney & Bradbury, 1995). Poverty, unemployment, crowded living conditions, and limited social support all can cause substantial distress in family life. In fact, many family problems are societal concerns in the United States today. Teenage pregnancy, nonmarital childbirth, divorce, and family violence are pressing social issues, not just psychological ones.

Biological Factors Biological factors also contribute to problematic family transitions (Booth et al., 2000), which brings us to a central debate about individual and family distress: Does family conflict cause individual dysfunction, or do troubled individuals cause relationship problems? We have noted that people who have never been married, are divorced, or have conflicted marital relationships have more psychological problems than happily married partners. But this correlation has several potential explanations. Marital distress may cause psychopathology, or marital happiness might protect against its development. Or causality may work in the other direction.

People with emotional disorders may be less likely to get or stay married (South, Turkheimer, & Oltmanns, 2008).

Questions of interpretation stem from the fact that research only tells us that there is a correlation between family distress and individual psychopathology. And you know that correlation does not mean causation. One variable may be causing the other, or both may be caused by some third variable. A special case of this

RESEARCH METHODS Genes and the Environment

When behavior genetic researchers find that MZ twins have higher concordance rates than DZ twins for a particular characteristic, they rightly conclude that genes contribute to its development. Twin studies also yield important information about environmental contributions. Concordance rates for MZ twins would be perfect if a disorder were purely genetic, because MZ twins are genetically identical. Thus MZ concordance rates of less than 100 percent demonstrate environmental contributions to the development of a behavioral characteristic.

Because twin studies yield information about the contributions of both genes and environments, behavior geneticists have developed ways of measuring **heritability,** the relative contribution of genes to a characteristic. Defined more formally, heritability is the proportion of variance in a trait that is attributable to genetic factors. Researchers often estimate heritability with a statistic called the **heritability ratio,** which can be described according to the following simple formula:

Heritability ratio = Variance due to genetic factors / Total variance

where Total variance = Variance due to genetic factors + Variance due to environmental factors + Variance due to the interaction of genes and environment[3]

The heritability ratio is a useful summary when it is interpreted correctly. You should particularly note two cautions. First, any estimate of heritability is necessarily limited to the particular sample in a study. When a researcher finds a heritability of 50 percent for some trait, this does not mean that the trait has the same heritability in the population as a whole or that heritability ratios are unchangeable. In fact, heritability estimates do *not* reflect the range of environments that are *theoretically* possible. Consider this point. One political goal in the United States is to provide everyone with the same rich and fulfilling environment. If we ever achieved the goal of providing everyone with the identical environment, all differences between people would be caused by genetics. You can see this by setting the variance due to environmental factors to zero in the preceding equation. In this case, heritability always equals 1.0. Although there are dramatic and frightening exceptions, most contemporary environments vary relatively little from one another compared to what is possible in theory. This increases estimates of heritability (Stoolmiller, 1999).

The practical implication of this theoretical point is that environments may matter more than we are able to detect. Consider, for example, that the environmental variation found in today's research does not include historical changes that have produced notable increases in life expectancy, education, and material resources for the population as a whole. Thus estimates of heritability in today's samples may be high, in part because there is relatively limited environmental variation—notwithstanding ongoing social problems like poverty, racism, and sexism.

> ### Why do genes contribute to heritability more in consistently good environments?

The second caution about the heritability ratio is that genes and environments work together, not separately. Thus, dividing contributions into genetic and environmental components artificially separates them. For example, what is the appropriate heritability for PKU, a cause of mental retardation known to result from the pairing of two recessive genes *combined* with the ingestion of foods containing phenylalanine? PKU is not caused by some percentage of genes and some percentage of the environment. PKU is caused by a critical *gene–environment interaction.*

This brings us to another important point about genes and the environment. We think of family experiences as being purely environmental. However, behavior geneticists have emphasized that experience is not random (Scarr & McCartney, 1983). Rather, there is a **gene–environment correlation,** a nonrandom association between inborn propensities and environmental experience. The gene–environment correlation can be *active,* because different people seek out different environments. For example, risk takers constantly seek thrills, while risk-adverse people seek stable, predictable environments. Gene–environment correlations can also be *passive,* because parents provide children both with genes and a family environment. For example, genetically influenced impulsivity may make people both more likely to divorce and to pass on impulsive traits to their children. Because of gene–environment correlations, family transitions may be partly determined by biology.

Gene–environment correlations can be very important to recognize in trying to interpret the effects of environmental experiences. Because divorce does not occur at random, for example, children from divorced and married families differ in more ways than their parents' marital status. Thus, researchers who compare children from married and divorced families are comparing apples and oranges. Recent, genetically informed research suggests that this concern is more than theoretical. The internalizing problems found among children from divorced families can be explained by correlated genetic influences, while their externalizing problems are more likely to be true divorce consequences (D'Onofrio et al., 2006).

Genes and the environment are treated as separate in calculating the heritability ratio, but in real life they are connected through gene–environment correlations and gene–environment interactions.

---

[3]The variance due to environments can be further divided into shared and nonshared environmental components. An example of a shared environment is family income; an example of a nonshared environment is being the favorite child.

general issue is the *gene–environment correlation*, the likelihood that environmental experience is itself correlated with genetic background (see Critical Thinking Matters). We know from twin studies, for example, that even divorce is partly genetic (McGue & Lykken, 1992; D'Onofrio et al., 2006). This statement may seem startling—or foolish—when you first consider it, but if you pause to ponder this puzzle, it will begin to make sense. Divorce—or teen pregnancy or cohabitation or about any family event—do not occur at random. Empirical research, and common sense, tell us that these experiences are more likely when people differ in their background (for example, education and income), personality (for example, tendency toward risk taking or social conformity), and physical characteristics (for example, age at first menarche or physical appearance). To the extent that these background, personality, or physical characteristics are influenced by genes, the family experience associated with the characteristic also is correlated with those genes. That is, there is a gene–environment correlation.

A research example can illustrate the importance of recognizing gene–environment correlations. Jane Mendle and colleagues (2006) tested the well-established finding that girls who grow up with an unrelated male in their household (for example, a stepfather) reach menarche at a younger age than other girls. Researchers have struggled to explain this puzzling finding. For example, some have suggested this results from an evolutionary adaptation: Stressful family life causes early menarche because it contributes to the reproductive strategy (which is presumably is adaptive under condition of stress) of having many children and investing relatively little in their upbringing versus having only a few children and investing a great deal in their rearing (Belsky et al., 1991). You need not be concerned with the details of this theory, except for one point. The theory argues that being reared with an unrelated man causes early menarche.

Mendle and colleagues (2006) proposed an alternative explanation: A gene–environment correlation is responsible for the puzzling relation between growing up with an unrelated male in the household and early age at menarche. What is the genetic third variable? The *mother's* early age at menarche. We know that as a result of genetic influences, a mother's age at menarche strongly determines her daughter's age at menarche (which makes sense; Meyer et al., 1991). It also makes

sense, if you think about it, that a mother's age at menarche contributes to the likelihood that her daughter will grow up with an unrelated man in the household. How? Early maturing girls, in this case the mother, attract older men who are not particularly good long-term prospects. After all, these men are attracted to younger girls because of the girls prominent secondary sexual characteristics (early breast and hip development)—and surely for other bad reasons. As a result, young age at menarche is likely to be associated with relationship instability, and ultimately with your daughter growing up with an unrelated man in the household. Mendle and colleagues (2006) laid out this alternative logic, based on a possible gene–environment correlation but supported their reasoning in a study of thousands of twins and their children.

How is family experience partly genetic?

Researchers are only beginning to untangle all kinds of potential gene–environment correlations. Doing so is a challenging and exciting area of research. What you should know for now is this: It is undeniable that biological factors contribute to family experience. We also hope that consideration of this fact will cause you to think more deeply about what causes family distress—and about behavior genetic research (see Critical Thinking Matters on page 546).

Treatment During Family Transitions

Treatments for family conflict and distress include marital and family therapies and various community action projects designed to prevent family problems. In the following sections we introduce a few of these many and varied efforts.

Prevention Programs Programs designed to prevent marital distress have a long and informal history. Perhaps the most common efforts involve religious groups. Many religions encourage or require couples to attend counseling sessions or discussion groups about family life before marriage. These and secular marriage education programs lead to better communication and relationship satisfaction, but demonstrated benefits are limited to middle-income, white samples (Hawkins et al., 2008). Whether benefits translate to lower-income and minority groups is an important question for

CRITICAL THINKING MATTERS

A Divorce Gene?

Throughout the text, we have noted genetic contributions to various mental disorders. You may be a bit surprised, perhaps even taken aback, to learn that experience also is genetic. Divorce is one provocative example. Psychologists Matt McGue and David Lykken (1992) of the University of Minnesota found higher concordance rates for divorce among MZ than among DZ twin pairs in a sample of more than 1,500 twin pairs. In fact, the investigators calculated that the heritability of divorce was .525.

How could divorce be genetic? This is where critical thinking is, well, critical. Clearly, there is no divorce gene, but wait a minute. When you read that mood disorders or eating disorders were genetic, maybe you *did* think there was a gene for depression or bulimia. Just as you must do with divorce, you should think critically about *what mechanism* might make these mental disorders genetic.

> **If there is no divorce gene, how can divorce be genetic?**

One mechanism that might make divorce genetic is personality, at least that part of personality partially shaped by genetics—for example, a tendency toward thrill seeking or a relative insensitivity to social sanctions. But there are other possibilities. Maybe genes affect physical attractiveness or the age at menarche (Mendle et al., 2006). Physical appearance and early sexual maturation, in turn, may set a chain of events into motion: attention for something other than your good character, attracting less committed dates and eventual mates, and ultimately the increased risk of divorce. This would make divorce genetic, but not in the way you were probably thinking about what "genetic" means.

Today, "Genes" is a common answer to the question, "What causes mental disorders?" But this does not necessarily mean there is a gene for eating disorders, depression, and so on. Rather, the genetic mechanism might be indirect, affecting body type in the case of eating disorders and perhaps family experience in the case of depression. Critical thinking does not change the fact that mental disorders are influenced by genes. But critical thinking might help us to think more broadly, creatively, and we hope more accurately about possible genetic mechanisms.

research and for policy, as the U.S. government has tried to promote marriage and marital stability in recent years.

One best studied program is the Premarital Relationship Enhancement Program (PREP). PREP participants meet in small groups of couples, where they freely discuss their expectations about marital relationships, including difficult topics such as sexuality. Couples also learn specific communication and problem-solving skills as a part of the training. In one study, couples randomly assigned to participate in PREP maintained their marital satisfaction 3 years later, while the marital happiness of control couples declined during this time (Markman et al., 1988). Even 5 years after the intervention, PREP couples maintained their improved communication and reported lower rates of marital violence than control couples (Markman et al., 1993). Researchers reported similar benefits for a variation on the program implemented in Germany (Hahlweg et al., 1998).

The evidence on the success of the PREP is encouraging, but the systematic research conducted on the program is of broader importance. Formal and informal prevention programs have been developed to help family members at nearly every transition in the family life cycle. There are childbirth programs, parenting programs, and support groups for parents whose children are infants, preschoolers, school-aged, or teenagers. Courts have programs for helping parents cope with separation, divorce, and remarriage. Creativity in developing programs is not lacking. What is often missing, however, is systematic research on the effectiveness of prevention efforts.

▼ Many religious groups have long required couples to participate in counseling prior to marriage. Today, some government organizations are encouraging premarital counseling from religious figures, lay leaders, or therapists in the hope of strengthening marriage and reducing divorce rates.

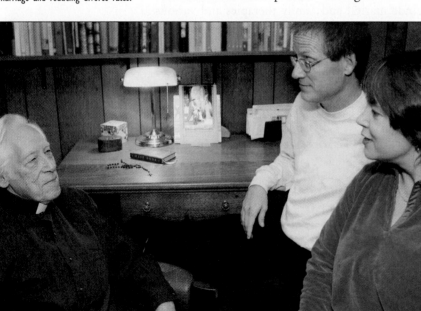

Couples Therapy and Family Therapy
Couples therapy and *family therapy* both focus on changing relationships rather than changing indi-

viduals (Gurman & Jacobson, 2002). The couples or family therapist acts as an objective outsider who helps family members to identify and voice their disagreements, work on improving their communication, solve some specific problems, and ultimately alter and hopefully enhance troubled family relationships. This very different approach to therapy is illustrated in the following brief case study.

Brief Case **Study**
Learning To Listen

Jan and Bill were seeking therapy for long-standing troubles in their marriage. Jan, a wife and homemaker, complained that Bill did not give her enough help with running the household or raising the couple's three children. More poignantly, Jan felt unloved because Bill did not seem to enjoy being around her and the children. Bill countered that he loved being with his children, but that Jan was a constant nag who did not appreciate the demands of his job as an insurance salesman. He also said that she was a "bottomless pit" in demanding his love and attention. The couple had been seen for several sessions when the following interaction occurred:

> **JAN:** Like you said, Bill and I were supposed to be working on a schedule so that he would only call on clients two evenings last week. But just like I knew would happen, Bill didn't follow through. (Jan begins to cry.) I just knew you wouldn't do it! Is that so much to ask? Couldn't you be home a few evenings during the week? Couldn't you at least tell me when you have to go out?
>
> **BILL:** (in a monotone) I got some new clients this week, and there's a sales push on. I couldn't reschedule. Next week will be better.
>
> **JAN:** Next week won't be any different! Or the week after that! You aren't going to change. Why should you? You have everything your way!
>
> **THERAPIST:** I can see you're upset, Jan, but let's give Bill a chance. Do you know your schedule for next week?
>
> **BILL:** Pretty much, but you never know.
>
> **THERAPIST:** Do you want to make a commitment to Jan right now about what nights you will be home in the evening next week?
>
> **BILL:** I suppose I can be home around six or so on Tuesday . . .
>
> **JAN:** You suppose! Go ahead and . . .
>
> **THERAPIST:** One second, Jan. OK, Bill. Tuesday is a start, but do you see what your tone of voice says to Jan?
>
> **BILL:** But she's always complaining about something! I said that I'd be home, OK? What else do you want me to do?
>
> **JAN:** I want you to want to be home.

> **THERAPIST:** Now we're getting to the real issue. Part of this is about schedules and time together, but part of this is about what these things mean. Jan, when it seems like Bill doesn't want to be around you and the kids, you feel unloved.
>
> **JAN:** That's what I just said. You heard me, but he didn't.
>
> **THERAPIST:** Bill, you feel controlled when Jan asks you about your work schedule. You have a lot to balance between work and home, and maybe you really don't want to be with Jan when you feel like she's forcing you to come home.
>
> **BILL:** That's exactly how I feel.
>
> **THERAPIST:** I want the two of you to talk with each other about these feelings. Then we will get back to work on the schedule that might help to solve some practical problems. Jan, tell Bill how you feel—and Bill, I only want you to listen to her feelings. Try to understand what she says. Don't worry about rebuttal. In a few minutes, we'll try this the other way around.

Several aspects of marital therapy are evident in this brief exchange. One goal was to help the couple negotiate tricky work and family schedules. Even an imperfect schedule might reduce some of the couple's conflict, because it would give them some clarity. Another goal was to break the couple's negative cycle of interaction by interrupting some fights, ignoring provocations, and encouraging Jan and Bill to talk about their own, deeper feelings. The discussion of feelings should be helpful in its own right. It also might allow the couple to develop a schedule in a way that would alleviate some hard feelings. If they could mutually agree on a plan, Jan would have one less reason to feel rejected, and Bill would have one less reason to feel controlled.

Cognitive Behavioral Couple Therapy Most research on marital therapy has examined cognitive behavioral approaches, the approach illustrated in the case of Bill and Jan. **Cognitive behavioral couple therapy (CBCT)** emphasizes the couple's moment-to-moment interaction, particularly their exchange of positive and negative behaviors, their style of communication, and their strategies for solving problems (Baucom et al., 2002). Systematic research comparing the effectiveness of CBCT versus no treatment indicates that marital therapy leads to significant improvements (Shadish & Baldwin, 2005). Still, approximately half of couples seen in CBCT do not improve significantly. Relapse at follow-up is also common, and other treatment approaches appear to be about as effective (Alexander, Holtzworth-Munroe, & Jameson, 1994).

There clearly is a need to expand on CBCT and perhaps integrate it with other approaches. Couple therapists increasingly focus on emotion, the core issue for Jan and Bill (Snyder, 1999), and the acceptance of differences that cannot be changed (Jacobson & Christensen, 1996). Emerging treatment research demonstrates the long-term importance of incorporating acceptance as well as change into couple therapy (Christensen et al., 2004; Christensen et al., 2006). There is also a need to extend research efforts to include treatments for other difficult family transitions, for example, coping with divorce (Emery, 1994).

▼ The transition to later life is not a time of despair for most people. Older adults who remain physically active and socially involved have better mental and physical health.

Treating Individual Problems with Couples Therapy or Family Therapy Couples therapy increasingly has been used not only to improve marriages, but also as an alternative to individual therapy in the treatment of psychological disorders, including depression, anxiety, alcoholism, and psychological disorders of childhood. In each area, research suggests that an improved marriage helps to alleviate individual disorders, particularly depression (Beach, Sandeen, & O'Leary, 1990; Jacobson, Holtzworth-Munroe, & Schmaling, 1989). These findings once again underscore the reciprocal nature of individual and family relationships. In some cases, successful marital therapy removes the cause of an individual spouse's psychopathology. In other cases, successful marital therapy enables well-adjusted spouses to understand and cope with their partner's psychological troubles.

THE TRANSITION TO LATER LIFE

Many people think of "old" as beginning at the age of 65, but aging and the transition to later life do not begin or end at any particular age. The aging transition extends over many years and includes a number of changes in appearance, health, family, friendships, work, and living arrangements. The nature, timing, and meaning of the transition also may differ for men and women.

Adults become increasingly aware of aging in their forties and fifties. Middle-aged men often worry about their physical performance in athletics and sex. Men also become more concerned about their physical health, especially as they learn of events like a friend's unexpected heart attack. Women also worry about their physical performance and appearance in middle age, but married women often are more concerned with their husbands' than with their own physical health. Men have a notably shorter life expectancy than women—7 years shorter on average. Thus, even as they encourage their husbands to follow good health practices, many middle-aged wives begin a mental "rehearsal for widowhood" (Neugarten, 1990).

Concerns about physical health increase for both men and women in their sixties, seventies, and eighties. Chronic diseases such as hypertension become common, all five sensory systems decline in acuity, and many cognitive abilities diminish with advancing age (Salthouse, 2004). All these physical changes occur gradually throughout adult life, but the decline in functioning accelerates, on average, around the age of 75. Major social transitions also take place during the later adult years. Most people retire in their early to late sixties, a transition that is eagerly anticipated by many people but dreaded by some. Whether retirement is seen as the end of a valued career or the beginning of a new life, it requires a redefinition of family roles as husbands and wives have more time and new expectations for each other. Parent–child relationships also change with age. Parents become more of a "friend" to children who are now adults themselves, while many older adults provide their children and grandchildren practical support and a sense of continuity in family life. As older adults move through their seventies and enter into their eighties, children who are now middle-aged themselves increasingly find themselves worrying about and caring for their parents.

Death is an inevitability that confronts all of us. With advancing age, we must face both the abstraction of our own mortality and specific fears about a painful and prolonged death. Bereavement is a part of life for older adults, as friends fall ill and die. Because of differences in life expectancy, women are particularly likely to become widows in their sixties, seventies, and eighties (see Figure 17–4).

Ageism

Older adults often confront a form of social prejudice known as **ageism,** a term that encompasses a number of misconceptions and prejudices about aging (Pasupathi, Carstensen, & Tsai, 1995). Young Americans, even mental health professionals, tend to view older adults as stubborn, irritable, bossy, and complaining. Some research does indicate that adults become more inwardly focused as they enter later life. Still, the major finding is that personality is consistent from middle age to old age (Magai, 2001). Some older adults *are* stubborn and irritable, much like they were as younger adults. Older adults experience the full range of human interests and concerns, and we must guard against forming stereotypes based on our prejudices or fears about aging.

Symptoms

We must be selective in reviewing typical experiences related to aging, because later life encompasses a large age range as well as numerous social

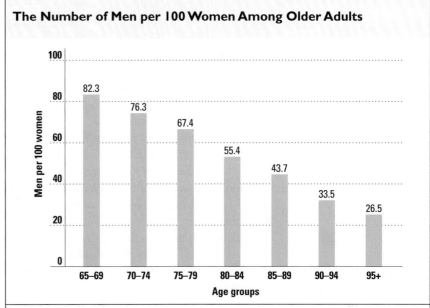

FIGURE 17–4   Women live longer than men; therefore, the ratio of men to women shrinks with increasing age.

Source: U.S. Bureau of the Census, 1996, "65+ in the United States," *Current Population Reports,* Series P23–190, pp. 2–10. Washington, DC: U.S. Government Printing Office.

and psychological transitions. We highlight only a few topics here, including changes in physical functioning and health; general psychological well-being, work, and relationships; bereavement and grief; and mental health.

Physical Functioning and Health Physical functioning and health decline with age, but the loss of health and vigor is not nearly as rapid as stereotypes suggest. Men and women can and do remain healthy and active well into their seventies and eighties. In fact, physical activity and physical health are among the better predictors of psychological well-being among older adults.

Menopause Menopause, the cessation of menstruation, is an important physical focus for middle-aged women. (Men do not experience a similar change in reproductive functioning.) Women in the United States have their last period at an average age of 51 years, although menstruation typically is erratic for at least 2 or 3 years prior to its complete cessation. Many women experience physical symptoms such as "hot flashes" during menopause, and some experience emotional swings as well. For example, they may find themselves crying for no apparent reason. Episodes of depression also increase during menopause.

Psychological adjustments to aging and the loss of fertility contribute to emotional volatility during menopause, but so do the physical symptoms that result from fluctuations in the female sex hormone **estrogen.** In fact, *hormone replacement therapy,* the administration of artificial estrogen, alleviates many of the adverse physical symptoms of menopause. The alleviation of symptoms, in turn, eases some of the psychological strains of menopause. Hormone replacement therapy also reduces the subsequent risk for heart and bone disease, but it is a controversial treatment because it simultaneously increases the risk for cancer.

Hormone replacement therapy has no direct effect on depression, which is unrelated to estrogen levels during menopause, or on other broad psychological consequences of the "change of life" (Rutter & Rutter, 1993). Some women struggle to redefine their identity as they face changes in their bodies, appearance, and family lives around the time of menopause. For others, menopause is *not* a trying time. They find the freedom from fear of pregnancy liberating, and enjoy the "empty nest." They value the time they now have for themselves and for their partners (Rutter & Rutter, 1993).

Sensation and Physical Movement Menopause is a rather "sudden" event in comparison to other physical changes that occur with age. For example, the functioning of all sensory systems declines gradually throughout adult life. Visual acuity declines slowly with age, as does the ability of the lens to accommodate from focusing on an object that is near to one that is far away. The eye also adapts to darkness or to light more slowly with age. Hearing loss also is gradual throughout adult life, particularly the ability to hear high tones. Sensitivity to taste, smell, and touch also decreases with advancing age. As with vision and hearing, however, declines in these senses typically are gradual until the seventies, when loss of sensitivity may accelerate notably (Fozard & Gordon-Salant, 2001).

The amount of muscle in our bodies also declines with age, but, like sensory function, the loss is gradual until advanced age. A 70-year-old retains 80 percent of his or her young adult muscle strength, but the loss may double in the next 10 years. Bone loss also occurs with advancing age, with women experiencing bone loss at twice the rate of men. After menopause, women are especially susceptible to the development of *osteoporosis,* a condition in which bones become honeycombed and can be broken easily. Many older adults develop other chronic illnesses, especially arthritis, cardiovascular diseases, cancer, diabetes, and sleep disorders (Longino & Mittelmark, 1996).

Life Satisfaction, Work, and Relationships
The fact that aging is accompanied by gradual declines in physical health does *not* mean that older adults experience similar declines in psychological well-being. In fact, older adults report more positive relationships and a greater sense of mastery over their environment than do adults who are young or in midlife. On the other hand, older adults report less of a sense of purpose in life and less satisfaction with personal growth in comparison to younger adults (Ryff, Kwan, & Singer, 2001). Perhaps this latter finding reflects that some older adults have trouble slowing down and adapting to less future-oriented goals.

Older adults also report greater satisfaction with their jobs than younger people, but this may be a result of self-selection. Older adults remain in a satisfying occupation, while younger adults struggle to find the right job. Most older adults view retirement positively, even though it can be a mixed blessing. Retirement leads to a loss of income and perhaps of status, and this can make retirement difficult for some older adults. On average, however, these costs are outweighed by the added benefits of increased leisure and freedom, especially for people with adequate financial resources (Kim & Moen, 2001).

Integrity Versus Despair Erik Erikson theorized that the conflict between integrity and despair is the central psychological struggle of the transition to later life. Many older adults do wonder about the meaning of their lives when they look back from the perspective of their later years. Identity conflicts also may accompany the changes that come from becoming a grandparent or retiring from a long-term occupation (Kaufman & Elder, 2003). Unfortunately, little research has been conducted on Erikson's conceptualization of the conflict between integrity and despair (see Reliving the Past).

Relationships People have more friendships as young adults than during later life, but the quality of relationships is more important than the

RELIVING THE PAST

Researchers have begun to study a common phenomenon among older adults: *reminiscence*—the recounting of personal memories of the distant past. Reminiscence, sometimes called *life-review*, may be helpful in facilitating adjustment during later life, and many senior centers offer life history discussion groups as a part of their services (Coleman, 2005).

All memories of the past are not equal, as suggested by Erikson's conflict between integrity and despair. Older adults may recall their journey through life with pride and acceptance or with disappointment and regret. As a way of studying how memories of the past can mark adjustment, the Canadian psychologists Paul Wong and Lisa Watt developed a taxonomy of six different categories of reminiscence.

Integrative reminiscence is an attempt to achieve a sense of self-worth, coherence, and reconciliation with the past. It includes a discussion of past conflicts and losses, but it is characterized by an overriding acceptance of events. *Instrumental reminiscence* involves the review of goal-directed activities and attainments. It reflects a sense of control and success in overcoming life's obstacles. *Transitive*

> **Is it healthy or unhealthy to relive the past?**

reminiscence serves the function of passing on cultural heritage and personal legacy, and it includes both direct moral instruction and storytelling that has clear moral implications. *Escapist reminiscence* is full of glorification of the past and deprecation of the present, a yearning for the "good old days." *Obsessive reminiscence* includes preoccupation with failure and is full of guilt, bitterness, and despair. Finally, *narrative reminiscence* is descriptive rather than interpretive. It involves "sticking to the facts" and does not serve clear intrapsychic or interpersonal functions.

Evidence indicates that integrative reminiscence and instrumental reminiscence are related to successful aging, whereas obsessive reminiscence is associated with less successful adjustment in later life (Wong & Watt, 1991). Other research similarly finds that reminiscence can be positively (focusing on communication or preparing for death) or negatively (reviving old problems, filling the void, or trying to maintain connections with the departed) related to better mental health (Cappeliez, O'Rourke, & Chaudhury, 2005). The next and needed step is to study whether reminiscence can be structured or guided in such a way that it helps older adults review and come to terms with their lives.

---

number (Antonucci, 2001). The presence of a supportive close relationship is an important predictor of psychological well-being during adult life. In fact, one reason why older adults have fewer friendships is because they become more selective in their companions. That is, older adults actively choose to spend their time with only the people they care for most, perhaps because they believe their time is limited and more precious (Carstensen, Isaacowitz, & Charles, 1999).

Family relationships strongly influence psychological well-being throughout the life span. Later in life, relationships with children become especially important, and in addition, sibling relationships often take on renewed practical and emotional importance (Cohler & Nakamura, 1996). The marital relationship is critical throughout life. If anything, marital satisfaction increases in later life, and conflicts become less embedded or intense. This, too, may be related to the foreshortened sense of time. The belief that "this may be the last time" encourages older adults to focus on the positive and overlook or forgive the negative (Carstensen, Isaacowitz, & Charles, 1999). Unfortunately, the loss of loved ones, including the loss of a spouse, is a fact of life for older adults, particularly for older women, as illustrated in the following case study.

Brief Case **Study**
Mrs. J's Loss

Mrs. Sylvia J. was 78 years old when she consulted a clinical psychologist for the first time in her life. Mrs. J. was physically fit, intellectually sharp, and emotionally vital. However, she remained terribly distressed by her husband's death. Eighteen months earlier, the 83-year-old Mr. J. had suffered a stroke. After a few weeks in the hospital, he was transferred to a nursing home, where his recuperation progressed slowly over the course of several months. According to his wife, Mr. J.'s care in the nursing home bordered on malpractice. He died as a result of infections from pervasive bedsores that he developed lying in the same position for hours on end. The staff was supposed to shift his position frequently in order to prevent bedsores from developing, but according to Mrs. J., they simply ignored her husband.

Mrs. J. was uncertain how to handle her grief, because she was stricken by many conflicting emotions. She had literally waited a lifetime to find the right man—she had married for the first time at the age of 71 after a long and successful career as a schoolteacher. She had been content throughout her life, but her marriage was bliss. She felt intensely sad over the loss of her husband, and she continued to make him part of her life. She would talk aloud to his picture when she awoke in the morning, and she visited his grave daily except when the weather was very bad.

Mrs. J. cried freely when discussing her loss, but she also chastised herself for not doing better in "getting on with her life." She had several female friends with whom she played bridge several times a week. Mrs. J. enjoyed the company of her friends, who also were widowed and who seemed more accepting of their losses.

A greater problem than acceptance was the intense anger Mrs. J. often felt but rarely acknowledged. She was furious at the nursing home, and she was vaguely considering legal action against the institution. During her career as a teacher, she had never tolerated incompetence, and the failures of the nursing home had robbed her of her happiness. She was confused, however, because her minister said that her anger was wrong. He said that she should forgive the nursing home and be happy to know that her husband was in heaven. Mrs. J. wanted to follow her minister's advice, but her emotions would not allow it. She wanted the psychologist to tell her if her feelings were wrong.

Clearly, it was not wrong for Mrs. J. to be distraught over her husband's death, but were some of her other reactions abnormal? Having constant thoughts of another person might seem obsessive in some circumstances, and talking out loud to a picture might indicate delusions or hallucinations. Mrs. J. was showing normal reactions to grief, however, as similar responses are common among other grief-stricken older people. Frequent thoughts of a loved one are a normal part of grief, and it also is normal for intense grief to continue for a year or two, or perhaps longer. But what about Mrs. J.'s anger? Whether she should forgive the nursing home or sue depends on many factors, of course, but she was not wrong—abnormal— for feeling angry. Evidence indicates that anger, too, is a common part of grief (Sbarra & Emery, 2005).

Is there a single, healthy way to grieve?

Grief and Bereavement **Grief** is the emotional and social process of coping with a separation or a loss. **Bereavement** is a specific form of grieving in response to the death of a loved one. The process of grieving in bereavement is com-

monly described as proceeding in a series of stages. For example, Elisabeth Kübler-Ross (1969) developed a popular model of bereavement in her work with terminally ill medical patients. She described their grief as occurring in five stages: (1) denial, (2) anger, (3) bargaining, (4) depression, and (5) acceptance.

Kübler-Ross's model is similar to Bowlby's (1979) four-stage outline of children's responses to separation or loss (see Chapter 16). Importantly, Bowlby's attachment theory offers an explanation for why someone might feel angry in the middle of intense sadness over a loss. Yearning and searching (his second stage of grief) is a pursuit of, and a signal to, the missing attachment figure—an attempt to bring about reunion. A child who is separated from a parent cries, screams angrily, and searches for the parent in order to get her or him back. Of course, a reunion is impossible following the death of a loved one, as bereaved people understand intellectually. But emotions are not rational, particularly at a time of loss.

Stage theories of grief have intuitive appeal, but research shows that few people grieve in a fixed sequence of stages. Rather, mourners vacillate among different emotions—for example, moving back and forth between sadness and anger (Sbarra & Emery, 2005). Many people apparently do not experience several of the stages described by Bowlby or Kübler-Ross, and still others show few observable reactions to bereavement—they suffer in silence. In short, although denial, sadness, and anger may be normal reactions to loss, there is no one "right" way to grieve, nor should people be forced to express their unexpressed grief. In fact, research generally indicates that *less* intense bereavement predicts *better* long-term adjustment to loss (Bonanno et al., 2005; Stroebe et al., 2002; Wortman & Silver, 2001).

In general, bereavement is more intense when a loss is "off time"—for example, when the loss of a mate occurs early in adult life or when a child dies before a parent (Cohler & Nakamura, 1996). There is no "good" time to lose a loved one, of course, but we are more prepared for the death of aged family members, and we often can find some solace in their long life.

Mrs. J.'s grief *was* a normal reaction to the loss of her husband, but there are cases where grief becomes problematic. Worden (1986) divided bereavement into normal, chronic, delayed, exaggerated, and masked grief. More generally,

▼ Grief is a part of life for older adults.

"complicated grief" has been proposed as a new diagnostic category (Bonanno et al., 2007; Shear et al., 2005). In our view, both normal and abnormal grief are critical topics for further study, but we believe that research is sufficiently developed to include a diagnosis for complicated grief in the DSM-V.

Mental Health With the exception of the cognitive disorders, mood and anxiety disorders are the most common emotional problems among older adults. Contrary to some stereotypes, however, later life is not a time of fear, disappointment, dejection, and despair. Affective disorders are less than half as common among older as among younger adults, and anxiety disorders also are less prevalent (Gatz & Smyer, 2001; Magai, 2001).

Despite the lower prevalence rates, psychological disorders are an important concern among older adults. This is especially true of depression, which may be more profound, lasting, and debilitating among older than younger adults. Suicide risk is a particular concern; adults over the age of 65 have the highest rate of completed suicide of any age group. The risk for completed suicide is notably higher among older white males, and, in fact, suicide is one of the top 10 causes of death among older adults (Koenig & Blazer, 1990). Many experts view the increase in suicide as a consequence not only of the emotional problems and adverse social circumstances, but also as a result of chronic pain, physical disease, and the prospect of a long terminal illness (Wrosch, Schulz, & Heckhausen, 2004). In fact, *rational suicide* is a controversial term for the decision some severely ill older adults make in ending their lives (Gallagher-Thompson & Osgood, 1997).

Even more controversial is *assisted suicide,* a hotly debated procedure where a medical professional helps terminally ill people to end their own lives. In the late 1990s, Oregon became the first, and as yet only, state where physicians can legally assist patients to hasten their death provided the patient is (1) over 18 years old; (2) a resident of Oregon; (3) diagnosed with a terminal illness with a life expectancy of 6 months or less; and (4) capable of making a reasonable decision (Rosenfeld, 2004). To date, the small number of legally assisted suicides in Oregon involved patients who were primarily older, white, well educated, and dying of cancer (see Table 17–4).

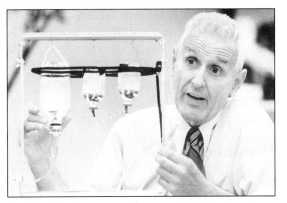

◄ Dr. Jack Kevorkian with his suicide machine. Kevorkian challenged Michigan law by helping dozens of terminally ill patients to take their own lives. He was imprisoned for eight years as a result but remains an advocate of assisted suicide.

Diagnosis of Aging

Experts often classify adults in later life based on their age and health status. In **gerontology,** the multidisciplinary study of aging, it is common to distinguish among the young-old, the old-old, and the oldest-old.

The *young-old* are adults roughly between the ages of 65 and 75. However, the category is defined less by age than by health and vigor. Notwithstanding the normal physical problems of aging, the young-old are in good health and are active members of their communities. The majority of older adults belong to this group.

The *old-old* are adults between the ages of approximately 75 and 85 who suffer from major physical, psychological, or social (largely economic) problems. They require some routine assistance in living, although only about 6 percent of Americans in this age group live in a nursing home. Despite advanced age, a healthy and active 80-year-old adult would be considered to be young-old instead of old-old.

Finally, the *oldest-old* are adults 85 years old or older, a group that as a result of male mortality and financial strains, including health care costs,

TABLE 17–4	Assisted Suicides in Oregon				
	1998	1999	2000	2001	2002
Number of assisted suicides	16	27	27	23	36
Average age	70	71	70	68	69
Percent female	50	41	56	62	29
Percent white	100	96	96	95	97
Percent cancer	88	63	78	86	84

Oregon is the only state in the United States where assisted suicide is legal. Most assisted suicides involve older whites who are dying of cancer.

Source: Adapted from B. Rosenfeld, 2004, *Assisted Suicide and the Right to Die,* Washington: American Psychological Association, p. 157.

is comprised of a disproportionate number of widowed women and low-income groups. Still, the oldest-old is a diverse group. Some people maintain their vigor; others need constant assistance. Twenty-two percent live in nursing homes (Neugarten, 1990).

Frequency of Aging

Approximately one out of every eight persons living in the United States is 65 years of age or older—over 33 million people. Approximately 10 percent, or 3.5 million, of these older adults are the oldest-old—people 85 years old or older (U.S. Census Bureau, 1996). Both the proportion and the absolute number of older Americans will increase through the middle of the twenty-first century. The increase is partly as a result of medical advances but primarily due to the aging of the post–World War II "baby boom" generation (see Figure 17–5).

The proportion of the U.S. population 65 years of age or older should peak around the year 2030. At that time, one out of every five Americans will be at least 65 years old. The number of the oldest-old will increase most dramatically. In fact, the proportion and absolute number of the oldest-old will continue to rise until halfway through the twenty-first century. By the year

2050, the oldest-old should comprise one-fourth of the population of older adults (U.S. Census Bureau, 1996).

Most older Americans are women, and the ratio of women to men increases at older ages (U.S. Census Bureau, 1996; see Figure 17–4). One important consequence of gender differences in longevity is that the majority of older men (75 percent) are married, whereas the majority of older women (60 percent) live alone (Longino & Mittelmark, 1996). Census data also indicate that poverty rates are higher among older Americans than among younger age groups (except children), and the percentage of older Americans living in poverty increases with advancing age. This is due, in part, to the lower economic status of widowed women.

Causes of Psychological Problems in Later Life

There is little doubt that the most important biological contribution to psychological well-being in later life is good physical health (Cohler & Nakamura, 1996). In fact, a study of adults over the age of 70 found that both men and women listed poor health as the most common contribution to a negative quality of life in their later years (Flanagan, 1982).

Health behavior is particularly important to the physical well-being of older adults. Increased vigor and good health are associated with proper diet, continued exercise, weight control, and the avoidance of cigarette smoking and excessive alcohol use (Leventhal et al., 2001). Many of these health behaviors also are tied to better cognitive functioning among older people (Colcombe & Kramer, 2003; Hess, 2005). It even has been suggested that the overriding goal of gerontology should be to promote healthy and active lifestyles among older adults, because in industrialized societies, current life expectancies probably are very close to the biological limits of the human species (Fries, 1990). Increasing longevity may be unrealistic, but it is possible to extend the number of vigorous and healthy years of life.

Psychological contributions to adjustment in later life include close relationships and loss. Bereavement and living alone are more strongly related to depression among men than among women (Siegel & Kuykendall, 1990). Among men over the age of 70, the most frequent posi-

The Growing Number of Older Adults

Legend: 65–74 | 75–84 | 85 and over

Y-axis: Population in millions (0, 20, 40, 60, 80)
X-axis: Year (1900, 1950, 2000, 2050)

FIGURE 17–5 The actual and projected number of older adults in the United States aged 65 or older. Note the particularly dramatic increase in the oldest-old population.

Source: U.S. Bureau of the Census, 1983, "America in Transition: An Aging Society," *Current Population Reports*, Series P23–128. Washington, DC: U.S. Government Printing Office.

◄ Social involvement and physical activity are two keys to healthy adjustment in later life.

tive contributions to quality of life include relationships with spouses, friends, and children. Because so many women over the age of 70 are widowed, they list relationships with friends and children, as well as general socializing as most important to their well-being (Flanagan, 1982).

Numerous social factors are linked with a happier transition to later life, especially material well-being and participation in recreational activities. Religion is also very important to many older adults, and religious affiliations have been found to moderate the ill effects of bereavement, particularly among men (Siegel & Kuykendall, 1990). Other research indicates that integration into the community is a major contribution to adjustment to later life.

Treatment of Psychological Problems in Later Life

Good medical care is of great importance to older adults, not only for treating disease but also for promoting physical health and psychological well-being. Because health behavior is critical to the quality of life among older adults, experts view health psychology and behavioral medicine as central components of medical care. In fact, a new subdiscipline of these fields, called **behavioral gerontology,** has been developed specifically for studying and treating the behavioral components of health and illness among older adults (Bromley, 1990).

The same psychological and biological therapies used to treat emotional disorders among younger adults can be used to treat these problems among the aged. An exception is that certain biological treatments may be more effective among older than among younger adults, particularly electroconvulsive therapy in the treatment of unremitting depression (Delano-Wood & Abeles, 2005). Older adults may have misconceptions about psychotherapy. Thus education about the therapeutic process can be critical to its success. A number of treatments have been developed specifically to help people through their grief, but they generally offer little benefit beyond expected improvements with time. The exception is that therapies do offer benefits for people whose grief is complicated, that is, more intense or long lasting that expected (Currier et al., 2008).

Health care professionals must focus not only on improving quality of life among older adults, but on maintaining integrity in death. *Living wills* are legal documents that direct health care professionals not to perform certain procedures in order to keep a terminally ill or severely disabled patient alive. Older adults often are much better at accepting death than are younger people, and living wills and other efforts to humanize dying allow dignity to be maintained through the end of life (Lawton, 2001; Rosenfeld, 2004).

How is health critical to successful aging?

GETTING HELP

The wide range of life-cycle transitions considered in this chapter makes it impossible to offer many generalizations about getting help. But we can make two broad suggestions. First, self-help and self-education are particularly important and effective in helping yourself, a friend, or family member cope with life-cycle transitions. We suggest that you find out more about the transition you or a loved one may be facing, how other people feel in similar circumstances, what coping strategies others have found helpful, what you can expect might happen as time passes, and where you might end up when you are through this phase of your life. Second, we also urge you—or your friends or family members—not to be shy about seeking professional help if you are stuck, suffering greatly, or just want the support of a caring expert to help you through this time. As we noted at the outset of the chapter, a quarter of the people who see mental health professionals do not have a diagnosable mental disorder, so you will be far from alone in seeking out a therapist.

Reading, writing, and talking to friends are three helpful activities when struggling with coming to terms with your goals, relationships, and identity. Erik Erikson's *Childhood and Society* and *Identity and the Life Cycle* are classics that you should find helpful even though they were written half a century ago. Another type of reading may also help—reading literature. Coming-of-age is a common theme in great (and not-so-great) books, and great writers are also insightful psychologists. Besides reading, keeping a journal is always a good idea, particularly when you are confused. Finally, we urge you to talk about your doubts and uncertainties with fellow students who are friends or strangers, even with your professors!

There are plentiful resources available in bookstores, on the Internet, or in therapy if you or someone you know is struggling through a family transition. In fact, the biggest problem may not be finding a resource, but finding a *credible* resource. We urge you to look for self-help resources and therapists that offer advice based on psychological science, not just "pop" psychology. As a good start, many of the psychological scientists whose research we have used in this chapter also have written books for the general public. Among the many books we recommend are Carolyn Cowan and Philip Cowan's *When Partners Become Parents;* John Gottman's *The Seven Principles for Making Marriage Work;* and Robert Emery's *The Truth About Children and Divorce.*

An excellent book on aging is George Vaillant's *Aging Well: Surprising Guideposts to a Happier Life* from the *Landmark Harvard Study of Adult Development.* Mitch Albom's *Tuesdays with Morrie* is another superb book on aging that is partly a self-help book, partly a journal, and partly a work of literature. As with coming of age, coming to grips with aging is another common theme in literature, and it is a genre you may want to explore yourself or recommend to a friend.

■ SUMMARY

One out of every four people who see a mental health professional has never met the criteria for the diagnosis of a mental disorder. Many of these people are seeking help with some difficult life problem. DSM-IV-TR categorizes such problems either as **adjustment disorders,** clinically significant symptoms in response to stress, or as part of a general list of other conditions that may be a focus of clinical attention. We prefer to view life problems in terms of **life-cycle transitions,** struggles in moving from one stage of adult development into a new one.

The experiences associated with diverse life-cycle transitions differ greatly, but conflict is one common theme. Many conflicts during life-cycle transitions are interpersonal; others reflect a search for identity, our global sense of self; and still others involve emotional conflicts such as grieving. The concept of adult development was first highlighted by Erik Erikson's work on psychosocial development.

The transition to adult life begins late in the teen years and may continue through the twen-

ties. The **identity crisis** is a central psychological conflict at this time, epitomized by the question "Who am I?" Many other things change during the transition to adulthood, including parent–child relationships, educational and career paths, and peer relationships. Emotional conflicts also mark the transition to adult life, as young people experience more intense and rapidly changing emotions than adults.

Family transitions are major changes in family relationships that often involve the addition or loss of members of a family household. Ongoing family conflict is closely linked with individual psychological problems, especially among women and children. Family researchers often blame difficulties in negotiating family transitions on problems with communication, but broader family roles, such as traditional gender roles, also may be responsible for distressed family relationships. Social factors like poverty and even genetics also contribute to difficulties in family transitions. Both marital and family therapies, as well as community prevention efforts, are designed to address family problems.

Declining physical health and death are inevitabilities of aging. Older adults also confront a form of social prejudice known as **ageism,** a number of misconceptions and prejudices about aging. **Menopause,** the cessation of menstruation, is an important physical focus for middle-aged women. Gradual declines in physical health do not mean that older adults experience similar declines in psychological well-being. The prevalence of most mental disorders is lower, not higher, among adults 65 years of age and older. Most adults also view retirement positively, and relationships with children, siblings, and partners take on renewed importance. Unfortunately, the loss of loved ones, including the loss of a spouse, is a fact of life for older adults, particularly for older women. **Bereavement** is **grief** in response to the death of a loved one; it is commonly described as proceeding in a series of stages.

Young-old adults are between the ages of 65 and 75, are in good health, and are active members of their communities. The old-old are between 75 and 85, and may suffer from major physical, psychological, or social problems. The oldest-old are adults 85 years old or older. Approximately one out of every eight persons living in the United States is 65 years of age or older, and both the proportion and the absolute number of older Americans are expected to increase through the middle of the twenty-first century.

The most important biological factor in psychological well-being in later life is good physical health. Psychological factors include the availability of close relationships and the experience of loss. Social factors include material well-being, participation in recreational activities, religious affiliation, and integration into the community. **Behavioral gerontology** is a central component of medical care for older adults, and the same therapies can be used to treat psychological disorders among older as younger adults.

THE BIG PICTURE   CRITICAL THINKING REVIEW

How is identity conflict a part of becoming an adult?

The resolution of the **identity crisis,** a period of uncertainty about self, provides the first complete answer to the question "Who am I"? (SEE PAGE 535)

Why do genes contribute to heritability more in consistently good environments?

If we ever achieved the goal of providing everyone with the identical, enriching environment, all differences between people would be caused by genetics. (SEE PAGE 544)

How is family experience partly genetic?

The gene-environment correlation suggests that family events do not occur at random. (SEE PAGE 545)

Is there a single, healthy way to grieve?

Although denial, sadness, and anger may be normal reactions to loss, there is no one "right" way to grieve, nor should people be forced to express their unexpressed grief. (SEE PAGE 552)

How is health critical to successful aging?

There is little doubt that the most important biological contribution to psychological well-being in later life is good physical health. (SEE PAGE 555)

■ KEY TERMS

adjustment disorders **532**
ageism **549**
behavioral gerontology **555**
bereavement **552**

cognitive behavioral couple
    therapy **547**
estrogen **550**
family life cycle **539**

gene–environment
    correlation **544**
gerontology **553**
grief **552**

heritability **544**
heritability ratio **544**
identity crisis **534**
life-cycle transitions **531**

menopause **549**
moratorium **535**
reciprocity **540**
social clocks **534**

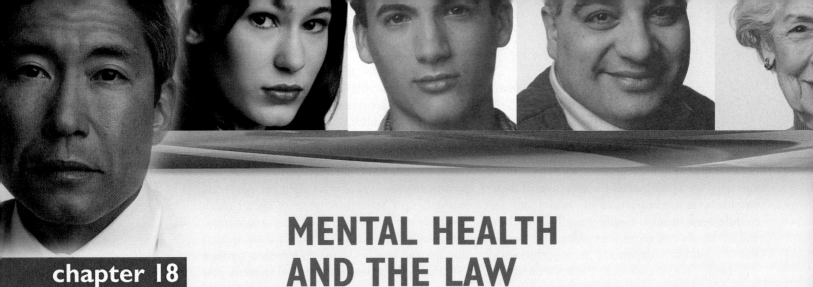

MENTAL HEALTH AND THE LAW

The legal system and mental health professionals view abnormal behavior very differently. Jeffrey Dahmer, who killed at least 17 people, chopped them up, and stored the body parts, was sane in the eyes of the law. So was 17-year-old Lee Malvo, who some claim was "brainwashed" by his fellow Beltway sniper, 42-year-old John Muhammad. Both were imprisoned for their crimes. Malvo is serving a life sentence. Dahmer was murdered by another inmate. Lorena Bobbitt, infamous for cutting off her husband's penis following an alleged rape, was found not guilty by reason of insanity—in the absence of any major mental illness. She was evaluated for 45 days in a mental hospital and released. A jury found psychotically depressed and schizophrenic Andrea Yates, who systematically drowned her five children in a bathtub, sane and guilty of murder. The Texas Court of Appeals later overturned the verdict on a technicality, and a retrial jury found Yates was not guilty by reason of insanity. She was moved from jail to a secure mental hospital. The paranoid schizophrenic "unabomber" Ted Kaczynski, who mailed exploding packages to unsuspecting victims, gained fame for *refusing* to try the insanity defense. These headline cases illustrate a basic and essential point: The legal definition of insanity is *not* the same as the psychological definition of mental illness.

OVERVIEW

In this chapter we consider a number of topics at the intersection of mental health and the law, including controversies that underscore the different goals and values of the two professions. We begin with a discussion of mental health in the criminal law, focusing on the insanity defense. Next, we consider mental health issues in the civil law, particularly the rights of mental patients. The confinement of the mentally ill against their will is a serious action. At best, it protects patients and society; at worst, it strips people of their human rights. Many political dissidents in the former Soviet Union were confined under the guise of "treating" their "mental illnesses." At the other extreme, many seriously mentally ill people in the United States today receive no therapy because they have the right to refuse treatment—a right they may exercise due to mental illness, not philosophical objections.

We also discuss legal intervention in families in this chapter, with an emphasis on child abuse and custody disputes after divorce. Concerns about serious mental illness are the exception, not the rule, in custody and abuse cases. However, predictions about children's emotional well-being often are vital in these cases. The legal decisions, in turn, can have far-reaching implications for children and their families.

Finally, we consider some of the legal responsibilities of mental health professionals, especially professional negligence and confidentiality. These issues, and all the topics in this chapter, are not only of interest to professionals; they also have broad implications for society. Our most basic legal rights and responsibilities are reflected, and defined, by the manner in which we treat the mentally ill.

We begin with a case study of an infamous and successful use of the insanity defense: the acquittal of John Hinckley. In 1981, Hinckley attempted to assassinate Ronald Reagan, the president of the United States. Our account is largely based on information in two books on the assassination attempt (Clarke, 1990; Low, Jeffries, & Bonnie, 1986).

CASE **STUDY** John Hinckley and the Insanity Defense

On March 30, 1981, John Hinckley stood outside the Washington Hilton hotel, drew a revolver from his raincoat pocket, and fired six shots at President Ronald Reagan. The president and three other men were wounded. The president rapidly recovered from his potentially fatal wound, but the presidential press

secretary, James Brady, was permanently crippled by a shot that struck him just above the left eye. Hinckley was charged with attempted assassination, but his trial resulted in a verdict of "not guilty by reason of insanity."

Hinckley, who came from a wealthy family, had never been convicted of a crime. He had a

history of unusual behavior, however, and had expressed violent intentions. Hinckley had read several books on famous assassinations and had joined the American Nazi Party. In fact, he was expelled from the Nazi Party in 1979 because of his continual advocacy of violence. A particular oddity was Hinckley's obsession with the

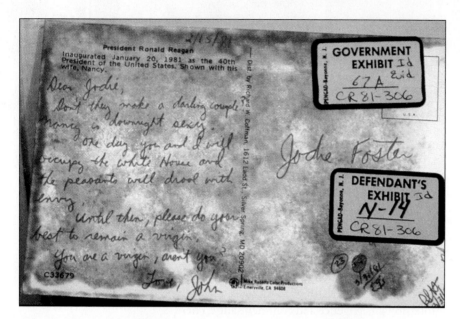

▲ One of several notes that John Hinckley wrote to actress Jodie Foster. Hinckley believed that he could win Foster's love by gaining notoriety, a delusion that apparently motivated him to attempt to assassinate former president Ronald Reagan.

actress Jodie Foster, whom he had seen play the role of a child prostitute in the movie *Taxi Driver*. In an attempt to win her favor, Hinckley adopted much of the style of Foster's movie rescuer, Travis Bickle. This included acquiring weapons and stalking the president, much as the movie character had stalked a political candidate. Hinckley repeatedly tried to contact Foster in real life and succeeded a few times, but his approaches were consistently rejected. He came to believe that the only way to win her over was through dramatic action. Less than 2 hours before he shot the president, he completed a letter to Foster, which said

Jodie, I would abandon this idea of getting Reagan in a second if I could only win your

heart and live out the rest of my life with you, whether it be in total obscurity or whatever.

> *All the prosecution's experts concluded that Hinckley was sane; all the defense's experts concluded that Hinckley was insane.*

I will admit to you that the reason I'm going ahead with this attempt now is because I just cannot wait any longer to impress you. I've got to do something now to make you

understand, in no uncertain terms, that I am doing all of this for your sake! By sacrificing my freedom and possibly my life, I hope to change your mind about me. This letter is being written only an hour before I leave for the Hilton Hotel. Jodie, I'm asking you to please look into your heart and at least give me the chance, with this historical deed, to gain your respect and love.

Hinckley's trial centered on the question of his sanity, or as one author put it, whether he was "mad" or merely angry (Clarke, 1990). Both the defense and the prosecution called numerous expert witnesses to determine whether Hinckley was legally sane or insane. According to the federal law in effect at the time, the prosecution had to prove "beyond a reasonable doubt" that Hinckley was indeed sane. That is, the prosecution had to establish that mental disease had not either (1) created an irresistible impulse that made it impossible for Hinckley to resist attempting to kill the president, or (2) so impaired Hinckley's thinking that he did not appreciate the wrongfulness of his actions. (The burden of proof and the definition of insanity in the federal law subsequently were changed because of Hinckley's acquittal.)

The prosecution's experts called attention to the fact that Hinckley's actions were planned in advance and to Hinckley's awareness that his actions would have consequences, including possible imprisonment or death. He chose six deadly "devastator" bullets from an abundance of ammunition, and he fired them all accurately in less than 3 seconds. Defense experts emphasized his erratic behavior, particularly his obsession with Jodie Foster. One psychiatrist suggested, for example, that the president and other victims were merely "bit players" in Hinckley's delusion that through his "historic deed" he would be united with Foster in death.

Hinckley was found not guilty by reason of insanity. We don't know what factors influenced the jury to come to this decision or whether they found him insane based on the "irresistible impulse" or the "right from wrong" part of the insanity defense. In any event, the verdict meant that Hinckley received no prison sentence. Instead, he was ordered into a mental hospital to be treated in confinement for an unspecified period of time. As of now, Hinckley remains confined in St. Elizabeth's Hospital, outside Washington, D.C. However, he is allowed to have brief, 3- or 4-day, unsupervised visits with his parents outside the

hospital. Hinckley could be released permanently if hospital staff concluded that he is no longer dangerous to himself or to others (and the court approves). On the other hand, Hinckley could remain in the hospital for the rest of his life.

John Hinckley obviously was emotionally disturbed, and legally he was determined to be insane when he shot the president. But in other cases, a defendant is clearly mentally ill but legally sane (e.g., Jeffrey Dahmer), and in still others, mentally healthy yet legally insane (e.g., Lorena Bobbitt). What is the basis for such conflicts between psychology and the law?

Expert Witnesses

One conflict between mental health and the law concerns the role of **expert witnesses,** specialists who the law allows to testify about specific matters of opinion (not just fact) that lie within their area of expertise. As they did in the Hinckley case, mental health experts often present conflicting testimony, creating a confusing and sometimes professionally embarrassing "battle of the experts" (Low, Jeffries, & Bonnie, 1986). In fact, some critics believe that mental health professionals should not serve as expert witnesses, because the mental health questions posed by the legal system cannot be answered reliably or validly (Faust & Ziskin, 1988).

The law does limit expert testimony to opinion based on established science (Faigman & Monahan, 2005). In *Daubert* v. *Merrell Dow Pharmaceuticals* (1993), the United States Supreme Court ruled that expert opinion must be based on an ". . . inference or assertion . . . derived by the scientific method," and courts must determine "whether the reasoning or methodology underlying the testimony is scientifically valid and . . . whether that reasoning or methodology can be applied to the facts in issue" (p. 2796). Still, the judge or jury, not science or an expert witness, is responsible for determining "truth" in the legal system. A judge or jury must decide the ultimate issue such as whether or not a defendant is legally insane.

The legal system and scientists differ in the procedures and goals in trying to determine truth. Lawyers are duty-bound to present the most convincing case for their side, not the most objective case. As such, lawyers expect challenges to their expert witnesses' testimony, and they anticipate that experts for the opposing side will present conflicting testimony (Fitch, Petrella, & Wallace, 1987). One trend to limit conflict, and hopefully improve expert testimony, is for courts to appoint neutral experts rather than having each side employ its own "hired gun" (Faigman & Monahan, 2005).

Free Will Versus Determinism

A more fundamental conflict between the legal and mental health systems involves the opposing assumptions made about the causes of and responsibility for human behavior. Criminal law assumes that human behavior is the product of **free will,** the capacity to make choices and freely act on them. The assumption of free will makes people responsible for their actions in the eyes of the law. The legal concept of **criminal responsibility** holds that, because people act out of free will, they are accountable for their actions when they violate the law.

In contrast, mental health professionals make an assumption of **determinism,** the view that human behavior is determined by biological, psychological, and social forces. The assumption of determinism is essential to science. While people obviously can exercise control over much of their behavior (Baumeister, 2008), scientists cannot study the causes of human behavior without assuming that it is determined by past and present factors that can be measured and perhaps controlled. Free will is an unscientific concept, which raises the question: Are people responsible for their behavior if they have no "free will"?

Assumptions about free will and determinism collide in the insanity defense. In U.S. law, **insanity** is an exception to criminal responsibility. The legally insane are assumed not to be acting out of free will. As a result, defendants like John Hinckley are not criminally responsible for their actions. Ironically, by calling attention to the rare exceptions when people are not responsible for their actions, the insanity defense reaffirms the legal system's view that most people are accountable.

Thus, debates about the insanity defense involve a broad conflict of philosophies, as well as differences about the specifics of a given case. Is human behavior a product of free will, or is it determined by biological, psychological, and social forces? Are people with mental disorders responsible for their actions, or are they not responsible?

Rights and Responsibilities

In the law, rights and responsibilities go hand in hand. When responsibilities are lost, rights are lost, too. When responsibilities are assumed, rights are gained. The profound implications of this simple relationship are evident in the provocative views of the American psychiatrist Thomas Szasz (1963, 1970). Szasz asserted that all people—even people with emotional disorders—are responsible for their actions. Consistent with this position, Szasz argued that the insanity defense should be abolished (1963). It also follows from Szasz's view that other exceptions made for mentally disturbed people in the legal system should be eliminated—for example, commitment to mental hospitals against their will (Moore, 1975).

In arguing for a broader concept of responsibility, Szasz also argued for a broader recognition of human dignity and individual rights of the mentally ill. Thus, while opposing the insanity defense, Szasz simultaneously supported greater recognition of the rights of mental patients. Since rights and responsibilities go hand in hand, one avenue to gaining rights might be to assume more responsibility through the abolition of the insanity defense.

Not surprisingly, Szasz's views generally are seen as extreme (Appelbaum, 1994). Nevertheless, they illustrate a fundamental conflict in mental health and the law. The dilemma is how to reconcile concepts of individual rights and responsibilities, which follow from an assumption of free will, with the deterministic view that is at the core of a scientific approach to understanding human behavior.

▶ Serial killer Jeffery Dahmer, who chopped up and stored his victims' bodies, was held to be legally sane. Lorena Bobbitt, who cut off her husband's penis following an alleged rape, was judged to be legally insane. The legal definition of insanity is *not* the same as the psychological definition of mental illness.

MENTAL ILLNESS AND CRIMINAL RESPONSIBILITY

The law assumes that mental disorders may affect an individual's capacity to exercise his or her rights and responsibilities. Defendants who are found not guilty by reason of insanity are determined not to be criminally responsible for their actions. Defendants who are incompetent to stand trial are judged to be unable to exercise their right to participate in their own trial defense. Finally, mental illness may be a mitigating factor that can lead to a less harsh sentence—or a harsher one.

The Insanity Defense

The idea that mental disability should limit criminal responsibility dates to ancient Greek and Hebrew traditions and was evident in early English law. Records indicate cases where English kings pardoned murderers because of "madness," and later judicial decisions similarly excused some criminals who were "madmen" or "idiots" (Reisner, Slobogin, & Rai, 2004). The emerging rationale underlying many of these insanity acquittals was not whether or not the perpetrator suffered from a mental illness. Instead, the issue was whether the defendant lacked the capacity to distinguish "good from evil," the inability to distinguish right from wrong. This ground for the **insanity defense** was codified in 1843, after Daniel M'Naghten was found not guilty of murder by reason of insanity.

M'Naghten Test   M'Naghten was a British subject who claimed that the "voice of God" ordered him to kill Prime Minister Robert Peel, but who mistakenly murdered Peel's private secretary instead. His insanity acquittal raised considerable controversy and caused the House of Lords to devise the following insanity test:

> To establish a defense on the ground of insanity, it must be clearly proved that, at the time of the committing of the act, the party accused was laboring under such a defect of reason, from disease of the mind, as not to know the nature and quality of the act he was doing; or, if he did know it, that he did not know he was doing what was wrong. [*Regina* v. *M'Naghten,* 8 Eng. Rep. 718, 722 (1843)]

Subsequently known as the *M'Naghten test,* this rule clearly articulated the "right from wrong" principle for determining insanity. If, at the time a criminal act is committed, a mental disease or defect prevents a criminal from knowing the wrongfulness of his or her actions, the criminal can be found to be *not guilty by reason of insanity (NGRI)*. The "right from wrong" ground established in the *M'Naghten* case continues to be the major focus of the insanity defense in U.S. law today. However, subsequent developments first broadened and later narrowed the grounds for determining insanity.

Irresistible Impulse and the Product Test

Later in the nineteenth century, the insanity defense was broadened in the United States. The so-called irresistible impulse test said that defendants were insane if they were unable to control their actions because of mental disease. *Parsons* v. *State* was one of the first cases in which the irresistible impulse test was adopted [81 Ala. 577, 596, 2 So. 854 (1886)]. In this 1886 case, an Alabama court ruled that defendants could be judged insane if they could not "avoid doing the act in question" because of mental disease. The rationale for the irresistible impulse test was that when people are unable to control their behavior, the law can have no effect on deterring crimes. Deterrence, the idea that people will avoid committing crimes because they fear being punished for them, is a major public policy goal of criminal law. In the *Parsons* case, however, the court reasoned that convicting people for acts that they could not control would serve no deterrence purpose. In such cases, a finding of NGRI was justified.

A 1954 ruling by the Washington, D.C. federal circuit court in *Durham* v. *United States* further broadened the insanity defense [214 F.2d 862 (D.C. Cir. 1954)]. Known as the *product test,* the Durham opinion indicated that an accused is not criminally responsible if his or her unlawful act was the product of mental disease or defect. The ruling made no attempt to define either *product* or *mental disease*. In fact, the terms were designed to be very broad to allow mental health professionals wide discretion in determining insanity and testifying in court.

Durham tried to align the definition of insanity more closely with the definition of mental illness, a superficially reasonable goal, but problems quickly arose with the product test. Some mental health professionals considered psychopathy (antisocial personality disorder in DSM-IV-TR) to be one of the "mental diseases" that justified the insanity defense. This created a cir-cular problem: Antisocial personality disorder is defined primarily by a pattern of criminal behavior, yet the same criminal behavior could be used to substantiate that the perpetrator was insane (Campbell, 1990). The problems came to a halt when the *Durham* decision was overruled in 1972 (Reisner et al., 2004).

Legislative Actions In 1955, a year after the original *Durham* decision, the American Law Institute drafted model legislation designed to address problems with the previous insanity rules. The model legislation is important because it subsequently was adopted by the majority of states. The rule indicates that

> A person is not responsible for criminal conduct if at the time of such conduct as a result of mental disease or defect he lacks substantial capacity either to appreciate the criminality [wrongfulness] of his conduct or to conform his conduct to the requirements of the law.

This definition of insanity combines the M'Naghten rule and the irresistible impulse test, although it softens the requirements somewhat with the term *substantial capacity*. (Compare this with the language used in the M'Naghten rule.) The American Law Institute's model statute also excluded a history of criminal behavior from the definition of "mental disease or defect." This provision, which also has been enacted by many states, eliminates the problem of circularity in the antisocial personality disorder diagnosis.

How does the law define "insanity?"

The most recent developments in the law governing the insanity defense occurred as a result of the acquittal of John Hinckley. Following the controversy over this case, both the American Bar Association and the American Psychiatric Association recommended the elimination of the irresistible impulse component of the insanity defense. These organizations judged this strand of the insanity defense to be more controversial and unreliable than the right from wrong standard (Mackay, 1988). Consistent with these recommendations, the Insanity Defense Reform Act was passed in 1984 and defined the insanity defense as follows:

> It is an affirmative defense to a prosecution under any federal statute that, at the time of the commission of acts constituting the offense, the defendant, as a result of severe mental disease or defect, was unable to appreciate the nature and quality or the wrongfulness of his acts. Mental disease or defect does not otherwise constitute a defense. (Title 18 of the United States Code)

▶ A jury declared Andrea Yates (in orange prison garb) legally sane, despite her psychosis, and guilty of murdering her five children. A prosecuting attorney argues that case (left). The Texas Court of Appeals overturned the verdict, and a retrial jury found her not guilty by reason of insanity.

Several states echoed this change in federal law by enacting similar, more restrictive legislation. Texas was one of these states. Thus, John Hinckley's assassination attempt is one reason why Andrea Yates initially was found sane and therefore guilty of drowning her five children in Texas (*New York Times,* March 13, 2002). The states of Montana, Idaho, Utah, Kansas, and Nevada went even further than Texas and completely abolished the insanity defense.

Guilty but Mentally Ill The verdict *guilty but mentally ill (GBMI)* has been enacted by a number of states in another attempt to reform the insanity defense (American Bar Association, 1995).

Defendants are GBMI if they are guilty of the crime, were mentally ill at the time it was committed, but were not legally insane at that time (see Table 18–1). A defendant found GBMI is sentenced in the same manner as any criminal, but the court can order treatment for the mental disorder as well. The GBMI verdict was designed as a compromise that would reduce NGRI verdicts, hold defendants criminally responsible, but acknowledge mental disorders and the need for treatment (Mackay, 1988). However, the GBMI verdict has not replaced NGRI. Instead, it is most often used in cases in which defendants simply would have been found guilty in the past (Smith & Hall, 1982). Others criticize GBMI for confusing

TABLE 18–1	Developments in the Insanity Defense		
GROUNDS FOR NGRI	**MENTAL INCAPACITY AT TIME OF CRIME**	**HOW BROAD?**	**BRIEF HISTORY OF RULE**
Right from wrong	Inability to distinguish right from wrong	Narrow	Formalized in 1843 *M'Naghten* case, many states again made this the only ground for NGRI following Hinckley.
Irresistible impulse	Unable to control actions	Broader	Dating to 1886, this broader rule remains in effect in some states.
Product test	Mental disease or defect	Broadest	Established in 1954 *Durham* case, this very broad rule was eliminated in 1972.
American Law Institute definition	Inability to distinguish right from wrong *or* unable to control actions	Broader	Combination of right from wrong and irresistible impulse tests, this hybrid model law was common before Hinckley.
Guilty but mentally ill	Legally responsible for crime but also mentally ill	Alternative	Recent alternative to NGRI. Defendant is *not* legally insane but may get treatment for mental illness.

the issues and suggest that interest in GBMI is rightfully declining (Melton et al., 1997).

Recent developments clearly led to a more restrictive insanity defense. The furor surrounding the high-profile *Hinckley* case was not unlike the controversy that surrounded the high profile *M'Naghten* case more than 100 years earlier. Ironically, the *Hinckley* case also caused the insanity defense to be revised to resemble the original M'Naghten test (Mackay, 1988). As it was for a time after 1843, the most common contemporary standard for determining legal insanity is the inability to distinguish right from wrong.

Burden of Proof Under U.S. criminal law, a defendant is innocent until proven guilty "beyond a reasonable doubt." The *burden of proof* thus rests with the prosecution, and the *standard of proof* is very high—beyond a reasonable doubt. Who has the burden of proof in insanity cases?

In the Hinckley trial, the prosecution was obliged to prove that Hinckley was sane beyond a reasonable doubt, a case it failed to make. The Insanity Defense Reform Act changed federal law. In federal courts the defense now must prove defendants' insanity rather than the prosecution having to prove their sanity. Insanity must be proven by "clear and convincing evidence," a stringent standard but not as exacting as "beyond a reasonable doubt." About two-thirds of states also now place the burden of proof on the defense, but the standard of proof typically is less restrictive than that found in federal law—"the preponderance of the evidence." Thus the insanity defense has been narrowed further by shifting the burden of proof from the prosecution to the defense (American Bar Association, 1995).

Defining "Mental Disease or Defect" An issue of obvious importance to the mental health professions is the precise meaning of the term *mental disease or defect*. The American Law Institute's proposal specifically excluded antisocial personality disorder, but would any other diagnosis listed in DSM qualify? The 1984 federal legislation indicates that the mental disease must be "severe," but what does this mean?

The question of which mental disorders qualify for the "mental disease or defect" component of the insanity defense is unresolved, although the legal definition of "mental disease" generally is more restrictive than the mental health definition (Campbell, 1990). Some legal and mental health professionals would allow any disorder listed in

DSM to qualify, provided that the other criteria for the legal definition of insanity also were met. Others have argued that some especially difficult circumstances—for example, being a victim of repeated violence—should qualify defendants for the "mental disease or defect" component of the insanity defense, even if the problems are *not* listed as DSM diagnoses (see The Battered Woman's Syndrome as a Defense on page 566). Still other commentators would sharply restrict the mental diseases or defects that can be used as a part of the insanity defense. One suggestion is to confine the insanity defense to mental retardation, schizophrenia, mood disorders, and cognitive disorders, excluding cognitive disorders induced by substance use or abuse (Appelbaum, 1994). Finally, the American Psychiatric Association (1983) has stated that mental diseases or defects are limited to "those severely abnormal mental conditions that grossly and demonstrably impair a person's perception or understanding of reality that are not attributable primarily to the voluntary ingestion of alcohol or other psychoactive substances."

Use of the Insanity Defense Given the intensive media coverage of high-profile cases, you might be surprised to learn that the insanity defense is used in only about 1 percent of all criminal cases in the United States. Only about 25 percent of defendants who offer the defense are actually found to be NGRI (Callahan et al., 1991; Steadman, Pantle, & Pasewark, 1983). Furthermore, over 90 percent of these acquittals result from plea bargains rather than jury trials (Callahan et al., 1991). In addition, the post-Hinckley shift in the burden of proof from the prosecution to the defense has reduced both the frequency and the success rate of the insanity defense (Steadman et al., 1993). In England, where the M'Naghten rule still stands, the insanity defense is virtually nonexistent. It is used in only a handful of cases each year (Mackay, 1988).

Do defendants "walk" if they are found NGRI? Some are incarcerated in mental institutions for much shorter periods of time than if they had been sentenced to prison. (Lorena Bobbitt was hospitalized for 45 days.) Others actually are incarcerated for much longer periods of time—yet another reminder that rights are lost when responsibilities are not assumed. On average, NGRI acquittees spend approximately the same amount of time in mental institutions as they would have served in prison (Pantle, Pasewark, & Steadman, 1980). Some

THE BATTERED WOMAN SYNDROME AS A DEFENSE

Battered women often remain in an abusive relationship for incomprehensibly long periods of time. To outsiders, the battered woman's reluctance to leave the relationship can seem foolish, even masochistic. To the battered woman, however, leaving the relationship often seems wrong or impossible. She may feel trapped by finances or by concern for her children; chronic abuse may cause her to lose perspective on the extent of her maltreatment. Some women eventually escape the abuse only by killing their tormentors. According to a report of the American Psychological Association (1995), approximately 1,000 women kill their current or former batterer each year. Is this violence in response to violence ever justified?

The killing of an abuser clearly is justified in U.S. law when the victim's life is in immediate danger. In this case, the action is committed in self-defense. In many battering cases, however, the killing takes place when the threat of abuse looms in the future but is not immediate. In this situation, a woman still might plead self-defense. According to contemporary trial practice, the defense may depend heavily on the battered woman syndrome.

The **battered woman syndrome** is a term coined by the psychologist Lenore Walker (1979) to describe her observations about the psychological effects of chronic abuse on

▲ A member of the "Framingham Eight," eight women imprisoned for killing their abusers. The women petitioned for early release from prison, claiming they acted in self-defense. The governor of Massachusetts eventually commuted their sentences.

victims. Two aspects of the syndrome are crucial to its use as a defense. First, Walker postulates a "cycle of violence," that includes three stages: (1) a tension-building phase leading up to violence; (2) the battering incident itself; and (3) a stage of loving contrition, during which the batterer apologizes and attempts to make amends. A second crucial aspect is Walker's assertion that the abused woman is prevented from leaving the relationship by learned helplessness. These two assertions imply that the battered woman expects to be beaten repeatedly but becomes immobilized and unable to leave the relationship.

Is it self-defense when a battered woman kills her abuser?

The battered woman's syndrome has been used successfully to acquit many battered women or, in other cases, to reduce their sentence. In fact, at least five states enacted statutes explicitly allowing the battered woman syndrome defense (Toffel, 1996). However, a similar defense arising when an abused child kills a parent or stepparent has met with much more resistance (Ryan, 1996). You may recall the battered child defense from the trial of the Menendez brothers, who murdered their parents. The first trial ended in a hung jury, but in a retrial, the court rejected the battered child defense and the brothers were sentenced to life in prison. (The circumstances of the Menendez case, where the murders were carefully premeditated, suggest that the guilty verdict was just in this case.)

Not surprisingly, the battered woman defense is controversial; some refer to it as the "abuse excuse." Criminal lawyer Alan Dershowitz (1994) is a notably vocal critic. He writes:

On the surface, the abuse excuse affects only a few handfuls of defendants. But at a deeper level, the abuse excuse is a symptom of a general abdication of responsibility. It also

endangers our collective safety by legitimating a sense of vigilantism. (p. 4)

A number of courts have ruled that expert testimony on the battered woman syndrome is inadmissible on various grounds, although the trend has been toward increasing acceptance (Brown, 1990; Faigman et al., 1997). Given the growing use of the defense, it may surprise you to learn that commentators generally agree about one point: The scientific evidence supporting the battered woman syndrome is weak to nonexistent (Faigman et al., 1997; Schopp, Sturgis, & Sullivan, 1994). One question that has been asked, for example, is: How can someone who is suffering from learned helplessness bring herself to kill?

Questions like this can make it difficult to plead self-defense based on the battered woman syndrome. The threat of imminent danger and questions about leaving the abuser usually play a lesser role in an alternative defense of *temporary insanity*, which may be more easily proved in court. (The legal definition of insanity refers to a defendant's mental state at the time of committing the criminal act; thus it is possible for a defendant to suffer from "temporary insanity.") An argument for temporary insanity based on the battered woman syndrome would stress that the physical abuse so impaired the battered woman's thinking that either she was unable to appreciate the consequences of her actions or she was driven to the point where she could no longer control her behavior (Cipparone, 1987).

In cases where women have killed their batterers, temporary insanity pleas are used less frequently than self-defense. Perhaps this is because the temporary insanity defense carries the stigma of an insanity determination, as well as the possibility of confinement in a mental institution. More broadly, a successful insanity defense relieves one woman of criminal responsibility for her actions. A successful self-defense defense makes a broader political statement that women have a right to take extreme action in the face of chronic battering (Walker, 1989).

---

state laws actually limit the length of confinement following an NGRI verdict to the maximum sentence the acquittee would have served if convicted. However, the U.S. Supreme Court has ruled that longer confinements are permitted because treatment, not punishment, is the goal of an NGRI verdict (American Bar Association, 1995).

Competence to Stand Trial

Many more people are institutionalized because of findings of incompetence than because of insanity rulings. **Competence** is a defendant's ability to understand the legal proceedings that are taking place against them and to participate in their own defense. Competence was defined as follows by the U.S. Supreme Court in *Dusky* v. *United States* [363 U.S. 402, 80 S. Ct. 788, 4 L. Ed.2d. 824 (1960)]:

> The test must be whether he [the defendant] has sufficient present ability to consult with his attorney with a reasonable degree of rational understanding and a rational as well as factual understanding of proceedings against him.

You should note several features of the legal definition of competence. First, competence refers to the defendant's current mental state, whereas insanity refers to the defendant's state of mind at the time of the crime. Second, as with insanity, the legal definition of incompetence is not the same as the psychologist's definition of mental illness. Even a psychotic individual may possess enough rational understanding to be deemed competent in the eyes of the law. Third, competence refers to the defendant's ability to understand criminal proceedings, not willingness to participate in them. For example, a defendant who simply refuses to consult with a court-appointed lawyer is not incompetent. Finally, the "reasonable degree" of understanding needed to establish competence is generally acknowledged to be fairly low. That is, only those who suffer from severe emotional disorders are likely to be found incompetent (Melton et al., 1997).

The legal definition of competence contains no reference to "mental disease or defect." The role of expert witnesses in determining competency is therefore quite different from their role in determining sanity. The evaluation focuses much more on specific behaviors and capacities than on DSM disorders. Table 18–2 summarizes the areas of legal understanding and reasoning necessary for competence formulated by a distinguished group of experts.

The most common finding of *incompetence* is incompetence to stand trial, but the issue may arise at several stages of the criminal process. Defendants must be competent to understand the *Miranda warning* issued during their arrest. (The Miranda warning details the suspect's rights to remain silent and to have an attorney present during police questioning.) Defendants also must be competent at the time of their sentencing, which takes place after they have been convicted of a crime. Finally, recent rulings indicate that defendants sentenced to death must be competent at the time of their execution, or the death sentence cannot be carried out. One issue that is currently working its way through the courts is whether a psychotic death-row inmate retains the right to refuse treatment (discussed shortly) or can be medicated against his wishes for the sole purpose of making him competent to be executed (Reisner et al., 2004).

What is "competence" in the eyes of the law?

TABLE 18–2 Measuring Legal Competence

A. Legal Understanding

1. Understanding the roles of defense attorney and prosecutor.
2. Understanding both the act and mental elements of a serious offense.
3. Understanding the elements of a less serious offense.
4. Understanding the role of a jury.
5. Understanding the responsibilities of a judge at a jury trial.
6. Understanding sentencing as a function of the severity of the offense.
7. Understanding the process of a guilty plea.
8. Understanding the rights waived in pleading guilty.

B. Legal Reasoning

9. Reasoning about evidence suggesting self-defense.
10. Reasoning about evidence related to criminal intent.
11. Reasoning about evidence of provocation.
12. Reasoning about motivation for one's behavior.
13. Reasoning about the potential impact of alcohol on one's behavior.
14. Capacity to identify information that might inform the decision to plead guilty versus plead not guilty.
15. Capacity to identify both potential costs and potential benefits of a legal decision (e.g., pleading guilty).
16. Capacity to compare one legal option (e.g., accepting a plea bargain) with another legal option (e.g., going to trial) in terms of advantages and disadvantages.

C. Legal Appreciation

17. Plausibility of defendant's beliefs about the likelihood of being treated fairly by the legal system.
18. Plausibility of defendant's beliefs about likelihood of being helped by his/her lawyer.
19. Plausibility of defendant's beliefs about whether to disclose case information to his/her attorney.
20. Plausibility of defendant's beliefs about likelihood of being found guilty.
21. Plausibility of defendant's beliefs about likelihood of being punished if found guilty.
22. Plausibility of defendant's beliefs about whether to accept a plea bargain.

Source: Items reprinted from the MacCAT-CA. Reprinted by permission of Professor R. Otto, University of South Florida.

▲ Zacarias Moussaoui, the "twentieth terrorist," pleaded guilty to conspiring in the September 11 attacks. His lawyers objected that he was not competent to plead guilty, but he eventually was found competent and his plea was accepted.

Competency hearings generally do not make front-page stories. Typically, a competency finding is accepted by agreement or reached in a relatively informal hearing. An exception arose in the trial of Zacarias Moussaoui, the so-called "twentieth terrorist" who was arrested before September 11 but was accused of being a conspirator in the attacks. Moussaoui first pleaded guilty to the charges against him, but his court-appointed lawyers objected that he was not competent to enter the guilty plea. Although the judge later found Moussaoui competent, she gave him a week to change his plea, which he did. After years of back and forth, a legally competent Moussaoui pleaded guilty to all counts on April 22, 2005, and the judge accepted the plea.

If defendants are determined to be incompetent, legal proceedings must be suspended until they can be understood by the defendant. The goal is to ensure fairness, but unfortunately, this has produced some very unfair results. Many defendants have been confined for periods of time much greater than they would have served if convicted. Although there is little doubt that they have severe mental disorders, incompetent defendants do not always receive the same protections as those hospitalized through civil commitment procedures, which we discuss shortly.

Sentencing and Mental Health

Mental health also is a consideration in sentencing the guilty. Mental disorders are one of several potential mitigating factors that judges are required to consider before sentencing a

guilty party (Reisner et al., 2004). The presence of a mental illness may justify a less harsh sentence, particularly in death penalty cases. Yet mental illness also can be used to justify longer periods of confinement, particularly for sex offenders.

Because death is the ultimate punishment, judicial scrutiny is particularly intense in death penalty cases. A thorough review of potential mitigating factors, including mental illness and duress at the time of the crime, is a major part of the scrutiny required by the court (Reisner et al., 2004). *Mitigation evaluations,* which include an assessment for mental disorders, are required in all death penalty cases.

Mental Retardation In the landmark case of *Atkins* v. *Virginia* (2002), the U.S. Supreme Court ruled—consistent with laws already in effect in many states—that mental retardation is a mitigating factor that makes the death penalty unconstitutional. In this case, Daryl Atkins, a man with an IQ of 59, was found guilty of robbing a 21-year-old man for beer money and subsequently shooting and killing him. According to the court, the death penalty would be cruel and unusual punishment in this case—and for all people with mental retardation. Writing for the majority, Justice John Paul Stevens reasoned:

> First, there is serious question whether either justification underpinning the death penalty—retribution and deterrence of capital crimes—applies to mentally retarded offenders. . . . Second, mentally retarded defendants in the aggregate face a special risk of wrongful execution because of the possibility that they will unwittingly confess to crimes they did not commit, their lesser ability to give their counsel meaningful assistance, and the facts that they typically are poor witnesses and that their demeanor may create an unwarranted impression of lack of remorse for their crimes. (536 U.S. 321, 2002, pp. 2–3)

As we noted in Chapter 16, a firestorm of debate about the precise definition of mental retardation is one practical consequence of the Supreme Court ruling. Whether or not a defendant has mental retardation literally may be a life or death question. In fact, in 2005 Virginia jury ruled that Daryl Atkins does *not* suffer from mental retardation. The prosecution argued that Atkins' low IQ did not begin before the age of 18 but was a consequence of later alcohol and drug abuse, and also that constant contact with his lawyers raised his IQ. He was again sentenced to death, but Atkins' sentence was recently commuted to life in prison based on prosecutorial misconduct during his first trial.

Although the issue of mental illness or mental retardation was not involved, the Supreme Court also recently ruled that the death penalty is cruel and unusual punishment for another category of defendants: Anyone who commits a capital crime when under the age of 18 [*Roper* v. *Simmons,* (03-633) (2005)].

Sexual Predators Mental retardation and mental illness may mitigate against harsh sentencing, but a history of and potential for sexual violence may lead to harsher sentencing. Several states have passed *sexual predator laws,* designed to keep sexual offenders confined for indefinite periods of time. These laws were challenged in the U.S. Supreme Court case of *Kansas* v. *Hendricks* (521 U.S. 346, 1997). In this case, Leroy Hendricks, who had a long and gruesome history of pedophilia, was about to be released from prison after serving a 10-year term for taking "indecent liberties" with two 13-year-old boys. Before he was released, however, Hendricks was confined indefinitely to a maximum security institution under a new Kansas sexual predator law.

In court, Hendricks admitted that when he "gets stressed out" he "can't control the urge" to molest children. Still, Hendricks argued against his continued confinement on several grounds, including "double jeopardy," that is, being punished twice for the same crime. The Supreme Court ruled in favor of the state of Kansas, however, concluding that Hendricks's indefinite confinement under the sexual predator law did not constitute punishment. Instead, the court viewed Hendricks's continued detention in a maximum security prison as justified on the basis of his dangerousness to others. While we may feel safer with someone like Hendricks in jail, the court's decision can be questioned. Other classes of criminals, for example burglars (who commit 60 percent of all rapes in the home), have notably higher rates of recidivism than sex offenders, yet they are not confined for dangerousness beyond their prison sentences (Reisner et al., 2004). Moreover, confined sex offenders typically get little or no treatment, a requirement for justifying civil commitment, our next topic.

◀ In 2002, the U.S. Supreme Court ruled that the death penalty would constitute cruel and unusual punishment for murderer Daryl Atkins (pictured), or for any person who, like Atkins, suffered from mental retardation. A Virginia jury later decided that Atkins no longer had mental retardation, foreshadowing a new area of debate about mental health and the law.

MENTAL HEALTH AND CIVIL LAW

The involuntary hospitalization of the severely mentally impaired raises questions of major importance in civil law. Three issues are of special relevance: (1) civil commitment, the legal process of sending someone to a mental hospital against his or her will; (2) patients' rights, especially their right to treatment, their right to treatment in the least restrictive alternative environment, and their right to refuse certain treatments; and (3) deinstitutionalization, the movement to treat patients in their communities instead of in mental hospitals. We begin our consideration of involuntary hospitalization with a brief review of the history of mental hospitals in the United States.

A Brief History of U.S. Mental Hospitals

In 1842, the famous British author Charles Dickens toured the United States and visited several mental institutions. In *American Notes and Pictures from Italy* (1842/1970), he wrote the following about one of the institutions that he visited:

I cannot say that I derived much comfort from the inspection of this charity. The different wards might have been cleaner and better ordered; I saw nothing of that salutary system which had impressed me so favorably elsewhere; and everything had a lounging, listless, madhouse air, which was very painful. The moping idiot, cowering down with long dishevelled hair; the gibbering maniac, with his hideous laugh

▲ Sadly, the horrors of mental institutions continue into the present, as documented in an April 28, 2002 *New York Times* exposé. The series documented inadequate care, poor staff training, and many suspicious and untimely deaths in the 100 adult homes that house over 15,000 residents in New York City alone. A state report dubbed one such home, "The New Warehouse for the Insane."

Nicole Bengiveno/The New York Times.

and pointed finger; the vacant eye, the fierce wild face, the gloomy picking of the hands and lips, and munching of the nails: there they were all without disguise, in naked ugliness and horror. In the dining-room, a bare, dull, dreary place, with nothing for the eye to rest on but the empty walls, a woman was locked up alone. She was bent, they told me, on committing suicide. If anything could have strengthened her in her resolution, it would certainly have been the insupportable monotony of such an existence. (p. 93)

Such cruel care of the mentally disturbed has been a problem throughout history. Ironically, many of the large mental institutions that still dot the U.S. countryside were built in the nineteenth century to fulfill the philosophy of *moral treatment,* the laudable but failed movement to alleviate mental illnesses by offering respite and humanistic care to the mentally disturbed. In 1830, there were only four public mental hospitals with under 200 patients in the United States. In 1880, there were 75 public mental hospitals with more than 35,000 residents (Torrey, 1988). As the moral treatment movement faded, many mental institutions simply became larger and more grotesque human warehouses, as more and more patients were housed in them. The squalid conditions in state mental hospitals began to be revealed to the public shortly after World War II. Many conscientious objectors who worked in mental hospitals instead of serving in the armed forces observed their horrors and brought the terrible conditions to the attention of politicians and the popular media (Torrey, 1988).

As can be seen in Figure 18–1, the number of patients living in mental hospitals began to shrink dramatically in the 1950s. This was due in large part to the discovery of antipsychotic medications and to the *deinstitutionalization movement*—the attempt to care for the mentally ill in their communities. Part of the decline was also due to the increase in private mental hospitals and psychiatric wards in general hospitals.

Even today, the mentally ill suffer in institutional care. An April 28, 2002 *New York Times* exposé documented inadequate care, poor staff training, and many suspicious and untimely deaths in the 100 adult homes housing over 15,000 mentally ill residents in New York City. A state report dubbed one such home "The New Warehouse for the Insane." The laudable deinstitutionalization movement, which has the same goal but the opposite solution as the moral treatment movement, also suffers from many problems. Finally, one more irony: Nineteenth-century reformers hoped to get the mentally disturbed out of jails and into hospitals. Today, fewer people with mental illness are housed in mental hospitals, and more are ending up in jail (Ditton, 1999). In fact, four times as many people with mental illnesses are incarcerated in prisons as are housed in state mental hospitals (U.S. Department of Justice, 1999). One new experiment for dealing with the flood of seriously mentally ill people into the legal system is establishing "mental health courts,"

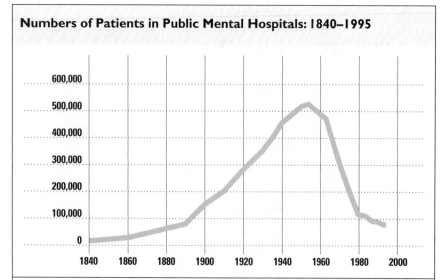

Numbers of Patients in Public Mental Hospitals: 1840–1995

FIGURE 18–1   The number of patients living in mental hospitals increased from the last part of the 1800s, when large mental hospitals were built, and declined from the 1950s with the development of antipsychotic medication and deinstitutionalization.

Source: E. F. Torrey, 1988, *Nowhere to Go: The Tragic Odyssey of the Homeless Mentally Ill*, p. 3, New York: HarperCollins; and E. F. Torrey, 1997, *Out of the Shadows*, p. 9. New York: Wiley.

designed to ensure that the accused and convicted who need mental health treatment get it. Whether these new courts will prove helpful is uncertain at this time (Reisner et al., 2004).

Libertarianism Versus Paternalism

What are society's legal and philosophical rationales for hospitalizing people against their will? Debates about involuntary hospitalization highlight the philosophical tension between libertarian views, which emphasize the protection of the rights of the individual, and paternalistic approaches, which emphasize the state's duty to protect its citizens. For example, the involuntary hospitalization of someone who appears to be dangerous to others serves a protective, paternalistic goal. Yet civil libertarians note that preventive detention—confinement before a crime is committed—can lead to substantial abuse. Our laws prohibit the confinement of someone simply on the suspicion that he or she is about to commit a crime, with a single exception: **civil commitment,** the involuntary hospitalization of the mentally ill.

The debate between the libertarian and paternalistic philosophies regarding civil commitment is very much alive. A major swing toward increased libertarianism began in the 1960s, including a closer scrutiny of civil commitment procedures, an increasing recognition of patients' rights, and the deinstitutionalization movement. Since at least 1990, however, the pendulum has swung in the direction of paternalism. Concern is growing about the failure to treat the mentally ill, and interest is increasing in aggressive, sometimes coercive, interventions with the seriously mentally ill (Appelbaum, 1994).

Civil Commitment

American law contains two broad rationales for civil commitment. The first is based on the state's *parens patriae* authority, the philosophy that the government has a humanitarian responsibility to care for its weaker members. (The literal translation of the Latin phrase *parens patriae* is the "state as parent.") Under the state's *parens patriae* authority, civil commitment may be justified when the mentally disturbed are either dangerous to themselves or unable to care for

themselves (Myers, 1983–1984). In addition to the confinement of the mentally ill, the concept of *parens patriae* is used to justify the state's supervision of minors and physically incapacitated adults.

How does the law justify civil commitment?

The second rationale is based on the state's police power—its duty to protect the public safety, health, and welfare. Our government restricts individual liberties for the public good in many ways. For the safety of others, we cannot yell "Fire!" in a crowded theater or drive an automobile at 100 miles an hour. The civil commitment of people who are dangerous to others is justified by similar police power rationales.

Grounds and Procedures Most states provide two types of civil commitment procedures: emergency procedures and formal procedures. *Emergency commitment procedures* allow an acutely disturbed individual to be temporarily confined in a mental hospital, typically for no more than a few days. Various states designate physicians, mental health professionals, or even police officers as qualified to determine whether an emergency commitment is required. Obviously, such action is taken only when a mental disorder is very serious, and the risk that the patient is dangerous to self or others appears to be very high.

Formal commitment procedures can lead to involuntary hospitalization for much longer periods of time, and formal commitment can be ordered only by a court. A hearing must be available to mental patients who object to involuntary hospitalization, and all of their due process rights must be protected. Following involuntary commitment, cases typically must be reviewed after a set period of time—for example, every 6 months.

Because civil commitment is a matter of state law, the specific grounds for involuntary hospitalization vary from state to state. Still, three grounds tend to dominate: (1) inability to care for self, (2) being dangerous to self, and (3) being dangerous to others. The broadest of these is *inability to care for self.* In some states, mental patients may be hospitalized against their will if they are unable to care for themselves adequately in the community or if they do not have family or friends who will care for them. The intention of this commitment standard is benevolent, but because it has been abused in some cases, newly articulated patient rights have been used to attack it (Appelbaum, 1994; Durham & LaFond, 1988). Debates continue in courtrooms and in state legislatures. Should we be paternalistic and sacrifice some individual rights by involuntarily committing mental patients who do not want, but who clearly need, inpatient treatment? Or do we run the danger of trampling on civil liberties if we hospitalize nondangerous people against their will?

The two other grounds for justifying civil commitment generally have not been attacked on philosophical grounds. Few civil libertarians object to hospitalizing people against their will when they clearly are either *dangerous to self* or *dangerous to others,* provided that the danger is "imminent." Thus a commonly accepted standard for civil commitment is "clear and convincing evidence of imminent danger to oneself or others." However, a case we discussed earlier, *Kansas* v. *Hendricks* (1997), created controversy about the *imminent* standard. Leroy Hendricks's risk of sexual molestation of minors was not imminent, but more general. Still, the Supreme Court ruled that civil commitment is justified for individuals "who suffer from a volitional impairment rendering them dangerous beyond their control." This vague position may signal a new trend, one that some fear will lead to overreaching in civil commitment cases (Falk, 1999).

Predicting Dangerousness and Suicidal Risk

The stakes are high in predicting a patient's dangerousness or suicidal risk. False positives—wrongly hospitalizing someone who is not dangerous or suicidal—unfairly restrict the patient's civil rights. False negatives—releasing someone who is dangerous to self or others—put lives at stake. Unfortunately, the prediction of violence is far from perfect, so one certainty is mental health professionals *will* make errors.

Predicting Dangerousness Research shows that mental illness increases the risk for violence. However, the public greatly overestimates that risk: The vast majority of people with a psychological disorder are *not* violent (see Critical Thinking Matters). If mental illness is a poor predictor of violence, can individual assessments improve prediction? Well, clinical predictions that someone will be violent are *wrong* approximately two out of three times (Ennis & Emery, 1978; Monahan, 1981). That is, the false-positive rate of a prediction of violence is about 67 percent. In fact, commentators have argued that it is unethical for mental health experts to offer specific predictions about dangerousness to the courts, because prediction is so inaccurate (Ewing, 1991; Foot, 1990; Melton et al., 1997).

The prediction of violence is better in the short term than in the long run, a key distinction because most research examines long-term outcomes (Monahan, 1981). For example, two out of three people who are hospitalized involuntarily are not violent after they are released. Would these people have been violent without the commitment? We cannot know for certain, but we do know that (1) clinicians commit patients only when they strongly believe that the risk of violence is imminent; and (2) clinicians release the same patients only if they believe that the patient no longer is a risk. Such urgent, real-life decisions confound research. For obvious ethical reasons, no one will ever do the unequivocal experiment: release or confine potentially violent people at random and compare clinical predictions with actual acts of violence.

Being wrong two out of three times may seem worse than chance, but it is not (Lidz, Mulvey, & Gardner, 1993). When predicting a very infrequent event (like violence), a false-positive rate of two-thirds is, in fact, much better than chance. This is because you must take **base rates**—population frequencies—into account. This is an important, if somewhat difficult, point, one for which U.S. Supreme Court Justice Harry Blackmun failed to grasp the concept. He wrongly claimed that a coin flip would be more accurate than clinical prediction (Reisner et al., 2004; see Research Methods on page 574).

In considering the imperfect prediction of violence, you also should remember the differ-

▼ Seung-Hui Cho showed frightening, erratic behavior long before he shot and killed 32 people and wounded many others on the Virginia Tech campus on April 16, 2007. He had been treated intermittently for mental health problems and declared a danger to himself by a Virginia court two years earlier. Can such horrors be prevented by more aggressive civil commitment and mandated treatment?

CRITICAL THINKING MATTERS

Violence and Mental Illness

Are mentally disturbed people dangerous? To many laypeople, the obvious answer is: "Yes!" In one survey, 61 percent of the respondents agreed that people with schizophrenia were "somewhat" or "very" likely to do something violent to others (Pescosolido et al., 1999). Ordinary people recall dramatic, frightening, and terribly sad cases like the Virginia Tech shootings or Kendra Webdale, a talented 32-year-old woman who was pushed in front of a subway train and killed in New York City. Her assailant was a complete stranger, a man with schizophrenia whose explanation for his impulsive and tragic act was that "an overwhelming force took over him."

Until recent years, most research suggested that the public was wrong: There was no empirical link between mental illness and violence. However, John Monahan (1992), a leading authority on the prediction of dangerousness, has marshaled new evidence demonstrating an increased risk after all. The rate of violence is about five times higher among people diagnosed with a major mental disorder than those with no diagnosis. People who abuse alcohol or drugs are even more likely to engage in violent behavior (see Table 18–3). Substance abuse symptoms actually increase the risk of violence in both former psychiatric inpatients and in the general community (Steadman et al., 1998).

Are mental patients as dangerous as many people fear?

Does this evidence translate into support for confining the seriously mentally ill based on their dangerousness? The answer is no, for several reasons. First, the risk for violence is far lower than is publicly perceived. Approximately 90 percent of the mentally disturbed have *no* history of violence (Monahan, 1992). Second, family and friends, not strangers in the street, are the victims of over 85 percent of violent acts perpetrated by the mentally ill

(Monahan et al., 2001a). Third, *current* psychotic symptoms predict violence, but a *past* history of psychosis does not (Link, Cullen, & Andrews, 1990).

Most importantly, numerous factors other than mental illness predict an increased risk for violence, but they obviously do not justify preventative detention. For example, people who live in poverty or who have a history of criminal behavior are more likely to be violent. But we would not consider confining the poor or those who have paid their debt to society based on their increased statistical risk. Basic civil liberties are at stake. And except in the extreme circumstances, our society must accord the same rights to the mentally ill.

TABLE 18–3 Mental Illness and Violence

DIAGNOSIS	PERCENTAGE VIOLENT
No disorder	2.1
Schizophrenia	12.7
Major depression	11.7
Mania or bipolar disorder	11.0
Alcohol abuse/dependence	24.6
Substance abuse/dependence	34.7

Source: Adapted from J. Monahan, 1992, "Mental Disorder and Violent Behavior: Perceptions and Evidence," *American Psychologist, 47,* pp. 516, 518.

ent responsibilities of the legal and the mental health systems. Mental health professionals must predict violence using the best research and individualized assessments; the legal system must translate these predictions into decisions about whether a given individual is "dangerous" in the legal sense (Grisso & Appelbaum, 1992). It also seems just to include the patient in this process. Many patients freely admit their intention to commit suicide or harm others. Even if they object to involuntary hospitalization, these patients will be more accepting when they are respectfully included in the decision-making process (Lidz et al., 1995; Monahan et al., 1999).

Assessing Suicide Risk Very similar issues arise in the assessment of suicide risk as in the assessment of dangerousness to others. Evidence on the clinical prediction of suicide risk also indicates very high false-positive rates (Pokony, 1983). Yet, concerns about inaccurate prediction are allayed by the fact that suicidal patients typically are committed only when they clearly and directly indicate an imminent likelihood of harming themselves.

Libertarianism and Paternalism in Civil Commitment Civil commitment obviously involves a dramatic restriction in individual liberty, however, as it constitutes confinement

RESEARCH METHODS

Base Rates and Prediction: Justice Blackmun's Error

The prediction of violence seems highly flawed when we learn this fact: Clinicians are wrong in predicting violence two-thirds of the time. However, predicting rare events is flawed for mathematical reasons. *Base rates* (population frequencies) strongly contribute to errors (Meehl & Rosen, 1955).

Consider a hypothetical example. Assume that (1) future, serious violence in a population has a base rate of 3 percent; (2) clinicians predict that violence will occur among 6 percent of the population; and (3) the clinical prediction of violence is wrong two-thirds of the time. These assumptions are portrayed in the following contingency table:

	ACTUALLY VIOLENT	ACTUALLY NOT VIOLENT
Predicted Violent	2% (true positive)	4% (false positive)
Predicted Not Violent	1% (false negative)	93% (true negative)

A quick check of the table will confirm our assumptions: The base rate of actual violence is 3 percent; the clinicians predict violence in 6 percent of the cases; and the prediction that patients will be violent is wrong two-thirds of the time. But examine the table more closely. Even though the prediction of violence is wrong two-thirds of the time, it is also true that the clinicians correctly detect 67 percent of violent patients and 96 percent of nonviolent patients in our example.

How does being wrong 2 out of 3 times beat a coin flip?

Now compare these figures with another hypothetical example: U.S. Supreme Court Justice Harry Blackmun's prediction that a coin flip is more accurate than the clinical prediction of violence. Justice Blackmun assumed that a coin flip would be right half of the time—it would come up heads or tails—while clinical prediction was right only one-third of the time. But the statistics are not as simple as Justice Blackmun thought. Assume that (1) the base rate of violence remains at 3 percent, (2) the coin predicts violence (heads) 50 percent of the time, and (3) the coin flip is random. These assumptions are portrayed in the following contingency table:

	ACTUALLY VIOLENT	ACTUALLY NOT VIOLENT
Predicted Violent	1.5%	48.5%
Predicted Not Violent	1.5%	48.5%

Sorry, Justice Blackmun, but a coin flip does *not* beat clinical prediction. The coin flip correctly detects only 50 percent of violent patients (versus 67 percent) and 50 percent of nonviolent patients (versus 96 percent). The percentage of false positives using Justice Blackmun's method is 48.5%, but using clinical prediction it is 4%. In our first example, the clinical prediction of violence was wrong 67 percent of the time. Justice Blackmun's coin flip was wrong in predicting violence 97 percent of the time [48.5/(48.5 + 1.5)].

A key to understanding Justice Blackmun's error is to recognize the influence of base rates. The base rate of predicting violence using the clinical method (6 percent) was fairly close to the base rate of the actual occurrence of violence (3 percent). However, the base rate of predicting violence using the coin flip (50 percent) was much higher than its actual occurrence. The statistical potential for accurate prediction is maximized when the predictor and the outcome have more similar base rates (Meehl & Rosen, 1955).

As a final illustration of how base rates affect prediction, we return to the coin flip example, but alter one aspect of it. We set the base rate of the occurrence of violence as identical to the base rate with which it is predicted to occur (50 percent). This is illustrated in the following contingency table:

	ACTUALLY VIOLENT	ACTUALLY NOT VIOLENT
Predicted Violent	25%	25%
Predicted Not Violent	25%	25%

The association between the coin flip and the occurrence of violence clearly is random in this example. However, the coin flip now "beats" the clinical prediction of violence. The coin flip is wrong half of the time, which is better than being wrong two-thirds of the time. But this is only a hypothetical example. In the real world, violence is a low-frequency event, and for statistical reasons alone, this makes it difficult to predict (like any infrequent event; Meehl & Rosen, 1955). The clinical prediction of violence is far from perfect, but it is better than chance. Justice Blackmun did not understand the influence of base rates. We hope that you do now.

---

without having committed a crime. Thus this severe restriction on individual liberty requires the highest degree of scrutiny.

Abuses of Civil Commitment The police power rationales for civil commitment have been invoked throughout the history of U.S. law. Even in colonial times the "furiously insane" could be detained in order to prevent them from doing harm to others (Myers, 1983–1984). In contrast, commitment under *parens patriae* rationales have been overused and abused. For example, an 1842 New York State statute required the confinement of all "lunatics" regardless of whether they were dangerous or able to care for themselves. The law commissioned "assessors" to round up lunatics and have them confined for a period of no less than 6 months (Reisner et al., 2004).

You may also be surprised to learn that a husband once could have his wife committed to a mental hospital, and father (and mother) still can. The first circumstance was changed through the efforts of Mrs. Elizabeth Parsons Ware Packard (Myers, 1983–1984). Mrs. Packard was committed to a mental hospital by her husband under an Illinois law that allowed a man to commit his children or his wife to a mental hospital against their will and without the usual evidence of insanity. The commitment was questionable at best. In presenting evidence in favor of her commitment, for example, one doctor noted that Mrs. Packard was rational but she was a "religious bigot" (Reisner et al., 2004). An apparent problem was that her religious beliefs differed from those of her preacher husband. After 3 years in a mental hospital, her suit for freedom was successful. A jury ruled her to be legally sane after only 7 minutes of deliberation. Mrs. Packard subsequently campaigned to revise commitment standards to prevent such abuses, and she influenced the laws in many states.

Commitment of Minors Parents still have the right to commit children to hospitals. According to the 1979 U.S. Supreme Court ruling in *Parham* v. *J.R.* [442 U.S. 584 (1979)], minors, unlike adults, are not entitled to a full hearing before they can be committed to a mental hospital. State laws may add requirements, but parents can commit a minor against the minor's wishes as long as an independent fact finder agrees (Weithorn, 1988). Most children and adolescents in mental hospitals therefore are "voluntary" patients. They were voluntarily committed by their parents.

Libertarians argue for an increased recognition of children's rights. Perhaps their strongest argument is that many minors are committed because they are troublesome to their parents—and because hospitalization is profitable to private psychiatric hospitals (Weithorn, 1988). On the other hand, paternalists are reluctant to interfere with parents' rights and family autonomy. Many also are concerned that mentally ill adolescents are particularly bad judges about what is best for them. Such libertarian and paternalist debates are not limited to children but echo throughout legal philosophies regarding civil commitment.

The Rights of Mental Patients

Several important court cases clarified the rights of mental patients following their civil commitment to a mental hospital. These rights include the right

◀ Elizabeth Parsons Ware Packard was committed to a mental hospital under a nineteenth-century law that allowed a husband to commit a wife against her will. Mrs. Packard later successfully campaigned to change commitment laws to prevent such abuses.

to treatment; the right to treatment in the least restrictive alternative environment; and the right to refuse treatment. Getting Help at the end of this chapter offers information on some of the advocacy groups working to protect mental patients' rights. These libertarian developments clearly offer important protections, yet as you will see, some paternalists think they have gone too far.

Why are most adolescents in mental hospitals voluntarily?

The Right to Treatment Two of the most significant cases for establishing that hospitalized mental patients have a constitutional right to treatment were *Wyatt* v. *Stickney* and *O'Connor* v. *Donaldson.*

Wyatt v. Stickney *Wyatt* v. *Stickney* (1972) began as a dispute over the dismissal of 99 employees from Bryce Hospital in Tuscaloosa, Alabama. The state mental hospital was built in the 1850s and housed nearly 5,000 patients when much-needed staff members were released due to budget cuts. All accounts indicate that conditions in the hospital were very bad even before the layoffs. The buildings were fire hazards, the food was inedible, sanitation was neglected, avoidable sickness was rampant, abuse of patients was frequent, and patients were regularly confined with no apparent therapeutic goal.

Why did Dr. Stickney support the suit against him?

Litigation was filed on behalf of Ricky Wyatt, a resident in the institution, as part of a class action suit against the Alabama mental health commissioner, Dr. Stonewall B. Stickney. The suit argued that institutionalized patients had a right to treatment that Bryce Hospital failed to fulfill. The commissioner was in the unusual position of being a proponent of a suit against him. He wanted to improve the care of the mentally ill in the state but was faced with budget problems. The case was tried and appealed several times, and the patients' suit eventually was upheld.

The victory forced the state of Alabama to provide services, but *Wyatt* had a broader impact. The judicial rulings clearly established that hospitalized mental patients have a right to treatment. Specifically, a federal district court ruled that, at a minimum, public mental institutions must provide (1) a humane psychological and physical environment, (2) qualified staff in numbers sufficient to administer adequate treatment, and (3) individualized treatment plans [334 F. Supp. 1341 (M.D. Ala. 1971) at 1343]. The court also ordered that the changes needed to fulfill patients' rights could not be delayed until funding was available.

The *Wyatt* decision helped focus national attention on the treatment of the mentally ill and the mentally retarded. Numerous "right to treatment" cases were filed. The threat of litigation impelled mental hospitals to improve patient care. *Wyatt* also helped to spur the *deinstitutionalization movement*, which we discuss shortly.

O'Connor v. Donaldson   The U.S. Supreme Court acknowledged mental patients' right to treatment in another landmark case, *O'Connor* v. *Donaldson* [422 U.S. 563 (1975)]. Kenneth Donaldson was confined in a Florida mental hospital for nearly 15 years. He repeatedly requested release, claiming that he was not mentally ill, was not dangerous to himself or others, and was receiving no treatment in the hospital. Eventually, he sued the hospital's superintendent, Dr. J. B. O'Connor, for release, based on the assertion that he had been deprived of his constitutional right to liberty.

The evidence presented at the trial indicated that Donaldson was not and never had been dangerous to himself or others. Testimony also revealed that reliable individuals and agencies in the community had made several offers to care for Donaldson, but Superintendent O'Connor repeatedly rejected them. O'Connor insisted that Donaldson could be released only to the custody of his parents, who were very old and unable to care for him. O'Connor's position on Donaldson's supposed inability to care for himself was puzzling, because Donaldson was employed and had lived on his own for many years before being committed to the hospital. Other evidence documented that Donaldson had received nothing but custodial care while he was hospitalized.

After a series of trials and appeals, the Supreme Court ruled that Donaldson was not dangerous either to himself or others. It further ruled that a state could not confine him as being in need of treatment and yet fail to provide him with that treatment. Specifically, it ordered that "the State cannot constitutionally confine a nondangerous individual who is capable of surviving safely in freedom by himself or with the help of willing and responsible family members or friends." Thus *O'Connor* not only underscored a patient's right to treatment but also set limitations on civil commitment standards. Commitment based on dangerousness to self or others remained unquestioned, but commitment based on inability to care for self became much more controversial, especially if institutionalization offered little treatment or therapeutic benefit.

Treatment in the Least Restrictive Alternative Environment   The patient's right to be treated in the least restrictive alternative environment was first developed in the 1966 case of *Lake* v. *Cameron* [364 F. 2d 657 (D.C. Cir. 1966)]. Catherine Lake was 60 years old when she was committed to St. Elizabeth's Hospital because of "a chronic brain syndrome associated with aging." A particular problem was her tendency to wander away from her home, which posed a threat to her life through exposure to the elements and other dangers.

▶ Kenneth Donaldson proudly displays a copy of the U.S. Supreme Court ruling in his case. The Court held that nondangerous mental patients cannot be confined against their will, a decision that freed Donaldson and set an important precedent for other hospitalized mental patients.

In contesting the commitment, Mrs. Lake did not object to her need for treatment, but she argued that appropriate treatment was available in a less restrictive setting. The court agreed, suggesting several less restrictive alternatives to institutionalization. These alternatives ranged from having Mrs. Lake carry an identification card to treating her in a public nursing home.

Several cases following *Lake* firmly established the doctrine of the least restrictive alternative. Litigation was quickly followed by legislation, as numerous states incorporated the right to treatment in the least restrictive alternative environment into their mental health statutes (Hoffman & Foust, 1977). Although the concept was quickly embraced, no one was or is absolutely certain what the expression "least restrictive alternative" means.

In theory, the least restrictive alternative can be seen as an attempt to balance paternalistic and libertarian concerns in the involuntary treatment of the mentally ill. The state provides mandatory care, but that care must restrict individual liberties to the minimal degree possible. However, questions arise about how to implement the theory. Who should determine what alternative is the least restrictive? Should the court monitor the consideration of alternatives? Should an independent party supervise these decisions?

Perhaps the most important issue about the least restrictive alternative concerns the problem that developed in the original *Lake* case: Less restrictive alternatives to hospitals often are not available. No suitable community care was found for Mrs. Lake, who was returned to the institution. Thus, *Lake* both established patients' right to treatment in the least restrictive alternative environment and foreshadowed the problem of insufficient alternative treatments in the community. The development of community resources has not kept up with the release of patients from mental hospitals. This is especially unfortunate, given that data suggest that community treatment can be more effective than inpatient care (Kiesler, 1982).

Olmstead v. L.C. A 1999 U.S. Supreme Court case, *Olmstead* v. *L.C.* (527 US 581[1999]), upheld the goals of placement in the least restrictive alternative environment but also accepted that the states face problems in providing community care. The case was brought against Tommy Olmstead, the Georgia commissioner

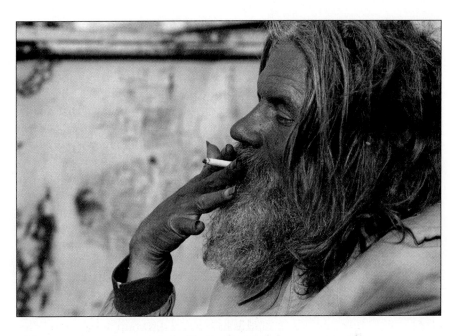

▲ Many homeless people suffer from serious mental illnesses.

of human resources, on behalf of two women with mental retardation and mental illness, L.C. and E.W., who were confined in a Georgia state hospital. The professionals who treated L.C. and E.W. agreed that the women should be treated in the community; however, no community placements were available. The suit was filed under the 1990 Americans with Disabilities Act (ADA), which, among other things, holds that public agencies must provide services to individuals with disabilities, including mental disabilities, "in the most integrated setting appropriate to the needs of qualified individuals with disabilities."

Why are many patients not treated in the "least restrictive" environment?

The Supreme Court upheld the ruling of lower courts indicating that Georgia had failed to comply with the ADA. The ruling held that states must demonstrate their efforts to find appropriate community placements, unless doing so would fundamentally alter the state's services and programs for the mentally disabled. *Olmstead* led to further litigation and some legislative change. As with *Lake's* least restrictive alternative goal, however, progress toward implementing *Olmstead's* antidiscrimination mandate for community placement has been remarkably slow and limited by the narrow interpretation of subsequent cases (Mathis, 2001; Reisner et al., 2004). For their part, both L.C. and E.W. were placed in their communities and have remained there for several years. According to the Legal Aid Society of Atlanta, which brought the suit on their behalf, their psychological well-being and quality of life improved immeasurably as a result.

The Right to Refuse Treatment The third and most recent development in litigation involving people committed to mental hospitals is the *right to refuse treatment,* particularly the right to refuse psychoactive medication. Several courts and state legislatures have concluded that mental health patients have the right to refuse treatment under certain conditions, although this right is on increasingly shaky ground.

The very concept of a patient refusing treatment is problematic in that involuntary hospitalization itself is treatment against a patient's will. The patient who is committed to a mental hospital has refused inpatient treatment but is receiving it anyway. On what grounds can subsequent treatment decisions be refused if the decision about hospitalization already has been taken out of the patient's hands? Many mental health professionals have noted this contradiction, and they argue that patients lose their right to refuse treatment once they are involuntarily hospitalized (Appelbaum, 1994; Gutheil, 1986; Torrey, 2008). After all, a mental health professional is in an awkward position if a patient is committed to a hospital for treatment yet retains the right to refuse medication.

> *Is it contradictory to give committed patients a right to refuse treatment?*

The question of the right to refuse treatment often turns on the issue of informed consent, one of several legal doctrines that can be used to justify a patient's refusal of mental health (or medical) treatments (Hermann, 1990). **Informed consent** requires that (1) a clinician tell a patient about a procedure and its associated risks, (2) the patient understands the information and freely consents to the treatment, and (3) the patient is competent to give consent. When the patient's competence to provide consent is in question, a common approach is to appoint an independent guardian who offers a *substituted judgment,* deciding not what is best for the patient but what the patient would have been likely to do if he or she were competent (Gutheil, 1986).

The rationales for and parameters of patients' right to refuse treatment are still being debated. Several courts have ruled that patients retain their competence to make treatment decisions even if they have been committed through civil procedures. Moreover, half the states have recognized the right to refuse psychoactive medications provided that patients are not dangerous to themselves or others (Hermann, 1990). The U.S. Supreme Court first ruled on this topic in the 1990 case of *Washington* v. *Harper* [110 S. Ct. 1028 (1990)]. This case involved a Washington state prison that overrode a patient's refusal of psychoactive medications. The Court decided in favor of the prison, ruling that the prison's review process sufficiently protected the patient's right to refuse treatment. The process stipulated that the patient's wishes could be overruled only after review by a three-member panel consisting of a psychologist, a psychiatrist, and a deputy warden.

In the subsequent case of *Riggins* v. *Nevada* [504 U.S. 127 (1992)], the Court *upheld* the right of a defendant who was being tried for murder to refuse an extremely high dose of antipsychotic medication. The medication ostensibly was being given to ensure the competence of the defendant to stand trial. In a recent case, *Sell* v. *United States* [123 U.S. 2174 (2003)], the Supreme Court again upheld the right of a defendant to refuse medication when the purpose was to establish competence to stand trial. However, the court signaled that it might have been permissible to medicate the same patient involuntarily if the purpose had been to reduce dangerous behavior (Reisner et al., 2004). Thus, a patient's right to refuse treatment may be limited if the rationale is to protect the patient or the public, but the right to refuse treatment trumps the state's interest when the purpose is to move prosecution forward for a nondangerous individual.

Almost a Revolution The libertarian cases and legislation of the 1960s, 1970s, and 1980s defined key patients' rights, producing what one commentator called "almost a revolution" (Appelbaum, 1994). The revolution ended in the 1990s, with the rise of paternalistic concerns. This new paternalism focuses especially on two issues: (1) treating severely disturbed patients who lack insight into their condition and (2) protecting the public from the violently mentally ill.

A newer, assertive approach to treating patients who lack insight is **outpatient commitment,** that is, mandatory, court-ordered treatment in the community (e.g., mandated therapy and/or medication). Outpatient commitment orders must be based on the same legal standards as inpatient commitment, that is, dangerousness and, in some states, inability to care for self. Because it involves less infringement on civil liberties, however, outpatient commitment criteria may be applied less stringently (Melton et al., 1997; Monahan et al., 2001a). In practice, for example, outpatient commitment is sometimes used to prevent future as opposed to imminent dangerousness. Other forms of "leverage" also may be used to get the seriously mentally ill to comply with treatment recommendations, including the threat of jail or help with obtaining public assistance (Monahan et al., 2005). Outpatient treatment of sufficient length reduces the rate of subsequent hospitalization; thus the coercive procedure can help the seriously mentally ill to receive help in a less restrictive environment (Swartz et al., 2001).

Concerns about public protection are not new, but fears have been fueled by the Virginia Tech shootings. Tech student Seung-Hui Cho had a history of anxiety, depression, and unusual, threatening behavior long before he shot and killed 32 people on April 16, 2007. In fact, a Virginia court declared him to be "an imminent danger to himself as a result of mental illness" in 2005. Unfortunately, the only outcome was an order for Cho to seek outpatient treatment. Could this horror have been prevented by more definitive action? No one knows. But perhaps foreshadowing a new paternalistic trend, Virginia altered its civil commitment law in 2008. The revised statute extends the time frame of potential dangerousness from "imminent" danger to danger "in the near future" (Cohen, Bonnie, & Monahan, 2008).

Deinstitutionalization

The **deinstitutionalization** movement embraces the philosophy that many of the mentally ill and mentally retarded can be better cared for in their community than in large mental hospitals. In 1963, Congress passed the Community Mental Health Centers (CMHC) Act with the strong support of President John F. Kennedy.[1] The act provided for the creation of community care facilities for the seriously mentally ill as alternatives to institutional care. This law began a broad change in the way mental health services are delivered in the United States.

Deinstitutionalization has occurred in dramatic fashion. In 1955, more than 500,000 people in the United States were confined to mental hospitals. By 1995, that number had shrunk to less than 69,000 (*New York Times,* July 12,

1999). The effects of deinstitutionalization are even greater than these numbers suggest, because the overall population grew during this time. Nearly 900,000 people would be in institutions today if the 1955 proportion of inpatients to the total population had remained unchanged (Torrey, 2008).

Unfortunately, CMHCs have not achieved many of their goals. In fact, the needed number of CMHCs were never built, and many in existence do not focus on serious mental illness. Many CMHCs do not even offer emergency treatment or inpatient care, despite the fact that they are mandated to do so by legislation (Torrey, 1997). Other community resources, such as halfway houses, simply have not been implemented in adequate numbers.

> **Has deinstitutionalization worked?**

Other problems with deinstitutionalization are evident. As public hospitalization has declined, the number of mental patients living in nursing homes and other for-profit institutions has grown. More people with a mental illness also are being confined in jail. In fact, 16 percent of the prison population suffers from a serious mental illness (Ditton, 1999). In addition, a *revolving door* phenomenon has developed in which more patients are admitted to psychiatric hospitals more frequently but for shorter periods of time. For example, one study found that 24 percent of inpatients in New York City had 10 or more previous admissions (Karras & Otis, 1987). Moreover, the deinstitutionalized mentally ill constitute a large part of the homeless population (Torrey, 2008). One study found that 31 percent of the homeless were in need of mental health services (Roth & Bean, 1986).

More Paternalism? Some of the problems of deinstitutionalization are compounded by restrictive civil commitment laws. One commentary graphically described the situation as one in which patients were "rotting with their rights on" (Appelbaum & Gutheil, 1980). Torrey (1988)

[1]President Kennedy had a special interest in mental health because of his sister Rosemary. She was mildly mentally retarded as a child, but she became psychotic as a young adult and underwent a failed lobotomy that left her so impaired that she had to be confined to a nursing home.

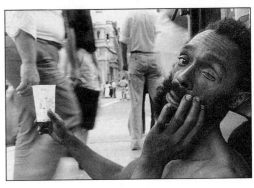

▼ These contrasting images illustrate how mental patients often are neglected both inside and outside of institutions. The photo on the left, taken several decades ago, shows some of the depressing and dehumanizing conditions that characterized many institutions for the mentally ill. The photo on the right depicts the contemporary problem of homelessness. Many homeless people are deinstitutionalized mental patients.

argued, "Freedom to be insane is an illusory freedom, a cruel hoax perpetrated on those who cannot think clearly by those who will not think clearly" (p. 34).

As noted, outpatient commitment is one important alternative that can balance some of these paternalistic concerns against the libertarian fears of restricted freedom. Other commentators call for the involuntary treatment of inpatients, but only following careful review (Appelbaum, 1994). Others support more paternalism in civil commitment laws but argue that a broader reorientation is needed. Most psychiatrists, clinical psychologists, and social workers treat only the "worried well." Perhaps new incentives are needed to direct more of their efforts toward helping the seriously mentally ill (Torrey, 2008).

MENTAL HEALTH AND FAMILY LAW

Mental health professionals involved with family law issues typically work with people whose problems are less severe than those involved in mental health law. This is evident in the major issues that form the focus of family law: divorce, spousal abuse, foster care, adoption, juvenile delinquency, child custody disputes, and child abuse and neglect. Any one of these problems can involve serious psychopathology, but they more commonly involve family members who are only mildly disturbed or are functioning normally.

We consider both family law and mental health law issues together in this chapter because the opinions and advice of mental health professionals are frequently sought by legal professionals working in both areas. However, family and mental health law are distinct in the legal system. The two areas have different historical roots and practices. Much of mental health law is based on the state's police power obligations, but virtually all of family law is premised on *parens patriae* duties. Attorneys may specialize in one or the other area, but rarely both. In fact, family law cases typically are tried in separate courts, known variously as "juvenile courts," "domestic relations courts," or "family courts."

What does "children's best interests" mean?

In theory, family courts are supposed to help and protect children and families, a goal that is psychological as well as legal. Psychological issues carry great weight in family court because of this philosophy—and because family law often is vague. For example, the guiding principle in custody and abuse cases is to make decisions according to the "child's best interest." This may sound laudable, but the law does not clearly define "best." This leaves family court judges in a position of making very difficult decisions with very little legal guidance. As law professor Robert Mnookin (1975) has pointed out:

> Deciding what is best for a child poses a question no less ultimate than the purposes and values of life itself. Should the judge be primarily concerned with the child's happiness? Or with the child's spiritual and religious training? Should the judge be concerned with the economic "productivity" of the child when he grows up? Are the primary values of life in warm interpersonal relationships, or in discipline and self-sacrifice? Is stability and security for a child more desirable than intellectual stimulation? These questions could be elaborated endlessly. And yet, where is the judge to look for the set of values that should inform the choice of what is best for the child? (pp. 260–261)

Judges are supposed to look to the law to define the values that define "best," but few answers can be found there. As a result, courts frequently turn to mental health professionals for guidance in trying to decide what might be best for any given child in a custody dispute or an abuse/neglect proceeding, the two issues we briefly consider.

Child Custody Disputes

About 40 percent of children in the United States today will experience their parents' divorce, a circumstance that can lead to a custody dispute (Emery, 1999a). Child custody disputes also may occur between cohabiting couples and even between extended family members. For example, the case of Elian Gonzalez involved a Cuban boy whose mother died while trying to come to the United States. A national debate focused on whether Elian should be returned to live with his father in Cuba (the parents were divorced) or stay in the United States with distant relatives. He eventually was returned to live with his father.

Although the legal terminology differs from state to state, **child custody** involves two issues: *physical custody*, or where the children will live at what times; and *legal custody*, or how the parents will make decisions about their children's lives. *Sole custody* refers to a situation in which only one parent retains physical or legal custody of the children; in contrast, in *joint custody* both parents retain legal or physical custody or both.

The majority of custody decisions are made outside of court through attorneys who negotiate for the parents. A growing number of custody decisions are being made by the parents themselves, however, typically with the help of a *mediator*—a neutral third party who facilitates the parents' discussions. Only a small percentage of custody disputes are decided in court by a judge (Maccoby & Mnookin, 1992). Mental health professionals may be involved in providing recommendations during attorney negotiations, they may provide expert testimony in court, or they may act as mediators themselves.

Expert Witnesses in Custody Determinations The law directs judges to consider only very general factors in evaluating a child's best interests, including the quality of the child's relationship with each parent, the family environment provided by each parent, each parent's mental health, the relationship between the parents, and the child's expressed wishes, if any (Emery, Sbarra, & Grover, 2005). Evaluating these broad family circumstances and drawing implications for child custody is a precarious task. In fact, some commentators have argued that, because of inexact scientific knowledge, mental health professionals should refrain from ever conducting custody evaluations (O'Donohue & Bradley, 1999).

Others suggest that the problem lies in the system for determining child custody (Emery et al., 2005). The "child's best interests" standard can increase conflict between parents, because the directive is so vague. Virtually any information that makes one parent look bad and the other look good may be construed as helping a parent's case—and people who have been married have much private and potentially damaging information about each other. This is a problem, because conflict between parents is strongly related to maladjustment among children following divorce (Emery, 1982, 1999; Grych & Fincham, 1990). Many mental health and legal experts believe they serve children and the legal system better if they help parents decide what is best for their own children by settling custody disputes outside of court (Emery et al., 2005).

Divorce Mediation In **divorce mediation**, parents meet with a neutral third party, who may be a mental health or legal professional, who helps them to identify, negotiate, and ultimately resolve their disputes. The role of mediator is very different from the evaluation role of mental health professionals, and mediation also is a major change in the practice of the law. Mediators adopt a cooperative approach to dispute resolution, treating separated parents as parents rather than as legal adversaries (Emery, 1994).

Mediation reduces custody hearings, helps parents reach decisions more quickly, and is viewed more favorably than litigation (Emery, 1994; Emery, Matthews, & Kitzmann, 1994; Emery, et al., 2005). One randomized trial found that 5 to 6 hours of mediation causes nonresidential parents to remain far more involved in their children's lives and work together better *12 years later* (Emery et al., 2001). Many states now require or mandate mediation as a more "family friendly" forum for dispute resolution. Consider the following brief case study.

Brief Case **Study**
A Custody Dispute

Jim and Suzanne had been divorced for 2 years when they first came to a mediator. The parents were disputing custody of their 8-year-old daughter, Ellen, and 10-year-old son, Will. The parents had maintained an uneasy joint physical custody arrangement. Every other week the children alternated between each of their parents' homes. However, Suzanne recently decided to sue for sole custody. She said she was worried about Will's increasingly difficult behavior, and Ellen's lack of activities with her father. Jim argued that Ellen's real concern was his recent remarriage. He said that he was eager to get on with his life with his new wife, Adriana, but Suzanne would not accept her.

Suzanne and Jim were referred to mediation by their lawyers, who urged their clients to avoid renewing the long and contentious negotiations that had surrounded their divorce. Suzanne and Jim had decided on joint custody as a last-minute compromise. They reached this decision literally on the courthouse steps.

The mediator urged Suzanne and Jim to take their children's perspective and, for the children's sake, to try to cooperate as parents even though they were not "friends." In private, the mediator also encouraged Suzanne to face her fears of losing her children to Jim's new family. Speaking to Jim alone, the mediator bluntly told him that, while he may have "moved on," Suzanne would always be a part of his life as the children's mother.

Following several frank discussions about their feelings, preferences, and past problems with joint custody, Suzanne and Jim reached a settlement. They would return to the week-to-week joint physical custody schedule but with a new commitment to communicate better, to support each other's efforts in parenting, and to make the children's routines more consistent across their homes. Adriana came for one of the last mediation sessions. All the adults agreed that Adriana would be an important part of raising Will and Ellen. Still, no one could or wanted to replace Suzanne or Jim as the children's parents.

Child Abuse

Child abuse involves the accidental or intentional infliction of harm to a child due to acts or omissions on the part of an adult responsible for the child's care. Such abuse of children was "discovered" to be a problem only relatively recently. The first child protection efforts in the United States did not begin until 1875. A much publicized case of foster parents who physically beat a young girl in their care led to the founding of the New York Society for the Prevention of Cruelty to Children. The society was given the power to police child abuse, and other states rapidly established similar organizations and legislation (Lazoritz, 1990).

Still, public attention did not consistently focus on child abuse until 1962, when the physi-

► A memorial for Elisa Izquierdo, a 6-year-old girl who was beaten to death by her mother. The child had been repeatedly abused by her mother and stepfather, but overwhelmed social service agencies found at least two reports of her abuse to be "unfounded."

cian Henry Kempe wrote about the "battered child syndrome." Kempe documented tragic cases of child abuse in which children suffered repeated injuries, fractured bones, and, in a substantial number of cases, death (Kempe et al., 1962). Kempe's influential article prompted legislation that defined child abuse (*abuse* is defined differently in different states) and required physicians to report suspected cases. This reporting requirement continues today, and in most states it extends to include mental health professionals, schoolteachers, and other professionals who have regular contact with children. In fact, mental health professionals not only can, but they must also break the confidentiality of psychotherapy if they suspect child abuse (Melton & Limber, 1989).

Four forms of child abuse generally are distinguished: physical abuse, sexual abuse, neglect, and psychological abuse (American Psychological Association, 1995). *Physical child abuse* involves the intentional use of physically painful and harmful actions. The definition of physical abuse is complicated by the fact that corporal punishments like spanking are widely accepted discipline practices (Emery & Laumann-Billings, 1998; Gershoff, 2002).

Child sexual abuse involves sexual contact between an adult and a child. Reports of child sexual abuse have increased astronomically in recent years, as the problem has been fully recognized only since the 1980s (Glaser, 2002; Haugaard & Reppucci, 1988). Although exact estimates are difficult to make, the sexual abuse of children is now known to be far more prevalent than would have been believed a short time ago.

Child neglect, the most commonly reported form of child abuse, involves placing children at risk for serious physical or psychological harm by failing to provide basic and expected care. Some children are severely neglected, and they experience extreme failure in their growth and development as a result (Wolfe, 1987). Some children also suffer *psychological abuse*—repeated denigration in the absence of physical harm.

Munchausen-by-proxy syndrome (MBPS) is a unique, rare, but potentially very harmful form of physical child abuse that merits special note. In MBPS, a parent feigns, exaggerates, or induces illness in a child. In benign cases, the parent simply fabricates the child's illness; in more serious cases, the parent actually induces illness. One study used covert video surveillance to monitor parents suspected of MBPS (Southall et al.,

1997). Of 39 children, video recordings captured 30 parents trying to harm their children through such extreme acts as attempting suffocation, trying to break a child's arm, and attempted poisoning with a disinfectant. Alarmingly, of the 41 siblings of the children, 12 had previously died suddenly and unexpectedly. These results clearly illustrate that MBPS can be a severe and ultimately deadly form of child abuse.

The number of reported cases of child abuse has increased dramatically in the United States since the 1970s and through today. As indicated in Figure 18–2, the number of reports of child abuse made to social service agencies climbed from 669,000 in 1976 to 3,353,000 in 2003. However, over two-thirds of all reports of abuse are found to be unsubstantiated. One reason for this, according to some critics, is that the concept of abuse and neglect is applied too broadly by primarily white, middle-class social workers who are evaluating primarily black, low-income families (Besharov, 1992).

When an allegation of abuse is substantiated, one of the major questions is whether to remove the child from the home. Each year over 100,000 maltreated children are placed in *foster care,* where they live temporarily with another family.

Foster care protects children who are in physical danger, but as many as half of all children placed in foster care are in no immediate danger of physical injury (Besharov, 1988). Stable foster care may offer psychological benefits, as well as physical protection (Wald, Carlsmith, & Leiderman, 1988). However, half the children placed in foster care remain there for at least 2 years, almost one-third are separated from their parents for over 6 years, and a substantial proportion live in many different foster homes during this time (Besharov, 1988).

Recent federal legislation encourages the adoption of children who are likely to be placed in foster care for long periods of time. However, this raises an even more controversial issue, the *termination of parental rights,* that is, the nonvoluntary removal of any right a parent has to care for and supervise his or her child. Obviously, this is an extreme step, and one that the courts take only with great reluctance.

PEARSON
mypsych lab **VIDEO CASE**

CHILDHOOD SEXUAL ABUSE

KAREN

"He used to lock me in the car, it would be 180 degrees, and he would leave me there for two or three hours ..."

As you watch the video, think about children's limited perspective on sexuality, trust, and protecting themselves, and how the nature of sexual abuse cannot be fully recognized until the child is older.

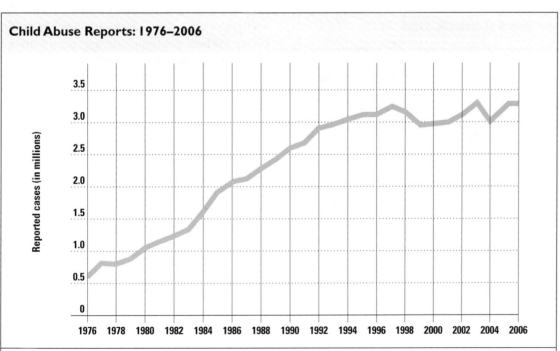

Child Abuse Reports: 1976–2006

FIGURE 18–2 Reports of child abuse made to social service agencies have increased sharply. Experts disagree about what has increased—actual abuse or the awareness and reporting of abuse.

Source: C.T. Wang, K. Harding, 1999, *Current Trends in Child Abuse Reporting and Fatalities: The Results of the 1998 Annual Fifty State Survey.* Chicago: National Center on Child Abuse Prevention and Research. Web site: www.acf.hhs.gov/programs/cb/stats_research/index.htm

As with child custody decisions, judicial determinations about foster care and other possible dispositions of child abuse cases are guided by the child's best interest standard. Psychologists frequently play a role in these legal proceedings by investigating allegations of abuse in interviews with children, making recommendations to the court about appropriate placements for children, and providing treatment to children and families (Becker et al., 1995; Melton & Limber, 1989).

Some have argued that too many of our legal and mental health efforts have been devoted to identifying families as abusive, while not enough resources are available for helping families (Huntington, 2007). The definition of abuse is applied broadly, and consequently the child protective service system has been overwhelmed by the need to investigate report after report (Emery & Laumann-Billings, 2002). In order to allow child protective service agencies to offer more supportive services to stressed families, many states are dividing reports of suspected abuse into more and less serious cases. More serious cases are investigated as usual, but social workers offer troubled parents support, counseling, and referral in less serious cases (Emery & Laumann-Billings, 1998). Initial evidence indicates that this more family friendly approach does *not* increase the risk for future abuse, but, in fact, reduces future recurrence, is liked better by parents, and saves agencies time and money (Loman & Siegel, 2005).

First, we'll look for repressed memories of malpractice suits.

PROFESSIONAL RESPONSIBILITIES AND THE LAW

Psychiatrists, clinical psychologists, and social workers all have **professional responsibilities,** obligations to meet the ethical standards of their profession and to uphold the laws of the states in which they practice. The duties of mental health professionals are numerous and varied. Here we focus on two important and examples: negligence and confidentiality.

Professional Negligence and Malpractice

Negligence occurs when a professional fails to perform in a manner that is consistent with the level of skill exercised by other professionals in the field. Simply put, negligence is substandard professional service. Malpractice refers to situations in which professional negligence results in harm to clients or patients. In the law, malpractice is demonstrated when (1) a professional has a duty to conform to a standard of conduct, (2) the professional is negligent in that duty, (3) the professional's client experiences damages or loss, and (4) it is reasonably certain that the negligence caused the damages (Reisner et al., 2004). When professionals are found to be guilty of malpractice, they are subject to disciplinary action both from their professional organizations and through state licensing boards, as well as to civil suits and possibly criminal actions.

The inappropriate use of medication and negligent treatment are two of the more common reasons for malpractice claims against mental health professionals (see Figure 18–3). Another is the existence of a sexual relationship between therapists and their clients. The ethical codes of the American Psychological Association and the American Psychiatric Association both prohibit sexual relationships between therapists and their clients. Other claims of professional negligence stem from the failure to prevent suicide, failure to prevent violence against others, and violations of confidentiality. In the future, a new area of professional negligence may become more important: the failure to inform clients about effective treatment alternatives.

Informed Consent on Alternative Treatments Patients may be given a wide range of alternative treatments for the same mental disorder. Unfortunately, the choice of treatment hinges, in part, on chance factors such as the professional's "theoretical orientation" (see Chapter 3). Should mental health professionals be required to reduce this element of chance by informing their patients about alternative treatments and research on their effectiveness?

This issue was raised in *Osheroff* v. *Chestnut Lodge* [62 Md. App. 519, 490 A. 2d. 720 (Md. App. 1985)]. In 1979, Dr. Rafael Osheroff, an internist, admitted himself to Chestnut Lodge, a private psychiatric hospital in Maryland that had long been famous as a center for psychoanalytic psychotherapy. Dr. Osheroff had a history of depression and anxiety, problems that previously had been treated on an outpatient basis with some success using tricyclic antidepressant medication. Apparently, Dr. Osheroff had not been taking his medication prior to his admission to Chestnut Lodge, and his condition had worsened. He was diagnosed by hospital staff as suffering primarily from a narcissistic personality disorder and secondarily from manic–depressive illness (Klerman, 1990b; Malcolm, 1987).

Hospital staff did not offer medication to Dr. Osheroff during his hospitalization. They hoped that, through therapy, he could achieve what they viewed as "more basic" changes in his personality. Dr. Osheroff was seen in individual psychoanalytic psychotherapy four times a week, and he participated in group therapy as well. During Dr. Osheroff's 7 months of hospitalization, his condition did not improve and actually may have deteriorated somewhat. After this time, his family discharged him from Chestnut Lodge and admitted him to another private psychiatric hospital, Silver Hill in Connecticut. At Silver Hill, Dr. Osheroff was diagnosed as suffering from a psychotic depressive reaction, and he was treated with phenothiazines and tricyclic antidepressants. He began to improve within 3 weeks after treatment began, and he was discharged from the hospital within 3 months. Although he continued to experience some problems, following his discharge Dr. Osheroff was able to resume his medical practice with the help of outpatient psychotherapy and antidepressants (Klerman, 1990b; Malcolm, 1987).

In 1982, Dr. Osheroff sued Chestnut Lodge for negligence. His claim stated that Chestnut Lodge had misdiagnosed his condition, failed to offer appropriate treatment, and failed to offer him informed consent about treatment alternatives (Malcolm, 1987). He argued that research available in 1979 provided clear support for the use of medication in the treatment of severe depression but offered no support for the use of psychoanalytic psychotherapy in the treatment of either depression or narcissistic personality disorder. As required by state law in Maryland, the matter was first heard by an arbitration panel. The panel initially awarded Dr. Osheroff $250,000 in damages, but it later reduced the amount of the award. Both sides appealed the decision of the arbitration board, but the matter was eventually settled out of court (Klerman, 1990b).

The private settlement of this case limits its precedent-setting value. Nevertheless, it suggests that mental health professionals will be held to increasingly higher standards in offering alternative treatments, or at least in informing patients about the risks and benefits of various treatments. As researchers demonstrate that certain approaches are more or less effective in treating particular disorders, offering informed consent about treatment

> *Is informing patients about alternative, effective treatments a professional responsibility?*

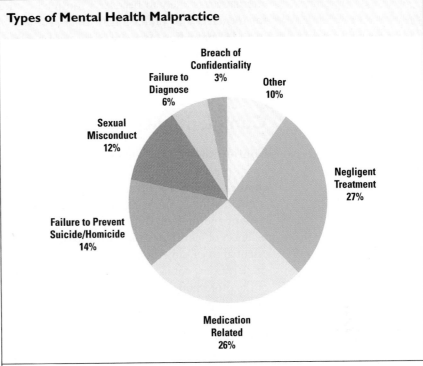

Types of Mental Health Malpractice

Breach of Confidentiality 3%

Failure to Diagnose 6%

Sexual Misconduct 12%

Failure to Prevent Suicide/Homicide 14%

Other 10%

Negligent Treatment 27%

Medication Related 26%

FIGURE 18–3 Categories of closed malpractice claims against psychiatrists among a sample of 188 closed cases from 1996–2005.

Source: From "Psychiatry Malpractice and Administrative Inquiries of Alleged Physician Misconduct" by D. L. Meyer, *Psychiatric Clinics of North America, 29* (2006), 616. Copyright © 2006. Reprinted by permission of Elsevier.

alternatives is likely to become a routine practice for mental health professionals. *Informed consent* includes providing accurate information about risks and benefits in an understandable and noncoercive manner.

Confidentiality

Confidentiality—the ethical obligation not to reveal private communications—is basic to psychotherapy. The therapist's guarantee of privacy is essential to encouraging clients to disclose important and difficult information, and the maintenance of confidentiality with past clients is essential to gaining the trust of future clients. For these reasons, confidentiality standards are a part of the professional ethics of all of the major mental health professions.

Despite the overriding importance of confidentiality, mental health professionals sometimes may be compelled by law to reveal confidential information. For example, all states require mental health professionals to break confidentiality and report suspected cases of child abuse. This requirement can create dilemmas for therapists (Smith & Meyer, 1985). Must a therapist make the limits on confidentiality clear before beginning therapy? If therapists tell their clients that their disclosures of child abuse will be reported, does this encourage clients to be something less than honest? Does reporting child abuse undermine the therapeutic relationship that might benefit an abused child?

When must therapists break confidentiality?

Confidentiality also must be broken when clients are dangerous to themselves or others, so that civil commitment can proceed. The influential case of *Tarasoff* v. *Regents of the University of California* [551 P.2d 334 (1976)] identified another obligation that therapists may assume when a client expresses violent intentions: the duty to warn the potential victim.

The Duty to Protect On October 27, 1969, a young woman named Tatiana Tarasoff was killed by Prosenjit Poddar, a foreign student at the University of California at Berkeley. Poddar had pursued a romantic relationship with Tarasoff, but after having been repeatedly rejected by her, he sought treatment at the Berkeley student health facility. Poddar was diagnosed as suffering from paranoid schizophrenia, and the clinical psychologist who treated Poddar concluded that he was dangerous to himself and others. After consulting with two psychiatrists, the psychologist decided to pursue civil commitment. He notified the campus police of his concerns and asked them to detain Poddar for the purpose of an emergency commitment. The police concluded that Poddar was not dangerous, however, and released him after he agreed to stay away from Tarasoff. Poddar subsequently discontinued therapy, and no one notified Tarasoff that Poddar posed a threat to her life. Poddar had never mentioned Tatiana Tarasoff by name, but the information he related to the psychologist was sufficient to deduce her identity. Two months after the police had questioned him, Poddar murdered Tarasoff after being rejected by her once more.

Tarasoff's parents sued the university, the therapists, and the police for negligence. The California Supreme Court ruled that the defendants were liable for failing to warn the woman of the impending danger. Subsequent California cases and legislation altered the *duty to warn* potential victims to a more general *duty to protect,* which may involve warning but alternatively might involve protective actions like hospitalizing the potentially dangerous patient (Weinstock et al., 2006).

The *Tarasoff* case prompted almost 20 states to enact laws outlining therapists' duty to protect potential victims of violence (Appelbaum, 1994). Still, the issues raised by *Tarasoff* are far from resolved. If he or she has a client with AIDS, must a psychologist warn unwitting sexual partners about the risk? In the case of the duty to protect, as with other issues in psychology and the law, psychologists sometimes must walk a thin line between their professional responsibilities and their legal obligations.

▶ Tatiana Tarasoff and Prosenjit Poddar, the man who killed her. The California Supreme Court ruled that Poddar's therapist should have warned Tarasoff that her life might be in danger.

GETTING HELP

Getting help for people with emotional disorders sometimes involves challenging various societal and legal obstacles. Advocacy can be a way of giving help as well as ensuring that you and those you care for can get help when it is needed. For serious mental illness, the National Alliance for the Mentally Ill (NAMI) is the largest and most effective national advocacy organization. In addition to its national efforts, you may be able to find a local chapter of NAMI in your community. Another advocacy group is the Judge David L. Bazelon Center for Mental Health Law. The Bazelon Center focuses more specifically on legal issues in the treatment of psychological disorders. The center tracks funding, legislation, and litigation, and it offers legal advice and assistance in selected cases. The center's Web site gives information on a number of their pressing priorities such as improving mental health treatment systems, increasing the availability of services for underserved populations (children, the aged), and addressing homelessness and housing needs. The American Bar Association's Commission on Mental and Physical Disability Law also collects and offers a wealth of information on mental health law and the rights of people disabled by mental illness.

An excellent book on these topics is *The Rights of People with Mental Disabilities: The Authoritative ACLU Guide to the Rights of People with Mental Illness and Mental Retardation,* by Robert Levy and Leonard Rubenstein. Another book (and author) that we highly recommend is E. Fuller Torrey's *Out of the Shadows: Confronting America's Mental Illness Crisis.*

Mental health advocacy involves individual as well as organized efforts. We encourage you to advocate directly in any number of small ways. You can educate yourself and others about the needs of the mentally ill and our society's failure to meet those needs. In everyday interactions, you can help by standing up for what you believe is right and just in our society's response to the immense problem of mental illness. Even more simply, you can respond receptively to agencies and individuals in your community. Advocacy, like therapy, begins by recognizing that the person with a psychological disorder is, first and foremost, a person.

■ SUMMARY

The legal system assumes that behavior is the product of **free will,** the capacity to make choices and therefore holds people responsible for their own actions. Scientific psychology instead emphasizes **determinism,** the idea that behavior is caused by biological, psychological, and social forces. Assumptions about free will and determinism conflict strongly in the **insanity defense.** The legally insane individual is assumed to have lost free will and, therefore, is not held responsible for his actions. Professionals who serve as **expert witnesses** offer opinions about a defendant's state of mind, but the court is responsible for determining the ultimate issue, insanity. According to the M'Naghten test, **insanity** is established if a mental disease or defect prevents a criminal from knowing the wrongfulness of his or her actions. The irresistible impulse test indicates that defendants are insane if they were unable to control their actions because of mental disease or defect.

Competence is the defendant's ability to understand legal proceedings and to participate in his or her own defense. Many more people accused of crimes are institutionalized because of incompetence than because of insanity. Mental health issues also arise in sentencing guilty parties. The death penalty was recently outlawed for people with mental retardation, while sexual predators are being confined for dangerousness even after completing their sentences.

Civil commitment—hospitalizing people against their will—reflects philosophical tensions between libertarian views, which emphasize protecting the rights of the individual, and paternalistic approaches, which emphasize the state's duty to protect its citizens. Three grounds dominate commitment laws: (1) unable to care for self, (2) dangerous to self, and (3) dangerous to others. There is some relation between mental illness and "dangerousness," and mental health professionals can predict dangerousness with some accuracy. The fact that violence has a low **base rate** is a major contributor to inaccurate prediction. Minors can be hospitalized by their parents, so strictly speaking they generally are not involuntarily committed.

The right to treatment indicates that hospitalized patients must receive therapy and not just custodial care. The right to treatment in the least restrictive environment indicates that therapy should be provided in community settings when it is possible and appropriate. The right to refuse treatment indicates that patients cannot be forced to receive certain treatments without **informed consent** or a careful substituted judgment. Concerns about patients' rights have given impetus to the **deinstitutionalization** movement, caring for many of the mentally ill and mentally retarded in their community rather than in large mental hospitals. Unfortunately, the lack of follow-up care undermines community care. **Outpatient commitment** may help to balance concerns about requiring treatment while protecting liberties.

Mental health professionals often are involved in family law as well as mental health law. **Child custody** decisions involve determinations about both physical custody—where the children will live—and legal custody—how the parents will make decisions about their children. Custody decisions are based on the child's best interests standard, a vague directive that creates problems for families. Parents can decide their custody arrangements themselves in **divorce mediation.**

Child abuse may involve physical abuse, sexual abuse, neglect, or psychological abuse. A rare but potentially dangerous form of abuse is **Munchausen-by-proxy syndrome.** Reports of child abuse have increased greatly in recent years, but neither the law nor mental health professionals determined how best to fulfill children's best interests in these cases. Currently, agencies are overloaded simply investigating abuse allegations.

Psychiatrists, clinical psychologists, and social workers all have **professional responsibilities** to meet the ethical standards of their profession and to uphold the law. Key professional issues include obtaining informed consent about alternative treatment procedures and maintaining **confidentiality.** A relatively new concern is the duty to protect potential victims when a client reveals violent intentions.

THE BIG PICTURE CRITICAL THINKING REVIEW

How does the law define "insanity?"

The rationale behind insanity acquittals is not whether the perpetrator suffers from a mental illness. The issue is whether the defendant lacks the capacity to distinguish "good from evil," the inability to distinguish right from wrong. (SEE PAGE 563)

How does the law justify civil commitment?

American law contains two broad rationales for civil commitment. The first is based on the state's *parens patriae* authority; the second is based on the state's *police power.* (SEE PAGE 571)

How does being wrong two out of three times beat a coin flip?

The statistics are not as simple as Justice Blackmun thought. (SEE PAGE 574)

Why are many patients not treated in the "least restrictive" environment?

Perhaps the most important issue about the least restrictive alternative is that less restrictive alternatives to hospitals often are not available. (SEE PAGE 577)

Has deinstitutionalization worked?

Problems with deinstitutionalization are evident. (SEE PAGE 579)

When must therapists break confidentiality?

Confidentiality must be broken when clients are dangerous to themselves or others, so that civil commitment can proceed. (SEE PAGE 586)

■ KEY TERMS

Glossary

Abnormal psychology The application of psychological science to the study of mental disorders. Includes investigation of the causes and treatment of psychopathological conditions.

Abstinence violation effect The guilt and perceived loss of control that the person feels whenever he or she slips and finds himself or herself returning to drug use after an extended period of abstinence.

Acquired immune deficiency syndrome (AIDS) A disease caused by the human immunodeficiency virus (HIV) that attacks the immune system and leaves the patient susceptible to unusual infections.

Actuarial interpretation Analysis of test results based on an explicit set of rules derived from empirical research.

Acute stress disorder (ASD) A category of mental disorder in DSM-IV that is defined as a reaction occurring within 4 weeks following a traumatic event and is characterized by dissociative symptoms, reexperiencing, avoidance, and marked anxiety or arousal. Contrasts with posttraumatic stress disorder, which either lasts longer or has a delayed onset.

Adjustment disorder A DSM-IV classification designating the development of clinically significant symptoms in response to stress in which the symptoms are not severe enough to warrant classification as another mental disorder.

Affect The pattern of observable behaviors that are associated with subjective feelings. People express affect through changes in their facial expressions, the pitch of their voices, and their hand and body movements.

Ageism A number of misconceptions and prejudices about aging and older adults.

Agnosia ("perception without meaning") The inability to identify objects. The person's sensory functions are unimpaired, but he or she is unable to recognize the source of stimulation.

Agoraphobia An exaggerated fear of being in situations from which escape might be difficult. Literally means "fear of the marketplace," and is sometimes described as fear of public spaces.

Allegiance effect A characterization of psychotherapy outcome research such that investigators commonly find the most effective treatment is the one to which they hold a theoretical allegiance.

Alogia A form of speech disturbance found in schizophrenia. Can include reductions in the amount of speech (poverty of speech) or speech that does not convey meaningful information (poverty of content of speech).

Alzheimer's disease A form of dementia in which cognitive impairment appears gradually and deterioration is progressive. A definite diagnosis of Alzheimer's desease requires the observation of two specific types of brain lesions: neurofibrillary tangles and senile plaques.

Amenorrhea The absence of at least three consecutive menstrual cycles; a defining symptom of anorexia nervosa in females.

Amnestic disorder A form of cognitive disorder characterized by memory impairments that are more limited or circumscribed than those seen in dementia or delirium.

Amniocentesis The extraction of fluid from the amniotic sac in order to test for chromosomal and genetic defects in the developing fetus.

Amyloid plaques A central core of homogeneous protein material know as beta-amyloid found in large numbers in the cerebral cortex of patients with Alzheimer's disease, but they are not unique to that condition.

Analogue study A research procedure in which the investigator studies behaviors that resemble mental disorders or isolated features of mental disorders. Usually employed in situations in which the investigator hopes to gain greater experimental control over the independent variable.

Androgyny The possession of both "female" and "male" gender-role characteristics.

Anhedonia The inability to experience pleasure. In contrast to blunted affect, which refers to the lack of outward expression, anhedonia is a lack of positive subjective feelings.

Anorexia nervosa A type of eating disorder characterized by the refusal to maintain a minimally normal body weight along with other symptoms related to body image.

Anterograde amnesia The inability to learn or remember new material after a particular point in time.

Antisocial personality disorder A pervasive and persistent disregard for, and frequent violation of, the rights of other people. Also known as *psychopathy.* In DSM-IV, it is defined in terms of a persistent pattern of irresponsible and antisocial behavior that begins during childhood or adolescence and continues into the adult years.

Antipsychotic drugs Various forms of medication that have a beneficial effect on positive symptoms (hallucinations and delusions) of psychosis and psychotic disorganization (e.g., disorganized speech). The effect of first generation antipsychotic drugs depends largely on the blockade of receptors in dopamine pathways in the brain. Second generation antipsychotics have a much broader effect on different neurotransmitters. All antipsychotic drugs have negative side effects, including motor side effects such as tardive dyskinesia.

Anxiety A diffuse emotional reaction that is out of proportion to threats from the environment. Rather than being directed toward the person's present, anxiety is typically associated with the anticipation of future problems.

Anxious attachment An insecure relationship in which an infant or child shows ambivalence about seeking reassurance or security from an attachment figure.

Aphasia The loss or impairment of previously acquired abilities in language comprehension or production that cannot be explained by sensory or motor defects or by diffuse brain dysfunction.

Apraxia The loss of a previously acquired ability to perform purposeful movements in response to verbal commands. The problem cannot be explained by muscle weakness or simple incoordination.

Asperger's disorder A subtype of pervasive developmental disorder that is identical to autism (oddities in social interaction, stereotyped behavior) with the exception that there is no clinically significant delay in language.

Assessment The process of gathering and organizing information about a person's behavior.

Attachments Selective bonds that develop between infants and their caregivers, usually their parents, and are theorized to be related to later development. Analogous to the process of imprinting, which has been observed in many animals.

Attention deficit Inattention characterized by distractibility, frequent shifts from one uncompleted activity to another, careless mistakes, and/or poor organization or effort. A key symptom of attention-deficit/hyperactivity disorder.

Attention-deficit/hyperactivity disorder (ADHD) A psychological disorder of childhood characterized by hyperactivity, inattention, and impulsivity. Typically has an onset by the early school years.

Attribution Perceived causes; people's beliefs about cause–effect relations.

Authoritative parenting A style of parenting that is both loving and firm and is often used by parents of well-adjusted children.

Autism Literally, "absorption in one's own mental activity." Formally, a severe pervasive developmental disorder characterized by profound problems in social interaction, communication, and stereotyped behavior, interests, and activities (see also *autistic disorder*).

Autistic disorder (autism) A severe form of pervasive developmental disorder characterized by oddities in social interaction (autistic aloneness), communication impairments, and stereotyped behavior, interests, and activities.

Autonomic nervous system The division of the peripheral nervous system that regulates the functions of various bodily organs such as the heart and stomach. The actions of the autonomic nervous system are largely involuntary, and it has two branches, the sympathetic and parasympathetic nervous systems.

Aversion therapy A classical conditioning technique for attempting to eliminate unwanted behavior by pairing an unpleasant (aversive) stimulus with the behavior—for example, inducing nausea when alcohol is consumed.

Avoidant personality disorder An enduring pattern of thinking and behavior that is characterized by pervasive social discomfort, fear of negative evaluation, and timidity. People with this disorder tend to be socially isolated outside of family circles. They want to be liked by others, but they are easily hurt by even minimal signs of disapproval from other people.

Avolition (lack of volition or will) A negative symptom of schizophrenia involving a loss of willpower, indecisiveness, and ambivalence. The person becomes apathetic and ceases to engage in purposeful actions.

Balanced placebo design A research design that combines the placebo and antiplacebo methods. It can be used to assess the effect of alcohol, the effect of expectations, and the interaction of alcohol by expectation.

Barbiturates Drugs that depress activities of the central nervous system; mostly for sedation.

Base rates Population frequencies. Relative base rates set statistical limits on the degree to which two variables can be associated with each other.

Battered woman syndrome A controversial classification of the common psychological effects of spousal abuse. Includes a tension-building phase leading up to violence, the battering incident itself, and a stage of loving contrition, during which the batterer apologizes. According to some experts, this induces learned helplessness in battered women.

Behavioral coding system (also known as a *formal observation schedule*) An observational assessment procedure that focuses on the frequency of specific behavioral events.

Behavioral family therapy (BFT) A form of family treatment that may include several variations, but always trains parents to use operant conditioning as a way of improving child discipline.

Behavioral gerontology A subspecialty within behavioral medicine developed specifically for studying and treating the behavioral components of illness among older adults.

Behavioral medicine A multidisciplinary field concerned with studying and treating the behavioral components of physical illness.

Behavior genetics The study of broad genetic contributions to the development of normal and abnormal behavior.

Behaviorism The belief within scientific psychology that observable behaviors, not unobservable cognitive or emotional states, are the appropriate focus of psychological study.

Benzodiazepines Group of drugs that have potent hypnotic, sedative, and anxiolytic action (also called antianxiety drugs).

Bereavement Grieving in response to the death of a loved one.

Beta-amyloid Protein material that forms the core of senile plaques, a type of brain lesion found in patients with Alzheimer's disease.

Binge eating Eating an amount of food in a fixed period of time that is clearly larger than most people would eat under similar circumstances. One part of the eating disorder of bulimia nervosa.

Binge eating disorder A controversial diagnosis defined by repeated episodes of binge eating but in the absence of compensatory behavior; included in an appendix of DSM-IV.

Biofeedback Behavioral medicine treatment that uses laboratory equipment to monitor physiological processes (that generally occur outside of conscious awareness) and provide feedback about them. Hypothesized to help patients to gain conscious control over problematic physiological processes such as hypertension.

Biological reductionism The assumption that biological explanations are more useful than psychological explanations because they deal with smaller units—with brain chemistry, for example, instead of emotional experience.

Biopsychosocial model A view of the etiology of mental disorders which assumes that disorders can best be understood in terms of the interaction of biological, psychological, and social systems.

Bipolar mood disorder A form of mood disorder in which the person experiences episodes of mania as well as episodes of depression.

Blunted affect A flattening or restriction of the person's nonverbal display of emotional responses. Blunted patients fail to exhibit signs of emotion or feeling.

Body dysmorphic disorder A type of somatoform disorder characterized by constant preoccupation with some imagined defect in physical appearance.

Body image A cognitive and affective evaluation of one's weight and shape, often a critical one.

Borderline personality disorder An enduring pattern of thinking and behavior whose essential feature is a pervasive instability in mood, self-image, and interpersonal relationships. Manifestations of this disorder include frantic efforts to avoid real or imagined abandonment. People who fit this description frequently hold opinions of significant others that vacillate between unrealistically positive and negative extremes.

Boundaries Rules defining a relationship, particularly the rules that separate a third person from an individual or another relationship. For example, the boundary of the marital relationship is defined, in part, by the limited discussion of intimate topics outside the relationship.

Brief psychotic disorder A diagnostic category in DSM-IV that includes people who exhibit psychotic symptoms for at least 1 day but no more than 1 month. After the symptoms are resolved, the person returns to the same level of functioning that had been achieved prior to the psychotic episode.

Bulimia nervosa A type of eating disorder characterized by repeated episodes of binge eating followed by inappropriate compensatory behaviors (such as self-induced vomiting) together with other symptoms related to eating and body image.

Cardiovascular disease (CVD) A group of disorders that affect the heart and circulatory system. Hypertension (high blood pressure) and coronary heart disease are the most important forms of CVD.

Cardiovascular reactivity A measure of the intensity of an individual's cardiovascular reactions to stress in the laboratory; a predictor of future cardiovascular disease.

Case study A careful description and analysis of the problems experienced by one person.

Catatonia Motor symptoms that can include either immobility and marked muscular rigidity or excitement and overactivity.

Catatonic type A subtype of schizophrenia that is characterized by symptoms of motor immobility (including rigidity and posturing) or excessive and purposeless motor activity.

Categorical approach to classification A view of classification based on the assumption that there are qualitative differences between normal and abnormal behavior as well as between one form of abnormal behavior and other forms of abnormal behavior.

Central nervous system The major communication system in the body, comprising the brain and the spinal cord.

Cerebral cortex The uneven surface of the brain that lies just underneath the skull and controls and integrates sophisticated memory, sensory, and motor functions.

Cerebral hemispheres The two major structures of the forebrain and the site of most sensory, emotional, and cognitive processes. The functions of the cerebral hemispheres are lateralized. In general, the left cerebral hemisphere is involved in language and related functions, and the right side is involved in spatial organization and analysis.

Child abuse A legal decision that a parent or other responsible adult has inflicted damage or offered inadequate care to a child; may include physical abuse, sexual abuse, neglect, and psychological abuse.

Child custody A legal decision, especially common in separation and divorce, that involves determining where children will reside and how parents will share legal rights and responsibilities for child rearing.

Chorea Unusual, involuntary muscle movements associated with disorders such as Huntington's disease.

Chromosomes Chainlike structures found in the nucleus of cells that carry genes and information about heredity. Humans normally have 23 pairs of chromosomes.

Civil commitment The involuntary hospitalization of the mentally ill; the decision typically is justified based on dangerousness to self or others (or inability to care for self).

Classical conditioning Pavlov's form of learning through association. A conditioned response eventually is elicited by a conditioned stimulus after repeated pairings with an unconditioned stimulus (which produces an unconditioned response).

Classification system A system for grouping together objects or organisms that share certain properties in common. In psychopathology, the set of categories in DSM-IV that describes mental disorders.

Client-centered therapy Carl Rogers's humanistic therapy that follows the client's lead. Therapists offer warmth, empathy, and genuineness, but clients solve their own problems.

Clinical depression A syndrome of depression in which a depressed mood is accompanied by several other symptoms, such as fatigue, loss of energy, difficulty in sleeping, and changes in appetite. Clinical depression also involves a variety of changes in thinking and overt behavior.

Clinical psychology The profession and academic discipline that is concerned with the application of psychological science to the assessment and treatment of mental disorders.

Coercion A pattern of interaction in which unwitting parents positively reinforce children's misbehavior (by giving in to their demands), and children negatively reinforce parents' capitulation (by ending their obnoxious behavior).

Cognitive behavioral couple therapy A variation on couples therapy that emphasizes the partners' moment-to-moment interaction, particularly their exchange of positive and negative behaviors, their style of communication, and their strategies for solving problems.

Cognitive behavior therapy The expansion of the scope of behavior therapy to include cognition and research on human information processing. Includes various general techniques, such as Beck's cognitive therapy and Ellis's RET.

Cognitive therapy A psychotherapy technique and important part of cognitive behavior therapy that was developed by Aaron Beck specifically as a treatment. Beck's cognitive therapy involves challenging negative cognitive distortions through a technique called collaborative empiricism.

Cohort A group whose members share some feature in common, particularly their date of birth.

Cohort effects Differences that distinguish one cohort from another. Cohorts share some feature in common, especially their date of birth, and cohort effects often distinguish people born in one time period (e.g., the 1960s) from those born in another.

Comorbidity The simultaneous manifestation of more than one disorder.

Competence Defendants' ability to understand legal proceedings and act rationally in relation to them. Competence evaluations can take place at different points in the legal process, but competence to stand trial (the ability to participate in one's own defense) is particularly important.

Compulsion A repetitive, ritualistic behavior that is aimed at the reduction of anxiety and distress or the prevention of some dreaded event. Compulsions are considered by the person to be senseless or irrational. The person feels compelled to perform the compulsion; he or she attempts to resist but cannot.

Concordance rate The rate, often a percentage, at which two, related individuals are found to both have a disorder or problem or neither has a disorder or problem, i.e., they are concordant. In discordant pairs, only one individual is disordered. Concordance rates often are computed for twin pairs.

Conduct disorder (CD) A psychological disorder of childhood that is defined primarily by behavior that is illegal as well as antisocial.

Confidentiality The ethical obligation not to reveal private communications in psychotherapy and in other professional contacts between mental health professionals and their clients.

Construct validity The overall strength of the network of relations that have been observed among variables that are used to define a construct. The extent to which the construct possesses some systematic meaning.

Contingency management A form of operant behavior therapy that focuses on directly changing rewards and punishments in order to increase desired and decrease undesired behavior. A contingency is the relationship between a behavior and its consequences; contingency management involves changing this relationship.

Control group The group of participants in an experiment that receives no treatment or perhaps a placebo treatment. Participants in the control group are compared with participants in the experimental group (who are given an active treatment).

Controlled drinking A controversial goal for some alcohol abusers. This concept refers to moderate consumption of alcohol in a pattern that avoids drinking to the point of intoxication.

Conversion disorder A type of somatoform disorder characterized by physical symptoms that often mimic those found in neurological diseases, such as blindness, numbing, or paralysis. The symptoms often make no anatomic sense.

Coping An attempt to adapt to stress by changing the stressor or by altering one's thinking or emotional response.

Coronary heart disease (CHD) A group of diseases of the heart that includes angina pectoris (chest pains) and myocardial infarction (heart attack).

Correlational study A scientific research method in which the relation between two factors (their co-relation) is studied in a systematic fashion. Has the advantage of practicality, as correlations between many variables can be studied in the real world, but also has the disadvantage that "correlation does not mean causation."

Correlation coefficient A number that always ranges between −1.00 and +1.00 and indicates the strength and direction of the relation between two variables. A higher absolute value indicates a stronger relation, while a correlation coefficient of 0 indicates no relation. The sign indicates the direction of the correlation.

Cortisol A corticosteroid secreted by the adrenal cortex. Cortisol is known as the "stress hormone" because its release is so closely linked with stress.

Countertransference The therapist's own feelings toward the client, particularly as described in psychoanalysis.

Couples therapy Partners who are involved in an intimate relationship are seen together in psychotherapy; sometimes called *marital therapy* or *marriage counseling*. Improving communication and negotiation are common goals.

Creutzfeldt-Jakob disease A type of dementia caused by a specific viral infection.

Criminal responsibility A legal concept that holds a person responsible for committing a crime if he or she (a) has been proven to have committed the act and (b) was legally sane at the time.

Critical incident stress debriefing (CISD) An early intervention following trauma involving a single 1- to 5-hour group meeting offered within one to three days following a disaster. CISD is used frequently, although data supporting its effectiveness are limited and some studies suggest that it may actually be harmful.

Cross-cultural psychology The scientific study of ways that human behavior and mental processes are influenced by social and cultural factors.

Cross-sectional study A research design in which subjects are studied only at one point in time. (Contrast with *longitudinal study*.)

Culture The shared way of life of a group or people; a complex system of accumulated knowledge that helps the people in a particular society adapt to their environment.

Culture-bound syndrome Patterns of erratic or unusual thinking and behavior that have been identified in diverse societes around the world and do not fit easily into the other diagnostic categories that are listed in the main body of DSM-IV-TR.

Culture-fair test A test that contains material that is equally familiar to people who differ in ethnicity, native language, or immigrant status, i.e., the test is not biased. Concerns about culture-fair tests often have been raised in measuring intelligence.

Cultural-familial retardation Typically mild mental retardation that runs in families and is linked with poverty. Thought to be the most common cause of mental retardation. There is controversy about the relative roles of genes or psychosocial disadvantage.

Cybernetics A communication and control process that uses feedback loops in order to adjust progress toward a goal, for example, the operation of a thermostat.

Cyclothymia A chronic, less severe form of bipolar disorder. The bipolar equivalent of dysthymia.

Defense mechanisms Unconscious processes that service the ego and reduce conscious anxiety by distorting anxiety-producing memories, emotions, and impulses—for example, projection, displacement, or rationalization.

Deinstitutionalization The movement to treat the mentally ill and mentally retarded in communities rather than in large mental hospitals.

Delirium A confusional state that develops over a short period of time and is often associated with agitation and hyperactivity. The primary symptom is clouding of consciousness or reduced awareness of one's surroundings.

Delusion An obviously false and idiosyncratic belief that is rigidly held in spite of its preposterous nature.

Delusional disorder Describes persons who do not meet the full symptomatic criteria for schizophrenia, but who are preoccupied for at least 1 month with delusions that are not bizarre.

Dementia A gradually worsening loss of memory and related cognitive functions, including the use of language as well as reasoning and decision making.

Dementia with Lewy bodies (DLB) A form of progressive dementia in which the central feature is progressive cognitive decline, combined with three additional defining features: (1) pronounced "fluctuations" in alertness and attention, such as frequent drowsiness, lethargy, lengthy periods of time spent staring into space, or disorganized speech; (2) recurrent visual hallucinations, and (3) parkinsonian motor symptoms, such as rigidity and the loss of spontaneous movement.

Dependent personality disorder An enduring pattern of dependent and submissive behavior. These people are exceedingly dependent on other people for advice and reassurance. Often unable to make everyday decisions on their own, they feel anxious and helpless when they are alone.

Dependent variable The outcome that is hypothesized to vary according to manipulations in the independent variable in an experiment.

Depersonalization disorder A type of dissociative disorder characterized by severe and persistent feelings of being detached from oneself (depersonalization experiences). For example, the repeated and profound sensation of floating above your body and observing yourself act.

Depressed mood Depressed feelings such as of disappointment and despair, but which are not yet necessarily part of a clinical syndrome.

Depression Can refer to a *symptom* (subjective feelings of sadness), a *mood* (sustained and pervasive feelings of despair), or to a clinical *syndrome* (in which the presence of a depressed mood is accompanied by several additional symptoms, such as fatigue, loss of energy, sleeping difficulties, and appetite changes).

Determinism The philosophical assumption (made by all psychologists except humanistic psychologists) that behavior is a potentially predictable consequence of biological, psychological, and social factors. Contrasts with the assumption that behavior is the product of free will.

Detoxification The process of short-term medical care (medication, rest, diets, fluids, and so on)

during removal of a drug upon which a person has become dependent. The aim is to minimize withdrawal symptoms.

Developmental deviation Significant departures from age-appropriate norms in some specific area of functioning. Some developmental deviations are considered disorders in their own right.

Developmental norms Behavior that is typical for children of a given age.

Developmental psychopathology An approach to abnormal psychology that emphasizes the importance of normal development to understanding abnormal behavior.

Developmental stage A distinct period of development focused on certain central "tasks" and marked by boundaries defined by changing age or social expectations.

Diagnosis The process of determining the nature of a person's disorder. In the case of psychopathology, deciding that a person fits into a particular diagnostic category, such as schizophrenia or major depressive disorder.

Diathesis A predisposition to disorder. Also known as *vulnerability*. A diathesis only causes abnormal behavior when it is combined with a stress or challenging experience.

Dimensional approach to classification A view of classification based on the assumption that behavior is distributed on a continuum from normal to abnormal. Also includes the assumption that differences between one type of behavior and another are quantitative rather than qualitative in nature.

Disorganized speech (also known as *formal thought disorder*) Severe disruptions of verbal communication, involving the form of the person's speech.

Disorganized type A subtype of schizophrenia (formerly known as *hebephrenia*) that is characterized by disorganized speech, disorganized behavior, and flat or inappropriate affect. If delusions or hallucinations are present, their content is not well organized.

Dissociation The separation of mental processes such as memory or consciousness that normally are integrated. Normal dissociative experiences include fleeting feelings of unreality and *déjà vu* experiences—the feeling that an event has happened before. Extreme dissociative experiences characterize dissociative disorders.

Dissociative amnesia A type of dissociative disorder characterized by the sudden inability to recall extensive and important personal information. The onset often is sudden and may occur in response to trauma or extreme stress.

Dissociative disorders A category of psychological disorders characterized by persistent, maladaptive disruptions in the integration of memory, consciousness, or identity. Examples include dissociative fugue and dissociative identity disorder (multiple personality).

Dissociative fugue A rare dissociative disorder characterized by sudden, unplanned travel, the inability to remember details about the past, and

confusion about identity or the assumption of a new identity. The onset typically follows a traumatic event.

Dissociative identity disorder (DID) An unusual dissociative disorder characterized by the existence of two or more distinct personalities in a single individual (also known as *multiple personality disorder*). At least two personalities repeatedly take control over the person's behavior, and some personalities have limited or no memory of the other.

Distorted body image A perceptual inaccuracy in evaluating body size and shape that sometimes is found in anorexia nervosa.

Diversion A practice of directing problem youth away from the juvenile justice system and into some alternative treatment or program. For example, a juvenile offender may be referred to counseling instead of having a hearing held in court.

Divorce mediation A procedure in which former partners attempt to resolve child custody or other disputes that arise from a divorce with the help of an impartial third party (a mediator).

Dizygotic (DZ) twins Fraternal twins produced from separate fertilized eggs. Like all siblings, DZ twins share an average of 50 percent of their genes.

Dominance The hierarchical ordering of a social group into more and less powerful members. Dominance rankings are indexed by the availabilty of uncontested privileges.

Dose-response effects Different treatment responses to different dosages of a medication.

Double-blind study A study in which neither the therapist nor the patient knows whether the patient receives the real treatment (for example, a medication) or a placebo.

Down syndrome A chromosomal disorder that is the most common known biological cause of mental retardation. It is caused by an extra chromosome (usually on the 21st pair) and associated with a characteristic physical appearance.

Drug of abuse (also called a *psychoactive substance*) A chemical substance that alters a person's mood, level of perception, or brain functioning.

Dualism The philosophical view that the mind and body are separate. Dates to the writings of the philosopher René Descartes, who attempted to balance the dominant religious views of his times with emerging scientific reasoning. Descartes argued that many human functions have biological explanations, but some human experiences have no somatic representation. Thus, he argued for a distinction—a dualism—between mind and body.

Dyskinesia Involuntary movements, such as tics, chorea, or tremors, that are often associated with certain types of dementia.

Dyspareunia Persistent genital pain during or after sexual intercourse. The problem can occur in either men or women.

Dysphoric An unpleasant or uncomfortable mood, often associated with disorders such as major depression, dysthymia, and various forms of anxiety disorder. The opposite of euphoric.

Dysthymia One of the mood disorders; a form of mild depression characterized by a chronic course (the person is seldom without symptoms).

Eating disorders A category of psychological disorders characterized by severe disturbances in eating behavior, specifically anorexia nervosa and bulimia nervosa.

Eclectic The term used to describe the therapeutic approach of a group of mental health professionals who do not identify themselves with a specific paradigm, but instead use different treatments for different disorders.

Ego One of Freud's three central personality structures. In Freudian theory, the ego must deal with reality as it attempts to fulfill id impulses as well as superego demands. The ego operates on the reality principle, and much of the ego resides in conscious awareness.

Ego analysis Originated in the work of different therapists trained in Freudian psychoanalysis, but who focus much more on the ego than on the id. Ego analysts are concerned with the patient's dealings with the external world.

Electroconvulsive therapy (ECT) A treatment that involves the deliberate induction of a convulsion by passing electricity through one or both hemispheres of the brain. Modern ECT uses restraints, medication, and carefully controlled electrical stimulation to minimize adverse consequences. Can be an effective treatment for severe depression, especially following the failure of other approaches.

Emotion A state of arousal that is defined by subjective feeling states, such as sadness, anger, and disgust. Emotions are often accompanied by physiological changes, such as in heart rate and respiration rate.

Emotion-focused coping Internally oriented coping in an attempt to alter one's emotional or cognitive responses to a stressor.

Emotional processing A process of facing and coming to accept powerful emotions following trauma. Emotional processing involves confronting fear, diminishing its intensity, and coming to some new understanding of the trauma and its consequences.

Emotion regulation The process of learning to control powerful emotions according to the demands of a situation. Children learn to regulate their emotions initially through interactions with their parents and others in their social world, and eventually children learn to regulate their own emotions.

Empathy Emotional understanding. Empathy involves understanding others' unique feelings and perspectives. Highlighted by Rogers but basic to most forms of psychotherapy.

Encopresis Inappropriately controlled defecation among children old enough to maintain control of their bowels.

Endocrine system A collection of glands found at various locations throughout the body, including the ovaries or testes and the pituitary, thyroid, and adrenal glands. Releases hormones that sometimes act as neuromodulators and affect responses to stress. Also important in physical growth and development.

Endorphins The term is a contraction formed from the words *endogenous* (meaning "within") and *morphine*. Endorphins are relatively short chains of amino acids, or neuropeptides, that are naturally synthesized in the brain and are closely related to morphine (an opioid) in terms of their pharmacological properties.

Enmeshed family Families whose members are overly involved in one another's lives.

Enuresis Inappropriately controlled urination (during sleep or while awake) among children old enough to maintain control of their bladder.

Epidemiology The scientific study of the frequency and distribution of disorders within a population.

Equifinality A concept from systems theory that states that the same outcome (e.g., a psychological disorder) may have different causes. That is, there may be not one cause but multiple pathways that lead to a given outcome (disorder).

Erectile dysfunction Difficulty experienced by a man in obtaining an erection that is sufficient to accomplish intercourse or maintaining an erection long enough to satisfy himself or his partner during intercourse.

Essential hypertension A form of high blood pressure in which the hypertension is the principal disorder, as opposed to hypertension that is secondary to a known illness such as a kidney disorder.

Estrogen The female sex hormone.

Etiology The causes or origins of a disorder.

Eugenics The very controversial and widely discredited movement to improve the human stock by selectively breeding "desirable" characteristics (or individuals or races) and preventing "undesirable" characteristics (or individuals or races) from reproducing.

Euphoria An exaggerated feeling of physical and emotional well-being, typically associated with manic episodes in bipolar mood disorder.

Evolutionary psychology The application of the principles of evolution to understanding the mind and behavior, and identifying species-typical characteristics, that is, genetically influenced traits that people or animals share as a part of their nature. Evolutionary psychologists assume that animal and human psychology, like animal and human anatomy, have evolved and share similarities.

Exhibitionism One of the paraphilias, characterized by distress over, or acting on, urges to expose one's genitals to an unsuspecting stranger.

Experiment A powerful scientific method that allows researchers to determine cause-and-effect relations. Key elements include random assignment, the manipulation of the independent variable, and careful measurement of the dependent variable.

Experimental group The group of participants in an experiment that receives a treatment that is hypothesized to cause some measured effect. Participants in the experimental group are compared with untreated participants in a control group.

Experimental hypothesis A new prediction made by an investigator to be tested in an experiment.

Experimental method The powerful scientific method that allows researchers to determine cause and effect by randomly assigning participants to experimental and control groups. In an experiment, researchers systematically manipulate independent variables and observe their effects on dependent variables.

Expert witness An individual stipulated as an expert on some subject matter who, because of his or her expertise, is allowed to testify about matters of opinion and not just matters of fact. For example, mental health professionals may serve as expert witnesses concerning a defendant's sanity.

Expressed emotion (EE) A concept that refers to a collection of negative or intrusive attitudes sometimes displayed by relatives of patients who are being treated for a disorder. If at least one of a patient's relatives is hostile, critical, or emotionally overinvolved, the family environment typically is considered high in expressed emotion.

Externalizing disorders An empirically derived category of disruptive child behavior problems that create problems for the external world (for example, attention-deficit/hyperactivity disorder).

External validity Whether the findings of an experiment generalize to other people, places, and circumstances, particularly real-life situations.

Extinction The gradual elimination of a response when learning conditions change. In classical conditioning, extinction occurs when a conditioned stimulus no longer is paired with an unconditioned stimulus. In operant conditioning, extinction occurs when the contingent is removed between behavior and its consequences.

Factitious disorder A feigned condition that, unlike malingering, is motivated by a desire to assume the sick role, not by a desire for external gain.

Family life cycle The developmental course of family relationships throughout life; most family life cycle theories mark stages and transitions with major changes in family relationships and membership.

Family therapy Treatment that might include two, three, or more family members in the psychotherapy sessions. Improving communication and negotiation are common goals, although family therapy also may be used to help well members adjust to a family member's illness.

Fear An unpleasant emotional reaction experienced in the face of real, immediate danger. It builds quickly in intensity and helps to organize the person's responses to threats from the environment.

Fetal alcohol syndrome A disorder caused by heavy maternal alcohol consumption and repeated exposure of the developing fetus to alcohol. Infants have retarded physical development, a small head, narrow eyes, cardiac defects, and cognitive impairments. Intellectual functioning ranges from mild mental retardation to intelligence with learning disabilities.

Fetishism The use of nonliving objects as a focus of sexual arousal.

Fight or flight response A response to a threat in which psychophysiological reactions mobilize the body to take action against danger.

Fixation The psychodynamic concept that psychological development is arrested at a particular age or stage. The person stops growing emotionally.

Flashbacks Reexperienced memories of past events, particularly as occurs in posttraumatic stress disorder or following use of hallucinogenic drugs.

Flooding A treatment for fears and phobias that involves exposure to the feared stimulus at full intensity. Works through extinction.

Fragile-X syndrome The second most common known biological cause of mental retardation. Transmitted genetically and indicated by a weakening or break on one arm of the X sex chromosome.

Free association A basic technique in Freudian psychoanalysis in which patients are encouraged to speak freely about whatever thoughts cross their mind; presumed to give insight into the unconscious.

Free will The capacity to make choices and freely act upon them. A philosophical counterpoint to determinism, which is the scientific assumption that behavior is a predictable consequence of internal and external events. Humanistic psychology and the American legal system assume people act out of free will.

Frotteurism One of the paraphilias, characterized by recurrent, intense sexual urges involving touching and rubbing against a nonconsenting person; it often takes place in crowded trains, buses, and elevators.

Gender identity A person's sense of himself or herself as being either male or female.

Gender identity disorder A strong and persistent identification with the opposite sex coupled with a sense of discomfort with one's anatomic sex.

Gender roles Roles associated with social expectations about gendered behavior, for example, "masculine" or "feminine" activities.

General adaptation syndrome (GAS) Selye's three stages in reaction to stress: alarm, resistance, and exhaustion.

Generalization Making accurate statements that extend beyond a specific sample to a larger population.

Generalized anxiety disorder (GAD) One of the anxiety disorders, which is characterized by excessive and uncontrollable worry about a number of events or activities (such as work or school performance) and associated with symptoms of arousal (such as restlessness, muscle tension, and sleep disturbance).

General paresis (general paralysis) A set of severe symptoms including dementia, delusions of grandeur, and paralysis caused by the sexually transmitted disease syphilis. Discovery of the cause of general paresis spurred the biological model of mental illness.

Genes Ultramicroscopic units of DNA that carry information about heredity. Located on the chromosomes.

Genetic linkage A close association between two genes, typically the genetic locus associated with a disorder or a trait and the locus for a known gene. Two loci are said to be linked when they are sufficiently close together on the same chromosome.

Gene–environment correlation The empirical and theoretical observation that experience often, perhaps always, is correlated with genetic makeup. Genes influence personality and other characteristics, and these traits affect the environment parents provide children and the environments people seek or responses they elicit from others. Therefore, experience is associated with genes, and studies of environments are confounded by this correlation.

Gene–environment interaction Genetic risk and an environmental experience working together to produce a given outcome. Many psychological disorders are assumed to be caused by such combinations of genetic risk and difficult experience.

Genotype An individual's actual genetic structure, usually with reference to a particular characteristic.

Gerontology The multidisciplinary study of aging and older adults.

Gestalt therapy A variation of the humanistic approach to psychotherapy that underscores affective awareness and expression, genuineness, and experiencing the moment (living in the "here and now").

Grief The emotional and social process of coping with a separation or a loss, often described as proceeding in stages.

Group therapy The treatment of three or more people in a group setting, often using group relationships as a central part of therapy.

Hallucinations A perceptual experience in the absence of external stimulation, such as hearing voices that aren't really there.

Hallucinogens Drugs that produce hallucinations.

Harmful dysfunction A concept used in one approach to the definition of mental disorder. A condition can be considered a mental disorder if it causes some harm to the person and if the condition results from the inability of some mental mechanism to perform its natural function.

Hashish The dried resin from the top of the female cannabis plant. Ingestion of hashish leads to a feeling of being "high" (see *marijuana*).

Health behavior A wide range of activities that are essential to promoting good health, including positive actions such as proper diet and the avoidance of negative activities such as cigarette smoking.

Health psychologist A psychologist who specializes in reducing negative health behavior (e.g., smoking) and promoting positive health behavior (e.g., exercise). Health psychology is a part of the interdisciplinary field of behavioral medicine.

Heritability The variability in a behavioral characteristic that is accounted for by genetic factors.

Heritability ratio A statistic for computing the proportion of variance in a behavioral characteristic that is accounted for by genetic factors in a given study or series of studies.

High-risk research design A longitudinal study of persons who are selected from the general population based on some identified risk factor that has a fairly high risk ratio.

Histrionic personality disorder An enduring pattern of thinking and behavior that is characterized by excessive emotionality and attention-seeking behavior. People with this disorder are self-centered, vain, and demanding. Their emotions tend to be shallow and may vacillate erratically.

Human Immunodeficiency Virus (HIV) The virus that causes AIDS and attacks the immune system, leaving the patient susceptible to infection, neurological complications, and cancers that rarely affect those with normal immune function.

Holism The assumption that the whole is more than the sum of its parts. A central tenet of systems theory, and counterpoint to reductionism.

Homeostasis The tendency to maintain a steady state. A familiar concept in biology that also is widely applicable in psychology.

Hopelessness theory A theory regarding the role of cognitive events in the etiology of depression; depression is associated with the expectation that very desirable events probably will not occur and that aversive events probably will occur regardless of what the person does.

Hormones Chemical substances that are released into the bloodstream by glands in the endocrine system. Hormones affect the functioning of distant body systems and sometimes act as neuromodulators.

Humanistic psychotherapy An approach that assumes that the most essential human quality is the ability to make choices and freely act on them (free will). Promoted as a "third force" to counteract the deterministic views of psychodynamic and the behavioral approaches to psychotherapy.

Huntington's disease A primary, differentiated dementia characterized by the presence of unusual involuntary muscle movements. Many Huntington's patients also exhibit a variety of personality changes and symptoms of mental disorders, including depression and anxiety.

Hyperactivity A symptom of attention-deficit/hyperactivity disorder (ADHD), often manifested as squirming, fidgeting, or restless behavior. Found across, but particularly notable in, structured settings.

Hypertension High blood pressure.

Hypnosis An altered state of consciousness during which hypnotized subjects are particularly susceptible to suggestion. There is considerable debate as to whether hypnosis is a unique state of consciousness or merely a form of relaxation.

Hypoactive sexual desire Diminished desire for sexual activity and reduced frequency of sexual fantasies.

Hypochondriasis A type of somatoform disorder characterized by a person's preoccupying fear or belief that he or she is suffering from a physical illness.

Hypomania An episode of increased energy that is not sufficiently severe to qualify as a full-blown manic episode.

Hypothalamus A part of the limbic system that plays a role in sensation, but more importantly it controls basic biological urges, such as eating, drinking, and activity, as well as much of the functioning of the autonomic nervous system.

Hypothesis A prediction about the expected findings in a scientific study.

Hypothetical construct A theoretical device that refers to events or states that reside within a person and are proposed to help understand or explain a person's behavior.

Hysteria An outdated but influential diagnostic category that included both somatoform and dissociative disorders. Attempts to treat hysteria had a major effect on Charcot, Freud, and Janet, among others. In Greek, *hysteria* means "uterus," a reflection of ancient speculation that hysteria was restricted to women and caused by frustrated sexual desires.

Iatrogenesis A creation of a disorder by an attempt to treat it.

Id One of Freud's three central personality structures. In Freudian theory, the id is present at birth and is the source of basic drives and motivations. The id houses biological drives (such as hunger), as well as Freud's two key psychological drives, sex and aggression. Operates according to the pleasure principle.

Identification A process wherein children not only imitate adults but also want to be like them and adopt their values. In Freudian theory, identification is to the Oedipal and Electra conflicts. In developmental psychology, a similar but broader concept than modeling.

Identity Erikson's term for the broad definition of self; in his view, identity is the product of the adolescent's struggle to answer the question "Who am I?"

Identity crisis Erikson's period of basic uncertainty about self during late adolescence and early adult life. A consequence of the psychosocial stage of identity versus role confusion.

Implicit memory Implicit memory is indicated by changes in behavior apparently based on a memory of a prior event but with nonconscious remembering of the event. *Explicit memory* is the conscious recollection of a past event.

Impulse control disorder A disorder characterized by failure to resist an impulse or a temptation to perform some pleasurable or tension-releasing act that is harmful to oneself or others; examples are pathological gambling, setting fires, and stealing.

Inappropriate affect A form of emotional disturbance seen in schizophrenia. The central features of inappropriate affect are incongruity and lack of adaptability in emotional expression.

Incest Sexual activity between close blood relatives, such as father–daughter, mother–son, or siblings.

Incidence The number of new cases of a disorder that appear in a population during a specific period of time.

Independent variable The variable in an experiment that is controlled and deliberately manipulated by the experimenter (for example, whether or not a subject receives a treatment). Affects the dependent variable.

Infarct The area of dead tissue produced by a stroke.

Informed consent A legal and ethical safeguard concerning risks in research and in treatment. Includes (a) accurate information about potential risks and benefits, (b) competence on the part of subjects/patients to understand them, and (c) the ability of subjects/patients to participate voluntarily.

Inhibited sexual arousal Difficulty experienced by a woman in achieving or maintaining genital responses, such as lubrication and swelling, that are necessary to complete sexual intercourse.

Insanity A legal term referring to a defendant's state of mind at the time of committing a crime. An insane individual is not held legally responsible for his or her actions because of a mental disease or defect.

Insanity defense An attempt to prove that a person with a mental illness did not meet the legal criteria for sanity at the time of committing a crime. The inability to tell right from wrong and an "irresistible impulse" are the two most common contemporary grounds for the defense.

Insight Self-understanding; the extent to which a person recognizes the nature (or understands the potential causes) of his or her disorder. In psychoanalysis, insight is the ultimate goal, specifically, to bring formerly unconscious material into conscious awareness.

Intelligence quotient (IQ) A measure of intellectual ability that typically has a mean of 100 and a standard deviation of 15. An individual's IQ is determined by comparisons with norms for same-aged peers.

Internalizing disorders An empirically derived category of psychological problems of childhood that affect the child more than the external world (for example, depression).

Internal validity Whether changes in the dependent variable can be accurately attributed to changes in the independent variable in an experiment, that is, there are no experimental confounds.

Interpretation A tool in psychotherapy and psychoanalysis in which the therapist suggests new meanings about a client's accounts of his or her past and present life.

Introceptive awareness Recognition of internal cues, including various emotional states as well as hunger.

In vivo desensitization A treatment for overcoming fears and phobias that involves gradual exposure to feared stimuli in real life while simultaneously maintaining a state of relaxation. Contrast with *systematic desensitization*.

Juvenile delinquency A legal term that refers to a minor who has violated the law and been judged responsible for the lawbreaking.

Kappa A statistical index of reliability (diagnostic agreement between clinicians) that reflects the proportion of agreement that occurred above and beyond that which would have occurred by chance.

Korsakoff's syndrome An amnestic disorder sometimes associated with chronic alcoholism. Memory is impaired but other cognitive functions are not.

Labeling theory A perspective on mental disorders that is primarily concerned with the social context in which abnormal behavior occurs. Labeling theory is more interested in social factors that determine whether or not a person will be given a psychiatric diagnosis than in psychological or biological reasons for the behaviors.

La belle indifference A flippant lack of concern about physical symptoms that may accompany somatoform disorders.

Lateralization The specialized functioning of each cerebral hemisphere. In general, the left hemisphere is involved in language and related functions, and the right side is involved in spatial organization and analysis.

Lateralized Functions or sites that are located primarily or solely in one hemisphere of the brain (the left or the right).

Lead poisoning Ingestion of toxic levels of lead (mainly through environmental pollutants) that can cause brain damage and a number of adverse behavioral and cognitive impairments, including mental retardation.

Learning disorders (LDs) A heterogenous group of educational problems characterized by academic performance that is notably below academic aptitude.

Life-cycle transitions Movements from one social or psychological "stage" of adult development into a new one; often characterized by interpersonal, emotional, and identity conflict.

Life-span development The study of continuities and changes in behavior, affect, and cognition from infancy through the last years of life.

Limbic system A variety of brain structures, including the thalamus and hypothalamus, that are central to the regulation of emotion and basic learning processes.

Linkage A process used to locate the position of a gene on a particular chromosome. Two genetic loci are said to be linked if they are close together on the same chromosome.

Longitudinal study A type of research design in which subjects are studied over a period of time (contrasts with the cross-sectional approach of studying subjects only at one point in time). Longitudinal studies attempt to establish whether hypothesized causes precede their putative effects in time.

Mainstreaming The educational philosophy that mentally retarded children should be taught, as much as possible, in regular classrooms rather than in "special" classes.

Malingering Pretending to have a psychological disorder in order to achieve some external gain such as insurance money or avoidance of work.

Mania A disturbance in mood characterized by such symptoms as elation, inflated self-esteem, hyperactivity, and accelerated speaking and thinking. An exaggerated feeling of physical and emotional well-being.

Marijuana The dried leaves and flowers of the female cannabis plant. "Getting high" on marijuana refers to a pervasive sense of well-being and happiness.

Mean The arithmetic average of a distribution of scores; the sum of scores divided by the number of observations.

Median The midpoint of a frequency distribution; half of all subjects fall above and half fall below the median.

Medulla The part of the hindbrain that controls various body functions involved in sustaining life, including heart rate, blood pressure, and respiration.

Melancholia A particularly severe type of depression. In DSM-IV, melancholia is described in terms of a number of specific features, such as loss of pleasure in activities and lack of reactivity to events in the person's environment that are normally pleasurable.

Menopause The cessation of menstruation and the associated physical and psychological changes that occur among middle-aged women (the so-called "change of life").

Mental retardation Substantial limitations in present functioning characterized by significantly subaverage intellectual functioning (IQ of 70 to 75 or below), concurrent limitations in adaptive skills, and an onset before age 18.

Meta-analysis A statistical technique that allows the results from different studies to be combined in a standardized way.

Midbrain Part of the brain between the hindbrain and forebrain that is involved in the control of some motor activities, especially those related to fighting and sex.

Minimal brain damage (MBD) Damage to the brain too slight to be detected with objective instruments but sometimes inferred from behavior. Was once held to be the cause of attention-deficit/hyperactivity disorder but now widely rejected.

Mode The most frequent score in a frequency distribution.

Modeling A social learning concept describing the process of learning through imitation. Contrasts with the broader concept of identification.

Monoamine oxidase inhibitors (MAO-Is) A group of antidepressant drugs that inhibit the enzyme monoamine oxidase (MAO) in the brain and raise the levels of neurotransmitters, such as norepinephrine, dopamine, and serotonin.

Monozygotic (MZ) twins Identical twins produced from a single fertilized egg; thus MZ twins have identical genotypes.

Mood A pervasive and sustained emotional response that, in its extreme, can color the person's perception of the world.

Mood disorders A broad category of psychopathology that includes depressive disorders and bipolar disorders. These conditions are defined in terms of episodes in which the person's behavior is dominated by either clinical depression or mania.

Moral treatment A historically important movement in the treatment of the mentally ill that led to improved hospital conditions. This movement was based on the belief that the mentally ill deserve adequate care and that good care would promote their recovery.

Moratorium A period of allowing oneself to be uncertain or confused about identity. Erikson advocated a moratorium as an important step in the formation of an enduring identity.

Multiple personality disorder An unusual dissociative disorder characterized by the existence of two or more distinct personalities in a single individual (called *dissociative identity disorder* in DSM-IV).

Munchausen-by-Proxy Syndrome (MBPS) A unique, rare, but potentially very harmful form of physical child abuse in which a parent feigns, exaggerates, or induces illness in a child.

Myocardial infarction (MI) Commonly known as a heart attack, this most deadly form of coronary heart disease is caused by oxygen deprivation to the heart and results in the death of at least some heart tissue.

Narcissistic personality disorder An enduring pattern of thinking and behavior that is characterized by pervasive grandiosity. Narcissistic people are preoccupied with their own achievements and abilities.

Nature–nurture controversy The debate that pits genetic and biological factors against life experience as causes of abnormal behavior.

Negative symptoms (of schizophrenia) Include flat or blunted affect, avolition, alogia, and anhedonia.

Neurofibrillary tangles A type of brain lesion found in the cerebral cortex and the hippocampus in patients with Alzheimer's disease. A pattern of disorganized neurofibrils, which provide structural support for the neurons and help transport chemicals that are used in the production of neurotransmitters.

Neurologist A physician who has been trained to diagnose and treat disorders of the nervous system, including diseases of the brain, spinal cord, nerves, and muscles.

Neurons The nerve cells that form the basic building blocks of the brain. Each neuron is composed of the soma or cell body, the dendrites, the axon, and the terminal buttons.

Neuropsychological assessment Assessment procedures focused on the examination of performance on psychological tests to indicate whether a person has a brain disorder. An example is the Halstead-Reitan Neuropsychological Test Battery.

Neuropsychologists A psychologist who has particular expertise in the assessment of specific types of cognitive impairment, including those associated with dementia and amnestic disorders.

Neurosis A traditional term, often associated with psychoanalytic theory, that describes maladaptive behavior resulting from the ego's failure to control anxiety resulting from unconscious conflicts. In DSM-I and DSM-II, neurotic disorders were defined as those in which anxiety is the chief characteristic. Anxiety presumably could be felt and expressed directly, or it could be controlled unconsciously by defense mechanisms.

Neurotransmitters Chemical substances that are released into the synapse between two neurons and carry signals from the terminal button of one neuron to the receptors of another.

Nonshared environment The component of a sibling's environment inside or outside the family that is unique to that sibling, for example, being a favorite child or one's best friend. Contrasts with the shared environment, family experiences that are common across siblings.

Normal distribution A frequency distribution represented by a bell-shaped curve—the normal curve—that is important for making statistical inferences. Many psychological characteristics (e.g., intelligence) are assumed to follow the normal distribution.

Normalization The philosophy that mentally retarded or mentally ill people are entitled to live as much as possible like other members of the society. Often with deinstitutionalization in providing custodial care and mainstreaming in education.

Null hypothesis The prediction that an experimental hypothesis is not true. Scientists must assume that the null hypothesis holds until research contradicts it.

Obesity Excess body fat, a circumstance that roughly corresponds with a body weight 20 percent above the expected weight.

Obsession A repetitive, unwanted, intrusive cognitive event that may take the form of thoughts, images, or impulses. Obsessions intrude suddenly into consciousness and lead to an increase in subjective anxiety.

Obsessive–compulsive personality disorder An enduring pattern of thinking and behavior that is characterized by perfectionism and inflexibility. These people are preoccupied with rules and efficiency. They are excessively conscientious, moralistic, and judgmental.

Operant conditioning A learning theory asserting that behavior is a function of its consequences. Specifically, behavior increases if it is rewarded, and it decreases if it is punished.

Operational definition A procedure that is used to measure a theoretical construct.

Opiates (sometimes called *opioids*) Drugs that have properties similar to opium. The main active ingredients in opium are morphine and codeine.

Oppositional defiant disorder (ODD) A psychological disorder of childhood characterized by persistent but relatively minor transgressions, such as refusing to obey adult requests, arguing, and acting angry.

Optimism A general and effective style of coping with stress involving a positive attitude when a stressor cannot be changed.

Orgasmic disorder A sexual disorder in which the person has recurrent difficulties reaching orgasm after a normal sexual arousal.

Outpatient Commitment Outpatient commitment generally requires the same dangerousness standards as inpatient commitment, but the patient is court-ordered to comply with treatment in the community (e.g., making regular office visits, taking medication). Outpatient commitment is permitted by 39 states, and because it involves less infringement on civil liberties, commitment criteria may be applied less stringently for outpatient versus inpatient commitment.

Pain disorder A type of somatoform disorder characterized by preoccupation with pain, and complaints are motivated at least in part by psychological factors.

Panic attack A sudden, overwhelming experience of terror or fright. While anxiety involves a blend of several negative emotions, panic is more focused.

Panic disorder A form of anxiety disorder in which a person experiences recurrent, unexpected panic attacks. At least one of the attacks must have been followed by a period of one month or more in which the person has either persistent concern about having additional attacks, worry about the implications of the attack or its consequences, or a significant change in behavior related to the attacks. Panic disorder is divided into two subtypes, depending on the presence or absence of agoraphobia.

Paradigm A set of assumptions both about the substance of a theory and about how scientists should collect data and test theoretical propositions. The term was applied to the progress of science by Thomas Kuhn, an influential historian and philosopher.

Paranoid personality disorder An enduring pattern of thinking and behavior characterized by a pervasive tendency to be inappropriately suspicious of other people's motives and behaviors. People who fit the description for this disorder expect that other people are trying to harm them, and they take extraordinary precautions to avoid being exploited or injured.

Paranoid type A subtype of schizophrenia that is characterized by systematic delusions with persecutory or grandiose content. Preoccupation with frequent auditory hallucinations can also be associated with the paranoid type.

Paraphilias Forms of sexual disorder that involve sexual arousal in association with unusual objects and situations, such as inanimate objects, sexual contacts with children, exhibiting their genitals to strangers, and inflicting pain on another person.

Parkinson's disease A disorder of the motor system that is caused by a degeneration of a specific area of the brain stem known as the *substantia nigra* and loss of the neurotransmitter dopamine, which is produced by cells in this area.

Pedophilia One of the paraphilias, characterized by marked distress over, or acting on urges involving, sexual activity with a prepubescent child.

Peer sociometrics A method of assessing children's social relationships and categorizing children's social standing by obtaining information on who is "liked most" and who is "liked least" from a group of children who know each other.

Peripheral nervous system Nerves that stem from the central nervous system and connect to the body's muscles, sensory systems, and organs. Divided into two subdivisions, the somatic and the autonomic nervous systems.

Personality The combination of persistent traits or characteristics that, taken as a whole, describe a person's behavior. In DSM-IV, personality is defined as "enduring patterns of perceiving, relating to, and thinking about the environment and oneself, which are exhibited in a wide range of important social and personal contexts."

Personality disorder Inflexible and maladaptive patterns of personality that begin by early adulthood and result in either social or occupational problems or distress to the individual.

Personality inventory Sometimes called an *objective personality test,* it consists of a series of straightforward statements that the person is required to rate or endorse as being either true or false in relation to himself or herself.

Pervasive developmental disorders (PDDs) A category of unusual psychological problems that begin early in life and involve severe impairments in a number of areas of functioning. Autistic disorder is one example.

Phenomenology The study of events and symptoms (including subjective experiences) in their own right rather than in terms of inferred causes.

Phenotype The observed expression of a given genotype or genetic structure, for example, eye color.

Phenylketonuria (PKU) A cause of mental retardation transmitted by the pairing of recessive genes that results in the deficiency of the enzyme that metabolizes phenylalanine. Infants have normal intelligence at birth, but the ingestion of foods containing phenylalanine causes phenylketonuria and produces brain damage. Can be prevented with a phenylalanine-free diet.

Phobias A persistent and irrational narrowly defined fear that is associated with a specific object or situation.

Pick's disease A form of primary dementia that is associated with atrophy of the frontal and temporal lobes of the brain. Very similar to Alzheimer's disease in terms of both behavioral symptoms and cognitive impairment.

Placebo control group A group of subjects given a treatment with no known specific ingredients for the purpose of comparison with alternative treatments that are thought to contain specific, therapeutic benefits.

Placebo effect The improvement in a condition produced by a placebo (sometimes a substantial change). An overriding goal of scientific research is to identify treatments that exceed placebo effects.

Polygenic Caused by more than one gene. Characteristics become normally distributed as more genes are involved in the phenotypic expression of a trait.

Polysubstance abuse (also known as *multidrug abuse*) A disorder characterized by the abuse of at least three different psychoactive drugs (not including nicotine or caffeine). No single substance predominates in the pattern of abuse.

Pons Part of the hindbrain that serves various functions in regulating stages of sleep.

Population The entire group of people about whom a researcher wants to generalize.

Positive symptoms (of schizophrenia) Include hallucinations, delusions, disorganized speech, inappropriate affect, and disorganized behavior.

Posttraumatic stress disorder (PTSD) A psychological disorder characterized by recurring symptoms of numbing, reexperiencing, and hyperarousal following exposure to a traumatic stressor.

Prefrontal lobotomy A psychosurgery technique introduced in 1935 by Egas Moniz in which the two hemispheres of the brain are severed. Moniz won a Nobel Prize for the treatment, which now is discredited.

Premature ejaculation A type of sexual disorder, in which a man is unable to delay ejaculation long enough to accomplish intercourse.

Premorbid history A pattern of behavior that precedes the onset of an illness. Adjustment prior to the disorder.

Preparedness theory The notion that organisms are biologically prepared, on the basis of neural pathways in their central nervous systems, to learn certain types of associations (also known as *biological constraints on learning*).

Prevalence An epidemiological term that refers to the total number of cases that are present within a given population during a particular period of time.

Primary appraisal The cognitive evaluation of the challenge, threat, or harm posed by a stressful life event.

Primary prevention An attempt to prevent new cases of disorder by improving the environment; promotes health, not just the treatment of illness.

Primary sleep disorder A condition where a sleeping difficulty is the principal complaint. In DSM-IV, either a dyssomnia—a difficulty in the amount, quality, or timing of sleep, or a parasomnia—an abnormal event that occurs during sleep; for example, nightmares.

Probands Index cases. In behavior genetic studies, probands are family members who have a disorder, and the relatives of the index cases are examined for concordance.

Problem-focused coping Externally oriented coping in an attempt to change or otherwise control a stressor.

Prodromal phase Precedes the active phase of schizophrenia and is marked by an obvious deterioration in role functioning. Prodromal signs and symptoms are less dramatic than those seen during the active phase of the disorder.

Professional responsibilities A professional's obligation to follow the ethical standards of his or her profession and to uphold the laws of the states in which he or she practices, for example, confidentiality.

Prognosis Predictions about the future course of a disorder with or without treatment.

Projective tests Personality tests, such as the Rorschach inkblot test, in which the person is asked to interpret a series of ambiguous stimuli.

Prospective design A research design in which people are studied longitudinally and forward in time. Supposed causes of future outcomes are assessed in the present, and subjects are then followed to see if the hypothesized effects develop over time.

Psychiatry The branch of medicine that is concerned with the study and treatment of mental disorders.

Psychoactive substance A drug that alters a person's mood, level of perception, or brain functioning.

Psychoanalysis Freud's orthodox form of psychotherapy that is practiced rarely today because of its time, expense, and questionable effectiveness in treating mental disorders. Freud viewed the task of psychoanalysis as promoting insight by uncovering the unconscious conflicts and motivations that cause psychological difficulties.

Psychoanalytic theory A paradigm for conceptualizing abnormal behavior based on the concepts and writings of Sigmund Freud. Highlights unconscious processes and conflicts as causing abnormal behavior and emphasizes psychoanalysis as the treatment of choice.

Psychodynamic A variation on the Freudian approach that searches for unconscious conflicts and motivations, but does not adhere to Freud literally as in psychoanalysis.

Psychodynamic psychotherapy An "uncovering" form of psychotherapy in which the therapist typically is more engaged and directive; the process is considerably less lengthy than in psychoanalysis.

Psychological dependence A term used to describe forceful, subjective urges to use drugs, often as a means of relieving negative mood states. Contrasts with the term "physiological dependence," which involves symptoms of tolerance and withdrawal.

Psychology The science, profession, and academic discipline concerned with the study of mental processes and behavior in humans and animals.

Psychometric approach A method of classification that forms diagnostic categories from statistical analysis of symptom checklists. Particularly used in classifying and internalizing disorders of childhood.

Psychomotor retardation A generalized slowing of physical and emotional reactions. The slowing of movements and speech; frequently seen in depression.

Psychomotor stimulants Drugs such as amphetamine and cocaine that produce their effect by simulating the effects of certain neurotransmitters, specifically norepinephrine, dopamine, and serotonin.

Psychoneuroimmunology (PNI) Research on the effects of stress on the functioning of the immune system.

Psychopathology The manifestations of (and the study of the causes of) mental disorders. Generally used as another term to describe abnormal behavior.

Psychopathy Another term for *antisocial personality disorder*. Usually associated with Cleckley's definition of that concept, which included features such as disregard for the truth, lack of empathy, and inability to learn from experience.

Psychopharmacology The study of the effects of psychoactive drugs on behavior. Clinical psychopharmacology involves the expert use of drugs in the treatment of mental disorders.

Psychophysiology The study of changes in the functioning of the body that result from psychological experiences.

Psychosis A term that refers to several types of severe mental disorder in which the person is out of contact with reality. Hallucinations and delusions are examples of psychotic symptoms.

Psychosomatic disorder A term indicating that a physical disease is a product both of the psyche (mind) and the soma (body).

Psychostimulants Medications that heighten energy and alertness when taken in small dosages, but lead to restless, even frenetic, behavior when misused. Often used in the treatment of attention-deficit/hyperactivity disorder.

Psychosurgery A controversial treatment that involves the surgical destruction of specific regions of the brain. Modern psychosurgery involves relatively little destruction of brain tissue, unlike the discredited prefrontal lobotomy.

Psychotherapy The use of psychological techniques in an attempt to produce change in the context of a special, helping relationship.

Psychotropic medications Chemical substances that when taken internally affect a person's psychological state.

Purging An intentional act designed to eliminate consumed food from the body. Self-induced vomiting is the most common form.

Random assignment Any of several methods of ensuring that each subject has a statistically equal chance of being exposed to any level of an independent variable.

Random selection A method of selecting samples from a larger population that ensures that each subject has a statistically equal chance of being selected.

Rape Acts involving nonconsensual sexual penetration obtained by physical force, by threat of bodily harm, or when the victim is incapable of giving consent by virtue of mental illness, mental retardation, or intoxication.

Rating scale An assessment tool in which the observer is asked to make judgments that place the person somewhere along a dimension.

Rational–emotive therapy (RET) A cognitive behavior therapy technique designed to challenge irrational beliefs about oneself and the world. Developed by Albert Ellis as a treatment for anxiety, depression, and related problems.

Reaction range A behavior genetic concept for conceptualizing the joint influence of genes and environment; specifically, that heredity determines the upper and lower limits of a trait and experience determines the extent to which people fulfill their genetic potential.

Reactivity The influence of an observer's presence on the behavior of the person who is being observed.

Receptors Sites on the dendrites or soma of a neuron that are sensitive to certain neurotransmitters.

Recidivism Repeat offending in violating the law.

Reciprocal causality The concept of causality as bidirectional (or circular). Interaction is a process of mutual influence, not separable causes and effects.

Reciprocity The social exchange of cooperation and conflict. Family members with happy relationships reciprocate positive actions; family members with troubled relationships reciprocate negative ones.

Recovered memories Dramatic recollections of long-forgotten traumatic experiences; a controversial topic because the "memories" often are impossible to validate and many such memories may be created rather than recovered.

Reductionism The scientific perspective that the whole is the sum of its parts, and that the task of scientists is to divide the world into its smaller and smaller components.

Regression A return or retreat to an earlier stage or style of coping or behaving.

Relapse The reappearance of active symptoms following a period of remission (such as a return to heavy drinking by an alcoholic after a period of sustained sobriety).

Reliability The consistency of measurements, including diagnostic decisions. One index of reliability is agreement among clinicians.

Remission A stage of disorder characterized by the absence of symptoms (i.e., symptoms that were previously present are now gone).

Representative sample A sample that accurately represents the larger population of an identified group (e.g., a representative sample of all children in the United States).

Residual phase Follows the active phase of a disorder such as schizophrenia. At this point, psychotic symptoms have improved, but the person continues to be impaired in various ways. Negative symptoms may be more pronounced during the residual phase.

Residual type A subtype of schizophrenia that includes patients who no longer meet the criteria for active phase symptoms but nevertheless demonstrate continued signs of negative symptoms or attenuated forms of delusions, hallucinations, or disorganized speech.

Resilience The ability to "bounce back" from adversity despite life stress and emotional distress.

Retrograde amnesia The loss of memory for events prior to the onset of an illness or the experience of a traumatic event.

Retrospective reports Recollections about past experiences that are often questioned in terms of reliability and validity.

Reuptake The process of recapturing some neurotransmitters in the synapse before they reach the receptors of another cell and returning the chemical substances to the terminal button. The neurotransmitter then is reused in subsequent neural transmission.

Reverse causality Indicates that causation could be operating in the opposite direction: Y could be causing X instead of X causing Y. A threat to interpretation in correlational studies, and a basic reason why correlation does not mean causation.

Risk A statement about the probability that a certain outcome will occur.

Risk factor A variable that is associated with a higher probability of developing a disorder.

Role playing Improvisational play acting that may be used in therapy to teach clients alternative ways of acting in problematic situations.

Savant performance An exceptional ability in a highly specialized area of functioning typically involving artistic,musical, or mathematical skills.

Schema A general cognitive pattern that guides the way a person perceives and interprets events in his or her environment.

Schizoaffective disorder A disorder defined by a period of disturbance during which the symptoms of schizophrenia partially overlap with a major depressive episode or a manic episode.

Schizoid personality disorder An enduring pattern of thinking and behavior characterized by pervasive indifference to other people, coupled with a diminished range of emotional experience and expression. People who fit this description prefer social isolation to interactions with friends or family.

Schizophrenia A type of (or group of) psychotic disorders characterized by positive and negative symptoms and associated with a deterioration in role functioning. The term was originally coined by Eugen Bleuler to describe the *splitting of mental associations,* which he believed to be the fundamental disturbance in schizophrenia (previously known as *dementia praecox*).

Schizophrenic spectrum A group of disorders that, on the basis of family history and adoption study data, are presumed to be genetically related to schizophrenia. These disorders may include schizotypal personality disorder, schizoaffective disorder, and delusional disorder.

Schizophreniform disorder A condition characterized by the same symptoms as schizophrenia, in which the patient has exhibited symptoms for less than the 6-month period required by DSM-IV for a diagnosis of schizophrenia.

Schizotypal personality disorder An enduring pattern of discomfort with other people coupled with peculiar thinking and behavior. The latter symptoms take the form of perceptual and cognitive disturbances. Considered by some experts to be part of the schizophrenic spectrum.

School refusal *(school phobia)* Extreme reluctance to go to school, accompanied by various symptoms of anxiety such as stomachaches and headaches. May be a fear of school or an expression of separation anxiety disorder.

Seasonal affective disorder A type of mood disorder (either unipolar or bipolar) in which there has been a regular temporal relation between onset (or disappearance) of the person's episodes and a particular time of the year. For example, the person might become depressed in the winter.

Secondary appraisal The assessment of one's abilities and resources for coping with a stressful life event.

Secondary gain The psychoanalytic concept that conversion (or other somatoform) symptoms can help a patient avoid responsibility or receive attention (reinforcement).

Secondary prevention Focuses on the early detection of emotional problems (for instance, "at-risk" groups) in an attempt to prevent problems from becoming more serious and difficult to treat.

Selective serotonin reuptake inhibitors (SSRIs) A group of antidepressant drugs that inhibit the reuptake of serotonin into the presynaptic nerve endings and therefore promote neurotransmission in serotonin pathways.

Self-control Appropriate behavior guided by internal (rather than external) rules.

Senile plaques A type of brain lesion found in Alzheimer's disease that consists of a central core of homogeneous protein material known as *amyloid* surrounded by clumps of debris left over from destroyed neurons.

Sensate focus A procedure for the treatment of sexual dysfunction that involves a series of simple exercises in which the couple spends time in a quiet, relaxed setting, learning to touch each other.

Separation anxiety A normal fear that begins to develop around 8 months and peaks around 15 months. The infant expresses distress following separation from an attachment figure, typically a parent or other close caregiver.

Separation anxiety disorder A psychological disorder of childhood characterized by persistent and excessive worry for the safety of an attachment figure and related fears such as getting lost, being kidnapped, nightmares, and refusal to be alone. Distinct from normal separation anxiety, which typically develops shortly before an infant's first birthday.

Sexual aversion disorder A form of sexual dysfunction in which a person has an extreme aversion to, and avoids, genital sexual contact with a partner.

Sexual dysfunctions Forms of sexual disorder that involve inhibitions of sexual desire or interference with the physiological responses leading to orgasm.

Sexual masochism A form of paraphilia in which sexual arousal is associated with the act of being humiliated, beaten, bound, or otherwise made to suffer.

Sexual sadism A form of paraphilia in which sexual arousal is associated with desires to inflict physical or psychological suffering, including humiliation, on another person.

Shared environment The component of the family environment that offers the same or highly similar experiences to all siblings, for example, socioeconomic status. Stands in contrast to the nonshared environment, experiences inside and outside the family that are unique to one sibling.

Social clocks Age-related goals people set for themselves and later use to evaluate life achievements.

Socialization The process of shaping children's behavior and attitudes to conform to the expectations of parents, teachers, and society.

Social phobia A type of phobic disorder in which the person is persistently fearful of social situations that might expose him or her to scrutiny by others, such as fear of public speaking.

Social skills training A behavior therapy technique in which clients are taught new skills that are desirable and likely to be rewarded in the everyday world.

Social support The emotional and practical assistance received from others.

Social work A profession whose primary concern is how human needs can be met within society.

Somatic symptoms Symptoms of mood disorders that are related to basic physiological or bodily functions, including fatigue, aches and pains, and serious changes in appetite and sleep patterns.

Somatization disorder A type of somatoform disorder characterized by multiple, somatic complaints in the absence of organic impairments.

Somatoform disorders A category of psychological disorders characterized by unusual physical symptoms that occur in the absence of a known physical pathology. Examples include hypochondriasis and conversion disorder. Somatoform disorders are somatic in form only, thus their name (note the distinction from psychosomatic disorders, which do involve real physical pathology).

Standard deviation A measure of dispersion of scores around the mean. Technically, the square root of the variance.

Standard scores A standardized frequency distribution in which each score is subtracted from the mean and the difference is divided by the standard deviation.

State-dependent learning Learning that occurs in one state of affect or consciousness is best recalled in the same state of affect or consciousness.

Statistically significant A statistical statement that a research result has a low probability of having occurred by chance alone. By convention, a result is said to be statistically significant if the probability is 5% or less that it was obtained by chance. This probability is often written as $p < .05$.

Status offense An act that is illegal only because of a youth's status as a minor, for example, running away from home, truancy from school.

Stigma A negative stamp or label that sets the person apart from others, connects the person to undesirable features, and leads others to reject the person.

Stress An event that creates physiological or psychological strain for the individual. Stress has been defined differently by various scientists.

Stress management   A treatment used in behavioral medicine and health psychology to teach more effective coping skills, reduce adverse reactions to stress, and improve health behavior.

Substance abuse   The less severe form of substance use disorder listed in DSM-IV. Describes a pattern of drug use that is defined in terms of interference with the person's ability to fulfill major role obligations, the recurrent use of a drug in dangerous situations, or the experience of repeated legal difficulties that are associated with drug use.

Substance dependence   The more severe form of substance use disorder listed in DSM-IV. Refers to a pattern of repeated self-administration that results in tolerance, withdrawal, or compulsive drug-taking behavior.

Superego   One of Freud's three central personality structures, roughly equivalent to the "conscience." In Freudian theory, the superego contains societal standards of behavior, particularly rules that children learn from identifying with their parents. The superego attempts to control id impulses.

Synapse   A small gap filled with fluid that lies between the axon of one neuron and a dendrite or soma of another neuron.

Syndrome   A group of symptoms that appear together and are assumed to represent a specific type of disorder.

Systematic desensitization   A treatment for overcoming fears and phobias developed by Joseph Wolpe. Involves learning relaxation skills, developing a fear hierarchy, and systematic exposure to imagined, feared events while simultaneously maintaining relaxation.

Systems theory   An innovation in the philosophy of conceptualizing and conducting science that emphasizes interdependence, cybernetics, and especially holism—the idea that the whole is more than the sum of its parts. Often traced to the biologist and philosopher Ludwig von Bertalanffy.

Temperament   Characteristic styles of relating to the world that are often conceptualized as inborn traits. Generally emphasizes the "how" as opposed to the "what" of behavior.

Tend and befriend   An alternative response to stress hypothesized to be more common among females. Tending involves caring for offspring in a way that protects them from harm, and also alters the offspring's neuroendocrine responses in a healthful manner. Befriending is responding to threat with social affiliation, thereby reducing the risk of physical danger and encouraging the exchange of resources.

Tertiary prevention   Involves treatment for a disorder, but also attempts to address some of the adverse consequences of mental illness (such as unemployment).

Thalamus   A part of the limbic system that is involved in receiving and integrating sensory information both from the sense organs and from higher brain structures.

Theory of mind   The cognitive capacity to appreciate that other people have a point of reference that differs from your own, to recognize that other minds exist. The idea that people with autism lack a theory of mind generated considerable research.

Therapeutic alliance   The emotional bond of confidence and trust between a therapist and client believed to facilitate therapy.

Third variable   An unmeasured factor that may account for a correlation observed between any two variables. A threat to interpretation in correlational studies, and a basic reason why correlation does not mean causation.

Threshold model   A perspective on etiology that holds that people can exhibit characteristics of a disorder without experiencing any adverse impact on their adjustment until they pass a critical threshold. Beyond that level, there is presumably a dramatic increase in the number of problems that are encountered.

Time-out   A discipline technique that involves briefly isolating a child as a punishment for misbehavior.

Token economy   A type of contingency management program that has been adopted in many institutional settings. Desired and undesired behaviors are identified, contingencies are defined, behavior is monitored, and rewards or punishments are given according to the rules of the economy.

Tolerance   The process through which the nervous system becomes less sensitive to the effects of a psychoactive substance. As a result, the person needs to consume increased quantities of the drug to achieve the same subjective effect.

Transference   In psychoanalysis, the process whereby patients transfer feelings about a key figure in their lives onto the analyst. In psychotherapy, the client's feelings toward the therapist.

Transsexualism   A severe form of gender identity disorder in adults.

Transvestic fetishism   A form of paraphilia in which sexual pleasure is derived from dressing in the clothing of the opposite gender.

Trauma desensitization   A treatment for posttraumatic stress disorder where the client is first taught to relax, and while maintaining a state of relaxation, he or she relives the traumatic event through discussions or fantasies.

Traumatic stress   A catastrophic event that involves real or perceived threat to life or physical well-being.

Tricyclics (TCAs)   A group of antidepressant drugs that block the uptake of neurotransmitters, such as norepinephrine and dopamine, from the synapse.

Two-factor theory   A combination of classical conditioning and operant conditioning that is hypothesized to explain the acquisition and maintenance of fear. Fears are acquired through classical conditioning and maintained through operant conditioning (the reduction in anxiety that stems from avoidance).

Type A behavior pattern   A characterological response to challenge that is competitive, hostile, urgent, impatient, and achievement-striving. Linked to an increased risk for coronary heart disease.

Undifferentiated type   A subtype of schizophrenia that includes patients who display prominent psychotic symptoms and either meet the criteria for several subtypes or otherwise do not meet the criteria for the catatonic, paranoid, or disorganized types.

Unipolar mood disorder   A form of mood disorder in which the person experiences episodes of depression but has never experienced an episode of mania or hypomania.

Vaginismus   A form of sexual dysfunction in which the outer muscles of the vagina snap tightly shut when penetration is attempted, thus preventing insertion of any object.

Validity   The meaning or systematic importance of a construct or a measurement.

Variance   A measure of dispersion of scores around the mean. Technically, the average squared difference from the mean (see also *standard deviation*).

Vascular dementia   (also known as *multi-infarct dementia*) A type of dementia associated with vascular disease. The cognitive symptoms of vascular dementia are the same as those for Alzheimer's disease, but a gradual onset is not required.

Ventricles   Four connected chambers in the brain filled with cerebrospinal fluid. The ventricles are enlarged in some psychological and neurological disorders.

Victimization   A pattern of responses often observed among victims of violent crimes, particularly rape, that includes fear, guilt, self-blame, powerlessness, and lowered self-esteem.

Voyeurism   A form of paraphilia (also known as *peeping*) in which a person becomes sexually aroused by observing unsuspecting people (usually strangers) while they are undressing or engaging in sexual activities.

Vulnerability marker   A specific measure, such as a biochemical assay or a psychological test, that might be useful in identifying people who are vulnerable to a disorder such as schizophrenia.

Weight set point   Fixed weights or small ranges of weight around which the body regulates weight, for example, by increasing or decreasing metabolism.

Withdrawal   The constellation of symptoms that are experienced shortly after a person stops taking a drug after heavy or prolonged use.

Worry   A relatively uncontrollable sequence of negative, emotional thoughts and images that are concerned with possible future threats or danger.

References

Abel, G. G., Becker, J. V., Mittelman, M., Cunningham-Rathner, J., et al. (1987). Self-reported sex crimes of nonincarcerated paraphiliacs. *Journal of Interpersonal Violence, 2*, 3–25.

Abel, G. G., & Gouleau, J. L. (1990). Male sex offenders. In M. E. Thase, B. A. Edelstein, & M. Hersen (Eds.), *Handbook of Outpatient Treatment of Adults: Nonpsychotic Mental Disorders*, pp. 271–290. New York: Plenum.

Abel, G. G., & Osborn, C. (1992). The paraphilias: The extent and nature of sexually deviant and criminal behavior. *Psychotic Clinics of North America, 15*, 675–687.

Abraído-Lanza, A. F., Vásquez, E. & Echeverría, S. E. (2004). En las manos de Dios [in God's hands]: Religious and other forms of coping among Latinos with arthritis. *Journal of Consulting and Clinical Psychology, 72*, 91–102.

Abramowitz, J. S. (1997). Effectiveness of psychological and parmacological treatments for obsessive-compulsive disorder: A quantitative review. *Journal of Consulting and Clinical Psychology, 65*, 44–52.

Abramowitz, J. S. (1998). Does cognitive-behavioral therapy cure obsessive-compulsive disorder? A meta-analytic evaluation of clinical significance. *Behavior Therapy, 29*, 339–355.

Abramowitz, J. S. (2006). The psychological treatment of obsessive-compulsive disorder. *Canadian Journal of Psychiatry, 51*, 407–416.

Abramowitz, J. S., Tolin, D. F., & Street, G. P. (2001). Paradoxical effects of thought suppression: A meta-analysis of controlled studies. *Clinical Psychology Review, 21*, 683–703.

Abrams, R. (2002). *Electroconvulsive Therapy* (4th ed.). New York: Oxford University Press.

Abramson, L. Y., Alloy, L. B., Hankin, B. L., Haeffel, G. J., MacCoon, D. G., & Gibb, B. E. (2002). Cognitive vulnerability-stress models of depression in a self-regulatory and psychobiological context. In I. H. Gotlib & C. L. Hammen (Eds.), *Handbook of Depression*, pp. 268–294. New York: Guilford.

Adams, C., Fenton, M., Quraishi, S., & David, A. (2001). Systematic meta-review of depot antipsychotic drugs for people with schizophrenia. *British Journal of Psychiatry, 179*, 290–299.

Adams, G. R., Abraham, K. G., & Markstrom, C. A. (1987). The relation among identity development, self-consciousness and self-focusing during middle and late adolescence. *Developmental Psychology, 23*, 292–297.

Adams, G. R., & Adams, C. M. (1989). Developmental issues. In L. K. G. Hsu & M. Hersen (Eds.), *Recent Developments in Adolescent Psychiatry*, pp. 13–30. New York: Wiley.

Adams, G. R., Ryan, J. H., Hoffman, J. J., Dobson, W. R., & Nielsen, E. C. (1985). Ego identity status, conformity behavior and personality in late adolescence. *Journal of Personality and Social Psychology, 47*, 1091–1104.

Addis, M. E., & Mahalik, J. R. (2003). Men, masculinity, and the contexts of help seeking. *American Psychologist, 58*, 5–14.

Adler, R. (2001). Psychoneuroimmunology. *Current Directions in Psychological Science, 10*, 94–98.

Agras, W. S. (1987). *Eating Disorders: Management of Obesity, Bulimia, and Anorexia Nervosa.* Elmsford, NY: Pergamon.

Agras, W. S., Rossiter, E. M., Arnow, B., et al. (1992). Pharmacologic and cognitive-behavioral treatment for bulimia nervosa. *American Journal of Psychiatry, 149*, 82–87.

Agras, W. S., Walsh, T., Fairburn, C. G., Wilson, G. T., & Kraemer, H. C. (2000). A multicenter comparison of cognitive-behavioral therapy and interpersonal psychotherapy for bulimia nervosa. *Archives of General Psychiatry, 57*(5), 459–466.

Agrawal, A., Dick, D. M., Bucholz, K. K., Madden, P. A. F., Cooper, M. L., Sher, K. J., & Heath, A. C. (2008). Drinking expectancies and motives: A genetic study of young adult women. *Addiction, 103*, 194–204.

Ainsworth, M. D. S. (1989). Attachments beyond infancy. *American Psychologist, 44*, 709–716.

Ainsworth, M. S. (1979). Infant-mother attachment. *American Psychologist, 34*(10), 932–937.

Akagi, H., & House, A. (2001) Epidemiology of Conversion Hysteria. In P. Halligan, C. Bass, & J. Marshall (Eds.), *Contemporary Approaches to the Study of Hysteria*, pp. 73–86. Oxford: Oxford University Press.

Akiskal, H. S. (1992). Borderline: An adjective still in search of a noun. In D. Silver & M. Rosenbluth (Eds.), *Handbook of Borderline Disorders*, pp. 155–176. Madison, CT: International Universities Press.

Akyuz, G., Dogan, O., Sar, V., Yargic, L. I., & Tutkun, H. (1999). Frequency of dissociative identity disorder in the general population in Turkey. *Comprehensive Psychiatry, 40*, 151–159.

Alarcon, R. D. (2005). Cross-cultural issues. In J. M. Oldham & A. E. Skodol (Eds.), *American Psychiatric Publishing Textbook of personality disorders*, pp. 561–578. Washington, DC: American Psychiatric Publishing.

Albarracín, D., Durantini, M. R., & Earl, A. (2006). Empirical and theoretical conclusions of an analysis of outcomes of HIV-prevention interventions. *Current Directions in Psychological Science, 15*, 73–78.

Albarracín, D., Gillette, J. C., Earl, A. N., Glasman, L. R., Durantini, M. R., & Ho, M. (2005). A test of major assumptions about behavior change: A comprehensive look at the effects of passive and active HIV-prevention interventions since the beginning of the epidemic. *Psychological Bulletin, 131*, 856–897.

Aldridge-Morris, R. (1989). *Multiple Personality: An Exercise in Deception.* Hillsdale, NJ: Erlbaum.

Alexander, F. (1950). *Psychosomatic Medicine: Its Principles and Applications.* New York: Norton.

Alexander, F., & French, T. M. (1946). *Psychoanalytic Therapy: Principles and Application.* Oxford, England: Ronald Press.

Alexander, F., French, T. M., & Pollock, G. H. (1968). *Psychosomatic Specificity.* Chicago: University of Chicago Press.

Alexander, J. F., Holtzworth-Munroe, A., & Jameson, P. B. (1994). The process and outcome of marital and family therapy: Research, review, and evaluation. In A. E. Bergin & S. L. Garfield (Eds.), *Handbook of Psychotherapy and Behavior Change*, 4th ed., pp. 595–630. New York: Wiley.

Alexander, J. F., & Parsons, B. V. (1982). *Functional Family Therapy.* Monterey, CA: Brooks/Cole.

Allen, A. (2006). Cognitive-behavior therapy and other psychosocial interventions in the treatment of obsessive-compulsive disorder. *Psychiatric Annals, 36*, 474–479.

Allen, J. P., et al. (2002). Attachment and autonomy as predictors of the development of social skills and delinquency during midadolescence. *Journal of Consulting and Clinical Psychology, 70*, 56–66.

Alloy, L. B., Abramson, L. Y., & Francis, E. L. (1999). Do negative cognitive styles confer vulnerability to depression? *Current Directions in Psychological Science, 8*, 128–132.

Alloy, L. B., Abramson, L. Y., Gibb, B. E., Crossfield, A. G., Pieracci, A. M., Spasojevic, J., & Steinberg, J. A. (2004). Developmental antecedents of cognitive vulnerability to depression: Review of findings from the cognitive vulnerability to depression project. *Journal of Cognitive Psychotherapy, 18*, 115–133.

Alloy, L. B., Abramson, L. Y., Walshaw, P. D., & Neeren, A. M. (2006). Cognitive vulnerability to unipolar and bipolar mood disorders. *Journal of Social and Clinical Psychology, 25*, 726–754.

Alloy, L. B., Reilly-Harrington, N., Fresco, D. M., Whitehouse, W. G., & Zechmeister, J. S. (1999). Cognitive styles and life events in subsyndromal unipolar and bipolar disorders. *Journal of Cognitive Psychotherapy, 13*, 21–40.

Almeida, D. M. (2005). Resilience and vulnerability to daily stressors assessed via diary methods. *Current Directions in Psychological Science, 14*, 64–68.

Al-Sawaf, M, & Al-Issa, I. (2000). Sex and sexual dysfunction in an Arab-Islamic society. In I. Al-Issa (Ed.), *Mental Illness in the Islamic World*, pp. 295–311. International Universities Press.

Altemus, M. (2006). Sex differences in depression and anxiety disorders: Potential biological determinants. *Hormones and Behavior, 50*, 534–538.

Amato, P. R. (2001). Children of divorce in the 1990s: An update of the Amato and Keith (1991) meta-analysis. *Journal of Family Psychology, 15*, 355–370.

America's Children: Key National Indicators of Well-Being. (1999). Federal Interagency Forum on Child and Family Statistics. Washington, DC: U.S. Government Printing Office.

American Association on Mental Retardation. (2002). *Mental Retardation: Definition, Classification, and Systems of Supports*, 10th ed. Washington, DC: Author.

American Association on Intellectual and Developmental Disabilities. (2002). *Mental Retardation: Definition, Classification, and Systems of Supports*, 10th ed. Washington, DC: AAIDD.

American Bar Association. (1995). *Mental Disability Law*, 5th ed. Washington, DC: Author.

American Cancer Society. (1994). *Cancer Facts and Figures, 1993.* New York: Author.

The American College of Obstetricians and Gynecologists. (2007, January 2). New recommendations for down syndrome call for screening of all pregnant women. Retrieved January 4, 2007, from www.acog.org/from_ home/publications/press_releases/nr01-02-07-1.cfm

American Psychiatric Association. (1980). *Psychiatric Glossary*. Washington, DC: American Psychiatric Press.

American Psychiatric Association. (1983). American Psychiatric Association statement on the insanity defense. *American Journal of Psychiatry, 140,* 681–688.

American Psychiatric Association (1994). *Diagnostic and Statistical Manual of Mental Disorders,* 1st ed. 1952; 2nd ed. 1968; 3rd ed. 1980; rev. 3rd ed. 1987; 4th ed. 1994. Washington, DC: Author.

American Psychological Association. (1995). *Violence in the Family.* Washington, DC: Author.

American Psychiatric Association. (2000). *Diagnostic and Statistical Manual of Mental Disorders* (DSM-IV-TR, 4th edition, text revision). Washington, DC: Author.

Anda, R., Williamson, D., Jones, D., Macera, C., Eaker, E., Glasman, A., et al. (1993). Depressed affect, hopelessness, and the risk of ischemic heart disease. *Epidemiology, 4,* 285–294.

Andersen, A. E. (1995). Eating disorders in males. In K. D. Brownell & C. G. Fairburn (Eds.), *Eating Disorders and Obesity: A Comprehensive Handbook,* pp. 177–182. New York: Guilford.

Anderson, A. E. (2002). Eating disorders in males. In C. G. Fairburn & K. D. Brownell (Eds.). *Eating Disorders and Obesity,* 2nd ed., pp. 188–192. New York: Guilford.

Andersen, B. L., & Cyranowski, J. M. (1995). Women's sexuality: Behaviors, responses, and individual differences. *Journal of Consulting and Clinical Psychology, 63,* 891–906.

Anderson, B. L., Kiecolt-Glaser, J. K., & Glaser, R. (1994). A biobehavioral model of cancer stress and disease course. *American Psychologist, 49,* 389–404.

Anderson, C. A., Berkowitz, L., Donnerstein, E., Huesmann, L. R., Johnson, J. D., Linz, D., et al., (2003). The influence of media violence on youth. *Psychological Science in the Public Interest, 4*(3), 81–110.

Anderson, D. K., Lord, C., Risi, S., DiLavore, P. S., Shulman, C., Thurm, A., et al. (2007). Patterns of growth in verbal abilities among children with autism spectrum disorder. *Journal of Consulting and Clinical Psychology, 75,* 594-604.

Anderson, I. (2006). The new guidelines from the British Association for Psychopharmacology for anxiety disorders. *International Journal of Psychiatry in Clinical Practice, 10* (Suppl. 3), 10–17.

Anderson, P. (1996 May 21). Obsessive compulsion and tics linked to sore throats. *The Medical Post.* Retrieved October 18, 2008, from www.mentalhealth.com/ mag1/p5m-ocd1.html

Andreasen, N. C. (2000). Schizophrenia: The fundamental questions. *Brain Research Reviews, 31,* 106–112.

Andreasen, N. C. (2001). *Brave New Brain: Conquering Mental Illness in the Era of the Genome.* New York: Oxford University Press.

Andreasen, N. C., Arndt, S., Alliger, R., Miller, D., & Flaum, M. (1995). Symptoms of schizophrenia: Methods, meanings, and mechanisms. *Archives of General Psychiatry, 52,* 341–351.

Andrews, G. (1996). Comorbidity and the general neurotic syndrome. *British Journal of Psychiatry, 168,* 76–84.

Andrews, G., MacMahon, S. W., Austin, A., & Byrne, D. G. (1984). Hypertension: Comparison of drug and non-drug treatments. *British Medical Journal, 284,* 1523–1530.

Angst, J., Sellaro, R., & Merikangas, K. R. (2000). Depressive spectrum diagnoses. *Comprehensive Psychiatry, 41,* 39–47.

Anthony, J. C., & Helzer, J. E. (1991). Syndromes of drug abuse and dependence. In L. N. Robins & D. A. Regier (Eds.), *Psychiatric Disorders in America: The Epidemiologic Catchment Area Study,* pp. 116–154. New York: Free Press.

Anthony, J. C., Warner, L. A., & Kessler, R. C. (1994). Comparative epidemiology of dependence on tobacco, alcohol, controlled substances, and inhalants: Basic findings from the National Comorbidity Survey. *Experimental and Clinical Psychopharmacology, 2,* 1–24.

Antoni, M. H., Lechner, S. C., Kazi, A., Wimberly, S. R., Sifre, T., Urcuyo, K. R., et al. (2006). How stress management improves quality of life after treatment for breast cancer. *Journal of Consulting and Clinical Psychology, 74,* 1143–1152.

Antonucci, T. C. (2001). Social relations. In J. E. Birren & K. W. Schaie (Eds.), *Handbook of the Psychology of Aging,* 5th ed., pp. 427–453. San Diego, CA: Academic Press.

Appelbaum, P. S. (1994). *Almost a Revolution: Mental Health Law and the Limits of Change.* New York: Oxford University Press.

Appelbaum, P. S., & Gutheil, T. G. (1980). The Boston State Hospital case: 'Involuntary mind control,' the Constitution, and the 'right to rot.' *American Journal of Psychiatry, 137*(6), 720–723.

Appels, M. C. M., Sitskoorn, M. M., Vollema, M. G., & Kahn, R. S. (2004). Elevated levels of schizotypal features in parents of patients with a family history of schizophrenia spectrum disorders. *Schizophrenia Bulletin, 30,* 781–790.

Arnett, J. J. (1999). Adolescent storm and stress, reconsidered. *American Psychologist, 54,* 317–326.

Arnold, L. E., Elliot, M., Sachs, L., Bird, H., Kraemer, H. C., Wells, K. C., et al. (2003). Effects of ethnicity on treatment attendance, stimulant response/dose, and 14-month outcome in ADHD. *Journal of Consulting and Clinical Psychology, 71*(4), 713–727.

Asher, S. R., & Wheeler, V. A. (1985). Children's loneliness: A comparison of rejected and neglected peer status. *Journal of Consulting and Clinical Psychology, 53,* 500–505.

Asperger, H. (1944/1991). "Autistic psychopathy" in childhood. In U. Frith (Ed. and Trans.), *Autism and Asperger Syndrome,* pp. 37–92. Cambridge: Cambridge University Press. (Original published in 1944.)

Astin, M. C., Ogland-Hand, S. M., Coleman, E. M., & Foy, D. W. (1995). Posttraumatic stress disorder and childhood abuse in battered women: Comparisons with maritally distressed women. *Journal of Consulting and Clinical Psychology, 63,* 308–312.

Atalay, F., & Atalay, H. (2006). Gender differences in patients with schizophrenia in terms of sociodemographic and clinical characteristics. German Journal of Psychiatry, 9, 41–47.

Atkinson, D. R., Morten, G., & Sue, D. W. (1993). Counseling American minorities: A cross-cultural perspective, 4th ed., Madison, Wl and England: Brown & Benchmark and Wm. C. Brown Publ.

Attie, I., & Brooks-Gunn, J. (1989). Development of eating problems in adolescent girls: A longitudinal study. *Developmental Psychology, 25,* 70–79.

Averill, P. M., Reas, D. L., Shack, A., Shah, N. N., Cowan, K., Krajewski, K., et al. (2004). Is schizoaffective disorder a stable diagnostic category? A retrospective examination. *Psychiatric Quarterly, 75,* 215–227.

Ayres, J. J. B. (1998). Fear conditioning and avoidance. In W. T. O'Donohue (Ed.), *Learning and Behavior Therapy,* pp. 122–145. Needham Heights, MA: Allyn and Bacon.

Babior, S., & Goldman, C. (1996). *Overcoming Panic, Anxiety, and Phobias: New Strategies for Free Yourself from Worry and Fear.* Duluth, MN: Whole Person Associates.

Babor, T. F. (2008). Treatment for persons with substance use disorders: Mediators, moderators, and the need for a new research approach. *International Journal of Methods in Psychiatric Research, 17* (Suppl. 1), S45–S49.

Babor, T. F., & Del Boca, F. K. (Eds.). (2002). *Treatment Matching in Alcoholism.* New York: Cambridge University Press.

Babor, T., & Del Boca, F. (2003). Treatment Matching in Alcoholism. New York: Cambridge University Press.

Bach, A. K., Brown, T. A., & Barlow, D. H. (1999). The effects of false negative feedback on efficacy expectancies and sexual arousal in sexually functional males. *Behavior Therapy, 30,* 79–95.

Bachar, K., & Koss, M. P. (2001). From prevalence to prevention: Closing the gap between what we know about rape and what we do. In C. M. Renzetti and J. L. Edleson (Eds.), *Sourcebook on Violence Against Women,* pp. 117–142. Thousand Oaks, CA: Sage.

Baer, J. S. (2002). Student factors: Understanding individual variation in college drinking. *Journal of Studies on Alcohol* (Supp. 14), 40–53.

Bailey, A., Le Couteur, A., Gottesman, I., Bolton, P., Simonoff, E., Yuzda, E., et al. (1995). Autism as a strongly genetic disorder: Evidence from a British twin study. *Psychological Medicine, 25,* 63–77.

Bailey, S. (2002). Treatment of delinquents. In M. Rutter & E. Taylor (Eds.), *Child and Adolescent Psychiatry,* 4th ed., pp. 1019–1037. Oxford, England: Blackwell.

Baker, J. D., Capron, E. W., & Azorlosa, J. (1996). Family environment characteristics of persons with histrionic and dependent personality disorders. *Journal of Personality Disorders, 10,* 82–87.

Baldwin, S. A., Wampold, B. E., & Imel, Z. E. (2007). Untangling the alliance-outcome correlation: Exploring the relative importance of therapist and patient variability in the alliance. *Journal of Consulting and Clinical Psychology, 75,* 842–852.

Ballard, E. (2007). Support groups: Meeting the needs of families caring for persons with Alzheimer's disease. In C. B. Cox (Ed.), *Dementia and Social Work Practice: Research and Interventions,* pp. 321–337. New York: Springer Publishing Co.

Ballard, C. G., O'Brien, J. T., Swann, A. G., Thompson, P., Neill, D., & McKeith, I. G. (2001). The natural history of psychosis and depression in dementia with Lewy bodies and Alzheimer's disease: Persistence and new cases over 1 year of follow-up. *Journal of Clinical Psychiatry, 62,* 46–49.

Ballenger, J. C. (2001). Overview of different pharmacotherapies for attaining remission in generalized anxiety disorder. *Journal of Clinical Psychiatry, 62* (suppl. 19), 11–19.

Ballenger, J. C., et al. (2000). Consensus statement on posttraumatic stress disorder from the International Consensus on Depression and Anxiety. *Journal of Clinical Psychiatry, 61,* 60–66.

Balon, R. (1998). Pharmacological treatment of paraphilias with a focus on antidepressants. *Journal of Sex and Marital Therapy, 24,* 241–254.

Baltes, P., & Smith, J. (2008). The fascination of wisdom: Its nature, ontogeny, and function. *Perspectives on Psychological Science, 3,* 56–64.

Baltes, P. B. (1993). The aging mind: Potential and limits. *Gerontologist, 33,* 580–594.

Baltes, P. B. (1997). On the incomplete architecture of human ontogeny. Selection, optimization, and compensation as foundation of developmental theory. *American Psychologist, 52,* 366–380.

Bancroft, J., Loftus, J., & Long, J. (2003). Distress about sex: A national survey of women in heterosexual relationships. *Archives of Sexual Behavior, 32,* 193–208.

Bangs, M. E., Tauscher-Wisniewski, S., Polzer, J., Zhang, S., Acharya, N., Desaiah, D., Trzepacz, P. T., et al.

(2008). Meta-analysis of suicide-related behavior events in patients with atomoxetine. *Journal of the Academy of Child & Adolescent Psychiatry, 47,* 209–218.

Bankier, B., Aigner, M., & Bach, M. (2001). Alexithymia in DSM-IV disorder: Comparative evaluation of somatoform disorder, panic disorder, obsessive-compulsive disorder, and depression. *Psychosomatics, 42,* 235–240.

Barbaree, H. E., & Seto, M. C. (1997). Pedophilia: Assessment and treatment. In D. R. Laws & W. T. O'Donohue (Eds.), *Handbook of Sexual Deviance: Theory and Application.* New York: Guilford.

Barbaree, H. E., Seto, M. C., Serin, R. C., Amos, N. L., & Preston, D. L. (1994). Comparisons between sexual and nonsexual rapist subtypes: Sexual arousal to rape, offense precursors, and offense characteristics. *Criminal Justice and Behavior, 21,* 95–114.

Barbaresi, W. J., Katusic, S. K., Colligan, R. C., Weaver, A. L., & Jacobsen, S. J. (2005). The incidence of autism in Olmsted County, Minnesota, 1976–1997: Results from a population-based study. *Archives of Pediatric & Adolescent Medicine, 159,* 37–44.

Barber, C. (2008, February 27). The medicated Americans: Antidepressant prescriptions on the rise. *Scientific American Mind.*

Barch, D. M. (2005). The cognitive neuroscience of schizophrenia. *Annual Review of Clinical Psychology, 1,* 321–353.

Bargh, J. A., & Morsella, E. (2008). The unconscious mind. *Perspectives on Psychological Science, 3,* 73–79.

Barkley, R. A. (1995). *Taking Charge of ADHD.* New York: Guilford.

Barkley, R. A. (Ed.). (2006). *Attention-Deficit Hyperactivity Disorder,* 3rd ed. New York: Guilford Press.

Barkley, R. A. (1998). *Attention-Deficit/Hyperactivity Disorder* (2nd ed.). New York: Guilford.

Barlow, D. H. (1997). Cognitive-behavioral therapy for panic disorder: Current status. *Journal of Clinical Psychiatry, 58* (Suppl. 2), 32–37.

Barlow, D. H. (2001). *Anxiety and Its Disorders* (2nd ed.). New York: Guilford.

Barlow, D. H. (2001). *Clinical Handbook of Psychological Disorders* (3rd ed.). New York: Guilford.

Barlow, D. H. (2004). *Anxiety and Its Disorders: The Nature and Treatment of Anxiety and Panic* 2nd ed., New York: Guilford.

Barlow, D. H. (Ed.). (2008). *Clinical Handbook of Psychological Disorders,* 4th ed. New York: Guilford.

Barlow, D. H., Brown, T. A., & Craske, M. G. (1994). Definitions of panic attacks and panic disorder in the DSM-IV: Implications for research. *Journal of Abnormal Psychology, 103,* 553–564.

Barlow, D. H., & Campbell, L. A. (2000). Mixed anxiety-depression and its implications for models of mood and anxiety disorders. *Comprehensive Psychiatry, 41* (Suppl. 1), 55–60.

Barlow, D. H., Pincus, D. B., Heinrichs, N., & Choate, M. L. (2003). Anxiety disorders. In G. Stricker and T. Widiger (Eds.), *Handbook of Psychology: Clinical Psychology,* Vol. 8, pp. 119–147. New York: Wiley.

Barlow, D. H., Raffa, S. D., & Cohen, E. M. (2002). Psychosocial treatments for panic disorders, phobias, and generalized anxiety disorder. In P. E. Nathan & J. M. Gorman (Eds.), *A Guide to Treatments That Work,* 2nd ed., pp. 301–336. New York: Oxford.

Barlow, D. H. (2004). *Anxiety and Its Disorders: The Nature and Treatment of Anxiety and Panic,* 2nd ed. New York: Guilford.

Barnes, G. M., & Farrell, M. P. (1992). Parental support and control as predictors of adolescent drinking, delinquency, and related problem behaviors. *Journal of Marriage and the Family, 54,* 763–776.

Barnier, A. J. (2002). Posthypnotic amnesia for autobiographical episodes: A laboratory model of functional amnesia? *Psychological Science, 13,* 232–237.

Baroff, G. S. (1986). *Mental Retardation: Nature, Cause, and Management* (2nd ed.). Washington, DC: Hemisphere.

Baroff, G. S., & Olley (1999). *Mental Retardation* (3rd ed.). Philadelphia: Brunner/Mazel.

Baron-Cohen, S., Leslie, A. M., & Frith, U. (1985). Does the autistic child have a "theory of mind"? *Cognition, 21,* 37–46.

Baron-Cohen, S., Tager-Flusberg, H., & Cohen, D. J. (Eds.). (1993). *Understanding Other Minds.* Oxford: Oxford University Press.

Barrett, J. E., Williams, J. W., Jr., Oxman, T. E., Frank, E., Katon, W., Sullivan, M., et al. (2001). Treatment of dysthymia and minor depression in primary care: A randomized trial in patients aged 18 to 59 years. *Journal of Family Practice, 50,* 405–412.

Barrett, M. S., & Berman, J. S. (2001). Is psychotherapy more effective when therapists disclose information about themselves? *Journal of Consulting and Clinical Psychology, 69,* 597–603.

Barrett, P. M., Dadds, M. R., & Rapee, R. M. (1996). Family treatment of childhood anxiety: A controlled trial. *Journal of Consulting and Clinical Psychology, 64,* 333–342.

Barrowclough, C., & Lobban, F. (2008). *Family Intervention. Clinical handbook of schizophrenia,* pp. 214–225. New York: Guilford Press.

Bartz, J. A., & Hollander, E. (2006). Is obsessive compulsive disorder an anxiety disorder? *Progress in Neuro-Psychopharmacology & Biological Psychiatry, 30,* 338–352.

Baskin, T. W., Tierney, S. C., Minami, T., & Wampold, B. E. (2003). Establishing specificity in psychotherapy: A meta-analysis of structural equivalence of placebo controls. *Journal of Consulting and Clinical Psychology, 71,* 973–979.

Basoglu, M., Mineka, S., Paker, M., Aker, T., Livanou, M., & Gok, S. (1997). Psychological preparedness for trauma as a protective factor in survivors of torture. *Psychological Medicine, 27,* 1421–1433.

Bass, C., Peveler, R., & House, A. (2001). Somatoform disorders: Severe psychiatric illnesses neglected by psychiatrists. *British Journal of Psychiatry, 179,* 11–14.

Bass, E., & Davis, L. (1988). *The Courage to Heal.* New York: Harper & Row.

Basson, R. (2001). Human sex-response cycles. *Journal of Sex and Marital Therapy, 27,* 33–43.

Basson, R. (2002). A model of women's sexual arousal. *Journal of Sex & Marital Therapy, 28,* 1–10.

Basson, R., Berman, J., Burnett, A., Derogatis, L., Ferguson, D., Fourcroy, J., et al. (2000). Report of the international consensus development conference on female sexual dysfunction: Definitions and classification. *Journal of Urology, 163,* 888–896.

Basson, R., Brotto, L. A., Laan, E., Redmond, G., & Utian, W. H. (2005). Assessment and management of women's sexual dysfunctions: Problematic desire and arousal. *Journal of Sexual Medicine, 2,* 291–300.

Bastiani, A. M., Rao, R., Weltzin, T., & Kaye, W. H. (1995). Perfectionism in anorexia nervosa. *International Journal of Eating Disorders, 17,* 147–152.

Bastien C. H., et al., (2004). Cognitive-behavioral therapy for insomnia: Comparison of individual therapy, group therapy, and telephone consultations. *Journal of Consulting and Clinical Psychology, 72,* 653–659.

Bates, J. E., Wachs, T. D., & Emde, R. N. (1994). Toward practical uses for biological concepts of temperament. In J. E. Bates & T. D. Wachs (Eds.), *Temperament: Individual Differences at the Interface of Biology and Behavior,* 275–306. Washington, DC: American Psychological Association.

Battaglia, M., & Torgersen, S. (1996). Schizotypal disorder: At the crossroads of genetics and nosology. *Acta Psychiatrica Scandinavica, 94,* 303–310.

Baucom, D. H., Epstein, N., & LaTaillade, J. J. (2002). Cognitive-behavioral couple therapy. In A. Gurman & N. Jacobson (Eds.), *Clinical Handbook of Couple Therapy,* 3rd ed., pp. 26–58. New York: Guilford.

Baucom, D. H., Notarius, C. I., Burnett, C. K., & Haefner, P. (1990). Gender differences and sex-role identity in marriage. In F. D. Fincham & T. N. Bradbury (Eds.), *The Psychology of Marriage: Basic Issues and Applications,* pp. 150–171. New York: Guilford.

Bauer, M. S., & Mitchner, L. (2004). What is a "mood stabilizer"? An evidence-based response. *American Journal of Psychiatry, 161,* 3–18.

Bauer, R. M., & Demery, J. A. (2003). Agnosia. In K. M. Heilman and E. Valenstein (Eds.), *Clinical Neuropsychology,* 4th ed., pp. 236–295. London: Oxford University Press.

Baum, A., Davidson, L. M., Singer, J. E., & Street, S. W. (1987). Stress as a psychophysiological response. In A. Baum & J. E. Singer (Eds.), *Handbook of Psychology and Health Stress,* Vol. 5, pp. 1–24. Hillsdale, NJ: Erlbaum.

Bauman, M. L. (1996). Neuroanatomic observations of the brain in pervasive developmental disorders. *Journal of Autism and Developmental Disorders, 26,* 199–203.

Baumeister, R. F. (1990). Suicide as escape from self. *Psychological Review, 97,* 90–113.

Baumeister, R. F. (1997). Identity, self-concept, and self-esteem: The self lost and found. In R. Hogan, J. Johnson, & S. Briggs (Eds.), *Handbook of Personality Psychology,* pp. 681–710. San Diego, CA: Academic Press.

Baumeister, R. F. (2008). Free will in scientific psychology. *Perspectives on Psychological Science, 3,* 14–19.

Baumeister, R. F., & Butler, J. L. (1997). Sexual masochism. In D. R. Laws & W. T. O'Donohue (Eds.), *Handbook of Sexual Deviance: Theory and Application.* New York: Guilford.

Baumeister, R. F., Campbell, J. D., Krueger, J. L., & Vohs, K. D. (2003). Does high self-esteem cause better performance, interpersonal success, happiness, or healthier lifestyles? *Psychological Science in the Public Interest, 4,* 1–44.

Bay-Cheng, L. Y., et al. (2002). Linking femininity, weight concern, and mental health among Latina, Black and White women. *Psychology of Women Quarterly, 26,* 36–45.

Beach, S. R. H., Wamboldt, M. Z., Kaslow, N. J., Heyman, R. E., & Reiss, D. (2006). Describing relationship problems in *DSM-V:* Toward better guidance for research and clinical practice. *Journal of Family Psychology, 20,* 359–368.

Beach, S. R. H., Wamboldt, M. Z., & Kaslow, N. J. (2006). *Relational processes and DSM-V: Neuroscience, assessment, prevention, and treatment.* Washington, DC: American Psychiatric Association.

Beach, S. R. H., Sandeen, E. E., & O'Leary, K. D. (1990). *Depression in Marriage: A Model for Etiology and Treatment.* New York: Guilford.

Beauchaine, T. P., Webster-Stratton, C., & Reid, M. J. (2005). Mediators, moderators, and predictors of 1-year outcomes among children treated for early-onset conduct problems: A latent growth curve analysis. *Journal of Consulting and Clinical Psychology, 73,* 371–388.

Bebbington, P., & Kuipers, L. (1994). The predictive utility of expressed emotion in schizophrenia: An aggregate analysis. *Psychological Medicine, 24,* 707–718.

Bechtoldt, H., Norcross, J. C., Wyckoff, L. A., Pokrywa, M. L., & Campbell, L. F. (2001). Theoretical orientations and employment settings of clinical and counseling psychologists: A comparative study. *The Clinical Psychologist, 54,* 3–6.

Beck, A. (1974). The development of depression: A cognitive model. In *The Psychology of Depression: Contemporary Theory and Research*, pp. 3–20, Oxford, England: John Wiley & Sons.

Beck, A. T. (1967). *Depression: Clinical, Experimental, and Theoretical Aspects*. New York: Harper & Row.

Beck, A. T. (1974). The development of depression. In R. J. Friedman & M. M. Katz (Eds.), *The Psychology of Depression: Contemporary Theory and Research*, pp. 3–20. New York: Winston-Wiley.

Beck, A. T. (1976). *Cognitive Therapy and the Emotional Disorders*. New York: International Universities Press.

Beck, A. T., Freeman, A., & Davis, D. D. (2004). *Cognitive Therapy of Personality Disorders* (2nd ed.). New York: Guilford.

Beck, A. T., Rush, A. J., Shaw, B. F., & Emery, G. (1979). *Cognitive Therapy of Depression*. New York: Guilford.

Beck, J. G. (1995). Hypoactive sexual desire disorder: An overview. *Journal of Consulting and Clinical Psychology, 63*, 919–927.

Becker, D., & Lamb, S. (1994). Sex bias in the diagnosis of borderline personality disorder and posttraumatic stress disorder. *Professional Psychology: Research and Practice, 25*, 55–61.

Becker, J. V., Alpert, J. L., BigFoot, D. S., Bonner, B. L., Geddie, L. F., Henggeler, S. W., et al. (1995). Empirical research on child abuse treatment: Report by the Child Abuse and Neglect Treatment Working Group, American Psychological Association. *Journal of Clinical Child Psychology, 24*, 23–46.

Beidel, D. C., Turner, S. M., & Cooley, M. R. (1993). Assessing reliable and clinically significant change in social phobia: Validity of the social phobia and anxiety inventory. *Behaviour Research and Therapy, 31*, 331–337.

Beidel, D. C., Turner, S. M., & Morris, T. L. (2000). Behavioral treatment of childhood social phobia. *Journal of Consulting and Clinical Psychology, 68*, 1072–1080.

Belkin, L. (2005, May 22). Can you catch obsessive-compulsive disorder? *New York Times Magazine.* 65–69.

Bell, L. G., & Bell, D. C. (2005). Family dynamics in adolescence affect midlife well-being. *Journal of Family Psychology, 19*, 198–207.

Bell, R. Q. (1968). A reinterpretation of the direction of effects in studies of socialization. *Psychological Review, 75*(2), 81–95.

Bellack, A. S., Haas, G. L., Schooler, N. R., & Flory, J. D. (2000). Effects of behavioural family management on family communication and patient outcomes in schizophrenia. *British Journal of Psychiatry, 177*, 434–439.

Belsky, J., Steinberg, L., & Draper, P. (1991). Childhood experience, interpersonal development and reproductive strategy: an evolutionary theory of socialization. *Child Development, 62*, 647–670.

Bender, L. (1947). Childhood schizophrenia, clinical study of one hundred schizophrenic children. *American Journal of Orthopsychiatry, 17*, 40–56.

Benitez, C. I. P., Smith, K., Vasile, R. G., Rende, R., Edelen, M. O., & Keller, M. B. (2008). Use of benzodiazepines and selective serotonin reuptake inhibitors in middle-aged and older adults with anxiety disorders. *American Journal of Geriatric Psychiatry, 16*, 5–13.

Benjamin, L. S. (2003). *Interpersonal Reconstructive Therapy: Promoting Change in Nonresponders*. New York: Guilford.

Bennett, F. C., & Sherman, R. (1983). Management of childhood "hyperactivity" by primary care physicians. *Journal of Developmental and Behavioral Pediatrics, 4*, 88–93.

Berenbaum, H., & Barch, D. (1995). The categorization of thought disorder. *Journal of Psycholinguistic Research, 24*, 349–376.

Berman, A. L., & Jobes, D. A. (1994). Treatment of the suicidal adolescent. In A. A. Leenaars, J. T. Maltsberger, &

R. A. Neimeyer (Eds.), *Treatment of Suicidal People*, pp. 89–100. Washington, DC: Taylor & Francis.

Berman, J. R., Berman, L. A., Werbin, T. J., Flaherty, E. E., Leahy, N. M., & Goldstein, I. (1999). Clinical evaluation of female sexual function: Effects of age and estrogen status on subjective and physiologic sexual responses. *International Journal of Impotence Research, 11* (Suppl. 1), 31–38.

Bernard, S. H. (2002). Services for children and adolescents with severe learning disabilities (mental retardation). In M. Rutter & E. Taylor (Eds.), *Child and Adolescent Psychiatry*, 4th ed., pp. 1114–1127. Oxford: Blackwell.

Bernlef, J. (1988). *Out of Mind*. London: Faber.

Bernstein, D. P., Cohen, P., Velez, C. N., Schwab-Stone, M., Siever, L. J., & Shinsato, L. (1993). Prevalence and stability of the DSM-III-R personality disorders in a community-based survey of adolescents. *American Journal of Psychiatry, 150*, 1237–1243.

Bernstein, G. A., Borchardt, C. M., Perwien, A. R., Crosby, R. D., Kushner, M. G., Thuras, P. D., et al. (2000). Imipramine plus cognitive-behavioral therapy in the treatment of school refusal. *Journal of the Academy of Child & Adolescent Psychiatry, 39*, 276–283.

Berrios, G. E. (1992). Research into the history of psychiatry. In C. Freeman & P. Tyrer (Eds.), *Research Methods in Psychiatry: A Beginner's Guide*, 2nd ed. London: Gaskell.

Berry, J. W., Poortinga, Y. H., Segall, M. H., & Dasen, P. R. (2002). *Cross-cultural Psychology: Research and Applications*, 2nd ed. New York: Cambridge University Press.

Bersoff, D. N. (1999). *Ethical Conflicts in Psychology*, 2nd ed. Washington, DC: American Psychological Association.

Bertelson, A., Harvald, B., & Hauge, M. (1977). A Danish twin study of manic-depressive disorders. *British Journal of Psychiatry, 130*, 330–351.

Besharov, D. J. (1992). A balanced approach to reporting child abuse. *Child, Youth, and Family Services Quarterly, 15*, 5–7.

Besharov, D. J. (Ed.). (1998). *Protecting Children from Abuse and Neglect: Policy and Practice*. Springfield, IL and England: Charles C. Thomas.

Bettleheim, B. (1967). *The Empty Fortress*. New York: Free Press.

Beumont, P. J. V., Garner, D. M., & Touyz, S. W. (1994). Diagnoses of eating or dieting disorders: What may we learn from past mistakes? *International Journal of Eating Disorders, 16*, 349–362.

Beutler, L. E., Clarkin, J. F., Crago, M., & Bergan, J. (1991). Client-therapist matching. In C. R. Snyder and D. R. Forsyth, *Handbook of Social and Clinical Psychology*, pp. 699–716. Elmsford, NY: Pergamon Press.

Beutler, L. E., Machado, P. P. P., & Neufeldt, S. A. (1994). Therapist variables. In A. E. Bergin and S. L. Garfield, *Handbook of Psychotherapy and Behavior Change*, 4th ed., pp. 229–269. Oxford England: John Wiley & Sons.

Bieling, P. J., Beck, A. T., & Brown, G. K. (2000). The sociotropy-autonomy scale: Structure and implications. *Cognitive Therapy and Research, 24*, 763–780.

Bierut, L. M., Dinwiddie, S. H., Begleiter, H., Crowe, R. R., Hesselbrock, V., Nurnberger, J. I., et al. (1998). Familial transmission of substance dependence: Alcohol, marijuana, cocaine, and habitual smoking. *Archives of General Psychiatry, 55*, 982–988.

Biklen, D. (1992b). Facilitated communication: Biklen responds, *American Journal of Speech and Language Pathology, 1*(2), 21–22.

Binik, Y. M. (2005). Should dyspareunia be retained as a sexual dysfunction in DSM-V? *Archives of Sexual Behavior, 34*, 11–21.

Binik, Y. M., Reissing, E., Pukall, C., Flory, N., Payne, K. A., & Khalife, S. (2002). The female sexual pain disorders: Genital pain or sexual dysfunction? *Archives of Sexual Behavior, 31*, 425–431.

Birditt, K. S., & Antonucci, T. C. (2007). Relationship quality profiles and well-being among married adults. *Journal of Family Psychology, 21*, 595–604.

Bishop, S. J. (2007). Neurocognitive mechanisms of anxiety: An integrative account. *Trends in Cognitive Sciences, 11*, 307–316.

Bisson, J. I., Ehlers, A., Matthews, R., Pilling, S., Richards, D., & Turner, S. (2007). Psychological treatments for chronic post-traumatic stress disorder: Systematic review and meta-analysis. *British Journal of Psychiatry, 190*, 97–104.

Bjorklund, P. (2006). No man's land: Gender bias and social constructivism in the diagnosis of borderline personality disorder. *Issues in Mental Health Nursing, 27*, 3–23.

Black, D. W., Kehrberg, L. D., Flumerfelt, D. L., & Schlosser, S. S. (1997). Characteristics of 36 subjects reporting compulsive sexual behavior. *American Journal of Psychiatry, 154*, 243–250.

Black, P. H., & Garbutt, L. D. (2002). Stress, inflammation and cardiovascular disease. *Journal of Psychosomatic Research, 52*, 1–23.

Blair, R. J. R., et al. (2001). A selective impairment in the processing of sad and fearful expressions in children with psychopathic tendencies. *Journal of Abnormal Child Psychology, 29*, 491–498.

Blanchard, E. B. (Ed.). (1992). Special issue on behavioral medicine. *Journal of Consulting and Clinical Psychology, 60*.

Blanchard, E. B. (1994). Behavioral medicine and health psychology. In A. E. Bergin & S. L. Garfield (Eds.), *Handbook of Psychotherapy and Behavior Change*, 4th ed., pp. 701–733. New York: Wiley.

Blanchard, J., Cohen, A., & Carreño, J. (2007). *Emotion and Schizophrenia. Emotion and Psychopathology: Bridging Affective and Clinical Science* pp. 103–122. Washington, DC: American Psychological Association.

Blanchard, R. (1989). The classification and labeling of nonhomosexual gender dysphorias. *Archives of Sexual Behavior, 18*, 315–334.

Blashfield, R. (2000). Growth of the literature on the topic of personality disorders. *American Journal of Psychiatry, 157*, 472–473.

Blashfield, R. K., & McElroy, R. A. (1987). The 1985 literature on the personality disorders. *Comprehensive Psychiatry, 28*, 536–546.

Blashfield, R., & McElroy, R. (1989). Ontology of personality disorder categories. *Psychiatric Annals, 19*, 126–131.

Blazer, D. G. (2004). The epidemiology of depressive disorders in late life. In S. P. Roose and H. A. Sackheim (Eds.), *Late-Life Depression*, pp. 3–11. New York: New York University Press.

Bleiberg, K. L., & Markowitz, J. C. (2008). Interpersonal psychotherapy for depression. In D. H. Barlow (Ed.), *Clinical Handbook of Psychological Disorders: A Step-by-Step Treatment Manual*, 4th ed., pp. 306–327. New York: Guilford.

Bleuler, M. (1978). *The Schizophrenic Disorders: Long-Term Patient and Family Studies*. New Haven, CT: Yale University Press.

Bliss, E. L. (1986). *Multiple Personality, Allied Disorders, and Hypnosis*. New York: Oxford University Press.

Blum, N., St. John, D., Pfohl, B., Stuart, S., McCormick, B., Allen, J., Arndt, S., & Black, D. W. (2008). Systems, training for emotional predictability and problem solving (STEPPS) for outpatients with borderline personality disorder: A randomized controlled trial and 1-year follow-up. *American Journal of Psychiatry, 165*, 468–478.

Blundell, J. E. (1995). The psychobiological approach to appetite and weight control. In K. D. Brownell & C. G. Fairburn (Eds.), *Eating Disorders and Obesity: A Comprehensive Handbook*, pp. 13–20. New York: Guilford.

Blustein, D. L., Juntunen, C. L., Worthington, R. L. (2000). The school-to-work transition: Adjustment challenges of the forgotten half. In S. D. Brown & R. W. Lent (Eds.), *Handbook of Counseling Psychology*, 3rd ed, pp. 435–470. New York: Wiley.

Bogg, T. & Roberts, B. W. (2004). Conscientiousness and health-related behaviors: A meta-analysis of the leading behavioral contributors to mortality. *Psychological Bulletin, 130*, 887–919.

Bohus, M., Haaf, B., Simms, T., Limberger, M. F., Schmahl, C., Unckel, C., et al. (2004). Effectiveness of inpatient dialectical behavioral therapy for borderline personality disorder: A controlled trial. *Behaviour Research & Therapy, 42*, 487–499.

Bolla, K. I., Cadet, J., & London, E. D. (1998). The neuropsychiatry of chronic cocaine abuse. *Journal of Neuropsychiatry and Clinical Neurosciences, 10*, 280–289.

Bonanno, G. A. (2004). Loss, trauma, and human resilience: Have we underestimated the human capacity to thrive after extremely aversive events? *American Psychologist, 59*, 20–28.

Bonanno, G. A., Galea, S., Bucciarelli, A., & Vlahov, D. (2006). Psychological resilience after disaster: New York City in the aftermath of the September 11th terrorist attack. *Psychological Science, 17*, 181–186.

Bonanno, G. A., Neria, Y., Mancini, A., Coifman, K. G., Litz, B., & Insel, B. (2007). Is there more to complicated grief than depression and posttraumatic stress disorder? A test of incremental validity. *Journal of Abnormal Psychology, 116*, 342–351.

Bonanno, G. A., Papa, A., Lalande, K., Westphal, M., & Coifman, K. (2004). The importance of being flexible: The ability to both enhance and suppress emotional expression predicts long-term adjustment. *Psychological Science, 15*, 482–487.

Bonanno, G. A., Papa, A., Lalande, K., Zhang, N., & Noll, J. G. (2005). Grief processing and deliberate grief avoidance: A prospective comparison of bereaved spouses and parents in the United States and the People's Republic of China. *Journal of Consulting and Clinical Psychology, 73*, 86–98.

Bonner-Jackson, A., Haul, K., Csernansky, J., & Barch, D. (2005). The influence of encoding strategy on episodic memory and cortical activity in schizophrenia. *Biological Psychiatry, 58*, 47–55.

Booth, A., et al. (2000). Biosocial perspectives on the family. *Journal of Marriage and the Family, 62*, 1018–1034.

Booth-Kewley, S., & Friedman, H. S. (1987). Psychological predictors of heart disease: A quantitative review. *Psychological Bulletin, 101*, 343–362.

Bootzin, R. R. (2000). Cognitive-behavioral treatment of insomnia: Knitting up the ravell'd sleave of care. In D. T. Kenny et al. (Eds.), *Stress and Health*. Sydney, Australia: Harwood Academic Press.

Borduin, C. M., Mann, B. J., Cone, L. T., Henggeler, S. W., Fucci, B. R., Blaske, D. M., et al. (1995). Multisystemic treatment of serious juvenile offenders: Long-term prevention of criminality and violence. *Journal of Consulting and Clinical Psychology, 63*, 569–578.

Borkovec, T. D., Alcaine, O. M., & Behar, E. (2004). Avoidance theory of worry and generalized anxiety disorder. In R. G. Heimberg and C. L. Turk (Eds.), *Generalized Anxiety Disorder: Advances in Research and Practice*, pp. 77–108. New York: Guilford.

Borkovec, T. D., Newman, M. G., Pincus, A. L., & Lytle, R. (2002). A component analysis of cognitive-behavioral therapy for generalized anxiety disorder and the role of interpersonal problems. *Journal of Consulting and Clinical Psychology, 70*, 288–298.

Bornstein, R. F. (1996). Dependency. In C. G. Costello (Ed.), *Personality Characteristics of the Personality Disordered*, pp. 120–145. New York: Wiley-Interscience.

Bornstein, R. F. (2007). Dependent personality disorder. In W. O'Donohue, K. A. Fowler, & S. O. Lilienfeld (Eds.), *Personality Disorders: Toward the DSM-V*, pp. 307–324. Thosand Oaks, CA: Sage.

Bosma, H. A., & Kunnen, E. S. (2001). Determinants and mechanisms in ego identity development: A review and synthesis. *Developmental Review, 21*, 39–66.

Bouchard, C. (2002). Genetic influences on body weight. In C. G. Fairbum & K. D. Brownell (Eds.), *Eating Disorders and Obesity*, 2nd ed., pp. 16–21. New York: Guilford.

Bourne, R., Tahir, T., Borthwick, M., & Sampson, E. (2008). Drug treatment of delirium: Past, present and future. *Journal of Psychosomatic Research, 65*, 273–282.

Bouton, M. E., Mineka, S., & Barlow, D. (2001). A modern learning theory perspective on the etiology of panic disorder. *Psychological Review, 108*, 4–32.

Bower, G. H. (1990). Awareness, the unconscious, and repression: An experimental psychologist's perspective. In J. L. Singer (Ed.), *Repression and Dissociation*, pp. 209–232. Chicago: University of Chicago Press.

Bower, G. (2001). The gender identity disorder in the DSM-IV classification: A critical evaluation. *Australian & New Zealand Journal of Psychiatry, 35*, 1–8.

Bowker, G. C., & Star, S. L. (1999). *Sorting Things Out: Classification and Its Consequences*. Cambridge, MA: MIT Press.

Bowlby, J. (1969). *Attachment*. New York: Basic Books.

Bowlby, J. (1973). *Separation: Anxiety and Anger*. New York: Basic Books.

Bowlby, J. (1979). *The Making and Breaking of Affectional Bonds*. London: Tavistock.

Bowlby, J. (1980). *Loss: Sadness and Depression*. New York: Basic Books.

Boydell, J., & Murray, R. (2003). Urbanization, migration and risk of schizophrenia. In R. M. Murray and P. B. Jones (Eds.), *The Epidemiology of Schizophrenia*, pp. 49–67. New York: Cambridge University Press.

Bracha, H. S., Tyler C. Ralston, T. C., Matsukawa, J. M., Williams, A. E., Adam S. Bracha, A. S. (2004). Does "Fight or Flight" Need Updating? *Psychosomatics, 45*, 448–449.

Bradbury, T. N., & Fincham, F. D. (1990). Attributions in marriage: Review and critique. *Psychological Bulletin, 107*, 3–33.

Bradbury, T. N., Fincham, F. D., & Beach, S. R. H. (2000). Research on the nature and determinants of marital satisfaction: A decade in review. *Journal of Marriage and the Family, 62*, 964–980.

Bradford, J. (1997). Medical interventions in sexual deviance. In D. R. Laws & W. T. O'Donohue (Eds.), *Handbook of Sexual Deviance: Theory and Application*. New York: Guilford.

Bradford, J. M. W. (2001). The neurobiology, neuropharmacology, and pharmacological treatment of the paraphilias and compulsive sexual behaviour. *Canadian Journal of Psychiatry, 46*, 26–34.

Bradford, J. M. W., & Pawlak, A. (1993). Double-blind placebo cross-over study of cyproterone acetate in the treatment of paraphilias. *Archives of Sexual Behavior, 22*, 383–402.

Bradley, C. (1937). The behavior of children receiving benzedrine. *American Journal of Psychiatry, 94*, 577–585.

Bradley, S. J., & Zucker, K. J. (1997). Gender identity disorder: A review of the past 10 years. *Journal of the American Academy of Child and Adolescent Psychiatry, 36*, 872–880.

Brady, K. T., Back, S. E., & Coffey, S. F. (2004). Substance abuse and posttraumatic stress disorder. *Current Directions in Psychological Science, 13*, 206–209.

Braff, D., Schork, N., & Gottesman, I. (2007). Endophenotyping schizophrenia. *American Journal of Psychiatry, 164*, 705–707.

Bramlett, M. D., & Mosher, W. D. (2001). *First Marriage Dissolution, Divorce, and Remarriage: United States* (Advance Data From Vital and Health Statistics No. 323). Hyattsville, MD: National Center for Health Statistics.

Brand, M. (2007). Cognitive profile of patients with alcoholic Korsakoff's syndrome. *International Journal on Disability and Human Development, 6*, 161–170.

Brandon, T. H., Wetter, D. W., & Baker, T. B. (1996). Affect, expectancies, urges, and smoking: Do they conform to models of drug motivation and relapse? *Experimental and Clinical Psychopharmacology, 4*, 29–36.

Braun, B. G. (1989). Psychotherapy of the survivor of incest with a dissociative disorder. *Psychiatric Clinics of North America, 12*, 307–324.

Braun, D. L., Sunday, S. R., & Halmi, K. A. (1994). Psychiatric comorbidity in patients with eating disorders. *Psychological Medicine, 24*, 859–867.

Braun, P., Kochansky, G., Shapiro, R., et al. (1981). Overview: Deinstitutionalization of psychiatric patients: A critical review of outcome studies. *American Journal of Psychiatry, 138*, 736–749.

Brébion, G., Ohlsen, R., Pilowsky, L., & David, A. (2008). Visual hallucinations in schizophrenia: Confusion between imagination and perception. *Neuropsychology, 22*(3), 383–389.

Breggin, P. R. (2004). Recent U. S., Canadian and British regulatory agency actions concerning antidepressant-induced harm to self and others: A review and analysis. *International Journal of Risk and Safety in Medicine, 16*, 247–259.

Bregman, J. D., Dykens, E., Watson, M., Ort, S. I., & Leckman, J. F. (1987). Fragile-X syndrome: Variability of phenotypic expression. *Journal of the American Academy of Child and Adolescent Psychiatry, 26*, 463–471.

Breitner, J. C. S., Gatz, M., Bergem, A. L. M., Christian, J. C., Mortimer, J. A., McClearn, G. E., et al. (1993). Use of twin cohorts for research in Alzheimer's disease. *Neurology, 43*, 261–267.

Bremner, J. D. (2005). *Brain Imaging Handbook*. New York: Norton.

Brenner, M. H. (1973). *Mental Illness and the Economy*. Cambridge, MA: Harvard University Press.

Brent, D. A. (2004). Antidepressants and pediatric depression—The risk of doing nothing. *New England Journal of Medicine, 351*, 1598–1601.

Brent, D. A., & Bridge, J. (2003). Firearms availability and suicide: Evidence, interventions, and future directions. *American Behavioral Scientist, 46*, 1192–1210.

Breslau, N., Davis, G. C., & Andreski, P. (1995). Risk factors for PTSD-related traumatic events: A prospective analysis. *American Journal of Psychiatry, 152*, 529–535.

Breslau, N., Davis, G. C., Andreski, P., and Peterson, E. (1991). Traumatic events and posttraumatic stress disorder in an urban population of young adults. *Archives of General Psychiatry, 48*, 216–222.

Breslau, N., Kessler, R. C., Chilcoat, H. D., Schultz, L. R., Davis, G. C., & Andreski, P. (1998). Trauma and post traumatic stress disorder in the community: The 1996 Detroit Area Survey of Trauma. *Archives of General Psychiatry, 55*, 626–632.

Breslau, N., Peterson, E. L., & Schultz, L. R. (2008). A second look at prior trauma and the posttraumatic stress disorder effects of subsequent trauma: A prospective epidemiological study. *Archives of General Psychiatry, 65*, 431–437.

Brestan, E. V., & Eyberg, S. M. (1998). Effective psychosocial treatments of conduct-disordered children and adolescents: 29 years, 82 studies, and 5,272 kids. *Journal of Clinical Child Psychology, 27*, 180–189.

Breteler, M. M. B., Ott, A., & Hofman, A. (1998). The new epidemic: Frequency of dementia in the Rotterdam study. *Haemostasis, 28*, 117–123.

Brewerton, T. D., Lydiard, R. B., Herzog, D. B., Brotman, A. W., O'Neil, P. M., & Ballenger, J. (1995). Comorbidity of Axis I psychiatric disorders in bulimia nervosa. *Journal of Clinical Psychiatry, 56,* 77–80.

Brewin, C. R., Andrews, B., & Gotlib, I. H. (1993). Psychopathology and early experience: A reappraisal of retrospective reports. *Psychological Bulletin, 113,* 82–98.

Brewin, C. R., MacCarthy, B., Duda, K., et al. (1991). Attributions and expressed emotion in the relatives of patients with schizophrenia. *Journal of Abnormal Psychology, 100,* 546–554.

Brezo, J., Klempan, T., & Turecki, G. (2008). The genetics of suicide: A critical review of molecular studies. *Psychiatric Clinics of North America, 31,* 179–203.

Bridle, N., Pantelis, C., Wood, S., Coppola, R., Velakoulis, D., McStephen, M., et al. (2002). Thalamic and caudate volumes in monozygotic twins discordant for schizophrenia. *Australian and New Zealand Journal of Psychiatry, 36,* 347–354.

Briken, P., Habermann, N., Berner, W., & Hill, A. (2007). Diagnosis and treatment of sexual addiction: A survey among German sex therapists. *Sexual Addiction & Compulsivity, 14,* 131–143.

Broderick, G. (2006). Premature ejaculation: On defining and quantifying a common male sexual dysfunction. *Journal of Sexual Medicine, 3,* 295–302.

Brody, E. M., Saperstein, A. R., & Lawton, M. P. (1989). A multi-service respite program for caregivers of Alzheimer's patients. *Journal of Gerontological Social Work, 14,* 41–75.

Bromet, E., Naz, B., Fochtmann, L., Carlson, G., & Tanenberg-Karant, M. (2005). Long-term diagnostic stability and outcome in recent first-episode cohort studies of schizophrenia. *Schizophrenia Bulletin, 31,* 639–649.

Bromley, D. B. (1990). *Behavioral Gerontology: Central Issues in the Psychology of Ageing.* New York: Wiley.

Brown, A. (2006). Prenatal infection as a risk factor for schizophrenia. *Schizophrenia Bulletin, 32,* 200–202.

Brown, A. S. (2003). A review of the déjà vu experience. *Psychological Bulletin, 129,* 394–413.

Brown, C. H., Wyman, P. A., Brinales, J. M., & Gibbons, R. D. (2007). The role of randomized trials in testing interventions for the prevention of youth suicide. *International Review of Psychiatry, 19,* 1–15.

Brown, G. W. (1998). Genetic and population perspectives on life events and depression. *Social Psychiatry and Psychiatric Epidemiology, 33,* 363–372.

Brown, G. W. (2002). Social roles, context and evolution in the origins of depression. *Journal of Health and Social Behavior, 43,* 255–276.

Brown, G. W., Bifulco, A., & Harris, T. O. (1987). Life events, vulnerability and onset of depression: Some refinements. *British Journal of Psychiatry, 150,* 30–42.

Brown, G. W., Birley, J. L. T., & Wing, J. K. (1972). Influence of family life on the course of schizophrenic disorders: A replication. *British Journal of Psychiatry, 121,* 241–258.

Brown, G. W., & Harris, T. O. (1978). *Social Origins of Depression: A Study of Psychiatric Disorder in Women.* London: Tavistock.

Brown, G. W., & Harris, T. O. (1993). An etiology of anxiety and depressive disorders in an inner-city population. 1. Early adversity. *Psychological Medicine, 23,* 143–154.

Brown, M. L. & Rounsley, C. A. (2003). *True Selves: Understanding Transsexualism–For Families, Friends, Coworkers, and Helping Professionals.* San Francisco: Jossey-Bass.

Brown, P. (1994). Toward a psychobiological model of dissociation and post-traumatic stress disorder. In S. J. Lynn & J. W. Rhue (Eds.), *Dissociation: Clinical and Theoretical Perspectives,* pp. 94–122. New York: Guilford.

Brown, R. (1990). Limitations on expert testimony on the battered women syndrome in homicide cases: The return of the ultimate issue rule. *Arizona Law Review, 32,* 665–689.

Brown, R. J. (2004). Psychological mechanisms of medically unexplained syndromes: An integrative conceptual model. *Psychological Bulletin, 130,* 793–812.

Brown, S. A., Tate, S. R., Vik, P. W., Haas, A. L., & Aarons, G. A. (1999). Modeling of alcohol use mediates the effect of family history of alcoholism on adolescent alcohol expectancies. *Experimental and Clinical Psychopharmacology, 7,* 20–27.

Brown, S. L., Nesse, R. M., Vinokur, A. D., Smith, D. M. (2003). Providing social support may be more beneficial than receiving it: Results from a prospective study of mortality. *Psychological Science, 14,* 320–327.

Brown, T. A., & Barlow, D. H. (1992). Comorbidity among anxiety disorders: Implications for treatment and DSM-IV. *Journal of Consulting and Clinical Psychology, 60,* 835–844.

Brown, T. A., Barlow, D. H., & Liebowitz, M. R. (1994). The empirical basis of generalized anxiety disorder. *American Journal of Psychiatry, 151,* 1272–1280.

Brown, T. A., Chorpita, B. F., & Barlow, D. H. (1998). Structural relationships among dimensions of the DSM-IV anxiety and mood disorders and dimensions of negative affect, positive affect, and autonomic arousal. *Journal of Abnormal Psychology, 107,* 179–192.

Brownell, K. D. (1995). Definition and classification of obesity. In K. D. Brownell & C. G. Fairburn (Eds.), *Eating Disorders and Obesity: A Comprehensive Handbook,* pp. 386–390. New York: Guilford.

Brownell, K. D., & Fairburn, C. G. (Eds.). (1995). *Eating Disorders and Obesity: A Comprehensive Handbook.* New York: Guilford.

Brownell, K. D., & Rodin, J. (1994). The dieting maelstrom: Is it possible and advisable to lose weight? *American Psychologist, 49,* 781–791.

Browning, C. R., & Laumann, E. O. (1997). Sexual contact between children and adults: A life course perspective. *American Sociological Review, 62,* 540–560.

Bruch, H. (1982). Anorexia nervosa: Therapy and theory. *American Journal of Psychiatry, 132,* 1531–1538.

Bryant, R. A., & Guthrie, R. M. (2005). Maladaptive appraisals as a risk factor for posttraumatic stress: A study of trainee firefighters. *Psychological Science, 16,* 749–752.

Bryant, R. A., & Harvey, A. G. (2000). *Acute Stress Disorder: A Handbook of Theory Assessment and Treatment.* Washington, DC: American Psychological Association.

Bryant, R. A., Moulds, M. L., & Nixon, R. D. V. (2003). Cognitive behaviour therapy of acute stress disorder: A four-year follow-up. *Behaviour Research and Therapy, 41,* 489–494.

Bryant, R. A., Moulds, M. L., Guthrie, R. M., Dang, S. T. & Nixon, R. D. V. (2003). Imaginal exposure alone and imaginal exposure with cognitive restructuring in treatment of posttraumatic stress disorder. *Journal of Consulting and Clinical Psychology, 71,* 706–712.

Bryant, R. A., Moulds, M. L., Guthrie, R. M., & Nixon, R. D. V. (2005). The additive benefit of hypnosis and cognitive behavior therapy in treating acute stress disorder. *Journal of Consulting and Clinical Psychology.*

Bryant, R. A., Moulds, M. L., Nixon, R. D. V., Mastrodomenico, J., Felmingham, K., & Hopwood, S. (2006). Hypnotherapy and cognitive behaviour therapy of acute stress disorder: A 3-year follow-up. *Behaviour Research and Therapy, 44,* 1331–1335.

Bryne, S. M. (2002). Sport, occupation, and eating disorders. In C. G. Fairburn & K. D. Brownell (Eds.), *Eating Disorders and Obesity,* 2nd ed., pp. 256–259. New York: Guilford.

Bryson, S. E. (1996). Epidemiology of autism. *Journal of Autism and Developmental Disorders, 26,* 165–167.

Bucholz, K. K. (1999). Nosology and epidemiology of addictive disorders and their comorbidity. *Psychiatric Clinics of North America, 22,* 221–240.

Buchanan, R. (2007). Persistent negative symptoms in schizophrenia: An overview. *Schizophrenia Bulletin, 33,* 1013–1022.

Buck, R. (1999). The biological affects: A typology. *Psychological Review, 106,* 301–336.

Buckley, P., & Stahl, S. (2007). Pharmacological treatment of negative symptoms of schizophrenia: Therapeutic opportunity or cul-de-sac?. *Acta Psychiatrica Scandinavica, 115,* 93–100.

Budney, A. J. (2007). Are specific dependence criteria necessary for different substances? In J. B. Saunders, M. A. Schuckit, P. J. Sirovatka, & D. A. Regier, (Eds.), *Diagnostic issues in substance use disorders,* pp. 221–236. Washington, DC: American Psychiatric Press.

Bugg, J., Zook, N., DeLosh, E., Davalos, D., & Davis, H. (2006). Age differences in fluid intelligence: Contributions of general slowing and frontal decline. *Brain and Cognition, 62,* 9–16.

Buka, S. L., & Gilman, S. E. (2002). Psychopathology and the life course. In J. E. Helzer and J. J. Hudziak (Eds.), *Defining Psychopathology in the 21st Century,* pp. 129–142. Washington, DC: American Psychiatric Press.

Bulik, C. M., Sullivan, P. F., Tozzi, F., Furberg, H., Lichtenstein, P., & Pedersen, N. L. (2006). Prevalence, heritability, and prospective risk factors for anorexia nervosa. *Archives of General Psychiatry, 63,* 305–312.

Bulik, C. M., Wade, T. D., & Kendler, K. S. (2000). Characteristics of monozygotic twins discordant for bulimia nervosa. *International Journal of Eating Disorders, 19,* 1–10.

Bullough, B., & Bullough, V. (1997). Are transvestites necessarily heterosexual? *Archives of Sexual Behavior, 26,* 1–11.

Bullough, V. L. (1976). *Sexual Variance in Society and History.* New York: Wiley.

Burke, B. L., & McGee, D. P. (1990). Sports deficit disorder. *Pediatrics, 85,* 1118.

Burke, C. (1995). Foreword. In L. Nadel & D. Rosenthal (Eds.), *Down Syndrome: Living and Learning in the Community,* p. ix. New York: Wiley.

Burns, D. D. (1999). *Feeling Good: The New Mood Therapy* (Rev. ed.). Wholecare.

Burns, D. D. (1999). *Feeling Good: The New Mood Therapy.* New York: Avon.

Burns, J. (2004). An evolutionary theory of schizophrenia: Cortical connectivity, metarepresentation, and the social brain. *Behavioral and Brain Sciences, 27,* 831–885.

Burt, S. A., Krueger, R. F., McGue, M., & Iancono, W. G. (2001). Sources of covariation among attention-deficit/hyperactivity disorder, oppositional defiant disorder, and conduct disorder: The importance of shared environment. *Journal of Abnormal Psychology, 110,* 516–525.

Buss, A. (1991). The EAS theory of temperament. In J. Strelau & A. Angleitner (Eds.), *Explorations in Temperament.* New York: Plenum.

Buss, D. M. (1999). Human nature and individual differences: The evolution of human personality. In L. A. Pervin and O. P. John (Eds.), *Handbook of Personality: Theory and Research,* 2nd ed., pp. 31–56. New York: Guilford.

Butcher, J. N., & Williams, C. L. (2000). *Essentials of MMPI2 and MMPI-A Interpretation* (2nd ed.). Minneapolis: University of Minnesota Press.

Butler, S. M., Ashford, J. W., & Snowdon, D. A. (1996). Age, education, and changes in the Mini-Mental State Exam scores of older women: Findings from the Nun

Study. *Journal of the American Geriatrics Society, 44,* 675–681.

Button, T. M. M., Scourfield, J., Martin, N., Purcell, S., & McGuffin, P. (2005). Family dysfunction interacts with genes in the causation of antisocial symptoms. *Behavior Genetics, 35*(2), 115–120.

Butzlaff, R. L., & Hooley, J. M. (1998). Expressed emotion and psychiatric relapse. *Archives of General Psychiatry, 55,* 547–552.

Byrne, C. A., Resnick, H. S., Kilpatrick, D. G., Best, C. L., & Saunders, B. E. (1999). The Socioeconomic impact of interpersonal violence on women. *Journal of Consulting and Clinical Psychology, 67*(3), 362–366.

Bystritsky, A., Pontillo, D., Powers, M., Sabb, F. W., Craske, M. G., & Bookheimer, S. Y. (2001). Functional MRI changes during panic anticipation and imagery exposure. *NeuroReport, 12,* 3953–3957.

Cacioppo, J. T., Bernston, G. G., Sheridan, J. F., & McClintock, M. K. (2000). Multilevel integrative analyses of human behavior: Social neuroscience and the complementing nature of social and biological approaches. *Psychological Bulletin, 126,* 829–843.

Cadieux, R. J. (1996). Azapirones: An alternative to benzodiazepines for anxiety. *American Family Physician, 53,* 2349–2353.

Cadòret, R. J., Yates, W. R., Troughton, E., Woodworth, G., & Stewart, M. A. (1995). Genetic-environmental interaction in the genesis of aggressivity and conduct disorders. *Archives of General Psychiatry, 52,* 916–924.

Cafri, G., Yamamiya, Y., Brannick, M., & Thompson, J. K. (2005). The influence of sociocultural factors on body image: A meta-analysis. *Clinical Psychology: Science and Practice, 12,* 421–433.

Cale, E. M., & Lilienfeld, S. O. (2002). Histrionic personality disorder and antisocial personality disorder: Sex-differentiated manifestations of psychopathy? *Journal of Personality Disorders, 16,* 52–72.

Callahan, L. A., Steadman, H. J., McGreevy, M. A., Robbins, P. C. (1991). The volume and characteristics of insanity defense pleas: An eight-state study. *Bulletin of the American Academy of Psychiatry and the Law, 19,* 331–338.

Campbell-Sills, L., Barlow, D. H., Brown, T. A., & Hofmann, S. G. (2006). Acceptability and suppression of negative emotion in anxiety and mood disorders. *Emotion, 6,* 587–595.

Campbell, E. (1990). The psychopath and the definition of "mental disease of defect" under the Model Penal Code test of insanity: A question of psychology or a question of law? *Nebraska Law Review, 69,* 190–229.

Campbell, M., Green, W. H., & Deutsch, S. I. (1985). *Child and Adolescent Psychopharmacology.* Beverly Hills, CA: Sage.

Campbell, R., Sefl, T., Barnes, H. E., Ahrens, C. E., Wasco, S. M., & Zaragoza-Diesfeld, Y. (1999). Community services for rape survivors: Enhancing psychological well-being or increasing trauma? *Journal of Consulting and Clinical Psychology, 67,* 847–858.

Canino, G. L., Bird, H. R., et al. (1987). Prevalence of specific psychiatric disorders in Puerto Rico. *Archives of General Psychiatry, 44,* 727–735.

Cannon, M., Jones, P. B., & Murray, R. M. (2002). Obstetric complications and schizophrenia: Historical and meta-analytic review. *American Journal of Psychiatry, 159,* 1080–1092.

Cannon, T. D. (1998). Neurodevelopmental influences in the genesis and epigenesis of schizophrenia: An overview. *Applied and Preventive Psychology, 7,* 47–62.

Cannon, T. D., Kaprio, J., Loennqvist, J., Huttunen, M., & Koskenvuo, M. (1998). The genetic epidemiology of schizophrenia in a Finnish twin cohort: A population-based modeling study. *Archives of General Psychiatry, 55,* 67–74.

Cannon, T. D., Mednick, S. A., & Parnas, J. (1990). Antecedents of predominantly negative and predominantly positive-symptom schizophrenia in a high-risk population. *Archives of General Psychiatry, 47,* 622–632.

Cannon, T. D., van Erp, T. G., Glahn, D. C. (2002). Elucidating continuities and discontinuities between schizotypy and schizophrenia in the nervous system. *Schizophrenia Research, 54,* 151–156.

Cannon, W. B. (1935). Stress and strains of homeostasis. *American Journal of Medical Science, 189,* 1–14.

Cantor-Graae, E., & Selten, J. (2005). Schizophrenia and migration: A meta-analysis and review. *American Journal of Psychiatry, 162,* 12–24.

Cantwell, D. P., Baker, L., & Rutter, M. (1979). Families of autistic and dysphasic children. I. Family life and interactions patterns. *Archives of General Psychiatry, 36,* 682–687.

Caplan, P. J. (1995). *They Say You're Crazy: How the World's Most Powerful Psychiatrists Decide Who's Normal.* Reading: MA: Addison-Wesley.

Cappeliez, P., O'Rourke, N., & Chaudhury, H. (2005). Functions of reminiscence and mental health in later life. *Aging & Mental Health, 9,* 95–301.

Capron, C., & Duyme, M. (1989). Assessment of effects of socioeconomic status on IQ in a full cross-fostering study. *Nature, 340,* 552–554.

Cardno, A. G., Jones, L. A., Murphy, K. C., Sanders, R. D., Asherson, P., Owen, M. J., & McGuffin, P. (1998). Sibling pairs with schizophrenia or schizoaffective disorder: Associations of subtypes, symptoms and demographic variables. *Psychological Medicine, 28,* 815–823.

Carey, G., & Gottesman, I. I. (1996). Genetics and antisocial behavior: Substance versus sound bytes. *Politics and the Life Sciences* (March), 88–90.

Carlat, D. J., Camargo, C. A., & Herzog, D. B. (1997). Eating disorders in males: A report on 135 patients. *American Journal of Psychiatry, 154,* 1127–1132.

Carlson, E. A., & Sroufe, A. (1995). Contribution of attachment theory to developmental psychopathology. In D. Cicchetti & D. J. Cohen (Eds.), *Developmental Psychopathology,* Vol. 1, pp. 581–617. New York: Wiley.

Carlsson, A., & Lindqvist, M. (1963). Effect of chlorpromazine and haloperidol on the formation of 3-methoxytyramine and normetanephrine in mouse brain. *Acta Pharmacology, 20,* 140.

Carlsson, A., Waters, N., Holm-Waters, S., Tedroff, J., Nilsson, M., & Carlsson, M. L. (2001). Interactions between monoamines, glutamate, and GABA in schizophrenia: New evidence. *Annual Review of Pharmacology and Toxicology, 41,* 237–260.

Carmen, B., Angeles, M., Munoz, A., & Amate, J. (2004). Efficacy and safety of naltrexone and acamprosate in the treatment of alcohol dependence: A systematic review. *Addiction, 99,* 811–823.

Carmin, C. N., Pollard, C. A., & Gillock, K. L. (1999). Assessment of anxiety disorders in the elderly. In P. A. Lichtenberg (Ed.), *Handbook of Assessment in Clinical Gerontology,* pp. 59–90. New York: Wiley.

Carney, R. M., Freeland, K. E., Rich, M. W., & Jaffe, A. S. (1995). Depression as a risk factor for cardiac events in established coronary heart disease: A review of possible mechanisms. *Annals of Behavioral Medicine, 17,* 142–149.

Carpenter, W. (2006). The schizophrenia paradigm: A hundred-year challenge. *Journal of Nervous and Mental Disease, 194,* 639–643.

Carpenter, W. T., & Strauss, J. S. (1991). The prediction of outcome in schizophrenia. IV. Eleven-year follow-up of the Washington IPSS cohort. *Journal of Nervous and Mental Disease, 179,* 517–525.

Carr, E. G. (1977). *The motivation of self-injurious behavior: A review of some hypotheses. Psychological Bulletin, 84*(4), 800–816.

Carr, E. G. (1982). *How to Teach Sign Language to Developmentally Disabled Children.* Lawrence, KS: H & H Enterprises.

Carstensen, L. L., Isaacowitz, D. M., & Charles, S. T. (1999). Taking time seriously: A theory of socioemotional selectivity. *American Psychologist, 54,* 165–181.

Carter, J. C., & Fairburn, C. G. (1998). Cognitive-behavioral self-help for binge eating disorder: A controlled effectiveness study. *Journal of Consulting and Clinical Psychology, 66,* 616–623.

Carter, R. (1999) *Mapping the Mind.* Berkeley: University of California Press.

Carver, C. S., &. Scheier, M. F. (1999). Optimism. In C. R. Snyder (Ed.), *Coping: The Psychology of What Works,* pp. 182–204. New York: Oxford University Press.

Casas, J. M. (1995). Counseling and psychotherapy with racial/ethnic minority groups in theory and practice. In B. M. Bongar and L. E. Beutler, *Comprehensive Textbook of Psychotherapy: Theory and Practice,* pp. 311–335. New York: Oxford University Press.

Caselli, R., Beach, T., Yaari, R., & Reiman, E. (2006). Alzheimer's disease a century later. *Journal of Clinical Psychiatry, 67,* 1784–1800.

Casey, P. (2001). Multiple personality disorder. *Primary Care Psychiatry, 7,* 7–11.

Cash, T. F., & Henry, P. E. (1995). Women's body images: The results of a national survey in the U.S.A. *Sex Roles, 33,* 19–28.

Cash, T. F., Morrow, J. A., Hrabosky, J. I., & Perry, A. A. (2004). How has body image changed? A cross-sectional investigation of college women and men from 1983–2001. *Journal of Consulting and Clinical Psychology, 72,* 1081–1089.

Caspi, A., Henry, B., McGee, R. O., Moffitt, T. E., et al. (1995). Temperamental origins of child and adolescent behavior problems: From age three to fifteen. *Child Development, 66,* 55–68.

Caspi, A., McClay, J., Moffitt, T. E., Mill, J., Martin, J., Craig, I. W., et al. (2002). Role of genotype in the cycle of violence in maltreated children. *Science, 297,* 851–854.

Caspi, A., & Moffitt, T. E. (1995). The continuity of maladaptive behavior: From description to understanding in the study of antisocial behavior. In D. Cicchetti & D. J. Cohen (Eds.), *Developmental Psychopathology,* Vol. 1, pp. 472–511. New York: Wiley.

Caspi, A., & Roberts, B. W. (1999). Personality continuity and change across the life course. In L. A. Pervin & O. P. John (Eds.), *Handbook of Personality: Theory and Research,* 2nd ed., pp. 300–326. New York: Guilford.

Caspi, A. Sugden, K., Moffitt, T. E., Taylor, A., Craig, I. W., Harrington, H., et al. (2003). Influence of life stress on depression: Moderation by a polymorphism in the 5-HTT gene. *Science, 301,* 386–389.

Cassidy, J. (1988). Child-mother attachment and the self in six-year-olds. *Child Development, 59,* 121–134.

Cassidy, J., & Mohr, J. J. (2001). Unsolvable fear, trauma, and psychopathology: Theory, research, and clinical considerations related to disorganized attachment, across the life span. *Clinical Psychology: Science and Practice, 8,* 275–298.

Cattarin, J. A., & Thompson, J. K. (1994). A three-year longitudinal study of body image, eating disturbance, and general psychological functioning in adolescent females. *Eating Disorders: Journal of Treatment and Prevention, 2,* 114–125.

Cavell, T. A. (2001). Updating our approach to parent training. I: The case against targeting noncompliance. *Clinical Psychology: Science and Practice, 8,* 299–318.

CDC. (2006). Health hazard evaluation of police officers and firefighters after Hurricane Katrina—New Orleans, Louisiana, October 17–28 and November

30–December 5, 2005. *Morbidity and Weekly Reports, 55,* 456–458.

CDC. (2007). Suicide trends among youths and young adults aged 10–24 years—United States, 1990–2004. *Morbidity and Mortality Weekly Report, 56,* 905–908.

Celio, A. A., Winzelberg, A. J., Wilfley, D. E., Eppstein-Herald, D., Springer, E. A., Dev, P., et al. (2000). Reducing risk ractors for eating disorders: Comparison of an internet and a classroom-delivered psychoeducational program. *Journal of Consulting and Clinical Psychology, 68,* 650–657.

Centers for Disease Control and Prevention (1999b). Data presented at the 1999 National HIV Prevention Conference, Atlanta, August 29–September 1.

Centers for Disease Control and Prevention (2000). National Center for HIV, STD, and TB Prevention. Special data run.

Chakrabarti, S., & Fombonne, E. (2001). Pervasive developmental disorders in preschool children. *Journal of the American Medical Association 285,* 3093–3099.

Chaloupka, F. (2005). Explaining recent trends in smoking prevalence. *Addiction, 100,* 1394–1395.

Chamberlain, P., & Reid, J. B. (1998). Comparison of two community alternatives to incarceration for chronic juvenile offenders. *Journal of Consulting and Clinical Psychology, 66,* 624–633.

Chambless, D. L., & Ollendick, T. H. (2000). Empirically supported psychological interventions. Controversies and evidence. *Annual Review of Psychology, 52,* 685–716.

Chambless, D. L., et al. (2002). Marital interaction of agoraphobic women: A controlled, behavioral observation study. *Journal of Abnormal Psychology, 111,* 502–512.

Charman, T. (2002). The prevalence of autism spectrum disorders: Recent evidence and future challenges. *European Child & Adolescent Psychiatry, 11,* 249–256.

Chassin, L., & Handley, E. D. (2006). Parents and families as contexts for the development of substance use and substance use disorders. *Psychology of Addictive Behaviors, 20,* 135–137.

Chassin, L., Ritter, J., Trim, R. S., & King, K. M. (2003). Adolescent substance use disorders. In E. J. Mash and R. A. Barkley (Eds.), *Child Psychopathology,* 2nd ed., pp. 199–230. New York: Guilford.

Chen, R. T., & DeStefano, R. (1998). Vaccine adverse events: Causal or coincidental? *Lancet, 351,* 611–612.

Chen, S., Boucher, H. C., & Tapias, M. P. (2006). The relational self revealed: Integrative conceptualization and implications for interpersonal life. *Psychological Bulletin, 132,* 151–179.

Chen, W., Landau, S., & Sham, P. (2004). No evidence for links between autism, MMR and measles virus. *Psychological Medicine, 34,* 545–553.

Cheng, A. T. A., Hawton, K., Chen, T. H. H., Yen, A. M. F., Chen, C., Chen, L., & Teng, P. (2007). The influence of media coverage of a celebrity suicide on subsequent suicide attempts. *Journal of Clinical Psychiatry, 68,* 862–866.

Cherlin, A. J. (1992). *Marriage, Divorce, Remarriage* (2nd ed.). Cambridge, MA: Harvard University Press.

Chesselet, M., & Delfs, J. M. (1996). Basal ganglia and movement disorders: An update. *Trends in Neurosciences, 19,* 417–423.

Chiu, H. F. K., Lam, L. C. W., Chi, I., Leung, T., Li, S. W., Law, W. T., et al. (1998). Prevalence of dementia in Chinese elderly in Hong Kong. *Neurology, 50,* 1002–1009.

Chorpita, B. F., Brown, T. A., & Barlow, D. H. (1998). Diagnostic reliability of the DSM-III-R anxiety disorders: Mediating effects of patient and diagnostician characteristics. *Behavior Modification, 22,* 307–320.

Christensen, A., Atkins, D. C., Berns, S., Wheeler, J., Baucom, D. H., & Simpson, L. E. (2004). Traditional versus integrative behavioral couple therapy for significantly and chronically distressed married couples. *Journal of Consulting and Clinical Psychology, 72,* 176–191.

Christensen, A., Atkins, D. C., Yi, J., Baucom, D. H., & George, W. H. (2006). Couple and individual adjustment for 2 years following a randomized clinical trial comparing traditional versus integrative behavioral therapy. *Journal of Consulting and Clinical Psychology, 74,* 1180–1191.

Cicchetti, D., & Beegly, M. (1990). *Children with Down Syndrome: A Developmental Perspective.* New York: Cambridge University Press.

Ciompi, L. (1980). Catamnestic long-term study on the course of life and aging of schizophrenics. *Schizophrenia Bulletin, 6,* 606–618.

Cipparone, R. C. (1987). The defense of battered women who kill. *University of Pennsylvania Law Review, 135,* 427–452.

Claar, R. L. & Blumenthal, J. A. (2003). The value of stress-management interventions in life-threatening medical conditions. *Current Directions in Psychological Science, 12,* 133–137.

Clark, D. A., Beck, A. T., & Alford, B. A. (1999). *Scientific Foundations of Cognitive Theory and Therapy of Depression.* New York: Wiley.

Clark, D. C., & Goebel-Fabbri, A. E. (1999). Lifetime risk of suicide in major affective disorders. In D. G. Jacobs et al. (Eds.), *The Harvard Medical School Guide to Suicide Assessment and Intervention,* pp. 270–286. San Francisco: Jossey-Bass.

Clark, D. M. (1986b). Cognitive therapy for anxiety. *Behavioral Psychotherapy, 14,* 283–294.

Clark, D. M., Salkovskis, P. M., Hackmann, A., Wells, A., Fennell, M., Ludgate, J., et al. (1998). Two psychological treatments for hypochondriasis: A randomised controlled trial. *British Journal of Psyrchiatry, 173,* 218–225.

Clark, D. M., Salkovskis, P. M., Hackmann, A., Wells, A., Ludgate, J., & Gelder, M. (1999). Brief cognitive therapy for panic disorder: A randomized controlled trial. *Journal of Consulting and Clinical Psychology, 67,* 583–589.

Clark, L. A. (1999). Dimensional approaches to personality disorder assessment and diagnosis. In C. R. Cloninger (Ed.), *Personality and Psychopathology,* pp. 219–244. Washington, DC: American Psychiatric Press.

Clark, L. A. (2007). Assessment and diagnosis of personality disorder: Perennial issues and an emerging reconceptualization. *Annual Review of Psychology, 58,* 227–257.

Clark, L. A., Livesley, W. J., & Morey, L. (1997). Personality disorder assessment: The challenge of construct validity. *Journal of Personality Disorders, 11,* 205–231.

Clark, L. A., & Watson, D. (1991). Tripartite model of anxiety and depression: Psychometric evidence and taxonomic implications. *Journal of Abnormal Psychology, 100,* 316–336.

Clark, R., Anderson, N. B., Clark, V. R., & Williams, D. R. (1999). Racism as a stressor for African Americans: A biopsychosocial model. *American Psychologist, 54,* 805–816.

Clarke, J. W. (1990). *On Being Mad or Merely Angry.* Princeton, NJ: Princeton University Press.

Clarkin, J. F., Foelsch, P. A., Levy, K. N., Hull. J. W., Delaney, J. C., & Kernberg, O. F., (2001). The development of a psychodynamic treatment for patients with borderline personality disorder: A preliminary study of behavioral change. *Journal of Personality Disorders, 15,* 487–495.

Clayton, A. (2007). Epidemiology and neurobiology of female sexual dysfunction. *Journal of Sexual Medicine, 4,* 260–268.

Clayton, A. H., & West, S. G. (2003). The effects of antidepressants on human sexuality. *Primary Psychiatry, 10,* 62–70.

Cleckley, H. (1976). *The Mask of Sanity* (5th ed.). St. Louis, MO: Mosby.

Clifton, A., Turkheimer, E., & Oltmanns, T. F. (2004). Contrasting perspectives on personality problems: Descriptions from the self and others. *Personality and Individual Differences, 36,* 1499–1514.

Cloninger, C. R. (1987). Neurogenetic adaptive mechanisms in alcoholism. *Science, 236,* 410–416.

Cloninger, C. R., Sigvardsson, S., & Bohman, M. (1996). Type I and type II alcoholism: An update. *Alcohol Health and Research World, 20,* 18–23.

Coan, J. A., Schaefer, H. S., & Davidson, R. J. (2006). Lending a hand: Social regulation of the neural response to threat. *Psychological Science, 17,* 1032–1039.

Coccaro, E. F., Posternak, M. A., & Zimmerman, M. (2005). Prevalence and features of intermittent explosive disorder in a clinical setting. *Journal of Clinical Psychiatry, 66,* 1221–1227.

Cohen, A. N., Hammen, C., Henry, R. M., & Daley, S. E. (2004). Effects of stress and social support on recurrence in bipolar disorder. *Journal of Affective Disorders, 82,* 143–147.

Cohen, B. J., Bonnie, R. J., & Monahan, J. (2008). *Understanding and applying Virginia's new statutory civil commitment criteria.* Unpublished manuscript, University of Virginia, Charloffesville, VA.

Cohen, L. J., & Galynker, I. I. (2002). Clinical features of pedophilia and implications for treatment. *Journal of Psychiatric Practice, 8,* 276–289.

Cohen, P., Chen, H., Crawford, T. N., Brook, J. S., & Gordon, K. (2007). Personality disorders in early adolescence and the development of later substance use disorders in the general population. *Drug and Alcohol Dependence, 88,* S71–S84.

Cohen, S., & Pressman, S. D. (2006). Positive affect and health. *Current Directions in Psychological Science, 15,* 122–125.

Cohen, S., Kaplan, J. R., Cunnick, J. E., Manuck, S. B., & Rabin, B. S. (1992). Chronic social stress, affiliation, and cellular immune response in nonhuman primates. *Psychological Science, 3,* 301–304.

Cohen, S., & Williamson. G. M. (1991). Stress and infectious disease in humans. *Psychological Bulletin, 109,* 5–24.

Cohen-Kettenis, P. T., & Gooren, L. J. (1999). Transsexualism: A review of etiology, diagnosis and treatment. *Journal of Psychosomatic Research, 46,* 315–333.

Cohler, B. J., & Nakamura, J. E. (1996). In J. Sadavoy, L. W. Lazarus, L. F. Jarvik, & G. T. Grossberg (Eds.), *Comprehensive Review of Geriatric Psychiatry II,* pp. 153–194. Washington, DC: American Psychiatric Press.

Coid, J., Yang, M., Tyrer, P., Roberts, A., & Ullrich, S. (2006). Prevalence and correlates of personality disorder among adults aged 16 to 74 in Great Britain. *British Journal of Psychiatry, 188,* 423–431.

Coie, J., & Kupersmidt, J., (1983). A behavioral analysis of emerging social status in boys' groups. *Child Development, 54,* 1400–1416.

Colcombe, S., & Kramer, A. F. (2003). Fitness effects on the cognitive function of older adults: A meta-analytic study. *Psychological Science, 14,* 125–130.

Cole, M. G., McCusker, J., Dendukuri, N., & Han, L. (2002). Symptoms of delirium among elderly medical inpatients with or without dementia. *Journal of Neuropsychiatry and Clinical Neuroscience, 14,* 167–175.

Cole, W. (1992). Incest perpetrators: Their assessment and treatment, *Psychiatric Clinics of North America, 15,* 689–670.

Coleman, P. G. (2005). Uses of reminiscence: Functions and benefits. *Aging & Mental Health, 9,* 291–294.

Collaer, M. L., & Hines, M. (1995). Human behavioral sex differences: A role for gonadal hormones during early development. *Psychological Bulletin, 118,* 55–107.

Comas-Diaz, L. (2000). An ethnopolitical approach to working with people of color. *American Psychologist, 55,* 1319–1325.

Compton, W. M., Thomas, Y. F., Stinson, F. S., & Grant, B. F. (2007). Prevalence, correlates, disabilities, and comorbidities of DSM-IV drug abuse and dependence in the United States. *Archives of General Psychiatry, 64,* 566–576.

Conduct Problems Prevention Research Group. (1999). Initial impact of the Fast Track prevention trial for conduct problems: II. Classroom effects. *Journal of Consulting and Clinical Psychology, 67,* 648–657.

Conger, J. J. (1956). Alcoholism: Theory, problem, and challenge. II. Reinforcement theory and the dynamics of alcoholism. *Quarterly Journal of Studies on Alcohol, 17,* 296–305.

Conley, R. R., & Kelly, D. L. (2001). Management of treatment resistance in schizophrenia. *Biological Psychiatry, 50,* 898–911.

Conners, C. K. (1980). Artificial colors and the diet of disruptive behavior: Current status of research. In R. M. Knights & D. J. Bakker (Eds.), *Treatment of Hyperactive and Learning Disabled Children.* Baltimore: University Park Press.

Consumer Reports. (1995, November). Mental health: Does therapy help? 734–739.

Constable, N. (2004). *This Is Cocaine (Addiction).* New York: Sanctuary Publishing.

Contrada, R. J., et al., (2001). Ethnicity-related sources of stress and their effects on well-being. *Current Directions in Psychological Science, 9,* 136–139.

Cook, J. M., Riggs, D. S., Thompson, R., Coyne, J. C., & Sheikh, J. I. (2004). Posttraumatic stress disorder and current relationship functioning among World War II ex-prisoners of war. *Journal of Family Psychology, 18,* 36–45.

Coombs, R. H., Howatt, W. A., & Coombs, K. (2005). Addiction recovery tools. In R. H. Coombs (Ed.), *Addiction Counseling Review,* pp. 425–446. Mahwah, NJ: Erlbaum.

Coons, P. (1986). The prevalence of multiple personality disorder. *Newsletter of the International Society for the Study of Multiple Personality and Dissociation, 4,* 6–8.

Coons, P., & Milstein, V. (1988). Psychogenic amnesia: A clinical investigation of 25 consecutive cases. Unpublished data cited in D. Spiegel & E. Cardena (1991), Disintegrated experience: The dissociative disorders revisited. *Journal of Abnormal Psychology, 100,* 366–378.

Coons, P. M., & Bowman, E. S. (2001). Ten-year follow-up study of patients with dissociative identity disorder. *Journal of Trauma and Dissociation, 2,* 73–89.

Cooper, M. H. (1994). Regulating tobacco: Can the FDA break America's smoking habit? *CQ Research, 4,* 843–858.

Cooper, P. J. (1995). Eating disorders and their relationship to mood and anxiety disorders. In K. D. Brownell & C. G. Fairburn (Eds.), *Eating Disorders and Obesity: A Comprehensive Handbook,* pp. 159–164. New York: Guilford.

Coovert, D. L., Kinder, B. N., & Thompson, J. K. (1989). The psychosexual aspects of anorexia nervosa and bulimia nervosa: A review of the literature. *Clinical Psychology Review, 9,* 169–180.

Corbitt, E. M. (2002). Narcissism from the perspective of the five-factor model. In P. T. Costa, Jr., & T. A. Widiger (Eds.), *Personality Disorders and the Five-Factor Model of Personality,* 2nd ed., pp. 293–298. Washington, DC: American Psychological Association.

Cordova, J. V., Jacobson, N. S., Gottman, J. M., Rushe, R., & Cox, G. (1993). Negative reciprocity and communication in couples with a violent husband. *Journal of Abnormal Psychology, 102,* 559–564.

Cornelius, J. R., Reynolds, M., Martz, B. M., Clark, D. B., Kirisci, L., & Tarter, R. (2008). Premature mortality among males with substance use disorders. *Addictive Behaviors, 33,* 156–160.

Correll, C., & Schenk, E. (2008). Tardive dyskinesia and new antipsychotics. *Current Opinion in Psychiatry, 21,* 151–156.

Corse, C. D., Manuck, S. B., Cantwell, J. D., Giordani, B., & Matthews, K. A. (1982). Coronary-prone behavior pattern and cardiovascular response in persons with and without coronary heart disease. *Psychosomatic Medicine, 44,* 449–459.

Coryell, W., Solomon, D., Turvey, C., Keller, M., Leon, A. C., Endicott, J., et al. (2003). The long-term course of rapid-cycling bipolar disorder. *Archives of General Psychiatry, 60,* 914–920.

Coser, L. A. (1977). *Masters of Sociological Thought: Ideas in Historical and Social Context.* San Diego, CA: Harcourt Brace Jovanovich.

Costello, E. J., Compton, S. N., Keeler, G., & Angold, A. (2003). Relationships between poverty and psychopathology: A natural experiment. *JAMA, 290*(15), 2023–2029.

Costello, E. J., Erkanli, A., & Angold, A. (2006). Is there an epidemic of child or adolescent depression? *Journal of Child Psychology and Psychiatry, 47,* 1263–1273.

Courchesne, E., et al. (2001). Unusual brain growth patterns in early life in patients with autistic disorder: An MRI study. *Neurology, 57,* 245–254.

Couture, S. M., & Penn, D. L. (2003). Interpersonal contact and the stigma of mental illness. A review of the literature. *Journal of Mental Health, 12,* 291–305.

Covault, J., Gelernter, J., Hesselbrock, V., Nellissery, M., & Kranzler, H. R. (2004). Allelic and haplotypic association of GABRA2 with alcohol dependence. *American Journal of Medical Genetics (Neuropsychiatric Genetics), 129B,* 104–109.

Cowan, C. P., & Cowan, P. A. (1992). *When Partners Become Parents.* New York: Basic Books.

Cox, B. J., Enns, M. W., Walker, J. R., Kjernisted, K., & Pidlubny, S. R. (2001). Psychological vulnerabilities in patients with major depression vs panic disorder. *Behaviour Research and Therapy, 39,* 567–573.

Coyne, J. C., Thompson, R., & Palmer, S. C. (2002). Marital quality, coping with conflict, marital complaints, and affection in couples with a depressed wife. *Journal of Family Psychology, 16,* 26–37.

Crabbe, J. C. (2002). Genetic contributions to addiction. *Annual Review of Psychology, 53,* 435–462.

Craddock, N., O'Donovan, M., & Owen, M. (2006). Genes for schizophrenia and bipolar disorder? Implications for psychiatric nosology. *Schizophrenia Bulletin, 32,* 9–16.

Craig, T. J., Siegel, C., Hopper, K., Lin, S., et al. (1997). Outcome in schizophrenia and related disorders compared between developing and developed countries: A recursive partitioning re-analysis of the WHO. *British Journal of Psychiatry, 170,* 229–233.

Craighead, W. E., & Miklowitz, D. J. (2000). Psychosocial interventions for bipolar disorder. *Journal of Clinical Psychiatry, 61* (Suppl. 13), 58–64.

Cramer, P. (2000). Defense mechanisms in psychology today: Further processes for adaptation. *American Psychologist, 55,* 637–646.

Craske, M. G., & Rowe, M. K. (1997). Nocturnal panic. *Clinical Psychology: Science and Practice, 4,* 153–174.

Crawford, T. N., Cohen, P., & Brook, J. S. (2001). Dramatic-erratic personality disorder symptoms: I. Continuity from early adolescence to adulthood. *Journal of Personality Disorders, 15,* 319–335.

Creed, F., & Barsky A. (2004). A systematic review of the epidemiology of somatisation disorder and hypochondriasis. *Journal of Psychosomatic Research, 56,* 391–408.

Crews, F., Collins, M., Dlugos, C., Littleton, J., Wilkins, L., Neafsey, E., et al. (2004). Alcohol-induced neurodegeneration: When, where and why? *Alcoholism: Clinical and Experimental Research, 28,* 350–364.

Crick, N. R., & Dodge, K. A. (1994). A review and reformulation of social information-processing mechanisms in children's social adjustment. *Psychological Bulletin, 115,* 74–101.

Crimlisk, H., Bhatia, K., Cope, H., et al. (1998). Slater revisited: 6-year follow-up study of patients with medically unexplained motor symptoms. *British Medical Journal, 316,* 582–586.

Crits-Christoph, P. (1998). Psychosocial treatments for personality disorders. In P. E. Nathan & J. M. Gorman (Eds.), *A Guide to Treatments that Work,* pp. 544–553. New York: Oxford University Press.

Cronbach, L. J., & Meehl, P. E. (1955). Construct validity in psychological tests. *Psychological Bulletin, 52,* 281–302.

Crosby, J. P., & Sprock, J. (2004). Effect of patient sex, clinician sex, and sex role on the diagnosis of antisocial personality disorder: Models of underpathologizing and overpathologizing biases. *Journal of Clinical Psychology, 60,* 583–604.

Cross-National Collaborative Panic Study. Second Phase Investigators. (1992). Drug treatment of panic disorder: Comparative efficacy of alprazolam, imipramine, and placebo. *British Journal of Psychiatry, 160,* 191–202.

Csikszentmihalyi, M., & Larson, R. (1984). *Being Adolescent.* New York: Basic Books.

Cuckle, H. (2001). Time for a total shift to first trimester screening for Down syndrome. *The Lancet, 358,* 1658–1659.

Cuellar, A. K., Johnson, S. L., & Winters, R. (2005). Distinctions between bipolar and unipolar depression. *Clinical Psychology Review, 25,* 307–339.

Cummings, E. M., & Davies, P. (1994). *Children and Marital Conflict.* New York: Guilford.

Cummings, J. L., & Cole, G. (2002). Alzheimer disease. *Journal of the American Medical Association, 287,* 2335–2338.

Cummings, J. L., Vinters, H. V., Cole, G. M., & Khachaturian, Z. S. (1998). Alzheimer's disease: Etiologies, pathophysiology, cognitive reserve, and treatment opportunities. *Neurology, 51* (Suppl. 1), S2–S17.

Currier, D., & Mann, J. J. (2008). Stress, genes and the biology of suicidal behavior. *Psychiatric Clinics of North America, 31,* 247–269.

Currier, J. M., Neimeyer, R. A., & Berman, J. S. (2008). The effectiveness of psychotherapeutic interventions for bereaved persons: A comprehensive review. *Psychological Bulletin, 134,* 648–661.

Curtis, C. E., Calkins, M. E., & Iacono, W. G. (2001). Saccadic disinhibition in schizophrenia patients and their first-degree biological relatives. *Experimental Brain Research, 137,* 228–236.

Curtis, N. M., Ronan, K. R., & Borduin, C. M. (2004). Multisystemic treatment: A meta-analysis of outcome studies. *Journal of Family Psychology, 18*(3), 411–419.

D'Emilio, J., & Freedman, E. B. (1988). *Intimate Matters: A History of Sexuality in America.* New York: Harper & Row.

D'Onofrio, B., Turkheimer, E., Emery, R., Slutske, W., Heath, A., Madden, P., et al. (in press). A genetically informed study of marital instability and its association with offspring psychopathology. *Journal of Abnormal Psychology.*

D'Onofrio, B., Turkheimer, E., Emery, R., Slutske, W., Heath, A., Madden, P., & Martin, N. (2006). A genetically informed study of the processes underlying the association between parental marital instability and offspring life course patterns. *Developmental Psychology, 42,* 486–499.

D'Onofrio, B. M., Turkheimer, E., Emery, R. E., Harden, K. P., Slutske, W. S., Heath, A. C., Madden, P. A. F., & Martin, N. G. (2007). A genetically informed study of the intergenerational transmission of relationship instability. *Journal of Marriage and the Family, 69,* 793–809.

Da Rocha, F. F., Correa, H., & Teixeira, A. L. (2008). Obsessive-compulsive disorder and immunology: A review. *Progress in Neuro-Psychopharmacology & Biological Psychiatry, 32,* 1139–1146.

Danforth, J. S., Barkley, R. A., & Stokes, T. F. (1991). Observations of parent-child interactions with hyperactive children: Research and clinical implications. *Clinical Psychology Review, 11,* 703–727.

Das-Munshi, J., Goldberg, D., Bebbington, P. E., Bhugra, D. K., Brugha, T. S., Dewey, M. E., et al. (2008). Public health significance of mixed anxiety and depression: Beyond current classification. *British Journal of Psychiatry, 192,* 171–177.

Davidson, J. R., DuPont, R. L., Hedges, D., & Haskins, J. T. (1999). Efficacy, safety, and tolerability of venlafaxine extended release and buspirone in outpatients with generalized anxiety disorder. *Journal of Clinical Psychiatry, 60,* 528–535.

Davidson, L., & McGlashan, T. (2005). *The Varied Outcomes of Schizophrenia. Recovery from Severe mental illnesses: Research Evidence and Implications for practice,* Vol 1, pp. 236–259. Boston, MA: Center for Psychiatric Rehabilitation/Boston University.

Davidson, L. L., & Heinrichs, R. W. (2003). Quantification of frontal and temporal lobe brain-imaging findings in schizophrenia: A meta-analysis. *Psychiatry Research: Neuroimaging, 122,* 69–87.

Davidson, P. R., & Parker, K. C. H. (2001). Eye movement desensitization and reprocessing (EMDR): A metaanalysis. *Journal of Consulting and Clinical Psychology, 69,* 305–316.

Davidson, R. J., Pizzagalli, D., Nitschke, J. B., & Putnam, K. (2002). Depression: Perspectives from affective neuroscience. *Annual Review of Psychology, 53,* 545–574.

Davidson, W. S., Redner, R., Blakely, C. H., Mitchell, C. M., & Emshoff, J. G. (1987). Diversion of juvenile offenders: An experimental comparison. *Journal of Consulting and Clinical Psychology, 55,* 68–75.

Davila, J. (2001). Refining the association between excessive reassurance seeking and depressive symptoms: The role of related interpersonal constructs. *Journal of Social and Clinical Psychology, 20,* 538–559.

Davis, B., Sheeber, L., Hops, H., & Tildesley, E. (2000). Adolescent responses to depressive parental behaviors in problem-solving interactions: Implications for depressive symptoms. *Journal of Abnormal Child Psychology, 28,* 541–465.

Davis, D., & Herdt, G. (1997). Cultural issues and sexual disorders. In T. A. Widiger, A. J. Frances, H. A. Pincus, R. Ross, M. B. First, & W. Davis (Eds.), *DSM-IV Sourcebook,* Vol. 3, pp. 951–958. Washington, DC: American Psychiatric Press.

Davis, G. C., & Akiskal, H. S. (1986). Descriptive, biological, and theoretical aspects of borderline personality disorder. *Hospital and Community Psychiatry, 37,* 685–692.

Davis, H. J., & Reissing, E. D. (2007). Relationship adjustment and dyadic interaction in couples with sexual pain disorders: A critical review of the literature. *Sexual & Marital Therapy, 22,* 245–254.

Dawes, R. M. (1994). *House of Cards: The Collapse of Modern Psychotherapy.* New York: Free Press.

Dawson, D. A. (2000). Drinking patterns among individuals with and without DSM-IV alcohol use disorders. *Journal of Studies on Alcohol, 61,* 111–125.

Deblinger, E., McLeer, S. V., Atkins, M. S., Ralphe, D., & Foa, E. (1989). Post-traumatic stress in sexually abused, physically abused, and nonabused children. *Child Abuse and Neglect, 13,* 403–408.

De Cuypere, G., Van Hemelruck, M., Michel, A., Cael, B., Heylens, G., Rubens, R., Hoebeke, P., & Monstrey, S. (2007). Prevalence and demography of transsexualism in Belgium. *European Psychiatry, 22,* 137–141.

Delano-Wood, L., Abeles, N. (2005). Late-life depression: Detection, risk reduction, and somatic intervention. *Clinical Psychology: Science and Practice, 12,* 207–217.

Delgado, P. L., & Moreno, F. A. (2006). Neurochemistry of mood disorders. In D. J. Stein, D. J. Kupfer, and A. F. Schatzberg (Eds.), *The American Psychiatric Publishing Textbook of Mood Disorders,* pp. 101–116. Washington, DC: American Psychiatric Publishing.

DeLisi, L. (2008). The concept of progressive brain change in schizophrenia: Implications for understanding schizophrenia. *Schizophrenia Bulletin, 34,* 312–321.

DeLisi, L., & Fleischhaker, W. (2007). Schizophrenia research in the era of the genome, 2007. *Current Opinion in Psychiatry, 20,* 109–110.

DeLuca, N., Moser, L., & Bond, G. (2008). Assertive Community Treatment. Clinical Handbook of Schizophrenia, pp. 329-338. New York: Guilford Press.

Dell'Osso, B., Nestadt, G., Allen, A., & Hollander, E. (2006). Serotonin-norepinephrine reuptake inhibitors in the treatment of obsessive-compulsive disorder: A critical review. *Journal of Clinical Psychiatry, 67,* 600–610.

DePaulo, J. R., & Horvitz, L. A. (2002). *Understanding Depression: What We Know and What You Can Do About it.* New York: Wiley.

Dershowitz, A. M. (1994). *The Abuse Excuse and Other Cop-outs, Sob Stories, and Evasions of Responsibility.* Boston: Little, Brown.

DeRogatis, L. R., & Burnett, A. L. (2008). The epidemiology of sexual dysfunctions. *Journal of Sexual Medicine, 5,* 289–300.

DeRubeis, R. J., Brotman, M. A., & Gibbons, C. J. (2005). A conceptual and methodological analysis of the nonspecifics argument. *Clinical Psychology: Science and Practice, 12,* 174–183.

DeRubeis, R. J., Gelfand, L. A., Tang, T. Z, & Simons, A. D. (1999). Medications versus cognitive behavior therapy for severely depressed outpatients: Mega-analysis of four randomized comparisons. *American Journal of Psychiatry, 156,* 1007–1013.

De Silva, P., & Rachman, S. (2004). *Obsessive–Compulsive Disorders: The Facts* (3rd ed.). Oxford: Oxford University Press.

Detera-Wadleigh, S., & McMahon, F. J. (2004). Genetic association studies in mood disorders: Issues and promise. *International Review of Psychiatry, 16,* 301–310.

Detterman, D. K., & Gabriel, L. (2007). Look before you leap: Implications of the 1992 and 2002 definitions of mental retardation. In H. N. Switzky & S. Greenspan, Eds., *What is Mental Retardation? Ideas for an Evolving Disability in the 21st Century,* pp. 133–144. Washington: AAIDD.

DeVane, C. L., & Sallee, F. R. (1996). Serotonin selective reuptake inhibitors in child and adolescent psychopharmacology: A review of published evidence. *Journal of Clinical Psychiatry, 57,* 55–66.

Dick, D. M. (2007). Identification of genes influencing a spectrum of externalizing psychopathology. *Current Directions in Psychological Science, 16,* 331–335.

Dick, D. M., & Foroud, T. (2003). Candidate genes for alcohol dependence: A review of genetic evidence from human studies. *Alcoholism: Clinical and Experimental Research, 5,* 868–879.

Dick, D. M., Jones, K., Saccone, N., Hinrichs, A. L., Wang, J. C., Goate, A. et al. (2006). Endophenotypes successfully lead to gene identification: Results from the collaborative study on the genetics of alcoholism. *Behavior Genetics, 36.*

Dick, D. M., Pagan, J. L., Holliday, C., Viken, R., Pulkkinen, L., Kaprio, J., & Rose, R. J. (2007). Gender differences in friends' influences on adolescent drinking: A genetic epidemiological study. *Alcoholism: Clinical and Experimental Research, 31,* 2012–2019.

Dick, D. M., Pagan, J. L., Viken, R., Purcell, S., Kaprio, J., Pulkkinen, L., & Rose, R. J. (2007). Changing environmental influences on substance use across development. *Twin Research and Human Genetics, 10,* 315–326.

Dickens, C. (1842/1970). *American Notes and Pictures from Italy.* New York: Oxford University Press.

Dickens, W. T., & Flynn, J. R. (2001). Heritability estimates versus large environmental effects: The IQ paradox resolved. *Psychological Review, 108,* 346–369.

Dickerson, F., Tenhula, W., & Green-Paden, L. (2005). The token economy for schizophrenia: Review of the literature and recommendations for future research. *Schizophrenia Research, 75,* 405–416.

Dickerson, S. S., & Kemeny, M. E. (2004). Acute stressors and cortisol responses: A theoretical integration and synthesis of laboratory research. *Psychological Bulletin, 130,* 355–391.

Dickson, D. W. (2001). Neuropathology of Alzheimer's disease and other dementias. *Clinics in Geriatric Medicine, 17,* 209–228.

Digman, J. M. (2002). Historical antecedents of the five-factor model. In P. T. Costa, Jr., & T. A. Widiger (Eds.), *Personality Disorders and the Five-Factor Model of Personality,* 2nd ed., pp. 17–22. Washington, DC: American Psychological Association.

Diliberto, G. (1999). *A Useful Woman: The Early Life of Jane Addams.* New York HarperCollins.

Dishion, T. J, McCord, J., & Poulin, F. (1999). When interventions harm: Peer groups and problem behavior. *American Psychologist, 54,* 755–764.

Dishion, T. J., French, D. C., & Patterson, G. R. (1995). The development and ecology of antisocial behavior. In D. Cicchetti & D. J. Cohen (Eds.), *Developmental Psychopathology,* Vol. 1, pp. 421–471. New York: Wiley.

Ditton, P. M. (1999). *Mental Health and Treatment of Inmates and Probationers.* Washington, DC: Bureau of Justice Statistics.

Dobson, K. S. (2008). Cognitive therapy for depression. In M. A. Whisman (Ed.), *Adapting Cognitive Therapy for Depression: Managing Complexity and Comorbidity,* pp. 3–35. New York: Guilford.

Docherty, N. M., DeRosa, M., & Andreasen, N. C. (1996). Communication disturbances in schizophrenia and mania. *Archives of General Psychiatry, 53,* 358–364.

Dodge, K. A., Lansford, J. E., Burks, V. S., Bates, J. E., Pettit, G. S., Fontaine, R., et al. (2003). Peer rejection and social information-processing factors in the development of aggressive behavior problems in children. *Child Development, 74*(2), 374–393.

Dohrenwend, B. P. (2006). Inventorying stressful life events as risk factors for psychopathology: Toward resolution of the problem of intracategory variability. *Psychological Bulletin, 132,* 477–495.

Dohrenwend, B. P., Link, B. G., Kern, R., Shrout, P. E., & Markowitz, J. (1990). Measuring life events: The problem of variability within event categories. *Stress Medicine, 6,* 179–187.

Dolan-Sewell, R. T., Krueger, R. F., & Shea, M. T. (2001). Co-occurrence with syndrome disorders. In W. J. Livesley (Ed.), *Handbook of Personality Disorders: Theory, Research, and Treatment,* pp. 84–104. New York: Guilford.

Donahey, K. M., & Carroll, R. A. (1993). Gender differences in factors associated with hypoactive sexual desire. *Journal of Sex and Marital Therapy, 19,* 25–40.

Donavan, D. M. (1999). Efficacy and effectiveness: Complementary findings from two multisite trials evaluating outcomes of alcohol treatments differing in theoretical orientations. *Alcoholism: Clinical and Experimental Research, 23,* 564–572.

Doss, B. D. (2004). Changing the way we study change in psychotherapy. *Clinical Psychology: Science and Practice, 11,* 368–386.

Dotti, M. T., et al. (2002). A Rett syndrome MECP2 mutation that causes mental retardation in men. *Neurology, 58,* 226–230.

Dougherty, D. D., & Rauch, S. L., (2007). Somatic therapies for treatment-resistant depression: New neurotherapeutic interventions. *Psychiatric Clinics of North America, 30,* 1–7.

Douglas, V. I. (1983). Attention and cognitive problems. In M. Rutter (Ed.), *Developmental Neuropsychiatry,* pp. 280–329. New York: Guilford.

Downar, J., & Kapur, S. (2008). Biological Theories. Clinical Handbook of Schizophrenia, pp. 25–34. New York: Guilford Press.

Draguns, J. G. (2006). Culture in psychopathology—psychopathology in culture: Taking a new look at an old problem. In T. G. Plante (Ed.), *Mental Disorders of the New Millennium: Public and Social Problems,* Vol. 2, pp. 215–233. Westport, CT: Praeger Publishers/Greenwood Publishing Group.

Draguns, J. G., & Tanaka-Matsumi, J. (2003). Assessment of psychopathology across and within cultures: Issues and findings. *Behaviour Research & Therapy, 41,* 755–776.

Drevets, W. C. (2002). Neuroimaging studies of mood disorders. In J. E. Helzer & J. J. Hudziak (Eds.), *Defining Psychopathology in the 21st Century: DSM-IV and Beyond,* pp. 71–106. Washington, DC: American Psychiatric Press.

Dreyfuss, R. (1996). Tobacco, enemy number 1. *Mother Jones, 21,* 42–48.

Drobes, D. J., Stritzke, W. G. K., & Coffey, S. F. (2000). Psychophysiological factors. In M. Hersen & A. S. Bellack (Eds.), *Psychopathology in Adulthood,* 2nd ed., pp. 112–130. Needham Heights, MA: Allyn & Bacon.

Duchek, J., Balota, D., Storandt, M., & Larsen, R. (2007). The power of personality in discriminating between healthy aging and early-stage Alzheimer's disease. *Journals of Gerontology: Series B: Psychological Sciences and Social Sciences, 62B,* P353–P361.

Duhig, A. M., Renk, K., Epstein, M. K., & Phares, V. (2000). Interparental agreement on internalizing, externalizing, and total behavior problems: A metaanalysis. *Clinical Psychology: Science and Practice, 7,* 435–453.

Dunmore, E., Clark, D. M., & Ehlers, A. (2001). A prospective investigation of the role of cognitive factors in persistent Posttraumatic Stress Disorder (PTSD) after physical and sexual assault. *Behaviour Research and Therapy, 39,* 1063–1084.

Dupéré, V., Lacourse, É., Willms, J. D., Vitaro, F., & Tremblay, R. E. (2007). Affiliation to youth gangs during adolescence: The interaction between childhood psychopathic tendencies and neighborhood disadvantage. *Journal of Abnormal Child Psychology, 35,* 1035–1045.

Durham, M. L., & LaFond, J. Q. (1988). A search for the missing premise of involuntary therapeutic commitment: Effective treatment of the mentally ill. *Rutgers Law Review, 40,* 303–368.

Durkheim, E. (1897/1951). *Suicide: A Study in Sociology.* New York: Free Press.

Dusseldorp, E., van Elderen, T., Maes, S., Meulman, J., & Kraaij, V. (1999). A meta-analysis of psychoeducational programs for coronary heart disease patients. *Health Psychology, 18,* 506–519.

Dutere, E., Segraves, T., & Althof, S. (2007). Psychotherapy and pharmacotherapy for sexual dysfunctions. In P. E. Nathan & J. M. Gorman (Eds), *A Guide to Treatments That Work* 3rd ed, pp. 531–560. New York: Oxford University Press.

Dyk, P. H., & Adams, G. R. (1990). Identity and intimacy: An initial investigation of three theoretical models using cross-lag panel correlations. *Journal of Youth and Adolescence, 19,* 91–110.

Earls, F., & Mezzacappa, E. (2002). Conduct and oppositional disorders. In M. Rutter & E. Taylor (Eds.), *Child and Adolescent Psychiatry,* 4th ed., pp. 419–436. Oxford, England: Blackwell.

Eberhard, J., Lindström, E., & Levander, S. (2006). Tardive dyskinesia and antipsychotics: A 5-year longitudinal study of frequency, correlates and course. *International Clinical Psychopharmacology, 21,* 35–42.

Eberlin, M., McConnachie, G., Igel, S., & Volpe, L. (1993). Facilitated communication: A failure to replicate the phenomenon. *Journal of Autism and Developmental Disorders, 23,* 507–530.

Eddy K. T., Keel, P. K., Dorer, D. J., Delinsky, S. S., Franko, D. L., & Herzog, D. B. (2002). Longitudinal comparison of anorexia nervosa subtypes. *International Journal of Eating Disorders, 31,* 191–201.

Edenberg, H. J., Dick, D. M., Xuei, X., Tian, H., Almasy, L., Bauer, L. O., et al. (2004). Variations in GABRA2, encoding the a2 subunit of the GABA-A receptor are associated with alcohol dependence and with brain oscillations. *American Journal of Human Genetics, 74,* 705–714.

Edwards, W., & Hensley, C. (2001). Contextualizing sex offender management legislation and policy: Evaluating the problem of latent consequences in community notification laws. *International Journal of Offender Therapy and Comparative Criminology, 45,* 83–101.

Ehlers, A., & Clark, D. M. (2000). A cognitive model of persistent posttraumatic stress disorder. *Behavior Research and Therapy, 38,* 319–345.

Ehlers, A., Mayou, R. A., & Bryant, B. (1998). Psychological predictors of chronic posttraumatic stress disorders after motor vehicle accidents. *Journal of Abnormal Psychology, 107,* 508–519.

Eich, E., Macaulay, D., Lowenstein, R. J., & Dihle, P. H. (1997). Memory, amnesia, and dissociative identity disorder. *Psychological Science, 8,* 417–422.

Eifert, G. H., Zvolensky, M. J., & Lejuez, C. W. (2000). Heart-focused anxiety and chest pain: A conceptual and clinical review. *Clinical Psychology: Science and Practice, 7,* 403–417.

Eisenberg, N., Shepard, S. A., Fabes, R. A., Murphy, B. C., & Guthrie, I. K. (1998). Shyness and children's emotionality, regulation, and coping: Contemporaneous, longitudinal, and across-context relations. *Child Development, 69,* 767–790.

Eliason, M. J., & Amodia, D. S. (2007). An integral approach to drug craving. *Addiction Research & Theory, 15,* 343–364.

Elkis, H. (2007). Treatment-resistant schizophrenia. Psychiatric Clinics of North America, 30, 511-533.

Ellason, J. W., & Ross, C. A. (1997). Two-year follow-up of inpatients with dissociative identity disorder. *American Journal of Psychiatry, 154,* 832–839.

Ellis, A. (1962). *Reason and Emotion in Psychotherapy.* New York: Lyle Stuart.

Ellis, A. (1999). Early theories and practices of rational-emotive behavior therapy and how they have been augmented and revised during the last three decades. *Journal of Rational-Emotive and Cognitive Behavior Therapy, 17,* 69–93.

Ellis, B. J. (2004). Timing of pubertal maturation in girls: An integrated life history approach. *Psychological Bulletin, 130*(6), 920–958.

Emery, R. E. (1982). Interparental conflict and the children of discord and divorce. *Psychological Bulletin, 92,* 310–330.

Emery, R. E. (1992). Family conflict and its developmental implications: A conceptual analysis of deep meanings and systemic processes. In C. U. Shantz & W. W. Hartup (Eds.), *Conflict in Child and Adolescent Development,* pp. 270–298. London: Cambridge University Press.

Emery, R. E. (1994). *Renegotiating Family Relationships: Divorce, Child Custody, and Mediation.* New York: Guilford.

Emery, R. E. (1999a). *Marriage, Divorce, and Children's Adjustment* (2nd ed.). Thousand Oaks, CA: Sage.

Emery, R. E. (1999b). Changing the rules for determining child custody in divorce cases. *Clinical Psychology: Science and Practice, 6,* 323–327.

Emery, R. E. (2004). *The Truth About Children and Divorce: Dealing with the Emotions So You and Your Children Can Thrive.* New York: Viking/Penguin.

Emery, R. E. (in press). *Renegotiating Family Relationships.* New York: Guilford.

Emery, R. E., Fincham, F. D., & Cummings, E. M. (1992). Parenting in context: Systemic thinking about parental conflict and its influence on children. *Journal of Consulting and Clinical Psychology, 60,* 909–912.

Emery, R. E., & Laumann-Billings, L. (1998). An overview of the nature, causes, and consequences of abuse family relationships: Toward differentiating maltreatment and violence. *American Psychologist, 53,* 121–135.

Emery, R. E., & Laumann-Billings, L. (2002). In M. Rutter & E. Taylor (Eds.), *Child and Adolescent Psychiatry,* 4th ed., pp. 325–339. Oxford, England: Blackwell.

Emery, R. E., Laumann-Billings, L., Waldron, M., Sbarra, D. A., and Dillon, P. (2001). Child custody mediation and litigation: Custody, contact, and co-parenting 12 years after initial dispute resolution. *Journal of Consulting and Clinical Psychology, 69,* 323–332.

Emery, R. E., Matthews, S., & Kitzmann, K. (1994). Child custody mediation and litigation: Parents' satisfaction and functioning a year after settlement. *Journal of Consulting and Clinical Psychology, 62,* 124–129.

Emery, R. E., Otto, R. K., & O'Donohue, W. (in press). A Critical Assessment of Child Custody Evaluations: Weak Science in a Flawed System. *Psychological Science in the Public Interest.*

Emery, R. E., & Rogers, K. C. (1990). The role of behavior therapists in child custody cases. In M. Hersen & R. M. Eisler (Eds.), *Progress in Behavior Modification,* pp. 60–89. Beverly Hills, CA: Sage.

Emery, R. E., Sbarra, D. S., & Grover, T. (2005). Divorce mediation: Research and reflections. *Family Court Review, 43,* 22–37.

Emery, R. E., Waldron, M. C., Kitzmann, K. M., & Aaron, J. (1999). Delinquent behavior, future divorce or non-marital childbearing, and externalizing behavior among offspring: A 14 year prospective study. *Journal of Family Psychology, 13,* 1–12.

Emery, R. E., & Marholin, D. (1977). An applied behavior analysis of delinquency: The irrelevancy of relevant behavior. *American Psychologist, 32,* 860–873.

Emmons, R. A. (1997). Motives and goals. In R. Hogan, J. Johnson, & S. Briggs (Eds.), *Handbook of Personality Psychology,* pp. 486–512. San Diego, CA: Academic Press.

Emrick, C. D. (1999). Alcoholics anonymous and other 12-step groups. In M. Galanter & H. D. Kleber (Eds.), *Textbook of Substance Abuse Treatment,* 2nd ed., pp. 403–411. Washington, DC: American Psychiatric Press.

Ennis, B., & Emery, R. (1978). *The Rights of Mental Patients.* New York: Avon.

ENRICHD Investigators (2003). Effects of treating depression and low percieved social support on clinical events after myocardial infarction. *Journal of the American Medical Association, 289,* 3106.

Epstein, J. N., Erkanli, A., Conners, C. K., Klaric, J., Costello, J. E., & Angold, A. (2003). Relations between continuous performance test performance measures and ADHD behaviors. *Journal of Abnormal Child Psychology, 31*(5), 543–554.

Epstein, S. (1994). Integration of the cognitive and the psychodynamic unconscious. *American Psychologist, 49,* 709–724.

Erdelyi, M. H. (1990). Repression, reconstruction, and defense: History and integration of the psychoanalytic and experimental frameworks. In J. L. Singer (Ed.), *Repression and Dissociation,* pp. 1–32. Chicago: University of Chicago Press.

Erickson, C. A., Stigler, K. A., Posey, D. J., & McDougle, C. J. (2007). Psychopharmacology. In F. R. Volkmar (Ed.), *Autism and Pervasive Developmental Disorders,* pp. 221–253. New York: Cambridge University Press.

Erikson, E. H. (1950). *Childhood and Society.* New York: Norton (Rev. ed. 1963), Harmondsworth, England: Penguin.

Erikson, E. H. (1959, 1980). *Identity and the Life Cycle.* New York: Norton.

Erikson, E. H. (1963). *Childhood and Society,* rev. ed. Harmondsworth, England Penguin.

Erikson, E. H. (1968). *Identity: Youth and Crisis.* New York: Norton.

Ernulf, K. E., & Innala, S. M. (1995). Sexual bondage: A review and unobtrusive investigation. *Archives of Sexual Behavior, 24,* 631–655.

Eron, L. D. (1982). Parent-child interaction, television violence, and aggression in children. *American Psychologist, 37,* 197–211.

Esterling, B. A., L'Abate, L., Murray, E. J., & Pennebaker, J. W. (1999). Empirical foundations for writing in prevention and psychotherapy: Mental and physical health outcomes. *Clinical Psychology Review, 19,* 79–96.

Etkin, A., & Wager, T. D. (2007). Functional neuroimaging of anxiety: A meta-analysis of emotional processing in PTSD, social anxiety disorder, and specific phobia. *American Journal of Psychiatry, 164,* 1476–1488.

Eubanks-Carter, C., Burckell, L. A., & Goldfried, M. R. (2005). Enhancing therapeutic effectiveness with lesbian, gay, and bisexual clients. *Clinical Psychology: Science and Practice, 12,* 1–18.

Evans, D. L., Leserman, J., Perkins, D. O., et al. (1997). Severe life stress as a predictor of early disease progression in HIV infection. *American Journal of Psychiatry, 154,* 630–634.

Evans, G. W. (2004). The environment of childhood poverty. *American Psychologist, 59,* 7–92.

Ewing, C. (1991). Preventive detention and execution: The constitutionality of punishing future crimes. *Law and Human Behavior, 15,* 139–163.

Exner, J. E., Jr. (1993). *The Rorschach: A Comprehensive System,* Vol. 1: *Basic Foundations* (3rd ed.). New York: Wiley.

Exner, J. E., Jr. (1999). The Rorschach: Measurement concepts and issues of validity. In S. E. Embretson & S. L. Hershberger (Eds.), *The New Rules of Measurement: What Every Psychologist and Educator Should Know,* pp. 159–183. Mahwah, NJ: Erlbaum.

Eysenck, H. J. (1992). The effects of psychotherapy: An evaluation. *Journal of Consulting and Clinical Psychology, 60*(5), 659–663. Originally in *Journal of Consulting Psychology,* 1952, *16,* 319–324.

Factor, S. A. (2002). Pharmacology of atypical antipsychotics. *Clinical Neuropharmacology, 25,* 153–157.

Fagan, P. J., Wise, T. N., Schmidt, C. W., & Berlin, F. S. (2002). Pedophilia. *Journal of the American Medical Association, 288,* 2458–2465.

Faigman, D. L., & Monahan, J. (2005). Psychological evidence at the dawn of the law's scientific age. *Annual Review of Psychology, 56,* 631–659.

Faigman, D. L., Kaye, D. H., Saks, M. J., & Sanders, J. (1997). *Modern Scientific Evidence: The Law and Science of Expert Testimony.* St. Paul, MN: West.

Fairburn, C. G. (1996). *Overcoming Binge Eating.* New York: Guilford.

Fairburn, C. G. (2002). Cognitive-behavioral therapy for bulimia nervosa. In C. G. Fairburn & K. D. Brownell (Eds.), *Eating Disorders and Obesity,* 2nd ed., pp. 302–307. New York: Guilford.

Fairburn, C. G., & Beglin, S. J. (1990). Studies of the epidemiology of bulimia nervosa. *American Journal of Psychiatry, 147,* 401–480.

Fairburn, C. G., & Brownell, K. D. (Eds.), *Eating Disorders and Obesity* (2nd ed.). New York: Guilford.

Fairburn, C. G., Hay, P. J., & Welch, S. L. (1993). Binge eating and bulimia nervosa: Distribution and determinants. In C. G. Fairburn & G. T. Wilson (Eds.), *Binge Eating: Nature, Assessment, and Treatment,* pp. 123–143. New York: Guilford.

Fairburn, C. G., Jones, R., Peveler, R. C., Carr, S. J., Solomon, R. A., O'Connor, M. E., et al. (1991). Three psychological treatments for bulimia nervosa. *Archives of General Psychiatry, 48,* 463–469.

Fairburn, C. G., Jones, R., Peveler, R. C., Hope, R. A., & O'Connor, M. (1993). Psychotherapy and bulimia nervosa: Longer-term effects of interpersonal psychotherapy, behavior therapy, and cognitive behavior therapy. *Archives of General Psychiatry, 50,* 419–428.

Fairburn, C. G., Stice, E., Cooper, Z., Doll, H. A., Norman, P. A. & O'Connor, M. E. (2003). Understanding persistence in bulimia nervosa: A 5-year naturalistic study. *Journal of Consulting and Clinical Psychology, 71,* 103–109.

Fairburn, C. G., Welch, S. L., Doll, H. A., Davies, B. A., & O'Connor, M. E. (1997). Risk factors for bulimia nervosa: A community-based case-control study. *Archives of General Psychiatry, 54,* 509–517.

Fairburn, C. G., & Wilson, G. T. (Eds.). (1993). *Binge Eating: Nature, Assessment, and Treatment.* New York: Guilford.

Falk, A. J. (1999). Sex offenders, mental illness, and criminal responsibility: The constitutional boundaries of civil commitment after *Kansas v. Hendricks. American Journal of Law and Medicine, 25,* 117–147.

Falkai, P. (2008). Limitations of current therapies: Why do patients switch therapies? *European Neuropsychopharmacology, 18,* S135–S139.

Fallon, P., Katzman, M. A., & Wooley, S. C. (1994). *Feminist Perspectives on Eating Disorders.* New York: Guilford.

Fann, J. R. (2000). The epidemiology of delirium: A review of studies and methodological issues. *Seminars in Clinical Neuropsychiatry, 5,* 64–74.

Farah, M. J., O'Reilly, R. C., & Vecera, S. P. (1993). Dissociated overt and covert recognition as an emergent property of a lesioned neural network. *Psychological Review, 100,* 571–588.

Faraone, S. V. (2003). Report from the 4th international meeting of the attention deficit hyperactivity disorder molecular genetics network. *American Journal of Medical Genetics, 121B,* 55–59.

Faraone, S. V., Tsuang, M. T., & Tsuang, D. W. (1999). *Genetics of Mental Disorders.* New York: Guilford.

Faris, R. E. L., & Dunham, H. W. (1939). *Mental Disorders in Urban Areas: An Ecological Study of Schizophrenia and Other Psychoses.* Chicago: University of Chicago Press.

Farmer, A. E., McGuffin, P., & Gottesman, I. I. (1987). Twin concordance for DSM-III schizophrenia: Scrutinizing the validity of the definition. *Archives of General Psychiatry, 44,* 634–641.

Farquhar, J. W., Macoby, N., Wood, P. D., et al. (1977). Community education for cardiovascular health. *Lancet, i,* 1192–1195.

Farrer, L. A., Cupples, A., Haines, J. L., Hyman, B., Kukull, W. A., Mayeux, R., et al. (1997). Effects of age, sex, and ethnicity on the association between apolipoprotein E genotype and Alzheimer disease: A meta-analysis. *Journal of the American Medical Association. 278,* 1349–1356.

Farrington, D., Ohlin, L., & Wilson, J. Q. (1986). *Understanding and Controlling Crime.* New York: Springer.

Farrington, D. P. (2006). Family background and psychopathy. In C. J. Patrick (Ed.). *Handbook of Psychopathy,* pp. 229–250. New York: Guilford.

Faust, D., & Ziskin, J. (1988). The expert witness in psychology and psychiatry. *Science, 241,* 31–35.

Fawzy, F. I., Fawzy, N. W., Hyun, C. S., Gutherie, D., Fahey, J. L., & Morton, D. (1993). Malignant melanoma. Effects of an early structured psychiatric intervention, coping, and affective state on recurrence and survival six years later. *Archives of General Psychiatry, 50,* 681–689.

Fearon, P., & Morgan, C. (2006). Environmental Factors in Schizophrenia: The Role of Migrant Studies. *Schizophrenia Bulletin, 32,* 405–408.

Federal Bureau of Investigation. (1999). *Uniform Crime Reports, 1998.* Washington, DC: U.S. Department of Justice.

Federal Bureau of Investigation. (2004). *Uniform Crime Reports.* Washington, DC.

Fedoroff, J. P. (2003). The paraphilic world. In S. B. Levine and C. B. Risen (Eds.), *Handbook of Clinical Sexuality for Mental Health Professionals,* pp. 333–356. New York: Brunner-Routledge.

Feingold, A., & Mazzella, R. (1998). Gender differences in body image are increasing. *Psychological Science, 9,* 190–195.

Feingold, B. F. (1975). *Why Your Child Is Hyperactive.* New York: Random House.

Fenning, R. M., Baker, J. K., Baker, B. L., & Crinic, K. A. (2007). Parenting children with borderline intellectual functioning: A unique risk population. *American Journal on Mental Retardation, 112,* 107–121.

Fenton, W. S. (2000). Heterogeneity, subtypes, and longitudinal course in schizophrenia. *Psychiatric Annals, 30,* 638–644.

Fernandez, H. (1998). *Heroin.* Center City, MN: Hazeldon.

Ferster, C. B. (1961). Positive reinforcement and behavioral deficits of autistic children. *Child Development, 32,* 437–456.

Figley, C. R. (1978). *Stress Disorders Among Vietnam Veterans.* New York: Brunner/Mazel.

Fingarette, H. (1988). *Heavy Drinking: The Myth of Alcoholism as a Disease.* Berkeley: University of California Press.

Fink, H. A., MacDonald, R., Rutks, I. R., Nelson, D. B., and Wilt, T. J. (2002). Sildenafil for male erectile dysfunction: A systematic review and meta-analysis. *Archives of Internal Medicine, 162,* 1349–1360.

Finney, J. W., & Moos, R. H. (2002). Psychosocial treatments for alcohol use disorders. In P. E. Nathan & J. M. Gorman (Eds.), *A Guide to Treatments That Work,* 2nd ed., pp. 157–168. New York: Oxford.

Finney, J. W., Moos, R. H., & Humphreys, K. (1999). A comparative evaluation of substance abuse treatment. II. Linking proximal outcomes of 12-step and cognitive-behavioral treatment to substance use outcomes. *Alcoholism: Clinical and Experimental Research, 23,* 537–544.

First, M. B., Bell, C. C., Cuthbert, B., Krystal, J. H., Malison, R., Offord, D. R., et al. (2002). Personality disorders and relational disorders: A research agenda for addressing crucial gaps in DSM. In D. J. Kupfer, M. B. First, & D. A. Regier (Eds.), *A Research Agenda for DSM-V,* pp. 123–200. Washington, DC: American Psychiatric Association.

Fischer, C., Bozanovic-Sosic, R., & Norris, M. (2004). Review of delusions in dementia. *American Journal of Alzheimer's Disease & Other Dementias, 19,* 19–23.

Fischer, M., Barkley, R. A., Smallish, L., & Fletcher, K. (2002). Young adult follow-up of hyperactive children: Self-reported psychiatric disorders, comorbidity, and the role of childhood conduct problems and teen CD. *Journal of Abnormal Child Psychology, 30*(5), 463–475.

Fishbain, D. A., Cutler, R. B, Rosomoff, H. L., Rosomoff, R., & Steele, R. (1998). Do antidepressants have an analgesic effect in psychogenic pain and somatoform pain disorder? A meta-analysis. *Psychosomatic Medicine, 60,* 503–509.

Fisher, P. J., & Breakey, W. R. (1991). The epidemiology of alcohol, drug, and mental disorders among homeless persons. *American Psychologist, 46,* 1115–1128.

Fitch, S. A., & Adams, G. R. (1983). Ego-identity and intimacy status: Replication and extension. *Developmental Psychology, 19,* 839–845.

Fitch, W. L., Petrella, R. C., & Wallace, J. (1987). Legal ethics and the use of mental health experts in criminal cases. *Behavioral Sciences and the Law, 5,* 105–117.

Fitzpatrick, A. L., Kuller, L. H., Ives, D. G., Lopez, O. L., Jagust, W., Breitner, J. C. S., et al. (2004). Incidence and prevalence of dementia in the cardiovascular health study. *Journal of the American Geriatrics Society, 52,* 195–204.

Flanagan, J. C. (1982). *New Insights to Improve the Quality of Life at Age 70.* Palo Alto, CA: American Institutes for Research.

Floyd, F. J., Singer, G. H. S., Powers, L. E., & Costigan, C.L. (1996). Families coping with mental retardation; Assessment and therapy. In J. W. Jacobson & J. A. Mulick, *Manual of Diagnosis and Professional Practice in Mental Retardation,* pp. 277–288. Washington, DC: American Psychological Association.

Foa, E. B., Dancu, C. V., Hembree, E. A., Jaycox, L. H., Meadows, E. A., & Street, G. P. (1999). A comparison of exposure therapy, stress inoculation training, and their combination for reducing post-traumatic stress disorder in female assault victims. *Journal of Consulting and Clinical Psychology, 67,* 194–200.

Foa, E. B., Hembree, E. A., Cahill, S. P., Rauch, S. A. M., Riggs, D. S., Feeny, N. C., et al. (2005). Randomized trial of prolonged exposure for posttraumatic stress disorder with and without cognitive restructuring: Outcome at academic and community clinics. *Journal of Consulting and Clinical Psychology, 73,* 953–964.

Foa, E. B., & Riggs, D. S. (1995). Post traumatic stress disorder following assault: Theoretical considerations and empirical findings. *Current Directions in Psychological Science, 5,* 61–65.

Foa, E. B., & Street, G. P. (2001). Women and traumatic events. *Journal of Clinical Psychiatry, 62* 29–34.

Foa, E. B., & Wilson, R. (2001). *Stop Obsessing: How to Overcome Your Obsessions and Compulsions* (Rev. ed.). New York: Bantam Doubleday.

Foa, E. B., Rothbaum, B. O., Riggs, D. S., Murdock, T. B. (1991). Treatment of posttraumatic stress disorder in rape victims: A comparison between cognitive-behavioral procedures and counseling. *Journal of Consulting and Clinical Psychology, 59*(5), 715–723.

Foa, E. B., Zoellner, L. A., Feeny, N. C., Hembree, E. A., & Alvarez-Conrad, J. (2002). Does imaginal exposure exacerbate PTSD symptoms? *Journal of Consulting and Clinical Psychology, 70,* 1022–1028.

Folkman, S., & Moskowitz, J. T. (2000). Stress, positive emotion, and coping. *Current Directions in Psychological Science, 9,* 115–118.

Fombonne, E. (2007). Epidemiological surveys of pervasive developmental disorders. In F. R. Volkmar (Ed.), *Autism and Pervasive Developmental Disorders,* pp. 33–68. New York: Cambridge University Press.

Fonagy, P., & Bateman, A. (2008). The development of borderline personality disorder—a mentalizing model. *Journal of Personality Disorders, 22,* 4–21.

Foot, P. (1990). Ethics and the death penalty: Participation of forensic psychiatrists in capital trials. In R. Rosner & R. Weinstock (Eds.), *Ethical Practice in Psychiatry and the Law,* pp. 202–217. New York: Plenum.

Fordyce, W. E. (1976). *Behavioral Methods for Chronic Pain and Illness.* St. Louis, MO: Mosby.

Forehand, R., & Long, N. (2002). *Parenting the Strong-willed Child.* New York: McGraw-Hill.

Foreman, M. C., Wakefield, B., Culp, K., & Milisen, K. (2001). Delirium in elderly patients: An overview of the state of the science. *Journal of Gerontological Nursing, 27,* 12–20.

Fornari, V., Wlodarczyk-Bisaga, K., Matthews, M., Sandberg, D., Mandel, F. S., & Katz, J. L. (1999). Perception of family functioning and depressive symptomatology in individuals with anorexia nervosa or bulimia nervosa. *Comprehensive Psychiatry, 40,* 434–444.

Forrest, K. A. (2001). Toward an etiology of dissociative identity disorder: A neurodevelopmental approach. *Consciousness and Cognition, 10,* 259–293.

Fountoulakis, K. N., Thessaloniki, T., Grunze, H., Panagiotidis, P., & Kaprinis, G. (2008). Treatment of bipolar depression: An update. *Journal of Affective Disorders, 109,* 21–34.

Fournier, J. C., DeRubeis, R. J., Shelton, R. C., Gallop, R., Amsterdam, J. D., & Hollon, S. D. (2008). Antidepressant medications v. cognitive therapy in people with depression with or without personality disorder. *British Journal of Psychiatry, 192,* 124–129.

Fowles, D. C., & Dindo, L. (2006). A dual-deficit model of psychopathy. In C. J. Patrick (Ed.), *Handbook of Psychopathy,* pp. 14–34. New York: Guilford.

Fox, P. J., Kelly, S. E., & Tobin, S. L. (1999). Defining dementia: Social and historical background of Alzheimer disease. *Genetic Testing, 3,* 13–19.

Fozard, J. L., & Gordon-Salant, S. (2001). Changes in vision and hearing with aging. In J. E. Birren & K. W. Schaie (Eds.), *Handbook of the Psychology of Aging,* 5th ed., pp. 241–266. San Diego, CA: Academic Press.

Frances, A., First, M. B., & Pincus, H. A. (1995). *DSM-IV Guidebook.* Washington, DC: American Psychiatric Press.

Frank, E. (2005). *Treating Bipolar Disorder: A Clinician's Guide to Interpersonal and Social Rhythm Therapy.* New York: Guilford.

Frank, E., & Thase, M. E. (1999). Natural history and preventative treatment of recurrent mood disorders. *Annual Review of Medicine, 50,* 453–468.

Frank, J. D. (1973). *Persuasion and Healing: A Comparative Study of Psychotherapy,* Baltimore, MD: Johns Hopkins University Press.

Franklin, J. A., & Andrews, G. (1989). Stress and the onset of agoraphobia. *Australian Psychologist, 24,* 203–219.

Franklin, M. E., & Foa, E. B. (2002). Cognitive behavioral treatments for obsessive compulsive disorder. In P. E. Nathan and J. M. Gorman (Eds.), *A Guide to Treatments That Work,* 2nd ed. London: Oxford University Press.

Frasure-Smith, N. & Lespérance, F. (2005). Depression and coronary heart disease: Complex synergism of mind, body, and environment. *Current Directions in Psychological Science, 14,* 39–43.

Frasure-Smith, N., & Prince, R. (1985). Long-term follow-up of the ischemic heart disease life stress monitoring program. *Psychosomatic Medicine, 51,* 485–513.

Frattaroli, J. (2006). Experimental disclosure and its moderators: A meta-analysis. Psychological *Bulletin, 132,* 823–865.

Fredrickson, B. L., & Losada, M. (2005). Positive emotions and the complex dynamics of human flourishing. *American Psychologist, 60,* 678–686.

Freud, S. (1917/1961). Mourning and melancholia. In J. Strachey (Ed. and Trans.), *The Standard Edition of the Complete Psychological Works of Sigmund Freud,* Vol. 14. London: Hogarth Press.

Freud, S. (1924/1962). The aetiology of hysteria. In J. Strachey (Ed. and Trans.), *The Standard Edition of the Complete Psychological Works of Sigmund Freud,* Vol. 3, pp. 191–221. London: Hogarth Press.

Freund, A. M., & Baltes, P. B. (2002). Life-management strategies of selection, optimization, and compensation: Measurement by self-report and construct validity. *Journal of Personality and Social Psychology, 82,* 642–662.

Freund, K., & Blanchard, R. (1993). Erotic target location errors in male gender dysphorics, paedophiles, and fetishists. *British Journal of Psychiatry, 162,* 558–563.

Freund, K., & Seto, M. C. (1998). Preferential rape in the theory of courtship disorder. *Archives of Sexual Behavior, 27,* 433–445.

Frick, P. J., Bodin, S. D., & Barry, C. T. (2000). Psychopathic traits and conduct problems in community and clinic-referred samples of children: Further development of the psychopathy screening device. *Psychological Assessment, 12,* 382–393.

Friedman, M., & Rosenman, R. H. (1959). Association of specific overt behavior pattern with blood and cardiovascular findings: Blood cholesterol level, blood clotting time, incidence of arcus senilis and clinical coronary artery disease. *Journal of the American Medical Association, 169,* 1286–1296.

Friedman, M., Thoresen, C. D., Gill, J. J., et al. (1986). Alteration of Type A behavior and its effect on cardiac recurrences in post-myocardial infarction patients: Summary results of the recurrent coronary prevention project. *American Heart Journal, 112,* 653–665.

Friedman, R. A., & Leon, A. C. (2007). Expanding the black box—Depression, antidepressants, and the risk of suicide. *New England Journal of Medicine, 356,* 2343–2346.

Fries, J. F. (1990). Medical perspectives upon successful aging. In P. B. Baltes & M. M. Baltes (Eds.), *Successful Aging: Perspectives from the Behavioral Sciences,* pp. 35–49. Cambridge: Cambridge University Press.

Frith, C., & Dolan, R. J. (2000). The role of memory in the delusions associated with schizophrenia. In D. L. Schacter and E. Scarry (Eds.), *Memory, Brain, and Belief,* pp. 115–135. Cambridge, MA: Harvard University Press.

Frith, U. (2003). *Autism: Explaining the Enigma* (2nd ed.). Oxford, England: Blackwell.

Froehlich, J. (1997). Opioid peptides. *Alcohol Health & Research World, 21,* 132–136.

Froehlich, J. C. (1997). Opioid peptides. *Alcohol Health and Research World, 21,* 144–148.

Frueh, B. C., Turner, S. M., & Beidel, D. C. (1995). Exposure therapy for combat-related PTSD: A critical review. *Clinical Psychology Review, 15,* 799–817.

Fuller, R. K., & Gordis, E. (2004). Does disulfiram have a role in alcoholism treatment today? *Addiction, 99,* 115–135, 21–24.

Funtowicz, M. N., & Widiger, T. A. (1999). Sex bias in the diagnosis of personality disorders: An evaluation of DSM-IV criteria. *Journal of Abnormal Psychology, 108,* 195–201.

Furr, R. M., & Funder, D. C. (2007). Behavioral observation. In R. C. Fraley and R. F. Krueger (Eds.), *Handbook of Research Methods in Personality Psychology,* pp. 273–291. New York: Guilford.

Furstenberg, F. F. (2000). The sociology of adolescence and youth in the 1990s: A critical commentary. *Journal of Marriage and the Family, 62,* 896–910.

Gabbard, G. O. (2000). Psychodynamic psychotherapy of borderline personality disorder: A contemporary approach. *Bulletin of the Menninger Clinic, 65,* 41–57.

Gabbard, G. O. (2001). Musings on the report of the international consensus development conference on female sexual dysfunction: Definitions and classification. *Journal of Sex and Marital Therapy, 27,* 145–147.

Gadde, K. M., & Krishman, R. R. (1997). Recent advances in the pharmacologic treatment of bipolar illness. *Psychiatric Annals, 27,* 496–506.

Galea, S., Ahern, J., Resnick, H., Kilpatrick, D., Bucuvalas, M., Gold, J., et al. (2002). Psychological sequelae of the September 11 terrorist attacks. *New England Journal of Medicine, 346,* 982–987.

Galea, S., Boscarino, J., Resnick, H., & Vlahov, D. (2003). Mental health in New York City after September 11 terrorist attacks: Results from two population surveys. In R. W. Manderscheid & M. J. Henderson (Eds.), *Mental Health, United States, 2002.* Washington, DC: U.S. Government Printing Office.

Galea, S., Vlahov, D., Resnick, H., Ahern, J., Susser, E., Gold, J., et al. (2003). Trends of probable posttraumatic stress disorder in New York City after the September 11 terrorist attacks. *American Journal of Epidemiology, 158,* 514–524.

Gallagher-Thompson, D., & Osgood, N. J. (1997). Suicide in later life. *Behavior Therapy, 28,* 23–41.

Gallagher, N., South, S., & Oltmanns, T. (2003). Attentional coping style obsessive-compulsive personality disorder: A test of the intolerance of uncertainty hypothesis. *Personality and Individual Differences, 34,* 41–57.

Garb, H. N. (2005). Clinical judgment and decision making. *Annual Review of Clinical Psychology, 1,* 67–89.

Garb, H. N., Klein, D. F., & Grove, W. M. (2002). Comparison of medical and psychological tests. *American Psychologist, 57,* 13–138.

Garb, H. N., Wood, J. M., Lilienfeld, S. O., & Nezworski, M. T. (2005). Roots of the Rorschach controversy. *Clinical Psychology Review, 25,* 97–118.

Garber, H. I. (1988). *The Milwaukee Project: Preventing Mental Retardation in Children at Risk.* Washington, DC: American Association on Mental Retardation.

Garber, J. (1984). Classification of childhood psychopathology: A developmental perspective. *Child Development, 55,* 30–48.

Garber, J., & Hollon, S. D. (1991). What can specificity designs say about causality in psychopathology research? *Psychological Bulletin, 110,* 129–136.

Garber, J., Keiley, M. K., & Martin, N. C. (2002). Developmental trajectories of adolescents' depressive symptoms: Predictors of change. *Journal of Consulting and Clinical Psychology, 70*(1), 79–95.

Gardner, F., Shaw, D. S., Dishion, T. J., Burton, J., & Supplee, L. (2007). Randomized prevention trial for early conduct problems: Effects on proactive parenting and links to toddler disruptive behavior. *Journal of Family Psychology, 21,* 398–406.

Garfinkel, P. E., & Garner, D. M. (1982). *Anorexia Nervosa: A Multidimensional Perspective.* New York: Basic Books.

Garfinkel, P. E., Kennedy, S. H., & Kaplan, A. S. (1995). Views on classification and diagnosis of eating disorders. *Canadian Journal of Psychiatry, 40,* 445–456.

Garfinkel, P. E., Lin, B., & Goering, P. (1996). Purging and nonpurging forms of bulimia nervosa in a community sample. *International Journal of Eating Disorders.*

Garmezy, N. (1978). DSM-III: Never mind the psychologists; Is it good for the children? *Clinical Psychologist, 31,* 1–6.

Garmezy, N., & Rutter, M. (Eds.) (1983). *Stress, Coping, and Development in Children.* New York: McGraw-Hill.

Garner, D. M., & Bemis, K. M. (1982). A cognitive-behavioral approach to anorexia nervosa. *Cognitive Therapy and Research, 6,* 123–150.

Garner, D. M., Garfinkel, P. E., Schwartz, D., & Thompson, M. (1980). Cultural expectations of thinness in women. *Psychological Reports, 47,* 483–491.

Garner, D. M., Garner, M. V., & Rosen, L. W. (1993). Anorexia nervosa "restrictors" who purge: Implications for subtyping anorexia nervosa. *International Journal of Eating Disorders, 13,* 171–185.

Garner, D. M., & Needleman, L. D. (1996). Stepped-care and decision-tree models for treating eating disorders. In J. K. Thompson, *Body Image, Eating Disorders, and Obesity,* pp. 225–252. Washington, DC: American Psychological Association.

Garner, D. M., Olmstead, M. P., & Polivy, J. (1983). The Eating Disorder Inventory: A measure of cognitive-behavioral dimensions of anorexia nervosa and bulimia. In P. L. Darby, P. E. Garfinkel, D. M. Garner, & D. V. Coscina (Eds.), *Anorexia Nervosa: Recent Developments in Research,* pp. 173–184. New York: Liss.

Garratt, G., Ingram, R. E., Rand, K. L., & Sawalani, G. (2007). Cognitive processes in cognitive therapy: Evaluation of the mechanisms of change in the treatment of depression. *Clinical Psychology: Science and Practice, 14,* 224–239.

Garssen, B., de Ruiter, C., & Van Dyck, R. (1992). Breathing retraining: A rational placebo? *Clinical Psychology Review, 12,* 141–153.

Gatchel, R. J., Peng, Y. B., Peters, M. L., Fuchs, P. N., & Turk, D. C. (2007). The biopsychosocial approach to chronic pain: Scientific advances and future directions. *Psychological Bulletin, 133,* 581–624.

Gatz, M., & Smyer, M. A. (2001). Mental health and aging at the outset of the twenty-first century. In J. E. Birren & K. W. Schaie (Eds.), *Handbook of the Psychology of Aging,* 5th ed., pp. 523–544. San Diego, CA: Academic Press.

Gaulin, S. J. C., & McBurney, D. H. (2001). *Psychology: An Evolutionary Approach.* Upper Saddle River, NJ: Prentice-Hall.

Geddes, J. R., Burgess, S., Hawton, K., Jamison, K., & Goodwin, G. M. (2004). Long-term lithium therapy for bipolar disorder: Systematic review and metaanalysis of randomized controlled studies. *American Journal of Psychiatry, 161,* 217–222.

Gehlbach, S. H. (1988). *Interpreting the Medical Literature: Practical Epidemiology for Clinics* (2nd ed.). New York: Macmillan.

Geraerts, E., Schooler, J. W., Merckelbach, H., Jelicic, M., Hauer, B. J. A., & Ambadar, Z. (2007). The reality of recovered memories: Corroborating continuous and discontinuous memories of childhood sexual abuse. *Psychological Science, 18,* 564–568.

Gershoff, E. T. (2002). Corporal punishment by parents and associated child behaviors and experience: A meta-analytic and theoretical review. *Psychological Bulletin, 128,* 539–579.

Ghanem, H., & El-Sakka, A. (2007). Sex and Sexual Dysfunctions in the Middle Eastern Culture. *Sexual Health,* Vol. 3: *Moral and Cultural Foundations,* pp. 279–295. Westport, CT: Praeger Publishers/Greenwood Publishing Group.

Ghisletta, P., & Lindenberger, U. (2003). Age-based structural dynamics between perceptual speed and knowledge in the Berlin Aging Study: Direct evidence for ability dedifferentiation in old age. *Psychology and Aging, 18,* 696–713.

Gianoulakis, C., DeWaele, J. P., & Thavundayil, J. (1996). Implications of the endogenous opioid system in excessive ethanol consumption. *Alcohol, 13,* 19–23.

Gibbons, R. D., Brown, C. H., Hur, K., Marcus, S. M., Bhaumik, D. K., & Mann, J. J. (2007). Relationship between antidepressants and suicide attempts: An analysis of the Veterans Health Administration data sets. *American Journal of Psychiatry, 164,* 1044–1049.

Gibbs, N. A., South, S. C., & Oltmanns, T. F. (2002). Attentional coping style in obsessive-compulsive personality disorder: A test of the intolerance of uncertainty hypothesis. *Personality and Individual Differences, 33,* 1205–1222.

Gilbert, P. (2001). Evolutionary approaches to psychopathology: The role of natural defences. *Australian and New Zealand Journal of Psychiatry, 35,* 17–27.

Gilbert, P. (2006). Evolution and depression: Issues and implications. *Psychological Medicine, 36,* 287–297.

Gilbertson, M. W., et al. (2002). Smaller hippocampal predicts pathologic vulnerability to psychological trauma. *Nature Neuroscience, 5,* 1242–1247.

Gilbertson, M. W., Paulus, L. A., Williston, S. K., Gurvits, T. V., Lasko, N. B., Pitman, R. K., et al. (2006). Neurocognitive function in monozygotic twins discordant for combat exposure: Relationship to posttraumatic stress disorder. *Journal of Abnormal Psychology, 115,* 484–495.

Gillberg, C. (1988). The role of the endogenous opioids in autism and possible relationships to clinical features. In L. Wing (Ed.), *Aspects of Autism: Biological Research,* pp. 31–37. London: Gaskell.

Gillberg, C. (1991). Outcome in autism and autistic-like conditions. *Journal of the American Academy of Child & Adolescent Psychiatry, 30*(3).

Gillberg, C., Rastam, M., & Gillberg, C. (1995). Anorexia nervosa 6 years after onset. I. Personality disorders. *Comprehensive Psychiatry, 36,* 61–69.

Gillberg, C., & Schaumann, H. (1982). Social class and infantile autism. *Journal of Autism and Developmental Disorders, 12,* 223–228.

Gilligan, C. (1982). *In a Different Voice.* Cambridge, MA: Harvard University Press.

Gladis, M. M., Gosch, E. A., Dishuk, N. M., Crits-Christoph, P. (1999). Quality of life: Expanding the scope of clinical significance. *Journal of Consulting and Clinical Psychology, 6,* 320–331.

Glaser, D. (2002). Child sexual abuse. In M. Rutter & E. Taylor (Eds.), *Child and Adolescent Psychiatry,* 4th ed., pp. 340–358. Oxford, England: Blackwell.

Glatt, S. J., Faraone, S. V., & Tsuang, M. T. (2003). Association between a functional catechol o-methyltransferase gene polymorphism and schizophrenia: Meta-analysis of case-control and family-based studies. *American Journal of Psychiatry, 160,* 469–476.

Gleaves, D. H. (1996). The sociocognitive model of dissociative identity disorder: A reexamination of the evidence. *Psychological Bulletin, 120,* 42–59.

Gleaves, D. H., Smith, S. M., Butler, L. D., & Spiegel, D. (2004). False and recovered memories in the laboratory and clinic: A review of experiment and clinical evidence. *Clinical Psychology: Science & Practice, 11,* 3–28.

Gold, M. S., Tabrah, H., & Frost-Pineda, K. (2001). Psychopharmacology of MDMA (Ecstasy). *Psychiatric Annals, 31,* 675–681.

Gold, S. N., & Heffner, C. L. (1998). Sexual addiction: Many conceptions, minimal data. *Clinical Psychology Review, 18,* 367–381.

Goldberg, J., True, W. R., Eisen, S. A., & Henderson, W. G. (1990). A twin study of the effects of the Vietnam War on posttraumatic stress disorder. *Journal of the American Medical Association, 263,* 2725–2729.

Goldberg, J. F., & Truman, C. J. (2003). Antidepressant-induced mania: An overview of current controversies. *Bipolar Disorders, 5,* 407–420.

Goldberg, T. E., & Weinberger, D. R. (1995). A case against subtyping in schizophrenia. *Schizophrenia Research, 17,* 147–152.

Goldman, M. S., Darkes, J., & Del Boca, F. K. (1999). Expectancy mediation of biopsychosocial risk for alcohol use and alcoholism. In I. Kirsch (Ed.), *How Expectancies Shape Experience*, pp. 233–262. Washington, DC: American Psychological Association.

Goldman-Rakic, P. S., Muly, E. C., & Williams, G. V. (2000). D1 receptors in prefrontal cells and circuits. *Brain Research Review, 31,* 295–301.

Goldsmith, S. K. (2001). *Risk Factors for Suicide.* Washington, DC: National Academy Press.

Goldstein, A. J., & Chambless, D. L. (1978). A reanalysis of agoraphobia. *Behavior Therapy, 9,* 47–59.

Goldstein, G. (2003). Delirium, dementia, and amnestic and other cognitive disorders. In M. Hersen & S. M. Turner (Eds.), *Adult Psychopathology and Diagnosis,* 4th ed., pp. 153–191. New York: Wiley.

Goldstein, I. (2004). Epidemiology of erectile dysfunction. *Sexuality & Disability, 22,* 113–120.

Goldstein, J. J., Rosenfarb, I., Woo, S., & Nuechterlein, K. (1997). Transactional processes which can function as risk or protective factors in the family treatment of schizophrenia. In H. D. Brenner and W. Boeker (Eds.), *Towards a Comprehensive Therapy for Schizophrenia,* pp. 147–157. Kirkland, WA: Hogrefe & Huber.

Goldstein, M. J. (1988). The family and psychopathology. *Annual Review of Psychology, 39,* 283–299.

Golier, J. A., Legge, J., & Yehuda, R. (2007). Pharmacological treatment of posttraumatic stress disorder. In P. E. Nathan & J. M. Gorman (Eds.), *A Guide to Treatments That Work,* 3rd ed., pp. 475–512. New York: Oxford University Press.

Golub, E. S. (1994). *The Limits of Medicine: How Science Shapes Our Hope for the Cure.* New York: Random House.

Golwyn, D. H., & Sevlie, C. P. (1992). Paraphilias, nonparaphilic sexual addictions, and social phobia. *Journal of Clinical Psychiatry, 53,* 330.

Good, B., & Kleinman, A. (1985). Culture and anxiety: Cross-cultural evidence for the patterning of anxiety disorders. In A. H. Tuma & J. Maser (Eds.), *Anxiety and the Anxiety Disorders.* Hillsdale, NJ: Erlbaum.

Gooding, D. G., Miller, M. D., & Kwapil, T. R. (2000). Smooth pursuit eye tracking and visual fixation in psychosis-prone individuals. *Psychiatry Research, 93,* 41–54.

Goodman, G. S., Ghetti, S., Quas, J. A., Edelstein, R. S., Alexander, K. W., Redlich, A. D., et al. (2003). A prospective study of memory for child sexual abuse: New findings relevant to the repressed-memory controversy. *Psychological Science, 14,* 113–118.

Goodman, L. A., Koss, M. P., Fitzgerald, L. F., Russo, N. F., & Keita, G. P. (1993). Male violence against women: Current research and future directions. *American Psychologist, 48,* 1054–1058.

Goodman, L. A., Koss, M. P., & Russo, N. F. (1993). Violence against women: Physical and mental health effects. Part I. Research findings. *Applied and Preventive Psychology, 2,* 79–89.

Goodman, S. H., & Gotlib, I. H. (1999). Risk for psychopathology in the children of depressed mothers: A developmental model for understanding mechanisms of transmission. *Psychological Review, 106*(3), 458–490.

Goodman, T. A. (1985). From Tarasoff to Hopper: The evolution of the therapist's duty to protect third parties. *Behavioral Sciences and the Law, 3,* 195–225.

Goodman, W. K., Price, L. H., Rasmussen, S. A., Mazure, C., Fleischman, R. L., Hill, C. L., et al. (1989). The Yale-Brown Obsessive-Compulsive Scale. 1. Development, use, and reliability. *Archives of General Psychiatry, 46,* 1006–1011.

Goodwin, D. W. (1991). The genetics of alcoholism. In P. R. McHugh & V. A. McKusick (Eds.), *Genes, Brain, and Behavior.* New York: Raven Press.

Goodwin, P. J., et al. (2001). The Effect of Group Psychosocial Support on Survival in Metastatic Breast Cancer. *New England Journal of Medicine, 345,* 1719–1726.

Gordis, L. (2004). *Epidemiology* (3rd ed.). Philadelphia: Elsevier Saunders.

Gosselin, C. C., & Wilson, G. D. (1980). *Sexual Variations.* London: Faber & Faber.

Gotlib, I. H., & Hamilton, J. P. (2008). Neuroimaging and depression: Current status and unresolved issues. *Current Directions in Psychological Science, 17,* 159–163.

Gotlib, I. H., & Hammen, C. (1992). *Psychological Aspects of Depression: Toward a Cognitive-Interpersonal Integration.* New York: Wiley.

Gotlib, I. H., Joormann, J., Minor, K. L, & Hallmaer, J. (2008). HPA axis reactivity: A mechanism underlying the associations among 5-HTLPR, stress, and depression. *Biological Psychiatry, 63,* 847–851.

Gotlib, I. H., & Neubauer, D. L. (2000). Information-processing approaches to the study of cognitive biases in depression. In S. L. Johnson & A. M. Hayes (Eds.), *Stress, Coping, and Depression,* pp. 117–143. Mahwah, NJ: Erlbaum.

Gottesman, I. G. (1963). Genetic aspects of intelligent behavior. In N. Ellis (Ed.), *The Handbook of Mental Deficiency: Psychological Theory and Research,* pp. 253–296. New York: McGraw-Hill.

Gottesman, I. I. (1987). The psychotic hinterlands or, the fringes of lunacy. *British Medical Bulletin, 43,* 1–13.

Gottesman, I. I. (1991). *Schizophrenia Genesis: The Origins of Madness.* New York: Freeman.

Gottesman, I. I., & Goldsmith, H. H. (1994). Developmental psychopathology of antisocial behavior: Inserting genes into its ontogenesis and epigenesis. In C. A. Nelson (Ed.), *Threats to Optimal Development: Integrating Biological, Psychological, and Social Risk Factors,* pp. 69–104. Hillsdale, NJ: Erlbaum.

Gottesman, I. I., & Gould, T. D. (2003). The endophenotype concept in psychiatry: Etymology and strategic intentions. *American Journal of Psychiatry, 160,* 636–645.

Gottesman, I. I., & Hanson, D. R. (2005). Human development: Biological and genetic processes. *Annual Review of Psychology, 56,* 10.1–10.24.

Gottman, J., Notarius, C., Gonso, J., & Markman, H. (1976). *A Couple's Guide to Communication.* Champaign, IL: Research Press.

Gottman, J. M. (1994). *Why Marriages Succeed or Fail.* New York: Simon & Schuster.

Gottman, J. M. (1999). *The Marriage Clinic: A Scientifically Based Marital Therapy.* New York: Norton.

Gottman, J. M. (1997). *Why Marriages Succeed or Fail: And How You Can Make Yours Last.* London: Bloomsbury, 1997.

Gottman, J. M., & Katz, L. F. (1989). Effects of marital discord on young children's peer interaction and health. *Developmental Psychology, 25,* 373–381.

Gottman, J. M., & Levenson, R. W. (1986). Assessing the role of emotion in marriage. *Behavioral Assessment, 8,* 31–48.

Gottman, J. M., & Levenson, R. W. (1988). The social psychophysiology of marriage. In P. Noller & M. A. Fitzpatrick (Eds.), *Perspectives on Marital Interaction,* pp. 182–200. Clevedon, England: Multilingual Matters.

Gottman, J. M., & Notarius, C. I. (2000). Decade review: Observing marital interaction. *Journal of Marriage and the Family, 62,* 927–947.

Gove, W. R. (1990). Labeling theory's explanation of mental illness: An update of recent evidence. In M. Nagler (Ed.), *Perspectives on Disability.* Palo Alto, CA: Health Markets Research.

Grabe, S., & Shibley-Hyde, J. (2006). Ethnicity and body dissatisfaction among women in the United States: A meta-analysis. *Psychological Bulletin, 132,* 622–640.

Grandin, T. (1995). *Thinking in Pictures: And Other Reports from My Life with Autism,* with a foreword by Oliver Sacks. New York: Vintage Books.

Grant, B. F., Stinson, F. S., Dawson, D. A., Chous, S. P., Dufour, M. C., Compton, W., et al. (2004). Prevalence and co-occurrence of substance use disorders and independent mood and anxiety disorders: Results from the national epidemiologic survey on alcohol and related conditions. *Archives of General Psychiatry, 61,* 807–816.

Grant, B. F., Stinson, F. S., Dawson, D. A., Chous, S. P., & Ruan, W. J. (2005). Co-occurrence of DSM-IV personality disorders in the United States: Results from the National Epidemiologic Survey on Alcohol and Related Conditions. *Comprehensive Psychiatry, 46,* 1–5.

Grant, B. F., Stinson, F .S., Dawson, D. A., Chous, S. P., Dufour, M. C., Compton, W., Pickering, R. P., & Kaplan, K. (2006). Prevalence and co-occurrence of substance use disorders and independent mood and anxiety disorders: Results from the National Epidemiologic Survey on Alcohol and Related Conditions. *Alcohol Research & Health, 29,* 107–120.

Grant, J. E., & Potenza, M. N. (2006). Compulsive aspects of impulse-control disorders. *Psychiatric Clinics of North America, 29,* 539–551.

Grant, William T., Foundation. (1988). *The Forgotten Half: Pathways to Success for America's Youth and Young Families.* Washington, DC: Youth and America's Future: William T. Grant Foundation Commission on Work, Family and Citizenship.

Grasel, E. (1997). Temporary institutional respite in dementia cases: Who utilizes this form of respite care and what effect does it have? *International Psychogeriatrics, 9,* 437–448.

Gratzer, T., & Bradford, J. M. W. (1995). Offender and offense characteristics of sexual sadists: A comparative study. *Journal of Forensic Sciences, 40,* 450–455.

Graves, A. B., et al. (1999). Cognitive decline and Japanese culture in a cohort of older Japanese-Americans in King County, WA: The Kame Project. *Journals of Gerontology Series B-Psychological Sciences and Social Sciences, 54B,* S154–S161.

Gray, J., & Roth, B. (2007). The pipeline and future of drug development in schizophrenia. *Molecular Psychiatry, 12,* 904–922.

Grawe, R., Falloon, I., Widen, J., & Skogvoll, E. (2006). Two years of continued early treatment for recent-onset schizophrenia: A randomised controlled study. *Acta Psychiatrica Scandinavica, 114,* 328–336.

Greaves, G. B. (1980). Multiple personality disorder: 165 years after Mary Reynolds. *Journal of Nervous and Mental Disease, 168,* 577–596.

Green, B. L., Epstein, S. A., Krupnick, J. L., & Rowland, J. H. (1997). Trauma and medical illness: Assessing trauma-related disorders in medical settings. In J. P. Wilson & T. M. Keane (Eds.), *Assessing Psychological Trauma and PTSD.* New York: Guilford.

Green, M. F. (2001). *Schizophrenia Revealed: From Neurons to Social Interactions.* New York: Norton.

Green, M. F., Nuechterlein, K. H., Gold, J. M., Barch, D. M., Cohen, J., Essock, S., et al. (2004). Approaching a consensus cognitive battery for clinical trials in schizophrenia: The NIMH-MATRICS conference to select cognitive domains and test criteria. *Biological Psychiatry, 56,* 301–307.

Greenberg, R. P., Bornstein, R. F., Zborowski, M. J., Fisher, S., & Greenberg, M. D. (1994). A meta-analysis of fluoxetine outcome in the treatment of depression. *Journal of Nervous and Mental Disease, 182,* 547–551.

Greene, R. W., et al. (2001). Social impairment in girls with ADHD: Patterns, gender comparisons, and correlates. *Journal of the American Academy of Child and Adolescent Psychiatry, 40,* 704–710.

Greene, R. L. (2006). Use of the MMPI-2 in outpatient mental health settings. In J. N. Butcher (Ed.),

MMPI-2: A Practitioner's Guide, pp. 253–271. Washington, DC: American Psychological Association.

Greenley, J. R. (1995). Madison, Wisconsin, United States: Creation and implementation of the Program of Assertive Community Treatment (PACT). In R. Schulz & J. R. Greenley (Eds.), *Innovating in Community Mental Health: International Perspectives*, pp. 83–96. Westport, CT: Praeger.

Greenspan, S. & Switzky, H.N. (2007). Lessons from the Atkins decision for the next AAMR manual. In H. N. Switzky & S. Greenspan (Eds.), *What is Mental Retardation? Ideas for and Evolving Disability in the 21st Century*, pp. 281–300. Washington: AAIDD.

Griffin, M. G., Resick, P. A., & Mechanic, M. B. (1997). Objective assessment of peritraumatic dissociation: Psychophysiological indicators. *American Journal of Psychiatry, 154*, 1081–1088.

Grilo, C. M., Shea, M. T., Sanislow, C. A., Skodol, A. E., Gunderson, J. G., Stout, R. L., et al. (2004). Two-year stability and change of schizotypal, borderline, avoidant, and obsessive-compulsive personality disorders. *Journal of Consulting and Clinical Psychology, 72*, 767–775.

Grisso, T., & Appelbaum, P. S. (1992). Is it unethical to offer predictions of future violence? *Law and Human Behavior, 16*, 621–633.

Grob, G. N. (1994). *The Mad Among US: A History of the Care of America's Mentally Ill*. New York: Free Press.

Grossman, H. J. (1983). *Classification in Mental Retardation*. Washington, DC: American Association on Mental Deficiency.

Group for the Advancement of Psychiatry. (1966). *Psychopathological Disorders of Childhood: Theoretical Considerations and a Proposed Classification. Report 62*. New York: Mental Health Memorials Center.

Group for the Advancement of Psychiatry. (1995). A model for the classification and diagnosis of relational disorders. *Psychiatric Services, 46*, 926–931.

Grove, A. S. (1996). *Only the Paranoid Survive: How to Exploit the Crisis Points That Challenge Every Company*. New York: Doubleday.

Grych, J. H., & Fincham, F. D. (1990). Marital conflict and children's adjustment: A cognitive-contextual framework. *Psychological Bulletin, 101*, 267–290.

Guarnaccia, P., & Pincay, I. M. (2008). Culture-specific diagnoses and their relationship to mood disorders (pp. 32–53). In S. Loue and M. Sajatovic (Eds.), *Diversity Issues in the Diagnosis, Treatment and Research of Mood Disorders*, pp. 32–53. New York: Oxford University Press.

Guarnaccia, P. J. (1996). The experiences of ataques de nervios: Towards an anthropology of emotions in Puerto Rico. *Culture, Medicine and Psychiatry, 20*, 343–367.

Guarnaccia, P. J. (1997). A cross-cultural perspective on anxiety disorders. In S. Friedman (Ed.), *Cultural Issues in the Treatment of Anxiety*, pp. 3–20. New York: Guilford.

Gunderson, J. (1984). *Borderline Personality Disorder*. Washington, DC: American Psychiatric Press.

Gunderson, J. G. (1994). Building structure for the borderline construct. *Acta Psychiatrica Scandinavica, 89* (Suppl. 379), 12–18.

Gupta, N., de Jonghe, J., Schieveld, J., Leonard, M., & Meagher, D. (2008). Delirium phenomenology: What can we learn from the symptoms of delirium?. *Journal of Psychosomatic Research, 65*, 215–222.

Gureje, O., Simon, G. E., Ustun, T. B., & Goldberg, D. P. (1997). Somatization in cross-cultural perspective: A world health organization study in primary care. *American Journal of Psychiatry, 154*, 989–995.

Gurman, A. S., & Jacobson, N. S. (2002). *Clinical Handbook of Couple Therapy*, 3rd ed. New York: Guilford.

Gusella, J. F., Wexler, N. S., Conneally, P. M., Naylor, S. L., Anderson, M. A., Tanzi, R. E., et al. (1983). A polymorphic DNA marker genetically linked to Huntington's disease. *Nature, 306*, 234–238.

Gutheil, T. G. (1986). The right to refuse treatment: Paradox, pendulum and the quality of care. *Behavioral Sciences and the Law, 4*, 265–277.

Gutierrez-Lobos, K., Schmid-Siegel, B., Bankier, B., & Walter, H. (2001). Delusions in first-admitted patients: Gender, themes, and diagnoses. *Psychopathology, 34*, 1–7.

Guzder, J., Paris, J., Zelkowitz, P., & Marchessault, K. (1996). Risk factors for borderline psychology in children. *Journal of the American Academy of Child and Adolescent Psychiatry, 35*, 26–33.

Haefner, H., Heiden, W., Behrens, S., Gattaz, W. F., Hambrecht, M., Loeffler, W., et al. (1998). Causes and consequences of the gender difference in age at onset of schizophrenia. *Schizophrenia Bulletin, 24*, 99–113.

Hafner, H., Maurer, K., Loffler, W., an der Heiden, W., Hambrecht, M., & Schultze-Lutter, F. (2003). Modeling the early course of schizophrenia. *Schizophrenia Bulletin, 29*, 325–340.

Hagedoorn, M., Sanderman, R., Bolks, H. N., Tuinstra, J., & Coyne, J. C. (2008). Distress in couples coping with cancer: A meta-analysis and critical review of role and gender effects. *Psychological Bulletin, 134*, 1–30.

Hahlweg, K., Fiegenbaum, W., Frank, M., Schroeder, B., & Witzleben, I. (2001). Short- and long-term effectiveness of an empirically supported treatment for agoraphobia. *Journal of Consulting and Clinical Psychology, 69*, 375–382.

Hahlweg, K., Markman, H. J., Thurmaier, F., Engl, J., & Eckert, V. (1998). Prevention of martial distress: Results of a German prospective longitudinal study *Journal of Family Psychology, 12*, 543–556.

Halbreich, U., Alarcon, R. D., Calil, H. I., Douki, S., Gaszner, P., Jadresic, E., et al. (2007). Culturally-sensitive complaints of depressions and anxieties in women. *Journal of Affective Disorders, 102*, 159–176.

Hall, G. C. N. (2001). Psychotherapy research with ethnic minorities: Empirical, ethical, and conceptual issues. *Journal of Consulting and Clinical Psychology, 69*, 502–510.

Hall, W., & Pacula, R. L. (2003). Cannabis Use and Dependence: Public Health and Public Policy. Cambridge: Cambridge University Press.

Halligan, S. L., Michael, T., Clark, D. M., & Ehlers, A. (2003). Posttraumatic stress disorder following assault: The role of cognitive processing, trauma memory, and appraisals. *Journal of Consulting and Clinical Psychology, 71*, 419–431.

Halliwell, E., & Dittmar, H. (2004). Does size matter? The impact of model's body size on women's body-focused anxiety and advertising effectiveness. *Journal of Social & Clinical Psychology, 23*, 104–122.

Halmi, K. A. (1997). Models to conceptualize risk factors for bulimia nervosa. *Archives of General Psychiatry, 54*, 507–509.

Hamilton, N. A., Gallagher, M. W., Preacher, K. J., Stevens, N., Nelson, C. A., Karlson, C., et al. (2007). Insomnia and well-being. *Journal of Consulting and Clinical Psychology, 75*, 939–946.

Hammand, T. A., Laughren, T., & Racoosin, J. (2006). Suicidality in pediatric patients treated with antidepressant drugs. *Archives of General Psychiatry, 63*, 332–339.

Hammen, C. (2002). Context of stress in families of children with depressed parents. In S. H. Goodman and I. H. Gotlib (Eds.), *Children of Depressed Parents: Mechanisms of Risk and Implications for Treatment*, pp. 175–199. Washington, DC: American Psychological Association.

Hammen, C. (2005). Stress and Depression. *Annual Review of Clinical Psychology, 55*, 11.1–11.27.

Hammen, C., & Garber, J. (2001). Vulnerability to depression across the lifespan. *Vulnerability to Psychopathology: Risk Across the Lifespan*, pp. 258–267. New York: Guilford Press.

Hankin, B. L., et al. (1998). Development of depression from preadolescence to young adulthood: Emerging gender differences in a 10-year longitudinal study. *Journal of Abnormal Psychology, 107*, 128–140.

Hankin, B. L., & Abramson, L. Y. (2001). Development of gender differences in depression: An elaborated cognitive vulnerability-transactional stress theory. *Psychological Bulletin, 127*, 773–796.

Hansen, N. B., Lambert, M. J., & Forman, E. M. (2002). The psychotherapy dose–response effect and its implications for treatment service delivery. *Clinical Psychology: Science and Practice, 9*, 329–343.

Hanson, D. R., & Gottesman, I. I. (1976). The genetics, if any of infantile autism and childhood schizophrenia. *Journal of Autism & Childhood Schizophrenia, 6*(3), 209–234.

Happe, F. (1995). *Autism*. Cambridge, MA: Harvard University Press.

Hardin, S., & Schooley, B. (2002). A story of Pick's disease: A rare form of dementia. *Journal of Neuroscience Nursing, 34*, 117–122.

Harding, C. M. (1988). Course types in schizophrenia: An analysis of European and American studies. *Schizophrenia Bulletin, 14*, 633–643.

Hare, R. D. (1993). *Without Conscience: The Disturbing World of the Psychopaths Among Us*. New York: Pocket Books.

Harkness, K. L., & Wildes, J. E. (2002). Childhood adversity and anxiety versus dysthymia co-morbidity in major depression. *Psychological Medicine, 32*, 1239–1249.

Harkness, K. L., Monroe, S. M., Simons, A. D., & Thase, M. (1999). The generation of life events in recurrent and non-recurrent depression. *Psychological Medicine, 29*, 135–144.

Harpur, T. J., & Hare, R. D. (1994). Assessment of psychopathy as a function of age. *Journal of Abnormal Psychology, 103*, 604–609.

Harrington, R. (2002). Affective disorders. In M. Rutter & E. Taylor (Eds.), *Child and Adolescent Psychiatry*, 4th ed., pp. 463–485. Oxford, England: Blackwell.

Harrington, R., Fudge, H., Rutter, M., Pickles, A., & Hill, J. (1990). Adult outcomes of childhood and adolescent depression. I. Psychiatric status. *Archives of General Psychiatry, 47*, 465–473.

Harrington, R. C., & Harrison, L. (1999). Unproven assumptions about the impact of bereavement on children. *Journal of the Royal Society of Medicine, 92*, 230–233.

Harris, A. H. S. (2006). Does expressive writing reduce health care utilization? A meta-analysis of randomized trials. *Journal of Consulting and Clinical Psychology, 74*, 243–252.

Harris, G. T., & Rice, M. E. (2006). Treatment of psychopathy: A review of empirical findings. In C. J. Patrick (Ed.), *Handbook of Psychopathy*, pp. 555–572. New York: Guilford.

Harris, J. R. (1995). Where is the child's environment? A group socialization theory of development. *Psychological Review, 102*, 458–489.

Harrison, G., Gunnell, D., Glazebrook, C., Page, K., & Kwiecinski, R. (2001). Association between schizophrenia and social inequality at birth: Case control study. *British Journal of Psychiatry, 179*, 346–350.

Harrison, P. J. (1999). The neuropathology of schizophrenia: A critical review of the data and their interpretation. *Brain, 122,* 593–624.

Hart, A. B., Craighead, W. E., & Craighead, L. W. (2001). Predicting recurrence of major depressive disorder in young adults: A prospective study. *Journal of Abnormal Psychology, 110,* 633–643.

Hart, C., McCance-Katz, E. F., & Kosten, T. R. (2001). Pharmacotherapies used in common substance use disorders. In F. M. Tims and C. G. Leukefeld (Eds.), *Relapse and Recovery in Addictions,* pp. 303–333. New Haven, CT: Yale University Press.

Hart, E. L., Lahey, B. B., Loeber, R., Applegate, B., & Frick, P. J. (1995). Developmental change in attention-deficit hyperactivity disorder in boys: A four-year longitudinal study. *Journal of Abnormal Child Psychology, 23,* 729–750.

Hart, S. D., & Hare, R. D. (1997). Psychopathy: Assessment and association with criminal conduct. In D. M. Stoff, J. Breiling, & J. Maser (Eds.), *Handbook of Antisocial Behavior,* pp. 22–35. New York: Wiley.

Harvey, A. G., & Bryant, R. A. (1998). The relationship between acute stress disorder and posttraumatic stress disorder: A prospective evaluation of motor vehicle accident survivors. *Journal of Consulting and Clinical Psychology, 66,* 507–512.

Harvey, A. G., & Bryant, R. A. (1999). The relationship between acute stress disorder and posttraumatic stress disorder: A 2-year prospective evaluation. *Journal of Consulting and Clinical Psychology, 67,* 985–988.

Harvey, A. G., & Bryant, R. A. (2002). Acute stress disorder: A synthesis and critique. *Psychological Bulletin, 128,* 886–902.

Harvey, A. G., Bryant, R. A., & Dang, S. T. (1998). Autobiographical memory in acute stress disorder. *Journal of Consulting and Clinical Psychology, 66,* 500–506.

Harvey, R. J. (1996). Review: Delusions in dementia. *Age and Ageing, 25,* 405–409.

Hasin, D., Paykin, A., Endicott, J., & Grant, B. (1999). The validity of DSM-IV alcohol abuse: Drunk drivers versus all others. *Journal of Studies on Alcohol, 60,* 746–755.

Hasin, D. S., Stonson, F.S., Ogburn, E., & Grant, B.F. (2007). Prevalence, correlates, disability, and comorbidity of DSM-IV alcohol abuse and dependence in the United States. *Archives of General Psychiatry, 64,* 830–842.

Haslam, N. (2003). Categorical versus dimensional models of mental disorder: The taxometric evidence. *Australian & New Zealand Journal of Psychiatry, 3,* 696–704.

Haugaard, J. J., & Reppucci, N. D. (1988). *The Sexual Abuse of Children.* San Francisco: Jossey-Bass.

Hawkins, A. J., Blanchard, V. L., Baldwin, S. A., & Fawcett, E. B. (2008). Does marriage and relationship education work? A meta-analytic study. *Journal of Consulting and Clinical Psychology, 76,* 723-734.

Hawley, K. M., & Weisz, J. R. (2003). Child, parent, and therapist (dis)agreement on target problems in outpatient therapy: The therapist's dilemma and its implications. *Journal of Consulting and Clinical Psychology, 71*(1), 62–70.

Hayes, R. D., Dennerstein, L., Bennett, C. M., & Fairley, C. K. (2008). What is the 'true' prevalence of female sexual dysfunctions and does the way we assess these conditions have an impact? *Journal of Sexual Medicine, 5,* 777–787.

Hayes, S. C. (2004). Acceptance and commitment therapy, relational frame theory, and the third wave of behavioral and cognitive therapies. *Behaviour Therapy, 35,* 639–665.

Haynes, S. G., & Feinleib, M. (1980). Women, work, and coronary heart disease: Prospective findings from the Framingham heart study. *American Journal of Public Health, 70,* 133–141.

Hazell, P. L., & Stuart, J. E. (2003). A randomized controlled trial of clonidine added to psychostimulant medication for hyperactive and aggressive children. *Journal of the American Academy of Child and Adolescent Psychiatry, 42*(8), 886–894.

Head, D., Rodrigue, K., Kennedy, K., & Raz, N. (2008). Neuroanatomical and cognitive mediators of age-related differences in episodic memory. *Neuropsychology, 22*(4), 491–507.

Heath, A. C., Bucholz, I. I., Madden, P. A. F., Dinwiddie, S. H., Slutske, W. S., Bierut, L. J., et al. (1997). Genetic and environmental contributions to alcohol dependence risk in a national twin sample: Consistency of findings in women and men. *Psychological Medicine, 27,* 1381–1396.

Heatherton, T. F., & Polivy, J. (1992). Chronic dieting and eating disorders: A spiral model. In J. Crowther, S. E. Hobfall, M. A. P. Stephens, & D. L. Tennenbaum (Eds.), *The Etiology of Bulimia: The Individual and Familial Context,* pp. 135–155. Washington, DC: Hemisphere.

Heavey, C. L., Christensen, A., & Malamuth, N. M. (1995). The longitudinal impact of demand and withdrawal during marital conflict. *Journal of Consulting and Clinical Psychology, 63,* 797–801.

Heber, R. (1959). A manual on terminology and classification in mental retardation. *American Journal on Mental Deficiency, 64* (Monograph Suppl.).

Heerey, E. A., & Kring, A. M. (2007). Interpersonal consequences of social anxiety. *Journal of Abnormal Psychology, 116,* 125–134.

Heiman, J. R. (1998). Psychophysiological models of female sexual response. *International Journal of Impotence Research, 10* (Suppl. 2), 94–97.

Heiman, J. R., & LoPiccolo, J. (1988). *Becoming Orgasmic: A Sexual and Personal Growth Program for Women.* Fireside.

Heinberg, L. J., Thompson, J. K., & Matzon, J. L. (2001). Body image dissatisfaction as a motivator for healthy lifestyle change: Is some distress beneficial? In R. H. Striegel-Moore & L. Smolak (Eds.), *Eating Disorders: Innovative Directions in Research and Practice,* pp. 215–232. Washington, DC: American Psychological Association.

Heinberg, L. J., Thompson, J. K., & Stormer, S. (1995). Development and validation of the sociocultural attitudes towards appearance questionnaire. *International Journal of Eating Disorders, 17,* 81–89.

Heinssen, R. K., Liberman, R. P., & Kopelowicz, A. (2000). Psychosocial skills training for schizophrenia: Lessons from the laboratory. *Schizophrenia Bulletin 26,* 21–46.

Heisel, M. (2008). Suicide. Clinical Handbook of Schizophrenia, pp. 491–504. New York: Guilford Press.

Helgeland, M. I., & Torgersen, S. (2004). Developmental antecedents of borderline personality disorder. *Comprehensive Psychiatry, 45,* 138–147.

Helgeson, V. S., Reynolds, K. A., & Tomich, P. L. (2006). A meta-analytic review of benefit finding and growth. *Journal of Consulting and Clinical Psychology, 74,* 797–816.

Helzer, J. E., Bucholz, K. K., & Gosson, M. (2008). A dimensional option for the diagnosis of substance dependence in DSM-V. In J. E. Helzer, H. C. Kraemer, R. F. Krueger, H. Wittchen, & P. J. Sirovatka (Eds.), *Dimensional Approaches in Diagnostic Classification: Refining the Research Agenda for DSM-V,* pp. 19–34. Washington, DC: American Psychiatric Press.

Helzer, J. E., Robins, L. N., & McEvoy, L. (1987). Posttraumatic stress disorder in the general population: Findings of the Epidemiologic Catchment Area Survey. *New England Journal of Medicine, 317,* 1630–1634.

Hempel, C. G. (1961). Introduction to problems of taxonomy. In J. Zubin (Ed.), *Field Studies in the Mental Disorders.* New York: Grune & Stratton.

Hendin, H. (1995). *Suicide in America.* New York: Norton.

Hendricks, C. L. (1993–94). The trend toward mandatory mediation in custody and visitation disputes of minor children: An overview. *Journal of Family Law, 32,* 491–510.

Hendrie, H. C. (1998). Epidemiology of dementia and Alzheimer's disease. *American Journal of Geriatric Psychiatry, 6* (Suppl. 1), 3–18.

Hendrie, H. C., Osuntokun, B. O., Hall, K. S., et al. (1995). Prevalence of Alzheimer's disease and dementia in two communities: Nigerian Africans and African Americans. *American Journal of Psychiatry, 152,* 1485–1492.

Henggeler, S. W. (1994). *Treatment Manual for Family Preservation Using Multisystemic Therapy.* Charleston: Medical University of South Carolina.

Henggeler, S. W., & Borduin, C. M. (1990). *Family Therapy and Beyond: A Multisystemic Approach to Treating the Behavior Problems of Children and Adolescents.* Pacific Grove, CA: Brooks/Cole.

Henker, B., & Whalen, C. K. (1989). Hyperactivity and attention deficits. *American Psychologist, 44,* 216–223.

Herbener, E. S., & Harrow, M. (2002). The course of anhedonia during 10 years of schizophrenic illness. *Journal of Abnormal Psychology, 111,* 237–248.

Herbert, M. (2002). Behavioural therapies. In M. Rutter & E. Taylor (Eds.), *Child and Adolescent Psychiatry,* 4th ed., pp. 900–920. Oxford, England: Blackwell.

Herman, C. P., & Polivy, J. (1988). Excess and restraint in bulimia. In K. Pirke, W. Vandereycken, & D. Ploog (Eds.), *The Psychobiology of Bulimia,* pp. 33–41. Munich, Germany: Springer-Verlag.

Hermann, D. H. J. (1990). Autonomy, self determination, the right of involuntarily committed persons to refuse treatment, and the use of substituted judgment in medication decisions involving incompetent persons. *International Journal of Law and Psychiatry, 13,* 361–385.

Hernandez, D. J. (1993). *America's Children: Resources from Family, Government, and the Economy.* New York: Russell Sage.

Herpertz, S. C., Werth, U., Lucas, G., Qunaibi, M., Schuerkens, A., Kunert, H., et al. (2001). Emotion in criminal offenders with psychopathy and borderline personality disorders. *Archives of General Psychiatry, 58,* 737–745.

Herzog, D. B. & Delinsky, S. S. (2001). Classification of eating disorders. In R. H. Striegel-Moore & L. Smolak (Eds.), *Eating Disorders: Innovative Directions in Research and Practice,* pp. 31–50. Washington, DC: American Psychological Association.

Herzog, D. B., Dorer, D. J., Keel, P. K., Selwyn, S. E., Ekeblad, E. R., Flores, A. T., et al. (1999). Recovery and relapse in anorexia and bulimia nervosa: A 75-year follow-up study. *Journal of the American Academy of Child & Adolescent Psychiatry, 38,* 829–837.

Hess, T. M. (2005). Memory and aging in context. *Psychological Bulletin, 131,* 383–406.

Hesselbrook, V. M., & Hesselbrook, M. N. (2007). Are there empirically supported and clinically useful subtypes of alcohol dependence? In J. B. Saunders, M. A. Schuckit, P. J. Sirovatka, & D. A. Regier (Eds.), *Diagnostic Issues in Substance Use Disorders,* pp. 171–182. Washington, DC: American Psychiatric Press.

Heston, L. L. (1966). Psychiatric disorders in foster home reared children of schizophrenic mothers. *British Journal of Psychiatry, 112,* 819–825.

Heston, L. L., & White, J. A. (1991). *The Vanishing Mind: A Practical Guide to Alzheimer's Disease and Other Dementias.* New York: Freeman.

Hettema, J. M., Prescott, C. A., Myers, J. M., Neale, M. C., & Kendler, K. S. (2005). The structure of genetic and environmental risk factors for anxiety disorders in men and women. *Archives of General Psychiatry, 62,* 182–189.

Heyman, I., & Santosh, P. (2002). Pharmacological and other physical treatments. In M. Rutter & E. Taylor (Eds.), *Child and Adolescent Psychiatry,* 4th ed., pp. 998–1018. Oxford, England: Blackwell.

Heyman, R. E., & Slep, A. M. S. (2006). Creating and field-testing diagnostic criteria for partner and child maltreatment. *Journal of Family Psychology, 20,* 379–408.

Hiatt, K. D., & Newman, J. P. (2006). Understanding psychopathy: The cognitive side. In C. J. Patrick (Ed.), *Handbook of Psychopathy,* pp. 334–352. New York: Guilford.

Hill, A., Briken, P., Kraus, C., Strohm, K., & Berner, W. (2003). Differential pharmacological treatment of paraphilias and sex offenders. *International Journal of Offender Therapy, 47,* 407–421.

Hill, J., & Holmbeck, G. (1986). Attachment and autonomy during adolescence. In G. Whitehurst (Ed.), *Annals of Child Development,* Vol. 3, pp. 145–189. Greenwich, CT: JAI.

Hill, M. A. (1992). Light, circadian rhythms, and mood disorders: A review. *Annals of Clinical Psychiatry, 4,* pp. 131–146.

Hill, P. C., & Pargament, K. I. (2003). Advances in the conceptualization and measurement of religion and spirituality: Implications for physical and mental health research. *American Psychologist, 58*(1), 64–74.

Hilliard, R. B., & Spitzer, R. L. (2002). Change in criterion for paraphilias in DSM-IV-TR. *American Journal of Psychiatry, 159,* 1249.

Hillman, J. L. (2000). *Clinical Perspectives on Elderly Sexuality.* New York: Kluwer Academic/Plenum.

Hinshaw, et al. (2000). Family processes and treatment outcome in the MTA: Negative/ineffective parenting practices in relations to multimodal treatment. *Journal of Abnormal Child Psychology, 28,* 555–568.

Hinshaw, S. P. (1994). *Attention Deficits and Hyperactivity in Children.* Thousand Oaks, CA: Sage.

Hirschfeld, R. M. A. (2001). Antidepressants in the United States: Current status and future needs. In M. M. Weissman (Ed.), *Treatment of Depression: Bridging the 21st Century,* pp. 123–134. Washington, DC: American Psychiatric Press.

Hirschfeld, R. M. A., Shea, M. T., & Weise, R. (1995). Dependent personality disorder. In W. J. Livesley (Ed.), *The DSM-IV Personality Disorders,* pp. 239–256. New York: Guilford.

Hittner, J. B. (1997). Alcohol-related expectancies: Construct overview and implications for primary and secondary prevention. *Journal of Primary Prevention, 17,* 297–314.

Hlastala, S. A., Frank, E., Kowalski, J., Tu, X. M., Anderson, B., & Kupfer, D. J. (2000). Stressful life events, bipolar disorder, and the "kindling model." *Journal of Abnormal Psychology, 109,* 777–786.

Hobfoll, S. E., Canetti-Nisim, D., & Johnson, R. J. (2006). Exposure to terrorism, stress-related mental health symptoms, and defensive coping among Jews and Arabs in Israel. *Journal of Consulting and Clinical Psychology, 74,* 207–218.

Hoek, H. W. (1995). The distribution of eating disorders. In K. D. Brownell & C. G. Fairburn (Eds.), *Eating Disorders and Obesity: A Comprehensive Handbook,* pp. 207–211. New York: Guilford.

Hoek, H. W. (2002). Distribution of eating disorders. In C. G. Fairburn & K. D. Brownell (Eds.), *Eating Disorders and Obesity,* 2nd ed., pp. 233–237. New York: Guilford.

Hoenig, J. (1985). Etiology of transsexualism. In B. W. Steiner (Ed.), *Gender Dysphoria: Development,* *Research, Management,* pp. 33–74. New York: Plenum.

Hoeve, M., Blokland, A., Dubas, J. S., Loeber, R., Gerris, J. R. M., & van der Laan, P. H. (2008). Trajectories of delinquency and parenting styles. *Journal of Abnormal Child Psychology, 36,* 223–235.

Hoff, A. L., & Kremen, W. S. (2002). Is there a cognitive phenotype for schizophrenia? The nature and course of the disturbance in cognition. *Current Opinion in Psychiatry, 15,* 43–48.

Hoffman, P. B., & Foust, L. L. (1977). Least restrictive treatment of the mentally ill: A doctrine in search of its senses. *San Diego Law Review, 14,* 1100–1154.

Hofmann, S. G. (2004). Cognitive mediation of treatment change in social phobia. *Journal of Consulting and Clinical Psychology, 72,* 392–399.

Hofmann, S. G., Heinrichs, N., & Moscovitch, D. A. (2004). The nature and expression of social phobia: Toward a new classification. *Clinical Psychology Review, 24,* 769–797.

Hofmann, S. G., Moscovitch, D. A., & Heinrichs, N. (2004). Evolutionary mechanisms of fear and anxiety. In P. Gilbert (Ed.), *Evolutionary Theory and Cognitive Therapy,* pp. 119–136. New York: Springer.

Hogan, D. R. (1990). Sexual dysfunctions: A historical perspective. In C. E. Walker (Ed.), *History of Clinical Psychology,* pp. 279–309. Pacific Grove, CA: Brooks/Cole.

Hogarty, G. E., Flesher, S., Ulrich, R., Carter, M., Greenwald, D., Pogue-Geile, M., et al. (2004). Cognitive enhancement therapy for schizophrenia: Effects of a 2-year randomized trial on cognition and behavior. *Archives of General Psychiatry, 61,* 866–876.

Hoge, E. A., Tamraker, S. M., Christian, K. M., Mahara, N., Nepal, M. K. Pollack, M. H., et al. (2006). Cross-cultural differences in somatic presentation in patients with generalized anxiety disorder. *Journal of Nervous and Mental Disease, 194,* 962–966.

Holland, J. (2001). *Ecstasy: The Complete Guide: A Comprehensive Look at the Risks and Benefits of MDMA.* Inner Traditions.

Hollander, E., & Stein, D. J. (Eds.). (2006). *Clinical Manual of Impulse-Control Disorders.* Arlington, VA: American Psychiatric Publishing.

Hollon, S. D., Shelton, R. C., & Davis, D. D. (1993). Cognitive therapy for depression: Conceptual issues and clinical efficacy. *Journal of Consulting and Clinical Psychology, 61,* 270–275.

Hollon, S. D., Stewart, M. O., & Strunk, D. (2006). Enduring effects for cognitive behavior therapy in the treatment of depression and anxiety. *Annual Review of Psychology, 57,* 285–315.

Hollon, S. D., Thase, M. E., & Markowitz, J. C. (2002). Treatment and prevention of depression. *Psychological Science in the Public Interest, 3,* 39–77.

Holmes, C. (2002). Genotype and phenotype in Alzheimer's disease. *British Journal of Psychiatry, 180,* 131–134.

Holmes, T. H., & Rahe, R. H. (1967). The Social Readjustment Rating Scale. *Journal of Psychosomatic Research, 11,* 213–218.

Holsinger, T., Steffens, D. C., Phillips, C., Helms, M. J., Havlik, R. J., Breitner, J. C. S., et al. (2002). Head injury in early adulthood and the lifetime risk of depression. *Archives of General Psychiatry, 59,* 17–22.

Holtzworth-Munroe, A. Meehan, J. C., Herron, K., Rehman, U., & Stuart, G. L. (2000). Testing the Holtzworth-Munroe and Stuart (1994). Batterer typology. *Journal of Consulting and Clinical Psychology, 68,* 1000–1019.

Holzman, P. S. (2000). Eye movements and the search for the essence of schizophrenia. *Brain Research Reviews, 31,* 350–356.

Homewood, J., & Bond, N. W. (1999). Thiamin deficiency and Korsakoff's syndrome: Failure to find memory impairments following nonalcoholic Wernicke's encephalopathy. *Alcohol, 19,* 75–84.

Honda, H. et al. (2005). No effect of MMR withdrawal on the incidence of autism: A total population study. *Journal of Child Psychology and Psychiatry, 46,* 572–579.

Hong, L., Turano, K., O'Neill, H., Hao, L., Wonodi, I., McMahon, R., et al. (2008). Refining the predictive pursuit endophenotype in schizophrenia. *Biological Psychiatry, 63,* 458–464.

Hooley, J. M., & Gotlib, I. H. (2000). A diathesis-stress conceptualization of expressed emotion and clinical outcome. *Applied and Preventive Psychology, 9,* 135–151.

Hopper, K., Harrison, G., Janca, A., & Sartorius, N. (2007). *Recovery from schizophrenia: An International Perspective:* A Report from the WHO Collaborative Project, the International Study of Schizophrenia. New York: Oxford University Press.

Horevitz, R., & Loewenstein, R. J. (1994). The rational treatment of multiple personality disorder. In S. J. Lynn & J. W. Rhue (Eds.), *Dissociation: Clinical and Theoretical Perspectives,* pp. 289–316. New York: Guilford.

Horley, J. (2001). Frotteurism: A term in search of an underlying disorder. *Journal of Sexual Aggression, 7,* 51–55.

Horn, J. M., Loehlin, J. C., & Willerman, L. (1979). Intellectual resemblance among adoptive and biological relatives: The Texas Adoption Project. *Behavior Genetics, 9,* 177–205.

Horney, K. (1939). *New Ways in Psychoanalysis.* New York: International Universities Press.

Horowitz, L. M. (2004). Dependent and avoidant personality disorders. In L. M. Horowitz (Ed.), *Interpersonal Foundations of Psychopathology,* pp. 103–129. Washington, DC: American Psychological Association.

Horowitz, M. J., Siegel, B., Holen, A., Bonanno, G. A., Milbrath, C., & Stinson, C. H. (1997). Diagnostic criteria for complicated grief disorder. *American Journal of Psychiatry, 154,* 904–910.

Horvath, K., Stefanatos, G., Sokolski, K. N., Wachtel, R., Nabors, L, & Tildon, J. T. (1998). Improved social and language skills after secretin administration in patients with autistic spectrum disorders. *Journal of the Association of the Academy of Minority Physicians, 9,* 9–15.

Horwath, E., Cohen, R. S., & Weissman, M. M. (2002). Epidemiology of depressive and anxiety disorders. In M. T. Tsuang & M. Tohen (Eds.), *Textbook in Psychiatric Epidemiology,* 2nd ed., pp. 389–426. New York: Wiley-Liss.

Horwitz, A. V. (2002). *Creating Mental Illness.* Chicago: University of Chicago Press.

Horwitz, A. V., & Wakefield, J. C. (2007). *The Loss of Sadness: How Psychiatry Transformed Normal Sorrow into Depressive Disorder.* New York: Oxford University Press.

Houezec, J. L. (1998). Pharmacokinetics and pharmacodynamics of nicotine. In J. Snel & M. M. Lorist (Eds.), *Nicotine, Caffeine and Social Drinking: Behaviour and Brain Function,* pp. 3–20. Amsterdam: Harwood.

Houts, A. C. (1991). Nocturnal enuresis as a biobehavioral problem. *Behavior Therapy, 22,* 133–151.

Houts, A. C. (2002). Discovery, invention, and the expansion of the modern Diagnostic and Statistical Manuals of Mental Disorders. In L. E. Beutler and M. L. Malik (Eds.), *Rethinking the DSM: A Psychological Perspective,* pp. 17–68. Washington, DC: American Psychological Association.

Howard, K. I., Cornille, T. A., Lyons, J. S., Vessey, J. T., Lueger, R. J., & Saunders, S. M. (1996), "Patterns of service utilization," *Archives of General Psychiatry, 53,* pp. 696–703.

Howard, K. J., Kopta, S. M., Krause, M. S., & Orlinsky, D. E. 1986, "The Dose–Effect Relationship in Psychotherapy," *American Psychologist, 41,* pp. 159–164. © 1996 by American Psychological Association. Reprinted by permission of D.E. Orlinsky.

Howe, M. L. (2003). Memories from the cradle. *Current Directions in Psychological Science, 12,* 62–65.

Howes, O. D., McDonald, C., Cannon, M., Arseneault, L., Boydell, J., & Murray, R. M. (2004). Pathways to schizophrenia: The impact of environmental factors. *International Journal of Neuropsychopharmacology, 7* (Suppl. 1), S7–S13.

Howlin, P. (2007). The outcome in adult life for people with ASD. In F. R. Volkmar (Ed.), *Autism and Pervasive Developmental Disorders,* pp. 269–306. New York: Cambridge University Press.

Hoza, B., et al. (2005). What aspects of peer relationships are impaired in children with attention-deficit/hyperactivity disorder? *Journal of Consulting and Clinical Psychology, 73,* 411–423.

Hsu, L. G. (1989). The gender gap in eating disorders: Why are the eating disorders more common among women? *Clinical Psychology Review, 9*(3), 393–407.

Hsu, L. K. G. (1990). *Eating Disorders.* New York: Guilford.

Hsu, L. K. G. (1995). Outcome of bulimia nervosa. In K. D. Brownell & C. G. Fairburn (Eds.), *Eating Disorders and Obesity: A Comprehensive Handbook,* pp. 238–244. New York: Guilford.

Hubbs-Tait, L., Nation, J. R., Krebs, N. F., & Bellinger, D. C. (2005). Neurotoxicants, micronutrients, and social environments: Individual and combined effects on children's development. *Psychological Science in the Public Interest, 6,* 57–121.

Hucker, S. J. (1997). Sexual sadism: Theory and psychopathology. In D. R. Laws & W. T. O'Donohue (Eds.), *Handbook of Sexual Deviance: Theory and Application.* New York: Guilford.

Huettel, S. A., Song, A. W., & McCarthy, G. (2004). *Functional Magnetic Resonance Imaging.* Sunderland, MA: Sinauer.

Hughes, C. C. (1998). The glossary of culture-bound syndromes in DSM-IV: A critique. *Transcultural Psychiatry, 35,* 413–421.

Hughes, J. R. (2007a). Should criteria for drug dependence differ across drugs? In J. B. Saunders, M. A. Schuckit, P. J. Sirovatka, & D. A. Regier (Eds.), *Diagnostic Issues in Substance Use Disorders,* pp. 237–250. Washington, DC: American Psychiatric Press.

Hughes, J. R. (2007b). Measurement of the effects of abstinence from tobacco: A qualitative review. *Psychology of Addictive Behaviors, 21,* 127–137.

Hulshoff, H. E., Hoek, H. W., Susser, E., Brown, A. S., Dingemans, A., Schnack, H. G., et al. (2000). Prenatal exposure to famine and brain morphology in schizophrenia. *American Journal of Psychiatry, 157,* 1170–1172.

Human Capital Initiative. (1996). *Doing the Right Thing: A Research Plan for Healthy Living.* Washington, DC: American Psychological Society.

Humphrey, L. L. (1987). Comparison of bulimic-anorexic and nondistressed families using structural analysis of social behavior. *Journal of the American Academy of Child and Adolescent Psychiatry, 26,* 248–255.

Hunsley, J., & Bailey, M. J. (2001). Whither the Rorschach? An analysis of the evidence. *Psychological Assessment, 13,* 472–485.

Huntington, C. (2007). Mutual independence in child welfare. *Notre Dame Law Review, 82,* 1485–1536.

Huntington's Disease Collaborative Research Group (1993). A novel gene containing a trinucleotide repeat that is expanded and unstable on Huntington's disease chromosomes. *Cell, 72,* 971–983.

Hurt, S. W., Reznikoff, M., & Clarkin, J. F. (1991). *Psychological Assessment, Psychiatric Diagnosis, and Treatment Planning.* New York: Brunner/Mazel.

Husain, S. S., Kevan, I. M., Linnell, R., & Scott, A. I. F. (2004). Electroconvulsive therapy in depressive illness that has not responded to drug treatment. *Journal of Affective Disorders, 83,* 121–126.

Husak, D. N. (2002). *Legalize This: The Case for Decriminalizing Drugs.* New York: Verso.

Husted, D. S., Shapira, N. A., & Goodman, W. K. (2006). The neurocircuitry of obsessive-compulsive disorder and disgust. *Progress in Neuro-Psychopharmacology & Biological Psychiatry, 30,* 389–399.

Hviid, A., Stellfeld, M., Wohlfahrt, J., & Melbye, M. (2003). Association between thimerosal-containing vaccine and autism. *Journal of the American Medical Association, 290,* 1763–1766.

Hwang, W. (2006). The psychotherapy adaptation and modification framework: Application to Asian Americans. *American Psychologist, 61,* 702–715.

Hwang, W., Myers, H. F., Abe-Kim, J., & Ting, J. Y. (2008). A conceptual paradigm for understanding culture's impact on mental health. *Clinical Psychology Review, 28,* 211–227.

Hyman, S. E., & Malenka, R. C. (2001). Addiction and the brain: The neurobiology of compulsion and its persistence. *Nature Reviews Neuroscience, 2,* 695–703.

Hyman, S. E., & Moldin, S. O. (2001). Genetic science and depression: Implications for research and treatment. In M. M. Weissman (Ed.), *Treatment of Depression: Bridging the 21st Century,* pp. 83–103. Washington, DC: American Psychiatric Press.

Imperato-McGinley, J., Guerrero, L., Gautier, T., & Peterson, R. E. (1974). Steroid 5a-reductase deficiency in man: An inherited form of male pseudohermaphroditism. *Science, 186,* 1213–1215.

Ingram, J. L., Stodgell, C. J., Hyman, S. L., Figlewicz, D. A., Weitkamp, L. R., & Rodier, P. M. (2000). Discovery of allelic variants of HOXA1 and HOXB1: Genetic susceptibility to autism spectrum disorders. *Teratology, 62,* 396–409.

Ingram, R. E., & Ritter, J. (2000). Vulnerability to depression: Cognitive reactivity and parental bonding in high-risk individuals. *Journal of Abnormal Psychology, 109,* 588–596.

Insel, K. C., & Badger, T. A. (2002). Deciphering the 4 D's: Cognitive decline, delirium, depression and dementia—a review. *Journal of Advanced Nursing, 38,* 360–368.

Izard, C., et al. (2001). Emotion knowledge as a predictor of social behavior and academic competence in children at risk. *Psychological Science, 12,* 18–25.

Jablensky, A. (1985). Approaches to the definition and classification of anxiety and related disorders in European psychiatry. In A. H. Tuma & J. Maser (Eds.), *Anxiety and the Anxiety Disorders.* Hillsdale, NJ: Erlbaum.

Jablensky, A. (1999). The nature of psychiatric classification: Issues beyond ICD-10 and DSM-IV. *Australian and New Zealand Journal of Psychiatry, 33,* 137–144.

Jablensky, A. (2000). Epidemiology of schizophrenia: The global burden of disease and disability. *European Archives of Psychiatry and Clinical Neuroscience, 250,* 274–285.

Jacobi, C., Hayward, C., de Zwaan, M., Kraemer, H. C., & Agras, W. S. (2004). Coming to terms with risk factors for eating disorders: Application of risk terminology and suggestions for a general taxonomy. *Psychological Bulletin, 130,* 19–65.

Jacobson, E. (1938). *Progressive Relaxation.* Chicago: University of Chicago Press.

Jacobson, J. W., Mulick, J. A., & Schwartz, A. A. (1995). A history of facilitated communication: Science, pseudoscience, and antiscience. *American Psychologist, 50,* 750–765.

Jacobson, N. S., & Christensen, A. (1996). *Integrative Couple Therapy: Promoting Acceptance and Change.* New York: Norton.

Jacobson, N. S., Holtzworth-Munroe, A., & Schmaling, K. B. (1989). Marital therapy and spouse involvement in the treatment of depression, agoraphobia, and alcoholism. *Journal of Consulting and Clinical Psychology, 57,* 5–10.

Jacobson, N. S., & Truax, P. (1991). Clinical significance: A statistical approach to defining meaningful change in psychotherapy research. *Journal of Consulting and Clinical Psychology, 59,* 12–19.

Jacobson, S. A. (1997). Delirium in the elderly. *Psychiatric Clinics of North America, 20,* 91–110.

Jaffe, J. H. (1995). Pharmacological treatment of opioid dependence: Current techniques and new findings. *Psychiatric Annals, 25,* 369–375.

Jaffee, S. R., Caspi, A., Moffitt, T. E., Dodge, K. A., Rutter, M., Taylor, A., et al. (2005). Nature × nurture: Genetic vulnerabilities interact with physical maltreatment to promote conduct problems. *Development and Psychopathology, 17,* 67–84.

Jaffee, S. R., Caspi, A., Moffitt, T. E., & Taylor, A. (2004). Physical maltreatment victim to antisocial child: Evidence of an environmentally mediated process. *Journal of Abnormal Psychology, 113*(1), 44–55.

Jaffe, J. H., & Jaffe, A. R. (1999). Neurobiology of opiates/opioids. In M. Galanter & H. D. Kleber (Eds.), *Textbook of Substance Abuse Treatment,* 2nd ed., pp. 11–20. Washington, DC: American Psychiatric Press.

Jain, A., & Bradbeer, C. (2007). Gender identity disorder: Treatment and post-transition care in transsexual adults. *International Journal of STD & AIDS, 18,* 147–150.

James, J. E., & Keane, M. A. (2007). Caffeine, sleep and wakefulness: Implications of new understanding about withdrawal reversal. *Human Psychopharmacology: Clinical and Experimental, 22,* 549–558.

Jamison, K. R. (1995). *An Unquiet Mind: A Memoir of Moods and Madness.* New York: Knopf.

Jamison, K. R. (1999). *Night Falls Fast: Understanding Suicide.* New York: Knopf.

Janet, P. (1914/1915). Psychoanalysis. *Journal of Abnormal Psychology, 1*(35), 187–253.

Janssen, E. (2002). Psychophysiological measurement of sexual arousal. In M. W. Wiederman & B. E. Whitley Jr. (Eds), *Handbook for Conducting Research on Human Sexuality,* pp. 139–171. Mahwah, NJ: Erlbaum.

Jefferson, J. W. (1997). Antidepressants in panic disorder. *Journal of Clinical Psychiatry, 58* (Suppl. 2), 20–24.

Jemal, A., Siegel, R., Ward, E., Murray, T., Xu, J., Smigal, C., et al. (2006). Cancer statistics, 2006. *CA Cancer Journal for Clinicians, 56,* 106–130.

Jenkins, C. D. (1988). Epidemiology of cardiovascular diseases. *Journal of Consulting and Clinical Psychology, 56,* 324–332.

Jenkins, J. H. (1993). Too close for comfort: Schizophrenia and emotional overinvolvement among Mexican families. In A. D. Gaines (Ed.), *Ethnopsychiatry,* pp. 203–221. Albany: State University of New York Press.

Jensen, P. S., Arnold, E., Swanson, J. M., Vitiello, B., Abikoff, H. B., Greenhill, L. L., et al. (2007). 3-Year follow-up of the NIMH MTA study. *Journal of the American Academy of Child & Adolescent Psychiatry, 46,* 989–1002.

Jiang, W., Babyak, M., Krantz, D. S., Waugh, R. A., et al. (1996). Mental stress-induced myocardial ischemia and cardiac events. *Journal of the American Medical Association, 275,* 1651–1656.

Johnson, C. C., Rybicki, B. A., Brown, G., D'Hondt, E., Herpolsheimer, B., Roth, D., et al. (1997). Cognitive impairment in the Amish: A four county survey. *International Journal of Epidemiology, 26,* 387–394.

Johnson, J. G., Cohen, P., Brown, J., Smailes, E. M., & Bernstein, D. P. (1999). Childhood maltreatment increases risk for personality disorders during early adulthood. *Archives of General Psychiatry, 56,* 600–606.

Johnson, P. (1989). Hemingway: Portrait of the artist as an intellectual. *Commentary, 87,* 49–59.

Johnson, S. L, Sandrow, D., Meyter, B., Winters, R., Miller, I., Solomon, D., et al. (2000). Increases in manic symptoms after life events involving goal attainment. *Journal of Abnormal Psychology, 109,* 721–727.

Johnson, S. L., & Kizer, A. (2002). Bipolar and unipolar depression: A comparison of clinical phenomenology and psychosocial predictors. In I. H. Gotlib and C. L. Hammen (Eds.), *Handbook of Depression,* pp. 141–165. New York: Guilford.

Johnson, S. L., Winett, C. A., Meyer, B., Greenhouse, W. J., & Miller, I. (1999). Social support and the course of bipolar disorder. *Journal of Abnormal Psychology, 108,* 558–566.

Johnson, S. K. (2008). *Medically Unexplained Illness: Gender and Biopsychosocial Implications.* Washington, DC: American Psychological Association.

Johnston, D. W. (1985). Psychological interventions in cardiovascular disease. *Journal of Psychosomatic Research, 29,* 447–456.

Johnston, D. W. (1989). Prevention of cardiovascular disease by psychological methods. *British Journal of Psychiatry, 154,* 183–194.

Joiner, T. (2005). *Why People Die by Suicide.* Cambridge, MA: Harvard University Press.

Joiner, T. E., Jr., Brown, J. S., & Wingate, L. R. (2005). The psychology and neurobiology of suicidal behavior. *Annual Review of Psychology, 56,* 287–314.

Jones, B. T., Corbin, W., & Fromme, K. (2001). A review of expectancy theory and alcohol consumption. *Addiction, 96,* 57–72.

Jones, D. M. (1985). Bulimia: A false self identity. *Clinical Social Work, 13,* 305–316.

Jones, E., Thomas, A., & Ironside, S. (2007). Shell shock: An outcome study of a First World War "PIE" unit. *Psychological Medicine, 37,* 215–223.

Jones, J. C., & Barlow, D. H. (1990). The etiology of posttraumatic stress disorder. *Clinical Psychology Review, 10,* 299–328.

Jones, J. H. (1997). *Alfred C. Kinsey: A Public/Private Life.* New York: Norton.

Jones, M. A., & Krisberg, B. (1994). *Images and Reality: Juvenile Crime, Youth Violence, and Public Policy.* San Francisco: National Council on Crime and Delinquency.

Jones, P. B., Bebbington, P., Foerster, A., Lewis, S. W., et al. (1993). Premorbid social underachievement in schizophrenia: Results from the Camberwell Collaborative Psychosis Study. *British Journal of Psychiatry, 162,* 65–71.

Jones, R. T., & Ollendick, T. H. (in press). The impact of residential fire on children and their families. In A. La Greca, W. Silverman, E. Vernberg, & M. Roberts (Eds.), *Helping Children Cope with Disasters: Integrating Research and Practice.* Washington, DC: American Psychological Association Books.

Josephs, L. (1994). Psychoanalytic and related interpretations. In B. B. Wolman & G. Stricker (Eds.), *Anxiety and Related Disorders: A Handbook,* pp.11–29. New York: Wiley-Interscience.

Julien, R. M. (2001). *A Primer of Drug Action: A Concise, Nontechnical Guide to the Actions Uses and Side Effects of Psychoactive Drugs* (9th ed.). New York: Worth.

Junginger, J. (1997). Fetishism. In D. R. Laws & W. T. O'Donohue (Eds.), *Handbook of Sexual Deviance: Theory and Application.* New York: Guilford.

Kagan, J. (1998). *Three Seductive Ideas.* Cambridge, MA: Harvard University Press.

Kagan, J. (2007). A trio of concerns. *Perspectives on Psychological Science, 2,* 361–376.

Kagan, J., & Snidman, N. (1991). Temperamental factors in human development. *American Psychologist, 46,* 856–862.

Kahneman, D. (2003). A perspective on judgment and choice: Mapping bounded rationality. *American Psychologist. 58,* 697–720.

Kallman, W. M., & Feuerstein, M. J. (1986). Psychophysiological procedures. In A. R. Ciminero, K. S. Calhoun, & H. E. Adams (Eds.), *Handbook of Behavioral Assessment,* 2nd ed., pp. 325–350. New York: Wiley-Interscience.

Kalra, S., Bergeron, C., & Lang, A. E. (1996). Lewy body disease and dementia: A review. *Archives of Internal Medicine, 156,* 487–493.

Kalueff, A. V., & Nutt, D. J. (2007). Role of GABA in anxiety and depression. *Depression and Anxiety, 24,* 495–517.

Kalueff, A. V., Wheaton, M., & Murphy, D. L. (2007). What's wrong with my mouse model? Advances and strategies in animal modeling of anxiety and depression. *Behavioural Brain Research, 179,* 1–18.

Kamarck, T., & Jennings, J. R. (1991). Biobehavioral factors in sudden cardiac death. *Psychological Bulletin, 109,* 42–75.

Kanaya, T., Scullin, M. H., & Ceci, S. J. (2003). The Flynn effect and U.S. policies: The impact of rising IQ scores on American society via mental retardation diagnoses. *American Psychologist, 58*(10), 778–790.

Kane, J. M. (1999). Pharmacologic treatment of schizophrenia. *Biological Psychiatry, 46,* 1396–1408.

Kane, J. M. (2001a). Extrapyramidal side effects are unacceptable. *European Neuropsychopharmacology, 11* (Suppl. 4), S397–S403.

Kane, J. M. (2001b). Long-term therapeutic management in schizophrenia. In A. Breier, and P. V. Tran (Eds.), *Current Issues in the Psychopharmacology of Schizophrenia,* pp. 430–446. Philadelphia: Lippincott.

Kaneko, K. (2001). Penetration disorder: Dyspareunia exists on the extension of vaginismus. *Journal of Sex and Marital Therapy, 27,* 153–155.

Kangas, M., Henry, J. L., & Bryant, R. A. (2005). A prospective study of autobiographical memory and posttraumatic stress disorder following cancer. *Journal of Consulting and Clinical Psychology, 73*(2), 293–299.

Kanner, L. (1943). Autistic disturbances of affective contact. *Nervous Child, 2,* 217–250.

Kaplan, H. S. (1974). *The New Sex Therapy: Active Treatment of Sexual Dysfunctions.* New York: Brunner/Mazel.

Kaplan, L. J. (1989). *Female Perversions: The Temptations of Emma Bovary.* New York: Doubleday.

Kaptchuk, T. J., Kelley, J. M., Conboy, L. A., Davis, R. B., Kerr, C. E., Jacobson, E. E., et al. (2008). Components of placebo effect: Randomised controlled trial in patients with irritable bowel syndrome. *British Medical Journal, 48,* 409–419.

Kapur, S., & Remington, G. (2001). Antypical antipsychotics: New directions and new challenges in the treatment of schizophrenia. *Annual Review of Medicine, 52,* 503–517.

Kapusta, N. D., Etzersdorfer, E., Krall, C., & Sonneck, G. (2007). Firearm legislation reform in the European Union: Impact on firearm availability, firearm suicide and homicide rates in Austria. *British Journal of Psychiatry, 19,* 253–257.

Karasek, R. A., Theorell, T. G., Schwartz, J., Pieper, C., & Alfredsson, L. (1982). Job, psychological factors and coronary heart disease: Swedish prospective findings and U.S. prevalence findings using a new occupational inference method. *Advances in Cardiology, 29,* 62–67.

Karney, B. R., & Bradbury, T. N. (1995). The longitudinal course of marital quality and stability: A review of theory, method, and research. *Psychological Bulletin, 118,* 3–34.

Karon, J. M., et al. (1996). Prevalence of HIV infection in the United States, 1984 to 1992. *Journal of the American Medical Association, 276,* 126–131.

Karras, A., & Otis, D. B. (1987). A comparison of inpatients in an urban state hospital in 1975 and 1982. *Hospital and Community Psychiatry, 38,* 963–967.

Kasari, C., Paparella, T., Freeman, S., & Jahromi, L. B. (2008). Language outcome in autism: Randomized comparison of joint attention and play interventions. *Journal of Consulting and Clinical Psychology, 76,* 125–137.

Kasen, S., Cohen, P., Brook, J. S., & Hartmark, C. (1996). A multiple-risk interaction model: Effects of temperament and divorce on psychiatric disorders in children. *Journal of Abnormal Child Psychology, 24,* 121–150.

Kaskutas, L. A., Turk, N., Bond, J., & Weisner, C. (2003). The role of religion, spirituality and Alcoholics Anonymous in sustained sobriety. *Alcoholism Treatment Quarterly, 21,* 1–16.

Kaslow, N. J., & Thompson, M. P. (1998). Applying the criteria for empirically supported treatments to studies of psychosocial interventions for child and adolescent depression. *Journal of Clinical Child Psychology, 27,* 146–155.

Kasvikis, Y. G., Tsakiris, F., Marks, I. M., Basogulu, M., & Noshirvani, H. V. (1986). Past history of anorexia nervosa in women with obsessive-compulsive disorders. *International Journal of Eating Disorders, 5,* 1069–1075.

Kato, T. (2007). Molecular genetics of bipolar disorder and depression. *Psychiatry and Clinical Neurosciences, 61,* 3–19.

Katschnig, H., & Amering, M. (1990). Panic attacks and panic disorder in cross-cultural perspective. In J. C. Ballenger (Ed.), *Clinical Aspects of Panic Disorder.* New York: Wiley.

Katz, R., & McGuffin, P. (1993). The genetics of affective disorders. In D. Fowles (Ed.), *Progress in Experimental Personality and Psychopathology Research.* New York: Springer.

Katz, R. J., DeVeaugh-Geiss, J., & Landau, P. (1990). Clomipramine in obsessive-compulsive disorder. *Biological Psychiatry, 28,* 401–414.

Katzman, R. (1976). The prevalence and malignancy of Alzheimer's disease. *Archives of Neurology, 33,* 217–218.

Katzman, R. (1993). Education and the prevalence of dementia and Alzheimer's disease. *Neurology, 43,* 13–20.

Kaufman, G., & Elder, G. H., Jr. (2003). Grandparenting and age identity. *Journal of Aging Studies, 17,* 269–282.

Kaufman, J., Aikins, D., & Krystal, J. (2004). Neuroimaging studies in PTSD. In J. P. Wilson & T. M. Keane (Eds.), *Assessing Psychological Trauma and PTSD,* 2nd ed. New York: Guilford.

Kawas, C. (2003). Early Alzheimer's disease. *New England Journal of Medicine, 349,* 1056–1063.

Kaye, D. W. K. (1995). The epidemiology of age-related neurological disease and dementia. *Reviews in Clinical Gerontology, 5,* 39–56.

Kaye, W. H., Weltzin, T. E., Hsu, L. K. G., McConahan, C. W., & Bolton, B. (1993). Amount of calories retained after binge eating and vomiting. *American Journal of Psychiatry, 150,* 969–971.

Kaysen, S. (2001). *The Camera My Mother Gave Me.* New York: Knopf.

Kazdin, A. E. (1989). Identifying depression in children: A comparison of alternative selection criteria. *Journal of Abnormal Child Psychology, 17,* 437–455.

Kazdin, A. E. (1994a). Methodology, design, and evaluation in psychotherapy research. In A. E. Bergin and S. L. Garfield (Eds.), *Handbook of Psychotherapy and Behavior Change,* 4th ed., pp. 19–71, New York: Wiley.

Kazdin, A. E. (1994b). Psychotherapy for children and adolescents. In A. E. Bergin & S. L. Garfield (Eds.), *Handbook of Psychotherapy and Behavior Change*, 4th ed., pp. 543–594. New York: Wiley.

Kazdin, A. E. (1995). *Conduct Disorders in Childhood and Adolescence* (2nd ed.). Thousand Oaks, CA: Sage.

Kazdin, A. E. (1997). Parent management training: Evidence, outcomes, and issues. *Journal of the American Academy of Child and Adolescent Psychiatry, 36,* 1349–1365.

Kazdin, A. E. (2008). Evidence-based treatment and practice: New opportunities to bridge clinical research and practice, enhance the knowledge base, and improve patient care. *American Psychologist, 63,* 146–159.

Kazdin, A. E., French, N. H., & Unis, A. S. (1983). Child, mother, and father evaluations of depression in psychiatric inpatient children. *Journal of Abnormal Child Psychology, 11,* 167–180.

Kazdin, A. E., & Petti, T. A. (1982). Self-report and interview measures of childhood and adolescent depression. *Journal of Child Psychology and Psychiatry, 23,* 437–457.

Kazdin, A. E., Siegel, T. C., & Bass, D. (1992). Cognitive problem-solving skills training and parent management training in the treatment of antisocial behavior in children. *Journal of Consulting and Clinical Psychology, 60,* 753–747.

Kazdin, A. E., & Whitley, M. K. (2003). Treatment of parental stress to enhance therapeutic change among children referred for aggressive and antisocial behavior. *Journal of Consulting and Clinical Psychology, 71*(3), 504–515.

Keane, T. M., Marshall, A. D., & Taft, C. T. (2006). Posttraumatic stress disorder: Etiology, epidemiology, and treatment outcome. *Annual Review of Clinical Psychology, 2,* 161–197.

Keane, T. M., Zimering, R. T., & Caddell, J. M. (1985). A behavioral formulation of posttraumatic stress disorder in Vietnam veterans. *Behavior Therapist, 8,* 9–12.

Keefe, F. J., Lumley, M., Anderson, T., Lynch, T., & Carson, K. L. (2001). Pain and emotion: New research directions. *Journal of Clinical Psychology, 57,* 587–607.

Keel, P. K., Baxter, M. G., Heatherton, T. F., & Joiner, Jr., T. E. (2007). A 20-year longitudinal study of body weight, dieting, and eating disorder symptoms. *Journal of Abnormal Psychology, 116,* 422–432.

Keel, P. K., et al. (2000). Predictive validity of bulimia nervosa as a diagnostic category. *American Journal of Psychiatry, 157,* 136–138.

Keel, P. K., et al. (In press). Predictors of treatment utilization among women with anorexia and bulimia nervosa. *American Journal of Psychiatry.*

Keel, P. K., & Klump, K. L. (2003). Are eating disorders culture-bound syndromes? Implications for conceptualizing their etiology. *Psychological Bulletin, 129,* 747–769.

Keel, P. K., & Mitchell, J. E. (1997). Outcome in bulimia nervosa. *American Journal of Psychiatry, 154,* 313–321.

Keel, P. K., Mitchell, J. E., Davis, T. L., & Crow, S. J. (2002). Long-term impact of treatment in women diagnosed with bulimia nervosa. *International Journal of Eating Disorders, 31,* 151–158.

Keenan, K., & Shaw, D. (1997) Developmental and social influences on young girls' early problem behavior. *Psychological Bulletin, 121,* 95–113.

Keesey, R. E. (1995). A set-point model of body weight regulation. In K. D. Brownell & C. G. Fairburn (Eds.), *Eating Disorders and Obesity: A Comprehensive Handbook,* pp. 46–50. New York: Guilford.

Keller, J., Hicks, B. D., & Miller, G. A. (2000). Psychophysiology in the study of psychopathology. In J. T. Cacioppo, L. G. Tassinary, and G. G. Berntson

(Eds.), *Handbook of Psychophysiology,* 2nd ed., pp. 719–750. New York: Cambridge University Press.

Keller, M. B. (2003). The lifelong course of social anxiety disorder: A clinical perspective. *Acta Psychiatrica Scandinavica, 108* (Suppl. 417), 85–94.

Kellner, R. (1985). Functional somatic symptoms in hypochondriasis. *Archives of General Psychiatry, 42,* 821–833.

Kelly, M. P., Strassberg, D. S., & Turner, C. M. (2004). Communication and associated relationship issues in female anorgasmia. *Journal of Sex & Marital Therapy, 30,* 263–276.

Kelly, T., Soloff, P. H., Cornelius, J., George, A., Lis, J. A., & Ulrich, R. (1992). Can we study (treat) borderline patients? Attrition from research and open treatment. *Journal of Personality Disorders, 6,* 417–433.

Kempe, C. H., Silverman, F., Steele, B., Droegueller, W., & Silver, H. (1962). The battered child syndrome. *Journal of the American Medical Association, 181,* 17–24.

Kendall, P. C. (1994). Treating anxiety disorders in children: Results of a randomized clinical trial. *Journal of Consulting and Clinical Psychology, 62,* 100–110.

Kendall, P. C., Hudson, J. L., Gosch, E., Flannery-Schroeder, E., & Suveg, C. (2008). Cognitive-behavioral therapy for anxiety disordered youth: A randomized clinical trial evaluating child and family modalities. *Journal of Consulting and Clinical Psychology, 76,* 282–297.

Kendall, P. C., Safford, S., Flannery-Schroeder, E., & Webb, A. (2004). Child anxiety treatment: Outcomes in adolescence and impact on substance use and depression at 7.4-year follow-up. *Journal of Consulting and Clinical Psychology, 72*(2), 276–287.

Kendell, R. E. (1989). Clinical validity. *Psychological Medicine, 19,* 45–55.

Kendell, R. E. (2002) The distinction between personality disorder and mental illness. *British Journal of Psychiatry, 180,* 110–115.

Kendell, R. E. (2002). Five criteria for an improved taxonomy of mental disorders. In J. E. Helzer and J. J. Hudziak (Eds.), *Defining Psychopathology in the 21st Century,* pp. 3–17. Washington, DC: American Psychiatric Press.

Kendell, R., & Jablensky, A. (2003). Distinguishing between the validity and utility of psychiatric diagnoses. *American Journal of Psychiatry, 160,* 4–12.

Kendler, K. S. (1990). The super-normal control group in psychiatric genetics: Possible artifactual evidence for coaggregation. *Psychiatric Genetics, 1,* 45–53.

Kendler, K. S. (2006). Reflections on the relationship between psychiatric genetics and psychiatric nosology. *American Journal of Psychiatry, 7,* 1138–1146.

Kendler, K. S., & Diehl, S. R. (1993). The genetics of schizophrenia: A current, genetic-epidemiologic perspective. *Schizophrenia Bulletin, 19,* 261–285.

Kendler, K. S., & Gardner, C. O. (1997). The risk for psychiatric disorders in relatives of schizophrenic and control probands: A comparison of three independent studies. *Psychological Medicine, 27,* 411–419.

Kendler, K. S., & Prescott, C. A. (2006). *Genes, Environment, and Psychopathology: Understanding the Causes of Psychiatric and Substance Use Disorders.* New York: Guilford.

Kendler, K. S., Hettema, J. M., Butera, F., Gardner, C. O., & Prescott, D. A. (2003). Life event dimensions of loss, humiliation, entrapment, and danger in the prediction of onsets of major depression and generalized anxiety. *Archives of General Psychiatry, 60,* 789–796.

Kendler, K. S., MacLean, C., Neale, M., Kessler, R., Heath, A., & Eaves, L. (1991). The genetic epidemiology of bulimia nervosa. *American Journal of Psychiatry, 148,* 1627–1637.

Kendler, K. S., McGuire, M., Gruenberg, A. M., & Walsh, D. (1994). Outcome and family study of the

subtypes of schizophrenia in the west of Ireland. *American Journal of Psychiatry, 151,* 849–856.

Kendler, K. S., Neale, M. C., Kessler, R. C., Heath, A. C., & Eaves, L. J. (1992a). Generalized anxiety disorder in women: A population-based twin study. *Archives of General Psychiatry, 49,* pp. 267–272.

Kendler, K. S., Neale, M. C., Kessler, R. C., Heath, A. C., & Eaves, L. J. (1992b). The genetic epidemiology of phobias in women: The interrelationship of agoraphobia, social phobia, situational phobia, and simple phobia. *Archives of General Psychiatry, 49,* pp. 273–281.

Kendler, K. S., Prescott, C., Myers, J., & Neale, M. C. (2003). The structure of genetic and environmental risk factors for common psychiatric and substance use disorders in men and women. *Archives of General Psychiatry, 60,* 929–937.

Kendler, K. S., Walters, E. E., Neale, M. C., Kessler, R. C., Heath, A. C., & Eaves, L. J. (1995). The structure of the genetic and environmental risk factors for six major psychiatric disorders in women. *Archives of General Psychiatry, 52,* 374–383.

Kernberg, O. F. (1967). Borderline personality organization. *Journal of the American Psychoanalytic Association, 15,* 641–685.

Kernberg, O. F. (1975). *Borderline Conditions and Pathological Narcissism.* New York: Aronson.

Kerns, J. G., & Berenbaum, H. (2002). Cognitive impairments associated with formal thought disorder in people with schizophrenia. *Journal of Abnormal Psychology, 111,* 211–224.

Kessler, R. C, Keller, M. B., & Wittchen, H. (2001). The epidemiology of generalized anxiety disorder. *Psychiatric Clinics of North America, 24,* 19–39.

Kessler, R. C. (1995). The national comorbidity survey: Preliminary results and future directions. *International Journal of Methods in Psychiatric Research, 5,* 139–151.

Kessler, R. C. (2002). Epidemiology of depression. In I. H. Gotlib and C. L. Hammen (Eds.), *Handbook of depression.* New York: Guilford.

Kessler, R. C., Berglund, P., Demler, O., Jin, R., & Walters, E. E. (2005). Lifetime prevalence and age-of-onset distributions of DSM-IV disorders in the National Comorbidity Survey Replication. *Archives of General Psychiatry, 52,* 1048–1060.

Kessler, R. C., Berglund, P., Demler, O., Jin, R., Merikangas, K. R., & Walters, E. E. (2005). Lifetime prevalence and age-of-onset distributions of DSM-IV disorders in the National Comorbidity Survey Replication. *Archives of General Psychiatry, 62,* 593–603.

Kessler, R. C., Coccaro, E. F., Fava, M., Jaeger, S., Jin, R. & Walters, E. (2006). The prevalence and correlates of DSM-IV intermittent explosive disorder in the National Comorbidity Survey Replication. *Archives of General Psychiatry, 63,* 669–678.

Kessler, R. C., Gruber, M., Hettema, J. M., Hwang, I., Sampson, N., & Yonkers, K. A. (2008). Co-morbid major depression and generalized anxiety disorders in the National Comorbidity Survey follow-up. *Psychological Medicine, 38,* 365–374.

Kessler, R. C., McGonagle, K. A., Zhao, S., Nelson, C. R., Highes, M., Eshleman, S., et al. (1994). Lifetime and 12-month prevalence of DSM-III-R psychiatric disorders in the United States: Results from the National Comorbidity Survey. *Archives of General Psychiatry, 51,* 8–19.

Kessler, R. C., Merikangas, K. R., & Wang, P. S. (2007). Prevalence, comorbidity, and service utilization for mood disorders in the United States at the beginning of the twenty-first century. *Annual Review of Clinical Psychology, 3,* 137–158.

Kessler, R. C., Sonnega, A., Bromet, E., Hughes, M., & Nelson, C. B. (1995). Posttraumatic stress disorder in the National Comorbidity Survey. *Archives of General Psychiatry, 52,* 1048–1060.

Kessler, R. C., Stang, P. E., Wittchen, H., Ustun, T. B., Roy-Burne, P. P., & Walters, E. (1998). Lifetime panic-depression comorbidity in the National Comorbidity Survey. *Archives of General Psychiatry, 55,* 801–808.

Kessler, R., Berglund, P., Demler, O., Jin, R., & Walters, E. (2005). Lifetime prevalence and age-of-onset distributions of DSM-IV disorders in the National Comorbidity Survey Replication. *Archives of General Psychiatry, 62*(6), 593–602.

Kessler, R., Merikangas, K., & Wang, P. (2007). Prevalence, comorbidity, and service utilization for mood disorders in the United States at the beginning of the twenty-first century. *Annual Review of Clinical Psychology, 3,* 137–158.

Keteyian, A. (1986, March 10). The straight-arrow addict: Compulsive gambling of A. Schlichter. *Sports Illustrated,* 74–77.

Kettl, P. A. (1993). 10 basic rules for managing dementia. *Patient Care, 27,* 79–86.

Keyes, C. L. M. (2007). Promoting and protecting mental health as flourishing. *American Psychologist, 62,* 95–108.

Keys, A., Brozek, J., Henschel, A., Mickelsen, O., & Taylor, H. L. (1950). *The Biology of Human Starvation,* 2 vols. Minneapolis: University of Minnesota Press.

Khalid, N., Atkins, M., Tredget, J., Giles, M., Champney-Smith, K., & Kirov, G. (2008). The effectiveness of electroconvulsive therapy in treatment-resistant depression: A naturalistic study. *Journal of ECT, 24,* 141–145.

Kiecolt-Glaser, J. K. (1999). Stress, personal relationships, and immune function: Health implications. *Brain, Behavior, and Immunity, 13,* 61–72.

Kiecolt-Glaser, J. K., Bane, C., Glaser, R., & Malarkey, W. B. (2003). Love, marriage, and divorce: Newlyweds' stress hormones foreshadow relationship changes. *Journal of Consulting and Clinical Psychology, 71,* 176–188.

Kiecolt-Glaser, J. K., Malarkey, W. B., Chee, M., Newton, T., Cacioppo, J. T., Mao, H., et al. (1993). Negative behavior during marital conflict is associated with immunological down-regulation. *Psychosomatic Medicine, 55,* 395–409.

Kiecolt-Glaser, J. K., & Newton, T. L. (2001). Marriage and health: His and hers. *Psychological Bulletin, 127,* 472–503.

Kiesler, C. (1982). Mental hospitals and alternative care: Coninstitutionalization as potential public policy for mental patients. *American Psychologist, 37,* 349–360.

Kihara, T., & Shimohama, S. (2004). Alzheimer's disease and acetylcholine receptors. *Acta Neurobiologiae Experimentalis, 64,* 99–105.

Kihlstrom, J. F. (1998a). Exhumed memory. In S. J. Lynn & K. M. McConkey (Eds.), *Truth in Memory,* pp. 3–31. New York: Guilford.

Kihlstrom, J. F. (1998b). Dissociations and dissociation theory in hypnosis: A comment on Kirch and Lynn (1998). *Psychological Bulletin, 123,* 186–191.

Kihlstrom, J. F. (2002). To honor Kraepelin: From symptoms to pathology in the diagnosis of mental illness. In L. E. Beutler and M. L. Malik (Eds.). *Rethinking the DSM: A Psychological Perspective,* pp. 279–303. Washington, DC: American Psychological Association.

Kihlstrom, J. F. (2005). Dissociative disorders. *Annual Reviews in Clinical Psychology, 1,* 10.1–10.27.

Kihlstrom, J. F., Glisky, M. L., & Angiulo, M. J. (1994). Dissociative tendencies and dissociative disorders. *Journal of Abnormal Psychology, 103,* 117–124.

Kihlstrom, J. F., & Hastie, R. (1997). Mental representations of persons and personality. In R. Hogan, J. Johnson, & S. Briggs (Eds.), *Handbook of Personality Psychology,* pp. 712–735. San Diego, CA: Academic Press.

Kilmann, P. R., et al. (1982). The treatment of sexual paraphilias: A review of the outcome research. *Journal of Sex Research, 18,* 193–252.

Kilpatrick, D. G., & Acierno, R. (2003). Mental health needs of crime victims: Epidemiology and outcomes. *Journal of Traumatic Stress, 16,* 119–132.

Kilpatrick, D. G., Edmunds, C. N., & Seymour, A. K. (1992). *Rape in America: A Report to the Nation.* Arlington, VA: National Victim Center.

Kilpatrick, D. G., Ruggiero, K. J., Acierno, R., Saunders, B. E., Resnick, H. S., & Best, C. L. (2003). Violence and risk of PTSD, major depression, substance abuse/dependence, and comorbidity: Results from the national survey of adolescents. *Journal of Consulting and Clinical Psychology, 71,* 692–700.

Kilpatrick, D. G., Saunders, B. E., Amick-McMullan, A., Best, C. L., Veronen, L. J., & Resnick, H. S. (1989). Victim and crime factors associated with the development of crime-related posttraumatic stress disorder. *Behavior Therapy, 20,* 199–214.

Kim, J. E., & Moen, P. (2001). Is retirement good or bad for subjective well-being? *Current Directions in Psychological Science, 10,* 83–86.

Kimble, G. A. (1989). Psychology from the standpoint of a generalist. *American Psychologist, 44,* 491–499.

Kimmel, S. B., & Mahalik, J. R. (2005). Body image concerns of gay men: The roles of minority stress and conformity to masculine norms. *Journal of Consulting and Clinical Psychology, 73,* 1185–1190.

King, B. M. (1996). *Human Sexuality Today.* Upper Saddle River, NJ: Prentice Hall.

King, N. J., Ollier, K., Iacuone, R., Schuster, S., Bays, K., Gullone, E., et al. (1989). Fears of children and adolescents: A cross-sectional Australian study using the Revised-Fear Survey Schedule for Children. *Journal of Child Psychology and Psychiatry, 30,* 775–784.

King, R. A., Segman, R. H., & Anderson, G. M. (1994). Serotonin and suicidality: The impact of acute fluoxetine administration. I. Serotonin and suicide. *Israel Journal of Psychiatry and Related Sciences, 31,* 271–279.

Kingsberg, S. A., & Janata, J. W. (2003). The sexual aversions. In S. B. Levine and C. B. Risen (Eds.), *Handbook of Clinical Sexuality for Mental Health Professionals,* pp. 153–165. New York: Brunner-Routledge.

Kinsey, A. C., Pomeroy, W. B., & Martin, C. E. (1948). *Sexual Behavior in the Human Male.* Philadelphia: Saunders.

Kirisci, L., Tarter, R., Mezzich. A., & Vanyukov, M. (2007). Developmental trajectory classes in substance use disorder etiology. *Psychology of Addictive Behaviors, 21,* 287–296.

Kirk, S. A., & Kutchins, H. (1992). *The Selling of DSM: The Rhetoric of Science in Psychiatry.* New York: Aldine.

Kirmayer, L. J. (2001). Cultural variations in the clinical presentation of depression and anxiety: Implications for diagnosis and treatment. *Journal of Clinical Psychiatry, 62* (Suppl. 13), 22–28.

Kirmayer, L. J., Robbins, J. M., & Paris, J. (1994). Somatoform disorders: Personality and the social matrix of somatic distress. *Journal of Abnormal Psychology, 103,* 125–136.

Kirmayer, L. J. (2006). Beyond the new cross-cultural psychiatry: Cultural biology, discursive psychology and the ironies of globalization. *Transcultural Psychiatry, 43,* 126–144.

Kirsch, I., & Lynn, S. J. (1995). The altered state of hypnosis: Changes in the theoretical landscape. *American Psychologist, 50,* 846–858.

Kirsch, I., & Lynn, S. J. (1998). Dissociation theories of hypnosis. *Psychological Bulletin, 123,* 100–115.

Klein, D. F. (1996). Preventing hung juries about therapy studies. *Journal of Consulting and Clinical Psychology, 64,* 81–87.

Klein, D. F. (1999). Harmful dysfunction, disorder, disease, illness, and evolution. *Journal of Abnormal Psychology, 108,* 421–429.

Klein, D. F., & Klein, H. M. (1989). The definition and psychopharmacology of spontaneous panic and phobia. In P. Tyrer (Ed.), *Psychopharmacology of Anxiety.* New York: Oxford University Press.

Klein, D. N. (2003). Patients' versus informants' reports of personality disorders in predicting 71/2 year outcome in outpatients with depressive disorders. *Psychological Assessment, 15,* 216–222.

Klein, R. G., & Pine, D. S. (2002). Anxiety disorders. In M. Rutter & E. Taylor (Eds.), *Child and Adolescent Psychiatry,* 4th ed., pp. 486–509. Oxford, England: Blackwell.

Kleinman, A. (1988). *Rethinking Psychiatry: From Cultural Category to Personal Experience.* New York: Free Press.

Kleinman, A. (2004). Culture and depression. *New England Journal of Medicine, 352,* 951–953.

Klerman, G. L. (1990a). History and development of modern concepts of anxiety and panic. In J. Ballenger (Ed.), *Clinical Aspects of Panic Disorder,* pp. 3–12. New York: Wiley.

Klerman, G. (1990b). The psychiatric patient's right to effective treatment: Implications of Osheroff vs. Chestnut Lodge. *American Journal of Psychiatry, 147,* 409–418.

Klonsky, E. D. (2007). The functions of deliberate self-injury: A review of the evidence. *Clinical Psychology Review, 27,* 226–239.

Klonsky, E. D., Oltmanns, T. F., & Turkheimer, E. (2003). Deliberate self-harm in a nonclinical population: Prevalence and psychological correlates. *American Journal of Psychiatry, 160,* 1501–1508.

Kluft, R. P. (1987). An update on multiple personality disorder. *Hospital and Community Psychiatry, 38,* 363–373.

Klump, K. L., & Culbert, K. M. (2007). Molecular genetic studies of eating disorders: Current status and future directions. *Current Directions in Psychological Science, 16,* 37–41.

Klump, K. L., McGue, M., & Iacono, W. G. (2000). Age differences in genetic and environmental influences on eating attitudes and behaviors in preadolescent and adolescent female twins. *Journal of Abnormal Psychology, 109,* 239–251.

Kluznik, J. C., Speed, N., Van Valkenburg, C., & Magraw, R. (1986). Forty-year follow-up of United States prisoners of war. *American Journal of Psychiatry, 143,* 1443–1446.

Kneebone, I., & Martin, P. (2003). Coping and caregivers of people with dementia. *British Journal of Health Psychology, 8,* 1–17.

Knight, R. A. (1999). Validation of a typology for rapists. *Journal of Interpersonal Violence, 14,* 303–330.

Knight, R. A. & Guay, J. P. (2006). The role of psychopathy in sexual coercion against women. In C. J. Patrick (Ed.), *Handbook of Psychopathy,* pp. 512–532. New York: Guilford.

Knop, J., Penick, E., Jensen, P., Nickel, E., Gabrielli, W., Mednick, S., et al. (2003). Risk factors that predicted problem drinking in Danish men at age thirty. *Journal of Studies on Alcohol, 64,* 745–755.

Koch, H., & Knapp, D. E. (1987). Highlights of drug utilization in office practice. National Ambulatory Medical Survey, 1885. *Advance Data from Vital and Health Statistics,* No. 134. U.S. Department of Health and Human Services Publication No. (PHS) 87-1250.

Kochanek, K. D., Murphy, S. L., Anderson, R. N., & Scott, C. (2004). *Deaths: Final Data for 2002.* National Vital Statistics Reports. DHHS Publication No. (PHS) 2005–1120, *53* (5). Hyattsville, MD: National Center for Health Statistics.

Koegel, R. L., Koegel, L. K., & McNerney, E. K. (2001). Pivotal areas intervention for autism. *Journal of Clinical Child Psychology, 30,* 19–32.

Koenen, K. C., Stellman, J. M., Stellman, S. D., & Sommer, J. F. (2003). Risk factors for course of posttraumatic stress disorder among Vietnam veterans: A 14-year follow-up of American Legionnaires. *Journal of Consulting and Clinical Psychology, 71,* 980–986.

Koenig, H. G., & Blazer, D. G. (1990). Depression and other affective disorders. In C. K. Cassel, D. E. Riesenberg, L. B. Sorenson, & J. R. Walsh (Eds.), *Geriatric Medicine,* 2nd ed., pp. 473–489. New York: Springer.

Koenigsberg, H. W., Reynolds, D., Goodman, M., New, A. S., Mitropoulou, V., Trestman, R. L., et al. (2003). Risperidone in the treatment of schizotypal personality disorder. *Journal of Clinical Psychiatry, 64,* 628–634.

Koenigsberg, H., Woo-Ming, A., & Siever, L. (2002). *Pharmacological Treatments for Personality Disorders. A Guide to Treatments That Work,* 2nd ed., pp. 625–641.

Koerner, S. S., Wallace, S., Lehman, S. J., Lee, S. A., & Escalante, K. A. (2004). Sensitive mother-to-adolescent disclosures after divorce: Is the experience of sons different from that of daughters? *Journal of Family Psychology, 18*(1), 46–57.

Kohlberg, L. (1985). *The Psychology of Moral Development.* San Francisco: Harper & Row.

Kolassa, I., & Elbert, T. (2007). Structural and functional neuroplasticity in relation to traumatic stress. *Current Directions in Psychological Science, 16,* 321–325.

Koluchova, J. (1972). Severe deprivation in twins: A case study of marked IQ change after age 7. *Journal of Child Psychology and Psychiatry, 13,* 107–114.

Kontakos, N., & Stokes, J. (1999). Parkinson's disease—Recent developments and new directions. *Chronic Diseases in Canada, 20,* 58–76.

Koob, G. F. (2000). Neurobiology of addiction: Toward the development of new therapies. *Annals of the New York Academy of Sciences, 909,* 170–185.

Koob, G. F. (2006). Neurobiology of addiction: A neuroadaptational view relevant for diagnosis. *Addiction, 101* (Suppl. 1), 23–30.

Koons, C. R., Robins, C. J., Tweed, J. L., Lynch, T. R., Gonzales, A. M., Morse, J. Q., et al. (2001). Efficacy of dialectical behavior therapy in women veterans with borderline personality disorder. *Behavior Therapy, 32,* 371–390.

Kop, W. J. (1999). Chronic and acute psychological risk factors for liar clinical manifestations of coronary artery disease. *Psychosomatic Medicine, 61,* 476–487.

Kopelowicz, A., Liberman, R. P., & Zarate, R. (2002). Psychosocial treatments for schizophrenia. In P. E. Nathan & J. M. Gorman (Eds.). *A Guide to Treatments that Work,* 2nd ed., pp. 201–228. London: Oxford University Press.

Koranyi, E. K. (1989). Physiology of stress reviewed. In S. Cheren (Ed.), *Psychosomatic Medicine: Theory, Physiology, and Practice,* Vol. 1, pp. 241–278. Madison, CT: International Universities Press.

Koskenvuo, M., Kaprio, J., Rose, R. J., Kesaniemi, A., Sarna, S., Heikkila, K., et al. (1988). Hostility as a risk factor for mortality and ischemic heart disease in men. *Psychosomatic Medicine, 50,* 330–340.

Koski, L, Iacoboni, M., & Mazziotta, J. C. (2002). Deconstructing apraxia: Understanding disorders of intentional movement after stroke. *Current Opinion in Neurology, 15,* 71–77.

Koss, M. P., Tromp, S., & Tharan, M. (1995). Traumatic memories: Empirical foundations, forensic, and clinical implications. *Clinical Psychology: Science and Practice, 2,* 111–132.

Kovacs, M., Feinberg, T. L., Crouse-Novak, M. A., Paulaukas, S., Pollock, M., & Finkelstein, R. (1984). Depressive disorders in childhood. II. A longitudinal study of the risk for a subsequent major depression. *Archives of General Psychiatry, 41,* 643–649.

Kovas, Y., & Polmin, R. (2007). Learning abilities and disabilities: Generalist genes, specialist environments. *Current Directions in Psychological Science, 16,* 284–288.

Kowalski, K. M. (1998). The dangers of alcohol. *Current Health, 24,* 6–13.

Kozak, M. J., Liebowitz, M. R., & Foa, E. G. (2000). Cognitive behavior therapy and pharmacotherapy for obsessive-compulsive disorder: The NIMH-sponsored collaborative study. In W. K. Goodman & M. V. Rudorfer (Eds.), *Obsessive-Compulsive Disorder: Contemporary Issues in Treatment,* pp. 501–530. Mahwah, NJ: Erlbaum.

Kozlowski, L. T., Henningfield, J. E., & Brigham, J. (2001). *Cigarettes, Nicotine, and Health: A Biobehavioral Approach.* Thousand Oaks, CA: Sage Publications.

Kraemer, H. C. (2008). DSM categories and dimensions in clinical and research contexts. In J. E. Helzer, H. C. Kraemer, R. F. Krueger, H. Wittchen, P. J. Sirovotka et al. (Eds.), *Dimensional Approaches in Diagnostic Classification: Refining the Research Agenda for DSM-V,* pp. 5–17. Washington, DC: American Psychiatric Publishing.

Kraepelin, E. (1921). *Manic-Depressive Insanity and Paranoia.* Edinburgh, Scotland: Livingstone.

Krakow, B., et al. (2001). Imagery rehearsal therapy for chronic nightmares in sexual assault survivors with posttraumatic stress disorder: A randomized clinical trial. *Journal of the American Medical Association, 286,* 537–545.

Krantz, D. S., Contrada, R. J., Hill, D. R., & Friedler, E. (1988). Environmental stress and biobehavioral antecedents of coronary heart disease. *Journal of Consulting and Clinical Psychology, 56,* 333–341.

Krantz, D. S., Gabbay, F. H., Hedges, S. M., Leach, S. G., Gottdiener, J. S., & Rozanski, A. (1993). Mental and physical triggers of silent myocardial ischemia: Ambulatory studies using self-monitoring diary methodology. *Annals of Behavioral Medicine, 15,* 33–40.

Kreuger, A. B., & Stone, A. A. (2008). Assessment of pain: A community-based diary survey in the USA. *The Lancet, 371,* 1519–1525.

Kroenke, K., Spitzer, R. L., deGruy, F. V., Hahn, S. R., Linzer, M., Williams, J. B. W., et al. (1997). Multisomatoform disorder: An alternative to undifferentiated somatoform disorder for the somatizing patient in primary care. *Archives of General Psychiatry, 54,* 352–358.

Kroenke, K., & Swindle, R. (2000). Cognitive behavioural therapy for somatization and symptom syndromes: A critical review of controlled clinical trials. *Psychotherapy and Psychosomatics, 69,* 205–215.

Kroenke, K., West, S. L., Gilsenan, A., Eckert, G. J., Dolor, R., Stang, et al. (2001). Similar effectiveness of paroxetine, fluoxetine, and sertraline in primary care: A randomized trial. *Journal of the American Medical Association, 286,* 2947–2955.

Kroska, A., & Harkness, S.K. (2006). Stigma sentiments and self-meanings: Exploring the modified labeling theory of mental illness. *Social Psychology Quarterly, 69,* 325–348.

Krueger, R. B., & Kaplan, M. S. (1997). Frotteurism: Assessment and treatment, In D. R. Laws and W. O'Donohue (Eds.), *Sexual Deviance: Theory, Assessment, and Treatment.* New York: Guilford.

Krueger, R. F. (1999). Personality traits in late adolescence predict mental disorders in early adulthood: A prospective-epidemiological study. *Journal of Personality, 67,* 39–65.

Krueger, R. F. (2002). Psychometric perspectives on comorbidity. In J. E. Helzer and J. J. Hudziak (Eds.), *Defining Psychopathology in the 21st Century,* pp. 41–54. Washington, DC: American Psychiatric Press.

Kubzansky, L. D., Sparrow, D., Vokonas, P., & Kawachi, I. (2001). Is the glass half empty or half full? A prospective study of optimism and coronary heart disease in the normative aging study. *Psychosomatic Medicine, 63,* 910–916.

Kuehner, C. (2003). Gender differences in unipolar depression: An update of epidemiological findings and possible explanations. *Acta Psychiatrica Scandinavica, 108,* 163–174.

Kukull, W. A., & Bowen, J. D. (2002). Dementia epidemiology. *Medical Clinics of North America, 86,* 573–590.

Kumagai, R., Matsumiya, M., Tada, Y., Miyakawa, K., Ichimiya, Y., & Arai, H. (2008). Long-term effect of donepezil for Alzheimer's disease: Retrospective clinical evaluation of drug efficacy in Japanese patients. *Psychogeriatrics, 8,* 19–23.

Kunzmann, U., & Baltes, P. (2003). Wisdom-related knowledge: Affective, motivational, and interpersonal correlates. *Personality and Social Psychology Bulletin, 29,* 1104–1119.

Kupfer, D. J., Chengappa, K. N. R., Gelenberg, A. J., Hirschfeld, R. M. A., Goldberg, J. F., Sachs, G. S., et al. (2001). Citalopram as adjunctive therapy in bipolar depression. *Journal of Clinical Psychiatry, 62,* 985–990.

Kupfer, D. J., & Frank, E. (2001). The interaction of drug- and psychotherapy in the longterm treatment of depression. *Journal of Affective Disorders, 62,* 131–137.

Kurlan, R. (2004). The PANDAS hypothesis: Losing its bite? *Movement Disorders, 19,* 371–374.

Kurlan, R., & Kaplan, E. L. (2004). The pediatric autoimmune neuropsychiatric disorders associated with streptococcal infection (PANDAS) etiology for tics and obsessive-compulsive symptoms: Hypothesis or entity? *Pediatrics, 113,* 883–886.

Kurlan, R., Johnson, D., & Kaplan, E. L. (2008). Streptococcal infection and exacerbations of childhood tics and obsessive-compulsive symptoms: A prospective blinded cohort study. *Pediatrics, 121,* 1188–1197.

Kurtz, M., & Mueser, K. (2008). A meta-analysis of controlled research on social skills training for schizophrenia. *Journal of Consulting and Clinical Psychology, 76*(3), 491–504.

Kushner, M. G., Sher, K. J., & Erickson, D. J. (1999). Prospective analysis of the relation between DSM-III anxiety disorders and alcohol use disorders. *American Journal of Psychiatry, 156,* 723–732.

Kutscher, E. (2008). Antipsychotics. *Clinical Handbook of Schizophrenia,* pp. 159–167. New York: Guilford.

Kwapil, T. R. (1998). Social anhedonia as a predictor of the development of schizophrenia-spectrum disorders. *Journal of Abnormal Psychology, 107,* 558–565.

Kymalainen, J., & Weisman de Mamani, A. (2008). Expressed emotion, communication deviance, and culture in families of patients with schizophrenia: A review of the literature. *Cultural Diversity and Ethnic Minority Psychology, 14,* 85–91.

Lacey, J. I. (1967). Somatic response patterning and stress: Some revisions of activation theory. In M. H. Appley & R. Trumball (Eds.), *Psychological Stress.* New York: McGraw-Hill.

LaCroix, A. Z., & Haynes, S. G. (1987). Gender differences in the stressfulness of workplace roles: A focus on work and health. In R. Barnett, G. Baruch, & L. Biener (Eds.), *Gender and Stress,* pp. 96–121. New York: Free Press.

Ladwig, K., Marten-Mittag, B., Erazo, N., & Guendel, H. (2001). Identifying somatization disorder in a population-based health examination survey: Psychosocial burden and gender differences. *Psychosomatics, 42,* 511–518.

Lahey, B. B., et al. (1994). DSM-IV field trials for attention deficit/hyperactivity disorder in children and adolescents. *Journal of the American Academy of Child and Adolescent Psychiatry, 151,* 1673–1685.

Lahey, B. B., Loeber, R., Burke, J. D., & Applegate, B. (2005). Predicting future antisocial personality disorder in males from a clinical assessment in childhood. *Journal of Consulting and Clinical Psychology, 73,* 389–399.

Lahey, B. B., Schwab-Stone, M., Goodman, S. H., Waldron, I. D., Canino, G., Rathouz, P. J., et al. (2000). Age and gender differences in oppositional behavior and conduct problems: A cross-sectional household study of middle childhood and adolescence. *Journal of Abnormal Psychology, 109,* 488–503

Lahti, R. A., Roberts, R. C., Conley, R. R., Cochrane, E. V., et al. (1996). D2 type receptors in postmortem human brain sections from normal and schizophrenic subjects. *Neuroreport: An International Journal for the Rapid Communication of Research in Neuroscience, 7*(12), 1945–1948.

Lake, C., & Hurwitz, N. (2007). Schizoaffective disorder merges schizophrenia and bipolar disorders as one disease—there is no schizoaffective disorder. *Current Opinion in Psychiatry, 20,* 365–379.

Lam, R. W., Levitt, A., Levitan, R. D., Enns, M. W., Morehouse, R., Michalak, E., & Tam, E. M. (2006). The Can-SAD Study: A randomized controlled trial of the effectiveness of light therapy and fluoxetine in patients with winter seasonal affective disorder. *American Journal of Psychiatry, 163,* 805–812.

Lamberg, L. (1998). New drug for erectile dysfunction boon for many, "viagravation" for some. *Journal of the American Medical Association, 280,* 867–869.

Lambert, M. J., & Bergin, A. E. (1994). In A. E. Bergin & S. L. Garfield, *The Effectiveness of Psychotherapy and Behavior Change,* 4th ed. Oxford, England: John Wiley & Sons.

Lancet (1991). Editorial. Phenylketonuria grows up. *337,* 1256–1257.

Landis, D., Gaylord-Harden, N. K., & Malinowski, S. L. (2007). Urban adolescent stress and hopelessness. *Journal of Adolescence, 30,* 1051–1070.

Lanfumey, L., Mongeau, R., & Cohen-Salmon, C. (2008). Corticosteroid-serotonin interactions in the neurobiological mechanisms of stress-related disorders. *Neuroscience & Biobehavioral Reviews, 32,* 1174–1184.

Langevin, R. (1992). Biological factors contributing to paraphilic behavior. *Psychiatric Annals, 22,* 307–314.

Lara, M. E., & Klein, D. N. (1999). Psychosocial processes underlying the maintenance and persistence of depression: Implications for understanding chronic depression. *Clinical Psychology Review, 19,* 553–570.

Larsen, R. J., & Buss, D. J. (2002). *Personality Psychology.* New York: McGraw-Hill.

Larson, R., Csikszentmihalyi, M., & Graef, R. (1980). Mood variability and the psychosocial adjustment of adolescents. *Journal of Youth and Adolescence, 9,* 469–490.

Last, C. G., & Strauss, C. C. (1990). School refusal in anxiety-disordered children and adolescents. *Journal of the American Academy of Child and Adolescent Psychiatry, 29,* 31–35.

Latendresse, S. J., Rose, R. J., Viken, R. J., Pulkkinen, L., Kaprio, J., & Dick, D. M. (2008). Parenting mechanisms in links between parents' and adolescents' alcohol use behaviors. *Alcoholism: Clinical and Experimental Research, 32,* 322–330.

Laumann-Billings, L. &. Emery, R. E. (2000). Distress among young adults from divorced families. *Journal of Family Psychology, 14,* 671–687.

Laumann, E., & Gagnon, J. (1995). A sociological perspective on sexual action. *Conceiving Sexuality: Approaches to Sex Research in a Postmodern World,* pp. 183–213. Florence, KY: Taylor & Frances/Routledge.

Laumann, E. O., Gagnon, J. H., Michael, R. T., & Michaels, S. (1994). *The Social Organization of Sexuality: Sexual Practices in the United States.* Chicago: University of Chicago Press.

Laumann, E. O., Paik, A., & Rosen, R. (1999). Sexual dysfunction in the United States: Prevalence and predictors. *Journal of the American Medical Association, 281,* 537–544.

Lauterbach, E. C., Carter, W. G., Rathke, K. M., Thomas, B. H., Shillcutt, S. D., Vogel, R. L., et al. (2001). Tardive dyskinesia—Diagnostic issues, subsyndromes, and concurrent movement disorders. *Schizophrenia Bulletin, 27,* 601–614.

Lavender, H., Khondoker, A. H., & Jones, R. (2006). Understandings of depression: An interview study of Yoruba, Bangladeshi and White British people. *Family Practice, 23,* 651–658.

Lawton, M. P. (1989). Environmental approaches to research and treatment of Alzheimer's disease. In E. Light & B. D. Lebowitz (Eds.), *Alzheimer's Disease Treatment and Family Stress: Directions for Research.* U.S. Department of Health and Human Services, Publication No. (ADM) 89-1569, 340–362.

Lawton, M. P. (2001). Quality of life and the end of life. In J. E. Birren & K. W. Schaie (Eds.), *Handbook of the Psychology of Aging,* 5th ed., pp. 592–616. San Diego, CA: Academic Press.

Lazarus, R. S. (1966). *Psychological Stress and the Coping Process.* New York: McGraw-Hill.

Lazarus, R. S. (2000). Toward better research on stress and coping. *American Psychologist, 55,* 665–673.

Lazarus, R. S., & Folkman, S. (1984). *Stress, Appraisal, and Coping,* New York: Springer.

Lazoritz, S. (1990). What ever happened to Mary Ellen? *Child Abuse and Neglect, 14,* 143–149.

Ledoux, J. E., & Gorman, J. M. (2001). A call to action: Overcoming anxiety through active coping. *American Journal of Psychiatry, 158,* 1953–1955.

LeDoux. J. E. (2000). Emotion circuits in the brain. *Annual Review of Neuroscience, 23,* 155–184.

Leenaars, A. A. (2004). Altruistic suicide: A few reflections. *Archives of Suicide Research, 8,* 1–7.

Leesfield, I. H. (1987). Negligence of mental health professionals. *Trial, 23,* 57–61.

LeFever, G. B., et al., (2003). ADHD among American schoolchildren: Evidence of overdiagnosis and overmedication. *The Scientific Review of Mental Health Practice, 2.*

Leff, J. (1992). Transcultural aspects. In E. S. Paykel (Ed.), *Handbook of Affective Disorders,* 2nd ed., pp. 539–550. New York: Guilford.

Leff, J., Sartorius, N., Jablensky, A., Korten, A., & Ernberg, G. (1992). The International Pilot Study of Schizophrenia: Five-year follow-up findings. *Psychological Medicine, 22,* 131–145.

Leff, J., & Vaughn, C. (1985). *Expressed Emotion in Families: Its Significance for Mental Illness,* New York: Guilford.

Leff, J. P. (1988). *Psychiatry Around the Globe: A Transcultural View.* London: Royal College of Psychiatrists.

Lehman, A. F., Dixon, L. B., Hoch, J. S., DeForge, B., Kernan, E., & Frank, R. (1999). Cost-effectiveness of assertive community treatment for homeless persons with severe mental illness. *British Journal of Psychiatry, 174,* 346–352.

Lehman, A. F., Kreyenbuhl, J., Buchanan, R. W., Dickerson, F. B., Dixon, L. B., Goldberg, R., et al. (2004). The schizophrenia patient outcomes research team (PORT): Updated treatment recommendations. *Schizophrenia Bulletin, 30,* 193–217.

Lehrer, P., & Carr, R. (1997). Progressive relaxation. In W. T. Roth & I. D. Yalom (Eds.), *Treating Anxiety Disorders,* pp. 83–116. San Francisco: Jossey-Bass.

Leiblum, S. R. (1995). Relinquishing virginity: The treatment of a complex case of vaginismus. In R. C. Rosen & S. R. Leiblum (Eds.), *Case Studies in Sex Therapy,* pp. 250–263. New York: Guilford.

Leiblum, S. R. (1999). What every urologist should know about female sexual dysfunction. *International Journal of Impotence Research, 11* (Suppl. 1), 39–40.

Leiblum, S. R. (2001). Critical overview of the new consensus-based definitions and classification of female sexual dysfunction. *Journal of Sex and Marital Therapy, 27,* 159–168.

Leichtman, M. (1989). Evolving concepts of borderline personality disorders. *Bulletin of the Menninger Clinic, 53,* 229–249.

Lejoyeux, M., McLoughlin, M., & Ades, J. (2006). Pyromania. In E. Hollander & D.J. Stein (Eds.), *Clinical manual of impulse-Control Disorders,* pp. 229–250. Arlington, VA: American Psychiatric Publishing

Leland, J. (1996, August 26). The fear of heroin is shooting up. *Newsweek,* 55–56.

Lencz, T., Smith, C. W., Auther, A. M., Correll, C. U., & Cornblatt, B. A. (2003). The assessment of prodromal schizophrenia: Unresolved issues and future directions. *Schizophrenia Bulletin, 29,* 717–728.

Lenzenweger, M., & O'Driscoll, G. (2006). Smooth pursuit eye movement and schizotypy in the community. *Journal of Abnormal Psychology, 115,* 779–786.

Lenzenweger, M. F. (1999). Schizophrenia: Refining the phenotype, resolving endophenotypes. *Behaviour Research and Therapy, 37,* 281–295.

Lenzenweger, M. F., Lane, M.C., Loranger, A. W., & Kessler, R. C.(2007). DSM-IV personality disorders in the National Comorbidity Survey Replication. *Biological Psychiatry, 62,* 553–564.

Lenzenweger, M. F., & Willett, J. B. (2007). Predicting individual change in personality disorder features by simultaneous individual change in personality dimensions linked to neurobehavioral systems: The longitudinal study of personality disorders. *Journal of Abnormal Psychology, 116,* 684–700.

Leon, G., Fulkerson, J. A., Perry, C. L., & Cudeck, R. (1993). Personality and behavioral vulnerabilities associated with risk status for eating disorders in adolescent girls. *Journal of Abnormal Psychology, 102,* 438–444.

Leon, G. R., Fulkerson, J. A., Perry, C. L., & Early-Zald, M. B. (1995). Prospective analysis of personality and behavioral vulnerabilities and gender influences in the later development of disordered eating. *Journal of Abnormal Psychology, 104,* 140–149.

Leonard, K. E., & Eiden, R. D. (2007). Marital and family processes in the context of alcohol use and alcohol disorders. *Annual Review of Clinical Psychology, 3,* 285–310

Leonard, K. E., Eiden, R. D., Wong, M. M., Zucker, R. A., Puttler, L. I., Fitzgerald, H. E., et al., (2000). Developmental perspectives on risk and vulnerability in alcoholic families. *Alcoholism: Clinical and Experimental Research, 24,* 238–240.

Leonard, L. M., & Follette, V. M. (2002). Sexual functioning in women reporting a history of child sexual abuse: Review of the empirical literature and clinical implications. *Annual Review of Sex Research, 13,* 346–388.

Leonardo, E. D., & Hen, R. (2006). Genetics of affective and anxiety disorders. *Annual Review of Psychology, 57,* 117–137.

Leong, F. T. L. (2007). Cultural accommodation as method and metaphor. *American Psychologist, 62,* 916–927.

Leor, J., Poole, W. K., & Kloner, R. A. (1996). Sudden cardiac death triggered by an earthquake. *New England Journal of Medicine, 334*(7), 413–419.

Lerner, A. J. (1999). Women and Alzheimer's disease. *Journal of Clinical Endocrinology and Metabolism, 84,* 1830–1834.

Leserman, J., Jackson, E. D., Petitto, J. M., Golden, R. N., Silva, S. G., Perkins, D. O., et al. (1999). Progression to AIDS: The effects of stress, depressive symptoms, and social support. *Psychosomatic Medicine, 61,* 397–406.

Lesser, J., & O'Donohue, W. (1999). What is a delusion? Epistemological dimensions. *Journal of Abnormal Psychology, 108,* 687–694.

Lester, D. (2002). The effectiveness of suicide prevention and crisis intervention services. In D. Lester (Ed.), *Crisis Intervention and Counseling by Telephone,* 2nd ed., pp. 289–298. Springfield, IL: Charles C. Thomas.

Leucht, S., Pitschel-Walz, G., Engel, R. R., & Kissling, W. (2002). Amisulpride, an unusual "atypical" antipsychotic: A meta-analysis of randomized controlled trials. *American Journal of Psychiatry, 159,* 180–190.

Lev, A. I. (2005). Disordering gender identity: Gender identity disorder in the DSM-IV-TR. *Journal of Psychology & Human Sexuality, 17,* 35–69.

LeVay, S. (1993). *The Sexual Brain,* Cambridge, MA: MIT Press.

LeVay, S., & Valente, S. M. (2003). *Human Sexuality.* Sunderland, MA: Sinauer Associates.

Levenkron, S. (2006). *Cutting: Understanding and Overcoming Self-Mutiliation.* New York: W. W. Norton.

Levenson, M. R. (1992). Rethinking psychopathy. *Theory and Psychology, 2,* 51–71.

Levenson, R. W., Carstensen, L. L., & Gottman, J. M. (1994). The influence of age and gender on affect, physiology, and their interrelations: A study of long-term marriages. *Journal of Personality and Social Psychology, 67,* 56–68.

Levenson, R. W., & Miller, B. L. (2007). Loss of cells—loss of self: Frontotemporal lobar degeneration and human emotion. *Current Directions in Psychological Science, 16,* 289–294.

Leventhal, A. M., & Rehm, L. P. (2005). The empirical status of melancholia: Implications for psychology. *Clinical Psychology Review, 25,* 25–44.

Leventhal, H., et al. (2001). Heath risk behaviors and aging. In J. E. Birren & K. W. Schaie (Eds.), *Handbook of the Psychology of Aging,* 5th ed., pp. 186–214. San Diego, CA: Academic Press.

Leventhal, T., & Brooks-Gunn, J. (2000). The neighborhoods they live in: The effects of neighborhood residence on child and adolescent outcomes. *Psychological Bulletin, 126,* 309–337.

Levine, H. G. (1978). The discovery of addiction: Changing conceptions of habitual drunkenness in America. *Journal of Studies on Alcohol, 39,* 143–174.

Levine, S. B., Risen, C. B., & Althof, S. E. (1990). Essay on the diagnosis and nature of paraphilia. *Journal of Sex and Marital Therapy, 16,* 89–102.

Levinson, B. (1999). Erectile dysfunction and culture in South Africa. *Journal of Sex and Marital Therapy, 25,* 267–270.

Levinson, D. J. (1986). A conception of adult development. *American Psychologist, 41,* 3–13.

Levitan, R. D., Rector, N. A., Sheldon, T., & Goering, P. (2003). Childhood adversities associated with major depression and/or anxiety disorders in a community sample of Ontario: Issues of co-morbidity and specificity. *Depression & Anxiety, 17,* 34–42.

Levitt, E. E., Moser, C., & Jamison, K. V. (1994). The prevalence and some attributes of females in the sadomasochistic subculture: A second report. *Archives of Sexual Behavior, 23,* 465–474.

Levy, D. L., & Holzman, P. S. (1997). Eye tracking dysfunction and schizophrenia: An overview with special reference to the genetics of schizophrenia. *International Review of Psychiatry, 9,* 365–371.

Levy, F., Hay, D. A., McStephen, M., Wood, C., & Waldman, I. (1997). Attention-deficit/hyperactivity disorder: A category or a continuum? Genetic analysis of a large-scale twin study. *Journal of the American Academy of Child and Adolescent Psychiatry, 36,* 737–744.

Lewinsohn, P. M., Holm-Denoma, J. M., Small, J. W., Seeley, J. R., & Joiner, T. E. (2008). Separation anxiety disorder in childhood as a risk factor for future mental illness. *Journal of the American Academy of Child & Adolescent Psychiatry, 47,* 548–555.

Lewinsohn, P. M., Roberts, R. E., Seely, J. R., Rohde, P., Gotlib, I. H., & Hops, H. (1994). Adolescent psychopathology. II. Psychosocial risk factors for depression. *Journal of Abnormal Psychology, 103,* 302–315.

Lewinsohn, P. M., Rohde, P., & Seeley, J. R. (1998). Major depressive disorder in older adolescents: Prevalence, risk factors, and clinical implications. *Clinical Psychology Review, 18,* 765–794.

Lewis, M. H. (1996). Psychopharmacology of autism spectrum. *Journal of Autism and Developmental Disorders, 26,* 231–235.

Lewis, V., Allen-Byrd, L., & Rouhbakhsh, P. (2004). Understanding successful family recovery in treating alcoholism. *Journal of Systemic Therapies, 23,* 39.

Ley, R. (1999). The modification of breathing behavior: Pavlovian and operant control in emotion and cognition. *Behavior Modification, 23,* 441–479.

Leys, D., Pasquier, F., & Parnetti, L. (1998). Epidemiology of vascular dementia. *Haemostasis, 28,* 134–150.

Li, S. (2003). Biocultural orchestration of developmental plasticity across levels: The interplay of biology and culture in shaping the mind and behavior across the life span. *Psychological Bulletin, 129,* 171–194.

Lidz, C. W., Hoge, S. K., Gardner, W., Bennett, N. S., Monahan, J., Mulvey, E. P., et al. (1995). Perceived coercion in mental hospital admission: Pressures and process. *Archives of General Psychiatry, 52,* 1034–1039.

Lidz, C. W., Mulvey, E. P., & Gardner, W. (1993). The accuracy of predictions of violence to others. *Journal of the American Medical Association, 269,* 1007–1011.

Lieberman, J. (2006). Comparative effectiveness of antipsychotic drugs. *Archives of General Psychiatry, 63,* 1069–1072.

Lieberman, J., Chakos, M., Wu, H., Alvir, J., Hoffman, E., Robinson, D., et al. (2001). Longitudinal study of brain morphology in first episode schizophrenia. *Biological Psychiatry, 49,* 487–499.

Lieberman, J., Stroup, T., McEvoy, J., Swartz, M., Rosenheck, R., Perkins, D., et al. (2005). Effectiveness of Antipsychotic Drugs in Patients with Chronic Schizophrenia. *New England Journal of Medicine, 353,* 1209–1223.

Lilienfeld, S. O. (1992). The association between antisocial personality and somatization disorders: A review and integration of theoretical models. *Clinical Psychology Review, 12,* 641–662.

Lilienfeld, S. O. (1994). Conceptual problems in the assessment of psychopathy. *Clinical Psychology Review, 14,* 17–38.

Lilienfeld, S. O. (2007). Psychological treatments that cause harm. *Perspectives on Psychological Science, 2,* 53–70.

Lilienfeld, S. O., Lyn, S. J., Kirsch, I., Chaves, J. F., Sarbin, T. R., Ganaway, G. K., et al. (1999). Dissociative identity disorder and the sociocognitive model: Recalling lessons of the past. *Psychological Bulletin, 125,* 507–523.

Lock, J., Le Grange, D., Agras, W. S., Dare, C. (2001). *Treatment Manual for Anorexia Nervosa: A Family-based Approach.* New York: The Guilford Press.

Loeb, K. L., Walsh, B. T., Lock, J., Le Grange, D., Jones, J., Marcus, S., et al. (2007). Open trial of family-based treatment for full and partial anorexia nervosa in adolescence: Evidence of successful dissemination. *Journal of the American Academy of Child & Adolescent Psychiatry, 46,* 792–800.

Lilienfeld, S. O., Lynn, S. J., & Lohr, J. M. (2003). *Science and Pseudoscience in Clinical Psychology.* New York: Guilford.

Lindsay, D. S., Hagen, L., Read, J. D., Wade, K. A., & Garry, M. (2004). True photographs and false memories. *Psychological Science, 15,* 149–154.

Lincoln, Tania M. 2007. Relevant dimensions of delusions: Continuing the continuum versus category debate. *Schizophrenia Research, 93,* 211–220.

Linehan, M. M. (1993). *Cognitive-Behavioral Treatment of Borderline Personality Disorder.* New York: Guilford.

Linehan, M. M., Cochran, B. N., & Kehrer, C. A. (2001). Dialectical behavior therapy for borderline personality disorder. In D. H. Barlow (Ed.), *Clinical Handbook of Psychological Disorders: A Step By Step Treatment Manual,* 3rd ed., pp. 470–522. New York: Guilford.

Linehan, M. M., Kanter, J. W., & Comtois, K. A. (1999). Dialectical behavior therapy for borderline personality disorder: Efficacy, specificity, and cost effectiveness. In D. S. Janowsky (Ed.), *Psychotherapy Indications and Outcomes,* pp. 93–118. Washington, DC: American Psychiatric Press.

Linehan, M. M., Tutek, D. A., Heard, H. L., & Armstrong, H. E. (1994). Interpersonal outcome of cognitive-behavioral treatment for chronically suicidal borderline patients. *American Journal of Psychiatry, 151,* 1771–1776.

Link, B., Cullen, F., & Andrews, H. (1990, August). Violent and illegal behavior of current and former mental patients compared to community controls. Paper presented at the meeting of the Society for the Study of Social Problems.

Link, B. G., & Phelan, J. C. (1999). The labeling theory of mental disorder (II): The consequences of labeling. In A. V. Horwitz and T. L. Scheid (Eds.), *A Handbook for the Study of Mental Health: Social Contexts Theories and Systems,* pp. 361–376. New York: Cambridge University Press.

Linley, P. A. & Joseph, S. (2005). The human capacity for growth through adversity. *American Psychologist, 60,* 262–264.

Linney, Y. M., Murray, R. M., Peters, E. R., MacDonald, A. M., Rijskijk, F., & Sham, P. (2003). A quantitative genetic analysis of schizotypal personality traits. *Psychological Medicine, 33,* 803–816.

Lipowski, Z. J. (1988). Somatization: The concept and its clinical applications. *American Journal of Psychiatry, 145,* 1358–1368.

Lipsey, M.W., & Wilson, D.B. (1993). The efficacy of psychological, educational, and behavioral treatment: Confirmation from meta-analysis. *American Psychologist, 48*(12), 1181–1209.

Lisanby, S. H. (2007). Electroconvulsive therapy for depression. *New England Journal of Medicine, 357,* 1939–1945.

Lisanby, S. H., Maddox, J. H., Prudic, J., Devanand, D. P., & Sackheim, H. A. (2000). The effects of electroconvulsive therapy on memory of autobiographical and public events. *Archives of General Psychiatry, 57,* 581–590.

Litz, B. T. (2004). *Early Intervention for Trauma and Traumatic Loss.* New York: Guilford.

Litz, B. T. (2005). Has resilience to severe trauma been underestimated? *American Psychologist, 60,* 262.

Livesley, J. (2008). Toward a genetically-informed model of borderline personality disorder. *Journal of Personality Disorders, 22,* 42–71.

Livesley, W. J. (1995). Commentary on dependent personality disorder. In W. J. Livesley (Ed.), *The DSM-IV Personality Disorders,* pp. 257–260. New York: Guilford.

LoboPrabhu, Sheila M.; Molinari, Victor A.; Lomax, James W.; pp. 151–167. Baltimore, MD, US: Johns Hopkins University Press, 2006. xiv, 295 pp.

Lochman, J. E., & Wells, K. C. (2004). The coping power program for preadolescent aggressive boys and their parents: Outcome effects at the 1-year follow-up. *Journal of Consulting and Clinical Psychology, 72*(4), 571–578.

Loeb, T. B., Williams, J. K., Carmona, J. V., Rivkin, I., Wyatt, G. E., Chin, D., et al. (2002). Child sexual abuse: Associations with the sexual functioning of adolescents and adults. *Annual Review of Sex Research, 13*, 307–345.

Loeber, R. (1988). Natural histories of conduct problems, delinquency, and associated substance use: Evidence for developmental progression. In B. B. Lahey & A. E. Kazdin (Eds.), *Advances in Clinical Child Psychology,* Vol. 11, pp. 73–118. New York: Plenum.

Loeber, R., Lahey, B. B., & Thomas, C. (1991). Diagnostic conundrum of oppositional defiant disorder and conduct disorder. *Journal of Abnormal Psychology,* 100, 379–390.

Loftus, E. F. (1993). The reality of repressed memories. *American Psychologist, 48,* 518–537.

Loftus, E. F. (2003). Make-believe memories. *American Psychologist, 58,* 867–871.

Loftus, E. F. (2004). Memories of things unseen. *Current Directions in Psychological Science, 13,* 145–147.

Loftus, E., & Ketcham, K. (1994). *The Myth of Repressed Memory.* New York: St. Martin's Press.

Loftus, E. F., & Klinger, M. R. (1992). Is the unconscious smart or dumb? *American Psychologist, 47*(6), 761–765.

Lohr, J. M., Kleinknecht, R. A., Conley, A. T., Dal Cerro, S., Schmidt, J., & Sonntag, M. E. (1992). A methodological critique of the current status of eye movement desensitization (EMD). *Behavior Therapy and Experimental Psychiatry, 23,* 159–167.

Loman, L. A., & Siegel, G. (2005). Alternative response in Minnesota: Findings of the program evaluation. *Protecting Children, 20,* 78–92.

Lombardo, P. A. (2001). Carrie Buck's pedigree. *Journal of Laboratory and Clinical Medicine. 138,* 278–282.

Longino, C. F., & Mittelmark, M. B. (1996). In J. Sadavoy, L. W. Lazarus, L. F. Jarvik, & G. T. Grossberg (Eds.), *Comprehensive Review of Geriatric Psychiatry—II,* pp. 135–152. Washington, DC: American Psychiatric Press.

Looper, K. J, Kirmayer, L. J. (2001). Hypochondriacal concerns in a community population. *Psychological Medicine 31,* 577–584.

Looper, K. J. & Kirmayer, L. J. (2002). Behavioral medicine approaches to somatoform disorders. *Journal of Consulting and Clinical Psychology, 70,* 810–827.

Lopez, A. D., Mathers, C. D., Ezzati, M., Jamison, D. T., & Murray, C. J. L. (2006). *Global Burden of Disease and Risk Factors.* Washington, DC: The World Bank and Oxford University Press.

López, S., Nelson Hipke, K., Polo, A., Jenkins, J., Karno, M., Vaughn, C., et al. (2004). Ethnicity, expressed emotion, attributions, and course of schizophrenia: family warmth matters. *Journal of Abnormal Psychology, 113,* 428–439.

Lopez, S. R., & Guarnaccia, P. J. (2000). Cultural psychopathology: Uncovering the social world of mental illness. *Annual Review of Psychology, 51,* 571–598.

Lopez, S. R., Nelson, K., Snyder, K., & Mintz, J. (1999). Attributions and affective reactions of family members and course of schizophrenia. *Journal of Abnormal Psychology, 108,* 307–314.

Lord, C., & Bailey, A. (2002). Autism spectrum disorders. In M. Rutter & E. Taylor (Eds.), *Child and Adolescent Psychiatry,* 4th ed., pp. 636–663. Oxford, England: Blackwell.

Losh, M., & Capps, L. (2006). Understanding of emotional experience in autism: Insights from the personal accounts of high-functioning children with autism. *Developmental Psychology, 42,* 809–818.

Lotter, V. (1966). Epidemiology of autistic conditions in young children. *Social Psychiatry, 1,* 124–137.

Lovaas, O. I. (1987). Behavioral treatment and normal educational and intellectual functioning in young autistic children. *Journal of Consulting and Clinical Psychology, 55,* 3–9.

Lovaas, O. I., Schreibman, L., Koegel, R. L., & Rehm, R. (1971). Selective responding by autistic children to multiple sensory input. *Journal of Abnormal Psychology, 77,* 211–222.

Low, P. W., Jeffries, J. C., & Bonnie, R. J. (1986). *The Trial of John W. Hinckley, Jr.: A Case Study in the Insanity Defense,* Mineola, NY: Foundation Press.

Luborsky, L., Barber, J. P., & Beutler, L. (1993). Introduction to Special Section: A briefing on curative factors in dynamic psychotherapy. *Journal of Consulting and Clinical Psychology, 61*(4), 539–541.

Luborsky, L., Diguer, L., Seligman, D. A., Rosenthal, R., Krause, E. D., Johnson, S., Halperin, G., Bishop, M., Berman, J. S., & Schweizer, E. (1999). The researcher's own therapy allegiances: A "wild card" in comparisons of treatment efficacy. *Clinical Psychology: Science and Practice, 6*(1), 95–106.

Lubs, H. A. (1969). A marker X chromosome. *American Journal of Human Genetics, 21,* 231–244.

Lucas, A. R., Crowson, C. S., O'Fallon, W. M., & Melton, L. J. (1999). The ups and downs of anorexia nervosa. *International Journal of Eating Disorders, 26,* 397–405.

Lyketsos, C. G., Garrett, E., Liang, K., & Anthony, J. C. (1999). Cannabis use and cognitive decline in persons under 65 years of age. *American Journal of Epidemiology, 149,* 794–781.

Lynam, D. R., et al. (2000). The interaction between impulsivity and neighborhood context on offending: The effects of impulsivity are stronger in poor neighborhoods. *Journal of Abnormal Psychology, 109,* 563–574.

Lynam, D. R., Caspi, A., Moffitt, T. E., Loeber, R., & Stouthamer-Loeber, M. (2007). Longitudinal evidence that psychopathy scores in early adolescence predict adult psychopathy. *Journal of Abnormal Psychology, 116,* 155–165.

Lynam, D. R., & Widiger, T. A. (2001). Using the five-factor model to represent the DSM-IV personality disorders: An expert consensus approach. *Journal of Abnormal Psychology, 110,* 401–412.

Lynn, S. J., & McConkey, K. M. (1998). *Truth in Memory,* New York: Guilford.

Lyon, G. R. (1996). Learning disabilities. *Future of Children, 6,* 54–76.

Lyons, M. J. (1995). Epidemiology of personality disorders. In M. T. Tsuang, M. Tohen, & G. E. P. Zahner (Eds.), *Textbook in Psychiatric Epidemiology,* pp. 407–436. New York: Wiley.

Maccoby, E. E., & Martin, J. A. (1983). Socialization in the context of the family: Parent-child interaction. In E. M. Hetherington (Ed.), *Socialization, Personality, and Social Development,* Vol. 4, *Handbook of Child Psychology,* pp. 1–101. New York: Wiley.

Maccoby, E. E., & Mnookin, R. H. (1992). *Dividing the Child: Social and Legal Dilemmas of Custody,* Cambridge, MA: Harvard University Press.

Maccoby, E. E. (1998). *The Two Sexes: Growing Up Apart, Coming Together.* Cambridge, MA: Belknap Press.

MacCoun, R. J., Reuter, P., & Wolf, C. (2001). *Drug War Heresies: Learning from Other Vices, Times, and Places (RAND Studies in Policy Analysis).* New York: Cambridge University Press.

MacDonald, G., & Leary, M. R. (2005). Why does social exclusion hurt? The relationship between social and physical pain. *Psychological Bulletin, 131,* 202–223.

Mack, A. H., Forman, L., Brown, R., & Frances, A. (1994). A brief history of psychiatric classification: From the ancients to DSM-IV. *Psychiatric Clinics of North America, 17,* 515–523.

Mackay, R. D. (1988). Post-Hinckley insanity in the U.S.A. *Criminal Law Review,* 88–96.

MacLeod, C., Rutherford, E., Campbell, L., Ebsworthy, G., & Holker, L. (2002). Selective attention and emotional vulnerability: Assessing the causal basis of their association through the experimental manipulation of attentional bias. *Journal of Abnormal Psychology, 111,* 107–123.

MacMillan, D. L., Gresham, F. M., & Siperstein, G. N. (1995). Heightened concerns over the 1992 AAMR definition: Advocacy versus precision. *American Journal on Mental Retardation, 100,* 87–97.

Magai. C. (2001). Emotions over the life span. In J. E. Birren & K. W. Schaie (Eds.), *Handbook of the Psychology of Aging,* 5th ed., pp. 399–426. San Diego, CA: Academic Press.

Magenis, R. E., Overton, K. M., Chamberlin, J., Brady, T., & Lovrien, E. (1977). Parental origin of the extra chromosome in Down's syndrome. *Human Genetics, 37,* 7–16.

Mahe, V., & Balogh, A. (2000). Long-term pharmacological treatment of generalized anxiety disorder. *International Clinical Psychopharmacology, 15,* 99–105.

Maher, B. A. (2001). Delusions. In P. B. Sutker and H. E. Adams (Eds.), *Comprehensive Handbook of Psychopathology,* 3rd ed., pp. 309–339. New York: Kluwer Academic/Plenum.

Maier, S. & Watkins, L. R. (1998). Cytokines for psychologists: Implications of bidirectional immune-to-brain communication for understanding behavior, mood, and cognition. *Psychological Review, 105,* 83–107.

Maier, S.F., Watkins, L. R., & Fleshner, M. (1994). Psychoneuroimmunology: The interface between behavior, brain, and immunity. *American Psychologist, 49,* 1004–1017.

Malcolm, J. G. (1987). Treatment choices and informed consent in psychiatry: Implications of the Osheroff case for the profession. *Journal of Psychiatry and the Law, 15,* 9–81.

Malcolm, R. (2003). Pharmacologic treatments manage alcohol withdrawal, relapse prevention. *Psychiatric Annals, 33,* 593–601.

Maldonado, J. R., Butler, L. D., & Spiegel, D. (2001). Treatments for dissociative disorders. In P. E. Nathan & J. M. Gorman (Eds.), *A Guide to Treatments That Work,* pp. 463–469. London: Oxford University Press.

Maletzky, B. (1997). Exhibitionism: Assessment and treatment. *Sexual Deviance: Theory, Assessment, and Treatment,* pp. 40–74. New York: Guilford Press.

Maletzky, B. M. (2002). The paraphilias: Research and treatment. In P. E. Nathan & J. M. Gorman (Eds.), *A Guide to Treatments That Work,* 2nd ed., pp. 525–557. London: Oxford University Press.

Manassis, K. (1996). *Keys to Parenting Your Anxious Child.* New York: Barron's.

Manber, R., Kraemer, H. C., Arnow, B. A., Trivedi, M. H., Rush, A. J., Thase, M. E., et al. (2008). Faster remission of chronic depression with combined psychotherapy and medication than with each therapy alone. *Journal of Consulting and Clinical Psychology, 76,* 459–467.

Manderscheid, R.W., Henderson, M. J., Witkin, M. J., & Atay, J. E. (1999). Contemporary mental health systems and managed care. In A. V. Horwitz and T. L. Scheid (Eds.), *A Handbook for the Study of Mental Health: Social Contexts, Theories, and Systems,* pp. 412–426. Cambridge: Cambridge University Press.

Mann, K. (2004). Pharmacotherapy of alcohol dependence: A review of the clinical data. *CNS Drugs, 18,* 485–504.

Mann, K., Lehert, P., & Morgan, M. Y. (2004). The efficacy of acamprosate in the maintenance of abstinence in alcohol-dependent individuals: Results of a meta-analysis. *Alcoholism: Clinical & Experimental Research, 28,* 51–63.

Mannuzza, S., et al. (1998). Adult psychiatric status of hyperactive boys grown up. *American Journal of Psychiatry, 155,* 493–498.

Manson. S. E. (1994). Culture and depression: Discovering variations in the experience of illness. In W. J. Lonner & R. S. Malpass (Eds.), *Psychology and Culture,* pp. 285–290. Boston: Allyn & Bacon.

Manson, S. M., & Kleinman, A. (1998). DSM-IV, culture and mood disorders: A critical reflection on recent progress. *Transcultural Psychiatry, 35,* 377–386.

March, J. S., et al., (2004). Obsessive–compulsive disorder. In T. L. Morris & J. S. March (Eds.), *Anxiety Disorders in Children and Adolescents,* 2nd ed., pp. 212–240. New York: Guilford.

March, J. S., Leonard, H. L., & Swedo, S. E. (1995). Obsessive-compulsive disorder. In J. S. March (Ed.), *Anxiety Disorders in Children and Adolescents,* pp. 251–275. New York: Guilford.

March, J. S., Silva, S., Petrycki, S., Curry, J., Wells, K., Fairbank, J., et al. (2004). Fluoxetine, cognitive-behavioral therapy, and their combination for adolescents with depression: Treatment for Adolescents with Depression Study (TADS) randomized control trial. *Journal of the American Medical Association, 292,* 807–820.

March, J. S., Silva, S., Petrycki, S., Curry, J., Wells, K., Fairbank, J., et al. (2007). The Treatment for Adolescents with Depression Study (TADS): Long-term effectiveness and safety outcomes. *Archives of General Psychiatry, 64,* 1132–1144.

Marcia, J. E. (1966). Development and validation of ego-identity status. *Journal of Personality and Social Psychology, 24,* 551–558.

Marcia, J. E. (1994). The empirical study of ego identity. In H. A. Bosma, T. L. G. Graafsma, H. D. Grotevant, & D. J. de Levita (Eds.), *Identity and Development,* pp. 67–80. Thousand Oaks, CA: Sage.

Marder, K., Tang, M., Cote, L., & Stern, Y. (1995). The frequency and associated risk factors for dementia in patients with Parkinson's disease. *Archives of Neurology, 52,* 695–701.

Margolin, G., Christensen, A., & John, R. S. (1996). The continuance and spillover of everyday tensions in distressed and nondistressed families. *Journal of Family Psychology, 10,* 304–321.

Margraf, J., Taylor, C. B., Ehlers, A., Roth, W. T., & Agras, W. S. (1987). Panic attacks in the natural environment. *Journal of Nervous and Mental Disease, 175,* 558–565.

Markman, H. J., Floyd, F. J., Stanley, S. M., & Storaasli, R. D. (1988). Prevention of marital distress: A longitudinal investigation. *Journal of Consulting and Clinical Psychology, 56,* 210–217.

Markman, H. J., Renick, M. J., Floyd, F. J., Stanley, S. M., & Clements, M. (1993). Preventing marital distress through communication and conflict management training: A 4- and 5-year follow-up. *Journal of Consulting and Clinical Psychology, 61,* 70–77.

Marks, I. M., & Nesse, R. M. (1994). Fear and fitness: An evolutionary analysis of anxiety disorders. *Ethology and Sociobiology, 15,* 247–261.

Marks, I. M., Swinson, R. P., Basoglu, M., Kuch, K., Noshirvani, H., O'Sullivan, G., et al. (1993). Alprazolam and exposure alone and combined in panic disorder with agoraphobia: A controlled study in London and Toronto. *British Journal of Psychiatry, 162,* 776–787.

Marks, P. A., Seeman, W., & Haller, D. L. (1974). *The Actuarial Use of the MMPI with Adolescents and Adults.* New York: Oxford University Press.

Marlatt, G. A., Baer, J. S., Donovan, D. M., & Kivlahan, D. R. (1988). Addictive behaviors: Etiology and treatment. *Annual Review of Psychology, 39,* 223–252.

Marlatt, G. A., Blume, A. W., & Parks, G. A. (2001). Integrating harm reduction therapy and traditional substance abuse treatment. *Journal of Psychoactive Drugs, 33,* 13–21.

Marom, S., Munitz, H., Jones, P., Weizman, A., & Hermesh, H. (2005). Expressed emotion: Relevance to rehospitalization in schizophrenia over 7 years. *Schizophrenia Bulletin, 31,* 751–758.

Marques, J. K. (1999). How to answer the question "Does sexual offender treatment work?" *Journal of Interpersonal Violence, 14,* 437–451.

Marques, J. K., Day, D. M., Nelson, C., & West, M. A. (1993). Findings and recommendations from California's experimental treatment program. In G. C. N. Hall, R. Hirschman, J. R. Graham, & M. S. Zaragoza (Eds.), *Sexual Aggression: Issues in Etiology, Assessment, and Treatment,* pp. 197–214. Washington, DC: Hemisphere.

Marshall, W. L. (1989). Intimacy, loneliness, and sexual offenders. *Behaviour Research and Therapy, 27,* 491–503.

Marshall, W. L. (2007). Diagnostic issues, multiple paraphilias, and comorbid disorders in sexual offenders: Their incidence and treatment. *Aggression and Violent Behavior, 12,* 16–35.

Marshall, W. L., Bryce, P., Hudson, S. M., Ward, T., & Moth, B. (1996). The enhancement of intimacy and the reduction of loneliness among child molesters. *Journal of Family Violence, 11,* 219–236.

Marshall, W. L., Eccles, A., & Barbaree, H. E. (1991). The treatment of exhibitionists: A focus on sexual deviance versus cognitive and relationship features. *Behaviour Research and Therapy, 29,* 129–135.

Martin, C. S., Chung, T., & Langenbucher, J. W. (2008). How should we revise diagnostic criteria for substance use disorders in the DSM-V? *Journal of Abnormal Psychology, 117,* 561–575.

Martin, J. A., et al., (2007). Births: Final data for 2005. *National Vital Statistics Reports, 56* (6). Hyattsville, MD: National Center for Health Statistics.

Martin, R. L., Roberts, W. V., & Clayton, P. J. (1980). Psychiatric status after hysterectomy: A one-year prospective follow-up. *Journal of the American Medical Association, 244,* 350–353.

Martinez, M., Kurik, M. E. (2006). The role of pharmacotherapy for dementia patients with behavorial disturbances. In S. M. LoboPrabhu, V. A. Molinari, J. W. Lomax, *Supporting the Caregiver in Dementia: A Guide for Caregivers,* pp. 151–157. Baltimore, MD: Johns Hopkins Press.

Martire, L. M., & Schulz, R. (2007). Involving family in psychosocial interventions for chronic illness. *Current Directions in Psychological Science, 16,* 90–94.

Marwit, S. J. (1996). Reliability of diagnosing complicated grief: A preliminary investigation. *Journal of Consulting and Clinical Psychology, 64,* 563–568.

Mash, E. J., & Johnston, C. (1982). A comparison of the mother-child interactions of younger and older hyperactive and normal children. *Child Development, 53,* 1371–1381.

Mash, E. J., & Wolfe, D. A. (2005). *Abnormal Child Psychology,* 3rd ed. Belmont, CA: Thomson Wadsworth.

Mashour, G. A., Walker, E. E., & Martuza, R. L. (2005). Psychosurgery: Past, present, and future. *Brain Research Reviews, 48,* 409–419.

Maslow, A. H. (1954). *Motivation and Personality.* New York: Harper & Row.

Maslow, A. H. (1970). *Motivation and Personality* (2nd ed.). New York: Harper & Row.

Mason, J. W. (1975). A historical view of the "stress" field. II. *Journal of Human Stress, 1,* 12–16.

Masten, A. S. (2001). Ordinary magic: Resilience processes in development. *American Psychologist, 56,* 227–238.

Masters, W. H., & Johnson, V. E. (1966). *Human Sexual Response.* Boston: Little, Brown.

Masters, W. H., & Johnson, V. E. (1970). *Human Sexual Inadequacy.* Boston: Little, Brown.

Mate-Kole, C., Freschi, M., & Robin, A. (1988). Aspects of psychiatric symptoms at different stages in the treatment of transsexualism. *British Journal of Psychiatry, 152,* 550–553.

Mathews, A.(1990). Why worry: The cognitive function of anxiety. *Behaviour Research and Therapy, 28,* 455–468.

Mathews, A., & MacLeod, C. (2005). Cognitive vulnerability to emotional disorders. *Annual Review of Clinical Psychology, 1,* 167–195.

Mathis, J. (2001). Community integration of individuals with disabilities: An update on *Olmstead* implementation. *Journal of Poverty Law and Policy, 23,* 395–410.

Matson, J. L., & Frame, C. L. (1986). *Psychopathology Among Mentally Retarded Children and Adolescents.* Beverly Hills, CA: Sage.

Mavissakalian, M. R., & Ryan, M. T. (1998). Rational treatment of panic disorder with antidepressants. *Annals of Clinical Psychiatry, 10,* 185–195.

Mayes. S. D., Calhoun, S. L., & Crites, D. L. (2001). Does DSM-IV Asperger's Disorder Exist? *Journal of Abnormal Child Psychology, 29,* 263–271.

Mayeux, R., & Ottman, R. (1998). Alzheimer's disease genetics: Home runs and strikeouts. *Annals of Neurology, 44,* 716–719.

Mazure, C. M., Bruce, M. L., Maciejewski, P. K., & Jacobs, S. C. (2000). Adverse life events and cognitive-personality characteristics in the prediction of major depression and antidepressant response. *American Journal of Psychiatry, 157,* 896–903.

McAdams, D., & Pals, J. L. (2006). A new big five: Fundamental principles for an integrative science of personality. *American Psychologist, 61,* 204–217.

McCabe, M. P. (2001). Evaluation of a cognitive behavior therapy program for people with sexual dysfunction. *Journal of Sex and Marital Therapy, 27,* 259–271.

McCabe, M. P. (2005). The role of performance anxiety in the development and maintenance of sexual dysfunction in men and women. *International Journal of Stress Management, 12,* 379–388.

McCabe, M. P., & Wauchope, M. (2005). Behavioral characteristics of men accused of rape: Evidence for different types of rapists. *Archives of Sexual Behavior, 34,* 241–253.

McCabe, P. M., et al. (2002). Social environment influences the progression of atherosclerosis in the Watanabe heritable hyperlipidemic rabbit. *Circulation, 105,* 354–359.

McCann, U. D., Rossiter, E. M., King, R. J., & Agras, W. S. (1991). Nonpurging bulimia: A distinct subtype of bulimia nervosa. *International Journal of Eating Disorders, 10,* 679–687.

McCarroll, J. E., Ursano, R. J., Fullerton, C. S., Liu, X., & Lundy, A. (2002). Somatic symptoms in Gulf War mortuary workers. *Psychosomatic Medicine, 64,* 29–33.

McCarthy, B. W. (1989). Cognitive-behavioral strategies and techniques in the treatment of early ejaculation. In S. R. Leiblum & R. C. Rosen (Eds.), *Principles and Practice of Sex Therapy,* 2nd ed. New York: Guilford.

McCarthy, B. W. (1998). Integrating Viagra into cognitive-behavioral couples sex therapy. *Journal of Sex Education and Therapy, 23,* 302–308.

McCarthy, B. W. (1998). Sex therapy workshops: The Indian experience. *Journal of Sex Education and Therapy, 23,* 309–311.

McCarthy, B. W. (2004). An integrative cognitive-behavioral approach to understanding, assessing, and treating female sexual dysfunction. *Journal of Family Psychotherapy, 15,* 19–35.

McConaghy, N. (1999b). Methodological issues concerning evaluation of treatment for sexual offenders: Randomization, treatment dropouts, untreated controls, and within-treatment studies. *Sexual Abuse: Journal of Research and Treatment, 11,* 183–193.

McConaghy, N. (2005). Sexual dysfunctions and disorders. In J. E. Maddux & B. A. Winstead (Eds.), *Psychopathology: Foundations for a Contemporary Understanding,* pp. 255–280. Mahwah, NJ: Erlbaum.

McCullough, J. P., Jr., Klein, D. N., Borian, F. E., Howland, R. H., Riso, L. P., Keller, M. B., et al. (2003). Group comparisons of DSM-IV subtypes of chronic depression: Validity of the distinctions, Part 2. *Journal of Abnormal Psychology, 112,* 614–622.

McDonagh, A., Friedman, M., McHugo, G., Ford, J., Sengupta, A., Mueser, K., et al. (2005). Randomized trial of cognitive-behavioral therapy for chronic posttraumatic stress disorder in adult female survivors of childhood sexual abuse. *Journal of Consulting and Clinical Psychology, 73,* 515–524.

McDougle, C. J., Price, L. H., & Volkmar, F. R. (1994). Recent advances in the pharmacotherapy of autism and related conditions. *Child and Adolescent Psychiatric Clinics of North America, 3,* 71–89.

McEachin, J. J., Smith, T., Lovaas, O. I. (1993). Long-term outcome for children with autism who received early intensive behavioral treatment. *American Journal on Mental Retardation, 97*(4), 359–372.

McFall, R. M. (2001). New manifesto.

McFall, R. M. (2005). Theory and utility—Key themes in evidence-based assessment. *Psychological Assessment., 17,* 312–323.

McFall, R. M., & McDonel, E. C. (1986). The continuing search for units of analysis in psychology: Beyond persons, situations, and their interactions. In R. O. Nelson & S. C. Hayes (Eds.), *Conceptual Foundations of Behavioral Assessment,* pp. 201–241. New York: Guilford.

McFarlane, W. R., Dixon, L., Lukens, E., & Lucksted, A. (2003). Family psychoeducation and schizophrenia: A review of the literature. *Journal of Marital and Family Therapy, 29,* 223–245.

McGeer, P. L., & McGeer, E. G. (1996). Anti-inflammatory drugs in the fight against Alzheimer's disease. *Annals of the New York Academy of Sciences, 777,* 213–220.

McGlashan, T. (1986). The Chestnut Lodge follow-up study: III. Long-term outcome of borderline personalities. *Archives of General Psychiatry, 43,* 20–30.

McGlashan, T. H. (1998). The profiles of clinical deterioration in schizophrenia. *Journal of Psychiatric Research, 32,* 133–141.

McGlashan, T. H., & Fenton, W. S. (1991). Classical subtypes for schizophrenia: Literature review for DSM-IV. *Schizophrenia Bulletin, 17,* 609–623.

McGrath, J. (2005). Myths and plain truths about schizophrenia epidemiology—The NAPE lecture 2004. *Acta Psychiatrica Scandinavica, 111,* 4–11.

McGrath, J. J., & Welham, J. L.(1999). Season of birth and schizophrenia: A systematic review and meta-analysis of data from the Southern Hemisphere. *Schizophrenia Research, 35,* 237–242.

McGue, M. (1993). From proteins to cognitions: The behavioral genetics of alcoholism. In R. Plomin & G.E. McClearn (Eds.), *Nature, Nurture, and Psychology.* Washington, DC: American Psychological Association.

McGue, M., & Iacono, W. G. (2008). The adolescent origins of substance use disorders. *International Journal of Methods in Psychiatric Research, 17* (Suppl. 1), S30–S38.

McGue, M., & Lykken, D. T. (1992). Genetic influence on risk of divorce. *Psychological Science, 3,* 368–373.

McGue, M., Iacono, W., Legrand, L., & Elkins, I. (2001). Origins and consequences of age at first drink: II. Familial risk and heritability. *Alcoholism: Clinical and Experimental Research, 25,* 1166–1173.

McGuffin, P., & Farmer, A. E. (2005) Are there phenotype problems? In C. F. Zorumski and E. H. Rubin (Eds.), *Psychopathology in the Genome and Neuroscience Era,* pp. 65–84. Washington, DC: American Psychiatric Publishing.

McGuffin, P., & Thapar, A. (1998). Genetics and antisocial personality disorder. In T. Millon and E. Simonsen (Eds.), *Psychopathy: Antisocial, Criminal, and Violent Behavior,* pp. 215–230. New York: Guilford.

McGuffin, P., Katz, R., Watkins, S., & Rutherford, J. (1996). A hospital-based twin register of the heritability of DSM-IV unipolar depression. *Archives of General Psychiatry, 53,* 129–136.

McGuffin, P., Rijsdijk, F., Andrew, M., Sham, P., Katz, R., & Cardno, A. (2003). The heritability of bipolar affective disorder and the genetic relationship to unipolar depression. *Archives of General Psychiatry, 60,* 497–502.

McGurk, S., Twamley, E., Sitzer, D., McHugo, G., & Mueser, K. (2007, December). A meta-analysis of cognitive remediation in schizophrenia. *American Journal of Psychiatry, 164*(12), 1791–1802.

McKeith, I. G. (2002). Dementia with Lewy bodies. *British Journal of Psychiatry, 180,* 144–147.

McKenna, M. C., Zevon, M. A., Corn, B., & Rounds, J. (1999). Psychosocial factors and the development of breast cancer: A meta-analysis. *Health Psychology, 18,* 520–531.

McKey, R. H., Condelli, L., Granson, H., Barrett, B., McConkey, C., & Plantz, M. (1985, June). *The Impact of Head Start on Children, Families, and Communities.* Final Report of the Head Start Evaluation, Synthesis and Utilization Project. Washington, DC: Corporate Social Responsibility.

McKim, W. (2000). *Drugs and Behavior: An Introduction to Behavioral Pharmacology,* 4th ed. Upper Saddle River, NJ: Prentice Hall.

McKim, W. A. (2006). *Drugs and Behavior: An Introduction to Behavioral Pharmacology,* 6th ed. Upper Saddle River, NJ: Prentice Hall.

McLaughlin, K., Borkovec, T., & Sibrava, N. (2007). The effects of worry and rumination on affect states and cognitive activity. *Behavior Therapy, 38,* 23–38.

McLemore, C. W., & Benjamin, L. A. (1979). Whatever happened to interpersonal diagnosis? A psychosocial alternative to DSM-III. *American Psychologist, 34,* 17–34.

McNally, R. J. (1994). Cognitive bias in panic disorder. *Current Directions in Psychological Science, 3,* 129–132.

McNally, R. J. (2003). Recovering memories of trauma: A view from the laboratory. *Current Directions in Psychological Science, 12,* 32–35.

McNally, R. J. (2007). Mechanisms of exposure therapy: How neuroscience can improve psychological treatments for anxiety disorders. *Clinical Psychology Review, 27,* 750–759.

McNally, R. J., Bryant, R. A., & Ehlers, A. (2003). Does early psychological intervention promote recovery from posttraumatic stress? *Psychological Science in the Public Interest, 4,* 45–79.

McNeil, T. F., & Cantor-Graae, E. (1999). Does preexisting abnormality cause labor-delivery complications in fetuses who will develop schizophrenia? *Schizophrenia Bulletin, 25,* 425–435.

McQueen, M., & Blacker, D. (2008). *Genetics of Alzheimer's Disease. Psychiatric Genetics: Applications in Clinical Practice,* pp. 177–193. Arlington, VA: American Psychiatric Publishing, Inc.

Meaney, M. J. (2001). Nature, nurture, and the disunity of knowledge. *Annals of the New York Academy of Sciences, 935,* 50–61.

Medine, J. (1999). *What You Need to Know About Alzheimer's.* Oakland, CA: New Harbinger.

Mednick, S. A., & Schulsinger, F. (1968). Some premorbid characteristics related to breakdown in children with schizophrenic mothers. *Journal of Psychiatric Research* (Suppl. 1), 6, 354–362.

Meehl, P. E. (1990). Toward an integrated theory of schizotaxia, schizotypy, and schizophrenia. *Journal of Personality Disorders, 4,* 1–99.

Meehl, P. E. (1993). The origins of some of my conjectures concerning schizophrenia. In L. J. Chapman, J. P. Chapman, & D. Fowles (Eds.), *Progress in Experimental Personality and Psychopathology Research,* pp. 1–11. New York: Springer.

Meehl, P. E., & Rosen, A. (1955). Antecedent probability and the efficiency of psychometric signs, patterns, or cutting scores. *Psychological Bulletin, 52,* 194–216.

Meichenbaum, D. (1977). *Cognitive-Behavior Modification: An Integrative Approach.* New York: Plenum Press.

Mejeur, J. (1999). There's more to TEA-21 than .08. *State Legislatures, 25,* 33.

Melman, A., & Tiefer, L. (1992). Surgery for erectile disorders: Operative procedures and psychological issues. In R. C. Rosen & S. R. Leiblum (Eds.), *Erectile Disorders: Assessment and Treatment,* pp. 255–282. New York: Guilford.

Melton, G. B., & Limber, S. (1989). Psychologists' involvement in cases of child maltreatment: Limits of roles and expertise. *American Psychologist, 44,* 1225–1233.

Melton, G. B., Petrila, J., Poythress, N. G., & Slobogin, C. (1997). *Psychological Evaluations for the Courts* (2nd ed.). New York: Guilford.

Mendle, J., Turkheimer, E., D'Onofrio, B. M., Lynch, S. K., Emery, R. E., Slutske, W. S. & Martin, N. G. (2006). Family structure and age at menarche: A children-of-twins approach. *Developmental Psychology, 42,* 533–542.

Mendez, M., Lauterbach, E., & Sampson, S. (2008). An evidence-based review of the psychopathology of frontotemporal dementia: A report of the ANPA committee on research. *Journal of Neuropsychiatry & Clinical Neurosciences, 20,* 130–149.

Mendlewicz, J., Souery, D., & Rivelli, S. K. (1999). Short-term and long-term treatment for bipolar patients: Beyond the guidelines. *Journal of Affective Disorders, 55,* 79–85.

Menzies, L., Chamberlain, S. R., Laird, A. R., Thelen, S. M., Sahakian, B. J. & Bullmore, E. T. (2008). Integrating evidence from neuroimaging and neuropsychological studies of obsessive-compulsive disorder: The orbitofronto-striatal model revisited. *Neuroscience and Biobehavioral Reviews, 32,* 525–549.

Merckelbach, H., Muris, P., & Schouten, E. (1996). Pathways to fear in spider phobic children. *Behaviour Research and Therapy, 34,* 935–938.

Merkin, D. (1996, February 26 and March 4). Unlikely obsession: Confronting a taboo. *The New Yorker,* 98–115.

Mersky, H. (1992). The manufacture of personalities: The production of multiple personality disorder. *British Journal of Psychiatry, 160,* 327–340.

Mervielde, I., DeClercq, B., DeFruyt, F., & Van Leeuwen, K. (2005). Temperament, personality, and developmental psychopathology as childhood antecedents of personality disorders. *Journal of Personality Disorders, 19,* 171–201.

Messias, E., Chen, C., & Eaton, W. (2007). Epidemiology of schizophrenia: Review of findings and myths. *Psychiatric Clinics of North America, 30,* 323–338.

Meston, C.M., & Rellini, A. (2008). Sexual dysfunction In W. E. Craighead, D. J. Miklowitz, & L. W. Craighead (Eds), *Psychopathology: History, Diagnosis, and Empirical Foundations,* pp. 544-564. Hoboken, NJ: Wiley.

Meston, C.M., & Bradford, A. (2007). Sexual dysfunctions in women. *Annual Review of Clinical Psychology, 3,* 233–256.

Mesulam, M. (2007). Primary progressive aphasia: A 25-year retrospective. *Alzheimer Disease & Associated Disorders, 21,* S8–S11.

Meston, C. M., Trapnell, P. D., & Gorzalka, B. B. (1996). Ethnic and gender differences in sexuality: Variations in sexual behavior between Asian and non-Asian university students. *Archives of Sexual Behavior, 25,* 33–72.

Metalsky, G. I., Joiner, T. E., Hardin, T. S., & Abramson, L. Y. (1993). Depressive reactions to failure in a naturalistic setting: A test of the hopelessness and self-esteem theories of depression. *Journal of Abnormal Psychology, 102,* 101–109.

Metz, M. E., & Epstein, N. (2002). Assessing the role of relationship conflict in sexual dysfunction. *Journal of Sex and Marital Therapy, 28,* 139–164.

Metz, M. E., & Pryor, J. L. (2000). Premature ejaculation: A psychophysiological approach for assessment and management. *Journal of Sex and Marital Therapy, 26,* 293–320.

Metzl, J. M. (2004). Voyeur nation? Changing definitions of voyeurism, 1950–2004. *Harvard Review of Psychiatry, 12,* 127–131.

Meuret, A. E., Ritz, T., Wilhelm, F. H., & Roth, W. T. (2005). Voluntary hyperventilation in the treatment of panic disorder. *Clinical Psychology Review, 25,* 285–306.

Meyer, D. J. (2006). Psychiatry malpractice and administrative inquiries of alleged physician misconduct. *Psychiatric Clinics of North America, 29,* 615–628.

Meyer, G. J., & Archer, R. P. (2001). The hard science of Rorschach research: What do we know and where do we go? *Psychological Assessment, 13,* 486–502.

Meyer, G. J., Finn, S. E., Eyde, L. D., Kay, G. G., Moreland, K. L., Dies, R. R., Eisman, E. J. Kubiszyn, T. W., & Reed, G. M. (2001). Psychological testing and psychological assessment: A review of evidence and issues. *American Psychologist, 56,* 128–165.

Meyer, I. H. (2003). Prejudice, social stress, and mental health in lesbian, gay, and bisexual populations: Conceptual issues and research evidence. *Psychological Bulletin, 129,* 674–697.

Meyer, J. M., Eaves, L. J., Heath, A. C., & Martin, N. G. (1991). Estimating genetic influences on the age-at-menarche: A survival analysis approach. *American Journal of Medical Genetics, 39,* 148–154.

Mezzich, J. E., Berganza, C. E., & Ruiperez, M. A. (2001). Culture in DSM-IV, ICD-10, and evolving diagnostic systems. *Psychiatric Clinics of North America, 24,* 407–419.

Michelini, S., Cassano, G. B., Frare, F., & Perugi, G. (1996). Long-term use of benzodiazepines: Tolerance, dependence and clinical problems in anxiety and mood disorders. *Pharmacopsychiatry, 29,* 127–134.

Mickelson, K. D., Kessler, R. C., & Shaver, P. R. (1997). Adult attachment in a nationally representative sample. *Journal of Personality and Social Psychology, 73,* 1092–1106.

Miklowitz, D. (2004). The role of family systems in severe and recurrent psychiatric disorders: A developmental psychopathology view. *Development and Psychopathology, 16,* 667–688.

Miklowitz, D. J. (1995). The evolution of family-based psychopathology. In R. H. Mikesell, D. Losterman, & S. H. McDaniel (Eds.), *Integrating Family Therapy: Handbook of Family Psychology and Systems Theory,* pp. 183–197. Washington, DC: American Psychological Association.

Miklowitz, D. J. (2002). *The Bipolar Disorder Survival Guide: What You and Your Family Need to Know.* New York: Guilford.

Miklowitz, D. J., & Johnson, S. L. (2008). Bipolar disorder. In W. E. Craighead, D. J. Miklowitz, and L. W.

Craighead (Eds.), *Psychopathology: History, Diagnosis, and Empirical Foundations,* pp. 366–401. New York: Wiley.

Miklowitz, D. J., Goldstein, M. J., & Nuechterlein, K. H. (1995). Verbal interactions in the families of schizophrenic and bipolar affective patients. *Journal of Abnormal Psychology, 104,* 268–276.

Miklowitz, D. J., Otto, M. W., & Frank, E. (2007). Intensive psychosocial intervention enhances functioning in patients with bipolar depression: Results from a 9-month randomized controlled trial. *American Journal of Psychiatry, 164,* 1340–1347.

Miklowitz, D. J., Otto, M. W., Frank, E., Reilly-Harrington, N. A., Kogan, J. N., et al. (2007). Intensive psychosocial intervention enhances functioning in patients with bipolar depression: Results from a 9-month randomized controlled trial. *American Journal of Psychiatry, 164,* 1340–1347.

Milich, R., Balentine, A. C., & Lynam, D. R. (2001). ADHD combined type and ADHD predominantly inattentive type are distinct and unrelated disorders. *Clinical Psychology: Science and Practice, 8,* 463–488.

Milich, R., Wolraich, M., & Lindgren, S. (1986). Sugar and hyperactivity: A critical review of empirical findings. *Clinical Psychology Review, 6,* 493–513.

Miller, C. J., Sanchez, J., & Hynd, G. W. (2003). Neurological correlates of reading disabilities. In H. L. Swanson, K. R. Harris, & S. Graham (Eds.), *Handbook of Learning Disabilities,* pp. 242–255. New York: Guilford.

Miller, G. A., & Keller, J. (2000). Psychology and neuroscience: Making peace. *Current Directions in Psychological Science, 9,* 212–215.

Miller, M. W., Kaloupek, D. G., Dillon, A. L., & Keane, T. M. (2004). Externalizing and internalizing subtypes of combat-related PTSD: A replication and extension using the PSY-5 scales. *Journal of Abnormal Psychology, 113,* 636–645.

Miller, T. Q., Smith, T. W., Turner, C. W., Guijarro, M. L., & Hallet, A. J. (1996). A meta-analytic review of research on hostility and physical health. *Psychological Bulletin, 119,* 322–348.

Miller, T. Q., Turner, C. W., Tindale, R. S., Posavac, E. J., & Dugoni, B. L. (1991). Reasons for the trend toward null findings in research on Type A behavior. *Psychological Bulletin, 110,* 469–485.

Miller, T., & Swartz, L. (1990). Clinical psychology in general hospital settings: Issues in interprofessional relationships. *Professional Psychology: Research and Practice, 21*(1), 48–53.

Miller, T. W. (1989). *Stressful Life Events.* Madison, CT: International Universities Press.

Miller, W. R. (1995). Increasing motivation for change. In R. K. Hester & W. R. Miller (Eds.), *Handbook of Alcoholism Treatment Approaches,* 2nd ed., pp. 89–104. Boston: Allyn & Bacon.

Miller, W. R., & Longabaugh, R. (2003). Summary and conclusions. In T. F. Babor & F. K. Del Boca (Eds.), *Treatment Matching in Alcoholism,* pp. 207–221. New York: Cambridge University Press.

Miller-Johnson, S., Emery, R. E., Marvin, R. S., Clarke, W., Lovinger, R., & Martin, M. (1994). Parent-child relationships and the management of insulin-dependent diabetes mellitus. *Journal of Consulting and Clinical Psychology, 62,* 603–610.

Millon, T., & Martinez, A. (1995). Avoidant personality disorder. In W. J. Livesley (Ed.), *The DSM-IV Personality Disorders,* pp. 218–233. New York: Guilford.

Mineka, S., & Cook, M. (1993). Mechanisms involved in the observational conditioning of fear. *Journal of Experimental Psychology: General, 122,* 23–38.

Mineka, S., & Kihlstrom, J. F. (1978). Unpredictable and uncontrollable events: A new perspective on experimental neurosis. *Journal of Abnormal Psychology, 87* (2), 256–271.

Mineka, S., & Oehlberg, K. (2008). The relevance of recent developments in classical conditioning to understanding the etiology and maintenance of anxiety disorders. *Acta Psychologica, 127,* 567–580.

Mineka, S., & Ohman, A. (2002). Born to fear: non-associative vs associative factors in the etiology of phobias. *Behaviour Research and Therapy, 40,* 173–184.

Mineka, S., Watson, D., & Clark, L. A. (1998). Comorbidity of anxiety and unipolar mood disorders. *Annual Review of Psychology, 49,* 377–412.

Mineka S., & Zinbarg R. (1998). Experimental approaches to the anxiety and mood disorders. In J. G. Adair & D. Belanger (Eds.), *Advances in Psychological Science,* Vol. 1: *Social, Personal, and Cultural Aspects,* pp. 429–454. Hove, England: Psychology Press/Erlbaum (UK) Taylor & Francis.

Minino, A. M., & Smith, B. L. (2001). Deaths: Preliminary data for 2000. *National Vital and Statistics Report, 49,* #12. Hyattsville, MD: National Center for Health Statistics.

Minton, H. L. (2002). *Departing from Deviance: A History of Homosexual Rights and Emancipatory Science in America.* Chicago: University of Chicago Press.

Minuchin, S., Rosman, B. L., & Baker, L. (1978). *Psychosomatic Families.* Cambridge, MA: Harvard University Press.

Mitchell, J. (1982). When disaster strikes . . . The critical incident stress debriefing process. *Journal of Emergency Medical Services, 8,* 36–39.

Mitchell, J., & Dyregrov, A. (1993). Traumatic stress in disaster workers and emergency personnel. In J. P. Wilson & B. Raphael (Eds.), *International Handbook of Traumatic Stress Syndromes,* pp. 905–914. New York: Plenum.

Mitchell, J. E., Pyle, R. L., Eckert, E. D., Hatsukami, D., Pomeroy, C., & Zimmerman, R. (1990). A comparison study of antidepressants and structured intensive group psychotherapy in the treatment of bulimia nervosa. *Archives of General Psychiatry, 47,* 149–157.

Mitchell, J. E., Raymond, N., & Specker, S.(1993). A review of controlled trials of pharmacotherapy and psychotherapy in the treatment of bulimia nervosa. *International Journal of Eating Disorders, 14,* 229–247.

Mitchell, K., & Graham, C. A. (2008). Two challenges for the classification of sexual dysfunction. *Journal of Sexual Medicine, 5,* 1552–1558.

Mittelman, M. S., Ferris, S. H., Shulman, E., Steinberg, G., Ambinder, A., & Mackell, J. (1997). Effects of a multicomponent support program on spouse-caregivers of Alzheimer's disease patients: Results of a treatment/control study. In L. Heston (Ed.), *Progress in Alzheimer's Disease and Similar Conditions.* Washington, DC: American Psychiatric Press.

Mizrahi, R., Bagby, R., Zipursky, R., & Kapur, S. (2005). How antipsychotics work: The patients' perspective. *Progress in Neuro-Psychopharmacology & Biological Psychiatry, 29,* 859–864.

Mnookin, R. H. (1975). Child-custody adjudication: Judicial functions in the face of indeterminancy. *Law and Contemporary Problems, 88,* 226–293.

Mnookin, R. H. (1985). *In the Interest of Children: Advocacy, Law Reform, and Public Policy.* New York: Freeman.

Modesto-Lowe, V. & Van Kirk, J. (2002). Clinical uses of naltrexone: A review of the evidence. *Experimental & Clinical Psychopharmacology, 10,* 213–227.

Moffitt, T., Caspi, A., Harrington, H., Milne, B., Melchior, M., Goldberg, D., et al. (2007). Generalized anxiety disorder and depression: Childhood risk factors in a birth cohort followed to age 32. *Psychological Medicine, 37,* 441–452.

Moffitt, T. E. (1993). Adolescence-limited and life-course-persistent antisocial behavior: A developmental taxonomy. *Psychological Review, 100,* 674–701.

Moffitt, T. E. (1997). Adolescence-limited and life-course-persistent offending: A complementary pair of developmental theories. In T. P. Thornberry (Ed.), *Developmental Theories of Crime and Delinquency. Advances in Criminological Theory*, Vol. 7, pp. 11–54. New Brunswick, NJ: Transaction.

Moffitt, T. E., Caspi, A., & Rutter, M. (2006). Measured gene-environment interactions in psychopathology: Concepts, research strategies, and implications for research, intervention, and public understanding of genetics. *Perspectives on Psychological Science, 1,* 5–27.

Moffitt, T. E. (2007). A review of research on the taxonomy of life-course persistent versus adolescence-limited antisocial behavior. In D. J. Flannery, A. T. Vazsonyi, & I. D. Waldman (Eds.), *The Cambridge Handbook of Violent Behavior and Aggression,* pp. 47–74. New York: Cambridge University Press.

Moldavsky, M., Dorit, L., & Lerman-Sagie, T. (2001). Behavioral phenotypes in genetic syndromes: A reference guide for psychiatrists. *Journal of the American Academy of Child and Adolescent Psychiatry, 40,* 749–761.

Moldin, S. O. (2003). Neurobiology of autism: The new frontier. *Genes, Brain and Behavior, 2,* 253–254.

Monahan, J. (1981). *The Clinical Prediction of Violent Behavior.* Rockville, MD: National Institute of Mental Health.

Monahan, J. (1992). Mental disorder and violent behavior: Perceptions and evidence. *American Psychologist, 47,* 511–521.

Monahan, J. (1993). Limiting therapist exposure to Tarasoff liability: Guidelines for risk containment. *American Psychologist, 48,* 242–250.

Monahan, J., et al. (2001a). Mandated community treatment: Beyond outpatient commitment. *Psychiatric Services, 52,* 1198–1205.

Monahan, J., et al. (2001b). *Rethinking Risk Assessment.* New York: Oxford.

Monahan, J., Redlich, A. D., Swanson, J., Robbins, P. C., Applebaum, P. S., Petrila, J., et al. (2005). Use of leverage to improve adherence to psychiatric treatment in the community. *Psychiatric Services, 56,* 37–44.

Money, J. (1984). Paraphilias: Phenomenology and classification. *American Journal of Psychotherapy, 38,* 164–179.

Monroe, S. M., & Harkness, K. L. (2005). Life stress, the "kindling" hypothesis, and the recurrence of depression: Considerations from a life stress perspective. *Psychological Review, 112,* 417–445.

Monroe, S. M., & Simons, A. D. (1991). Diathesis-stress theories in the context of life stress research: Implications for the depressive disorders. *Psychological Bulletin, 110,* 406–425.

Monson, C. M., Schnurr, P. P., Resick, P. A., Friedman, M. J., Young-Xu, Y., & Stevens, S. P. (2006). Cognitive processing therapy for veterans with military-related posttraumatic stress disorder. *Journal of Consulting and Clinical Psychology, 74,* 898–907.

Montgomery, H. A., Miller, W. R., & Tonigan, J. S. (1993). Differences among AA groups: Implications for research. *Journal of Studies on Alcohol, 54,* 502–504.

Moore, M. (1975). Some myths about "mental illness." *Inquiry, 18,* 233–240.

Moore, P. S., Whaley, S. E., Sigman, M. (2004). Interactions between mothers and children: Impacts of maternal and child anxiety. *Journal of Abnormal Psychology, 113*(3), 471–476.

Moos, R. H., Finney, J. W., Ouimette, P. C., & Suchinsky, R. T. (1999). A comparative evaluation of substance abuse treatment. I. Treatment orientation, amount of care, and 1-year outcomes. *Alcoholism: Clinical and Experimental Research, 23,* 529–536.

Moran, P. (1999). The epidemiology of antisocial personality disorder. *Social Psychiatry and Psychiatric Epidemiology, 34,* 231–242.

Morgentaler, A. (2003). *The Viagra Myth: The Surprising Impact on Love and Relationships.* New York: Jossey-Bass.

Moriarty, P. J., Lieber, D., Bennett, A., White, L., Parrella, M., Harvey, P. D., et al. (2001). Gender differences in poor outcome patients with lifelong schizophrenia. *Schizophrenia Bulletin, 27,* 103–113.

Morokoff, P. J. (1989). Sex bias and POD. *American Psychologist,* 73–75.

Morris, J. (1995). Dementia and cognitive changes in Huntington's disease. In W. J. Weiner & A. E. Lang (Eds.), *Behavioral Neurology of Movement Disorders. Advances in Neurology,* Vol. 65, pp. 187–200. New York: Raven Press.

Morris, J. C. (2003). Dementia update 2003. *Alzheimer Disease & Associated Disorders, 17,* 245–258.

Morrison, J., & Herbstein, J. (1988). Secondary affective disorder in women with somatization disorder. *Comprehensive Psychiatry, 29,* 433–440.

Morse, K. L. (1990). A uniform testimonial privilege for mental health professionals, *Ohio State Law Journal, 51,* 741–757.

Moscicki, E. K. (1995). Epidemiology of suicidal behavior. *Suicide and Life-Threatening Behavior, 25,* 22–35.

Moser, C. (2001). Paraphilia: A critique of a confused concept. In P. J. Kleinplatz (Ed.), *New Directions in Sex Therapy: Innovations and Alternatives,* pp. 91–108. Philadelphia: Brunner-Routledge.

Moskovitz, R. A. (1996). *Lost in the Mirror: An Inside Look at Borderline Personality Disorder.* Dallas, TX: Taylor Publishing.

Moussavi, S., Chatterji, S., Verdes, E., Tandon, A., Patel, V., & Ustun, B. (2007). Depression, chronic diseases, and decrements in health: Results from the World Health Surveys. *Lancet, 370,* 851–858.

MTA Cooperative Group. (1999). A 14-month randomized clinical trial of treatment strategies for attention-deficit/hyperactivity disorder. *Archives of General Psychiatry, 56,* 1073–1086.

Mueser, K. T., & Gingerich, S. (1994). *Coping with Schizophrenia: A Guide for Families.* Oakland, CA: New Harbinger.

Mueser, K. T., & Bellack, A.S. (2007). Social skills training: Alive and well? *Journal of Mental Health, 16,* 549–552.

Mulder, R. T. (2002). Personality pathology and treatment outcome in major depression: A review. *American Journal of Psychiatry, 159,* 359–371.

Multiple Risk Factor Intervention Trial Research Group (1982). Multiple Risk Factor Intervention Trial: Risk factor changes and mortality results. *Journal of the American Medical Association, 248,* 1465–1477.

Muris, P., Merckelbach, H., & Clavan, M. (1997). Abnormal and normal compulsions. *Behaviour Research and Therapy, 35,* 249–252.

Murphy, B., Chung, Y., Park, T., & McGorry, P. (2006). Pharmacological treatment of primary negative symptoms in schizophrenia: A systematic review. *Schizophrenia Research, 88,* 5–25.

Murphy, D. (2006). *Psychiatry in the Scientific Image.* Cambridge, MA: The MIT Press.

Murphy, W. D. (1997). Exhibitionism: Psychopathology and theory. In D. R. Laws & W. T. O'Donohue (Eds.), *Handbook of Sexual Deviance: Theory and Application.* New York: Guilford.

Murray, C. J. L., & Lopez, A. D. (1997). Global mortality, disability, and the contribution of risk factors: Global Burden of Disease Study. *Lancet, 349,* 1436–1442.

Myers, J. E. B. (1983–84). Involuntary civil commitment of the mentally ill: A system in need of change. *Villanova Law Review, 29,* 367–433.

Myers, T. C., Mittenberger, R. G., & Studa, K. T. (1998). A survey of the use of facilitated communication in community agencies serving persons with developmental disabilities. *Behavioral Interventions, 13*(3), 135–146.

Najman, J. M., Dunne, M. P., Purdie, D. M., Boyle, F. M., & Coxeter, P. D. (2005). Sexual abuse in childhood and sexual dysfunction in adulthood: An Australian population-based study. *Archives of Sexual Behavior, 34,* 517–526.

Narding, P., & Janzing, J. G. E. (2003). The neuropsychiatric manifestations of Huntington's disease. *Current Opinion in Psychiatry, 16,* 337–340.

Nasrallah, H. (2008). Atypical antipsychotic-induced metabolic side effects: Insights from receptor-binding profiles. *Molecular Psychiatry, 13,* 27–35.

Nathan, P. E. (1993). Alcoholism: Psychopathology, etiology, and treatment. In P. B. Sutker & H. E. Adams (Eds.), *Comprehensive Handbook of Psychopathology,* 2nd ed., pp. 451–476. New York: Plenum.

Nathan, P. E., & Gorman, J. M. (Eds.), *A Guide to Treatments That Work* (2nd ed) New York: Oxford.

Nathan, P. E., & Gorman, J. M. (Eds.). (2007). *A Guide to Treatments That Work,* 3rd ed. New York: Oxford.

Nathan, P. E., & Langenbucher, J. (2003). Diagnosis and classification. In G. Stricker, T. A. Widiger, et al. (Eds), *Handbook of Psychology: Clinical Psychology,* Vol. 8, pp. 3–26. New York: Wiley.

Nathan, P. E., Stuart, S. P., & Dolan, S. L. (2000). Research on psychotherapy efficacy and effectiveness: Between Scylla and Charybdis? *Psychological Bulletin, 126,* 964–981.

National Academy of Sciences, Institute of Medicine (1989). *Research on Children & Adolescents with Mental, Behavioral, and Developmental Disorders.* Washington, DC: National Academy Press.

National Institute of Mental Health. (1990). *Somatization Disorder in the Medical Setting.* Rockville, MD: Author.

National Institutes of Health (2000). Phenylketonuria (PKU): Screening and Management. *NIH Consensus Statement, 17,* 1–33.

National Victim Center. (1992). *Crime and Victimization in America: Statistical Overview.* Arlington, VA: Author.

Neale, J. M., & Oltmanns, T. F. (1980). *Schizophrenia.* New York: Wiley.

Neighbors, H. W., Caldwell, C., Williams, D. R., Nesse, R., Taylor, R. J., Bullard, K. M., Torres, M., et al. (2007). Race, ethnicity, and the use of services for mental disorders. *Archives of General Psychiatry, 64,* 485–494.

Neisser, U., & Harsch, N. (1992). Phantom flashbulbs: False recollections of hearing the news about *Challenger.* In E. Winograd & U. Neisser (Eds.), *Affect and Accuracy in Recall: Studies of "flashbulb" Memories,* pp. 9–31. New York: Cambridge University Press.

Nemeroff, C. (1998a). The neurobiology of depression. *Scientific American, 278,* 42–49.

Nemeroff, C. (1998b). Psychopharmacology of affective disorders in the 21st century. *Biological Psychiatry, 44*(7), 517–525.

Nemeroff, C. B. (1998). The neurobiology of depression. *Scientific American, 278,* 42–49.

Nemeroff, C. B. (1998). Psychopharmacology of affective disorders in the 21st century. *Biological Psychiatry, 44,* 517–525.

Neria, Y., & Galea, S. (2007). Post-traumatic stress disorder following disasters: A systematic review. *Psychological Medicine, 28,* 467–480.

Nesse, R. M. (1999). Proximate and evolutionary studies of anxiety, stress and depression: Synergy at the interface. *Neuroscience and Biobehavioral Reviews, 23,* 895–903.

Nestadt, G., Romanoski, A. J., Brown, C. H., Chahal, R., Merchant, A., Folstein, M. F., et al. (1991). DSM-III compulsive personality disorder: An epidemiological study. *Psychological Medicine, 21,* 461–471.

Neugarten, B. L. (1990). The changing meanings of age. In M. Bergener and S. I. Finkel (Eds.), *Clinical and Scientific Psychogeriatrics: The Holistic Approachs*, pp. 1–6. New York: Springer.

Nestler, E. J. (1998). Antidepressant treatments in the 21st century. *Biological Psychiatry, 44*, 526–533.

Neugebauer, R. (1979). Medieval and early modern theories of mental illness. *Archives of General Psychiatry, 36*(4), 477–483.

Neuner, F., Schauer, M., Klaschik, C., Karunakara, U., & Elbert, T.(2004). A comparison of narrative exposure therapy, supportive counseling, and psychoeducation for treating posttraumatic stress disorder in an African refugee settlement. *Journal of Consulting and Clinical Psychology, 72*, 579–587.

Newcomb, A. F., Bukowski, W. M., & Pattee, L. (1993). Children's peer relations: A meta-analytic review of popular, rejected, neglected, controversial, and average sociometric status. *Psychological Bulletin, 113*, 99–128.

Newcorn, J. H., Kratochvil, C. J., Allen, A. J., Casat, C. D., Ruff, D. D., Moore, R. J., et al. (2008). Atomoxetine/methylphenidate comparative study group: Atomoxetine and osmotically released methylphenidate for the treatment of attention deficit hyperactivity disorder: Acute comparison and differential response. *American Journal of Psychiatry, 165*, 721–730.

Newhouse, P. A. (1997). Alzheimer's disease and the cholinergic system: An introduction to clinical pharmacological research. In L. Heston (Ed.), *Progress in Alzheimer's Disease and Similar Conditions*. Washington, DC: American Psychiatric Press.

Newport, D. J., & Nemeroff, C. B. (2000). Neurobiology of posttraumatic stress disorder. *Cognitive Neuroscience, 10*, 211–218.

Newschaffer, C. J., Falb, M. D., & Gurney, J. G. (2005). National autism prevalence trends from United States Special Education Data. *Pediatrics, 115*(3), e277–e282.

Newsom, C., & Hovanitz, C. A. (in press). Autistic spectrum disorders. In E. J. Mash & R. A. Barkley (Eds.), *Treatment of Childhood Disorders*, 3rd ed. New York: Guilford Press.

Nichols, D.S. (2006). The trials of separating bath water from baby: A review and creitique of the MPPI-2 restructured clinical scales. *Journal of Personality Assessment, 87*, 121–138.

Niebuhr, R. (1951, February 13). To be abased and to abound. *Messenger*, 7.

Nigg, J. T. (2001). Is ADHD a disinhibitory disorder? *Psychological Bulletin, 127*, 571–598.

Nigg, J. T., Blaskey, L. G., Stawicki, J. A., & Sachek, J. (2004). Evaluating the endophenotype model of ADHD neuropsychological deficit: Results for parents and siblings of children with ADHD combined and inattentive subtypes. *Journal of Abnormal Psychology, 113*(4), 614–625.

Nigg, J. T., & Goldsmith, H. H. (1994). Genetics of personality disorders: Perspectives from personality and psychopathology research. *Psychological Bulletin, 115*, 346–380.

Nilsson, L. (2003). Memory function in normal aging. *Acta Neurologica Scandinavica, 107*, 7–13.

Ninan, P. T., & Dunlop, B. W. (2005). Neurobiology and etiology of panic disorder. *Journal of Clinical Psychiatry, 66* (Suppl. 4), 3–7.

Niznikiewicz, M. A., Kubicki, M., & Shenton, M. E. (2003). Recent structural and functional imaging findings in schizophrenia. *Current Opinion in Psychiatry, 16*, 123–147.

Nobre, P. J., & Pinto-Gouveia, J. (2006). Dysfuncitonal sexual beliefs as vulnerability factors for sexual dysfunction. *Journal of Sex Research, 43*, 68–75.

Nock, M. K., & Kessler, R. C. (2006). Prevalence of and risk factors for suicide attempts versus suicide gestures: Analysis of the National Comorbidity Survey. *Journal of Abnormal Psychology, 115*, 616–623.

Nolen-Hoeksema, S. (1994). An interactive model for the emergence of gender differences in depressive in adolescence. *Journal of Research on Adolescence, 4*, 519–534.

Nolen-Hoeksema, S. (2000). The role of rumination in depressive disorders and mixed anxiety/depressive symptoms. *Journal of Abnormal Psychology, 109*, 504–511.

Nolen-Hoeksema, S. (2002). Gender differences in depression. In I. H. Gotlib & C. L. Hammen (Eds.), *Handbook of Depression*. New York: Guilford.

Norcross, J. C. (2002). *Psychotherapy Relationships That Work*. New York: Oxford.

Norcross, J. C., & Hill, C. E. (2004). Empirically supported therapy relationships. *The Clinical Psychologist, 57*, 19–25.

Norris, F. H., Murphy, A. D., Baker, C. K., Perilla, J. L., Rodriguez, F. G., & Rodriguez, J. J. (2003). Epidemiology of trauma and posttraumatic stress disorder in Mexico. *Journal of Abnormal Psychology, 112*, 646–656.

North, C. S., et al. (2002). Psychiatric disorders in rescue workers after the Oklahoma City bombing. *American Journal of Psychiatry, 159*, 857–859.

Noyes, R., Garvey, M. J., & Cook, B. L. (1989). Follow-up study of patients with panic disorder and agoraphobia with panic attacks treated with tricyclic antidepressants. *Journal of Affective Disorders, 16*, 249–257.

Nuechterlein, K. H., Asarnow, R. F., Subotnik, K. L., Fogelson, D. L., Payne, D. L., Kendler, K. S., et al. (2002). The structure of schizotypy: Relationships between neurocognitive and personality disorder features in relatives of schizophrenic patients in the UCLA family study. *Schizophrenia Research, 54*, 121–130.

Nunes, E. V., Frank, K. A., & Kornfeld, J. (1987). Psychologic treatment for the Type A behavior pattern and for coronary heart disease: A meta-analysis of the literature. *Psychosomatic Medicine, 48*, 159–173.

Oberman, L. M., & Ramachandran, V. S. (2007). The simulating social mind: The role of the mirror neuron system and simulation in the social and communicative deficits of autism spectrum disorders. *Psychological Bulletin, 133*, 310–327.

O'Brien, C. P., & McKay, J. (2002). Pharmacological treatments for substance use disorders. In P. E. Nathan and J. M. Gorman (Eds.), *A Guide to Treatments That Work*, 2nd ed., pp. 125–156. London: Oxford University Press.

O'Brien, C. P., & Mckay, J. (2007). Psychopharmacological treatments for substance use disorders. In P. E. Nathan & J. M. Gorman (Eds.), *A Guide to Treatments That Work*, 3rd ed., pp. 145–177. New York: Oxford University Press.

O'Connor, D. W. (2006). Do older Australians truly have low rates of anxiety and depression? A critique of the 1997 National Survey of Mental Health and Wellbeing. *Australian and New Zealand Journal of Psychiatry, 40*, 623–631.

O'Connor, G. T., Buring, J. E., Yusuf, S., Goldhaber, S. Z., Olmstead, E. M., Paffenbarger, R. S., et al. (1989). An overview of randomized trials of rehabilitation with exercise after myocardial infarction. *Circulation, 80*, 234–244.

O'Donohue, W., & Bradley, A. R.(1999). Conceptual and empirical issues in child custody evaluations. *Clinical Psychology: Sciences and Practice, 6*, 310–322.

O'Donohue, W. T., Swingen, D. N., Dopke, C. A., & Regev, L. G. (1999). Psychotherapy for male sexual dysfunction: A review. *Clinical Psychology Review, 19*, 591–630.

O'Donovan, M. C., Williams, N. M., & Owen, M. J. (2003). Recent advances in the genetics of schizophrenia. *Human Molecular Genetics, 12* (Spec. no 2), R125–133.

O'Meara, E. S., Kukull, W. A., Sheppard, L., Bowen, J. D., McCormick, W. C., Teri, L., et al. (1997). Head injury and risk of Alzheimer's disease by apolipoprotein E genotype. *American Journal of Epidemiology, 146*, 373–384.

Oakley, R. (2004). How the mind hurts and heals the body. *American Psychologist, 59*(1), 29–40.

Oei, T. P. S., Lim, B., & Hennessy, B. (1990). Psychological dysfunction in battle: Combat stress reactions and posttraumatic stress disorder. *Clinical Psychology Review, 10*, 355–388.

Office of Special Education Programs. (2003). *Implementation of the Individuals with Disabilities Act: 25th Annual Report to Congress*. Washington, DC: U.S. Office of Education.

Ohayon, M. M. (2000). Prevalence of hallucinations and their pathological associations in the general population. *Psychiatry Research, 97*, 153–164.

Ohman, A., & Mineka, S. (2001). Fears, phobias, and preparedness: Toward an evolved module of fear and fear learning. *Psychological Review, 108*, 483–522.

Ohman, A., & Mineka, S. (2003): The malicious serpent: Snakes as a prototypical stimulus for an evolved module of fear. *Current Directions in Psychological Science, 12*, 5–9.

Öhman, A. (1996). Preferential preattentive processing of threat in anxiety: Preparedness and attentional biases. In R. M. Rapee (Ed.), *Current Controversies in the Anxiety Disorders*, pp. 253–290. New York: Guilford.

Olatunji, B., Cisler, J., & Tolin, D. (2007). Quality of life in the anxiety disorders: A meta-analytic review. *Clinical Psychology Review, 27*, 572–581.

Olfson, M., Marcus, S. C., & Druss, B. G. (2008). Effects of food and drug administration warnings on antidepressant use in a national sample. *Archives of General Psychiatry, 65*, 94–101.

Ollendick, T. H., & King, N. J. (1998). Empirically supported treatments for children with phobic and anxiety disorders: Current status. *Journal of Clinical Child Psychology, 27*, 156–167.

Olmstead, M. P., Kaplan, A. S., & Rockert, W. (1994). Rate and prediction of relapse in bulimia nervosa. *American Journal of Psychiatry, 151*, 738–743.

Olson, S. L., Schilling, E. M., & Bates, J. E. (1999). Measurement of impulsivity: Construct coherence, longitudinal stability, and relationship with externalizing problems in middle childhood and adolescence. *Journal of Abnormal Child Psychology, 27*(2), 151–165.

Olsson, S., & Moller, A. R. (2003). On the incidence and sex ratio of transsexualism in Sweden, 1972–2002. *Archives of Sexual Behavior, 32*, 381–386.

Oltmanns, T. F. (1988). Defining delusional beliefs. In T. F. Oltmanns & B. A. Maher (Eds.), *Delusional Beliefs*. New York: Wiley.

Oltmanns, T. F., Melley, A. H., & Turkheimer, E. (2002). Impaired social functioning and symptoms of personality disorders in a non-clinical population. *Journal of Personality Disorders, 16*, 438–453.

Oltmanns, T. F., & Turkheimer, E. (2006). Perceptions of self and others regarding pathological personality traits. In R. Krueger and J.Tackett (Eds.), *Personality and Psychopathology: Building Bridges*. New York: Guilford.

Olvera, R. L. (2002). Intermittent explosive disorder: Epidemiology, diagnosis and management, *CNS Drugs, 16*, 517–526.

Olweus, D. (1984). Aggressors and their victims: Bullying at school. In N. Frude & H. Gault (Eds.), *Disruptive Behavior in Schools*, pp. 57–76. New York: Wiley.

Onaivi, E. S. (2002). *Biology of Marijuana: From Gene to Behavior*. London: Taylor & Francis.

Oosterwegel, A., & Wicklund, R. A. (1995). *The Self in European and North American Culture: Development and Processes*. Boston: Kluwer.

Orne, M. T., Dingers, D. F., & Orne, E. C. (1984). On the differential diagnosis of multiple personality in the forensic context. *International Journal of Clinical and Experimental Hypnosis, 32*, 118–169.

Orth, U., & Wieland, E. (2006). Anger, hostility, and posttraumatic stress disorder in trauma-exposed adults: A meta-analysis. *Journal of Consulting and Clinical Psychology, 74*, 698–706.

Osman, A. K., & Al-Sawaf, M. H. (1995). Cross-cultural aspects of sexual anxieties and the associated dysfunction. *Journal of Sex Education and Therapy, 21*, 174–181.

Öst, L. (2008). Efficacy of the third wave of behavioral therapies: A systematic review and meta-analysis. *Behaviour Research and Therapy, 46*, 296–321.

Osterling, J. A., Dawson, G., & Munson, J. A. (2002). Early recognition of 1-year-old infants with autism spectrum disorder versus mental retardation. *Development and Psychopathology, 14*, 239–251.

Otto, J. W., Smits, J. A. J., & Reese, H. E. (2004). Cognitive-behavioral therapy for the treatment of anxiety disorders. *Journal of Clinical Psychiatry, 65* (Suppl. 5), 34–41.

Otto, J. W., Smits, J. A. J., & Reese, H. E. (2005). Combined psychotherapy and pharmacotherapy for mood and anxiety disorders in adults: Review and analysis. *Clinical Psychology: Science and Practice, 12*, 72–86.

Otto, M. W., Wilhelm, S., Cohen, L. S., Harlow, B. L. (2001). Prevalence of body dysmorphic disorder in a community sample of women. *American Journal of Psychiatry, 158*, 2061–2063.

Otto, R. K., Poythress, N. G., Nicholson, R. A., Edens, J. F., Monahan, J., Bonnie, R. J., et al. (1998). Psychometric properties of the MacArthur Competence Assessment Tool—Criminal Adjudication. *Psychological Assessment, 10*, 435–443.

Owen, P. L., Slaymaker, V., Torigan, J. S., McCrady, B. S., Epstein, E. E., Kaskutas, L. A., et al. (2003). Participation in Alcoholics Anonymous: Intended and unintended change mechanisms. *Alcoholism: Clinical & Experimental Research, 27*, 524–532.

Owen, P. R. & Laurel-Seller, E. (2000). Weight and shape ideals: Thin is dangerously in. *Journal of Applied Social Psychology, 30*, 979–990.

Ozer, E. J., & Weiss, D. S. (2004). Who develops posttraumatic stress disorder? *Current Directions in Psychological Science, 13*, 169–172.

Ozer, E. J., Best, S. R., Lipsey, T. L., & Weiss, D. S. (2003). Predictors of posttraumatic stress disorder and symptoms in adults: A meta-analysis. *Psychological Bulletin, 129*, 52–73.

Padilla, A. M. (2001). Issues in culturally appropriate assessment. In L. A. Suzuki, J. G. Ponterotto, & P. J. Metter (Eds.). *Handbook of Multicultural Assessment: Clinical Psychological, and Educational Applications*, 2nd ed. San Francisco: Jossey-Bass.

Paikoff, R. L., & Brooks-Gunn, J. (1991). Do parent-child relationships change during puberty? *Psychological Bulletin, 110*, 47–66.

Pallanti, S., & Sandner, C. (2007). Treatment of depression with selective serotonin inhibitors: The role of fluvoxamine. *International Journal of Psychiatry in Clinical Practice, 11*, 233–238.

Pally, R. (2002). The neurobiology of borderline personality disorder: The synergy of "nature and nurture." *Journal of Psychiatric Practice, 8*, 133–142.

Palmer, R. L. (1995). Sexual abuse and eating disorders. In K. D. Brownell & C. G. Fairburn (Eds.), *Eating Disorders and Obesity: A Comprehensive Handbook*, pp. 230–233. New York: Guilford.

Panksepp, J. (1998). *Affective Neuroscience: The Foundations of Human and Animal Emotions*. New York: Oxford University Press.

Panksepp, J. (2005). Why does separation distress hurt? Comment on MacDonald and Leary. *Psychological Bulletin, 131*, 224–230.

Pantle, M., Pasewark, R., & Steadman, H. (1980). Comparing institutionalization periods and subsequent arrests of insanity acquittees and convicted felons. *Journal of Psychiatry and the Law, 8*, 305–316.

Pargament, K. I. & Park, C. L. (1995). Merely a defense? The variety of religious means and ends. *Journal of Social Issues, 51*, 13–32.

Paris, J. (2003). Personality disorders over time: Precursors, course and outcome. *Journal of Personality Disorders, 17*, 479–488.

Park, C. L., & Helgeson, V. S. (2006). Introduction to the special section: Growth following highly stressful life events—Current status and future directions. *Journal of Consulting and Clinical Psychology, 74*, 791–796.

Park, D. C., Nisbett, R., & Hedden, T. (1999). Aging, culture, and cognition. *Journal of Gerontology* (Ser. B), p75–p84.

Parker, G., Roussos, J., Mitchell, P., Wilhelm, K., et al. (1997). Distinguishing psychotic depression from melancholia. *Journal of Affective Disorders, 42*, 155–167.

Parker, J. G., & Asher, S. R. (1987). Peer relations and later personality adjustment: Are low-accepted children at risk? *Psychological Bulletin, 102*, 357–389.

Parker, R. A., & Aldwin, C. M. (1997). Do aspects of gender identity change from early to middle adulthood? Disentangling age, cohort and period effects. In J. E. Lachman & J. B. James (Eds.), *Multiple Paths of Midlife Development*, 67–107. Chicago: University of Chicago Press.

Parks, F. M. (2003). The role of African American folk beliefs in the modern therapeutic process. *Clinical Psychology: Science and Practice, 10*, 456–467.

Parnas, J., Cannon T. D., Jacobsen, B., Schulsinger, H., Schulsinger, F., & Mednick, S. A. (1993). Lifetime DSM-III-R diagnostic outcomes in the offspring of schizophrenic mothers: Results from the Copenhagen high-risk study. *Archives of General Psychiatry, 50*, 707–714.

Parry-Jones, B. (1994). Merycism or rumination disorder: A historical investigation and current assessment. *British Journal of Psychiatry, 165*, 303–314.

Pascual-Leone, A., & Greenberg, L. S. (2007). Emotional processing in experiential therapy: Why "the only way is through." *Journal of Consulting and Clinical Psychology, 75*, 875–887.

Pasupathi, M. (2001). The social construction of the personal past and its implications for adult development. *Psychological Bulletin, 127*, 651–672.

Pasupathi, M., Carstensen, L. L., & Tsai, J. L. (1995). Ageism in interpersonal settings. In B. Lott & D. Maluso (Eds.), *The Social Psychology of Interpersonal Discrimination*, pp. 160–182. New York: Guilford.

Patrick, C. J., & Zempolich, K. A. (1998). Emotion and aggression in the psychopathic personality. *Aggression and Violent Behavior, 3*, 303–338.

Patterson, C. J., Kupersmidt, J. B., & Griesler, P. C. (1990). Children's perceptions of self and of relationships with others as a function of sociometric status. *Child Development, 61*, 1335–1349.

Patterson, C. M., & Newman, J. P. (1993). Reflectivity and learning from aversive events: Toward a psychological mechanism for the syndromes of disinhibition. *Psychological Review, 100*, 716–736.

Patterson, D. R. (2004). Treating pain with hypnosis. *Current Directions in Psychological Science, 13*, 252–255.

Patterson, G.R. (1982). *Coercive Family Process*. Eugene, OR: Castalia.

Patterson, G. R., DeBaryshe, B. D., & Ramsey, E. (1989). A developmental perspective on antisocial behavior. *American Psychologist, 44*, 329–325.

Patterson, G. R., & Fleischman, M. J. (1979). Maintenance of treatment effects: Some considerations concerning family systems and follow-up data. *Behavior Therapy, 10*, 168–185.

Patton, J. R., Beirne-Smith, M., & Payne, J. S. (1990). *Mental Retardation*. (3rd ed.). Columbus, OH: Merrill.

Paul, G. L., & Lentz, R. J. (1977). *Psychosocial Treatment of Chronic Mental Patients: Milieu Versus Social-Learning Programs*. Cambridge, MA: Harvard University Press.

Paul, R., Garrett, K., & Cohen, R. (2003). Vascular dementia: A diagnostic conundrum for the clinical neuropsychologist. *Applied Neuropsychology, 10*, 129–136.

Pauli, P., & Alpers, G. W. (2002). Memory bias in patients with hypochondriasis and somatoform pain disorder. *Journal of Psychosomatic Research, 52*, 45–53.

Payne, R. L. (1992). First person account: My schizophrenia. *Schizophrenia Bulletin, 18*, 725–728.

Pedersen, N. L., & Gatz, M. (1991). Twin studies as a tool for bridging the gap between genetics and epidemiology of dementia: The study of dementia in Swedish twins [abstract]. *Gerontologist, 31*, 333.

Pedersen, N. L., Gatz, M., Berg, S., & Johansson, B. (2004). How heritable is Alzheimer's disease late in life? Findings from Swedish twins. *Annals of Neurology, 55*, 180–185.

Pelham, W. E., Carlson, C., Sams, S. E., Vallano, G., Dixon, M. J., & Hoza, B. (1993). Separate and combined effects of methylphenidate and behavior modification with attention deficit-hyperactivity disorder in the classroom. *Journal of Consulting and Clinical Psychology, 61*, 506–515.

Pelham, W. E., et al. (1985). Methylphenidate and children with attention deficit disorder: Dose effects on classroom academic and social behavior. *Archives of General Psychiatry, 42*, 948–952.

Pelham, W. E., et al. (2000). Behavioral versus behavioral and pharmacological treatment in ADHD children attending a summer treatment program. *Journal of Abnormal Child Psychology, 28*, 507–525.

Pelham, W. E., et al. (2002). Effects of methylphenidate and expectancy on children with ADHD: Behavior, academic performance, and attributions in a summer treatment program and regular classroom settings. *Journal of Consulting and Clinical Psychology, 70*, 320–335.

Penn, D., Waldheter, E., Perkins, D., Mueser, K., & Lieberman, J. (2005). Psychosocial treatment for first-episode psychosis: A research update. *American Journal of Psychiatry, 162*, 2220–2232.

Pennebaker, J. W. (1990). *Opening Up: The Healing Power of Confiding in Others*. New York: Morrow.

Pennebaker, J. W., Kiecolt-Glaser, J., & Glaser, R. (1988). Disclosure of traumas and immune function: Health implications for psychotherapy. *Journal of Consulting and Clinical Psychology, 56*, 239–245.

Pennix, B., Van Tilburg, T., Kriegsman, D., Deeg, D., Boeke, A., & Van Eijk, J. (1997). Effects of social support and personal coping resources on mortality in older age: The Longitudinal Aging Study of Amsterdam. *American Journal of Epidemiology, 146*, 510–519.

Perkins, D., Miller-Andersen, L., & Lieberman, J. (2006). Natural History and Predictors of Clinical Course. The American Psychiatric Publishing Textbook of Schizophrenia, pp. 289–301. Arlington, VA: American Psychiatric Publishing, Inc.

Perry, C., & Laurence, J. (1984). Mental processing outside of awareness: The contributions of Freud and Janet. In K. S. Bowers & D. Meichenbaum (Eds.), *The Unconscious Reconsidered*, pp. 9–48. New York: Wiley.

Perry, J. C. (2005). Dependent personality disorder. In G. O. Gabbard, J. S. Beck, & J. Holmes (Eds.), *Oxford Textbook of Psychotherapy*, pp. 321–328. New York: Oxford University Press.

Pescosolido, B., et al. (1999). The public's view of the competence, dangerousness, and need for legal coercion among persons with mental illness. *American Journal of Public Health, 89*, 1339–1345.

Peters, K. D., Kochanek, K. D., and Murphy, S. L. (1998). Deaths: Final data for 1996. *National Vital*

Statistics Reports, vol. 47, no. 9. Hyattsville, MD: National Center for Health Statistics.

Petrie, K. J., Booth, R. J., Pennebaker, J. W., Davison, K. P., & Thomas, M. G. (1995). Disclosure of trauma and immune response to a hepatitis B vaccination program. *Journal of Consulting and Clinical Psychology, 63,* 787–792.

Pfohl, B. (1995). *Histrionic Personality Disorder. The DSM-IV Personality Disorders,* pp. 173–192. New York: Guilford Press.

Pfohl, B., Blum, N., & Zimmerman, M. (1995). *Structured Interview for DSM-IV Personality (SIDP-IV).* Iowa City: University of Iowa.

Pfohl, B., Coryell, W., Zimmerman, M., & Stangl, D. (1986). DSM-III personality disorders: Diagnostic overlap and internal consistency of individual DSMI-II-criteria. *Comprehensive Psychiatry, 27,* 21–34.

Phelan, J. C., & Link, B. G. (1999). The labeling theory of mental disorder (I): The role of social contingencies in the application of psychiatric labels. In A. V. Horwitz and T. L. Scheid (Eds.), *A Handbook for the Study of Mental Health: Social Contexts, Theories, and Systems,* pp. 139–150. New York: Cambridge University Press.

Phillips, E. L., Phillips, E. A., Fixsen, D. L., & Wolf, M. M. (1973). Behavior shaping works for delinquents. *Psychology Today, 7*(1), 74–79.

Phillips, K. A. (1991). Body dysmorphic disorder: The distress of imagined ugliness. *American Journal of Psychiatry, 148,* 1138–1149.

Phillips, K. A., Albertini, R. S., & Rasmussen, S. A. (2002). A randomized placebo-controlled trial of fluoxetine in body dysmorphic disorder. *Archives of General Psychiatry, 59,* 381–388.

Phillips, K. A., Grant, J., Siniscalchi, J., Albertini, R. S. (2001). Surgical and nonpsychiatric medical treatment of patients with body dysmorphic disorder. *Psychosomatics, 42,* 504–510.

Phillips, N. K., Hammen, C. L., Brennan, P. A., Najman, J. M., & Bor, W. (2005). Early adversity and the prospective prediction of depressive and anxiety disorders in adolescents. *Journal of Abnormal Child Psychology, 33,* 13–24.

Phillips, S. D., Burns, B. J., Edgar, E. R., Mueser, K. T., Linkins, K. W., Rosenheck, R. A., et al. (2001). Moving assertive community treatment into standard practice. *Psychiatric Services, 52,* 771–779.

Pilling, S., Bebbington, P., Kuipers, E., Garety, P., Geddes, J., Martindale, B., et al. (2002a). Psychological treatments in schizophrenia: II. Meta-analyses of randomized controlled trials of social skills training and cognitive remediation. *Psychological Medicine, 32,* 783–791.

Pilling, S, Bebbington, P., Kuipers, E., Garety, P., Geddes, J. Orbach, G., et al. (2002b). Psychological treatments in schizophrenia: II. Meta-analyses of family intervention and cognitive behavior therapy. *Psychological Medicine, 32,* 763–782.

Pincus, H. A., Tanielian, T. L., Marcus, S. C., Olfson, M., Zarin, D. A., Thompson, J., et al. (1998). Prescribing trends in psychotropic medications: Primary care, psychiatry, and other medical specialties. *Journal of the American Medical Association, 279,* 526–531.

Pincus, T., & Morley, S. (2001). Cognitive-processing bias in chronic pain: A review and integration. *Psychological Bulletin, 127,* 599–617.

Pinheiro, A. P., et al., (2007). Patterns of menstrual disturbance in eating disorders. *International Journal of Eating Disorders, 40,* 424–434.

Pinker, S. (1997). *How the Mind Works.* New York: Norton.

Pinto, C., Dhavale, H. S., Nair, S., Patil, B., & Dewan, M. (2000). Borderline personality disorder exists in India. *Journal of Nervous and Mental Disease, 188,* 386–388.

Piper, A. (1994). Multiple personality disorder. *British Journal of Psychiatry, 164,* 600–612.

Pitman, R. K. (1997). Overview of biological themes in PTSD. In R. Yehuda & A. C. McFarlane (Eds.), *Psychobiology of Posttraumatic Stress Disorder.* New York: New York Academy of Sciences.

Plassman, B. L., & Breitner, J. C. S. (1997). The genetics of dementia in late life. *Psychiatric Clinics of North America, 20,* 59–76.

Plaut, S. M. (1995). *Sex therapy following treatment by an exploitive therapist.* In R. C. Rosen & S. R. Leiblum (Eds.), *Case Studies in Sex Therapy,* pp. 264–278. New York: Guilford.

Plomin, R., & Crabbe, J. (2000). *Psychological Bulletin, 126,* 806–828.

Plomin, R., & Daniels, D. (1987). Why are children in the same family so different from one another? *Behavioral and Brain Sciences, 10,* 1–60.

Plomin, R., DeFries, J. C., McClearn, G.E., & McGuffin, P. (2001). *Behavioral genetics* (4th ed.). New York: Worth Publishers.

Plomin, R., Owen, M. J., & McGuffin, P. (1994). The genetic bases of complex human behaviors. *Science, 264,* 1733–1739.

Pogue-Geile, M., & Gottesman, I. (2007). Schizophrenia: Study of a Genetically Complex Phenotype. Neurobehavioral Genetics: Methods and Applications, 2nd ed., pp. 209–226. Boca Raton, FL: CRC Press.

Pohl, J., Olmstead, M. C., Wynne-Edwards, K. E., Harkness, K., & Menard, J. L. (2007). Repeated exposure to stress across the childhood-adolescent period alters rats' anxiety and depression-like behaviors in adulthood. *Behavioral Neuroscience, 121,* 462–474.

Pokony, A. (1983). Prediction of suicide in psychiatric patients: A prospective study. *Archives of General Psychiatry, 40,* 249–257.

Polaschek, D. L. (1997). New Zealand rapists: An examination of subtypes. In G. M. Habermann (Ed.), *Looking Back and Moving Forward: 50 Years of New Zealand Psychology,* pp 224–231. Wellington, New Zealand: New Zealand Psychological Society.

Pole, N. (2007). The psychopathology of posttraumatic stress disorder: A meta-analysis. *Psychological Bulletin, 133,* 725–749.

Pole, N., Gone, J. P., & Kulkarni, M. (2008). Posttraumatic stress disorder among ethnoracial minorities in the United States. *Clinical Psychology: Science and Practice, 15,* 35–61.

Polivy, J., & Herman, C. P. (2002). Causes of eating disorders. *Annual Review of Psychology, 53,* 187–213.

Pollak, S. D. & Tolley-Schell, S. A. Selective attention to facial emotion in physically abused children. (2003). *Journal of Abnormal Psychology, 112*(3), 323–338.

Polleux, F., & Lauder, J. M. (2004). Toward a developmental neurobiology of autism. *Mental Retardation and Developmental Disabilities Research Reviews, 10,* 303–317.

Pomeroy, C. (1996). Anorexia nervosa, bulimia nervosa, and binge eating disorder: The assessment of physical status. In J. K. Thompson, *Body Image, Eating Disorders, and Obesity,* pp. 177–204. Washington, DC: American Psychological Association.

Poole, D. A., Lindsay, D. S., Memon, A., & Bull, R. (1995). Psychotherapy and the recovery of memories of childhood sexual abuse: U.S. and British practitioners' opinions, practices, and experiences. *Journal of Consulting and Clinical Psychology, 63,* 426–437.

Pope, H. G., & Yurgelun-Todd, D. (1996). The residual cognitive effects of heavy marijuana use in college students. *Journal of the American Medical Association, 275,* 521–527.

Pope, H. G., Poliakoff, M. B., Parker, M. P., Boynes, M., & Hudson, J. I. (2007). Is dissociative amnesia a culture-bound syndrome? Findings from a survey of historical literature. *Psychological Medicine, 37,* 225–233.

Posner, M. I., & DiGirolamo, G. J. (2000). Cognitive neuroscience: Origins and promise. *Psychological Bulletin, 126,* 873.

Poulton, R., & Menzies, R. G. (2002). Non-associative fear acquisition: A review of the evidence from retrospective and longitudinal research. *Behaviour Research and Therapy, 40,* 127–149.

Powell, L. H., Shahabi, L., & Thoresen, C. E. (2003). Religion and spirituality: Linkages to physical health. *American Psychologist, 58*(1), 36–52.

Prentky, R. A. (1997). Arousal reduction in sexual offenders: A review of antiandrogen interventions. *Sexual Abuse: Journal of Research and Treatment, 9,* 335–347.

Prentky, R., Lee, A., Knight, R., & Cerce, D. (1997). Recidivism rates among child molesters and rapists: A methodological analysis. *Law and Human Behavior, 21,* 635–659.

Prescott, C. A., Hewitt, J. K., Heath, A. C., Truett, K. R., Neale, M. C., & Eaves, L. J. (1994). Environmental and genetic influences on alcohol use in a volunteer sample of older twins. *Journal of Studies on Alcohol, 55,* 18–32.

Presnell, K. & Stice, E. (2003). An experimental test of the effect of weight-loss dieting on bulimic pathology: Tipping the scales in a different direction. *Journal of Abnormal Psychology, 112,* 166–170.

Presta, S., Marazziti, D., Dell'Osso, L., Pfanner, C., Pallanti, S., & Cassano, G. B. (2002). Kleptomania: Clinical features and comorbidity in an Italian sample. *Comprehensive Psychiatry, 43,* 7–12.

Preti, A., & Miotto, P. (2005). Genetics, perinatal insult and schizophrenia: The mechanism underlying an increased prevalence of perinatal complications among individuals with a diagnosis of schizophrenia? *Current Psychiatry Reviews, 1,* 139–150.

Price, G., Cercignani, M., Bagary, M., Barnes, T., Barker, G., Joyce, E., et al. (2006). A volumetric MRI and magnetization transfer imaging follow-up study of patients with first-episode schizophrenia. *Schizophrenia Research, 87,* 100–108.

Price, J. S., Gardner, R., Jr., & Erickson, M. (2004). Can depression, anxiety and somatization be understood as appeasement displays? *Journal of Affective Disorders, 79,* 1–11.

Prigerson, H. G., Maciejewski, P. K., & Rosenheck, R. A. (2002). Population attributable fractions of psychiatric disorders and behavioral outcomes associated with combat exposure among U.S. men. *American Journal of Public Health, 92,* 59–63.

Prince, M., Acosta, D., Chiu, H., Scazufca, M., & Varghese, M. (2003). Dementia diagnosis in developing countries: A cross-cultural validation study. *Lancet, 361,* 909–917.

Prior, M., & Ozonoff, S. (2007). Psychological factors in autism. In F. R. Volkmar (Ed.), *Autism and Pervasive Developmental Disorders,* pp. 69–128. New York: Cambridge University Press.

Prochaska, J. O., & Norcross, J. C. (2006). *Systems of Psychotherapy: A Transtheoretical Analysis.* Belmont, CA: Wadsworth.

Pryor, J. P. (2002). Pharmacotherapy of erectile dysfunction. *Sexual & Relationship Therapy, 17,* 389–400.

Pryse-Phillips, W. (1999). Do we have drugs for dementia? *Archives of Neurology, 56,* 735–737.

Puig-Antich, J. (1986). Psychobiological markers: Effects of age and puberty. In M. Rutter, C. Izard, & P. Read (Eds.), *Depression in Young People,* pp. 341–382. New York: Guilford.

Purdon, C. (2004). Empirical investigations of thought suppression in OCD. *Journal of Behavior Therapy & Experimental Psychiatry, 35,* 121–136.

Putnam, F. W., Curoff, J. J., et al. (1986). The clinical phenomenology of multiple personality disorder: Review of 100 recent cases. *Journal of Clinical Psychiatry, 47,* 285–293.

Quadagno, D., Sly, D. F., Harrison, D. F., Eberstein, I. W., & Soler, H. R. (1998). Ethnic differences in sexual decisions and sexual behavior. *Archives of Sexual Behavior, 27,* 57–75.

Quay, H. C. (1993). The psychobiology and undersocialized aggressive conduct disorder: A theoretical perspective. *Development and Psychopathology, 5,* 165–180.

Quigley, B. M., & Leonard, (2006). Alcohol expectancies and intoxicated aggression. *Aggression and Violent Behavior, 11,* 484–496.

Rachman, S. (1991). *Fear and Courage* (2nd ed.). San Francisco: Freeman.

Rachman, S. (2002). *Anxiety* (2nd ed.). New York: Psychology Press (Taylor and Francis Group).

Rachman, S., & de Silva, P. (1978). Abnormal and normal obsessions. *Behaviour Research and Therapy, 16,* 233–248.

Rachman, S. J., & Hodgson, R. J. (1980). *Obsessions and Compulsions.* Englewood Cliffs, NJ: Prentice Hall.

Radel, M., Vallejo, R. L., Iwata, N., Aragon, R., Long, J. C., Virkkunen, M., et al. (2005). Haplotype-based localization of an alcohol dependence gene to the 5q34 gamma-aminobutyric acid type A gene cluster. *Archives of General Psychiatry, 62,* 47–55.

Raichle, M. E. (2001). Bold insights. *Nature, 412,* 128–130.

Raine, A., Moffit, T. E., Caspi, A., Loeber, R., Southamer-Loeber, M., & Lynam, D. (2005). Neurocognitive impairments in boys on the life-course persistent antisocial path. *Journal of Abnormal Psychology, 114*(1), 38–49.

Ramey, C. T., & Bryant, D. (1982). Evidence for primary prevention of developmental retardation. *Journal of the Division of Early Childhood, 5,* 73–78.

Rangaswamy, M., Porjesz, B., Chorlian, D. B., Wang, K., Jones, K. A., Kuperman, S., et al. (2004). Resting EEG in offspring of male alcoholics: beta frequencies. *International Journal of Psychophysiology, 51,* 239–251.

Rapee, R. M. (1995). Psychological factors influencing the affective response to biological challenge procedures in panic disorder. *Journal of Anxiety Disorders, 9,* 59–74.

Rapee, R. M., et al., (2005). Prevention and early intervention of anxiety disorders in inhibited preschool children. *Journal of Consulting and Clinical Psychology, 73,* 488–497.

Raphael, B., Wilson, J., Meldrum L., & McFarlane, A. C. (1996). Acute preventive interventions. In B. A. van der Kolk, A. C. McFarlane, & L. Weisaeth (Eds.), *Traumatic Stress,* pp. 463–479. New York: Guilford.

Rapoport, J., & Swedo, S. (2002). Obsessive-compulsive disorders. In M. Rutier & E. Taylor (Eds.), *Child and Adolescent Psychiatry,* 4th ed., pp. 571–592. Oxford, England: Blackwell.

Rapoport, J. L., Buchsbaum, M. S., Zahn, T. P., Weingartner, H., Ludlow, C., & Mikkelsen, E. J. (1978). Dextroamphetamine: Cognitive and behavioral effects in normal prepubertal boys. *Science, 199,* 560–563.

Raskind, M. A. (1998). The clinical interface of depression and dementia. *Journal of Clinical Psychiatry, 59* (Suppl. 10), 9–12.

Raskind, M. A., & Peskind, E. R. (1997). Neurotransmitter abnormalities and the psychopharmacology of Alzheimer's disease. In L. Heston (Ed.), *Progress in Alzheimer's Disease and Similar Conditions.* Washington, DC: American Psychiatric Press.

Rastam, M., Gillberg, C., & Gillberg, C. (1995). Anorexia nervosa 6 years after onset. Part II. Comorbid psychiatric problems. *Comprehensive Psychiatry, 36,* 70–76.

Rathod, S., & Turkington, D. (2005). Cognitive-behaviour therapy for schizophrenia: A review. *Current Opinion in Psychiatry, 18,* 159–163.

Ratner, C., & Hui, L. (2003). Theoretical and methodological problems in cross-cultural psychology. *Journal for the Theory of Social Behaviour, 33,* 67–94.

Read, J. (1995). Female sexual dysfunction. *International Review of Psychiatry, 7,* 175–182.

Regier, D., Rae, D., Narrow, W., Kaelber, C., & Schatzberg, A. (1998). Prevalence of anxiety disorders and their comorbidity with mood and addictive disorders. *British Journal of Psychiatry, 173,* 24–28.

Reich, J. (1996). The morbidity of DSM-III-R dependent personality disorder. *Journal of Nervous and Mental Disease, 184,* 22–26.

Reis, H. T., Collins, W. A., & Berscheid, E. (2000). The relationship context of human behavior and development. *Psychological Bulletin, 6,* 844–872.

Reisberg, B., & Sartorius, N. (2007). *Diagnostic Criteria in Dementia: A Comparison of Current Criteria, Research Challenges, and Implications for DSM-V and ICD-11. Diagnostic Issues in Dementia: Advancing the Research Agenda for DSM-V,* pp. 27–50. Washington, DC: American Psychiatric Association.

Reisner, R., Slobogin, C., & Rai, A. (1999). *Law and the Mental Health System. Civil and Criminal Aspects* (3rd ed.). St. Paul, MN: West.

Reisner, R., Slobogin, C., & Rai, A. (2004). *Law and the Mental Health System* (4th ed.). St. Paul, MN: West.

Reiss, A. L., Feinstein, C., & Rosenbaum, K. N. (1986). Autism and genetic disorders. *Schizophrenia Bulletin, 12,* 724–738.

Reissing, E. D., Binik, Y. M., Khalife, S., Cohen, D., & Amsel, R. (2004). Vaginal spasm, pain, and behavior: An empirical investigation of the diagnosis of vaginismus. *Archives of Sexual Behavior, 33,* 5–17.

Repetti, R. L., Taylor, S. E., & Seeman, T. E. (2002). Risky families. Family social environments and the mental and physical health of offspring. *Psychological Bulletin, 128,* 330–366.

Research Units on Pediatric Psychopharmacology (RUPP) Anxiety Group. (2001) *New England Journal of Medicine, 344,* 1279–1285.

Resick, P. A., & Calhoun, K. S. (2001). Posttraumatic stress disorder. In D. Barlow (Ed.), *Clinical Handbook of Psychological Disorders,* 3rd ed. New York: Guilford.

Resick, P. A., Nishith, P., Weaver, T. L., Astin, M. C., & Feuer, C. A. (2002). *Journal of Consulting and Clinical Psychology, 70,* 867–879.

Ressler, K. J., & Mayberg, H. S. (2007). Targeting abnormal neural circuits in mood and anxiety disorders: From the laboratory to the clinic. *Nature Neuroscience, 10,* 1116–1124.

Reynolds, C. F., et al. (1999). Nortriptyline and interpersonal psychotherapy as maintenance therapies for recurrent major depression. *Journal of the American Medical Association, 281,* 39–45.

Rhee, S. H., & Waldman, I. D. (2002). Genetic and environmental influences on antisocial behavior: A meta-analysis of twin and adoption studies. *Psychological Bulletin, 128,* 490–529.

Rhee, S. H., Hewitt, J. K., Young, S. E., Corley, R. P., Crowley, T. J., & Stallings, M. C. (2003). Genetic and environmental influences on substance initiation, use, and problem use in adolescents. *Archives of General Psychiatry, 60,* 1256–1264.

Ricciardelli, L. A., & McCabe, M. P. (2004). A biopsychosocial model of disordered eating and the pursuit of muscularity in adolescent boys. *Psychological Bulletin, 130,* 179–205.

Riccio, C. A., Reynolds, C. R., Lowe, P., & Moore, J. J. (2002). The continuous performance test: A window on the neural substrates for attention? *Archives of Clinical Neuropsychology, 17,* 235–272.

Rice, M. E., & Harris, G. T. (1997). The treatment of adult offenders. In D. M. Stoff, J. Breiling, & J. Maser (Eds.), *Handbook of Antisocial Behavior,* pp. 425–435. New York: Wiley.

Richardson, K. (2000). *Developmental Psychology: How Nature and Nurture Interact.* Mahwah, NJ: Erlbaum.

Richardson, S. (1996). The besieged brain: Immune cells in brain may further progression of Alzheimer's disease. *Discover, 17,* 30–32.

Richelson, E. (1999). Receptor pharmacology of neuroleptics: Relation to clinical effects. *Journal of Clinical Psychiatry, 60* (Suppl. 10), 5–14.

Richtand, N., Welge, J., Logue, A., Keck, P., Strakowski, S., & McNamara, R. (2007). Dopamine and serotonin receptor binding and antipsychotic efficacy. *Neuropsychopharmacology, 32,* 1715–1726.

Richters, J. E., & Hinshaw, S. P. (1999). The abduction of disorder in psychiatry. *Journal of Abnormal Psychology, 108,* 438–445.

Richters, J. E., & Martinez, P. (1993). The NIMH Community Violence Project: I. Children as victims of and witnesses to violence. *Psychiatry: Interpersonal and Biological Processes, 56*(1), Special issue: Children and violence, 7–21.

Rieber, R. W. (1999). Hypnosis, false memory and multiple personality: A trinity of affinity. *History of Psychiatry, 10,* 3–11.

Rief, W., Hiller, W., & Margraf, J. (1998). Cognitive aspects of hypochondriasis and the somatization syndrome. *Journal of Abnormal Psychology, 107,* 587–595.

Rietkerk, T., Boks, M., Sommer, I., Liddle, P., Ophoff, R., & Kahn, R. (2008). The genetics of symptom dimensions of schizophrenia: Review and meta-analysis. *Schizophrenia Research, 102,* 197–205.

Rind, B., Tromovitch, P., & Bauserman, R. (1998). A meta-analytic examination of assumed properties of child sexual abuse using college samples. *Psychological Bulletin, 124,* 22–53.

Rivas-Vazquez, R. A., Saffa-Biller, D., Ruiz, I., Blais, M. A., & Rivas-Vazquez, A. (2004). Current issues in anxiety and depression: Comorbid, mixed, and subthreshold disorders. *Professional Psychology: Research and Practice, 35,* 74–83.

Roberts, A., Cash, T. F., Feingold, A., & Thompson, B. T. (2006). Are black-white differences in females' body dissatisfaction decreasing? A meta-analytic review. *Journal of Consulting and Clinical Psychology, 74,* 1121–1131.

Roberts, J., & Rowland, M. (1981). *Hypertension in Adults 25–74 Years of Age: United States, 1971–75.* Vital and Health Statistics Series 11, No. 221, DHEW Publication No. PHS 81-1671. Washington, DC: U. S. Government Printing Office.

Roberts, L. J., & Marlatt, G. A. (1999). Harm reduction. In P. J. Ott, R. E. Tarter, & R. T.Ammerman (Eds.), *Sourcebook on Substance Abuse: Etiology, Epidemiology, Assessment, and Treatment,* pp. 389–398. Boston: Allyn & Bacon.

Robin, A. L., Siegel, P. T., Moye, A. W., Gilroy, M., Dennis, A. B., & Sikand, A.(1999). A controlled comparison of family versus individual therapy for adolescents with anorexia nervosa. *Journal of the American Academy of Child & Adolescent Psychiatry, 38,* 1482–1489.

Robiner, W. N., Bearman, D. L., Berman, M., Grove, W. M., Colon, E., Armstrong, J., et al. (2003). Prescriptive authority for psychologists: Despite deficits in education and knowledge? *Journal of Clinical Psychology in Medical Settings, 10,* 211–212.

Robins, C. J., & Chapman, A. L. (2004). Dialectical behavior therapy: Current status, recent developments, and future directions. *Journal of Personality Disorders, 18,* 73–89.

Robins, E., & Guze, S. (1989). Establishment of diagnostic validity in psychiatric illness. In L. N. Robins & J. E. Barrett (Eds.), *The Validity of Psychiatric Diagnosis,* pp. 177–197. New York: Raven Press.

Robins, L. N. (1966). *Deviant Children Grown up: A Sociological and Psychiatric Study of Sociopathic Personality.* Baltimore: Williams & Wilkins.

Robins, L. N., & Regier, D. A. (1991). *Psychiatric Disorders in America: The Epidemiologic Catchment Area Study.* New York: Free Press.

Robins, L. N., Tipp, J., & Przybeck, T. (1991). Antisocial personality. In L. N. Robins & D. A. Regier (Eds.), *Psychiatric Disorders in America: The Epidemiologic Catchment Area Study,* pp. 258–290. New York: Free Press.

Robinson, N. M., Zigler, E., & Gallagher, J. J. (2000). Two tails of the normal curve: Similarities and differences in the study of mental retardation and giftedness. *American Psychologist, 55,* 1413–1424.

Robinson, P. (1976). *The Modernization of Sex: Havelock Ellis, Alfred Kinsey, William Masters and Virginia Johnson.* New York: Harper & Row.

Rockwood, K., Black, S., Bedard, M., Tran, T., & Lussier, I. (2007). Specific symptomatic changes following donepezil treatment of Alzheimer's disease: A multi-centre, primary care, open-label study. *International Journal of Geriatric Psychiatry, 22,* 312–319.

Rockwood, K., & Middleton, L. (2007). Physical activity and the maintenance of cognitive function. *Alzheimer's & Dementia, 3,* S38–S44.

Roemer, L., & Borkovec, T. D. (1993). Worry: Unwanted cognitive activity that controls unwanted somatic experience. In D. M.Wegner & J. W. Pennebaker (Eds.), *Handbook of Mental Control.* Englewood Cliffs, NJ: Prentice Hall.

Rogers, M. P., Weinshenker, N. J., Warshaw, M. G., et al. (1996). Prevalence of somatoform disorders in a large sample of patients with anxiety disorders. *Psychosomatics, 37,* 17–22.

Rogers, S., Wehner, E. A., & Hagerman, R. (2001). The behavioral phenotype in fragile X: Symptoms of autism in very young children with fragile X syndrome, idiopathic autism, and other developmental.

Rohan, K. J., Roecklein, K. A., Lindsey, K. T., Johnson, L. G., Lippy. R. D., Lacy, T. J., et al. (2007). A randomized controlled trial of cognitive-behavioral therapy, light therapy, and their combination for seasonal affective disorder. *Journal of Consulting and Clinical Psychology, 75,* 489–500.

Rohrbaugh, M. J., Shoham, V., Coyne, J. C., Cranford, J. A., Sonnega, J. S., & Nicklas, J. M. (2004). Beyond the "self" in self-efficacy: Spouse confidence predicts patient survival following heart failure. *Journal of Family Psychology, 18,* 184–193.

Roisman, G. I. (2005). Conceptual clarifications in the study of resilience. *American Psychologist, 60,* 264–265.

Rojas-Fernandez, C. H., & MacKnight, C. (1999). Dementia with Lewy bodies: Review and pharmacotherapeutic implications. *Pharmacotherapy, 19,* 795–803.

Rojas-Fernandez, C. H., Lanctot, K. L., Allen, D. D., & MacKnight, C. (2001). Pharmacotherapy of behavioral and psychological symptoms of dementia: Time for a different paradigm? *Pharmacotherapy, 21,* 74–102.

Roman, G. C. (2002). Vascular dementia revisited: Diagnosis, pathogenesis, treatment, and prevention. *Medical Clinics of North America, 86,* 477–499.

Ronningstam, E., & Gunderson, J. (1991). Differentiating borderline personality disorder from narcissistic personality disorder. *Journal of Personality Disorders, 5,* 225–232.

Room, R. (2007). Cultural and societal influences on substance use diagnoses and criteria. In J.B. Saunders, M. A. Schuckit, P. J. Sirovatka, & D. A. Regier (Eds.), *Diagnostic Issues in Substance Use Disorders,* pp. 45–60. Washington, DC: American Psychiatric Press.

Rose, R. J., Dick, D. M., Viken, R. J., & Kaprio, J. (2001). Gene–environment interaction in patterns of

adolescent drinking: Regional residency moderates longitudinal influences on alcohol use. *Alcoholism: Clinical and Experimental Research, 25,* 637–643.

Rose, R. J., Viken, R. J., Dick, D. M., Bates, J., Pulkkinen, L., & Kaprio, J. (2003). It does take a village: Nonfamilial environments and children's behavior. *Psychological Science, 14,* 273–277.

Rosen, J. C., Reiter, J., & Orosan, P. (1995). Cognitive-behavioral body image therapy for body dysmorphic disorder. *Journal of Consulting and Clinical Psychology, 63,* 263–269.

Rosen, R. C. (2000). Medical and psychological interventions for erectile dysfunction: Toward a combined treatment approach. In *Principles and Practice of Sex Therapy,* pp. 276–304.

Rosen, R. C., & Leiblum, S. R. (1995). Treatment of sexual disorders in the 1990s: An integrated approach. *Journal of Consulting and Clinical Psychology, 63,* 877–890.

Rosen, R. C., & McKenna, K. E. (2002). PDE-5 inhibition and sexual response: Pharmacological mechanisms and clinical outcomes. *Annual Review of Sex Research, 13,* 36–88.

Rosen, R. C., Weigel, M., & Gendrano, N. (2007). Sexual dusfunction, sexual psychophysiology, and psychopharmacology: Laboratory studies in men and women. In E. Janssen (Ed.), *The Psychophysiology of Sex,* pp. 381–409. Bloomington: Indiana University Press.

Rosenfeld, B. (2004). *Assisted Suicide and the Right to Die.* Washington, DC: American Psychological Association.

Rosenheck, R. (2007). Evaluating the cost-effectiveness of reduced tardive dyskinesia with second-generation antipsychotics. *British Journal of Psychiatry, 191,* 238–245.

Rosenhan, D. L. (1973). On being sane in insane places. *Science, 179*(4070), 250–258.

Rosenstein, L. D. (1998). Differential diagnosis of the major progressive dementias and depression in middle and later adulthood: A summary of the literature of the early 1990s. *Neuropsychology Review, 8,* 109–167.

Rosenthal, D. (Ed.). (1963). *The Genain Quadruplets.* New York: Basic Books.

Rosenthal, N. E. (1998). *Winter Blues: Seasonal Affective Disorder.* New York: Guilford.

Rosler, A., & Witztum, E. (1998). Treatment of men with paraphilia with a long-acting analogue of gonadotripin-releasing hormone. *New England Journal of Medicine, 338,* 416–422.

Ross, C. A. (1991). Epidemiology of multiple personality disorder and dissociation. *Psychiatric Clinics of North America, 14,* 503–516.

Ross, C. A. (1997). *Dissociative Identity Disorder: Diagnosis, Clinical Features, and Treatment of Multiple Personality.* New York: Wiley.

Ross, C. A., Duffy, C. M., & Ellason, J. W. (2002). Prevalence, reliability, and validity of dissociative disorders in an inpatient setting. *Journal of Trauma and Dissociation, 3,* 7–17.

Ross, C. A., Norton, G. R., & Wozney, K. (1989). Multiple personality disorder: An analysis of 236 cases. *Canadian Journal of Psychiatry, 34,* 413–418.

Ross, G. W., & Bowen, J. D. (2002). The diagnosis and differential diagnosis of dementia. *Medical Clinics of North America, 86,* 455–476.

Ross, J., & Carter, R. (1995). *Triumph over Fear.* New York: Bantam Books.

Rossor, M. N. (2001). Pick's disease: A clinical overview. *Neurology, 56* (Suppl. 4), S3–S5.

Roth, D., & Bean, J. (1986). New perspectives on homelessness: Findings from a statewide epidemiological study. *Hospital and Community Psychiatry, 37,* 712–723.

Roth, W. T., Wilhelm, F. H., & Pettit, D. (2005). Are current theories of panic falsifiable? *Psychological Bulletin, 131,* 171–192.

Rothbart, M. K. (2007). Temperament, development, and personality. *Current Directions in Psychological Science, 16,* 207–212.

Rothbaum, B. O., & Foa, E. B. (1996). Cognitive behavioral therapy for posttraumatic stress disorder. In B. A. van der Kolk, A. C., McFarlane, & L. Weiseath (Eds.), *Traumatic Stress,* pp. 491–509. New York: Guilford.

Rounsaville, B. J., Alarcon, R. D., Andrews, G., Jackson, J. S., Kendell, R. E., & Kendler, K. (2002). Basic nomenclature issues for DSM-V. In D. J. Kupfer, M. B. First, & D. A. Regier (Eds.), *A Research Agenda for DSM-V.* Washington, DC: American Psychiatric Press.

Roy-Byrne, P. P., & Cowley, D. S. (2002). Pharmacological treatments for panic disorder, generalized anxiety disorder, specific phobia, and social anxiety disorder. In P. E. Nathan & J. M. Gorman (Eds.), *A Guide to Treatments That Work,* 2nd ed., pp. 337–365. London: Oxford University Press.

Rozanski, A., Blumenthal, J. A., & Kaplan, J. (1999). Impact of psychological factors on the pathogenesis of cardiovascular disease and implications for therapy. *Circulation, 99,* 2192–2217.

Rubio, G., & Lopez-Ibor, J. J. (2007). Generalized anxiety disorder: A 40-year follow-up study. *Acta Psychiatrica Scandinavica, 115,* 372–379.

Rubonis, A. V., & Bickman, L. (1991). Psychological impairment in the wake of disaster: The disaster-psychopathology relationship. *Psychological Bulletin, 109,* 384–399.

Rucklidge, J. J., & Tannock, R. (2001). Psychiatric, psychosocial, and cognitive functioning of female adolescents with ADHD. *Journal of the American Academy of Child and Adolescent Psychiatry, 40,* 530–540.

Rueter, M. A., Scaramella, L., Wallace, L. E., & Conger, R. D. (1999). First onset of depressive or anxiety disorders predicted by the longitudinal course of internalizing symptoms and parent-adolescent disagreements. *Archives of General Psychiatry, 56,* 726–732.

Ruitenberg, A., Ott, A. L., van Swieten, J. C., Hofman, A., & Breteler, M. M. B. (2001). Incidence of dementia: Does gender make a difference? *Neurobiology of Aging, 22,* 575–580.

Ruscio, A. M., Borkovec, T. D., & Ruscio, J. (2001). A taxometric investigation of the latent structure of worry. *Journal of Abnormal Psychology, 110,* 413–422.

Ruscio, J. (2004). Diagnoses and the behaviors they denote: A critical evaluation of the labeling theory of mental illness. *The Scientific Review of Mental Health Practice, 3,* 5–22.

Russell, C. J. & Keel, P. K. (2002). Homosexuality as a specific risk factor for eating disorders in men. *International Journal of Eating Disorders, 31,* 300–306.

Russell, D. E. H. (1984). *Sexual Exploitation: Rape, Child Sexual Abuse, and Workplace Harassment.* Beverly Hills, CA: Sage.

Russell, G. F. M. (1979). Bulimia nervosa: An ominous variant of anorexia nervosa. *Psychological Medicine, 9,* 429–448.

Russell, G. F. M., Szmukler, G. I., Dare, C., & Eisler, I. (1987). An evaluation of family therapy in anorexia nervosa and bulimia nervosa. *Archives of General Psychiatry, 44,* 1047–1056.

Rutherford, J., McGuffin, P., Katz, R. J., & Murray, R. M. (1993). Genetic influences on eating attitudes in a normal female twin population. *Psychological Medicine, 23,* 425–436.

Rutter, M. (1970). Autistic children: Infancy to adulthood. *Seminars in Psychiatry, 2,* 435–450.

Rutter, M. (1983). Introduction: Concepts of brain dysfunction syndromes. In M. Rutter (Ed.), *Developmental Neuropsychiatry,* pp. 1–14. New York: Guilford.

Rutter, M. (1989). Isle of Wight revisited: Twenty-five years of child psychiatric epidemiology. *Journal of the American Academy of Child & Adolescent Psychiatry, 28,* 633–653.

Rutter, M. (1996). Autism research: Prospects and priorities. *Journal of Autism and Developmental Disorders, 26,* 257–275.

Rutter, M. (2005). Incidence of autism spectrum disorders: Changes over time and their meaning. *ACTA Paediatrica, 94*(1), 2–15.

Rutter, M. (2007). Proceeding from observed correlation to causal inference: The use of natural experiments. *Perspectives on Psychological Science, 2,* 377–395.

Rutter, M., Greenfield, D., & Lockyer, L. (1967). A five- to fifteen-year follow-up study of infantile psychosis. II. Social and behavioral outcome. *British Journal of Psychiatry, 113,* 1187–1199.

Rutter, M., Moffitt, T. E., & Caspi, A. (2006). Gene-environment interplay and psychopathology: Multiple varieties but real effects. *Journal of Child Psychology and Psychiatry, 47,* 226–261.

Rutter, M., Pickles, A., Murray, R., & Eaves, L. (2001). Testing hypotheses on specific environmental causal effects on behavior. *Psychological Bulletin, 127,* 291–324.

Rutter, M., & Rutter, M. (1993). *Developing Minds.* New York: Basic Books.

Rutter, M., Silberg, J., O'Connor, T., & Simonoff, E. (1999). Genetics and child psychiatry. II. Empirical research findings. *Journal of Child Psychology and Psychiatry, 40,* 19–55.

Rutter, M. L. (1981). *Maternal Deprivation Reassessed* (2nd ed.). London: Penguin.

Rutter, M. L. (1997). Nature-nurture integration: The example of antisocial behavior. *American Psychologist, 52,* 390–398.

Ryan, C. S. (1996). Battered children who kill: Developing an appropriate legal response. *Notre Dame Journal of Law, Ethics, and Public Policy, 10,* 301–339.

Ryff, C. D., Kwan, C. M. L., & Singer, B. H. (2001). Personality and aging: Flourishing agendas and future challenges. In J. E. Birren & K. W. Schaie (Eds.), *Handbook of the Psychology of Aging,* 5th ed., pp. 477–499. San Diego, CA: Academic Press.

Saavedra, J. E., Messich, J. E., Salloum, I. M., & Kirisci, L. (2001). Predictive validity of the physical disorders axis of the DSM multiaxial diagnostic system. *Journal of Nervous and Mental Disease, 189,* 435–441.

Sabbagh, M., Richardson, S., & Relkin, N. (2008). Disease-modifying approaches to Alzheimer's disease: Challenges and opportunities—Lessons from donepezil therapy. *Alzheimer's & Dementia, 4,* S109–S118.

Sackeim, H. A., Prudic, J., & Devanand, D. P. (2000). A prospective, randomized, double-blind comparison of bilateral and right unilateral electroconvulsive therapy at different stimulus intensities. *Archives of General Psychiatry, 57,* 425–434.

Sacks, O. (1985). *The Man Who Mistook His Wife for a Hat and Other Clinical Tales.* New York: Summit.

Safer, D. J., Zito, J. M., & Fine, E. M. (1996). Increased methylphenidate usage for attention deficit disorder in the 1990s. *Pediatrics, 98,* 1084–1088.

Saffran, E. M. (2000). Aphasia and the relationship of language and brain. *Seminars in Neurology, 20,* 409–418.

Saha, S., Welham, J., Chant, D., & McGrath, J. (2006). Incidence of schizophrenia does not vary with economic status of the country: Evidence from a systematic review. *Social Psychiatry and Psychiatric Epidemiology, 41*(5), 338–340.

Saha, S., Chant, D., & McGrath, J. (2008). Meta-analyses of the incidence and prevalence of schizophrenia: Conceptual and methodological issues. *International Journal of Methods in Psychiatric Research, 17,* 55–61.

Sahley, T. L., & Panksepp, J. (1987). Brain opioids and autism: An updated analysis of possible linkages. *Journal of Autism and Developmental Disorders, 17*(2) 201–216.

Salkovskis, P. M., & Harrison, J. (1984). Abnormal and normal obsessions—A replication. *Behaviour Research and Therapy, 22,* 549–552.

Salthouse, T. A. (1999). Pressing issues in cognitive aging. In N. Schwarz and D. C. Park (Eds.), *Cognition, Aging, and Self-Reports,* pp. 185–198. Hove, England: Psychology Press/Erlbaum.

Salthouse, T. A. (2004). What and when of cognitive aging. *Current Directions in Psychological Science, 13,* 140–144.

San Miguel, V. E. F., Guarnaccia, P. J., Shrout, P. E., Lewis-Fernandez, R., Canino, G. J., & Ramirez, R. R. (2006). A quantitative analysis of ataque de nervios in Puerto Rico: Further examination of a cultural syndrome. *Hispanic Journal of Behavioral Science, 28,* 313–330.

Sanders, M. R., Montgomery, D. T., & Brechman-Toussaint, M. L. (2000). The mass media and the prevention of child behavior problems: The evaluation of a television series to promote better child and parenting outcomes. *Journal of Child Psychology and Psychiatry, 41,* 939–948.

Sanderson, W. C., Rapee, R. M., & Barlow, D. H. (1989). The influence of an illusion of control on panic attacks induced via inhalation of 5.5% carbon dioxide-enriched air. *Archives of General Psychiatry, 46,* 157–162.

Sandler, A. D., Sutton, K. A, DeWeese, J., Giradi, M. A., Sheeppard, V., & Bodfish, J. W. (1999). Lack of benefit of a single does of synthetic human secretin in the treatment of autism and pervasive developmental disorder. *New England Journal of Medicine, 341,* 1801–1806.

Sapolsky, R. (2003). Taming stress. *Scientific American, 286,* 86–95.

Sapolsky, R. M. (1992). Neuroendocrinology of the stress response. In J. B. Becker, S. M. Breedlove, & D. Crews (Eds.), *Behavioral Endocrinology,* pp. 288–324. Cambridge, MA: MIT Press.

Sartor, C. E., & Youniss, J. (2002). The relationship between positive parental involvement and identity achievement during adolescence. *Adolescence, 37,* 221–234.

Sartorius, N. (2007). Twenty-five years of WHO-Coordinated Activities Concerning Schizophrenia. Recovery from Schizophrenia: An International Perspective: A report from the WHO Collaborative Project, the International Study of Schizophrenia, pp. 3–9. New York: Oxford University Press.

Sartorius, N., Kaelber, C. T., Cooper, J. E., Roper, M. T., Rae, D. S., Gulbinat, W., et al. (1993). Progress toward achieving a common language in psychiatry: Results from the field trial of the clinical guidelines accompanying the WHO classification of mental and behavioral disorders in ICD-10. *Archives of General Psychiatry, 50,* 115–124.

Sayette, M. A., Shiffman, S., Tiffany, S. T., Niaura, R. S., Martin, C. S., & Shadel, W. G. (2000). The measurement of drug craving. *Addiction, 95* (Suppl. 2), S189–S210.

Sbarra, D. S. & Emery, R. E. (2005). The emotional sequelae of non-marital relationship dissolution: Descriptive evidence from a 28-day prospective study. *Personal Relationships, 12,* 213–232.

Scarr, S., & McCartney, K. (1983). How people make their own environments: A theory of genotype-environment effects. *Child Development, 54,* 424–435.

Scepkowski, L. A., Wiegel, M., Bach, A. K., Weisberg, R. B., Brown, T. A., & Barlow, D. H. (2004). Attributions for sexual situations in men with and without erectile disorder: Evidence from a sex-specific attributional style measure. *Archives of Sexual Behavior, 33,* 559–569.

Schachar, R., & Tannock, R. (2002). Syndromes of hyperactivity and attention deficit. In M. Rutter & E. Taylor (Eds.), *Child and Adolescent Psychiatry,* 4th ed., pp. 399–418. Oxford, England: Blackwell.

Schacter, D. L. (1987). Implicit memory: History and current status. *Journal of Experimental Psychology: Learning, Memory, and Cognition, 13,* 501–518.

Schaeffer, C. M. & Borduin, C. M. (2005). Long-term follow-up to a randomized clinical trial of multisystemic therapy with serious and violent juvenile offenders. *Journal of Consulting and Clinical Psychology, 73,* 445–453.

Schatzberg, A. F. (1999). Antidepressant effectiveness in severe depression and melancholia. *Journal of Clinical Psychiatry, 60,* 14–22.

Scheel, K. R. (2000). The empirical basis of dialectical behavior therapy: Summary, critique, and implications. *Clinical Psychology Science and Practice, 7,* 68–86.

Scheerenberger, R. C. (1982). Public residential services, 1981: Status and trends. *Mental Retardation, 20,* 210–215.

Scheff, T. J. (1984). *Being Mentally Ill: A Sociological Theory,* 3rd ed., Hawthorne, NY: Aldine de Gruyter.

Scheffler, R. M., Ivey, S. L., & Garrtt, A. B. (1998). Changing supply and earning patterns of the mental health workforce. *Administration and Policy in Mental Health, 26,* 85–99.

Schell, T. L., Marshall, G. N., & Jaycox, L. H. (2004). All symptoms are not created equal: The prominent role of hyperarousal in the natural course of posttraumatic psychological distress. *Journal of Abnormal Psychology, 113,* 189–197.

Schiavi, R. C., & Segraves, R. T. (1995). The biology of sexual function. *Psychiatric Clinics of North America, 18,* 7–23.

Schiavi, R. C., Stimmel, B. B., Mandeli, J., & White, D. (1995). Chronic alcoholism and male sexual function. *American Journal of Psychiatry, 152.*

Schiff, M., Duyme, M., Dumaret, A., & Tomkiewicz, S. (1982). How much could we boost scholastic achievement and IQ scores? A direct answer from a French adoption study. *Cognition, 12,* 165–196.

Schiffman, J., Abrahamson, A., Cannon, T., LaBrie, J., Parnas, J., Schulsinger, F., et al. (2001). Early rearing factors in schizophrenia. *International Journal of Mental Health, 30,* 3–16.

Schiller, J. S., Martinez, M., Hao, C., & Barnes, P. Early release of selected estimates based on data from the January–September 2004 National Health Interview Survey. National Center for Health Statistics. Retrieved on from www.cdc.gov/nchs/ nhis.htm

Schmidt, N. B., Kotov, R., Zvolensky, M. J., Joiner, T. E., & Lewinsohn, P. M. (2007). Mixed anxiety depression: Taxometric exploration of the validity of a diagnostic category in youth. *Journal of Affective Disorders, 98,* 83–89.

Schmitt, D. P. (2004). Evaluating evidence of psychological adaptation: How do we know one when we see one? *Psychological Science, 15,* 643–651.

Schneider, J. P., & Irons, R. (1996). Differential diagnosis of addictive sexual disorders using the DSM-IV. *Sexual Addiction and Compulsivity, 3,* 7–21.

Schneiderman, N., Chesney, M. A., & Krantz, D. S. (1989). Biobehavioral aspects of cardiovascular disease: Progress and prospects. *Health Psychology, 8,* 649–676.

Schneiderman, N., Ironson, G., & Siegel, S. D. (2004). Stress and health: Psychological, behavioral, and biological determinants. *Annual Review of Clinical Psychology, 1,* 19.1–19.22.

Schneidman, E. S. (1996). *The Suicidal Mind.* New York: Oxford.

Schneller, J. (1988). Terror on the A-train: Anatomy of a panic attack. *Mademoiselle, 94,* 148–159.

Schooler, N. R., Keith, S. J., Severe, J. B., et al. (1997). Relapse and rehospitalization during maintenance treatment of schizophrenia: The effects of dose reduction and family treatment. *Archives of General Psychiatry, 54,* 453–463.

Schopler, E. M., Andrews, C. E., & Strupp, K. (1979). Do autistic children come from upper-middle-class parents? *Journal of Autism and Developmental Disorders, 9,* 139–152.

Schopp, R. F., Sturgis, B. J., & Sullivan, M. (1994). Battered woman syndrome, expert testimony, and the distinction between justification and excuse. *University of Illinois Law Review, 54,* 45–113.

Schott, R. L. (1995). The childhood and family dynamics of tranvestites. *Archives of Sexual Behavior, 24,* 309–328.

Schotti, J. R., Evans, I. M., Meyer, L. H., & Walker, P. (1991). A meta-analysis of intervention research with problem behavior: Treatment validity and standards of practice. *American Journal on Mental Retardation, 96,* 233–256.

Schreibman, L. (1988). *Autism.* Beverly Hills, CA: Sage.

Schuckit, J. A., & Monteiro, J. G. (1988). Alcoholism, anxiety and depression. *British Journal of Addiction, 83,* 1373–1380.

Schuckit, M. (1998). *Educating Yourself About Alcohol and Drugs: A People's Primer.* New York: Plenum.

Schuckit, M. (1999). *Drug and Alcohol Abuse.* Norwell, MA: Kluwer.

Schuckit, M. A. (2000). *Drug and Alcohol Abuse: A Clinical Guide to Diagnosis and Treatment* (5th ed.). New York: Kluwer Academic/Plenum.

Schuckit, M., & Smith, T. L. (1997). Assessing the risk for alcoholism among sons of alcoholics. *Journal of Studies on Alcohol, 58,* 141–145.

Schuckit, M. A. (2005). *Drug and Alcohol Abuse: A Clinical Guide to Diagnosis and Treatment,* 6th ed., New York: Springer.

Schuckit, M. A., Daeppen, J., Danko, G. P. Tripp, M. L., Smith, T. L., Li, T. K., et al. (1998a). Clinical implications for four drugs of the DSM-IV distinction between substance dependence with and without a physiological component. *American Journal of Psychiatry, 156,* 41–49.

Schuckit, M. A., Smith, T. L., Daeppen, J., Eng, M., Li, T. K., Hesselbrock, V. M., et al. (1998b). Clinical relevance of the distinction between alcohol dependence with and without a physiological component. *American Journal of Psychiatry, 155,* 733–740.

Schuckit, M. A., Smith, T. L., Danko, G. P., Reich, T., Bucholz, K. K., & Bierut, L. J. (2002). Similarities in the clinical characteristics related to alcohol dependence in two populations. *American Journal on Addictions, 11,* 1–9.

Schuepbach, W. M. M., Adler., R. H., Sabbioni, M. E. E. (2002). Accuracy of clinical diagnosis of psychogenic disorders in the presence of physical symptoms suggesting a general medical condition: A 5-year follow-up in 162 patients. *Psychotherapy and Psychosomatics, 71,* 11–17.

Schulberg, H. C., Katon, W. J., Simon, G. E., & Rush, A. J. (1999). Best clinical practice: Guidelines for managing major depression in primary medical care. *Journal of Clinical Psychiatry, 60* (Suppl. 7), 19–26.

Schuyler, D. (1991). *A Practical Guide to Cognitive Therapy.* New York: Norton.

Schwartz, C. E., Covino, N., Morgenstaler, A., & De-Wolf, W. (2000). Quality of life after penile prosthesis placed at radical prostatectomy. *Psychology & Health, 15,* 651–661.

Schwartz, C. E., Snidman, N., & Kagan, J. (1999). Adolescent social anxiety as an outcome of inhibited temperament in childhood. *Journal of the American Academy of Child and Adolescent Psychiatry, 38,* 1008–1015.

Schwartz, G. E. (1989). Dysregulation theory and disease: Toward a general model for psychosomatic medicine. In S. Cheren (Ed.), *Psychosomatic Medicine: Theory, Physiology, and Practice,* Vol. 1, pp. 91–118. Madison, CT: International Universities Press.

Scott, S. (2002). Parent training programs. In M. Rutter & E. Taylor (Eds.), *Child and Adolescent Psychiatry,* 4th ed., pp. 949–967. Oxford, England: Blackwell.

Scotti, J. R., Evans, I. M., Meyer, L. H., & Walker, P. A meta-analysis of intervention research with problem behavior: Treatment, validity and standards of practices. *American Journal of Mental Retardation, 96*(3), 233–256.

Scroppo, J. C., Drob, S. L., Weinberger, J. L., & Eagle, P. (1998). Identifying dissociative identity disorder: A self-report and projective study. *Journal of Abnormal Psychology, 107,* 272–284.

Scurfield, R. M. (1985). Posttrauma stress assessment and treatment: Overview and formulations. In C. R. Figley (Ed.), *Trauma and Its Wake,* pp. 219–259. New York: Brunner/Mazel.

Searles, J. S. (1988). The role of genetics in the pathogenesis of alcoholism. *Journal of Abnormal Psychology, 97,* 153–167.

Searles, J. S. (1990). Methodological limitations of research on the genetics of alcoholism. In C. R. Cloninger & H. Begleiter (Eds.), *Genetics and Biology of Alcoholism,* pp. 89–100. Cold Spring Harbor, NY: Cold Spring Harbor Laboratory Press.

Sechrest, L., Stickle, T. R., & Stewart, M. (1998). The role of assessment in clinical psychology. In A. Bellack, Hersen, & C. R. Reynolds (Eds.), *Comprehensive Clinical Psychology:* Vol. 4, *Assessment,* pp. 2–28. New York: Pergamon.

Sedgwick, P. (1981). Illness—mental and otherwise. In A. L. Caplan, H. T. Engelhardt Jr., & J. J. McCartney (Eds.), *Concepts of Health and Disease: Interdisciplinary Perspectives,* pp. 119–129.

Seeman, M. (2008). Gender. Clinical Handbook of Schizophrenia, pp. 575–580. New York: Guilford Press.

Seeman, P. (2002). Atypical antipsychotics: Mechanisms of action. *Canadian Journal of Psychiatry, 47,* 27–38.

Segal, D. L. (1997). Structured interviewing and DSM classification. In S. M. Turner and M. Hersen (Eds.), *Adult Psychopathology and Diagnosis,* 3rd ed., pp. 24–57. New York: Wiley.

Segerstrom, S. C. (2007). Stress, energy, and immunity: An ecological view. *Current Directions in Psychological Science, 16,* 326–330.

Segerstrom, S. C. & Miller, G. E. (2004). Psychological stress and the human immune system: A meta-analytic study of 30 years of inquiry. *Psychological Bulletin, 130,* 601–630.

Segraves, R., Balon, R., & Clayton, A. (2007). Proposal for changes in diagnostic criteria for sexual dysfunctions. *Journal of Sexual Medicine, 4,* 567–580.

Segraves, R., & BlindtSegraves, K. (2001). Female sexual disorders. *Psychological Aspects of Women's Health Care: The Interface Between Psychiatry and Obstetrics and Gynecology,* 2nd ed., pp. 379–400. Arlington, VA: American Psychiatric Publishing, Inc.

Segraves, R.T., & Blindt, Segraves, K. (2001). Female sexual disorders. In N. L. Stotland and D. E. Stewart (Eds.), *Psychological Aspects of Women's Health Care: The Interface Between Psychiatry and Obstetrics and Gynecology,* 2nd ed., pp. 379–400. Washington, DC: American Psychiatric Press.

Segraves, T., & Althof, S. (2002). Psychotherapy and pharmacotherapy for sexual dysfunctions. In P. E. Nathan and J. M. Gorman (Eds.), *A Guide to Treatments That Work,* 2nd ed., pp. 497–524. London: Oxford University Press.

Seidman, B. T., Marshall, W. L., Hudson, S. M., & Robertson, P. J. (1994). An examination of intimacy and loneliness in sex offenders. *Journal of Interpersonal Violence, 9,* 518–534.

Self, D., & Tamminga, C. A. (2004). Drug dependence and addiction: Neural substrates. *American Journal of Psychiatry, 161,* 223.

Selfe, L. (1977). *Nadia: A Case of Extraordinary Drawing Ability in an Autistic Child.* London: Academic Press.

Seligman, M. E. (1996). *The Optimistic Child: A Proven Program to Safeguard Children Against Depression and Build Lifelong Resistance.* New York: HarperCollins.

Seligman, M. P. (1995). *What You Can Change, and What You Can't: The Complete Guide to Successful Self-Improvement.* Fawcett Books.

Selye, H. (1956). *The Stress of Life.* New York: McGraw-Hill.

Serdula, M. K., Collins, M. E., Williamson, D. F., Anda, R. F., Pamuk, E. R., & Byers, T. E. (1993). Weight control practices of U.S. adolescents and adults. *Annals of Internal Medicine, 119,* 667–671.

Seto, M. C., & Barbaree, H. E. (2000). Paraphilias. In V. B. Van Hasselt & M. Horsen (Eds.). *Aggression and Violence: An Introductory text.* Boston: Allyn and Bacon.

Seyfried, L. S., & Marcus, S. M. (2003). Postpartum mood disorders. *International Review of Psychiatry, 15,* 231–242.

Shadish, W. R., & Baldwin, S. A. (2005). Effects of behavioral marital therapy: A meta-analysis of randomized controlled trials. *Journal of Consulting and Clinical Psychology, 73,* 6–14.

Shadish, W. R., Matt, G. E., Navarro, A. N., & Phillips, G. (2000). The effects of psychological therapies under clinically representative conditions: A meta-analysis. *Psychological Bulletin, 126,* 512–529.

Shaffer, D., & Gutstein, J. (2002). Suicide and attempted suicide. In M. Rutter & E. Taylor (Eds.), *Child and Adolescent Psychiatry,* 4th ed., pp. 529–554. Oxford, England: Blackwell.

Shahinfar, A., Kupersmidt, J. B., & Matza, L. S. (2001). The relation between exposure to violence and social information processing among incarcerated adolescents. *Journal of Abnormal Psychology, 110,* 136–141.

Shakib, S., Mouttapa, M., Johnson, C. A., Ritt-Olson, A., Trinidad, D. R., Gallaher, P. E., et al. (2003). Ethnic variation in parenting characteristics and adolescent smoking. *Journal of Adolescent Health, 33,* 88–97.

Shalev, A., & Munitz, H. (1986). Conversion without hysteria: A case report and review of the literature. *British Journal of Psychiatry, 148,* 198–203.

Shalev, A. Y. (1996). Stress versus traumatic stress: From acute homeostatic reactions to chronic psychopathology. In B. A. van der Kolk, A. C. McFarlane, & L. Weisaeth (Eds.), *Traumatic Stress,* pp. 77–101. New York: Guilford.

Shalev, A. Y. (in press). Historical concepts and present patterns: Stress management and debriefing. In J. P Wilson & B. Raphael (Eds.), *Stress Debriefing: Theory, Practice, and Challenge.* Cambridge: Cambridge University Press.

Shalev, A. Y., Peri, T., Caneti, L., & Schreiber, S. (1996). Predictors of PTSD in injured trauma survivors. *American Journal of Psychiatry, 53,* 219–224.

Shankman, S. A., & Klein, D. N. (2003). The relation between depression and anxiety: An evaluation of the tripartite, approach-withdrawal and valence-arousal models. *Clinical Psychology Review, 23,* 605–637.

Shapiro, D. (1965). *Neurotic Styles.* New York: Basic Books.

Shapiro, F. (1995). *Eye Movement Desensitization and Reprocessing: Basic Principles, Protocols, and Procedures.* New York: Guilford Press.

Sharif, Z., Bradford, D., Stroup, S., & Lieberman, J. (2007). Pharmacological Treatment of Schizophrenia. A Guide to Treatments That Work (3rd ed.) (pp. 203–241). New York, NY US: Oxford University Press.

Sharpe, L. (2002). A reformulated cognitive-behavioral model of problem gambling: A biopsychosocial perspective. *Clinical Psychology Review, 22,* 1–25.

Shatte, A. J., Reivich, K., Gillham, J. E., & Seligman, M. E. P. (1999). Learned optimism in children. In C. R.

Snyder (Ed.), *Coping: The Psychology of What Works*, pp. 165–181. New York: Oxford University Press.

Shavelson, L. (2001). *Hooked: Five Addicts Challenge Our Misguided Drug Rehab System*. New York: New Press.

Shaw, D. S., & Bell, R. Q. (1993). Developmental theories of parental contributors to antisocial behavior. *Journal of Abnormal Child Psychology, 21*, 493–518.

Shaw, D. S., & Vondra, J. I. (1995). Infant attachment security and maternal predictors of early behavior problems: A longitudinal study of low-income families. *Journal of Abnormal Child Psychology, 23*, 335–357.

Shaw, D. S., Keenan, K., & Vondra, J. I. (1994). Developmental precursors of externalizing behavior: Ages 1 to 3. *Developmental Psychology, 30*, 355–364.

Shaw, D. S., Vondra, J. I., Hommerding, K. D., Keenan K., & Dunn, M. (1994). Chronic family adversity and early child behavior problems: A longitudinal study of low income families. *Journal of Child Psychology and Psychiatry, 35*, 1109–1122.

Shaw, D. S., Winslow, E. B., Owens, E. B., Vondra, J. I., Cohn, J. F., & Bell, R. Q. (1997). The development of early externalizing problems among children from low-income families: A transformational perspective. *Journal of Abnormal Child Psychology, 26*, 95–107.

Shaywitz, S. E., Mody, M., & Shaywitz, B. A. (2006). Neural mechanisms in dyslexia. *Current Directions in Psychological Science, 15*, 278–281.

Shear, K., Frank, E., Houck, P. R., & Reynolds, C. F. (2005). Treatment of complicated grief: A randomized controlled trial. *Journal of the American Medical Association, 293*, 2601–2608.

Shearer, D. E., & Shearer, M. S. (1976). The Portage Project: A model for early childhood intervention. In T. D. Tjossem (Ed.), *Intervention Strategies for High Risk Infants and Young Children*. Baltimore: University Park Press.

Shedler, J., Mayman, M., & Manis, M. (1993). The illusion of mental health. *American Psychologist, 48*, 1117–1131.

Sheffield, A. (1998). *How You Can Survive When They're Depressed: Living and Coping with Depression Fallout*. New York: Three Rivers Press.

Shen, W. W. (1999). A history of antipsychotic drug development. *Comprehensive Psychiatry, 40*, 407–417.

Shenton, M. E. (1996). Temporal lobe structural abnormalities in schizophrenia: A selective review and presentation of new magnetic resonance findings. In S. Matthysse & D. L. Levy (Eds.), *Psychopathology: The Evolving Science of Mental Disorder*, pp. 51–99. New York: Cambridge University Press.

Sher, K. J. (1993). Children of alcoholics and the intergenerational transmission of alcoholism: A biopsychosocial perspective. In J. S. Baer, G. A. Marlatt, & R. J. McMahon (Eds.), *Addictive Behaviors Across the Life Span: Prevention, Treatment, and Policy Issues*. pp. 3–33. Newbury Park, CA: Sage.

Sher, K. J., Grekin, E. R., & Williams, N. A. (2005). The development of alcohol use disorders. *Annual Review of Clinical Psychology, 1*, 493–523.

Shiffman, S., Paty, J. A., Gnys, M., Kassel, J. A., et al. (1996). *Journal of Consulting and Clinical Psychology, 64*, 366–379.

Shirk, S. R., & Karver, M. (2003). Prediction of treatment outcome from relationship variable in child and adolescent therapy: A meta-analytic review. *Journal of Consulting and Clinical Psychology, 71*(3), 452–464.

Short, A. B., & Schopler, E. (1988). Factors relating to age of onset in autism. *Journal of Autism and Developmental Disorders, 18*, 207–216.

Shorter, E. (1992). *From Paralysis to Fatigue: A History of Psychosomatic Illness in the Modern Era*. New York: Free Press.

Shoulson, I. (1990). Huntington's disease: Cognitive and psychiatric features. *Neuropsychiatry, Neuropsychology, and Behavioral Neurology, 3*, 15–22.

Showalter, E. (1997). *Hystories: Hysterical Epidemics and Modern Medicine*. New York: Columbia University Press.

Shulman, M. & Redmond, J. (in press). Access to psychoanalytic ideas in American undergraduate institutions. *Journal of the American Psychoanalytic Association*.

Sickmund, M., Snyder, H., and Poe-Yamagata, E. (1997). *Juvenile Offenders and Victims: 1997 Update on Violence*. Washington, DC: Office of Juvenile Justice and Delinquency Prevention.

Siegel, J. M., & Kuykendall, D. H. (1990). Loss, widowhood, and psychological distress among the elderly. *Journal of Consulting and Clinical Psychology, 58*, 519–524.

Siegel, S. (2005). Drug tolerance, drug addiction, and drug anticipation. *Current Directions in Psychological Science, 14*, 296–300.

Siev, J., & Chambless, D. L. (2007). Specificity of treatment effects: Cognitive therapy and relaxation for generalized anxiety and panic disorders. *Journal of Consulting and Clinical Psychology, 75*, 513–522.

Siever, L. J., Bernstein, D. P., & Silverman, J. M. (1995). Schizotypal personality disorder. In W. J. Livesley, (Ed.), *The DSM-IV Personality Disorders*, pp. 71–90. New York: Guilford.

Sigvardsson, S., Bohman, M., & Cloninger, C. R. (1996). Replication of the Stockholm adoption study of alcoholism: Confirmatory cross-fostering analysis. *Archives of General Psychiatry, 53*, 681–687.

Silverman, W. K., & Dick-Niederhauser, A. (2004). Separation anxiety disorder. In T. L. Morris & J. S. March (Eds.), *Anxiety Disorders in Children and Adolescents*, 2nd ed., pp. 164–188. New York: Guilford.

Silverman, W. K., et al. (1999). Contingency management, self-control, and education support in the treatment of childhood phobic disorders. A randomized clinical trial. *Journal of Consulting and Clinical Psychology, 67*, 675–687.

Simard, M., van Reekum, R., & Cohen, T. (2000). A review of the cognitive and behavioral symptoms in dementia with Lewy bodies. *Journal of Neuropsychiatry and Clinical Neuroscience, 12*, 425–450.

Simmons, R. A., Gordon, P. C., & Chambless, D. L. (2005). Pronouns in marital interaction: What do "You" and "I" say about marital health? *Psychological Science, 16*, 932–936.

Simon, G. E. (2002). Management of somatoform and factitious disorders. In P. E. Nathan & J. M. Gorman (Eds.), *A Guide to Treatments That Work*, 2nd ed., pp. 447–461. New York: Oxford.

Simon, J., Pilling, S., Burbeck, R., & Goldberg, D. (2006). Treatment options in moderate and severe depression: Decision analysis supporting a clinical guideline. *British Journal of Psychiatry, 189*, 494–501.

Singer, H. S., & Loiselle, C. (2003). PANDAS: A commentary. *Journal of Psychosomatic Research, 55*, 31–39.

Singer, M. T., & Lalich, J. (1996). *"Crazy" Therapies*. San Francisco: Jossey-Bass.

Singh, N. N., Guernsey, T. F., & Ellis, C. R. (1992). Drug therapy for persons with developmental disabilities: Legislation and litigation. *Clinical Psychology Review, 12*, 665–679.

Sitskoom, M. M., Aleman, A., Ebisch, S. J. H., Appels, M. C. M., & Kahn, R. S. (2004). Cognitive deficits in relatives of patients with schizophrenia: A metaanalysis. *Schizophrenia Research, 71*, 285–295.

Sizemore, C. C. (1989). *A Mind of Her Own*. New York: Morrow.

Sizemore, C. C., & Pittillo, E. S. (1977). *I'm Eve!* New York: Doubleday.

Skodak, M., & Skeels, H. (1949). A final follow-up study of one hundred adopted children. *Journal of Genetic Psychology, 75*, 85–125.

Skodol, A. E., & Bender, D. S. (2003). Why are women diagnosed borderline more than men? *Psychiatric Quarterly, 74*, 349–360.

Skodol, A. E., Dohrenwend, B. P., Link, B. G., & Shrout, P. E. (1990). The nature of stress: Problems of measurement. In J. D. Noshpit & K. D. Coddington (Eds.), *Stressors and the Adjustment Disorders*, pp. 3–20. New York: Wiley.

Skodol, A. E., Siever, L. J., Livesley, W. J., Gunderson, J. G., Pfohl, B., & Widiger, T. A. (2002). The borderline diagnosis II: Biology, genetics, and clinical course. *Biological Psychiatry, 51*, 951–963.

Skodol, A. E., Johnson, J. G., Cohen, P., Sneed, J. R., & Crawford, T. N. (2007). Personality disorder and impaired functioning from adolescence to adulthood. *British Journal of Psychiatry, 190*, 415–420.

Skoog, G., & Skoog, I. (1999). A 40-year follow-up of patients with obsessive-compulsive disorder. *Archives of General Psychiatry, 56*, 121–127.

Slade, P. D., & Russell, G. F. M. (1973). Awareness of body dimensions in anorexia nervosa and bulimia nervosa: Cross-sectional and longitudinal studies. *Psychological Medicine, 3*, 188–199.

Slater, E. (1965). Diagnosis of hysteria. *British Medical Journal, 1*, 1395–1399.

Sloan, D. M. & Marx, B. P. (2004). A closer examination of the structured written disclosure procedure. *Journal of Consulting and Clinical Psychology, 72*, 165–175.

Sloane, R. B., Staples, A. H., Cristo, N. J., & Whipple, K. (1975). In *Psychotherapy versus Behavior Therapy*, pp. 237–240. Cambridge, MA: Harvard University Press.

Slutske, W. S., Eisen, S., True, W. R., Lyons, M. J., Goldberg, J., & Tsuang, M. (2000). Common genetic vulnerability for pathological gambling and alcohol dependence in men. *Archives of General Psychiatry, 57*, 666–673.

Slutske, W. S., Eisen, S., Xian, H., True, W. R., Lyons, M. J., Goldberg, J., et al. (2001). A twin study of the association between pathological gambling and antisocial personality disorder. *Journal of Abnormal Psychology, 110*, 297–308.

Slutske, W. S., Heath, A. C., Madden, P. A. F., Bucholz, K. K., Statham, D. J., & Martin, N. G. (2002). Personality and the genetic risk for alcohol dependence. *Journal of Abnormal Psychology, 111*, 124–133.

Small, S. A., Tsai, W. Y., DeLaPaz, R., Mayeux, R., & Stern, Y. (2002). Imaging hippocampal function across the human life span: Is memory decline normal or not? *Annals of Neurology, 51*, 290–295.

Smalley, S. L., & Collins, F. (1996). Brief report: Genetic, prenatal, and immunologic factors. *Journal of Autism and Developmental Disorders, 26*, 195–197.

Smalley, S. L., Asarnow, R. F., & Spence, M. A. (1988). Autism and genetics: A decade of research. *Archives of General Psychiatry, 45*, 953–961.

Smetana, J. G. (1989). Adolescents' and parents' reasoning about actual family conflict. *Child Development, 60*, 1052–1067.

Smith, E. (1991). First person account: Living with schizophrenia. *Schizophrenia Bulletin, 17*, 689–691.

Smith, G., & Hall, M. (1982). Evaluating Michigan's guilty but mentally ill verdict: An empirical study. *University of Michigan Journal of Law Reform, 16*, 77–114.

Smith, G. R., Monson, R. A., & Ray, D. C. (1986). Psychiatric consultation in somatization disorder: A randomized controlled study. *New England Journal of Medicine, 314*, 1407–1413.

Smith, G. T., Goldman, M. S., Greenbaum, P. E., & Christiansen, A. (1995). Expectancy for social facilitation from drinking: The divergent paths of high-expectancy and low-expectancy adolescents. *Journal of Abnormal Psychology, 104*, 32–40.

Smith, M. L., & Glass, G. V. (1977). Meta-analysis of psychotherapy outcome studies. *American Psychologist, 32*(9), 752–760.

Smith, R. C., Gardiner, J. C., Lyles, J. S., Sirbu, C., Dwamena, F. C., Hodges, A., et al. (2005). Exploration of DSM-IV criteria in primary care patients with medically unexplained symptoms. *Psychosomatic Medicine, 67,* 123–129.

Smith, S. R., & Meyer, R. G. (1985). Child abuse reporting laws and psychotherapy: A time for reconsideration. *International Journal of Law and Psychiatry, 7,* 351–366.

Smith, T., Groen, A. D., & Wynn, J. W. Randomized trial of intensive early intervention for children with pervasive developmental disorder. *American Journal of Mental Retardation, 105,* 269–285.

Smith, T. W. (2006). Personality as risk and resilience in physical health. *Current Directions in Psychological Science, 15,* 227–231.

Smith, T. W. & Ruiz, J. M. (2002). Psychosocial influences on the development and course of coronary heart disease: Current status and implications for research and practice. *Journal of Consulting and Clinical Psychology, 70,* 548–568.

Smith, Y. L. S., van Goozen, S. H. M., & Cohen-Kettenis, P. T. (2001). Adolescents with gender identity disorder who were accepted or rejected for sex reassignment surgery: A prospective follow-up study. *Journal of the American Academy of Child and Adolescent Psychiatry, 40,* 472–481.

Smits, J. A. J., Powers, M. B., Cho, Y., & Telch, M. J. (2004). Mechanism of change in cognitive-behavioral treatment of panic disorder: Evidence for the fear of fear meditational hypothesis. *Journal of Consulting and Clinical Psychology, 72,* 646–652.

Smyth, J. M., Stone, A. A., Hurewitz, A., & Kaell, A. (1999). Effects of writing about stressful experiences on symptom reduction in patients with asthma or rheumatoid arthritis: A randomized trial. *Journal of the American Medical Association, 281,* 1304–1309.

Snitz, B., MacDonald, A., & Carter, C. (2006). Cognitive deficits in unaffected first-degree relatives of schizophrenia patients: A meta-analytic review of putative endophenotypes. *Schizophrenia Bulletin, 32,* 179–194.

Snowden, J. S., Neary, D., & Mann, D. A. (2002). Frontotemporal dementia. *British Journal of Psychiatry, 180,* 140–143.

Snowling, M. J. (2002). Reading and other learning difficulties. In M. Rutter & E. Taylor (Eds.), *Child and Adolescent Psychiatry,* 4th ed., pp. 682–696. Oxford, England: Blackwell.

Snyder, C. R. (Ed.). (1999). *Coping: The Psychology of What Works,* pp. 182–204. New York: Oxford University Press.

Snyder, D. K. (1999). Affective reconstruction in the context of a pluralistic approach to couple therapy. *Clinical Psychology: Science and Practice, 6,* 348–365.

Snyder, H. N. (2002, September). Juvenile arrests 2002. *Juvenile Justice Bulletin,* 1–12.

Sobell, L. C., & Sobell, M. B. (2003). Using motivational interviewing techniques to talk with clients about their alcohol use. *Cognitive & Behavioral Practice, 10,* 214–221.

Soble, A. G. (2004). Desire: Paraphilia and distress in DSM-IV. In J. Radden (Ed.), *The Philosophy of Psychiatry: A Companion,* pp. 54–63. New York: Oxford University Press.

Sohn, M., & Bosinski, H. A. G. (2007). Gender identity disorders: Diagnostic and surgical aspects. *Journal of Sexual Medicine, 4,* 1193–1208.

Solomon, A. (2001). *The Noonday Demon: An Atlas of Depression.* New York: Scribner.

Solomon, K., Manepalli, J., Ireland, G. A., & Mahon, G. M. (1993). Alcoholism and prescription drug abuse in the elderly: St. Louis University grand rounds. *Journal of the American Geriatrics Society, 41,* 57–69.

Somerfield, M. R., & McCrae, R. R. (2000). Stress and coping research: Methodological challenges, theoretical advances, and clinical applications. *American Psychologist, 55,* 620–625.

Song, C., & Leonard, B. E. (2000). *Fundamentals of Psychoneuroimmunology.* New York: Wiley.

South, S. C., Turkheimer, E., & Oltmanns, T. F. (2008). Personality disorder symptoms and marital functioning. *Journal of Consulting and Clinical Psychology, 76,* 769–780.

Southall, D. P., Plunkett, M. C., Banks, M. W., Falkov, A. F., & Samuels, M. P. (1997). Covert video recordings of life-threatening child abuse: Lessons for child protection. *Pediatrics, 100,* 735–774.

Spanos, N. P. (1994). Multiple identity enactments and multiple personality disorder: A sociocognitive perspective. *Psychological Bulletin, 116,* 143–165.

Spanos, N. P., Weekes, J. R., & Bertrand, L. D. (1985). Multiple personality: A social psychological perspective. *Journal of Abnormal Psychology, 94,* 362–376.

Spanos, N. P., Weekes, J. R., Menary, E., & Bertrand, L. D. (1986). Hypnotic interview and age regression procedures in the elicitation of multiple personality symptoms: A simulation study. *Psychiatry, 49,* 298–311.

Spector, S. G., & Volkmar, F. R. (2006). Autism spectrum disorders. In D. A. Wolfe & E. J. Mash (Eds.), *Behavioral and Emotional Disorders in Adolescents,* pp. 444–460. New York: Guilford Press.

Spencer, T. J., Biederman, J., & Wilens, T. (1998). Pharmacotherapy of ADHD with antidepressants. In R. A. Barkley (Ed.), *Attention-Deficit/Hyperactivity Disorder,* 2nd ed., pp. 552–563. New York: Guilford.

Spiegel, D., & Cardena, E. (1991). Disintegrated experience: The dissociative disorders revisited. *Journal of Abnormal Psychology, 100,* 366–378.

Spiegel, D. A., & Bruce, T. J. (1997). Benzodiazepines and exposure-based cognitive behavior therapies for panic disorder: Conclusions from combined treatment trials. *American Journal of Psychiatry, 154,* 773–781.

Spirito, A., & Esposito-Smythers, C. (2006). Attempted and completed suicide in adolescence. *Annual Review of Clinical Psychology, 2,* 237–266.

Spitzer, R. L., First, M. B., Williams, J. B. W., Kendler, K., Pincus, H. A., & Tucker, G. (1992). Now is the time to retire the term "organic mental disorders." *American Journal of Psychiatry, 149,* 240–244.

Spotts, E. L., Lichtenstein, P., & Pedersen, N. (2005). Personality and marital satisfaction: A behavioural genetic analysis. *European journal of personality, 19,* 205–227.

Sprague, R. L., & Sleator, E. K. (1977). Methlphenidate in hyperkinetic children: Differences in doses effects learning and social behavior. *Science, 198,* 1274–1276.

Sroufe, L. A., & Fleeson, J. (1986). Attachment and the construction of relationships. In W. W. Hartup & Z. Rubin (Eds.), *Relationships and Development,* pp. 51–72. Hillsdale, NJ: Erlbaum.

Stack, S. (2004). Emile Durkheim and altruistic suicide. *Archives of Suicide Research, 8,* 9–22.

Stahl, S., & Buckley, P. (2007). Negative symptoms of schizophrenia: A problem that will not go away. *Acta Psychiatrica Scandinavica, 115,* 4–11.

Stanton, A. L., et al. (2000). Emotional expressive coping predicts psychological and physical adjustment to breast cancer. *Journal of Consulting and Clinical Psychology, 68,* 875–882.

Stanton, B., & David, A. (2000). First-person accounts of delusions. *Psychiatric Bulletin, 24,* 333–336.

Starr, P. (1982). *The Social Transformation of American Medicine.* New York: Basic Books.

Steadman, H., et al. (1993). *Before and After Hinckley: Evaluating Insanity Defense Reform.* New York: Guilford.

Steadman, H., Pantle, R., & Pasewark, S. (1983). Factors associated with a successful insanity defense. *American Journal of Psychiatry, 140,* 401–405.

Steadman, H. J., Mulvey, E. P., Monahan, J., Robbins, P. C., Appelbaum, P. S., Grisso, T., et al. (1998). Violence by people discharged from acute psychiatric inpatient facilities and by others in the same neighborhoods. *Archives of General Psychiatry, 55,* 393–401.

Steen, R., Mull, C., McClure, R., Hamer, R., & Lieberman, J. (2006). Brain volume in first-episode schizophrenia: Systematic review and meta-analysis of magnetic resonance imaging studies. *British Journal of Psychiatry, 188,* 510–518.

Steffenburg, S., Gillberg, C., Hellgren, L., Andersson, L., Gillberg, I., Jakobsson, G., et al. (1989). A twin study of autism in Denmark, Finland, Iceland, Norway and Sweden. *Journal of Child Psychology and Psychiatry, 30,* 405–416.

Steffens, D., & Potter, G. (2008). Geriatric depression and cognitive impairment. *Psychological Medicine, 38,* 163–175.

Steggall, M. J., Gann, S. Y., & Chinegwundoh, F. I. (2004). Sexual dysfunction screening: The advantages of a culturally sensitive joint assessment clinic. *Sexual & Relationship Therapy, 19,* 179–189.

Steiger, H., Gauvin, L., Jabalpurwala, S., Seguin, J. R., & Stotland, S. (1999) Hypersensitivity to social interactions in bulimic syndromes: Relationship to binge eating. *Journal of Consulting & Clinical Psychology, 67,* 765–775.

Stein, D. J., Westenberg, H. G. M., & Liebowitz, M. R. (2002). Social anxiety disorder and generalized anxiety disorder: Serotonergic and dopaminergic neurocircuitry. *Journal of Clinical Psychiatry, 63* (Suppl. 6), 12–19.

Stein, L. I., & Santos, A. B. (1998). *Assertive Community Treatment of Persons with Severe Mental Illness.* New York: Norton.

Steinhausen, H. (1996). The course and outcome of anorexia nervosa. In K. D. Brownell & C. G. Fairburn (Eds.), *Eating Disorders and Obesity: A Comprehensive Handbook,* pp. 234–237. New York: Guilford.

Stern, Y., Gurland, B., Tatemichi, T. K., et al. (1994). Influence of education and occupation on the incidence of Alzheimer's disease. *JAMA, 271,* 1004–1010.

Stern, Y., Tang, M., Albert, M. S., Brandt, J., Jacobs, D. M., Bell, K., et al. (1997). Predicting time to nursing home care and death in individuals with Alzheimer disease. *Journal of the American Medical Association, 277,* 806–812.

Stevens, S. E., Hynan, M. T., & Allen, M. (2000). A metaanalysis of common factor and specific treatment effects across the outcome domains of the phase model of psychotherapy. *Clinical Psychology: Science and Practice, 7,* 273–290.

Stevens, V. J., et al. (2001). Long-Term Weight Loss and Changes in Blood Pressure: Results of the Trials of Hypertension Prevention, Phase II. *Annals of Internal Medicine, 134,* 1–11.

Stewart, A. J., & Ostrove, J. M. (1998). Women's personality in middle age: Gender, history, and midcourse corrections. *American Psychologist, 53,* 1185–1194.

Stewart, J. T. (1995). Management of behavior problems in the demented patient. *American Family Physician, 52,* 231–240.

Stewart, S., & Podd, J. (2004). The placebo effect: Dissolving the expectancy versus conditioning debate. *Psychological Bulletin, 130,* 324–340.

Stice, E. (2001). A prospective test of the dual-pathway model of bulimic pathology: Mediating effects of dieting and negative affect. *Journal of Abnormal Psychology, 110,* 124–135.

Stice, E. (2002). Risk and maintenance factors for eating pathology: A meta-analytic review. *Psychological Bulletin, 128,* 825–848.

Stice, E., & Agras, W. S. (1999). Subtyping bulimic women along dietary restraint and negative affect dimensions. *Journal of Consulting & Clinical Psychology, 67,* 460–469.

Stice, E., & Fairburn, C. G. (2003). Dietary and dietary-depressive subtypes of bulimia nervosa show differential symptom presentation, social impairment, comorbidity, and course of illness. *Journal of Consulting and Clinical Psychology, 71,* 1090–1094.

Stice, E., Schupak-Neuberg, E., Shaw, H. E., & Stein, R. I. (1994). Relation of media exposure to eating disorder symptomatology: An examination of mediating mechanisms. *Journal of Abnormal Psychology, 103,* 836–840.

Stice, E., & Shaw, H. (2004). Eating disorder prevention programs: A meta-analytic review. *Psychological Bulletin, 130,* 206–227.

Stice, E., Shaw, H., Burton, E., & Wade, E. (2006). Dissonance and healthy weight eating disorder prevention programs: A randomized efficacy trial. *Journal of Consulting and Clinical Psychology, 74,* 263–275.

Stice, E., Spangler, D., & Agras, W. S. (2001) Exposure to media-portrayed thin-ideal images adversely affects vulnerable girls: A longitudinal experiment. *Journal of Social & Clinical Psychology, 20,* 270–288.

Still, G. F. (1902). The Coulstonian Lectures on some abnormal physical conditions in children. *Lancet, 1,* 1008–1012, 1077–1082, 1163–1168.

Stirman, S. W., DeRubeis, R. J., Crits-Christoph, P., & Brody, P. E. (2003). Are samples in randomized controlled trials of psychotherapy representative of community outpatients? A new methodology and initial findings. *Journal of Consulting and Clinical Psychology, 71,* 963–972.

Stockard, J., & O'Brien, R. M. (2002). Cohort effects on suicide rates: International variations. *American Sociological Review, 67,* 854–872.

Stockmeier, C. A. (2003). Involvement of serotonin in depression: Evidence from postmortem and imaging studies of serotonin receptors and the serotonin transporter. *Journal of Psychiatric Research, 37,* 357–373.

Stokols, D. (1992). Establishing and maintaining healthy environments: Toward a social ecology of health promotion. *American Psychologist, 47,* 6–22.

Stoller, R. J. (1991). *Pain and Passion: A Psychoanalyst Explores the World of S & M.* New York: Plenum.

Stone, E. A., Lin, Y., & Quarermain, D. (2008). A final common pathway for depression? Progress toward a general conceptual framework. *Neuroscience and Biobehavioral Reviews, 32,* 508–524.

Stone, M. H. (1993). Long-term outcome in personality disorders. *British Journal of Psychiatry, 162,* 299–313.

Stone, M. H. (2001). Natural history and long-term outcome. In W. J. Livesley (Ed.), *Handbook of Personality Disorders: Theory Research, and Treatment,* pp. 259–273. New York: Guilford.

Storandt, M. (2008). Cognitive deficits in the early stages of Alzheimer's disease. *Current Directions in Psychological Science, 17,* 198–202.

Storandt, M., Grant, E., Miller, J., & Morris, J. (2006). Longitudinal course and neuropathologic outcomes in original vs revised MCI and in pre-MCI. *Neurology, 67,* 467–473.

Storch, E. A., Murphy, T. K., Geffken, G. R., Mann, G., Adkins, J., Merlo, L. J., et al. (2006). Cognitive-behavioral therapy for PANDAS-related obsessive-compulsive disorder: Findings from a preliminary waitlist controlled open trial. *Journal of the American Academy of Child and Adolescent Psychiatry, 45,* 1171–1177.

Stouthamer-Loeber, M., Loeber, R., Wei, E., Farrington D. P., & Wilkstrom, P. H. (2002). Risk and promotive effects in the explanation of persistent serious delinquency in boys. *Journal of Consulting and Clinical Psychology, 70*(1), pp. 111–123.

Stricker, G., & Gold, J. R. (1999). The Rorschach: Toward a nomothetically based, idiographically applicable configurational model. *Psychological Assessment, 11,* 240–250.

Striegel-Moore, R. H. (1995). A feminist perspective on the etiology of eating disorders. In K. D. Brownell & C. G. Fairburn (Eds.), *Eating Disorders and Obesity: A Comprehensive Handbook,* pp. 224–229. New York: Guilford.

Striegel-Moore, R. H., & Bulik, C. M. (2007). Risk factors for eating disorders. *American Psychologist, 62,* 181–198.

Striegel-Moore, R. H., Silberstein, L. R., & Rodin, J. (1993). The social self in bulimia nervosa: Public self-consciousness, social anxiety, and perceived fraudulence. *Journal of Abnormal Psychology, 102,* 297–303.

Striegel-Moore, R. H., & Smolak, L. (2001). *Eating Disorders: Innovative Directions in Research and Practice.* Washington, DC: American Psychological Association.

Strober, M. (1995). Family-genetic perspectives on anorexia nervosa and bulimia nervosa. In K. D. Brownell & C. G. Fairburn (Eds.), *Eating Disorders and Obesity: A Comprehensive Handbook,* pp. 212–218. New York: Guilford.

Strober, M., & Bulik, C. M. (2002). Genetic epidemiology of eating disorders. *Eating Disorders and Obesity,* 2nd ed., pp. 238–242. New York: Guilford.

Stroebe, M., Stroebe, W., Schut, H., Zech, E., & van den Bout, J. (2002). Does disclosure of emotions facilitate recovery from bereavement? Evidence from two prospective studies. *Journal of Consulting and Clinical Psychology, 70,* 169–178.

Stroud, J., Steiner, V., & Iwuagwu, C. (2008). Predictors of depression among older adults with dementia. *Dementia: The International Journal of Social Research and Practice, 7,* 127–138.

Stucki, S., & Rihs-Middel, M. (2007). Prevalence of adult problem and pathological gambling between 2000 and 2005: An update. *Journal of Gambling Studies, 23,* 245–257.

Substance Abuse and Mental Health Services Administration. (1999). *Report of the 1998 National Household Survey on Drug Abuse.* Retrieved on from www.samhsa.gov

Sue, S. (1998). In search of cultural competence in psychotherapy and counseling. *American Psychologist, 53*(4), 440–448.

Sugarman, S. D. (2007). Cases in vaccine court—legal battles over vaccines and autism. *New England Journal of Medicine, 357,* 1275–1277.

Sullivan, E. V., Lane, B., Deshmukh, A., Rosenbloom, M. J., Desmond, J. E., Lim, K. O., et al. (1999). In vivo mammillary body volume deficits in amnesic and nonamnesic alcoholics. *Alcoholism: Clinical and Experimental Research, 23,* 1629–1636.

Sullivan, K. T., & Bradbury, T. N. (1996). Preventing marital dysfunction: The primacy of secondary strategies. *Behavior Therapist, 19,* 33–36.

Suomi, S. J., & Harlow, H. F. (1972). Social rehabilitation of isolate-reared monkeys. *Developmental Psychology, 6,* 487–496.

Surgeon General. (2001). *Mental Health: Culture. Race, and Ethnicity.* Washington, DC: Department of Health and Human Services.

Susser, E., Neugebauer, R., Hoek, H. W., Brown, A. S., et al. (1996). Schizophrenia after prenatal famine: Further evidence. *Archives of General Psychiatry, 53,* 25–31.

Susser, E., Schwartz, S., Morabia, A., & Bromet, E. J. (2006). *Psychiatric Epidemiology: Searching for the Causes of Mental Disorders.* New York: Oxford University Press.

Susser, E., Varma, V. K., Mattoo, S. K., Finnerty, M., Mojtabi, R., Tripathi, B. M., et al. (1998). Long-term course of acute brief psychosis in a developing country setting. *British Journal of Psychiatry, 173,* 226–230.

Sussman, N., & Ginsberg, D. (1998). Rethinking side effects of the selective serotonin reuptake inhibitors: Sexual dysfunction and weight gain. *Psychiatric Annals, 28,* 89–97.

Sutker, P. B., Davis, J. M., Uddo, M., & Ditta, S. R. (1995). War zone stress, personal resources, and PTSD in Persian Gulf War returnees. *Journal of Abnormal Psychology, 104,* 444–452.

Swaab, D. F., & Gofman, M. A. (1995). Sexual differentiation of the human hypothalamus in relation to gender and sexual orientation. *Trends in Neurosciences, 18,* 264–270.

Swan, W. B., Chang-Schneider, C., & McClarty, K. L. (2007). Do people's self-views matter? Self-concept and self-esteem in everyday life. *American Psychologist, 62,* 84–94.

Swanson, H. L., Harris, K. R., & Graham S. (Eds.), *Handbook of Learning Disabilities.* New York: Guilford.

Swanson, J., Elliott, G. R., Greenhill, L. L., Wigal, T., Arnold, E., Vitiello, B., et al. (2007). Effects of stimulant medication on growth rates across 3 years in the MTA follow-up. *Journal of the American Academy of Child & Adolescent Psychiatry, 46,* 1015–1027.

Swanson, J., Elliott, G. R., Greenhill, L. L., Wigal, T., Arnold, E., Vitiello, B., et al. (2007). Effects of stimulant medication on growth rates across 3 years in the MTA follow-up. *Journal of the American Academy of Child & Adolescent Psychiatry, 46,* 1015–1027.

Swanson, J. M., & Wigal, T. (2004). Self-perceptions of competence in children with ADHD and comparison children. *Journal of Consulting and Clinical Psychology, 72*(3), 382–391.

Swanson, J. M., et al. (2001). Clinical relevance of the primary findings of the MTA: Success rates based on severity of ADHD and ODD symptoms at the end of treatment. *Journal of the American Academy of Child and Adolescent Psychiatry, 40,* 168–179.

Swartz, M. S., et al. (2001). Randomized controlled trial of outpatient commitment in North Carolina. *Psychiatric Services, 52,* 325–329.

Swartz, M. S., Hughes, D., Blazer, D. G., & George, L. K. (1987). Somatization disorder in the community: A study of diagnostic concordance among three diagnostic systems. *Journal of Nervous and Mental Disorder, 175,* 26–33.

Swedo, S. E., & Grant, P. J. (2005). Annotation: PANDAS: A model for human autoimmune disease. *Journal of Child Psychology & Psychiatry, 46,* 227–234.

Swedo, S. E., Leonard, H. L., Garvey, M., Mittleman, B., Allen, A. J., Perlmutter, S., et al. (1998). Pediatric autoimmune neuropsychiatric disorders associated with streptococcal infections: Clinical description of the first 50 cases. *American Journal of Psychiatry, 155,* 264–271.

Swendsen, J. D., & Merikangas, K. R. (2000). The comorbidity of depression and substance use disorders. *Clinical Psychology Review, 20,* 173–189.

Symonds, T., Roblin, D., Hart, K., & Althof, S. (2003). How does premature ejaculation impact a man's life? *Journal of Sex & Marital Therapy, 29,* 361–370.

Szasz, T. (1963). *Law, Liberty, and Psychiatry: An Inquiry into the Social Uses of Mental Health Practices.* New York: Macmillan.

Szasz, T. (1970). *Ideology and Insanity: Essays on the Psychiatric Dehumanization of Man.* New York: Doubleday.

Szatmari, P., & Jones, M. B. (2007). Genetic epidemiology of autism spectrum disorders. In F. R. Volkmar (Ed.), *Autism and Pervasive Developmental Disorders,* pp. 157–178. New York: Cambridge University Press.

Taft, C. T., Murphy, C. M., King, L. A., Dedeyn, J. M., & Musser, P. H. (2005). Posttraumatic stress disorder symptomatology among partners of men in treatment for relationship abuse. *Journal of Abnormal Psychology, 114,* 259–268.

Tager-Flusberg, H. (1996). Current theory and research on language and communication in autism. *Journal of Autism and Developmental Disorders, 26,* 169–171.

Tager-Flusberg, H. (2007). Evaluating the Theory-of-Mind hypothesis of autism. *Current Directions in Psychological Science, 16,* 311–315.

Tallal, P. (2003). Language learning disabilities: Integrating research approaches. *Current Directions in Psychological Science, 12,* 206–211.

Tandon, R., Keshavan, M., & Nasrallah, H. (2008). Schizophrenia, "just the facts" what we know in 2008. 2. Epidemiology and etiology. *Schizophrenia Research, 102,* 1–18.

Tannock, R., Schachar, R., & Logan, G. (1995). Methylphenidate and cognitive flexibility: Dissociated dose effects in hyperactive children. *Journal of Abnormal Child Psychology, 23,* 235–266.

Tarrier, N., & Barrowclough, C. (1995). Family interventions in schizophrenia and their long-term outcomes. *International Journal of Mental Health, 24,* 38–53.

Tarrier, N., Taylor, K., & Gooding, P. (2008). Cognitive-behavioral interventions to reduce suicide behavior: A systematic review and meta-analysis. *Behavior Modification, 32,* 77–108.

Tarter, R. E., & Vanyukov, M. M. (2001). Theoretical and operational framework for research into the etiology of substance use disorders. *Journal of Child and Adolescent Substance Abuse, 10,* 1–12.

Tarter, R. E., Vanyukov, M., & Kirisci, L. (2008). Etiology of substance use disorder: Developmental perspective. In Y. Kaminer & O. G. Bukstein (Eds.), *Adolescent Substance Abuse: Psychiatric Comorbidity and High-risk Behaviors,* pp. 5–27. New York: Routledge/Taylor & Francis.

Taschentke, T. M. (2001). Pharmacology and behavioral pharmacology of the mesocortical dopamine system. *Progress in Neurobiology, 63,* 241–320.

Taylor, C. B., & Luce, K. H. (2003). Computer- and Internet-based psychotherapy interventions. *Current Directions in Psychological Science, 12,* 18–22.

Taylor, E., & Rutter, M. (2002). Classification: Conceptual issues and substantive findings. In M. Rutter & E. Taylor (Eds.), *Child and Adolescent Psychiatry,* 4th ed., pp. 3–17. Oxford, England: Blackwell.

Taylor, J., Iacono, W. G., & McGue, M. (2000). Evidence for a genetic etiology of early-onset delinquency. *Journal of Abnormal Psychology, 109,* 634–643.

Taylor, M. A., & Fink, M. (2008). Restoring melancholia in the classification of mood disorders. *Journal of Affective Disorders, 105,* 1–14.

Taylor, R. L., Richards, S. B., & Brady, M. P. (2005). *Mental Retardation: Historical Perspectives, Current Practices, and Future Directions.* New York: Pearson Education.

Taylor, R., & Langdon, R. (2006). Understanding gender differences in schizophrenia: A review of the literature. *Current Psychiatry Reviews, 2,* 255–265.

Taylor, S. A. (2001). Breathing retraining in the treatment of panic disorder: Efficacy, caveats and indications. *Scandinavian Journal of Behaviour Therapy, 30,* 49–56.

Taylor, S. E. (1990). Health psychology: The science and the field. *American Psychologist, 45,* 40–50.

Taylor, S. E. (1995). *Health Psychology* (3rd ed.). New York: McGraw-Hill.

Taylor, S. E. (2006). Tend and befriend: Biobehavioral bases of affiliation under stress. *Current Directions in Psychological Science, 15,* 273–276.

Taylor, S. E., Klein, L. C., Lewis, B. P., Gruenewald, T. L., Gurung, R. A. R., & Updegraff, J. A. (2000). Biobehavioral responses to stress in females: Tend-and-befriend, not fight-or-flight. *Psychological Bulletin, 107,* 411–429.

Taylor, S. E., Lerner, J. S., Sherman, D. K., Sage, R. M., & McDowell, N. K. (2003). Portrait of the self-enhancer: Well adjusted and well liked or maladjusted and friendless? *Journal of Personality & Social Psychology, 84,* 165–176.

Taylor, S. E., Welch, W. T., Kim, H. S., & Sherman, D. K. (2007). Cultural differences in the impact of social support on psychological and biological stress responses. *Psychological Science, 18,* 831–837.

Teachman, B. A. (2006). Aging and negative affect: The rise and fall and rise of anxiety and depression symptoms. *Psychology and Aging, 21,* 201–207.

Teachman, B. A., Marker, C. D., & Smith-Janik, S. B. (in press). Automatic associations and panic disorder: Trajectories of change over the course of treatment. *Journal of Consulting and Clinical Psychology, 77.*

Teachman, B. A., Siedlecki, K. L., & Magee, J. C. (2007). Aging and symptoms of anxiety and depression: Structural invariance of the tripartite model. *Psychology and Aging, 22,* 160–170.

Teachman, B. A., Smith-Janik, S. B., & Saporito, J. (2007). Information processing biases and panic disorder: Relationships among cognitive and symptom measures. *Behaviour Research and Therapy, 45,* 1791–1811.

Tellegen, A. (1985). Structures of mood and personality and their relevance to assessing anxiety, with an emphasis on self-report. In A. H. Tuma & J. D. Maser (Eds.), *Anxiety and the Anxiety Disorders,* pp. 681–706. Hillsdale, NJ: Erlbaum.

Temple, S., & Ho, B. (2005). Cognitive therapy for persistent psychosis in schizophrenia: A case-controlled clinical trial. *Schizophrenia Research, 74,* 195–199.

Teplin, L. A., Abram, K. M., & McClelland, G. M. (1994). Does psychiatric disorder predict violent crime among released jail detainees? A six-year longitudinal study. *American Psychologist, 49,* 335–342.

Tesman, J. R., & Hills, A. (1994). Developmental effects of lead exposure in children. *Social Policy Report: Society for Research in Child Development, 8*(3), 1–16.

Testa, M., Fillmore, M. T., Norris, J., Abbey, A., Curtin, J. J., Leonard, K. E., et al. (2006). Understanding alcohol expectancy effects: Revisiting the placebo condition. Alcoholism: *Clinical and Experimental Research, 30,* 339–348.

Thaker, G. K., & Carpenter W. T. (2001). Advances in schizophrenia. *Nature Medicine, 7,* 667–71.

Thakker, J., & Ward, T. (1998). Culture and classification: The cross-cultural application of the DSM-IV. *Clinical Psychology Review, 18,* 501–529.

Thapar, A., Gottesman, I. I., Owen, M. J., O'Donovan, M. C., & McGuffin, P. (1994). The genetics of mental retardation. *British Journal of Psychiatry, 164,* 747–758.

Thase, M. (1988). The relationship between Down syndrome and Alzheimer's disease. In L. Nadel (Ed.), *The Psychobiology of Down Syndrome.* Cambridge, MA: MIT Press.

Thase, M. E. (2003). Achieving remission and managing relapse in depression. *Journal of Clinical Psychiatry, 64* (Suppl. 118), 3–7.

Thase, M. E. (2006). Preventing relapse and recurrence of depression: A brief review of therapeutic options. *CNS Spectrums, 11* (Suppl. 15), 12–21.

Thase, M. E., Ripu, J., & Howland, R. H. (2002). Biological aspects of depression. In I. H. Gotlib and C. L. Hammen (Eds.), *Handbook of Depression.* New York: Guilford.

Thigpen, C. H., & Cleckley, H. M. (1957). *The Three Faces of Eve.* New York: McGraw-Hill.

Thomas, A., & Chess, S. (1977). *Temperament and Development.* New York: Brunner/Mazel.

Thomas, E. (1996, May 27). A matter of honor. *Newsweek,* 24–29.

Thomas, K. M., Drevets, W. C., Dahl, R. E., Ryan, N. D., Birmaher, B., Eccard, C. H., et al. (2001). Amygdala response to fearful faces in anxious and depressed children. *Archives of General Psychiatry, 58,* 1057–1063.

Thomas, V. H., Melchert, T. P., & Banken, J. A. (1999). Substance dependence and personality disorders: Comorbidity and treatment outcome in an inpatient treatment population. *Journal of Studies on Alcohol, 60,* 271–277.

Thompson, J., Pogue-Geile, M., & Grace, A. (2004). Developmental pathology, dopamine, and stress: A model for the age of onset of schizophrenia symptoms. *Schizophrenia Bulletin, 30*(4), 875–900.

Thompson, J. K. (1996). *Body Image, Eating Disorders, and Obesity.* Washington, DC: American Psychological Association.

Thompson-Brenner, H., Glass, S., & Westen, D. (2003). A multidimensional meta-analysis of psychotherapy for bulimia nervosa. *Clinical Psychology, 10,* 269–287.

Thomson, J. B. & Raskind, W. H. (2003). Genetic influences on reading and writing disabilities. In H. L. Swanson, K. R. Harris, & S. Graham (Eds.), *Handbook of Learning Disabilities,* pp. 256–270. New York: Guilford.

Thoresen, C. E., & Powell, L. H. (1992). Type A behavior pattern: New perspectives on theory, assessment, and intervention. *Journal of Consulting and Clinical Psychology, 60,* 595–604.

Thornicroft, G., & Susser, E. (2001). Evidence-based psychotherapeutic interventions in the community care of schizophrenia. *British Journal of Psychiatry, 178,* 2–4.

Thorup, A., Waltoft, B., Pedersen, C., Mortensen, P., & Nordentoft, M. (2007). Young males have a higher risk of developing schizophrenia: A Danish register study. *Psychological Medicine, 37,* 479–484.

Tiefer, L. (1999). Challenging sexual naturalism, the shibboleth of sex research and popular sexology. In D. Bernstein (Ed.), *Gender and Motivation. Nebraska Symposium on Motivation,* Vol. 45, pp. 143–172. Lincoln: University of Nebraska Press.

Tiefer, L. (2001). The "consensus" conference on female sexual dysfunction: Conflicts of interest and hidden agendas. *Journal of Sex and Marital Therapy, 27,* 227–236.

Tiefer, L., & Kring, B. (1995). Gender and the organization of sexual behavior. *Psychiatric Clinics of North America, 18,* 25–37.

Tienari, P., Wynne, L., Läksy, K., Moring, J., Nieminen, P., Sorri, A., et al. (2003). Genetic boundaries of the schizophrenia spectrum: Evidence from the Finnish Adoptive Family Study of Schizophrenia. *American Journal of Psychiatry, 160,* 1587–1594.

Toffel, H. (1996). Crazy women, unharmed men, and evil children: Confronting the myths about battered people who kill their abusers, and the argument for extending battering syndrome self-defenses to all victims of domestic violence. *Southern California Law Review, 70,* 337–380.

Tolin, D. F., & Foa, E. B. (2006). Sex differences in trauma and posttraumatic stress disorder: A quantitative review of 25 years of research. *Psychological Bulletin, 132,* 959–992.

Tomkins, D. M., & Sellers, E. M. (2001). Addiction and the brain: The role of neurotransmitters in the cause and treatment of drug dependence. *Canadian Medical Association Journal. 164,* 817–821.

Tonigan, J. S., Connors, G. J., & Miller, W. R. (2003). Participation and involvement in Alcoholics Anonymous. In T. F. Babor and F. K. Del Boca (Eds.), *Treatment Matching in Alcoholism,* pp. 184–204. New York: Cambridge University Press.

Torgersen, S. (1986). Genetic factors in moderately severe and mild affective disorders. *Archives of General Psychiatry, 43,* 222–226.

Torgersen, S. (1994). Genetics in borderline conditions. *Acta Psychiatrica Scandinavica, 89* (Suppl. 379), 19–25.

Torgersen, S., Kringlen, E., & Cramer, V. (2001). The prevalence of personality disorders in a community sample. *Archives of General Psychiatry, 58,* 590–596.

Torres, A. R., Prince, M. J., Bebbington, P. E., Bhugra, D., Brugha, T. S., Farrell, M., et al. (2006). Obsessive-compulsive disorder: Prevalence, comorbidity, impact, and help-seeking in the British National Psychiatric Morbidity Survey of 2000. *American Journal of Psychiatry, 163,* 1978–1985.

Torrey, E., Barci, B., Webster, M., Bartko, J., Meador-Woodruff, J., & Knable, M. (2005). Neurochemical markers for schizophrenia, bipolar disorder, and major depression in postmortem brains. *Biological Psychiatry, 57,* 252–260.

Torrey, E. F. (1988). *Nowhere to Go: The Tragic Odyssey of the Homeless Mentally Ill.* New York: Harper & Row.

Torrey, E. F. (1997). *Out of the Shadows.* New York: Wiley.

Torrey, E. F. (2008). *The insanity offense: How America's failure to treat the seriously mentally ill endangers its citizens.* New York: Norton.

Torrey, E. F., Bowler, A. E., Taylor, E. H., & Gottesman, I. I. (1994). *Schizophrenia and Manic-Depressive Disorder: The Biological Roots of Mental Illness as Revealed by the Landmark Study of Identical Twins.* New York: Basic Books.

Trials of the Hypertension Prevention Collaborative Research Group. (1992). The effects of nonpharmacologic interventions on blood pressure of persons with high normal levels: Results of the Trials of Hypertension Prevention, Phase I. *Journal of the American Medical Association, 267,* 1213–1220.

Triandis, H. C. (1994). Culture and social behavior. In W. J. Lonner & R. S. Malpass (Eds.), *Psychology and Culture,* pp. 169–174. Boston: Allyn & Bacon.

True, W. R., Rice, J., Eisen, S. A., Heath, A. C., Goldberg, J., Lyons, M. J., et al. (1993). A twin study of genetic and environmental contributions to liability for posttraumatic stress symptoms. *Archives of General Psychiatry, 50,* 257–264.

Trull, T. J. (1995). Borderline personality disorder features in nonclinical young adults. 1. Identification and validation. *Psychological Assessment, 7,* 33–41.

Trull, T. J., & McCrae, R. R. (2002). A five-factor perspective on personality disorder research. In P. T. Costa, Jr., & T. A. Widiger (Eds.), *Personality Disorders and the Five-Factor Model of Personality,* 2nd ed., pp. 45–58. Washington, DC: American Psychological Association.

Trull, T. J., Stepp. S. D., & Solhan, M. (2006). Borderline personality disorder. In F. Andrasik (Ed.), *Comprehensive Handbook of Personality and Psychopathology,* Vol. 2, pp. 299–315. Hoboken, NJ: Wiley.

Tsai, J. L., & Chentsova-Dutton, Y. (2002). Understanding depression across cultures. In I. H. Gotlib and C. L. Hammen (Eds.), *Handbook of Depression.* New York: Guilford.

Tsai, L. Y. (1996). Comorbid psychiatric disorders of autistic disorder. *Journal of Autism and Developmental Disorders, 26,* 159–163.

Tsuang, M. T., Stone, W. S., Tarbox, S. I., & Faraone, S. V. (2003). Insights from neuroscience for the concepts of schizotaxia and the diagnosis of schizophrenia. In K. A. Phillips & M. B. First (Eds.), *Advancing DSM: Dilemmas in Psychiatric Diagnosis,* pp. 105–127. Washington, DC: American Psychiatric Association.

Tuckey, M. R. (2007). Issues in the debriefing debate for the emergency services: Moving research outcomes forward. *Clinical Psychology: Science and Practice, 14,* 106–116.

Tully, L. A., Arseneault, L., Caspi, A., Moffitt, T. E., & Morgan, J. (2004). Does maternal warmth moderate the effects of birth weight on twins' attention-deficit/hyperactivity disorder (ADHD) symptoms and

low IQ? *Journal of Consulting and Clinical Psychology, 72*(2), 218–226.

Tune, L. (2007). Treatments for dementia. A guide to treatments that work, 3rd ed., pp. 105–143. New York: Oxford University Press.

Turkat, I. D., & Carlson, C. R. (1984). Data-based versus symptomatic formulation of treatment: The case of a dependent personality. *Journal of Behavior Therapy and Experimental Psychiatry, 15,* 153–160.

Turkheimer, E. (1991). Individual and group differences in adoption studies of IQ. *Psychological Bulletin, 110,* 392–405.

Turkheimer, E., & Waldron, M. (2000). Nonshared environment: A theoretical, methodological and quantitative review. *Psychological Bulletin, 126,* 78–108.

Tyrer, P., Coombs, N., Ibrahimi, F., Mathilakath, A., Bajaj, P., Ranger, M., Rao, B., & Din, R. (2007). Critical developments in the assessment of personality disorder. *British Journal of Psychiatry, 190* (suppl. 49), s51–s59.

Tyrer, P., Seivewright, H., & Johnson, T. (2004). The Nottingham study of neurotic disorder: Predictors of 12-year outcome of dysthymic, panic and generalized anxiety disorder. *Psychological Medicine, 34,* 1385–1394.

Uchiyama, T., et al. (2007). MMR-vaccine and regression in autism spectrum disorders: Negative results presented from Japan. *Journal of Autism and Developmental Disorders, 37,* 210–217.

U.S. Census Bureau. (1996). Sixty-five plus in the United States. *Current Population Reports,* 23–190. Washington, DC: U.S. Government Printing Office.

U.S. Census Bureau. (2002, February 13). Historical poverty tables. Retrieved on from www.census.gov/_hhes/poverty/histpov/hstpov4.html3

U.S. Department of Health and Human Services. (1993). *AIDS Research: An NIMH Blueprint for the Second Decade.* NIH Publication No. 93-3563.Washington, DC: U.S. Government Printing Office.

U.S. Department of Health and Human Services, Administration on Children, Youth and Families. (2001). *Child Maltreatment 1999: Reports From the States to the National Child Abuse and Neglect Data Systems—National Statistics on Child Abuse and Neglect.* Washington, DC: U.S. Government Printing Office.

U.S. Department of Health and Human Services, Administration on Children, Youth and Families. (2002). *Child Maltreatment 2000: Reports from the States to the National Child Abuse and Neglect Data Systems—National Statistics on Child Abuse and Neglect.* Washington, DC: U.S. Government Printing Office.

U.S. Department of Health and Human Services, Administration on Children, Youth and Families. (2003). *Child Maltreatment 2001: Reports from the States to the National Child Abuse and Neglect Data Systems—National Statistics on Child Abuse and Neglect.* Washington, DC: U.S. Government Printing Office.

U.S. Department of Health and Human Services, Administration on Children, Youth and Families. (2004). *Child Maltreatment 2002: Reports from the States to the National Child Abuse and Neglect Data Systems—National Statistics on Child Abuse and Neglect.* Washington, DC: U.S. Government Printing Office.

U.S. Department of Health and Human Services, Administration on Children, Youth and Families. (2005). *Child Maltreatment 2003: Reports from the States to the National Child Abuse and Neglect Data Systems—National Statistics on Child Abuse and Neglect.* Washington, DC: U.S. Government Printing Office.

U.S. Department of Justice, Bureau of Justice Statistics. (1999). *Special Report: Mental Health and Treatment of Inmates and Probationers.* Washington, DC: National Criminal Justice.

Uchino, B. N., Cacioppo, J. T., & Kiecolt-Glaser, J. K. (1996). The relationship between social support and

physiological processes: A review with emphasis underlying mechanisms and implications for health. *Psychological Bullettin, 119,* 488–531.

Uhlenhuth, E. H., Leon, A. C., Matuzas, W. (2006). Psychopathology of panic attacks in panic disorder. *Journal of Affective Disorders, 92,* 55–62.

UK ECT Review Group. (2003). Efficacy and safety of electroconvulsive therapy in depressive disorders: A systematic review and meta-analysis. *Lancet, 361,* 799–808.

Updegraff, J. A., & Taylor, S. E. (2000). From vulnerability to growth: Positive and negative effects of stressful life events. In J. H. Harvey & E. D. Miller (Eds.), *Loss and Trauma: General and Close Relationship Perspectives,* pp. 3–28. Philadelphia: Brunner-Routledge.

Uttal, W. R. (2001). *The New Phrenology: The Limits of Localizing Cognitive Processes in the Brain.* Cambridge, MA: MIT Press.

Vaillant, G. (2003). A 60-year follow-up of alcoholic men. *Addiction. 98,* 1043–1051.

Vaillant, G. E. (1994). Evidence that the Type 1/Type 2 dichotomy in alcoholism must be re-examined. *Addiction, 89,* 1049–1057.

Vaillant, G. E. (1995). *The Natural History of Alcoholism Revisited.* Cambridge, MA: Harvard University Press.

Vaillant, G. E. (1996). A long-term follow-up of male alcohol abuse. *Archives of General Psychiatry, 53,* 243–249.

Valenstein, E. S. (1973). *Brain Control.* New York: Wiley.

Valenstein, E. S. (1986). *Great and Desperate Cures.* New York: Basic Books.

Valenstein, E. S. (1998). *Blaming the Brain.* New York: Free Press.

Valente, J. (1996, January). A long road to daylight: Football player's gambling problems. *People Weekly, 15,* 811.

van der Kolk, B. A. (1996). The psychobiology of PTSD. In B. A. van der Kolk, A. C. McFarlane, & L. Weisaeth (Eds.), *Traumatic Stress,* pp. 214–241. New York: Guilford.

van der Kolk, B. A., & McFarlane, A. C. (1996). The black hole of trauma. In B. A. van der Kolk, A. C. McFarlane, & L. Weisaeth (Eds.), *Traumatic Stress,* pp. 3–23. New York: Guilford.

van Haren, N., Bakker, S., & Kahn, R. (2008). Genes and structural brain imaging in schizophrenia. *Current Opinion in Psychiatry, 21,* 161–167.

Van Ommeren, M., de Jong, J., Sharma, B., Komproe, I., Thapa, S. B., & Cardena, E. (2001). Psychiatric disorders among tortured Bhutanese refugees in Nepal. *Archives of General Psychiatry, 58,* 475–482.

Van Orden, K. A., Witte, T. K., Gordon, K. H., Bender, T. W., & Joiner, T. E. (2008). Suicidal desire and the capability for suicide: Tests of the interpersonal-psychological theory of suicidal behavior among adults. *Journal of Consulting and Clinical Psychology, 76,* 72–83.

Van Os, J. & McGuffin, P. M. (2003). Can the social environment cause schizophrenia? *British Journal of Psychiatry, 182,* 291–292.

Vandereycken, W. (1995). The families of patients with an eating disorder. In K. D. Brownell & C. G. Fairburn (Eds.), *Eating Disorders and Obesity: A Comprehensive Handbook,* pp. 219–223. New York: Guilford.

Vandereycken, W. (2002.) Families of patients with eating disorders. In C. G. Fairburn & K. D. Brownell (Eds.), *Eating Disorders and Obesity,* 2nd ed., pp. 215–222. New York: Guilford.

Vanin, J. R. (2008). Psychopharmacotherapy. In J. R. Vanin & J. D. Helsley (Eds.). *Anxiety Disorders: A Pocket Guide for Primary Care,* pp. 63–112. Totowa, NJ: Humana Press.

Vasquez, M. J. T. (2007). Cultural difference and the therapeutic alliance: An evidence-based analysis. *American Psychologist, 62,* 878–885.

Vaughn, C. E., & Leff, J. P. (1976). The influence of family and social factors on the course of psychiatric illness: A comparison of schizophrenic and depressed neurotic patients. *British Journal of Psychiatry, 129,* 125–137.

Verheul, R., van den Bosch, L. M. C., Koeter, M. W. J., de Ridder, M. A. J., Stijnen, T., & van den Brink, W. (2003). Dialectical behaviour therapy for women with borderline personality disorder: 12-month, randomized clinical trial in The Netherlands. *British Journal of Psychiatry, 182,* 135–140.

Verma, K., Khaitan, B., & Singh, O. (1998). The frequency of sexual dysfunctions in patients attending a sex therapy clinic in North India. *Archives of Sexual Behavior, 27,* 309–314.

Vesga-Lopez, O., Schmidt, A., & Blanco, C. (2007). Update on sexual addictions. *Directions in Psychiatry, 27,* 143–158.

Viken, R. J., Treat, T. A., Nosofsky, R. M., McFall, R. M., & Palmeri, T. J. (2002). Modeling individual differences in perceptual and attentional processes related to bulimic symptoms. *Journal of Abnormal Psychology, 111,* 598–609.

Visintainer, M. A., Seligman, M. E. P., & Volpicelli, J. R. (1982). Tumor rejection in rats after inescapable or escapable electric shock. *Science, 216,* 437–439.

Vitiello, B., Abikoff, H. B., Chuang, S. Z., Kollins, S. H., McCracken, J. T., Riddle, M. A., et al. (2007). Effectiveness of methylphenidate in the 10-month continuation phase of the Preschoolers with ADHD Treatment Study (PATS). *Journal of Child and Adolescent Psychopharmacology, 17,* 593–603.

Vitousek, K. B. (2002). Cognitive-behavioral therapy for anorexia nervosa. In C. G. Fairburn & K. D. Brownell (Eds.), *Eating Disorders and Obesity,* 2nd ed., pp. 308–313. New York: Guilford.

Vohs, K. D., Bardone, A. M., Joiner, T. E., & Abramson, L. Y. (1999). Perfectionism, perceived weight status, and self-esteem interact to predict bulimic symptoms: A model of bulimic symptom development. *Journal of Abnormal Psychology, 108,* 695–700.

Volicer, L., McKee, A., & Hewitt, S. (2001). Dementia. *Neurologic Clinics, 19,* 867–885.

Volkmar, F., Chawarska, K., & Klin, A. (2005). Autism in infancy and early childhood. *Annual Review of Psychology, 56,* 315–336.

Volkmar, F., & Dykens, E. (2002). Mental retardation. In M. Rutter & E. Taylor (Eds.), *Child and Adolescent Psychiatry,* 4th ed., pp. 697–710. Oxford, England: Blackwell.

Volkmar, F. R. (1996). *Psychoses and pervasive Developmental Disorders in Childhood and Adolescence.* Washington, DC: American Psychiatric Association.

Volkmar, F. R., Klin, A., Siegel, B., et al. (1994). Field trial for autistic disorder in DSM-IV. *American Journal of Psychiatry, 151,* 1361–1367.

Volkmar, F. R., & Lord, C. (2007). Diagnosis and definition of autism and other pervasive developmental disorders. In F. R. Volkmar (Ed.), *Autism and Pervasive Developmental Disorders,* pp. 1–31. New York: Cambridge University Press.

Von Korff, M., Crane, P., Lane, M., Miglioretti, D. L., Simon, G., Saunders, K., et al. (2005). Chronic spinal pain and physical-mental comorbidity in the United States: Results from the National Comorbidity Survey Replication. *Pain, 113,* 331–339.

Waber, R. L., Shiv, B., Carmon, Z., & Ariely, D. (2008). Commercial features of placebo and therapeutic efficacy. *Journal of the American Medical Association, 299,* 1016–1017.

Waddington, J., Corvin, A., Donohoe, G., O'Tuathaigh, M., Mitchell, K., & Gill, M. (2007). Functional genomics and schizophrenia: Endophenotypes and mutant models. *Psychiatric Clinics of North America, 30,* 365–399.

Wager, T. D. (2005). The neural bases of placebo effects in pain. *Current Directions in Psychological Science, 14,* 175–179.

Wahl, R. L. (Ed.) (2002). *Principles and Practice of Position Emission Tomography.* Philadelphia: Lippincott, Williams and Wilkins.

Waite, L. J., & Gallagher, M. (2000). *The Case for Marriage: Why Married People are Happier, Healthier, and Better off Financially.* New York: Doubleday.

Wakefield, et al. (1998). Ileal lymphoid nodular hyperplasia, non-specific colitis, and regressive developmental disorder in children. *Lancet, 351,* 637–641.

Wakefield, J. C. (1992). The concept of mental disorder: On the boundary between biological facts and social values. *American Psychologist, 47,* 373–388.

Wakefield, J. C. (1999). The measurement of mental disorder. In A. V. Horwitz and T. L. Scheid (Eds.), *A Handbook for the Study of Mental Health: Social Contexts, Theories, and Systems.* Cambridge: Cambridge University Press.

Wald, M. S., Carlsmith, J. M., & Leiderman, P. H. (1988). *Protecting Abused and Neglected Children.* Stanford, CA: Stanford University Press.

Walden, B., McGue, M., Iacono, W. G., Burt, S. A., & Elkins, I. (2004). Identifying shared environmental contributions to early substance use: The respective roles of peers and parents. *Journal of Abnormal Psychology, 113*(3), 440–450.

Walden, J., Normann, C., Langosch, J., Berger, M., & Grunze, H. (1998). Differential treatment of bipolar disorder with old and new antiepileptic drugs. *Neuropsychobiology, 38,* 181–184.

Waldinger, M. D. (2003). Rapid ejaculation. In S. B. Levine and C. B. Risen (Eds.), *Handbook of Clinical Sexuality for Mental Health Professionals,* pp. 257–274. New York: Brunner-Routledge.

Waldman, I. D., & Rhee, S. H. (2006). Genetic and environmental influences on psychopathy and antisocial behavior. In C. J. Patrick (Ed.), *Handbook of Psychopathy,* pp. 205–228. New York: Guilford.

Walker, E., Davis, D., & Baum, K. (1993). Social withdrawal. In C. G. Costello (Ed.), *Symptoms of Schizophrenia,* pp. 227–260. New York: Wiley.

Walker, E., Kestler, L., Bollini, A., & Hochman, K. M. (2004). Schizophrenia: Etiology and course. *Annual Review of Psychology, 55,* 401–430.

Walker, L. (1979). *The Battered Woman.* New York: Harper & Row.

Walker, L. (1989). Psychology and violence against women. *American Psychologist, 44,* 695–702.

Wallace, J. (1999). The twelve-step recovery approach. In P. J. Ott, R. E. Tarter, & R. T. Ammerman (Eds.), *Sourcebook on Substance Abuse: Etiology, Epidemiology, Assessment, and Treatment,* pp. 293–302. Boston: Allyn & Bacon.

Wallace, J. F., & Newman, J. P. (2004). A theory-based treatment model for psychopathy. *Cognitive and Behavioral Practice, 11,* 178–189.

Waller, N. G., & Ross, C. A. (1997). The prevalence and biometric structure of pathological dissociation in the general population: Taxometric and behavior genetic findings. *Journal of Abnormal Psychology, 106,* 499–510.

Walsh, B. T. (1995). Pharmacotherapy of eating disorders. In K. D. Brownell & C. G. Fairburn (Eds.), *Eating Disorders and Obesity: A Comprehensive Handbook,* pp. 313–317. New York: Guilford.

Walsh, B. T., et al. (2004). Treatment of bulimia nervosa in a primary care setting. *American Journal of Psychiatry, 161,* 556–561.

Walsh, T., Wilson, G. T., Loeb, K. L., et al. (1997). Medication and psychotherapy in the treatment of bulimia nervosa. *American Journal of Psychiatry, 154,* 523–531.

Walters, G. D. (1999). *The Addiction Concept: Working Hypothesis or Self-Fulfilling Prophesy?* Boston: Allyn & Bacon.

Wampold, B. E. (2007). Psychotherapy: The humanistic (and effective) treatment. *American Psychologist, 62,* 857–873.

Wandersman, A., & Florin, P. (2003). Community interventions and effective prevention. *American Psychologist, 2003,* 441–448.

Wang, C. T., & Harding, K. (1999). *Current Trends in Child Abuse Reporting and Fatalities: The Results of the 1998 Annual Fifty Sate Survey.* Chicago: National Center on Child Abuse Prevention Research.

Waraich, P., Goldner, E. M., Somers, J. M., & Hsu, L. (2004). Prevalence and incidence studies of mood disorders: A systematic review of the literature. *Canadian Journal of Psychiatry, 49,* 124–138.

Warnock, J. K. (2002). Female hypoactive sexual desire disorder: Epidemiology, diagnosis and treatment. *CNS Drugs, 16,* 745–753.

Warren, S. T., & Ashley, C. T. (1995). Triplet repeat expansion mutations: The example of fragile X syndrome. *Annual Review of Neuroscience, 18,* 77–99.

Waschbusch, D. A. & Hill, G. P. (2004). Empirically supported, promising, and unsupported treatments for children with Attention-Deficit/Hyperactivity Disorder. In S. O. Lilienfeld et al. (Eds.), *Science and Pseudoscience in Clinical Psychology,* pp. 333–362. New York: Guilford.

Waschbusch, D. A. (2002). A meta-analytic examination of comorbid hyperactive-impulsive-attention problems and conduct problems. *Psychological Bulletin, 128*(1), 118–150.

Wassef, A., Baker, J., & Kochan, L. D. (2003). GABA and schizophrenia: A review of basic science and clinical studies. *Journal of Clinical Psychopharmacology, 23,* 601–640.

Waterhouse, L., Fein, D., & Modahl, C.(1996). Neurofunctional mechanisms in autism. *Psychological Review, 103*(3), 457–489.

Waterman, A. S., & Archer, S. (1990). A life-span perspective on identity formation: Development in form, function, and process. In P. B. Baltes, D. L. Featherman, & R. M. Lerner (Eds.), *Life-Span Development and Behavior,* Vol. 10, pp. 29–57. Hillsdale, NJ: Erlbaum.

Waterman, A. S., & Goldman, J. A. (1976). A longitudinal study of changes in ego identity development at a liberal arts college. *Journal of Youth and Adolescence.*

Waterman, G., Geary, P., & Waterman, C. (1974). Longitudinal study of changes in ego identity status from the freshman to the senior year at college. *Developmental Psychology, 10,* 387–392.

Waters, E., Hay, D., & Richters, J. (1986). Infant-parent attachment and the origins of prosocial and antisocial behavior. In D. Olweus, J. Block, & M. Radke-Yarrow (Eds.), *Development of Antisocial and Prosocial Behavior: Research, Theories, and Issues,* pp. 97–126. Orlando, FL: Academic Press.

Watkins, J. G. (1984). The Bianchi (L.A. Hillsdale Strangler) case: Sociopath or multiple personality. *International Journal of Clinical and Experimental Hypnosis, 32,* 67–101.

Watson, D., & Clark, L. A. (1990). *The Positive and Negative Affect Schedule-Expanded Form.* Unpublished manuscript. Southern Methodist University.

Watson, D., Clark, L. A., Weber, K., Assenheimer, J. S., Strauss, M. E., & McCormick, R. A. (1995). Testing a tripartite model. II. Exploring the symptom structure of anxiety and depression in student, adult, and patient samples. *Journal of Abnormal Psychology, 104,* 15–25.

Watson, J. B., & Rayner, R. (1920). Conditioned emotional reactions. *Journal of Experimental Psychology, 3,* 1–14.

Watts, C., & Zimmerman, C. (2002). Violence against women: Global scope and magnitude. *Lancet, 359,* 1232–1237.

Webster-Stratton, C. (1994). Advancing videotape parent training: A comparison study. *Journal of Consulting and Clinical Psychology, 62,* 583–593.

Wegner, D. M. (1994). Ironic processes of mental control. *Psychological Review, 101,* 34–52.

Wehr, T. A. (1989). Seasonal affective disorder: A historical overview. In N. E. Rosenthal, & M. C. Blehar. (Eds.), *Seasonal Affective Disorders and Phototherapy.* New York: Guilford.

Weiden, P. J., & Olfson, M. (1995). Cost of relapse in schizophrenia. *Schizophrenia Bulletin, 21,* 419–429.

Weinberger, D. R. (1997). The biological basis of schizophrenia: New directions. *Journal of Clinical Psychiatry, 58,* (Suppl. 10), 22–27.

Weinberger, D. R., & McClure, R. K. (2002). Neurotoxicity, neuroplasticity, and magnetic resonance imaging morphometry: What is happening in the schizophrenic brain? *Archives of General Psychiatry, 59,* 553–558.

Weiner, H., & Fawzy, F. I. (1989). An integrative model of health, disease, and illness. In S. Cheren (Ed.), *Psychosomatic Medicine: Theory, Physiology, and Practice,* Vol. 1, pp. 9–44. Madison, CT: International Universities Press.

Weiner, I. B. (2000). Using the Rorschach properly in practice and research. *Journal of Clinical Psychology, 56,* 435–438.

Weinstock, R., Vari, G., Leong, G. B., & Silva, J. A. (2006). Back to the past in California: A temporary retreat to a *Tarasoff* duty to warn. *Journal of the American Academy of Psychiatry and the Law, 34,* 523–528.

Weiss, L. A., Shen, Y., Korn, J. M., Arking, D. E., Miller, D. T., Fossdal, R., et al. (2008). Association between microdeletion and microduplication at 16p11.2 and autism. *The New England Journal of Medicine, 358,* 1–9.

Weissman, M. M. (1993). The epidemiology of personality disorders: A 1990 update. *Journal of Personality Disorders,* (Suppl.), 44–62.

Weissman, M. M., Markowitz, J. C., & Klerman, G. L. (2000). *Comprehensive Guide to Interpersonal Psychotherapy.* New York: Basic Books.

Weisz, J. R., & Hawley, K. M. (2002). Developmental factors in the treatment of adolescents. *Journal of Consulting and Clinical Psychology, 70,* 21–43.

Weithorn, L. A. (1988). Mental hospitalization of troublesome youth: An analysis of skyrocketing admission rates. *Stanford Law Review, 40,* 773–838.

Welch, S. L., & Fairburn, C. G. (1996). Childhood sexual and physical abuse as risk factors for the development of bulimia nervosa: A community-based case control study. *Child Abuse & Neglect, 20*(7), 633–642.

Wells, K. C., Chi, T. C., Hinshaw, S. P., Epstein, J. N., Pfiffner, L., Nebel-Schwalm, M., et al. (2006). Treatment-related changes in objectively measured parenting behaviors in the Multimodal Treatment Study of children with attention-deficit/hyperactivity disorder. *Journal of Consulting and Clinical Psychology, 74,* 649–657.

Welsh, R. S. (2003). Prescription privileges: Pro or con. *Clinical Psychology: Science & Practice, 10,* 371–372.

Welsh-Bohmer, K., & Attix, D. (2004). *Neuropsychological Assessment of Dementia. The American Psychiatric Publishing Textbook of Geriatric Psychiatry,* 3rd ed., pp. 189–203. Arlington, VA: American Psychiatric Publishing, Inc.

Werneke, U., Northey, S., & Bhugra, D. (2006). Antidepressants and sexual dysfunction. *Acta Psychiatric Scandinavica, 114,* 384–397.

Werner, J. S., & Smith, R. S. (1982). *Vulnerable but Invincible: A Longitudinal Study of Resilient Children and Youth.* New York: McGraw-Hill.

West, S. L., Vinikoor, L. C., & Zolnoun, D. (2004). A systematic review of the literature on female sexual dysfunction prevalence and predictors. *Annual Review of Sex Research, 15,* 40–172.

Westen, D., & Bradley, R. (2005). Empirically supported complexity: Rethinking evidence-based practice in psychotherapy. *Current Directions in Psychological Science, 14,* 266–271.

Westen, D., & Morrison, K. (2001). A multidimensional meta-analysis of treatments for depression, panic, and generalized anxiety disorder: An empirical examination of the status of empirically supported therapies. *Journal of Consulting and Clinical Psychology, 69,* 875–899.

Westermeyer, J. (1999). Cross-cultural aspects of substance abuse. In M. Galanter & H. D. Kleber (Eds.), *Textbook of Substance Abuse Treatment,* 2nd ed., pp. 75–88. Washington, DC: American Psychiatric Press.

Weston, D. (1998). The scientific legacy of Sigmund Freud: Toward a psychodynamically informed psychological science. *Psychological Bulletin, 124,* 333–371.

Weston, D., Novotny, C. M., & Thompson-Brenner, H. (2004). The empirical status of empirically supported psychotherapies: Assumptions, findings, and reporting in controlled clinical trials. *Psychological Bulletin, 130,* 631–663.

Westrin, A., & Lam, R. W. (2007). Seasonal affective disorder: A clinical update. *Annals of Clinical Psychiatry, 19,* 239–246.

Whalen, C., Henker, B., Hinshaw, S., Heller, T., & Huber-Dressler, A. (1991). Messages of medication: Effects of actual versus informed medication status on hyperactive boys's expectancies and self-evaluation. *Journal of Consulting and Clinical Psychology, 59,* 602–606.

Whaley, A. L. (2001). Cultural mistrust and the clinical diagnosis of paranoid schizophrenia in African American patients. *Journal of Psychopathology and Behavioral Assessment, 23,* 93–100.

Wheeler, B. W., Gunnell, D., Metcalfe, C., Stephens, P., & Martin, R. M. (2008). The population impact on incidence of suicide and non-fatal self harm of regulatory action against the use of selective serotonin reuptake inhibitors in under 18s in the United Kingdom: Ecological study. *British Medical Journal, 336,* 542–545.

Whisman, M. A., Beach, S. R. H., & Snyder, D. K. (2008). Is marital discord taxonic and can taxonic status be assessed reliably? Results from a national, representative sample of married couples. *Journal of Consulting and Clinical Psychology, 76,* 745–755.

Whisman, M. A., Sheldon, C. T., & Goering, P. (2000). Psychiatric disorders and dissatisfaction with social relationships: Does type of relationship matter? *Journal of Abnormal Psychology, 109,* 803–808.

Whisman, M. A., Tolejko, N., & Chatav, Y. (2007). Social consequences of personality disorders: probability and timing of marriage and probability of marital disruption. *Journal of Personality Disorders, 21,* 690–695.

Whittington, C. J., et al. (2004). Selective serotonin reuptake inhibitors in childhood depression: Systematic review of published versus unpublished data. *Lancet, 363,* 1341–1345.

Whybrow, P. C. (1997). *A Mood Apart: The Thinker's Guide to Emotion and Its Disorders.* New York: HarperCollins.

Wicks-Nelson, R., & Israel, A. C. (2000). *Behavior Disorders of Childhood* (4th ed.). Upper Saddle River, NJ: Prentice Hall.

Widiger, T. A. (1998). Sex biases in the diagnosis of personality disorders. *Journal of Personality Disorders, 12,* 95–118.

Widiger, T. A. (2001). Social anxiety, social phobia, and avoidant personality. In W. R. Crozier and L. E. Alden (Eds.), *International Handbook of Social Anxiety; Concepts, Research, and Interventions Relating to the Self and Shyness,* pp. 336–356. New York: Wiley.

Widiger, T. A. (2006). Psychopathy and DSM-IV psychopathology. In C. J. Patrick (Ed.), *Handbook of Psychopathy,* pp. 156–171. New York: Guilford.

Widiger, T. A., Cadoret, R., Hare, R., Robins, L., et al. (1996). DSM-IV antisocial personality disorder field trial. *Journal of Abnormal Psychology, 105,* 3–16.

Widiger, T. A., & Clark, L. A. (2000). Toward DSM-V and the classification of psychopathology. *Psychological Bulletin, 126,* 946–963.

Widiger, T. A., Costa, P. T., Jr., & McCrae, R. M. (2002). A proposal for Axis II: Diagnosing personality disorders using the five-factor model. In P. T. Costa, Jr., & T. A. Widiger (Eds.), *Personality Disorders and the Five-Factor Model of Personality,* 2nd ed., pp. 431–456. Washington, DC: American Psychological Association.

Widiger, T., & Simonsen, E. (2005). Alternative dimensional models of personality disorder: Finding a common ground. *Journal of Personality Disorders, 19,* 110–130.

Widiger, T. A., & Trull, T. J. (1993). Borderline and narcissistic personality disorders. In P. B. Sutker & H. E. Adams (Eds.), *Comprehensive Handbook of Psychopathology,* 2nd ed., pp. 371–394. New York: Plenum.

Widiger, T. A., Trull, T. J., Clarkin, J. F., Sanderson, C., & Costa, P. T., Jr. (2002). A description of the DSM-IV personality disorders with the five-factor model of personality. In P. T. Costa, Jr., & T. A. Widiger (Eds.), *Personality Disorders and the Five-Factor Model of Personality,* 2nd ed., pp. 89–102. Washington, DC: American Psychological Association.

Widiger, T. A., & Trull, T. J. (2007). Plate tectonics in the classification of personality disorder: Shifting to a dimensional model. *American Psychologist, 62,* 71–83.

Wiederman, M. W. (1997). Pretending orgasm during sexual intercourse: Correlates in a sample of young adult women. *Journal of Sex and Marital Therapy, 23,* 131–139.

Wiederman, M. W. (2003). Paraphilia and fetishism. *Family Journal-Counseling & Therapy for Couples & Families, 11,* 315–321.

Wiegel, M., Scepkowski, L. A., & Barlow, D. H. (2007). Cognitive-affective processes in sexual arousal and sexual dysfunction. In E. Janssen (Ed.), *The Psychophysiology of Sex,* pp. 143–165. Bloomington: Indiana University Press.

Wiegel, M., Wlncze, J. P., & Barlow, D. H. (2002). Sexual dysfunction. In M. M. Antony and D. H. Barlow (Eds.), *Handbook of Assessment and Treatment Planning for Psychological Disorders,* pp. 481–522. New York: Guilford.

Wiehe, V. R., & Richards, A. L. (1995). *Intimate Betrayal: Understanding and Responding to the Trauma of Acquaintance Rape.* Thousand Oaks, CA: Sage.

Wildes, J. E., Emery, R. E., & Simons, A. D. (2001). The roles of ethnicity and culture in the development of eating disturbance and body dissatisfaction: A meta-analytic review. *Clinical Psychology Review, 21,* 521–551.

Wileman, S. M., Eagles, J. M., Andrew, J. E., Howie, F. L., Cameron, I. M., McCormack, K., et al. (2001). Light therapy for seasonal affective disorder in primary care: Randomised controlled trial. *British Journal of Psychiatry, 178,* 311–316.

Wilfley, D. E., Bishop, M. E., Wilson, G. T., & Agras, W. S. (2008). Classification of eating disorders: Toward DSM-V. *International Journal of Eating Disorders, 40,* S123–S129.

Williams, K. E., Chambless, D. L., & Ahrens, A. (1997). Are emotions frightening? An extension of the fear of fear construct. *Behaviour Research and Therapy, 35,* 239–248.

Williams, L. M. (1994). Recall of childhood trauma: A prospective study of women's memories of child sexual abuse. *Journal of Consulting and Clinical Psychology, 62,* 1167–1176.

Williams, L. M., & Finkelhor, D. (1990). The characteristics of incestuous fathers: A review of recent studies. In W. L. Marshall, D. R. Laws, & H. E. Barbaree (Eds.), *Handbook of Sexual Assault: Issues, Theories, and Treatment of the Offender*, p. 231. New York: Plenum.

Williams, R. B., Barefoot, J. C., Califf, R. M., Haney, T. L., Saunders, W. B., et al. (1992). Prognostic importance of social and economic resources among medically treated patients with angiographically documented coronary artery disease. *Journal of the American Medical Association, 267*, 520–524.

Wilson, G. T., Grilo, C. M., & Vitousek, K. M. (2007). Psychological treatment of eating disorders. *American Psychologist, 62*, 199–216.

Wilson, G. T., Loeb, K. L., Walsh, B. T., Labouvie, E., Petkova, E., Liu, X., et al. (1999). Psychological versus pharmacological treatments of bulimia nervosa: Predictors and processes of change. *Journal of Consulting & Clinical Psychology, 67*, 451–459.

Wilson, T. D. (2002). *Strangers to Ourselves: Discovering the Adaptive Unconscious*. New York: Belknap.

Wilson, T. D., & Linville, P. W. (1982). Improving the academic performance of college freshmen: Attribution therapy revisited. *Journal of Personality and Social Psychology, 42*(2), 367–376.

Wimberly, S. R., et al. (2005). Perceived partner reactions to diagnosis and treatment of breast cancer: Impact on psychosocial and psychosexual adjustment. *Journal of Consulting and Clinical Psychology, 73*, 300–311.

Wincze, J. P. (1989). Assessment and treatment of atypical sexual behavior. In S. R. Lieblum & R. C. Rosen (Eds.), *Principles and Practice of Sex Therapy*, 2nd ed., pp. 382–404. New York: Guilford.

Wincze, J. P., Bach, A. K., & Barlow, D. H. (2008). Sexual dysfunction. In D. H. Barlow (Ed.), *Clinical Handbook of Psychological Disorders: A Step-by-step Treatment Manual*, 4th ed., pp. 615–661, New York: Guilford.

Wing, L. (1988). Autism: Possible clues to the underlying pathology. 1. Clinical facts. In L. Wing (Ed.), *Aspects of Autism: Biological Research*, pp. 11–18. London: Gaskell.

Wing, L., & Potter, D. (2002). The epidemiology of autistic spectrum disorders: Is the prevalence rising? *Mental Retardation and Developmental Disabilities Research Reviews, 8*(3), 151–161.

Winograd, E., & Killinger, W. A. (1983). Relating age at encoding in early childhood to adult recall: Development of flashbulb memories. *Journal of Experimental Psychology: General, 112*, 413–422.

Winokur, G., Coryell, W., Keller, M., Endicott, J., & Leon, A. (1995). A family study of manic-depressive (bipolar I) disease. *Archives of General Psychiatry, 52*, 367–373.

Winter, D. G., John, O. P., Stewart, A. J., Klohnen, E. C., & Duncan, L. E. (1998). Traits and motives: Toward an integration of two traditions in personality research. *Psychological Review, 105*, 230–250.

Wiseman, C. V., Gray, J. J., Mosimann, J. E., & Ahrens, A. H. (1992). Cultural expectations of thinness in women: An update. *International Journal of Eating Disorders, 11*, 85–89.

Witkiewitz, K., Marlatt, G. A., & Walker, D. (2005). Mindfulness-based relapse prevention for alcohol and substance use disorders. *Journal of Cognitive Psychotherapy, 19*, 221–228.

Wittchen, H., Holsboer, F., & Jacobi, F. (2001). Met and unmet needs in the management of depressive disorder in the community and primary care: The size and breadth of the problem. *Journal of Clinical Psychiatry, 62* (Suppl. 26), 23–28.

Wittchen, H., Knauper, B., & Kessler, R. C. (1994). Lifetime risk of depression. *British Journal of Psychiatry, 165* (Suppl. 26), 16–22.

Wittchen, H., Schuster, P., & Lieb, R. (2001). Comorbidity and mixed anxiety-depressive disorder: Clinical curiosity or pathophysiological need? *Human Psychopharmacology, 16* (Suppl. 1), S21–S30.

Witvliet, C., Ludwig, T. W., & Vander Laan, K. L. (2001). Granting forgiveness or harboring grudges: Implications for emotion, physiology, and health. *Psychological Science, 12*, 117–124.

Wolfe, D. (1987). *Child Abuse: Implications for Child Development and Psychopathology*. Beverly Hills, CA: Sage.

Wolpe, J. (1958). *Psychotherapy and Reciprocal Inhibition*. Stanford, CA: Stanford University Press.

Wonderlich, S. A., Joiner, Jr., T. E., Keel, P. K., Williamson, D. A., & Corsby, R. D. (2007). Eating disorder diagnoses: Empirical approaches to classification. *American Psychologist, 62*, 167–180.

Wong, P. T., & Watt, L. M. (1991). What types of reminiscence are associated with successful aging? *Psychology and Aging, 6*, 272–279.

Wood, J. M., Lilienfeld, S. O., Nezworski, M. T., & Garb, H. N. (2001). Coming to grips with negative evidence for the comprehensive system for the Rorschach. *Journal of Personality Assessment, 77*, 48–70.

Wood, J. M., Nezworski, M. T., Lilienfeld, S. O., & Garb, H. N. (2003). *What's Wrong with the Rorschach?* San Francisco: Jossey-Bass.

Woods, D. W., Adcock, A. C., & Conelea, C. A. (2008). Trichotillomania. In J. S. Abramowitz, D. McKay, & S. Taylor (Eds.), *Clinical Handbook of Obsessive-Compulsive Disorder and Related Problems*, pp. 205–221. Baltimore, MD: Johns Hopkins University Press.

Woodside, D. B., Garfinkel, P. E., Lin, E., Goering, P., & Kaplan, A. S. (2001). Comparisons of men with full or partial eating disorders, men without eating disorders, and women with eating disorders in the community. *American Journal of Psychiatry, 158*, 570–574.

Woody, E., & Sadler, P. (1998). On reintegrating dissociated theories: Comment on Kirsch and Lynn (1998). *Psychological Bulletin, 123*, 192–197.

Woody, S. R., Steketee, G., & Chambless, D. L. (1995). Reliability and validity of the Yale-Brown obsessive-compulsive scale. *Behaviour Research and Therapy, 33*, 597–605.

Woolfolk, R. L., Allen, L. A., & Tiu, J. E. (2007). New direction in the treatment of somatization. *Psychiatric Clinics of North America, 30*, 621–644.

Worden, J. W. (1986). *Grief Counseling and Grief Therapy: A Handbook for the Mental Health Practitioner*. New York: Springer.

Wortman, C. B., & Silver, R. C. (2001). The myths of coping with loss revisited. In M. S. Stroebe et al. (Eds.), *Handbook of Bereavement Research*, pp. 405–429. Washington, DC: American Psychological Association.

Wouda, J. C., Hartman, P. M., Bakker, R. M., Bakker, J. O., van de Wiel, H. B. M., & Weijmar Schultz, W. C. M. (1998). Vaginal plethysmography in women with dyspareunia. *Journal of Sex Research, 35*, 141–147.

Wrosch, C., Schulz, R., & Heekhausen, J. (2004). Health stresses and depressive symptomatology in the elderly: A control-process approach. *Current Directions in Psychological Science, 13*, 17–20.

Wu, E., Birnbaum, H., Shi, L., Ball, D., Kessler, R., Moulis, M., et al. (2005). The economic burden of schizophrenia in the United States in 2002. *Journal of Clinical Psychiatry, 66*(9), 1122–1129.

Wylie, K., & Machin, A. (2007). Erectile dysfunction. *Primary Psychiatry, 14*, 65–71.

Wynne, L. C., & Singer, M. T. (1963). Thought disorder and family relations of schizophrenics. II. A classification of forms of thinking. *Archives of General Psychiatry, 9*, 199–206.

Xian, H., Scherrer, J. F., Slutske, W. S., Shah, K. R., Volberg, R., & Eisen, S. A. (2007). Genetic and environmental contributions to pathological gambling symtoms in a 10-year follow-up. *Twin Research and Human Genetics, 10*, 174–179.

Yamashita, I., Koyama, T., & Ohmori, T. (1995). Ethnic differences in alcohol metabolism and physiological responses to alcohol: Implications in alcohol abuse. In B. Tabakoff & P. L. Hoffman (Eds.), *Biological Aspects of Alcoholism*, pp. 49–61. Seattle, WA: Hogrefe & Huber.

Yang, J., McCrae, R. R., Costa, P. T., Yao, S., Dai, X., Cai, T., et al. (2000). The cross-cultural generalizability of Axis-II constructs: An evaluation of two personality disorder assessment instruments in the People's Republic of China. *Journal of Personality Disorders, 14*, 249–263.

Yartz, A. R., & Hawk, L. W. (2001). Psychophysiological assessment of anxiety: Tales from the heart. In M. M. Antony, S. M. Orsillo, et al. (Eds.), *Practitioner's Guide to Empirically Based Measures of Anxiety*, pp. 25–30. Dordrecht The Netherlands: Netherlandshers.

Yates, A. (1990). Current perspectives on the eating disorders. II. Treatment, outcome, and research directions. *Journal of the American Academy of Child and Adolescent Psychiatry, 29*, 1–9.

Yates, W. R., Cadoret, R. J., & Troughton, E. P. (1999). The Iowa adoption studies: Methods and results. In M. C. LaBuda & E. L. Grigorenko (Eds.), *On the Way to Individuality: Current Methodological Issues in Behavioral Genetics*, pp. 95–125. Huntington. NY: Nova Science Publishers.

Yeh, M., & Weisz, J. R. (2001). Why are we here at the clinic? Parent-child (dis)agreement on referral problems at outpatient treatment entry. *Journal of Consulting and Clinical Psychology, 69*, 1018–1025.

Yehuda, R. (2002). Current concepts: Posttraumatic stress disorder. *New England Journal of Medicine, 346*, 108–114.

Yehuda, R., & McFarlane, A. C. (1995). Conflict between current knowledge about posttraumatic stress disorder and its original conceptual basis. *American Journal of Psychiatry, 152*, 1705–1713.

Yeung, P. P., & Greenwald, S. (1992). Jewish Americans and mental health: Results of the NIMH Epidemiologic Catchment Area study. *Social Psychiatry and Psychiatric Epidemiology, 27*, 292–297.

Yirmiya, N., & Sigman, M. D. (1996). High functioning individuals with autism: Diagnosis, empirical findings, and theoretical issues. *Clinical Psychology Review, 11*(6), 669–683.

Yoder, P., & Stone, W. L. (2006). Randomized comparison of two communication interventions for preschoolers with autism spectrum disorders. *Journal of Consulting and Clinical Psychology, 74*, 426–435.

Yonkers, K. A., Bruce, S. E., Dyck, I. R., & Keller, M. B. (2003). Chronicity, relapse, and illness—course of panic disorder, social phobia, and generalized anxiety disorder: Findings in men and women from 8 years of follow-up. *Depression & Anxiety, 17*, 173–179.

Yonkers, K. A., Zlotnick, C., Allsworth, J., Warshow, M., Shea, T., & Keller, M. B. (1998). Is the course of panic disorder the same in women and men? *American Journal of Psychiatry, 155*, 596–602.

Young, J., Leentjens, A., George, J., Olofsson, B., & Gustafson, Y. (2008). Systematic approaches to the prevention and management of patients with delirium. *Journal of Psychosomatic Research, 65*, 267–272.

Younglove, J. A., & Vitello, C. J. (2003). Community notification provisions of "Megan's Law" from a therapeutic jurisprudence perspective: A case study. *American Journal of Forensic Psychology, 21*, 25–38.

Yudofsky, S. C. (2005). *Fatal Flaws: Navigating Destructive Relationships with People with Disorders of Personality and Character*. Washington, DC: American Psychiatric Publishing.

Zachar, P., & Kendler, K. S. (2007). Psychiatric disorders: A conceptual taxonomy. *American Journal of Psychiatry, 164,* 557–565.

Zahn-Waxler, C., Kochanska, G., Krupnick, J., & McKnew, D. (1990). Patterns of guilt in children of depressed and well mothers. *Developmental Psychology, 26,* 51–59.

Zalta, A. K., & Keel, P. K. (2006). Peer influence on bulimic symptoms in college students. *Journal of Abnormal Psychology, 115,* 185–189.

Zanarini, M. C., & Frankenburg, F. R. (2001). Olanzapine treatment of female borderline personality disorder patients: A double-blind, placebo-controlled pilot study. *Journal of Clinical Psychiatry, 62,* 849–854.

Zarate, C. A., & Tohen, M. (1996). Epidemiology of mood disorders throughout the life cycle. In K. I. Shulman & M. Tohen (Eds.), *Mood Disorders Across the Lifespan.* New York: Wiley.

Zarit, S. H., Zarit, J. M., & Rosenberg-Thompson, S. (1990). A special treatment unit for Alzheimer's disease: Medical, behavioral, and environmental features. *Clinical Gerontologist, 9,* 47–63.

Zautra, A. J., Johnson, L. M., & Davis, M. C. (2005). Positive affect as a source of resilience for women in chronic pain. *Journal of Consulting and Clinical Psychology, 73,* 212–220.

Zebb, B. J., & Beck, J. G. (1998). Worry versus anxiety: Is there really a difference? *Behavior Modification, 22,* 45–61.

Zigler, E. (1967). Familial mental retardation: A continuing dilemma. *Science, 155,* 292–298.

Zigler, E., & Hodapp, R. M. (1986). *Understanding Mental Retardation.* New York: Cambridge University Press.

Zigler, E., & Styfco, S.J. (1993). Using research and theory to justify and inform Head Start expansion. *Social Policy Report for the Society Research in Child Development, 7*(2), 1–20.

Zilbergeld, B. (1995). The critical and demanding partner in sex therapy. In R. C. Rosen & S. R. Leiblum (Eds.), *Case Studies in Sex Therapy,* pp. 311–330. New York: Guilford.

Zilbergeld, B. (1999). *The New Male Sexuality* (rev. ed.). New York: Bantam Doubleday Dell.

Zill, N. (1978). *Divorce, Marital Happiness, and the Mental Health of Children: Findings from the FCD National Survey of Children.* Paper presented at the NIMH workshop on divorce and children. Bethesda, MD.

Zill, N., & Schoenborn, C. A. (1990). Developmental, learning, and emotional problems: Health of our nation's children. United States, 1988. *Advance Data from Vital and Health Statistics,* no. 190. Hyattsville, MD: National Center for Health Statistics.

Zisook, S., & Kendler, K. (2007). Is bereavement-related depression different than non-bereavement-related depression? *Psychological Medicine, 37,* 779–794.

Zito, J. M., Safer, D. J., dos Reis, S., Gardner, J. F., Boles, M., & Lynch, F. (2000). Trends in the prescribing of psychotropic medications to preschoolers. *Journal of the American Medical Association, 283,* 1025–1030.

Zito, J. M., Safer, D. J., dosReis, S., Gardner, J. F., Magder, L. S., Soeken, K., et al. (2003). Psychotropic practice patters for youth: A 10-year perspective. *Archives of Pediatrics and Adolescent Medicine, 157,* 17–25.

Zoccolillo, M., & Cloninger, C. R. (1986). Somatization disorder: Psychologic symptoms, social disability, and diagnosis. *Comprehensive Psychiatry, 27,* 65–73.

Zoellner, L. A., Foa, E. B., Bartholomew, D. B., & Przeworski, A. (2000). Are trauma victims susceptible to "false memories"? *Journal of Abnormal Psychology, 109,* 517–524.

Zorn, C. A. (1998). My private disorder. *Groton School Quarterly,* 19–21.

Zucker, K. J. (2005). Gender identity disorder in children and adolescents. *Annual Review of Clinical Psychology, 1,* 467–492.

Zucker, K. J., & Blanchard, R. (1997). Tranvestic fetishism: Psychopathology and theory. In D. R. Laws & W. T. O'Donohue (Eds.), *Handbook of Sexual Deviance: Theory and Application.* New York: Guilford.

Zuckerman, M. (1999). *Vulnerability to Psychopathology: A Biosocial Model.* Washington, DC: American Psychological Association Press.

Credits

Photographs / Cartoons

by E.S. Livingstone, Edinburgh, 1919; **p. 405**, © Walter Smith/CORBIS All Rights Reserved; **p. 408**, Ray Stubblebine/Reuters/Corbis/Bettmann; **p. 409**, Katharina Hesse/Katharina Hesse; **p. 412**, Antonio Scorza/Agence France Presse/Getty Images; **p. 414**, Dr. E. Fuller Torrey and Dr. Weinberger/National Institute of Mental Health; **p. 418**, Corbis Royalty Free; **p. 426**, AP Wide World Photos; **p. 427**, © JazzSign/Lebrecht/The Image Works.

Chapter 14 Page: 432, Photos.com.; **p. 433**, AP Wide World Photos; **p. 438**, AP Wide World Photos; **p. 439**, © Karin Cooper/Liaison/Getty Images, Inc.; **p. 443**, Paul Hoff, Psychiatric Hospital, Technical University of Aachen, Aachen, Germany; **p. 448, top**, AP Wide World Photos; **p. 448, bottom**, Lysia Forno/SPL/Photo Researchers, Inc./Photo Researchers, Inc.; **p. 450**, Beth A. Keiser/AP Wide World Photos; **p. 452**, © Jose Luis Magana/AP Wide World; **p. 455, top**, Nancy Andrews/Nancy Andrews; **p. 455, bottom**, Nancy Andrews/Nancy Andrews; **p. 457**, AP Wide World Photos.

Chapter 15 Page: 462, Photos.com.; **p. 463**, Bob D'amico/ABC Everett Collection; **p. 468**, Elaine Rebman/Photo Researchers, Inc.; **p. 471**, Bob Rowan/Corbis/Bettmann; **p. 472, top**, Used with permission from Warren & Nelson (JAMA, 2/16/94, 271; 536–542) Copyright 1994, American Medical Association.; **p. 472, bottom**, Used with permission from Warren & Nelson (JAMA, 2/16/94, 271; 536–542) Copyright 1994, American Medical Association.; **p. 474, top**, David Young-Wolff/PhotoEdit Inc.; **p. 474, bottom**, J. Griffin/The Image Works; **p. 478**, AP Wide World Photos; **p. 478**, Yoav Levy/Phototake NYC; **p. 479**, AP Wide World Photos; **p. 480**, AP Wide World Photos; **p. 481**, Michael A. Schwarz/Michael A. Schwarz Photography, Inc.; **p. 484, top**, ©Ellen B. Senisi/Ellen Senisi; **p. 484, bottom**, Waisman Brain Imaging Lab, University of Wisconsin–Madison; **p. 485**, Dr. Lorna Selfe, Principal Educational Psychologist, Herefordshire, UK. From "Nadia: A Case of Extraordinary Drawing Ability in an Autistic Child," Academic Press.; **p. 489**, AP Wide World Photos; **p. 490**, Alan Carey/The Image Works.

Chapter 16 Page: 496, Photos.com.; **p. 497**, Michael Newman/PhotoEdit Inc.; **p. 500**, Bob Daemmrich/The Image Works; **p. 505**, ©Bettmann/CORBIS; **p. 506**, Mary Kate Denny/PhotoEdit Inc.; **p. 509**, Rick Hunter/Rick Hunter; **p. 511**, Michael Gibson/Paramont/Picture Desk, Inc./Kobal Collection; **p. 512**, Cheryl Himmelstein Photography; **p. 514**, Bill Aron/PhotoEdit Inc.; **p. 515**, ©Vittoriano Rastelli/CORBIS; **p. 516, top**, Michael Newman/PhotoEdit Inc.; **p. 516, bottom**, Bill Kaczor/AP Wide World Photos; **p. 519, bottom**, Sybil Shackman/Sybil Shackman; **p. 520**, Tom McCarthy/Photolibrary.com; **p. 524**, A. Tannenbaum/Allen Tannenbaum; **p. 527**, Courtesy of U.S. Food and Drug Administration (FDA).

Chapter 17 Page: 530, Photos.com.; **p. 531, left**, Grant LeDuc/Grant LeDuc; **p. 531, center**, Simon Cherpitel/Magnum Photos, Inc.; **p. 531, right**, Roger Dollarhide/Roger Dollarhide; **p. 535**, Getty Images/Digital Vision; **p. 537**, Bob Daemmrich/Stock Boston; **p. 541**, G & M David de Lossy/Getty Images Inc.–Image Bank; **p. 546**, Lon C. Diehl/PhotoEdit Inc.; **p. 548, top**, Jon L. Barkan/Photolibrary.com; **p. 548, bottom**, Bob Daemmrich/The Image Works; **p. 552**, Michael S. Yamashita/Corbis/Bettmann; **p. 553**, Detroit News/Gary Porter/Getty Images, Inc.–Liaison; **p. 555**, Eric O'Connell/Taxi/Getty Images.

Chapter 18 Page: 558, Photos.com.; **p. 560**, Betty Mimms/Corbis/Sygma; **p. 562, top**, AP Wide World Photos; **p. 562, bottom**, Steve Helber/AP Wide World Photos; **p. 564, left**, Reuters/Landov Media; **p. 564, right**, AP Wide World Photos; **p. 566**, Marilyn Humphries/Marilyn Humphries Photography; **p. 568**, AP Wide World Photos; **p. 569**, AP Wide World Photos; **p. 572**, NBCU Photo Bank; **p. 575**, Courtesy of the Abraham Lincoln Presidential Library and Museum; **p. 576**, AP Wide World Photos; **p. 577**, Joel Stettenheim © Joel Stettenheim/CORBIS All Rights Reserved; **p. 579, left**, Jerry Cooke/Photo Researchers, Inc.; **p. 579, right**, Eugene Richards/Magnum Photos, Inc.; **p. 582**, © Alex Tehrani; **p. 586**, AP Wide World Photos.

Name Index

Subject Index

DSM-IV-TR Classification

NOS: Not otherwise specified

If criteria are currently met, one of the following severity specifiers may be noted after the diagnosis:

Mild
Moderate
Severe

If criteria are no longer met, one of the following specifiers may be noted:

In Partial Remission
In Full Remission
Prior History

Disorders Usually First Diagnosed in Infancy, Childhood, or Adolescence

Mental Retardation

Note: These are coded on Axis II.
Mild Mental Retardation
Moderate Mental Retardation
Severe Mental Retardation
Profound Mental Retardation
Mental Retardation, Severity Unspecified

Learning Disorders

Reading Disorder
Mathematics Disorder
Disorder of Written Expression
Learning Disorder NOS

Motor Skills Disorder

Developmental Coordination Disorder

Communication Disorders

Expressive Language Disorder
Mixed Receptive-Expressive Language Disorder
Phonological Disorder
Stuttering
Communication Disorder NOS

Pervasive Developmental Disorders

Autistic Disorder
Rett's Disorder
Childhood Disintegrative Disorder
Asperger's Disorder
Pervasive Developmental Disorder NOS

Attention-Deficit and Disruptive Behavior Disorders

Attention-Deficit/Hyperactivity Disorder
Attention-Deficit/Hyperactivity Disorder NOS
Conduct Disorder
Oppositional Defiant Disorder
Disruptive Behavior Disorder NOS

Feeding and Eating Disorders of Infancy or Early Childhood

Pica
Rumination Disorder
Feeding Disorder of Infancy or Early Childhood

Tic Disorders

Tourette's Disorder
Chronic Motor or Vocal Tic Disorder
Transient Tic Disorder
Tic Disorder NOS

Elimination Disorders

Encopresis
Enuresis (Not Due to a General Medical Condition)

Other Disorders of Infancy, Childhood, or Adolescence

Separation Anxiety Disorder
Selective Mutism
Reactive Attachment Disorder of Infancy or Early Childhood
Stereotypic Movement Disorder
Disorder of Infancy, Childhood, or Adolescence NOS

Delirium, Dementia, and Amnestic and Other Cognitive Disorders

Delirium

Delirium Due to . . . *[Indicate the General Medical Condition]*
Substance Intoxication Delirium
Substance Withdrawal Delirium
Delirium Due to Multiple Etiologies
Delirium NOS

Dementia

Dementia of the Alzheimer's Type, with Early Onset
Dementia of the Alzheimer's Type, with Late Onset
Vascular Dementia
Dementia Due to HIV Disease
Dementia Due to Head Trauma
Dementia Due to Parkinson's Disease
Dementia Due to Huntington's Disease
Dementia Due to Pick's Disease
Dementia Due to Creutzfeldt-Jakob Disease
Dementia Due to . . . *[Indicate the General Medical Condition not listed above]*
Substance-Induced Persisting Dementia
Dementia Due to Multiple Etiologies
Dementia NOS

Amnestic Disorders

Amnestic Disorder Due to . . . *[Indicate the General Medical Condition]*
Specify if: Transient/Chronic
Substance-Induced Persisting Amnestic Disorder
Amnestic Disorder NOS

Substance-Related Disorders

Alcohol Use Disorders

Alcohol Dependence
Alcohol Abuse

Alcohol-Induced Disorders

Alcohol Intoxication
Alcohol Withdrawal
Alcohol Intoxication Delirium
Alcohol-Induced Persisting Amnestic Disorder
Alcohol-Induced Psychotic Disorder

Amphetamine Use Disorders

Amphetamine Dependence
Amphetamine Abuse

Amphetamine-Induced Disorders

Amphetamine Intoxication
Amphetamine Withdrawal
Amphetamine Intoxication Delirium
Amphetamine-Induced Psychotic Disorder

Caffeine-Induced Disorders

Caffeine Intoxication
Caffeine-Induced Anxiety Disorder
Caffeine-Induced Sleep Disorder

Cannabis Use Disorders

Cannabis Dependence
Cannabis Abuse

Cannabis-Induced Disorders

Cannabis Intoxication
Cannabis Intoxication Delirium
Cannabis-Induced Psychotic Disorder
Cannabis-Induced Anxiety Disorder

Cocaine Use Disorders

Cocaine Dependence
Cocaine Abuse

Cocaine-Induced Disorders

Cocaine Intoxication
Cocaine Withdrawal
Cocaine Intoxication Delirium
Cocaine-Induced Psychotic Disorder

Hallucinogen Use Disorders

Hallucinogen Dependence
Hallucinogen Abuse

Hallucinogen-Induced Disorders

Hallucinogen Intoxication
Hallucinogen Persisting Disorder (Flashbacks)
Hallucinogen Intoxication Delirium
Hallucinogen-Induced Psychotic Disorder

Inhalant Use Disorders

Inhalant Dependence
Inhalant Abuse

Inhalant-Induced Disorders

Inhalant Intoxication
Inhalant Intoxication Delirium
Inhalant-Induced Persisting Dementia
Inhalant-Induced Psychotic Disorder

Nicotine Use Disorder

Nicotine Dependence

Nicotine-Induced Disorder

Nicotine Withdrawal

Opioid Use Disorders

Opioid Dependence
Opioid Abuse

Opioid-Induced Disorders

Opioid Intoxication
Specify if: With Perceptual Disturbances
Opioid Withdrawal
Opioid Intoxication Delirium
Opioid-Induced Psychotic Disorder

Phencyclidine Use Disorders

Phencyclidine Dependence
Phencyclidine Abuse

Phencyclidine-Induced Disorders

Phencyclidine Intoxication
Specify if: With Perceptual Disturbances
Phencyclidine-Induced Psychotic Disorder

Sedative, Hypnotic, or Anxiolytic Use Disorders

Sedative, Hypnotic, or Anxiolytic Dependence
Sedative, Hypnotic, or Anxiolytic Abuse

Sedative-, Hypnotic-, or Anxiolytic-Induced Disorders

Sedative, Hypnotic, or Anxiolytic Intoxication
Sedative, Hypnotic, or Anxiolytic Withdrawal
Specify if: With Perceptual Disturbances